Some Physical Constants

Quantity	Symbol	Value[a]
Atomic mass unit	u	$1.660\ 538\ 86\ (28) \times 10^{-27}$ kg $931.494\ 043\ (80)$ MeV/c^2
Avogadro's number	N_A	$6.022\ 141\ 5\ (10) \times 10^{23}$ particles/mol
Bohr magneton	$\mu_B = \dfrac{e\hbar}{2m_e}$	$9.274\ 009\ 49\ (80) \times 10^{-24}$ J/T
Bohr radius	$a_0 = \dfrac{\hbar^2}{m_e e^2 k_e}$	$5.291\ 772\ 108\ (18) \times 10^{-11}$ m
Boltzmann's constant	$k_B = \dfrac{R}{N_A}$	$1.380\ 650\ 5\ (24) \times 10^{-23}$ J/K
Compton wavelength	$\lambda_C = \dfrac{h}{m_e c}$	$2.426\ 310\ 238\ (16) \times 10^{-12}$ m
Coulomb constant	$k_e = \dfrac{1}{4\pi\epsilon_0}$	$8.987\ 551\ 788\ldots \times 10^9$ N·m^2/C^2 (exact)
Deuteron mass	m_d	$3.343\ 583\ 35\ (57) \times 10^{-27}$ kg $2.013\ 553\ 212\ 70\ (35)$ u
Electron mass	m_e	$9.109\ 382\ 6\ (16) \times 10^{-31}$ kg $5.485\ 799\ 094\ 5\ (24) \times 10^{-4}$ u $0.510\ 998\ 918\ (44)$ MeV/c^2
Electron volt	eV	$1.602\ 176\ 53\ (14) \times 10^{-19}$ J
Elementary charge	e	$1.602\ 176\ 53\ (14) \times 10^{-19}$ C
Gas constant	R	$8.314\ 472\ (15)$ J/mol·K
Gravitational constant	G	$6.674\ 2\ (10) \times 10^{-11}$ N·m^2/kg^2
Josephson frequency–voltage ratio	$\dfrac{2e}{h}$	$4.835\ 978\ 79\ (41) \times 10^{14}$ Hz/V
Magnetic flux quantum	$\Phi_0 = \dfrac{h}{2e}$	$2.067\ 833\ 72\ (18) \times 10^{-15}$ T·m^2
Neutron mass	m_n	$1.674\ 927\ 28\ (29) \times 10^{-27}$ kg $1.008\ 664\ 915\ 60\ (55)$ u $939.565\ 360\ (81)$ MeV/c^2
Nuclear magneton	$\mu_n = \dfrac{e\hbar}{2m_p}$	$5.050\ 783\ 43\ (43) \times 10^{-27}$ J/T
Permeability of free space	μ_0	$4\pi \times 10^{-7}$ T·m/A (exact)
Permittivity of free space	$\epsilon_0 = \dfrac{1}{\mu_0 c^2}$	$8.854\ 187\ 817\ldots \times 10^{-12}$ C^2/N·m^2 (exact)
Planck's constant	h	$6.626\ 069\ 3\ (11) \times 10^{-34}$ J·s
	$\hbar = \dfrac{h}{2\pi}$	$1.054\ 571\ 68\ (18) \times 10^{-34}$ J·s
Proton mass	m_p	$1.672\ 621\ 71\ (29) \times 10^{-27}$ kg $1.007\ 276\ 466\ 88\ (13)$ u $938.272\ 029\ (80)$ MeV/c^2
Rydberg constant	R_H	$1.097\ 373\ 156\ 852\ 5\ (73) \times 10^7$ m^{-1}
Speed of light in vacuum	c	$2.997\ 924\ 58 \times 10^8$ m/s (exact)

Note: These constants are the values recommended in 2002 by CODATA, based on a least-squares adjustment of data from different measurements. For a more complete list, see P. J. Mohr and B. N. Taylor, "CODATA Recommended Values of the Fundamental Physical Constants: 2002." *Rev. Mod. Phys.* **77**:1, 2005.

[a] The numbers in parentheses for the values represent the uncertainties of the last two digits.

Solar System Data

Body	Mass (kg)	Mean Radius (m)	Period (s)	Distance from the Sun (m)
Mercury	3.18×10^{23}	2.43×10^6	7.60×10^6	5.79×10^{10}
Venus	4.88×10^{24}	6.06×10^6	1.94×10^7	1.08×10^{11}
Earth	5.98×10^{24}	6.37×10^6	3.156×10^7	1.496×10^{11}
Mars	6.42×10^{23}	3.37×10^6	5.94×10^7	2.28×10^{11}
Jupiter	1.90×10^{27}	6.99×10^7	3.74×10^8	7.78×10^{11}
Saturn	5.68×10^{26}	5.85×10^7	9.35×10^8	1.43×10^{12}
Uranus	8.68×10^{25}	2.33×10^7	2.64×10^9	2.87×10^{12}
Neptune	1.03×10^{26}	2.21×10^7	5.22×10^9	4.50×10^{12}
Pluto[a]	$\approx 1.4 \times 10^{22}$	$\approx 1.5 \times 10^6$	7.82×10^9	5.91×10^{12}
Moon	7.36×10^{22}	1.74×10^6	—	—
Sun	1.991×10^{30}	6.96×10^8	—	—

[a] In August 2006, the International Astronomical Union adopted a definition of a planet that separates Pluto from the other eight planets. Pluto is now defined as a "dwarf planet" (like the asteroid Ceres).

Physical Data Often Used

Average Earth–Moon distance	3.84×10^8 m
Average Earth–Sun distance	1.496×10^{11} m
Average radius of the Earth	6.37×10^6 m
Density of air (20°C and 1 atm)	1.20 kg/m^3
Density of water (20°C and 1 atm)	1.00×10^3 kg/m^3
Free-fall acceleration	9.80 m/s^2
Mass of the Earth	5.98×10^{24} kg
Mass of the Moon	7.36×10^{22} kg
Mass of the Sun	1.99×10^{30} kg
Standard atmospheric pressure	1.013×10^5 Pa

Note: These values are the ones used in the text.

Some Prefixes for Powers of Ten

Power	Prefix	Abbreviation	Power	Prefix	Abbreviation
10^{-24}	yocto	y	10^1	deka	da
10^{-21}	zepto	z	10^2	hecto	h
10^{-18}	atto	a	10^3	kilo	k
10^{-15}	femto	f	10^6	mega	M
10^{-12}	pico	p	10^9	giga	G
10^{-9}	nano	n	10^{12}	tera	T
10^{-6}	micro	μ	10^{15}	peta	P
10^{-3}	milli	m	10^{18}	exa	E
10^{-2}	centi	c	10^{21}	zetta	Z
10^{-1}	deci	d	10^{24}	yotta	Y

Physics for Scientists and Engineers
/ with Modern Physics
Volume 1

Raymond A. Serway
James Madison University (Emeritus)

John W. Jewett
California State Polytechnic University, Pomona

THOMSON
™
BROOKS/COLE

Australia · Canada · Mexico · Singapore · Spain · United Kingdom · United States

Physics for Scientists and Engineers / with Modern Physics Vol. 1
Serway / Jewett

Executive Editors:
Michele Baird, Maureen Staudt &
Michael Stranz

Project Development Manager:
Linda deStefano

Sr. Marketing Coordinators:
Lindsay Annett and Sara Mercurio

Production/Manufacturing Manager:
Donna M. Brown

Production Editorial Manager:
Dan Plofchan

Pre-Media Services Supervisor:
Becki Walker

Rights and Permissions Specialist:
Kalina Ingham Hintz

Cover Image
Getty Images*

The Adaptable Courseware Program
consists of products and additions to
existing Brooks/Cole products that are
produced from camera-ready copy.
Peer review, class testing, and
accuracy are primarily the responsibility
of the author(s).

ISBN: 978-0-495-43517-4
ISBN: 0-495-43517-1

International Divisions List

Asia (Including India):
Thomson Learning
(a division of Thomson Asia Pte Ltd)
5 Shenton Way #01-01
UIC Building
Singapore 068808
Tel: (65) 6410-1200
Fax: (65) 6410-1208

Australia/New Zealand:
Thomson Learning Australia
102 Dodds Street
Southbank, Victoria 3006
Australia

Latin America:
Thomson Learning
Seneca 53
Colonia Polano
11560 Mexico, D.F., Mexico
Tel (525) 281-2906
Fax (525) 281-2656

Canada:
Thomson Nelson
1120 Birchmount Road
Toronto, Ontario
Canada M1K 5G4
Tel (416) 752-9100
Fax (416) 752-8102

UK/Europe/Middle East/Africa:
Thomson Learning
High Holborn House
50-51 Bedford Row
London, WC1R 4LS
United Kingdom
Tel 44 (020) 7067-2500
Fax 44 (020) 7067-2600

Spain (Includes Portugal):
Thomson Paraninfo
Calle Magallanes 25
28015 Madrid
España
Tel 34 (0)91 446-3350
Fax 34 (0)91 445-6218

© Thomson Learning/Charles D. Winters

NASA

Raymond A. Serway received his doctorate at Illinois Institute of Technology and is Professor Emeritus at James Madison University. In 1990, he received the Madison Scholar Award at James Madison University, where he taught for 17 years. Dr. Serway began his teaching career at Clarkson University, where he conducted research and taught from 1967 to 1980. He was the recipient of the Distinguished Teaching Award at Clarkson University in 1977 and of the Alumni Achievement Award from Utica College in 1985. As Guest Scientist at the IBM Research Laboratory in Zurich, Switzerland, he worked with K. Alex Müller, 1987 Nobel Prize recipient. Dr. Serway also was a visiting scientist at Argonne National Laboratory, where he collaborated with his mentor and friend, Sam Marshall. In addition to earlier editions of this textbook, Dr. Serway is the coauthor of *Principles of Physics,* fourth edition; *College Physics,* seventh edition; *Essentials of College Physics;* and *Modern Physics,* third edition. He also is the coauthor of the high school textbook *Physics,* published by Holt, Rinehart, & Winston. In addition, Dr. Serway has published more than 40 research papers in the field of condensed matter physics and has given more than 70 presentations at professional meetings. Dr. Serway and his wife, Elizabeth, enjoy traveling, golf, singing in a church choir, and spending quality time with their four children and eight grandchildren.

John W. Jewett, Jr., earned his doctorate at Ohio State University, specializing in optical and magnetic properties of condensed matter. Dr. Jewett began his academic career at Richard Stockton College of New Jersey, where he taught from 1974 to 1984. He is currently Professor of Physics at California State Polytechnic University, Pomona. Throughout his teaching career, Dr. Jewett has been active in promoting science education. In addition to receiving four National Science Foundation grants, he helped found and direct the Southern California Area Modern Physics Institute. He also directed Science IMPACT (Institute for Modern Pedagogy and Creative Teaching), which works with teachers and schools to develop effective science curricula. Dr. Jewett's honors include the Stockton Merit Award at Richard Stockton College in 1980, the Outstanding Professor Award at California State Polytechnic University for 1991–1992, and the Excellence in Undergraduate Physics Teaching Award from the American Association of Physics Teachers in 1998. He has given more than 80 presentations at professional meetings, including presentations at international conferences in China and Japan. In addition to his work on this textbook, he is coauthor of *Principles of Physics,* fourth edition, with Dr. Serway and author of *The World of Physics . . . Mysteries, Magic, and Myth.* Dr. Jewett enjoys playing keyboard with his all-physicist band, traveling, and collecting antiques that can be used as demonstration apparatus in physics lectures. Most importantly, he relishes spending time with his wife, Lisa, and their children and grandchildren.

In writing this seventh edition of *Physics for Scientists and Engineers,* we continue our ongoing efforts to improve the clarity of presentation and include new pedagogical features that help support the learning and teaching processes. Drawing on positive feedback from users of the sixth edition and reviewers' suggestions, we have refined the text to better meet the needs of students and teachers.

This textbook is intended for a course in introductory physics for students majoring in science or engineering. The entire contents of the book in its extended version could be covered in a three-semester course, but it is possible to use the material in shorter sequences with the omission of selected chapters and sections. The mathematical background of the student taking this course should ideally include one semester of calculus. If that is not possible, the student should be enrolled in a concurrent course in introductory calculus.

Objectives

This introductory physics textbook has two main objectives: to provide the student with a clear and logical presentation of the basic concepts and principles of physics and to strengthen an understanding of the concepts and principles through a broad range of interesting applications to the real world. To meet these objectives, we have placed emphasis on sound physical arguments and problem-solving methodology. At the same time, we have attempted to motivate the student through practical examples that demonstrate the role of physics in other disciplines, including engineering, chemistry, and medicine.

Changes in the Seventh Edition

A large number of changes and improvements have been made in preparing the seventh edition of this text. Some of the new features are based on our experiences and on current trends in science education. Other changes have been incorporated in response to comments and suggestions offered by users of the sixth edition and by reviewers of the manuscript. The features listed here represent the major changes in the seventh edition.

QUESTIONS AND PROBLEMS A substantial revision to the end-of-chapter questions and problems was made in an effort to improve their variety, interest, and pedagogical value, while maintaining their clarity and quality. Approximately 23% of the questions and problems are new or substantially changed. Several of the questions for each chapter are in objective format. Several problems in each chapter explicitly ask for qualitative reasoning in some parts as well as for quantitative answers in other parts:

> 19. ● Assume a parcel of air in a straight tube moves with a constant acceleration of -4.00 m/s^2 and has a velocity of 13.0 m/s at 10:05:00 a.m. on a certain date. (a) What is its velocity at 10:05:01 a.m.? (b) At 10:05:02 a.m.? (c) At 10:05:02.5 a.m.? (d) At 10:05:04 a.m.? (e) At 10:04:59 a.m.? (f) Describe the shape of a graph of velocity versus time for this parcel of air. (g) Argue for or against the statement, "Knowing the single value of an object's constant acceleration is like knowing a whole list of values for its velocity."

WORKED EXAMPLES All in-text worked examples have been recast and are now presented in a two-column format to better reinforce physical concepts. The left column shows textual information that describes the steps for solving the problem. The right column shows the mathematical manipulations and results of taking these steps. This layout facilitates matching the concept with its mathematical execution and helps students organize their work. These reconstituted examples closely follow a General Problem-Solving Strategy introduced in Chapter 2 to reinforce effective problem-solving habits. A sample of a worked example can be found on the next page.

> Each solution has been reconstituted to more closely follow the General Problem-Solving Strategy as outlined in Chapter 2, to reinforce good problem-solving habits.

A Vacation Trip

A car travels 20.0 km due north and then 35.0 km in a direction 60.0° west of north as shown in Figure 3.11a. Find the magnitude and direction of the car's resultant displacement.

SOLUTION

Conceptualize   The vectors $\vec{A}$ and $\vec{B}$ drawn in Figure 3.11a help us conceptualize the problem.

Categorize   We can categorize this example as a simple analysis problem in vector addition. The displacement $\vec{R}$ is the resultant when the two individual displacements $\vec{A}$ and $\vec{B}$ are added. We can further categorize it as a problem about the analysis of triangles, so we appeal to our expertise in geometry and trigonometry.

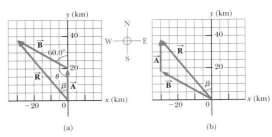

Figure 3.11   (Example 3.2) (a) Graphical method for finding the resultant displacement vector $\vec{R} = \vec{A} + \vec{B}$. (b) Adding the vectors in reverse order $(\vec{B} + \vec{A})$ gives the same result for $\vec{R}$.

> Each step of the solution is detailed in a two-column format. The left column provides an explanation for each mathematical step in the right column, to better reinforce the physical concepts.

Analyze   In this example, we show two ways to analyze the problem of finding the resultant of two vectors. The first way is to solve the problem geometrically, using graph paper and a protractor to measure the magnitude of $\vec{R}$ and its direction in Figure 3.11a. (In fact, even when you know you are going to be carrying out a calculation, you should sketch the vectors to check your results.) With an ordinary ruler and protractor, a large diagram typically gives answers to two-digit but not to three-digit precision.

The second way to solve the problem is to analyze it algebraically. The magnitude of $\vec{R}$ can be obtained from the law of cosines as applied to the triangle (see Appendix B.4).

Use $R^2 = A^2 + B^2 - 2AB \cos \theta$ from the law of cosines to find R:

$$R = \sqrt{A^2 + B^2 - 2AB \cos \theta}$$

Substitute numerical values, noting that $\theta = 180° - 60° = 120°$:

$$R = \sqrt{(20.0 \text{ km})^2 + (35.0 \text{ km})^2 - 2(20.0 \text{ km})(35.0 \text{ km}) \cos 120°}$$

$$= \boxed{48.2 \text{ km}}$$

Use the law of sines (Appendix B.4) to find the direction of $\vec{R}$ measured from the northerly direction:

$$\frac{\sin \beta}{B} = \frac{\sin \theta}{R}$$

$$\sin \beta = \frac{B}{R} \sin \theta = \frac{35.0 \text{ km}}{48.2 \text{ km}} \sin 120° = 0.629$$

$$\beta = \boxed{38.9°}$$

The resultant displacement of the car is 48.2 km in a direction 38.9° west of north.

Finalize   Does the angle β that we calculated agree with an estimate made by looking at Figure 3.11a or with an actual angle measured from the diagram using the graphical method? Is it reasonable that the magnitude of $\vec{R}$ is larger than that of both $\vec{A}$ and $\vec{B}$? Are the units of $\vec{R}$ correct?

Although the graphical method of adding vectors works well, it suffers from two disadvantages. First, some people find using the laws of cosines and sines to be awkward. Second, a triangle only results if you are adding two vectors. If you are adding three or more vectors, the resulting geometric shape is usually not a triangle. In Section 3.4, we explore a new method of adding vectors that will address both of these disadvantages.

What If?   Suppose the trip were taken with the two vectors in reverse order: 35.0 km at 60.0° west of north first and then 20.0 km due north. How would the magnitude and the direction of the resultant vector change?

Answer   They would not change. The commutative law for vector addition tells us that the order of vectors in an addition is irrelevant. Graphically, Figure 3.11b shows that the vectors added in the reverse order give us the same resultant vector.

> **What If?** statements appear in about 1/3 of the worked examples and offer a variation on the situation posed in the text of the example. For instance, this feature might explore the effects of changing the conditions of the situation, determine what happens when a quantity is taken to a particular limiting value, or question whether additional information can be determined about the problem situation. This feature encourages students to think about the results of the example and assists in conceptual understanding of the principles.

All worked examples are also available to be assigned as interactive examples in the Enhanced WebAssign homework management system (visit **www.pse7.com** for more details).

ONLINE HOMEWORK It is now easier to assign online homework with Serway and Jewett and Enhanced WebAssign. All worked examples, end-of-chapter problems, active figures, quick quizzes, and most questions are available in WebAssign. Most problems include hints and feedback to provide instantaneous reinforcement or direction for that problem. In addition to the text content, we have also added math remediation tools to help students get up to speed in algebra, trigonometry, and calculus.

SUMMARIES Each chapter contains a summary that reviews the important concepts and equations discussed in that chapter. A marginal note next to each chapter summary directs students to additional quizzes, animations, and interactive exercises for that chapter on the book's companion Web site. The format of the end-of-chapter summary has been completely revised for this edition. The summary is divided into three sections: Definitions, Concepts and Principles, and Analysis Models for Problem-Solving. In each section, flashcard-type boxes focus on each separate definition, concept, principle, or analysis model.

© Thomson Learning/Charles D. Winters

MATH APPENDIX The math appendix, a valuable tool for students, has been updated to show the math tools in a physics context. This resource is ideal for students who need a quick review on topics such as algebra, trigonometry, and calculus.

CONTENT CHANGES The content and organization of the textbook are essentially the same as in the sixth edition. Many sections in various chapters have been streamlined, deleted, or combined with other sections to allow for a more balanced presentation. Vectors are now denoted in boldface with an arrow over them (for example, $\vec{v}$), making them easier to recognize. Chapters 7 and 8 have been completely reorganized to prepare students for a unified approach to energy that is used throughout the text. A new section in Chapter 9 teaches students how to analyze deformable systems with the conservation of energy equation and the impulse-momentum theorem. Chapter 34 is longer than in the sixth edition because of the movement into that chapter of the material on displacement current from Chapter 30 and Maxwell's equations from Chapter 31. A more detailed list of content changes can be found on the instructor's companion Web site.

Content

The material in this book covers fundamental topics in classical physics and provides an introduction to modern physics. The book is divided into six parts. Part 1 (Chapters 1 to 14) deals with the fundamentals of Newtonian mechanics and the physics of fluids; Part 2 (Chapters 15 to 18) covers oscillations, mechanical waves, and sound; Part 3 (Chapters 19 to 22) addresses heat and thermodynamics; Part 4 (Chapters 23 to 34) treats electricity and magnetism; Part 5 (Chapters 35 to 38) covers light and optics; and Part 6 (Chapters 39 to 46) deals with relativity and modern physics.

Text Features

Most instructors believe that the textbook selected for a course should be the student's primary guide for understanding and learning the subject matter. Furthermore, the textbook should be easily accessible and should be styled and written to facilitate instruction and learning. With these points in mind, we have included many pedagogical features, listed below, that are intended to enhance its usefulness to both students and instructors.

Problem Solving and Conceptual Understanding

GENERAL PROBLEM-SOLVING STRATEGY A general strategy outlined at the end of Chapter 2 provides students with a structured process for solving problems. In all remaining chapters, the strategy is employed explicitly in every example so that students learn how it is applied. Students are encouraged to follow this strategy when working end-of-chapter problems.

MODELING   Although students are faced with hundreds of problems during their physics courses, instructors realize that a relatively small number of physical situations form the basis of these problems. When faced with a new problem, a physicist forms a *model* of the problem that can be solved in a simple way by identifying the common physical situation that occurs in the problem. For example, many problems involve particles under constant acceleration, isolated systems, or waves under refraction. Because the physicist has studied these situations extensively and understands the associated behavior, he or she can apply this knowledge as a model for solving a new problem. In certain chapters, this edition identifies Analysis Models, which are physical situations (such as the particle under constant acceleration, the isolated system, or the wave under refraction) that occur so often that they can be used as a model for solving an unfamiliar problem. These models are discussed in the chapter text, and the student is reminded of them in the end-of-chapter summary under the heading "Analysis Models for Problem-Solving."

© Thomson Learning/George Semple

PROBLEMS   An extensive set of problems is included at the end of each chapter; in all, the text contains approximately three thousand problems. Answers to odd-numbered problems are provided at the end of the book. For the convenience of both the student and the instructor, about two-thirds of the problems are keyed to specific sections of the chapter. The remaining problems, labeled "Additional Problems," are not keyed to specific sections. The problem numbers for straightforward problems are printed in black, intermediate-level problems are in blue, and challenging problems are in magenta.

- **"Not-just-a-number" problems** Each chapter includes several marked problems that require students to think qualitatively in some parts and quantitatively in others. Instructors can assign such problems to guide students to display deeper understanding, practice good problem-solving techniques, and prepare for exams.
- **Problems for developing symbolic reasoning** Each chapter contains problems that ask for solutions in symbolic form as well as many problems asking for numerical answers. To help students develop skill in symbolic reasoning, each chapter contains a pair of otherwise identical problems, one asking for a numerical solution and one asking for a symbolic derivation. In this edition, each chapter also contains a problem giving a numerical value for every datum but one so that the answer displays how the unknown depends on the datum represented symbolically. The answer to such a problem has the form of a function of one variable. Reasoning about the behavior of this function puts emphasis on the *Finalize* step of the General Problem-Solving Strategy. All problems developing symbolic reasoning are identified by a tan background screen:

> 53. ● A light spring has an unstressed length of 15.5 cm. It is described by Hooke's law with spring constant 4.30 N/m. One end of the horizontal spring is held on a fixed vertical axle, and the other end is attached to a puck of mass m that can move without friction over a horizontal surface. The puck is set into motion in a circle with a period of 1.30 s. (a) Find the extension of the spring x as it depends on m. Evaluate x for (b) $m = 0.070\,0$ kg, (c) $m = 0.140$ kg, (d) $m = 0.180$ kg, and (e) $m = 0.190$ kg. (f) Describe the pattern of variation of x as it depends on m.

- **Review problems** Many chapters include review problems requiring the student to combine concepts covered in the chapter with those discussed in previous chapters. These problems reflect the cohesive nature of the principles in the text and verify that physics is not a scattered set of ideas. When facing a real-world issue such as global warming or nuclear weapons, it may be necessary to call on ideas in physics from several parts of a textbook such as this one.
- **"Fermi problems"** As in previous editions, at least one problem in each chapter asks the student to reason in order-of-magnitude terms.

- **Design problems** Several chapters contain problems that ask the student to determine design parameters for a practical device so that it can function as required.
- **"*Jeopardy!*" problems** Some chapters give students practice in changing between different representations by stating equations and asking for a description of a situation to which they apply as well as for a numerical answer.
- **Calculus-based problems** Every chapter contains at least one problem applying ideas and methods from differential calculus and one problem using integral calculus.

The instructor's Web site, **www.thomsonedu.com/physics/serway,** provides lists of problems using calculus, problems encouraging or requiring computer use, problems with "**What If?**" parts, problems referred to in the chapter text, problems based on experimental data, order-of-magnitude problems, problems about biological applications, design problems, *Jeopardy!* problems, review problems, problems reflecting historical reasoning about confusing ideas, problems developing symbolic reasoning skill, problems with qualitative parts, ranking questions, and other objective questions.

QUESTIONS   The questions section at the end of each chapter has been significantly revised. Multiple-choice, ranking, and true–false questions have been added. The instructor may select items to assign as homework or use in the classroom, possibly with "peer instruction" methods and possibly with "clicker" systems. More than eight hundred questions are included in this edition. Answers to selected questions are included in the *Student Solutions Manual/Study Guide,* and answers to all questions are found in the *Instructor's Solutions Manual.*

> **19. O (i)** Rank the gravitational accelerations you would measure for (a) a 2-kg object 5 cm above the floor, (b) a 2-kg object 120 cm above the floor, (c) a 3-kg object 120 cm above the floor, and (d) a 3-kg object 80 cm above the floor. List the one with the largest-magnitude acceleration first. If two are equal, show their equality in your list. **(ii)** Rank the gravitational forces on the same four objects, largest magnitude first. **(iii)** Rank the gravitational potential energies (of the object–Earth system) for the same four objects, largest first, taking $y = 0$ at the floor.
>
> **23. O** An ice cube has been given a push and slides without friction on a level table. Which is correct? (a) It is in stable equilibrium. (b) It is in unstable equilibrium. (c) It is in neutral equilibrium (d) It is not in equilibrium.

WORKED EXAMPLES   Two types of worked examples are presented to aid student comprehension. All worked examples in the text may be assigned for homework in WebAssign.

The first example type presents a problem and numerical answer. As discussed earlier, solutions to these examples have been altered in this edition to feature a two-column layout to explain the physical concepts and the mathematical steps side by side. Every example follows the explicit steps of the General Problem-Solving Strategy outlined in Chapter 2.

The second type of example is conceptual in nature. To accommodate increased emphasis on understanding physical concepts, the many conceptual examples are labeled as such, set off in boxes, and designed to focus students on the physical situation in the problem.

WHAT IF?   Approximately one-third of the worked examples in the text contain a **What If?** feature. At the completion of the example solution, a **What If?** question offers a variation on the situation posed in the text of the example. For instance, this feature might explore the effects of changing the conditions of the situation, determine what happens when a quantity is taken to a particular limiting value, or question whether additional information can be determined about the situation. This feature encourages students to think about the results of the example, and it also assists in conceptual understanding of the principles. **What If?** questions also prepare students to encounter novel problems that may be included on exams. Some of the end-of-chapter problems also include this feature.

QUICK QUIZZES   Quick Quizzes provide students an opportunity to test their understanding of the physical concepts presented. The questions require students to make decisions on the basis of sound reasoning, and some of the questions have been written to help students overcome common misconceptions. Quick Quizzes have been cast in an objective format, including multiple-choice, true–false, and ranking. Answers to all Quick Quiz questions are found at the end of each chapter. Additional Quick Quizzes that can be used in classroom teaching are available on the instructor's companion Web site. Many instructors choose to use such questions in a "peer instruction" teaching style or with the use of personal response system "clickers," but they can be used in standard quiz format as well. Quick Quizzes are set off from the text by horizontal lines:

Quick Quiz 7.5   A dart is loaded into a spring-loaded toy dart gun by pushing the spring in by a distance x. For the next loading, the spring is compressed a distance $2x$. How much faster does the second dart leave the gun compared with the first? (a) four times as fast   (b) two times as fast   (c) the same   (d) half as fast (e) one-fourth as fast

---

PITFALL PREVENTION 16.2
Two Kinds of Speed/Velocity

Do not confuse v, the speed of the wave as it propagates along the string, with v_y, the transverse velocity of a point on the string. The speed v is constant for a uniform medium, whereas v_y varies sinusoidally.

PITFALL PREVENTIONS   More than two hundred Pitfall Preventions (such as the one to the left) are provided to help students avoid common mistakes and misunderstandings. These features, which are placed in the margins of the text, address both common student misconceptions and situations in which students often follow unproductive paths.

Helpful Features

STYLE   To facilitate rapid comprehension, we have written the book in a clear, logical, and engaging style. We have chosen a writing style that is somewhat informal and relaxed so that students will find the text appealing and enjoyable to read. New terms are carefully defined, and we have avoided the use of jargon.

IMPORTANT STATEMENTS AND EQUATIONS   Most important statements and definitions are set in **boldface** or are highlighted with a background screen for added emphasis and ease of review. Similarly, important equations are highlighted with a background screen to facilitate location.

MARGINAL NOTES   Comments and notes appearing in the margin with a ▶ icon can be used to locate important statements, equations, and concepts in the text.

PEDAGOGICAL USE OF COLOR   Readers should consult the **pedagogical color chart** (inside the front cover) for a listing of the color-coded symbols used in the text diagrams. This system is followed consistently throughout the text.

MATHEMATICAL LEVEL   We have introduced calculus gradually, keeping in mind that students often take introductory courses in calculus and physics concurrently. Most steps are shown when basic equations are developed, and reference is often made to mathematical appendices near the end of the textbook. Vector products are introduced later in the text, where they are needed in physical applications. The dot product is introduced in Chapter 7, which addresses energy of a system; the cross product is introduced in Chapter 11, which deals with angular momentum.

SIGNIFICANT FIGURES   Significant figures in both worked examples and end-of-chapter problems have been handled with care. Most numerical examples are worked to either two or three significant figures, depending on the precision of the data provided. End-of-chapter problems regularly state data and answers to three-digit precision.

UNITS   The international system of units (SI) is used throughout the text. The U.S. customary system of units is used only to a limited extent in the chapters on mechanics and thermodynamics.

APPENDICES AND ENDPAPERS   Several appendices are provided near the end of the textbook. Most of the appendix material represents a review of mathematical concepts and techniques used in the text, including scientific notation, algebra, geometry, trigonometry, differential calculus, and integral calculus. Reference to these appendices is made throughout the text. Most mathematical review sections in the appendices include worked examples and exercises with answers. In addition to the mathematical reviews, the appendices contain tables of physical data, conversion factors, and the SI units of physical quantities as well as a periodic table of the elements. Other useful information—fundamental constants and physical data, planetary data, a list of standard prefixes, mathematical symbols, the Greek alphabet, and standard abbreviations of units of measure—appears on the endpapers.

Course Solutions That Fit Your Teaching Goals and Your Students' Learning Needs

Recent advances in educational technology have made homework management systems and audience response systems powerful and affordable tools to enhance the way you teach your course. Whether you offer a more traditional text-based course, are interested in using or are currently using an online homework management system such as WebAssign, or are ready to turn your lecture into an interactive learning environment with JoinIn on TurningPoint, you can be confident that the text's proven content provides the foundation for each and every component of our technology and ancillary package.

Homework Management Systems

Enhanced WebAssign   Whether you're an experienced veteran or a beginner, Enhanced WebAssign is the perfect solution to fit your homework management needs. Designed by physicists for physicists, this system is a reliable and user-friendly teaching companion. Enhanced WebAssign is available for *Physics for Scientists and Engineers*, giving you the freedom to assign

- every end-of-chapter Problem and Question, enhanced with hints and feedback
- every worked example, enhanced with hints and feedback, to help strengthen students' problem-solving skills
- every Quick Quiz, giving your students ample opportunity to test their conceptual understanding.

- animated Active Figures, enhanced with hints and feedback, to help students develop their visualization skills
- a math review to help students brush up on key quantitative concepts

Please visit **www.thomsonedu.com/physics/serway** to view a live demonstration of Enhanced WebAssign.

The text also supports the following Homework Management Systems:

LON-CAPA: A Computer-Assisted Personalized Approach
   http://www.lon-capa.org/

The University of Texas Homework Service
   contact **moore@physics.utexas.edu**

Personal Response Systems

JoinIn on TurningPoint Pose book-specific questions and display students' answers seamlessly within the Microsoft® PowerPoint slides of your own lecture in conjunction with the "clicker" hardware of your choice. JoinIn on TurningPoint works with most infrared or radio frequency keypad systems, including Responsecard, EduCue, H-ITT, and even laptops. Contact your local sales representative to learn more about our personal response software and hardware.

Personal Response System Content Regardless of the response system you are using, we provide the tested content to support it. Our ready-to-go content includes all the questions from the Quick Quizzes, test questions, and a selection of end-of-chapter questions to provide helpful conceptual checkpoints to drop into your lecture. Our series of Active Figure animations have also been enhanced with multiple-choice questions to help test students' observational skills.

We also feature the Assessing to Learn in the Classroom content from the University of Massachusetts at Amherst. This collection of 250 advanced conceptual questions has been tested in the classroom for more than ten years and takes peer learning to a new level.

Visit **www.thomsonedu.com/physics/serway** to download samples of our personal response system content.

Lecture Presentation Resources

The following resources provide support for your presentations in lecture.

MULTIMEDIA MANAGER INSTRUCTOR'S RESOURCE CD   An easy-to-use multimedia lecture tool, the Multimedia Manager Instructor's Resource CD allows you to quickly assemble art, animations, digital video, and database files with notes to create fluid lectures. The two-volume set (Volume 1: Chapters 1–22; Volume 2: Chapters 23–46) includes prebuilt PowerPoint lectures, a database of animations, video clips, and digital art from the text as well as editable electronic files of the *Instructor's Solutions Manual* and *Test Bank*.

TRANSPARENCY ACETATES   Each volume contains approximately one hundred transparency acetates featuring art from the text. Volume 1 contains Chapters 1 through 22, and Volume 2 contains Chapters 23 through 46.

Assessment and Course Preparation Resources

A number of resources listed below will assist with your assessment and preparation processes.

INSTRUCTOR'S SOLUTIONS MANUAL by Ralph McGrew. This two-volume manual contains complete worked solutions to all end-of-chapter problems in the textbook as well as answers to the even-numbered problems and all the questions. The solutions to problems new to the seventh edition are marked for easy identification. Volume 1 contains

Chapters 1 through 22, and Volume 2 contains Chapters 23 through 46. Electronic files of the Instructor's Solutions are available on the Multimedia Manager CD as well.

PRINTED TEST BANK by Edward Adelson. This two-volume test bank contains approximately 2 200 multiple-choice questions. These questions are also available in electronic format with complete answers and solutions in the ExamView test software and as editable Word® files on the Multimedia Manager CD. Volume 1 contains Chapters 1 through 22, and Volume 2 contains Chapters 23 through 46.

EXAMVIEW This easy-to-use test generator CD features all of the questions from the printed test bank in an editable format.

WEBCT AND BLACKBOARD CONTENT For users of either course management system, we provide our test bank questions in the proper format for easy upload into your online course. In addition, you can integrate the ThomsonNOW for Physics student tutorial content into your WebCT or Blackboard course, providing your students a single sign-on to all their Web-based learning resources. Contact your local sales representative to learn more about our WebCT and Blackboard resources.

INSTRUCTOR'S COMPANION WEB SITE Consult the instructor's site by pointing your browser to **www.thomsonedu.com/physics/serway** for additional Quick Quiz questions, a detailed list of content changes since the sixth edition, a problem correlation guide, images from the text, and sample PowerPoint lectures. Instructors adopting the seventh edition of *Physics for Scientists and Engineers* may download these materials after securing the appropriate password from their local Thomson•Brooks/Cole sales representative.

Student Resources

STUDENT SOLUTIONS MANUAL/STUDY GUIDE by John R. Gordon, Ralph McGrew, Raymond Serway, and John W. Jewett, Jr. This two-volume manual features detailed solutions to 20% of the end-of-chapter problems from the text. The manual also features a list of important equations, concepts, and notes from key sections of the text in addition to answers to selected end-of-chapter questions. Volume 1 contains Chapters 1 through 22, and Volume 2 contains Chapters 23 through 46.

THOMSONNOW PERSONAL STUDY This assessment-based student tutorial system provides students with a personalized learning plan based on their performance on a series of diagnostic pre-tests. Rich interactive content, including Active Figures, Coached Problems, and Interactive Examples, helps students prepare for tests and exams.

Teaching Options

The topics in this textbook are presented in the following sequence: classical mechanics, oscillations and mechanical waves, and heat and thermodynamics followed by electricity and magnetism, electromagnetic waves, optics, relativity, and modern physics. This presentation represents a traditional sequence, with the subject of mechanical waves being presented before electricity and magnetism. Some instructors may prefer to discuss both mechanical and electromagnetic waves together after completing electricity and magnetism. In this case, Chapters 16 through 18 could be covered along with Chapter 34. The chapter on relativity is placed near the end of the text because this topic often is treated as an introduction to the era of "modern physics." If time permits, instructors may choose to cover Chapter 39 after completing Chapter 13 as a conclusion to the material on Newtonian mechanics.

For those instructors teaching a two-semester sequence, some sections and chapters could be deleted without any loss of continuity. The following sections can be considered optional for this purpose:

© Thomson Learning/Charles D. Winters

Acknowledgments

This seventh edition of *Physics for Scientists and Engineers* was prepared with the guidance and assistance of many professors who reviewed selections of the manuscript, the prerevision text, or both. We wish to acknowledge the following scholars and express our sincere appreciation for their suggestions, criticisms, and encouragement:

David P. Balogh, *Fresno City College*
Leonard X. Finegold, *Drexel University*
Raymond Hall, *California State University, Fresno*

Bob Jacobsen, *University of California, Berkeley*
Robin Jordan, *Florida Atlantic University*
Rafael Lopez-Mobilia, *University of Texas at San Antonio*
Diana Lininger Markham, *City College of San Francisco*
Steven Morris, *Los Angeles Harbor City College*
Taha Mzoughi, *Kennesaw State University*
Nobel Sanjay Rebello, *Kansas State University*
John Rosendahl, *University of California, Irvine*
Mikolaj Sawicki, *John A. Logan College*
Glenn B. Stracher, *East Georgia College*
Som Tyagi, *Drexel University*
Robert Weidman, *Michigan Technological University*
Edward A. Whittaker, *Stevens Institute of Technology*

This title was carefully checked for accuracy by Zinoviy Akkerman, *City College of New York;* Grant Hart, *Brigham Young University;* Michael Kotlarchyk, *Rochester Institute of Technology;* Andres LaRosa, *Portland State University;* Bruce Mason, *University of Oklahoma at Norman;* Peter Moeck, *Portland State University;* Brian A. Raue, *Florida International University;* James E. Rutledge, *University of California at Irvine;* Bjoern Seipel, *Portland State University;* Z. M. Stadnik, *University of Ottawa;* and Harry W. K. Tom, *University of California at Riverside.* We thank them for their diligent efforts under schedule pressure.

We are grateful to Ralph McGrew for organizing the end-of-chapter problems, writing many new problems, and suggesting improvements in the content of the textbook. Problems and questions new to this edition were written by Duane Deardorff, Thomas Grace, Francisco Izaguirre, John Jewett, Robert Forsythe, Randall Jones, Ralph McGrew, Kurt Vandervoort, and Jerzy Wrobel. Help was very kindly given by Dwight Neuenschwander, Michael Kinney, Amy Smith, Will Mackin, and the Sewer Department of Grand Forks, North Dakota. Daniel Kim, Jennifer Hoffman, Ed Oberhofer, Richard Webb, Wesley Smith, Kevin Kilty, Zinoviy Akkerman, Michael Rudmin, Paul Cox, Robert LaMontagne, Ken Menningen, and Chris Church made corrections to problems taken from previous editions. We are grateful to authors John R. Gordon and Ralph McGrew for preparing the *Student Solutions Manual/Study Guide.* Author Ralph McGrew has prepared an excellent *Instructor's Solutions Manual.* Edward Adelson has carefully edited and improved the test bank. Kurt Vandervoort prepared extra Quick Quiz questions for the instructor's companion Web site.

Special thanks and recognition go to the professional staff at the Brooks/Cole Publishing Company—in particular, Ed Dodd, Brandi Kirksey (who managed the ancillary program and so much more), Shawn Vasquez, Sam Subity, Teri Hyde, Michelle Julet, David Harris, and Chris Hall—for their fine work during the development and production of this textbook. Mark Santee is our seasoned marketing manager, and Bryan Vann coordinates our marketing communications. We recognize the skilled production service and excellent artwork provided by the staff at Lachina Publishing Services, and the dedicated photo research efforts of Jane Sanders Miller.

Finally, we are deeply indebted to our wives, children, and grandchildren for their love, support, and long-term sacrifices.

Raymond A. Serway
St. Petersburg, Florida

John W. Jewett, Jr.
Pomona, California

It is appropriate to offer some words of advice that should be of benefit to you, the student. Before doing so, we assume you have read the Preface, which describes the various features of the text and support materials that will help you through the course.

How to Study

Instructors are often asked, "How should I study physics and prepare for examinations?" There is no simple answer to this question, but we can offer some suggestions based on our own experiences in learning and teaching over the years.

First and foremost, maintain a positive attitude toward the subject matter, keeping in mind that physics is the most fundamental of all natural sciences. Other science courses that follow will use the same physical principles, so it is important that you understand and are able to apply the various concepts and theories discussed in the text.

Concepts and Principles

It is essential that you understand the basic concepts and principles before attempting to solve assigned problems. You can best accomplish this goal by carefully reading the textbook before you attend your lecture on the covered material. When reading the text, you should jot down those points that are not clear to you. Also be sure to make a diligent attempt at answering the questions in the Quick Quizzes as you come to them in your reading. We have worked hard to prepare questions that help you judge for yourself how well you understand the material. Study the **What If?** features that appear in many of the worked examples carefully. They will help you extend your understanding beyond the simple act of arriving at a numerical result. The Pitfall Preventions will also help guide you away from common misunderstandings about physics. During class, take careful notes and ask questions about those ideas that are unclear to you. Keep in mind that few people are able to absorb the full meaning of scientific material after only one reading; several readings of the text and your notes may be necessary. Your lectures and laboratory work supplement the textbook and should clarify some of the more difficult material. You should minimize your memorization of material. Successful memorization of passages from the text, equations, and derivations does not necessarily indicate that you understand the material. Your understanding of the material will be enhanced through a combination of efficient study habits, discussions with other students and with instructors, and your ability to solve the problems presented in the textbook. Ask questions whenever you believe that clarification of a concept is necessary.

© Thomson Learning/Charles D. Winters

Study Schedule

It is important that you set up a regular study schedule, preferably a daily one. Make sure that you read the syllabus for the course and adhere to the schedule set by your instructor. The lectures will make much more sense if you read the corresponding text material *before* attending them. As a general rule, you should devote about two hours of study time for each hour you are in class. If you are having trouble with the course, seek the advice of the instructor or other students who have taken the course. You may find it necessary to seek further instruction from experienced students. Very often, instructors offer review sessions in addition to regular class periods. Avoid the practice of delaying study until a day or two before an exam. More often than not, this approach has disastrous results. Rather than undertake an all-night study session before a test, briefly review the basic concepts and equations, and then get a good night's rest. If you believe that you need additional help in understanding the concepts, in preparing for exams, or in problem solving, we suggest that you acquire a copy of the *Student Solutions Manual/Study Guide* that accompanies this textbook; this manual should be available at your college bookstore or through the publisher.

Use the Features

You should make full use of the various features of the text discussed in the Preface. For example, marginal notes are useful for locating and describing important equations and concepts, and **boldface** indicates important statements and definitions. Many useful tables are contained in the appendices, but most are incorporated in the text where they are most often referenced. Appendix B is a convenient review of mathematical tools used in the text.

Answers to odd-numbered problems are given at the end of the textbook, answers to Quick Quizzes are located at the end of each chapter, and solutions to selected end-of-chapter questions and problems are provided in the *Student Solutions Manual/Study Guide*. The table of contents provides an overview of the entire text, and the index enables you to locate specific material quickly. Footnotes are sometimes used to supplement the text or to cite other references on the subject discussed.

After reading a chapter, you should be able to define any new quantities introduced in that chapter and discuss the principles and assumptions that were used to arrive at certain key relations. The chapter summaries and the review sections of the *Student Solutions Manual/Study Guide* should help you in this regard. In some cases, you may find it necessary to refer to the textbook's index to locate certain topics. You should be able to associate with each physical quantity the correct symbol used to represent that quantity and the unit in which the quantity is specified. Furthermore, you should be able to express each important equation in concise and accurate prose.

Problem Solving

R. P. Feynman, Nobel laureate in physics, once said, "You do not know anything until you have practiced." In keeping with this statement, we strongly advise you to develop the skills necessary to solve a wide range of problems. Your ability to solve problems will be one of the main tests of your knowledge of physics; therefore, you should try to solve as many problems as possible. It is essential that you understand basic concepts and principles before attempting to solve problems. It is good practice to try to find alternate solutions to the same problem. For example, you can solve problems in mechanics using Newton's laws, but very often an alternative method that draws on energy considerations is more direct. You should not deceive yourself into thinking that you understand a problem merely because you have seen it solved in class. You must be able to solve the problem and similar problems on your own.

The approach to solving problems should be carefully planned. A systematic plan is especially important when a problem involves several concepts. First, read the problem several times until you are confident you understand what is being asked. Look for any key words that will help you interpret the problem and perhaps allow you to make certain assumptions. Your ability to interpret a question properly is an integral part of problem solving. Second, you should acquire the habit of writing down the information given in a problem and those quantities that need to be found; for example, you might construct a table listing both the quantities given and the quantities to be found. This procedure is sometimes used in the worked examples of the textbook. Finally, after you have decided on the method you believe is appropriate for a given problem, proceed with your solution. The General Problem-Solving Strategy will guide you through complex problems. If you follow the steps of this procedure *(Conceptualize, Categorize, Analyze, Finalize),* you will find it easier to come up with a solution and gain more from your efforts. This Strategy, located at the end of Chapter 2, is used in all worked examples in the remaining chapters so that you can learn how to apply it. Specific problem-solving strategies for certain types of situations are included in the text and appear with a blue heading. These specific strategies follow the outline of the General Problem-Solving Strategy.

Often, students fail to recognize the limitations of certain equations or physical laws in a particular situation. It is very important that you understand and remember the assumptions that underlie a particular theory or formalism. For example, certain equations in kinematics apply only to a particle moving with constant acceleration. These equations are not valid for describing motion whose acceleration is not constant such as the motion of an object connected to a spring or the motion of an object through a fluid. Study the Analysis Models for Problem-Solving in the chapter summaries carefully so that you know how each model can be applied to a specific situation.

Experiments

Physics is a science based on experimental observations. Therefore, we recommend that you try to supplement the text by performing various types of "hands-on" experiments either at home or in the laboratory. These experiments can be used to test ideas and models discussed in class or in the textbook. For example, the common Slinky toy is excellent for studying traveling waves, a ball swinging on the end of a long string can be used to investigate pendulum motion, various masses attached to the end of a vertical spring or rubber band can be used to determine their elastic nature, an old pair of Polaroid sunglasses and some discarded lenses and a magnifying glass are the components of various experiments in optics, and an approximate measure of the free-fall acceleration can be determined simply by measuring with a stopwatch the time it takes for a ball to drop from a known height. The list of such experiments is endless. When physical models are not available, be imaginative and try to develop models of your own.

New Media

We strongly encourage you to use the **ThomsonNOW** Web-based learning system that accompanies this textbook. It is far easier to understand physics if you see it in action, and these new materials will enable you to become a part of that action. **Thomson-NOW** media described in the Preface and accessed at **www.thomsonedu.com/physics/serway** feature a three-step learning process consisting of a pre-test, a personalized learning plan, and a post-test.

It is our sincere hope that you will find physics an exciting and enjoyable experience and that you will benefit from this experience, regardless of your chosen profession. Welcome to the exciting world of physics!

The scientist does not study nature because it is useful; he studies it because he delights in it, and he delights in it because it is beautiful. If nature were not beautiful, it would not be worth knowing, and if nature were not worth knowing, life would not be worth living.

—Henri Poincaré

Mechanics

Physics, the most fundamental physical science, is concerned with the fundamental principles of the Universe. It is the foundation upon which the other sciences—astronomy, biology, chemistry, and geology—are based. The beauty of physics lies in the simplicity of its fundamental principles and in the manner in which just a small number of concepts and models can alter and expand our view of the world around us.

The study of physics can be divided into six main areas:

1. *classical mechanics,* concerning the motion of objects that are large relative to atoms and move at speeds much slower than the speed of light;

2. *relativity,* a theory describing objects moving at any speed, even speeds approaching the speed of light;

3. *thermodynamics,* dealing with heat, work, temperature, and the statistical behavior of systems with large numbers of particles;

4. *electromagnetism,* concerned with electricity, magnetism, and electromagnetic fields;

5. *optics,* the study of the behavior of light and its interaction with materials;

6. *quantum mechanics,* a collection of theories connecting the behavior of matter at the submicroscopic level to macroscopic observations.

The disciplines of mechanics and electromagnetism are basic to all other branches of classical physics (developed before 1900) and modern physics (c. 1900–present). The first part of this textbook deals with classical mechanics, sometimes referred to as *Newtonian mechanics* or simply *mechanics.* Many principles and models used to understand mechanical systems retain their importance in the theories of other areas of physics and can later be used to describe many natural phenomena. Therefore, classical mechanics is of vital importance to students from all disciplines.

An electric vehicle recharges from a public charging station. Electric cars, as well as gasoline-powered vehicles and hybrid vehicles, use many of the concepts and principles of mechanics that we will study in this first part of the book. Quantities that we can use to describe the operation of vehicles include position, velocity, acceleration, force, energy, and momentum. (© Mehau Kulyk/Photo Researchers, Inc.)

A close-up of the gears inside a mechanical clock. Complicated timepieces have been built for centuries in an effort to measure time accurately. Time is one of the basic quantities that we use in studying the motion of objects. (© Photographer's Choice/Getty Images)

1 Physics and Measurement

ThomsonNOW™ Throughout this chapter and others, there are opportunities for online self-study, linking you to interactive tutorials based on your level of understanding. Sign in at **www.thomsonedu.com** to view tutorials and simulations, develop problem-solving skills, and test your knowledge with these interactive resources.

WebAssign Interactive content from this chapter and others may be assigned online in WebAssign.

Like all other sciences, physics is based on experimental observations and quantitative measurements. The main objectives of physics are to identify a limited number of fundamental laws that govern natural phenomena and use them to develop theories that can predict the results of future experiments. The fundamental laws used in developing theories are expressed in the language of mathematics, the tool that provides a bridge between theory and experiment.

When there is a discrepancy between the prediction of a theory and experimental results, new or modified theories must be formulated to remove the discrepancy. Many times a theory is satisfactory only under limited conditions; a more general theory might be satisfactory without such limitations. For example, the laws of motion discovered by Isaac Newton (1642–1727) accurately describe the motion of objects moving at normal speeds but do not apply to objects moving at speeds comparable with the speed of light. In contrast, the special theory of relativity developed later by Albert Einstein (1879–1955) gives the same results as Newton's laws at low speeds but also correctly describes the motion of objects at speeds approaching the speed of light. Hence, Einstein's special theory of relativity is a more general theory of motion than that formed from Newton's laws.

Classical physics includes the principles of classical mechanics, thermodynamics, optics, and electromagnetism developed before 1900. Important contributions to classical physics were provided by Newton, who was also one of the originators of calculus as a mathematical tool. Major developments in mechanics continued in the 18th century, but the fields of thermodynamics and electromagnetism were not developed until the latter part of the 19th century, principally because before that time the apparatus for controlled experiments in these disciplines was either too crude or unavailable.

A major revolution in physics, usually referred to as *modern physics,* began near the end of the 19th century. Modern physics developed mainly because many physical phenomena could not be explained by classical physics. The two most important developments in this modern era were the theories of relativity and quantum mechanics. Einstein's special theory of relativity not only correctly describes the motion of objects moving at speeds comparable to the speed of light; it also completely modifies the traditional concepts of space, time, and energy. The theory also shows that the speed of light is the upper limit of the speed of an object and that mass and energy are related. Quantum mechanics was formulated by a number of distinguished scientists to provide descriptions of physical phenomena at the atomic level. Many practical devices have been developed using the principles of quantum mechanics.

Scientists continually work at improving our understanding of fundamental laws. Numerous technological advances in recent times are the result of the efforts of many scientists, engineers, and technicians, such as unmanned planetary explorations and manned moon landings, microcircuitry and high-speed computers, sophisticated imaging techniques used in scientific research and medicine, and several remarkable results in genetic engineering. The impacts of such developments and discoveries on our society have indeed been great, and it is very likely that future discoveries and developments will be exciting, challenging, and of great benefit to humanity.

1.1   Standards of Length, Mass, and Time

To describe natural phenomena, we must make measurements of various aspects of nature. Each measurement is associated with a physical quantity, such as the length of an object.

If we are to report the results of a measurement to someone who wishes to reproduce this measurement, a *standard* must be defined. It would be meaningless if a visitor from another planet were to talk to us about a length of 8 "glitches" if we do not know the meaning of the unit glitch. On the other hand, if someone familiar with our system of measurement reports that a wall is 2 meters high and our unit of length is defined to be 1 meter, we know that the height of the wall is twice our basic length unit. Whatever is chosen as a standard must be readily accessible and must possess some property that can be measured reliably. Measurement standards used by different people in different places—throughout the Universe—must yield the same result. In addition, standards used for measurements must not change with time.

In 1960, an international committee established a set of standards for the fundamental quantities of science. It is called the **SI** (Système International), and its fundamental units of length, mass, and time are the *meter, kilogram,* and *second,* respectively. Other standards for SI fundamental units established by the committee are those for temperature (the *kelvin*), electric current (the *ampere*), luminous intensity (the *candela*), and the amount of substance (the *mole*).

The laws of physics are expressed as mathematical relationships among physical quantities that we will introduce and discuss throughout the book. In mechanics, the three fundamental quantities are length, mass, and time. All other quantities in mechanics can be expressed in terms of these three.

Length

We can identify **length** as the distance between two points in space. In 1120, the king of England decreed that the standard of length in his country would be named the *yard* and would be precisely equal to the distance from the tip of his nose to the end of his outstretched arm. Similarly, the original standard for the foot adopted by the French was the length of the royal foot of King Louis XIV. Neither of these standards is constant in time; when a new king took the throne, length measurements changed! The French standard prevailed until 1799, when the legal standard of length in France became the **meter** (m), defined as one ten-millionth of the distance from the equator to the North Pole along one particular longitudinal line that passes through Paris. Notice that this value is an Earth-based standard that does not satisfy the requirement that it can be used throughout the universe.

As recently as 1960, the length of the meter was defined as the distance between two lines on a specific platinum–iridium bar stored under controlled conditions in France. Current requirements of science and technology, however, necessitate more accuracy than that with which the separation between the lines on the bar can be determined. In the 1960s and 1970s, the meter was defined as 1 650 763.73 wavelengths[1] of orange-red light emitted from a krypton-86 lamp. In October 1983, however, the meter was redefined as **the distance traveled by light in vacuum during a time of 1/299 792 458 second.** In effect, this latest definition establishes that the speed of light in vacuum is precisely 299 792 458 meters per second. This definition of the meter is valid throughout the Universe based on our assumption that light is the same everywhere.

Table 1.1 lists approximate values of some measured lengths. You should study this table as well as the next two tables and begin to generate an intuition for what is meant by, for example, a length of 20 centimeters, a mass of 100 kilograms, or a time interval of 3.2×10^7 seconds.

PITFALL PREVENTION 1.1
Reasonable Values

Generating intuition about typical values of quantities when solving problems is important because you must think about your end result and determine if it seems reasonable. If you are calculating the mass of a housefly and arrive at a value of 100 kg, this answer is *unreasonable* and there is an error somewhere.

TABLE 1.1

Approximate Values of Some Measured Lengths

	Length (m)
Distance from the Earth to the most remote known quasar	1.4×10^{26}
Distance from the Earth to the most remote normal galaxies	9×10^{25}
Distance from the Earth to the nearest large galaxy (Andromeda)	2×10^{22}
Distance from the Sun to the nearest star (Proxima Centauri)	4×10^{16}
One light-year	9.46×10^{15}
Mean orbit radius of the Earth about the Sun	1.50×10^{11}
Mean distance from the Earth to the Moon	3.84×10^{8}
Distance from the equator to the North Pole	1.00×10^{7}
Mean radius of the Earth	6.37×10^{6}
Typical altitude (above the surface) of a satellite orbiting the Earth	2×10^{5}
Length of a football field	9.1×10^{1}
Length of a housefly	5×10^{-3}
Size of smallest dust particles	$\sim 10^{-4}$
Size of cells of most living organisms	$\sim 10^{-5}$
Diameter of a hydrogen atom	$\sim 10^{-10}$
Diameter of an atomic nucleus	$\sim 10^{-14}$
Diameter of a proton	$\sim 10^{-15}$

[1] We will use the standard international notation for numbers with more than three digits, in which groups of three digits are separated by spaces rather than commas. Therefore, 10 000 is the same as the common American notation of 10,000. Similarly, $\pi = 3.14159265$ is written as 3.141 592 65.

(a)   (b)

Figure 1.1   (a) The National Standard Kilogram No. 20, an accurate copy of the International Standard Kilogram kept at Sèvres, France, is housed under a double bell jar in a vault at the National Institute of Standards and Technology. (b) The primary time standard in the United States is a cesium fountain atomic clock developed at the National Institute of Standards and Technology laboratories in Boulder, Colorado. The clock will neither gain nor lose a second in 20 million years.

Mass

The SI fundamental unit of **mass,** the **kilogram** (kg), is defined as **the mass of a specific platinum–iridium alloy cylinder kept at the International Bureau of Weights and Measures at Sèvres, France**. This mass standard was established in 1887 and has not been changed since that time because platinum–iridium is an unusually stable alloy. A duplicate of the Sèvres cylinder is kept at the National Institute of Standards and Technology (NIST) in Gaithersburg, Maryland (Fig. 1.1a). Table 1.2 lists approximate values of the masses of various objects.

Time

Before 1960, the standard of **time** was defined in terms of the *mean solar day* for the year 1900. (A solar day is the time interval between successive appearances of the Sun at the highest point it reaches in the sky each day.) The fundamental unit of a **second** (s) was defined as $\left(\frac{1}{60}\right)\left(\frac{1}{60}\right)\left(\frac{1}{24}\right)$ of a mean solar day. The rotation of the Earth is now known to vary slightly with time. Therefore, this motion does not provide a time standard that is constant.

In 1967, the second was redefined to take advantage of the high precision attainable in a device known as an *atomic clock* (Fig. 1.1b), which measures vibrations of cesium atoms. One second is now defined as **9 192 631 770 times the period of vibration of radiation from the cesium-133 atom.**[2] Approximate values of time intervals are presented in Table 1.3.

TABLE 1.2
Approximate Masses of Various Objects

	Mass (kg)
Observable Universe	$\sim 10^{52}$
Milky Way galaxy	$\sim 10^{42}$
Sun	1.99×10^{30}
Earth	5.98×10^{24}
Moon	7.36×10^{22}
Shark	$\sim 10^{3}$
Human	$\sim 10^{2}$
Frog	$\sim 10^{-1}$
Mosquito	$\sim 10^{-5}$
Bacterium	$\sim 1 \times 10^{-15}$
Hydrogen atom	1.67×10^{-27}
Electron	9.11×10^{-31}

TABLE 1.3
Approximate Values of Some Time Intervals

	Time Interval (s)
Age of the Universe	5×10^{17}
Age of the Earth	1.3×10^{17}
Average age of a college student	6.3×10^{8}
One year	3.2×10^{7}
One day	8.6×10^{4}
One class period	3.0×10^{3}
Time interval between normal heartbeats	8×10^{-1}
Period of audible sound waves	$\sim 10^{-3}$
Period of typical radio waves	$\sim 10^{-6}$
Period of vibration of an atom in a solid	$\sim 10^{-13}$
Period of visible light waves	$\sim 10^{-15}$
Duration of a nuclear collision	$\sim 10^{-22}$
Time interval for light to cross a proton	$\sim 10^{-24}$

[2] *Period* is defined as the time interval needed for one complete vibration.

TABLE 1.4

Prefixes for Powers of Ten

Power	Prefix	Abbreviation	Power	Prefix	Abbreviation
10^{-24}	yocto	y	10^3	kilo	k
10^{-21}	zepto	z	10^6	mega	M
10^{-18}	atto	a	10^9	giga	G
10^{-15}	femto	f	10^{12}	tera	T
10^{-12}	pico	p	10^{15}	peta	P
10^{-9}	nano	n	10^{18}	exa	E
10^{-6}	micro	μ	10^{21}	zetta	Z
10^{-3}	milli	m	10^{24}	yotta	Y
10^{-2}	centi	c			
10^{-1}	deci	d			

In addition to SI, another system of units, the *U.S. customary system,* is still used in the United States despite acceptance of SI by the rest of the world. In this system, the units of length, mass, and time are the foot (ft), slug, and second, respectively. In this book, we shall use SI units because they are almost universally accepted in science and industry. We shall make some limited use of U.S. customary units in the study of classical mechanics.

In addition to the fundamental SI units of meter, kilogram, and second, we can also use other units, such as millimeters and nanoseconds, where the prefixes *milli-* and *nano-* denote multipliers of the basic units based on various powers of ten. Prefixes for the various powers of ten and their abbreviations are listed in Table 1.4. For example, 10^{-3} m is equivalent to 1 millimeter (mm), and 10^3 m corresponds to 1 kilometer (km). Likewise, 1 kilogram (kg) is 10^3 grams (g), and 1 megavolt (MV) is 10^6 volts (V).

The variables length, time, and mass are examples of *fundamental quantities.* Most other variables are *derived quantities,* those that can be expressed as a mathematical combination of fundamental quantities. Common examples are *area* (a product of two lengths) and *speed* (a ratio of a length to a time interval).

Another example of a derived quantity is **density.** The density ρ (Greek letter rho) of any substance is defined as its *mass per unit volume:*

$$\rho \equiv \frac{m}{V} \tag{1.1}$$

▶ A table of the letters in the Greek alphabet is provided on the back endpaper of this book.

In terms of fundamental quantities, density is a ratio of a mass to a product of three lengths. Aluminum, for example, has a density of 2.70×10^3 kg/m³, and iron has a density of 7.86×10^3 kg/m³. An extreme difference in density can be imagined by thinking about holding a 10-centimeter (cm) cube of Styrofoam in one hand and a 10-cm cube of lead in the other. See Table 14.1 in Chapter 14 for densities of several materials.

Quick Quiz 1.1 In a machine shop, two cams are produced, one of aluminum and one of iron. Both cams have the same mass. Which cam is larger? (a) The aluminum cam is larger. (b) The iron cam is larger. (c) Both cams are the same size.

1.2 Matter and Model Building

If physicists cannot interact with some phenomenon directly, they often imagine a **model** for a physical system that is related to the phenomenon. For example, we cannot interact directly with atoms because they are too small. Therefore, we build a mental model of an atom based on a system of a nucleus and one or more electrons outside the nucleus. Once we have identified the physical components of the model, we make predictions about its behavior based on the interactions among the components of the system or the interaction between the system and the environment outside the system.

As an example, consider the behavior of *matter*. A 1-kg cube of solid gold, such as that at the top of Figure 1.2, has a length of 3.73 cm on a side. Is this cube nothing but wall-to-wall gold, with no empty space? If the cube is cut in half, the two pieces still retain their chemical identity as solid gold. What if the pieces are cut again and again, indefinitely? Will the smaller and smaller pieces always be gold? Such questions can be traced to early Greek philosophers. Two of them—Leucippus and his student Democritus—could not accept the idea that such cuttings could go on forever. They developed a model for matter by speculating that the process ultimately must end when it produces a particle that can no longer be cut. In Greek, *atomos* means "not sliceable." From this Greek term comes our English word *atom*.

The Greek model of the structure of matter was that all ordinary matter consists of atoms, as suggested in the middle of Figure 1.2. Beyond that, no additional structure was specified in the model; atoms acted as small particles that interacted with one another, but internal structure of the atom was not a part of the model.

In 1897, J. J. Thomson identified the electron as a charged particle and as a constituent of the atom. This led to the first atomic model that contained internal structure. We shall discuss this model in Chapter 42.

Following the discovery of the nucleus in 1911, an atomic model was developed in which each atom is made up of electrons surrounding a central nucleus. A nucleus of gold is shown in Figure 1.2. This model leads, however, to a new question: Does the nucleus have structure? That is, is the nucleus a single particle or a collection of particles? By the early 1930s, a model evolved that described two basic entities in the nucleus: protons and neutrons. The proton carries a positive electric charge, and a specific chemical element is identified by the number of protons in its nucleus. This number is called the **atomic number** of the element. For instance, the nucleus of a hydrogen atom contains one proton (so the atomic number of hydrogen is 1), the nucleus of a helium atom contains two protons (atomic number 2), and the nucleus of a uranium atom contains 92 protons (atomic number 92). In addition to atomic number, a second number—**mass number,** defined as the number of protons plus neutrons in a nucleus—characterizes atoms. The atomic number of a specific element never varies (i.e., the number of protons does not vary) but the mass number can vary (i.e., the number of neutrons varies).

Is that, however, where the process of breaking down stops? Protons, neutrons, and a host of other exotic particles are now known to be composed of six different varieties of particles called **quarks,** which have been given the names of *up, down, strange, charmed, bottom,* and *top*. The up, charmed, and top quarks have electric charges of $+\frac{2}{3}$ that of the proton, whereas the down, strange, and bottom quarks have charges of $-\frac{1}{3}$ that of the proton. The proton consists of two up quarks and one down quark, as shown at the bottom of Figure 1.2 and labeled u and d. This structure predicts the correct charge for the proton. Likewise, the neutron consists of two down quarks and one up quark, giving a net charge of zero.

You should develop a process of building models as you study physics. In this study, you will be challenged with many mathematical problems to solve. One of the most important problem-solving techniques is to build a model for the problem: identify a system of physical components for the problem and make predictions of the behavior of the system based on the interactions among its components or the interaction between the system and its surrounding environment.

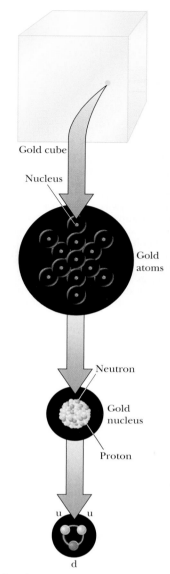

Figure 1.2   Levels of organization in matter. Ordinary matter consists of atoms, and at the center of each atom is a compact nucleus consisting of protons and neutrons. Protons and neutrons are composed of quarks. The quark composition of a proton is shown.

1.3   Dimensional Analysis

The word *dimension* has a special meaning in physics. It denotes the physical nature of a quantity. Whether a distance is measured in units of feet or meters or fathoms, it is still a distance. We say its dimension is *length*.

TABLE 1.5

Dimensions and Units of Four Derived Quantities

Quantity	Area	Volume	Speed	Acceleration
Dimensions	L^2	L^3	L/T	L/T^2
SI units	m^2	m^3	m/s	m/s^2
U.S. customary units	ft^2	ft^3	ft/s	ft/s^2

The symbols we use in this book to specify the dimensions of length, mass, and time are L, M, and T, respectively.[3] We shall often use brackets [ ] to denote the dimensions of a physical quantity. For example, the symbol we use for speed in this book is v, and in our notation, the dimensions of speed are written $[v] = L/T$. As another example, the dimensions of area A are $[A] = L^2$. The dimensions and units of area, volume, speed, and acceleration are listed in Table 1.5. The dimensions of other quantities, such as force and energy, will be described as they are introduced in the text.

In many situations, you may have to check a specific equation to see if it matches your expectations. A useful and powerful procedure called **dimensional analysis** can assist in this check because **dimensions can be treated as algebraic quantities.** For example, quantities can be added or subtracted only if they have the same dimensions. Furthermore, the terms on both sides of an equation must have the same dimensions. By following these simple rules, you can use dimensional analysis to determine whether an expression has the correct form. Any relationship can be correct only if the dimensions on both sides of the equation are the same.

To illustrate this procedure, suppose you are interested in an equation for the position x of a car at a time t if the car starts from rest at $x = 0$ and moves with constant acceleration a. The correct expression for this situation is $x = \frac{1}{2}at^2$. Let us use dimensional analysis to check the validity of this expression. The quantity x on the left side has the dimension of length. For the equation to be dimensionally correct, the quantity on the right side must also have the dimension of length. We can perform a dimensional check by substituting the dimensions for acceleration, L/T^2 (Table 1.5), and time, T, into the equation. That is, the dimensional form of the equation $x = \frac{1}{2}at^2$ is

$$L = \frac{L}{T^2} \cdot T^2 = L$$

The dimensions of time cancel as shown, leaving the dimension of length on the right-hand side to match that on the left.

A more general procedure using dimensional analysis is to set up an expression of the form

$$x \propto a^n t^m$$

where n and m are exponents that must be determined and the symbol $\propto$ indicates a proportionality. This relationship is correct only if the dimensions of both sides are the same. Because the dimension of the left side is length, the dimension of the right side must also be length. That is,

$$[a^n t^m] = L = L^1 T^0$$

Because the dimensions of acceleration are L/T^2 and the dimension of time is T, we have

$$(L/T^2)^n T^m = L^1 T^0 \quad \rightarrow \quad (L^n T^{m-2n}) = L^1 T^0$$

---

[3] The *dimensions* of a quantity will be symbolized by a capitalized, nonitalic letter, such as L or T. The *algebraic symbol* for the quantity itself will be italicized, such as L for the length of an object or t for time.

The exponents of L and T must be the same on both sides of the equation. From the exponents of L, we see immediately that $n = 1$. From the exponents of T, we see that $m - 2n = 0$, which, once we substitute for n, gives us $m = 2$. Returning to our original expression $x \propto a^n t^m$, we conclude that $x \propto at^2$.

Quick Quiz 1.2   True or False: Dimensional analysis can give you the numerical value of constants of proportionality that may appear in an algebraic expression.

EXAMPLE 1.1   **Analysis of an Equation**

Show that the expression $v = at$, where v represents speed, a acceleration, and t an instant of time, is dimensionally correct.

SOLUTION

Identify the dimensions of v from Table 1.5:

$$[v] = \frac{L}{T}$$

Identify the dimensions of a from Table 1.5 and multiply by the dimensions of t:

$$[at] = \frac{L}{T^2} T = \frac{L}{T}$$

Therefore, $v = at$ is dimensionally correct because we have the same dimensions on both sides. (If the expression were given as $v = at^2$, it would be dimensionally *incorrect*. Try it and see!)

EXAMPLE 1.2   **Analysis of a Power Law**

Suppose we are told that the acceleration a of a particle moving with uniform speed v in a circle of radius r is proportional to some power of r, say r^n, and some power of v, say v^m. Determine the values of n and m and write the simplest form of an equation for the acceleration.

SOLUTION

Write an expression for a with a dimensionless constant of proportionality k:

$$a = kr^n v^m$$

Substitute the dimensions of a, r, and v:

$$\frac{L}{T^2} = L^n \left(\frac{L}{T}\right)^m = \frac{L^{n+m}}{T^m}$$

Equate the exponents of L and T so that the dimensional equation is balanced:

$$n + m = 1 \quad \text{and} \quad m = 2$$

Solve the two equations for n:

$$n = -1$$

Write the acceleration expression:

$$a = kr^{-1} v^2 = k\frac{v^2}{r}$$

In Section 4.4 on uniform circular motion, we show that $k = 1$ if a consistent set of units is used. The constant k would not equal 1 if, for example, v were in km/h and you wanted a in m/s^2.

1.4 Conversion of Units

Sometimes you must convert units from one measurement system to another or convert within a system (for example, from kilometers to meters). Equalities between SI and U.S. customary units of length are as follows:

$$1 \text{ mile} = 1\,609 \text{ m} = 1.609 \text{ km} \qquad 1 \text{ ft} = 0.304\,8 \text{ m} = 30.48 \text{ cm}$$

$$1 \text{ m} = 39.37 \text{ in.} = 3.281 \text{ ft} \qquad 1 \text{ in.} = 0.025\,4 \text{ m} = 2.54 \text{ cm (exactly)}$$

A more complete list of conversion factors can be found in Appendix A.

Like dimensions, units can be treated as algebraic quantities that can cancel each other. For example, suppose we wish to convert 15.0 in. to centimeters. Because 1 in. is defined as exactly 2.54 cm, we find that

$$15.0 \text{ in.} = (15.0 \cancel{\text{ in.}})\left(\frac{2.54 \text{ cm}}{1 \cancel{\text{ in.}}}\right) = 38.1 \text{ cm}$$

where the ratio in parentheses is equal to 1. We must place the unit "inch" in the denominator so that it cancels with the unit in the original quantity. The remaining unit is the centimeter, our desired result.

Quick Quiz 1.3 The distance between two cities is 100 mi. What is the number of kilometers between the two cities? (a) smaller than 100 (b) larger than 100 (c) equal to 100

EXAMPLE 1.3 **Is He Speeding?**

On an interstate highway in a rural region of Wyoming, a car is traveling at a speed of 38.0 m/s. Is the driver exceeding the speed limit of 75.0 mi/h?

SOLUTION

Convert meters in the speed to miles:

$$(38.0 \cancel{\text{ m}}/s)\left(\frac{1 \text{ mi}}{1\,609 \cancel{\text{ m}}}\right) = 2.36 \times 10^{-2} \text{ mi/s}$$

Convert seconds to hours:

$$(2.36 \times 10^{-2} \text{ mi}/\cancel{s})\left(\frac{60 \cancel{s}}{1 \cancel{\text{ min}}}\right)\left(\frac{60 \cancel{\text{ min}}}{1 \text{ h}}\right) = 85.0 \text{ mi/h}$$

The driver is indeed exceeding the speed limit and should slow down.

What If? What if the driver were from outside the United States and is familiar with speeds measured in km/h? What is the speed of the car in km/h?

Answer We can convert our final answer to the appropriate units:

$$(85.0 \cancel{\text{ mi}}/h)\left(\frac{1.609 \text{ km}}{1 \cancel{\text{ mi}}}\right) = 137 \text{ km/h}$$

Figure 1.3 shows an automobile speedometer displaying speeds in both mi/h and km/h. Can you check the conversion we just performed using this photograph?

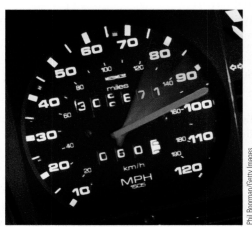

Figure 1.3 The speedometer of a vehicle that shows speeds in both miles per hour and kilometers per hour.

Phil Boorman/Getty Images

1.5 Estimates and Order-of-Magnitude Calculations

Suppose someone asks you the number of bits of data on a typical musical compact disc. In response, it is not generally expected that you would provide the exact number but rather an estimate, which may be expressed in scientific notation. An *order of magnitude* of a number is determined as follows:

1. Express the number in scientific notation, with the multiplier of the power of ten between 1 and 10 and a unit.
2. If the multiplier is less than 3.162 (the square root of ten), the order of magnitude of the number is the power of ten in the scientific notation. If the multiplier is greater than 3.162, the order of magnitude is one larger than the power of ten in the scientific notation.

We use the symbol $\sim$ for "is on the order of." Use the procedure above to verify the orders of magnitude for the following lengths:

$$0.008\ 6\ \text{m} \sim 10^{-2}\ \text{m} \qquad 0.002\ 1\ \text{m} \sim 10^{-3}\ \text{m} \qquad 720\ \text{m} \sim 10^{3}\ \text{m}$$

Usually, when an order-of-magnitude estimate is made, the results are reliable to within about a factor of 10. If a quantity increases in value by three orders of magnitude, its value increases by a factor of about $10^3 = 1\ 000$.

Inaccuracies caused by guessing too low for one number are often canceled by other guesses that are too high. You will find that with practice your guesstimates become better and better. Estimation problems can be fun to work because you freely drop digits, venture reasonable approximations for unknown numbers, make simplifying assumptions, and turn the question around into something you can answer in your head or with minimal mathematical manipulation on paper. Because of the simplicity of these types of calculations, they can be performed on a *small* scrap of paper and are often called "back-of-the-envelope calculations."

EXAMPLE 1.4   **Breaths in a Lifetime**

Estimate the number of breaths taken during an average human life span.

SOLUTION

We start by guessing that the typical human life span is about 70 years. Think about the average number of breaths that a person takes in 1 min. This number varies depending on whether the person is exercising, sleeping, angry, serene, and so forth. To the nearest order of magnitude, we shall choose 10 breaths per minute as our estimate. (This estimate is certainly closer to the true average value than 1 breath per minute or 100 breaths per minute.)

Find the approximate number of minutes in a year:
$$1\ \text{yr} \left(\frac{400\ \text{days}}{1\ \text{yr}} \right) \left(\frac{25\ \text{h}}{1\ \text{day}} \right) \left(\frac{60\ \text{min}}{1\ \text{h}} \right) = 6 \times 10^5\ \text{min}$$

Find the approximate number of minutes in a 70-year lifetime:
$$\text{number of minutes} = (70\ \text{yr})(6 \times 10^5\ \text{min/yr})$$
$$= 4 \times 10^7\ \text{min}$$

Find the approximate number of breaths in a lifetime:
$$\text{number of breaths} = (10\ \text{breaths/min})(4 \times 10^7\ \text{min})$$
$$= 4 \times 10^8\ \text{breaths}$$

Therefore, a person takes on the order of 10^9 breaths in a lifetime. Notice how much simpler it is in the first calculation above to multiply 400×25 than it is to work with the more accurate 365×24.

What If?   What if the average life span were estimated as 80 years instead of 70? Would that change our final estimate?

Answer   We could claim that $(80\ \text{yr})(6 \times 10^5\ \text{min/yr}) = 5 \times 10^7\ \text{min}$, so our final estimate should be 5×10^8 breaths. This answer is still on the order of 10^9 breaths, so an order-of-magnitude estimate would be unchanged.

1.6   Significant Figures

When certain quantities are measured, the measured values are known only to within the limits of the experimental uncertainty. The value of this uncertainty can depend on various factors, such as the quality of the apparatus, the skill of the experimenter, and the number of measurements performed. The number of **significant figures** in a measurement can be used to express something about the uncertainty.

As an example of significant figures, suppose we are asked to measure the area of a compact disc using a meter stick as a measuring instrument. Let us assume the accuracy to which we can measure the radius of the disc is ± 0.1 cm. Because of the uncertainty of ± 0.1 cm, if the radius is measured to be 6.0 cm, we can claim only that its radius lies somewhere between 5.9 cm and 6.1 cm. In this case, we say that the measured value of 6.0 cm has two significant figures. Note that **the significant figures include the first estimated digit.** Therefore, we could write the radius as (6.0 ± 0.1) cm.

Now we find the area of the disc by using the equation for the area of a circle. If we were to claim the area is $A = \pi r^2 = \pi (6.0 \text{ cm})^2 = 113 \text{ cm}^2$, our answer would be unjustifiable because it contains three significant figures, which is greater than the number of significant figures in the radius. A good rule of thumb to use in determining the number of significant figures that can be claimed in a multiplication or a division is as follows:

> When multiplying several quantities, the number of significant figures in the final answer is the same as the number of significant figures in the quantity having the smallest number of significant figures. The same rule applies to division.

Applying this rule to the area of the compact disc, we see that the answer for the area can have only two significant figures because our measured radius has only two significant figures. Therefore, all we can claim is that the area is $1.1 \times 10^2 \text{ cm}^2$.

Zeros may or may not be significant figures. Those used to position the decimal point in such numbers as 0.03 and 0.007 5 are not significant. Therefore, there are one and two significant figures, respectively, in these two values. When the zeros come after other digits, however, there is the possibility of misinterpretation. For example, suppose the mass of an object is given as 1 500 g. This value is ambiguous because we do not know whether the last two zeros are being used to locate the decimal point or whether they represent significant figures in the measurement. To remove this ambiguity, it is common to use scientific notation to indicate the number of significant figures. In this case, we would express the mass as 1.5×10^3 g if there are two significant figures in the measured value, 1.50×10^3 g if there are three significant figures, and 1.500×10^3 g if there are four. The same rule holds for numbers less than 1, so 2.3×10^{-4} has two significant figures (and therefore could be written 0.000 23) and 2.30×10^{-4} has three significant figures (also written 0.000 230).

For addition and subtraction, you must consider the number of decimal places when you are determining how many significant figures to report:

> When numbers are added or subtracted, the number of decimal places in the result should equal the smallest number of decimal places of any term in the sum.

For example, if we wish to compute $123 + 5.35$, the answer is 128 and not 128.35. If we compute the sum $1.000\ 1 + 0.000\ 3 = 1.000\ 4$, the result has five significant figures even though one of the terms in the sum, 0.000 3, has only one significant figure. Likewise, if we perform the subtraction $1.002 - 0.998 = 0.004$, the result

PITFALL PREVENTION 1.4
Read Carefully

Notice that the rule for addition and subtraction is different from that for multiplication and division. For addition and subtraction, the important consideration is the number of *decimal places*, not the number of *significant figures*.

has only one significant figure even though one term has four significant figures and the other has three.

> In this book, most of the numerical examples and end-of-chapter problems will yield answers having three significant figures. When carrying out order-of-magnitude calculations, we shall typically work with a single significant figure.

If the number of significant figures in the result of an addition or subtraction must be reduced, there is a general rule for rounding numbers: the last digit retained is increased by 1 if the last digit dropped is greater than 5. If the last digit dropped is less than 5, the last digit retained remains as it is. If the last digit dropped is equal to 5, the remaining digit should be rounded to the nearest even number. (This rule helps avoid accumulation of errors in long arithmetic processes.)

A technique for avoiding error accumulation is to delay rounding of numbers in a long calculation until you have the final result. Wait until you are ready to copy the final answer from your calculator before rounding to the correct number of significant figures.

EXAMPLE 1.5   **Installing a Carpet**

A carpet is to be installed in a room whose length is measured to be 12.71 m and whose width is measured to be 3.46 m. Find the area of the room.

SOLUTION

If you multiply 12.71 m by 3.46 m on your calculator, you will see an answer of 43.976 6 m². How many of these numbers should you claim? Our rule of thumb for multiplication tells us that you can claim only the number of significant figures in your answer as are present in the measured quantity having the lowest number of significant figures. In this example, the lowest number of significant figures is three in 3.46 m, so we should express our final answer as 44.0 m².

Summary

ThomsonNOW Sign in at **www.thomsonedu.com** and go to ThomsonNOW to take a practice test for this chapter.

DEFINITIONS

The three fundamental physical quantities of mechanics are **length, mass,** and **time,** which in the SI system have the units **meter** (m), **kilogram** (kg), and **second** (s), respectively. These fundamental quantities cannot be defined in terms of more basic quantities.

The **density** of a substance is defined as its *mass per unit volume:*

$$\rho \equiv \frac{m}{V} \qquad (1.1)$$

CONCEPTS AND PRINCIPLES

The method of **dimensional analysis** is very powerful in solving physics problems. Dimensions can be treated as algebraic quantities. By making estimates and performing order-of-magnitude calculations, you should be able to approximate the answer to a problem when there is not enough information available to specify an exact solution completely.

When you compute a result from several measured numbers, each of which has a certain accuracy, you should give the result with the correct number of **significant figures.** When multiplying several quantities, the number of significant figures in the final answer is the same as the number of significant figures in the quantity having the smallest number of significant figures. The same rule applies to division. When numbers are added or subtracted, the number of decimal places in the result should equal the smallest number of decimal places of any term in the sum.

Questions

☐ denotes answer available in *Student Solutions Manual/Study Guide;* **O** denotes objective question

1. Suppose the three fundamental standards of the metric system were length, *density,* and time rather than length, *mass,* and time. The standard of density in this system is to be defined as that of water. What considerations about water would you need to address to make sure the standard of density is as accurate as possible?

2. Express the following quantities using the prefixes given in Table 1.4: (a) 3×10^{-4} m   (b) 5×10^{-5} s   (c) 72×10^2 g

3. O Rank the following five quantities in order from the largest to the smallest: (a) 0.032 kg   (b) 15 g (c) 2.7×10^5 mg   (d) 4.1×10^{-8} Gg   (e) 2.7×10^8 μg. If two of the masses are equal, give them equal rank in your list.

4. O If an equation is dimensionally correct, does that mean that the equation must be true? If an equation is not dimensionally correct, does that mean that the equation cannot be true?

5. O Answer each question yes or no. Must two quantities have the same dimensions (a) if you are adding them? (b) If you are multiplying them? (c) If you are subtracting them? (d) If you are dividing them? (e) If you are using

one quantity as an exponent in raising the other to a power? (f) If you are equating them?

6. O The price of gasoline at a particular station is 1.3 euros per liter. An American student can use 41 euros to buy gasoline. Knowing that 4 quarts make a gallon and that 1 liter is close to 1 quart, she quickly reasons that she can buy (choose one) (a) less than 1 gallon of gasoline, (b) about 5 gallons of gasoline, (c) about 8 gallons of gasoline, (d) more than 10 gallons of gasoline.

7. O One student uses a meterstick to measure the thickness of a textbook and finds it to be 4.3 cm ± 0.1 cm. Other students measure the thickness with vernier calipers and obtain (a) 4.32 cm ± 0.01 cm, (b) 4.31 cm ± 0.01 cm, (c) 4.24 cm ± 0.01 cm, and (d) 4.43 cm ± 0.01 cm. Which of these four measurements, if any, agree with that obtained by the first student?

8. O A calculator displays a result as 1.365 248 0 $\times 10^7$ kg. The estimated uncertainty in the result is ±2%. How many digits should be included as significant when the result is written down? Choose one: (a) zero   (b) one (c) two   (d) three   (e) four   (f) five   (g) the number cannot be determined

Problems

WebAssign   The Problems from this chapter may be assigned online in WebAssign.

ThomsonNOW   Sign in at **www.thomsonedu.com** and go to ThomsonNOW to assess your understanding of this chapter's topics with additional quizzing and conceptual questions.

1, 2, 3 denotes straightforward, intermediate, challenging;   ☐ denotes full solution available in *Student Solutions Manual/Study Guide;*   ▲ denotes coached solution with hints available at **www.thomsonedu.com;**   denotes developing symbolic reasoning;   ● denotes asking for qualitative reasoning;   ▪ denotes computer useful in solving problem

Section 1.1 Standards of Length, Mass, and Time

Note: Consult the endpapers, appendices, and tables in the text whenever necessary in solving problems. For this chapter, Table 14.1 and Appendix B.3 may be particularly useful. Answers to odd-numbered problems appear in the back of the book.

1. ● Use information on the endpapers of this book to calculate the average density of the Earth. Where does the value fit among those listed in Table 14.1? Look up the density of a typical surface rock, such as granite, in another source and compare the density of the Earth to it.

2. The standard kilogram is a platinum-iridium cylinder 39.0 mm in height and 39.0 mm in diameter. What is the density of the material?

3. A major motor company displays a die-cast model of its first automobile, made from 9.35 kg of iron. To celebrate its one-hundredth year in business, a worker will recast the model in gold from the original dies. What mass of gold is needed to make the new model?

4. ● A proton, which is the nucleus of a hydrogen atom, can be modeled as a sphere with a diameter of 2.4 fm and a mass of 1.67×10^{-27} kg. Determine the density of the proton and state how it compares with the density of lead, which is given in Table 14.1.

5. Two spheres are cut from a certain uniform rock. One has radius 4.50 cm. The mass of the second sphere is five times greater. Find the radius of the second sphere.

Section 1.2 Matter and Model Building

6. A crystalline solid consists of atoms stacked up in a repeating lattice structure. Consider a crystal as shown in Figure P1.6a. The atoms reside at the corners of cubes of side $L = 0.200$ nm. One piece of evidence for the regular

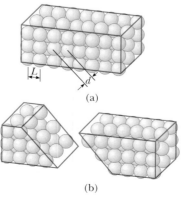

(a)

(b)

Figure P1.6

2 = intermediate;   3 = challenging;   ☐ = SSM/SG;   ▲ = ThomsonNOW;   = symbolic reasoning;   ● = qualitative reasoning

arrangement of atoms comes from the flat surfaces along which a crystal separates, or cleaves, when it is broken. Suppose this crystal cleaves along a face diagonal as shown in Figure P1.6b. Calculate the spacing d between two adjacent atomic planes that separate when the crystal cleaves.

Section 1.3 Dimensional Analysis

7. Which of the following equations are dimensionally correct?
(a) $v_f = v_i + ax$ (b) $y = (2 \text{ m}) \cos(kx)$, where $k = 2 \text{ m}^{-1}$

8. Figure P1.8 shows a *frustum of a cone*. Of the following mensuration (geometrical) expressions, which describes **(i)** the total circumference of the flat circular faces, **(ii)** the volume, and **(iii)** the area of the curved surface?
(a) $\pi(r_1 + r_2)[h^2 + (r_2 - r_1)^2]^{1/2}$,   (b) $2\pi(r_1 + r_2)$
(c) $\pi h(r_1^2 + r_1 r_2 + r_2^2)/3$

Figure P1.8

9. Newton's law of universal gravitation is represented by

$$F = \frac{GMm}{r^2}$$

Here F is the magnitude of the gravitational force exerted by one small object on another, M and m are the masses of the objects, and r is a distance. Force has the SI units $\text{kg} \cdot \text{m/s}^2$. What are the SI units of the proportionality constant G?

Section 1.4 Conversion of Units

10. Suppose your hair grows at the rate $1/32$ in. per day. Find the rate at which it grows in nanometers per second. Because the distance between atoms in a molecule is on the order of 0.1 nm, your answer suggests how rapidly layers of atoms are assembled in this protein synthesis.

11. A rectangular building lot is 100 ft by 150 ft. Determine the area of this lot in square meters.

12. An auditorium measures $40.0 \text{ m} \times 20.0 \text{ m} \times 12.0 \text{ m}$. The density of air is 1.20 kg/m^3. What are (a) the volume of the room in cubic feet and (b) the weight of air in the room in pounds?

13. ● A room measures 3.8 m by 3.6 m, and its ceiling is 2.5 m high. Is it possible to completely wallpaper the walls of this room with the pages of this book? Explain your answer.

14. Assume it takes 7.00 min to fill a 30.0-gal gasoline tank. (a) Calculate the rate at which the tank is filled in gallons per second. (b) Calculate the rate at which the tank is filled in cubic meters per second. (c) Determine the time interval, in hours, required to fill a 1.00-m^3 volume at the same rate. (1 U.S. gal = 231 in.^{3})

15. A solid piece of lead has a mass of 23.94 g and a volume of 2.10 cm^3. From these data, calculate the density of lead in SI units (kg/m^3).

16. An ore loader moves 1 200 tons/h from a mine to the surface. Convert this rate to pounds per second, using 1 ton = 2 000 lb.

17. At the time of this book's printing, the U.S. national debt is about \$8 trillion. (a) If payments were made at the rate of \$1 000 per second, how many years would it take to pay off the debt, assuming no interest were charged? (b) A dollar bill is about 15.5 cm long. If eight trillion dollar bills were laid end to end around the Earth's equator, how many times would they encircle the planet? Take the radius of the Earth at the equator to be 6 378 km. *Note:* Before doing any of these calculations, try to guess at the answers. You may be very surprised.

18. A pyramid has a height of 481 ft, and its base covers an area of 13.0 acres (Fig. P1.18). The volume of a pyramid is given by the expression $V = \frac{1}{3} Bh$, where B is the area of the base and h is the height. Find the volume of this pyramid in cubic meters. (1 acre = 43 560 ft^2)

Figure P1.18   Problems 18 and 19.

19. The pyramid described in Problem 18 contains approximately 2 million stone blocks that average 2.50 tons each. Find the weight of this pyramid in pounds.

20. A hydrogen atom has a diameter of 1.06×10^{-10} m as defined by the diameter of the spherical electron cloud around the nucleus. The hydrogen nucleus has a diameter of approximately 2.40×10^{-15} m. (a) For a scale model, represent the diameter of the hydrogen atom by the playing length of an American football field (100 yards = 300 ft) and determine the diameter of the nucleus in millimeters. (b) The atom is how many times larger in volume than its nucleus?

21. ▲ One gallon of paint (volume = 3.78×10^{-3} m^3) covers an area of 25.0 m^2. What is the thickness of the fresh paint on the wall?

22. The mean radius of the Earth is 6.37×10^6 m and that of the Moon is 1.74×10^8 cm. From these data calculate (a) the ratio of the Earth's surface area to that of the Moon and (b) the ratio of the Earth's volume to that of the Moon. Recall that the surface area of a sphere is $4\pi r^2$ and the volume of a sphere is $\frac{4}{3}\pi r^3$.

23. ▲ One cubic meter (1.00 m^3) of aluminum has a mass of 2.70×10^3 kg, and the same volume of iron has a mass of 7.86×10^3 kg. Find the radius of a solid aluminum sphere that will balance a solid iron sphere of radius 2.00 cm on an equal-arm balance.

24. Let ρ_{Al} represent the density of aluminum and ρ_{Fe} that of iron. Find the radius of a solid aluminum sphere that balances a solid iron sphere of radius r_{Fe} on an equal-arm balance.

Section 1.5 Estimates and Order-of-Magnitude Calculations

25. ▲ Find the order of magnitude of the number of table-tennis balls that would fit into a typical-size room (without being crushed). In your solution, state the quantities you measure or estimate and the values you take for them.

26. An automobile tire is rated to last for 50 000 miles. To an order of magnitude, through how many revolutions will it turn? In your solution, state the quantities you measure or estimate and the values you take for them.

27. Compute the order of magnitude of the mass of a bathtub half full of water. Compute the order of magnitude of the mass of a bathtub half full of pennies. In your solution, list the quantities you take as data and the value you measure or estimate for each.

28. ● Suppose Bill Gates offers to give you $1 billion if you can finish counting it out using only one-dollar bills. Should you accept his offer? Explain your answer. Assume you can count one bill every second, and note that you need at least 8 hours a day for sleeping and eating.

29. To an order of magnitude, how many piano tuners are in New York City? Physicist Enrico Fermi was famous for asking questions like this one on oral doctorate qualifying examinations. His own facility in making order-of-magnitude calculations is exemplified in Problem 48 of Chapter 45.

Section 1.6 Significant Figures

Note: Appendix B.8 on propagation of uncertainty may be useful in solving some problems in this section.

30. A rectangular plate has a length of (21.3 ± 0.2) cm and a width of (9.8 ± 0.1) cm. Calculate the area of the plate, including its uncertainty.

31. How many significant figures are in the following numbers: (a) 78.9 ± 0.2 (b) 3.788×10^9 (c) 2.46×10^{-6} (d) 0.005 3?

32. The radius of a uniform solid sphere is measured to be (6.50 ± 0.20) cm, and its mass is measured to be (1.85 ± 0.02) kg. Determine the density of the sphere in kilograms per cubic meter and the uncertainty in the density.

33. Carry out the following arithmetic operations: (a) the sum of the measured values 756, 37.2, 0.83, and 2   (b) the product $0.003\ 2 \times 356.3$ (c) the product $5.620 \times \pi$

34. The *tropical year,* the time interval from one vernal equinox to the next vernal equinox, is the basis for our calendar. It contains 365.242 199 days. Find the number of seconds in a tropical year.

Note: The next 11 problems call on mathematical skills that will be useful throughout the course.

35. Review problem. A child is surprised that she must pay $1.36 for a toy marked $1.25 because of sales tax. What is the effective tax rate on this purchase, expressed as a percentage?

36. ● **Review problem.** A student is supplied with a stack of copy paper, ruler, compass, scissors, and a sensitive balance. He cuts out various shapes in various sizes, calculates their areas, measures their masses, and prepares the graph of Figure P1.36. Consider the fourth experimental point from the top. How far is it from the best-fit straight line? (a) Express your answer as a difference in vertical-axis coordinate. (b) Express your answer as a difference in horizontal-axis coordinate. (c) Express both of the answers to parts (a) and (b) as a percentage. (d) Calculate the slope of the line. (e) State what the graph demonstrates, referring to the shape of the graph and the results of parts (c) and (d). (f) Describe whether this result should be expected theoretically. Describe the physical meaning of the slope.

Figure P1.36

37. Review problem. A young immigrant works overtime, earning money to buy portable MP3 players to send home as gifts for family members. For each extra shift he works, he has figured out that he can buy one player and two-thirds of another one. An e-mail from his mother informs him that the players are so popular that each of 15 young neighborhood friends wants one. How many more shifts will he have to work?

38. Review problem. In a college parking lot, the number of ordinary cars is larger than the number of sport utility vehicles by 94.7%. The difference between the number of cars and the number of SUVs is 18. Find the number of SUVs in the lot.

39. Review problem. The ratio of the number of sparrows visiting a bird feeder to the number of more interesting birds is 2.25. On a morning when altogether 91 birds visit the feeder, what is the number of sparrows?

40. Review problem. Prove that one solution of the equation

$$2.00x^4 - 3.00x^3 + 5.00x = 70.0$$

is $x = -2.22$.

41. Review problem. Find every angle θ between 0 and 360° for which the ratio of $\sin \theta$ to $\cos \theta$ is -3.00.

42. Review problem. A highway curve forms a section of a circle. A car goes around the curve. Its dashboard compass shows that the car is initially heading due east. After it travels 840 m, it is heading 35.0° south of east. Find the radius of curvature of its path. *Suggestion:* You may find it useful to learn a geometric theorem stated in Appendix B.3.

43. Review problem. For a period of time as an alligator grows, its mass is proportional to the cube of its length. When the alligator's length changes by 15.8%, its mass increases by 17.3 kg. Find its mass at the end of this process.

44. Review problem. From the set of equations

$$p = 3q$$

$$pr = qs$$

$$\tfrac{1}{2}pr^2 + \tfrac{1}{2}qs^2 = \tfrac{1}{2}qt^2$$

involving the unknowns p, q, r, s, and t, find the value of the ratio of t to r.

45. ● Review problem. In a particular set of experimental trials, students examine a system described by the equation

$$\frac{Q}{\Delta t} = \frac{k\pi\, d^2\, (T_h - T_c)}{4L}$$

We will see this equation and the various quantities in it in Chapter 20. For experimental control, in these trials all quantities except d and Δt are constant. (a) If d is made three times larger, does the equation predict that Δt will get larger or smaller? By what factor? (b) What pattern of proportionality of Δt to d does the equation predict? (c) To display this proportionality as a straight line on a graph, what quantities should you plot on the horizontal and vertical axes? (d) What expression represents the theoretical slope of this graph?

Additional Problems

46. In a situation in which data are known to three significant digits, we write 6.379 m = 6.38 m and 6.374 m = 6.37 m. When a number ends in 5, we arbitrarily choose to write 6.375 m = 6.38 m. We could equally well write 6.375 m = 6.37 m, "rounding down" instead of "rounding up," because we would change the number 6.375 by equal increments in both cases. Now consider an order-of-magnitude estimate, in which factors of change rather than increments are important. We write 500 m ~ 10^3 m because 500 differs from 100 by a factor of 5, whereas it differs from 1 000 by only a factor of 2. We write 437 m ~ 10^3 m and 305 m ~ 10^2 m. What distance differs from 100 m and from 1 000 m by equal factors so that we could equally well choose to represent its order of magnitude either as ~10^2 m or as ~10^3 m?

47. ● A spherical shell has an outside radius of 2.60 cm and an inside radius of a. The shell wall has uniform thickness and is made of a material with density 4.70 g/cm^3. The space inside the shell is filled with a liquid having a density of 1.23 g/cm^3. (a) Find the mass m of the sphere, including its contents, as a function of a. (b) In the answer to part (a), if a is regarded as a variable, for what value of a does m have its maximum possible value? (c) What is this maximum mass? (d) Does the value from part (b) agree with the result of a direct calculation of the mass of a sphere of uniform density? (e) For what value of a does the answer to part (a) have its minimum possible value? (f) What is this minimum mass? (g) Does the value from part (f) agree with the result of a direct calculation of the mass of a uniform sphere? (h) What value of m is halfway between the maximum and minimum possible values? (i) Does this mass agree with the result of part (a) evaluated for $a = 2.60$ cm/2 = 1.30 cm? (j) Explain whether you should expect agreement in each of parts (d), (g), and (i). (k) **What If?** In part (a), would the answer change if the inner wall of the shell were not concentric with the outer wall?

48. A rod extending between $x = 0$ and $x = 14.0$ cm has uniform cross-sectional area $A = 9.00$ cm^2. It is made from a continuously changing alloy of metals so that along its length its density changes steadily from 2.70 g/cm^3 to 19.3 g/cm^3. (a) Identify the constants B and C required in the expression $\rho = B + Cx$ to describe the variable density. (b) The mass of the rod is given by

$$m = \int_{\text{all material}} \rho\, dV = \int_{\text{all } x} \rho A\, dx = \int_0^{14\text{ cm}} (B + Cx)\,(9.00\text{ cm}^2)\; dx$$

Carry out the integration to find the mass of the rod.

49. The diameter of our disk-shaped galaxy, the Milky Way, is about 1.0×10^5 light-years (ly). The distance to Andromeda, which is the spiral galaxy nearest to the Milky Way, is about 2.0 million ly. If a scale model represents the Milky Way and Andromeda galaxies as dinner plates 25 cm in diameter, determine the distance between the centers of the two plates.

50. ● Air is blown into a spherical balloon so that, when its radius is 6.50 cm, its radius is increasing at the rate 0.900 cm/s. (a) Find the rate at which the volume of the balloon is increasing. (b) If this volume flow rate of air entering the balloon is constant, at what rate will the radius be increasing when the radius is 13.0 cm? (c) Explain physically why the answer to part (b) is larger or smaller than 0.9 cm/s, if it is different.

51. ▲ The consumption of natural gas by a company satisfies the empirical equation $V = 1.50t + 0.008\ 00t^2$, where V is the volume in millions of cubic feet and t is the time in months. Express this equation in units of cubic feet and seconds. Assign proper units to the coefficients. Assume a month is 30.0 days.

52. In physics it is important to use mathematical approximations. Demonstrate that for small angles ($< 20°$),

$$\tan \alpha \approx \sin \alpha \approx \alpha = \frac{\pi\alpha'}{180°}$$

where α is in radians and α' is in degrees. Use a calculator to find the largest angle for which $\tan \alpha$ may be approximated by α with an error less than 10.0%.

53. A high fountain of water is located at the center of a circular pool as shown in Figure P1.53. Not wishing to get his feet wet, a student walks around the pool and measures its circumference to be 15.0 m. Next, the student stands at the edge of the pool and uses a protractor to gauge the angle of elevation of the top of the fountain to be 55.0°. How high is the fountain?

Figure P1.53

54. ● Collectible coins are sometimes plated with gold to enhance their beauty and value. Consider a commemorative quarter-dollar advertised for sale at $4.98. It has a

---

2 = intermediate;   3 = challenging;   □ = SSM/SG;   ▲ = ThomsonNOW;   ▨ = symbolic reasoning;   ● = qualitative reasoning

diameter of 24.1 mm and a thickness of 1.78 mm, and it is completely covered with a layer of pure gold 0.180 μm thick. The volume of the plating is equal to the thickness of the layer times the area to which it is applied. The patterns on the faces of the coin and the grooves on its edge have a negligible effect on its area. Assume the price of gold is \$10.0 per gram. Find the cost of the gold added to the coin. Does the cost of the gold significantly enhance the value of the coin? Explain your answer.

55. One year is nearly $\pi \times 10^7$ s. Find the percentage error in this approximation, where "percentage error" is defined as

$$\text{Percentage error} = \frac{|\text{assumed value} - \text{true value}|}{\text{true value}} \times 100\%$$

56. ● A creature moves at a speed of 5.00 furlongs per fortnight (not a very common unit of speed). Given that 1 furlong = 220 yards and 1 fortnight = 14 days, determine the speed of the creature in meters per second. Explain what kind of creature you think it might be.

57. A child loves to watch as you fill a transparent plastic bottle with shampoo. Horizontal cross sections of the bottle are circles with varying diameters because the bottle is much wider in some places than others. You pour in bright green shampoo with constant volume flow rate 16.5 cm³/s. At what rate is its level in the bottle rising (a) at a point where the diameter of the bottle is 6.30 cm and (b) at a point where the diameter is 1.35 cm?

58. ● The data in the following table represent measurements of the masses and dimensions of solid cylinders of aluminum, copper, brass, tin, and iron. Use these data to calculate the densities of these substances. State how your results for aluminum, copper, and iron compare with those given in Table 14.1.

Substance	Mass (g)	Diameter (cm)	Length (cm)
Aluminum	51.5	2.52	3.75
Copper	56.3	1.23	5.06
Brass	94.4	1.54	5.69
Tin	69.1	1.75	3.74
Iron	216.1	1.89	9.77

59. Assume there are 100 million passenger cars in the United States and the average fuel consumption is 20 mi/gal of gasoline. If the average distance traveled by each car is 10 000 mi/yr, how much gasoline would be saved per year if average fuel consumption could be increased to 25 mi/gal?

60. The distance from the Sun to the nearest star is about 4×10^{16} m. The Milky Way galaxy is roughly a disk of diameter $\sim 10^{21}$ m and thickness $\sim 10^{19}$ m. Find the order of magnitude of the number of stars in the Milky Way. Assume the distance between the Sun and our nearest neighbor is typical.

Answers to Quick Quizzes

1.1 (a). Because the density of aluminum is smaller than that of iron, a larger volume of aluminum than iron is required for a given mass.

1.2 False. Dimensional analysis gives the units of the proportionality constant but provides no information about its numerical value. To determine its numerical value requires either experimental data or geometrical reasoning. For example, in the generation of the equation $x = \frac{1}{2}at^2$, because the factor $\frac{1}{2}$ is dimensionless there is no way to determine it using dimensional analysis.

1.3 (b). Because there are 1.609 km in 1 mi, a larger number of kilometers than miles is required for a given distance.

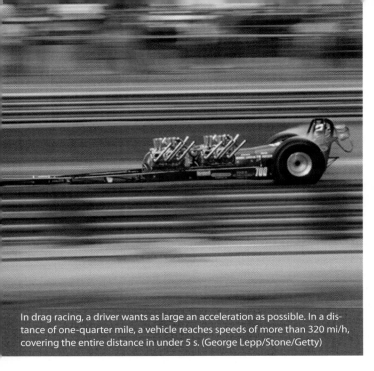

In drag racing, a driver wants as large an acceleration as possible. In a distance of one-quarter mile, a vehicle reaches speeds of more than 320 mi/h, covering the entire distance in under 5 s. (George Lepp/Stone/Getty)

2 Motion in One Dimension

As a first step in studying classical mechanics, we describe the motion of an object while ignoring the interactions with external agents that might be causing or modifying that motion. This portion of classical mechanics is called *kinematics*. (The word *kinematics* has the same root as *cinema*. Can you see why?) In this chapter, we consider only motion in one dimension, that is, motion of an object along a straight line.

From everyday experience we recognize that motion of an object represents a continuous change in the object's position. In physics, we can categorize motion into three types: translational, rotational, and vibrational. A car traveling on a highway is an example of translational motion, the Earth's spin on its axis is an example of rotational motion, and the back-and-forth movement of a pendulum is an example of vibrational motion. In this and the next few chapters, we are concerned only with translational motion. (Later in the book we shall discuss rotational and vibrational motions.)

In our study of translational motion, we use what is called the **particle model** and describe the moving object as a *particle* regardless of its size. In general, **a particle is a point-like object, that is, an object that has mass but is of infinitesimal size.** For example, if we wish to describe the motion of the Earth around the Sun, we can treat the Earth as a particle and obtain reasonably accurate data about its orbit. This approximation is justified because the radius of the Earth's orbit is large compared with the dimensions of the Earth and the Sun. As an example on a much smaller scale, it is possible to explain the pressure exerted by a gas on the walls of a container by treating the gas molecules as particles, without regard for the internal structure of the molecules.

2.1 Position, Velocity, and Speed

Position ▶

The motion of a particle is completely known if the particle's position in space is known at all times. A particle's **position** is the location of the particle with respect to a chosen reference point that we can consider to be the origin of a coordinate system.

Consider a car moving back and forth along the x axis as in Active Figure 2.1a. When we begin collecting position data, the car is 30 m to the right of a road sign, which we will use to identify the reference position $x = 0$. We will use the particle model by identifying some point on the car, perhaps the front door handle, as a particle representing the entire car.

We start our clock, and once every 10 s we note the car's position relative to the sign at $x = 0$. As you can see from Table 2.1, the car moves to the right (which we have defined as the positive direction) during the first 10 s of motion, from position Ⓐ to position Ⓑ. After Ⓑ, the position values begin to decrease, suggesting the car is backing up from position Ⓑ through position Ⓕ. In fact, at Ⓓ, 30 s after we start measuring, the car is alongside the road sign that we are using to mark our origin of coordinates (see Active Figure 2.1a). It continues moving to the left and is more than 50 m to the left of the sign when we stop recording information after our sixth data point. A graphical representation of this information is presented in Active Figure 2.1b. Such a plot is called a *position–time graph*.

Notice the *alternative representations* of information that we have used for the motion of the car. Active Figure 2.1a is a *pictorial representation*, whereas Active Figure 2.1b is a *graphical representation*. Table 2.1 is a *tabular representation* of the same information. Using an alternative representation is often an excellent strategy for understanding the situation in a given problem. The ultimate goal in many problems is a *mathematical representation*, which can be analyzed to solve for some requested piece of information.

TABLE 2.1

Position of the Car at Various Times

Position	t (s)	x (m)
Ⓐ	0	30
Ⓑ	10	52
Ⓒ	20	38
Ⓓ	30	0
Ⓔ	40	−37
Ⓕ	50	−53

(a)

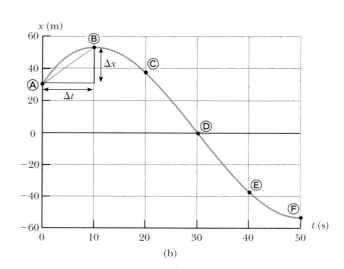

(b)

ACTIVE FIGURE 2.1

A car moves back and forth along a straight line. Because we are interested only in the car's translational motion, we can model it as a particle. Several representations of the information about the motion of the car can be used. Table 2.1 is a tabular representation of the information. (a) A pictorial representation of the motion of the car. (b) A graphical representation (position–time graph) of the motion of the car.

Sign in at www.thomsonedu.com and go to ThomsonNOW to move each of the six points Ⓐ through Ⓕ and observe the motion of the car in both a pictorial and a graphical representation as it follows a smooth path through the six points.

Given the data in Table 2.1, we can easily determine the change in position of the car for various time intervals. The **displacement** of a particle is defined as its change in position in some time interval. As the particle moves from an initial position x_i to a final position x_f, its displacement is given by

$$\Delta x \equiv x_f - x_i$$

(2.1)   ◀ Displacement

We use the capital Greek letter delta (Δ) to denote the *change* in a quantity. From this definition we see that Δx is positive if x_f is greater than x_i and negative if x_f is less than x_i.

It is very important to recognize the difference between displacement and distance traveled. **Distance** is the length of a path followed by a particle. Consider, for example, the basketball players in Figure 2.2. If a player runs from his own team's basket down the court to the other team's basket and then returns to his own basket, the *displacement* of the player during this time interval is zero because he ended up at the same point as he started: $x_f = x_i$, so $\Delta x = 0$. During this time interval, however, he moved through a *distance* of twice the length of the basketball court. Distance is always represented as a positive number, whereas displacement can be either positive or negative.

Displacement is an example of a vector quantity. Many other physical quantities, including position, velocity, and acceleration, also are vectors. In general, **a vector quantity requires the specification of both direction and magnitude**. By contrast, **a scalar quantity has a numerical value and no direction**. In this chapter, we use positive ($+$) and negative ($-$) signs to indicate vector direction. For example, for horizontal motion let us arbitrarily specify to the right as being the positive direction. It follows that any object always moving to the right undergoes a positive displacement $\Delta x > 0$, and any object moving to the left undergoes a negative displacement so that $\Delta x < 0$. We shall treat vector quantities in greater detail in Chapter 3.

One very important point has not yet been mentioned. Notice that the data in Table 2.1 result only in the six data points in the graph in Active Figure 2.1b. The smooth curve drawn through the six points in the graph is only a *possibility* of the actual motion of the car. We only have information about six instants of time; we have no idea what happened in between the data points. The smooth curve is a *guess* as to what happened, but keep in mind that it is *only* a guess.

If the smooth curve does represent the actual motion of the car, the graph contains information about the entire 50-s interval during which we watch the car move. It is much easier to see changes in position from the graph than from a verbal description or even a table of numbers. For example, it is clear that the car covers more ground during the middle of the 50-s interval than at the end. Between positions Ⓒ and Ⓓ, the car travels almost 40 m, but during the last 10 s, between positions Ⓔ and Ⓕ, it moves less than half that far. A common way of comparing these different motions is to divide the displacement Δx that occurs between two clock readings by the value of that particular time interval Δt. The result turns out to be a very useful ratio, one that we shall use many times. This ratio has been given a special name: the *average velocity*. **The average velocity $v_{x,\,avg}$ of a particle is defined as the particle's displacement Δx divided by the time interval Δt during which that displacement occurs:**

$$v_{x,\,avg} \equiv \frac{\Delta x}{\Delta t}$$

(2.2)   ◀ Average velocity

where the subscript x indicates motion along the x axis. From this definition we see that average velocity has dimensions of length divided by time (L/T), or meters per second in SI units.

The average velocity of a particle moving in one dimension can be positive or negative, depending on the sign of the displacement. (The time interval Δt is always positive.) If the coordinate of the particle increases in time (that is, if $x_f > x_i$), Δx is positive and $v_{x,\,avg} = \Delta x / \Delta t$ is positive. This case corresponds to a particle moving in the positive x direction, that is, toward larger values of x. If the coordinate decreases

Figure 2.2 On this basketball court, players run back and forth for the entire game. The distance that the players run over the duration of the game is nonzero. The displacement of the players over the duration of the game is approximately zero because they keep returning to the same point over and over again.

in time (that is, if $x_f < x_i$), Δx is negative and hence $v_{x, \text{avg}}$ is negative. This case corresponds to a particle moving in the negative x direction.

We can interpret average velocity geometrically by drawing a straight line between any two points on the position–time graph in Active Figure 2.1b. This line forms the hypotenuse of a right triangle of height Δx and base Δt. The slope of this line is the ratio $\Delta x/\Delta t$, which is what we have defined as average velocity in Equation 2.2. For example, the line between positions Ⓐ and Ⓑ in Active Figure 2.1b has a slope equal to the average velocity of the car between those two times, $(52 \text{ m} - 30 \text{ m})/(10 \text{ s} - 0) = 2.2$ m/s.

In everyday usage, the terms *speed* and *velocity* are interchangeable. In physics, however, there is a clear distinction between these two quantities. Consider a marathon runner who runs a distance d of more than 40 km and yet ends up at her starting point. Her total displacement is zero, so her average velocity is zero! Nonetheless, we need to be able to quantify how fast she was running. A slightly different ratio accomplishes that for us. The **average speed** v_{avg} of a particle, a scalar quantity, is defined as **the total distance traveled divided by the total time interval required to travel that distance:**

◀ Average speed

$$v_{\text{avg}} \equiv \frac{d}{\Delta t} \qquad (2.3)$$

PITFALL PREVENTION 2.1
Average Speed and Average Velocity

The magnitude of the average velocity is *not* the average speed. For example, consider the marathon runner discussed before Equation 2.3. The magnitude of her average velocity is zero, but her average speed is clearly not zero.

The SI unit of average speed is the same as the unit of average velocity: meters per second. Unlike average velocity, however, average speed has no direction and is always expressed as a positive number. Notice the clear distinction between the definitions of average velocity and average speed: average velocity (Eq. 2.2) is the *displacement* divided by the time interval, whereas average speed (Eq. 2.3) is the *distance* divided by the time interval.

Knowledge of the average velocity or average speed of a particle does not provide information about the details of the trip. For example, suppose it takes you 45.0 s to travel 100 m down a long, straight hallway toward your departure gate at an airport. At the 100-m mark, you realize you missed the restroom, and you return back 25.0 m along the same hallway, taking 10.0 s to make the return trip. The magnitude of your average *velocity* is +75.0 m/55.0 s = +1.36 m/s. The average *speed* for your trip is 125 m/55.0 s = 2.27 m/s. You may have traveled at various speeds during the walk. Neither average velocity nor average speed provides information about these details.

Quick Quiz 2.1 Under which of the following conditions is the magnitude of the average velocity of a particle moving in one dimension smaller than the average speed over some time interval? (a) a particle moves in the $+x$ direction without reversing (b) a particle moves in the $-x$ direction without reversing (c) a particle moves in the $+x$ direction and then reverses the direction of its motion (d) there are no conditions for which this is true

---

| EXAMPLE 2.1 | **Calculating the Average Velocity and Speed** |

Find the displacement, average velocity, and average speed of the car in Active Figure 2.1a between positions Ⓐ and Ⓕ.

SOLUTION

Consult Active Figure 2.1 to form a mental image of the car and its motion. We model the car as a particle. From the position–time graph given in Active Figure 2.1b, notice that $x_{Ⓐ} = 30$ m at $t_{Ⓐ} = 0$ s and that $x_{Ⓕ} = -53$ m at $t_{Ⓕ} = 50$ s.

Use Equation 2.1 to find the displacement of the car:

$$\Delta x = x_{Ⓕ} - x_{Ⓐ} = -53 \text{ m} - 30 \text{ m} = \boxed{-83 \text{ m}}$$

This result means that the car ends up 83 m in the negative direction (to the left, in this case) from where it started. This number has the correct units and is of the same order of magnitude as the supplied data. A quick look at Active Figure 2.1a indicates that it is the correct answer.

Use Equation 2.2 to find the average velocity:

$$v_{x, \text{avg}} = \frac{x_{\text{Ⓕ}} - x_{\text{Ⓐ}}}{t_{\text{Ⓕ}} - t_{\text{Ⓐ}}}$$

$$= \frac{-53 \text{ m} - 30 \text{ m}}{50 \text{ s} - 0 \text{ s}} = \frac{-83 \text{ m}}{50 \text{ s}} = \boxed{-1.7 \text{ m/s}}$$

We cannot unambiguously find the average speed of the car from the data in Table 2.1 because we do not have information about the positions of the car between the data points. If we adopt the assumption that the details of the car's position are described by the curve in Active Figure 2.1b, the distance traveled is 22 m (from Ⓐ to Ⓑ) plus 105 m (from Ⓑ to Ⓕ), for a total of 127 m.

Use Equation 2.3 to find the car's average speed:

$$v_{\text{avg}} = \frac{127 \text{ m}}{50 \text{ s}} = \boxed{2.5 \text{ m/s}}$$

Notice that the average speed is positive, as it must be. Suppose the brown curve in Active Figure 2.1b were different so that between 0 s and 10 s it went from Ⓐ up to 100 m and then came back down to Ⓑ. The average speed of the car would change because the distance is different, but the average velocity would not change.

2.2   Instantaneous Velocity and Speed

Often we need to know the velocity of a particle at a particular instant in time rather than the average velocity over a finite time interval. In other words, you would like to be able to specify your velocity just as precisely as you can specify your position by noting what is happening at a specific clock reading—that is, at some specific instant. What does it mean to talk about how quickly something is moving if we "freeze time" and talk only about an individual instant? In the late 1600s, with the invention of calculus, scientists began to understand how to describe an object's motion at any moment in time.

To see how that is done, consider Active Figure 2.3a, which is a reproduction of the graph in Active Figure 2.1b. We have already discussed the average velocity for the interval during which the car moved from position Ⓐ to position Ⓑ (given by the slope of the blue line) and for the interval during which it moved from Ⓐ to Ⓕ (represented by the slope of the longer blue line and calculated in Example 2.1). The car starts out by moving to the right, which we defined to be the positive direction. Therefore, being positive, the value of the average velocity during the interval from Ⓐ to Ⓑ is more representative of the initial velocity than is the value

PITFALL PREVENTION 2.2
Slopes of Graphs

In any graph of physical data, the *slope* represents the ratio of the change in the quantity represented on the vertical axis to the change in the quantity represented on the horizontal axis. Remember that a *slope has units* (unless both axes have the same units). The units of slope in Active Figure 2.1b and Active Figure 2.3 are meters per second, the units of velocity.

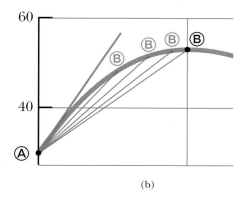

ACTIVE FIGURE 2.3

(a) Graph representing the motion of the car in Active Figure 2.1. (b) An enlargement of the upper-left-hand corner of the graph shows how the blue line between positions Ⓐ and Ⓑ approaches the green tangent line as point Ⓑ is moved closer to point Ⓐ.

Sign in at www.thomsonedu.com and go to ThomsonNOW to move point Ⓑ as suggested in part (b) and observe the blue line approaching the green tangent line.

of the average velocity during the interval from Ⓐ to Ⓕ, which we determined to be negative in Example 2.1. Now let us focus on the short blue line and slide point Ⓑ to the left along the curve, toward point Ⓐ, as in Active Figure 2.3b. The line between the points becomes steeper and steeper, and as the two points become extremely close together, the line becomes a tangent line to the curve, indicated by the green line in Active Figure 2.3b. The slope of this tangent line represents the velocity of the car at point Ⓐ. What we have done is determine the *instantaneous velocity* at that moment. In other words, **the instantaneous velocity v_x equals the limiting value of the ratio $\Delta x/\Delta t$ as Δt approaches zero:**[1]

$$v_x \equiv \lim_{\Delta t \to 0} \frac{\Delta x}{\Delta t} \tag{2.4}$$

In calculus notation, this limit is called the *derivative* of x with respect to t, written dx/dt:

◄ Instantaneous velocity

$$v_x \equiv \lim_{\Delta t \to 0} \frac{\Delta x}{\Delta t} = \frac{dx}{dt} \tag{2.5}$$

The instantaneous velocity can be positive, negative, or zero. When the slope of the position–time graph is positive, such as at any time during the first 10 s in Active Figure 2.3, v_x is positive and the car is moving toward larger values of x. After point Ⓑ, v_x is negative because the slope is negative and the car is moving toward smaller values of x. At point Ⓑ, the slope and the instantaneous velocity are zero and the car is momentarily at rest.

From here on, we use the word *velocity* to designate instantaneous velocity. When we are interested in *average velocity*, we shall always use the adjective *average*.

The **instantaneous speed** of a particle is defined as the magnitude of its instantaneous velocity. As with average speed, instantaneous speed has no direction associated with it. For example, if one particle has an instantaneous velocity of $+25$ m/s along a given line and another particle has an instantaneous velocity of -25 m/s along the same line, both have a speed[2] of 25 m/s.

PITFALL PREVENTION 2.3
Instantaneous Speed and Instantaneous Velocity

In Pitfall Prevention 2.1, we argued that the magnitude of the average velocity is not the average speed. The magnitude of the instantaneous velocity, however, *is* the instantaneous speed. In an infinitesimal time interval, the magnitude of the displacement is equal to the distance traveled by the particle.

Quick Quiz 2.2 Are members of the highway patrol more interested in (a) your average speed or (b) your instantaneous speed as you drive?

CONCEPTUAL EXAMPLE 2.2 **The Velocity of Different Objects**

Consider the following one-dimensional motions: **(A)** a ball thrown directly upward rises to a highest point and falls back into the thrower's hand; **(B)** a race car starts from rest and speeds up to 100 m/s; and **(C)** a spacecraft drifts through space at constant velocity. Are there any points in the motion of these objects at which the instantaneous velocity has the same value as the average velocity over the entire motion? If so, identify the point(s).

SOLUTION

(A) The average velocity for the thrown ball is zero because the ball returns to the starting point; therefore, its displacement is zero. There is one point at which the instantaneous velocity is zero: at the top of the motion.

(B) The car's average velocity cannot be evaluated unambiguously with the information given, but it must have some value between 0 and 100 m/s. Because the car will have every instantaneous velocity between 0 and 100 m/s at some time during the interval, there must be some instant at which the instantaneous velocity is equal to the average velocity over the entire motion.

(C) Because the spacecraft's instantaneous velocity is constant, its instantaneous velocity at *any* time and its average velocity over *any* time interval are the same.

---

[1] Notice that the displacement Δx also approaches zero as Δt approaches zero, so the ratio looks like $0/0$. As Δx and Δt become smaller and smaller, the ratio $\Delta x/\Delta t$ approaches a value equal to the slope of the line tangent to the x-versus-t curve.

[2] As with velocity, we drop the adjective for instantaneous speed. "Speed" means instantaneous speed.

| EXAMPLE 2.3 | **Average and Instantaneous Velocity** |

A particle moves along the x axis. Its position varies with time according to the expression $x = -4t + 2t^2$, where x is in meters and t is in seconds.[3] The position–time graph for this motion is shown in Figure 2.4. Notice that the particle moves in the negative x direction for the first second of motion, is momentarily at rest at the moment $t = 1$ s, and moves in the positive x direction at times $t > 1$ s.

(A) Determine the displacement of the particle in the time intervals $t = 0$ to $t = 1$ s and $t = 1$ s to $t = 3$ s.

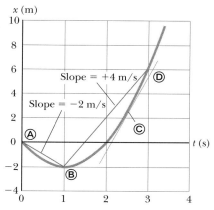

Figure 2.4 (Example 2.3) Position–time graph for a particle having an x coordinate that varies in time according to the expression $x = -4t + 2t^2$.

SOLUTION

From the graph in Figure 2.4, form a mental representation of the motion of the particle. Keep in mind that the particle does not move in a curved path in space such as that shown by the brown curve in the graphical representation. The particle moves only along the x axis in one dimension. At $t = 0$, is it moving to the right or to the left?

During the first time interval, the slope is negative and hence the average velocity is negative. Therefore, we know that the displacement between Ⓐ and Ⓑ must be a negative number having units of meters. Similarly, we expect the displacement between Ⓑ and Ⓓ to be positive.

In the first time interval, set $t_i = t_{Ⓐ} = 0$ and $t_f = t_{Ⓑ} = 1$ s and use Equation 2.1 to find the displacement:

$$\Delta x_{Ⓐ \to Ⓑ} = x_f - x_i = x_{Ⓑ} - x_{Ⓐ}$$
$$= [-4(1) + 2(1)^2] - [-4(0) + 2(0)^2] = \boxed{-2 \text{ m}}$$

For the second time interval ($t = 1$ s to $t = 3$ s), set $t_i = t_{Ⓑ} = 1$ s and $t_f = t_{Ⓓ} = 3$ s:

$$\Delta x_{Ⓑ \to Ⓓ} = x_f - x_i = x_{Ⓓ} - x_{Ⓑ}$$
$$= [-4(3) + 2(3)^2] - [-4(1) + 2(1)^2] = \boxed{+8 \text{ m}}$$

These displacements can also be read directly from the position–time graph.

(B) Calculate the average velocity during these two time intervals.

SOLUTION

In the first time interval, use Equation 2.2 with $\Delta t = t_f - t_i = t_{Ⓑ} - t_{Ⓐ} = 1$ s:

$$v_{x, \text{ avg } (Ⓐ \to Ⓑ)} = \frac{\Delta x_{Ⓐ \to Ⓑ}}{\Delta t} = \frac{-2 \text{ m}}{1 \text{ s}} = \boxed{-2 \text{ m/s}}$$

In the second time interval, $\Delta t = 2$ s:

$$v_{x, \text{ avg } (Ⓑ \to Ⓓ)} = \frac{\Delta x_{Ⓑ \to Ⓓ}}{\Delta t} = \frac{8 \text{ m}}{2 \text{ s}} = \boxed{+4 \text{ m/s}}$$

These values are the same as the slopes of the lines joining these points in Figure 2.4.

(C) Find the instantaneous velocity of the particle at $t = 2.5$ s.

SOLUTION

Measure the slope of the green line at $t = 2.5$ s (point Ⓒ) in Figure 2.4:

$$v_x = \boxed{+6 \text{ m/s}}$$

Notice that this instantaneous velocity is on the same order of magnitude as our previous results, that is, a few meters per second. Is that what you would have expected?

---

[3] Simply to make it easier to read, we write the expression as $x = -4t + 2t^2$ rather than as $x = (-4.00 \text{ m/s})t + (2.00 \text{ m/s}^2)t^{2.00}$. When an equation summarizes measurements, consider its coefficients to have as many significant digits as other data quoted in a problem. Consider its coefficients to have the units required for dimensional consistency. When we start our clocks at $t = 0$, we usually do not mean to limit the precision to a single digit. Consider any zero value in this book to have as many significant figures as you need.

2.3 Analysis Models: The Particle Under Constant Velocity

An important technique in the solution to physics problems is the use of *analysis models*. Such models help us analyze common situations in physics problems and guide us toward a solution. An **analysis model** is a problem we have solved before. It is a description of either (1) the behavior of some physical entity or (2) the interaction between that entity and the environment. When you encounter a new problem, you should identify the fundamental details of the problem and attempt to recognize which of the types of problems you have already solved might be used as a model for the new problem. For example, suppose an automobile is moving along a straight freeway at a constant speed. Is it important that it is an automobile? Is it important that it is a freeway? If the answers to both questions are no, we model the automobile as a *particle under constant velocity*, which we will discuss in this section.

This method is somewhat similar to the common practice in the legal profession of finding "legal precedents." If a previously resolved case can be found that is very similar legally to the current one, it is offered as a model and an argument is made in court to link them logically. The finding in the previous case can then be used to sway the finding in the current case. We will do something similar in physics. For a given problem, we search for a "physics precedent," a model with which we are already familiar and that can be applied to the current problem.

We shall generate analysis models based on four fundamental simplification models. The first is the particle model discussed in the introduction to this chapter. We will look at a particle under various behaviors and environmental interactions. Further analysis models are introduced in later chapters based on simplification models of a *system*, a *rigid object*, and a *wave*. Once we have introduced these analysis models, we shall see that they appear again and again in different problem situations.

Let us use Equation 2.2 to build our first analysis model for solving problems. We imagine a particle moving with a constant velocity. The **particle under constant velocity** model can be applied in *any* situation in which an entity that can be modeled as a particle is moving with constant velocity. This situation occurs frequently, so this model is important.

If the velocity of a particle is constant, its instantaneous velocity at any instant during a time interval is the same as the average velocity over the interval. That is, $v_x = v_{x,\,avg}$. Therefore, Equation 2.2 gives us an equation to be used in the mathematical representation of this situation:

$$v_x = \frac{\Delta x}{\Delta t} \qquad (2.6)$$

Remembering that $\Delta x = x_f - x_i$, we see that $v_x = (x_f - x_i)/\Delta t$, or

$$x_f = x_i + v_x \Delta t$$

This equation tells us that the position of the particle is given by the sum of its original position x_i at time $t = 0$ plus the displacement $v_x \Delta t$ that occurs during the time interval Δt. In practice, we usually choose the time at the beginning of the interval to be $t_i = 0$ and the time at the end of the interval to be $t_f = t$, so our equation becomes

$$x_f = x_i + v_x t \quad \text{(for constant } v_x) \qquad (2.7)$$

Equations 2.6 and 2.7 are the primary equations used in the model of a particle under constant velocity. They can be applied to particles or objects that can be modeled as particles.

Figure 2.5 is a graphical representation of the particle under constant velocity. On this position–time graph, the slope of the line representing the motion is constant and equal to the magnitude of the velocity. Equation 2.7, which is the equation of a straight line, is the mathematical representation of the particle under

Figure 2.5 Position–time graph for a particle under constant velocity. The value of the constant velocity is the slope of the line.

Position as a function ▶
of time

constant velocity model. The slope of the straight line is v_x and the y intercept is x_i in both representations.

EXAMPLE 2.4   **Modeling a Runner as a Particle**

A scientist is studying the biomechanics of the human body. She determines the velocity of an experimental subject while he runs along a straight line at a constant rate. The scientist starts the stopwatch at the moment the runner passes a given point and stops it after the runner has passed another point 20 m away. The time interval indicated on the stopwatch is 4.0 s.

(A) What is the runner's velocity?

SOLUTION

Think about the moving runner. We model the runner as a particle because the size of the runner and the movement of arms and legs are unnecessary details. Because the problem states that the subject runs at a constant rate, we can model him as a particle under constant velocity.

Use Equation 2.6 to find the constant velocity of the runner:

$$v_x = \frac{\Delta x}{\Delta t} = \frac{x_f - x_i}{\Delta t} = \frac{20 \text{ m} - 0}{4.0 \text{ s}} = \boxed{5.0 \text{ m/s}}$$

(B) If the runner continues his motion after the stopwatch is stopped, what is his position after 10 s has passed?

SOLUTION

Use Equation 2.7 and the velocity found in part (A) to find the position of the particle at time $t = 10$ s:

$$x_f = x_i + v_x t = 0 + (5.0 \text{ m/s})(10 \text{ s}) = \boxed{50 \text{ m}}$$

Notice that this value is more than twice that of the 20-m position at which the stopwatch was stopped. Is this value consistent with the time of 10 s being more than twice the time of 4.0 s?

The mathematical manipulations for the particle under constant velocity stem from Equation 2.6 and its descendent, Equation 2.7. These equations can be used to solve for any variable in the equations that happens to be unknown if the other variables are known. For example, in part (B) of Example 2.4, we find the position when the velocity and the time are known. Similarly, if we know the velocity and the final position, we could use Equation 2.7 to find the time at which the runner is at this position.

A particle under constant velocity moves with a constant speed along a straight line. Now consider a particle moving with a constant speed along a curved path. This situation can be represented with the **particle under constant speed** model. The primary equation for this model is Equation 2.3, with the average speed v_{avg} replaced by the constant speed v:

$$v = \frac{d}{\Delta t} \tag{2.8}$$

As an example, imagine a particle moving at a constant speed in a circular path. If the speed is 5.00 m/s and the radius of the path is 10.0 m, we can calculate the time interval required to complete one trip around the circle:

$$v = \frac{d}{\Delta t} \quad \rightarrow \quad \Delta t = \frac{d}{v} = \frac{2\pi r}{v} = \frac{2\pi (10.0 \text{ m})}{5.00 \text{ m/s}} = 12.6 \text{ s}$$

2.4 Acceleration

In Example 2.3, we worked with a common situation in which the velocity of a particle changes while the particle is moving. When the velocity of a particle changes with time, the particle is said to be *accelerating*. For example, the magnitude of the velocity of a car increases when you step on the gas and decreases when you apply the brakes. Let us see how to quantify acceleration.

Suppose an object that can be modeled as a particle moving along the x axis has an initial velocity v_{xi} at time t_i and a final velocity v_{xf} at time t_f, as in Figure 2.6a. The **average acceleration** $a_{x, \text{avg}}$ of the particle is defined as the *change* in velocity Δv_x divided by the time interval Δt during which that change occurs:

◀ Average acceleration

$$a_{x, \text{avg}} \equiv \frac{\Delta v_x}{\Delta t} = \frac{v_{xf} - v_{xi}}{t_f - t_i} \tag{2.9}$$

As with velocity, when the motion being analyzed is one dimensional, we can use positive and negative signs to indicate the direction of the acceleration. Because the dimensions of velocity are L/T and the dimension of time is T, acceleration has dimensions of length divided by time squared, or L/T². The SI unit of acceleration is meters per second squared (m/s²). It might be easier to interpret these units if you think of them as meters per second per second. For example, suppose an object has an acceleration of $+2$ m/s². You should form a mental image of the object having a velocity that is along a straight line and is increasing by 2 m/s during every interval of 1 s. If the object starts from rest, you should be able to picture it moving at a velocity of $+2$ m/s after 1 s, at $+4$ m/s after 2 s, and so on.

In some situations, the value of the average acceleration may be different over different time intervals. It is therefore useful to define the **instantaneous acceleration** as the limit of the average acceleration as Δt approaches zero. This concept is analogous to the definition of instantaneous velocity discussed in Section 2.2. If we imagine that point Ⓐ is brought closer and closer to point Ⓑ in Figure 2.6a and we take the limit of $\Delta v_x/\Delta t$ as Δt approaches zero, we obtain the instantaneous acceleration at point Ⓑ:

◀ Instantaneous acceleration

$$a_x \equiv \lim_{\Delta t \to 0} \frac{\Delta v_x}{\Delta t} = \frac{dv_x}{dt} \tag{2.10}$$

PITFALL PREVENTION 2.4
Negative Acceleration

Keep in mind that *negative acceleration does not necessarily mean that an object is slowing down.* If the acceleration is negative and the velocity is negative, the object is speeding up!

PITFALL PREVENTION 2.5
Deceleration

The word *deceleration* has the common popular connotation of *slowing down.* We will not use this word in this book because it confuses the definition we have given for negative acceleration.

That is, **the instantaneous acceleration equals the derivative of the velocity with respect to time**, which by definition is the slope of the velocity–time graph. The slope of the green line in Figure 2.6b is equal to the instantaneous acceleration at point Ⓑ. Therefore, we see that just as the velocity of a moving particle is the slope at a point on the particle's x–t graph, the acceleration of a particle is the slope at a point on the particle's v_x–t graph. One can interpret the derivative of the velocity with respect to time as the time rate of change of velocity. If a_x is positive, the acceleration is in the positive x direction; if a_x is negative, the acceleration is in the negative x direction.

For the case of motion in a straight line, the direction of the velocity of an object and the direction of its acceleration are related as follows. **When the object's velocity and acceleration are in the same direction, the object is speeding up. On the other hand, when the object's velocity and acceleration are in opposite directions, the object is slowing down.**

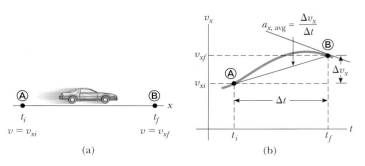

Figure 2.6 (a) A car, modeled as a particle, moving along the x axis from Ⓐ to Ⓑ, has velocity v_{xi} at $t = t_i$ and velocity v_{xf} at $t = t_f$. (b) Velocity–time graph (brown) for the particle moving in a straight line. The slope of the blue straight line connecting Ⓐ and Ⓑ is the average acceleration of the car during the time interval $\Delta t = t_f - t_i$. The slope of the green line is the instantaneous acceleration of the car at point Ⓑ.

To help with this discussion of the signs of velocity and acceleration, we can relate the acceleration of an object to the total *force* exerted on the object. In Chapter 5, we formally establish that **force is proportional to acceleration:**

$$F_x \propto a_x \qquad\qquad (2.11)$$

This proportionality indicates that acceleration is caused by force. Furthermore, force and acceleration are both vectors and the vectors act in the same direction. Therefore, let us think about the signs of velocity and acceleration by imagining a force applied to an object and causing it to accelerate. Let us assume the velocity and acceleration are in the same direction. This situation corresponds to an object that experiences a force acting in the same direction as its velocity. In this case, the object speeds up! Now suppose the velocity and acceleration are in opposite directions. In this situation, the object moves in some direction and experiences a force acting in the opposite direction. Therefore, the object slows down! It is very useful to equate the direction of the acceleration to the direction of a force, because it is easier from our everyday experience to think about what effect a force will have on an object than to think only in terms of the direction of the acceleration.

Quick Quiz 2.3   If a car is traveling eastward and slowing down, what is the direction of the force on the car that causes it to slow down? (a) eastward   (b) westward   (c) neither eastward nor westward

---

From now on we shall use the term *acceleration* to mean instantaneous acceleration. When we mean average acceleration, we shall always use the adjective *average*. Because $v_x = dx/dt$, the acceleration can also be written as

$$a_x = \frac{dv_x}{dt} = \frac{d}{dt}\left(\frac{dx}{dt}\right) = \frac{d^2x}{dt^2} \qquad\qquad (2.12)$$

That is, in one-dimensional motion, the acceleration equals the *second derivative* of x with respect to time.

Figure 2.7 illustrates how an acceleration–time graph is related to a velocity–time graph. The acceleration at any time is the slope of the velocity–time graph at that time. Positive values of acceleration correspond to those points in Figure 2.7a where the velocity is increasing in the positive x direction. The acceleration reaches a maximum at time $t_\text{Ⓐ}$, when the slope of the velocity–time graph is a maximum. The acceleration then goes to zero at time $t_\text{Ⓑ}$, when the velocity is a maximum (that is, when the slope of the v_x–t graph is zero). The acceleration is negative when the velocity is decreasing in the positive x direction, and it reaches its most negative value at time $t_\text{Ⓒ}$.

Quick Quiz 2.4   Make a velocity–time graph for the car in Active Figure 2.1a. The speed limit posted on the road sign is 30 km/h. True or False? The car exceeds the speed limit at some time within the time interval $0 - 50$ s.

(a)

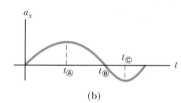

(b)

Figure 2.7   The instantaneous acceleration can be obtained from the velocity–time graph (a). At each instant, the acceleration in the graph of a_x versus t (b) equals the slope of the line tangent to the curve of v_x versus t (a).

CONCEPTUAL EXAMPLE 2.5   **Graphical Relationships Between x, v_x, and a_x**

The position of an object moving along the x axis varies with time as in Figure 2.8a (page 30). Graph the velocity versus time and the acceleration versus time for the object.

SOLUTION

The velocity at any instant is the slope of the tangent to the x–t graph at that instant. Between $t = 0$ and $t = t_\text{Ⓐ}$, the slope of the x–t graph increases uniformly, so the velocity increases linearly as shown in Figure 2.8b. Between $t_\text{Ⓐ}$ and $t_\text{Ⓑ}$, the slope of the x–t graph is con-

stant, so the velocity remains constant. Between $t_\text{Ⓑ}$ and $t_\text{Ⓓ}$, the slope of the x–t graph decreases, so the value of the velocity in the v_x–t graph decreases. At $t_\text{Ⓓ}$, the slope of the x–t graph is zero, so the velocity is zero at that instant. Between $t_\text{Ⓓ}$ and $t_\text{Ⓔ}$, the slope of the x–t graph and therefore the velocity are negative and decrease uniformly in this interval. In the interval $t_\text{Ⓔ}$ to $t_\text{Ⓕ}$, the slope of the x–t graph is still negative, and at $t_\text{Ⓕ}$ it goes to zero. Finally, after $t_\text{Ⓕ}$, the slope of the x–t graph is zero, meaning that the object is at rest for $t > t_\text{Ⓕ}$.

The acceleration at any instant is the slope of the tangent to the v_x-t graph at that instant. The graph of acceleration versus time for this object is shown in Figure 2.8c. The acceleration is constant and positive between 0 and $t_{\text{Ⓐ}}$, where the slope of the v_x-t graph is positive. It is zero between $t_{\text{Ⓐ}}$ and $t_{\text{Ⓑ}}$ and for $t > t_{\text{Ⓕ}}$ because the slope of the v_x-t graph is zero at these times. It is negative between $t_{\text{Ⓑ}}$ and $t_{\text{Ⓔ}}$ because the slope of the v_x-t graph is negative during this interval. Between $t_{\text{Ⓔ}}$ and $t_{\text{Ⓕ}}$, the acceleration is positive like it is between 0 and $t_{\text{Ⓐ}}$, but higher in value because the slope of the v_x-t graph is steeper.

Notice that the sudden changes in acceleration shown in Figure 2.8c are unphysical. Such instantaneous changes cannot occur in reality.

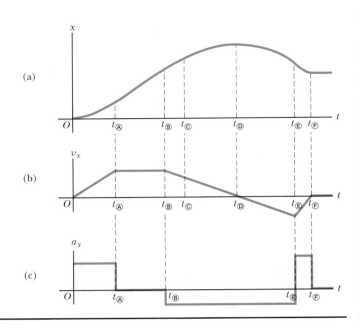

Figure 2.8 (Example 2.5) (a) Position–time graph for an object moving along the x axis. (b) The velocity–time graph for the object is obtained by measuring the slope of the position–time graph at each instant. (c) The acceleration–time graph for the object is obtained by measuring the slope of the velocity–time graph at each instant.

EXAMPLE 2.6 | Average and Instantaneous Acceleration

The velocity of a particle moving along the x axis varies according to the expression $v_x = (40 - 5t^2)$ m/s, where t is in seconds.

(A) Find the average acceleration in the time interval $t = 0$ to $t = 2.0$ s.

SOLUTION

Think about what the particle is doing from the mathematical representation. Is it moving at $t = 0$? In which direction? Does it speed up or slow down? Figure 2.9 is a v_x-t graph that was created from the velocity versus time expression given in the problem statement. Because the slope of the entire v_x-t curve is negative, we expect the acceleration to be negative.

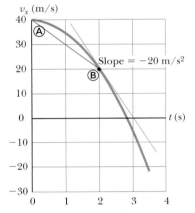

Figure 2.9 (Example 2.6) The velocity–time graph for a particle moving along the x axis according to the expression $v_x = (40 - 5t^2)$ m/s. The acceleration at $t = 2$ s is equal to the slope of the green tangent line at that time.

Find the velocities at $t_i = t_{\text{Ⓐ}} = 0$ and $t_f = t_{\text{Ⓑ}} = 2.0$ s by substituting these values of t into the expression for the velocity:

$$v_{x\text{Ⓐ}} = (40 - 5t_{\text{Ⓐ}}^2) \text{ m/s} = [40 - 5(0)^2] \text{ m/s} = +40 \text{ m/s}$$

$$v_{x\text{Ⓑ}} = (40 - 5t_{\text{Ⓑ}}^2) \text{ m/s} = [40 - 5(2.0)^2] \text{ m/s} = +20 \text{ m/s}$$

Find the average acceleration in the specified time interval $\Delta t = t_{\text{Ⓑ}} - t_{\text{Ⓐ}} = 2.0$ s:

$$a_{x,\text{ avg}} = \frac{v_{xf} - v_{xi}}{t_f - t_i} = \frac{v_{x\text{Ⓑ}} - v_{x\text{Ⓐ}}}{t_{\text{Ⓑ}} - t_{\text{Ⓐ}}} = \frac{(20 - 40) \text{ m/s}}{(2.0 - 0) \text{ s}}$$

$$= -10 \text{ m/s}^2$$

The negative sign is consistent with our expectations—namely, that the average acceleration, represented by the slope of the line joining the initial and final points on the velocity–time graph, is negative.

(B) Determine the acceleration at $t = 2.0$ s.

SOLUTION

Knowing that the initial velocity at any time t is $v_{xi} = (40 - 5t^2)$ m/s, find the velocity at any later time $t + \Delta t$:

$$v_{xf} = 40 - 5(t + \Delta t)^2 = 40 - 5t^2 - 10t\,\Delta t - 5(\Delta t)^2$$

Find the change in velocity over the time interval Δt:

$$\Delta v_x = v_{xf} - v_{xi} = [-10t\,\Delta t - 5(\Delta t)^2]\text{ m/s}$$

To find the acceleration at any time t, divide this expression by Δt and take the limit of the result as Δt approaches zero:

$$a_x = \lim_{\Delta t \to 0} \frac{\Delta v_x}{\Delta t} = \lim_{\Delta t \to 0} (-10t - 5\Delta t) = -10t\text{ m/s}^2$$

Substitute $t = 2.0$ s:

$$a_x = (-10)(2.0)\text{ m/s}^2 = \boxed{-20\text{ m/s}^2}$$

Because the velocity of the particle is positive and the acceleration is negative at this instant, the particle is slowing down.

Notice that the answers to parts (A) and (B) are different. The average acceleration in (A) is the slope of the blue line in Figure 2.9 connecting points Ⓐ and Ⓑ. The instantaneous acceleration in (B) is the slope of the green line tangent to the curve at point Ⓑ. Notice also that the acceleration is *not* constant in this example. Situations involving constant acceleration are treated in Section 2.6.

So far we have evaluated the derivatives of a function by starting with the definition of the function and then taking the limit of a specific ratio. If you are familiar with calculus, you should recognize that there are specific rules for taking derivatives. These rules, which are listed in Appendix B.6, enable us to evaluate derivatives quickly. For instance, one rule tells us that the derivative of any constant is zero. As another example, suppose x is proportional to some power of t, such as in the expression

$$x = At^n$$

where A and n are constants. (This expression is a very common functional form.) The derivative of x with respect to t is

$$\frac{dx}{dt} = nAt^{n-1}$$

Applying this rule to Example 2.5, in which $v_x = 40 - 5t^2$, we quickly find that the acceleration is $a_x = dv_x/dt = -10t$.

2.5   Motion Diagrams

The concepts of velocity and acceleration are often confused with each other, but in fact they are quite different quantities. In forming a mental representation of a moving object, it is sometimes useful to use a pictorial representation called a *motion diagram* to describe the velocity and acceleration while an object is in motion.

A motion diagram can be formed by imagining a *stroboscopic* photograph of a moving object, which shows several images of the object taken as the strobe light flashes at a constant rate. Active Figure 2.10 (page 32) represents three sets of strobe photographs of cars moving along a straight roadway in a single direction, from left to right. The time intervals between flashes of the stroboscope are equal in each part of the diagram. So as to not confuse the two vector quantities, we use red for velocity vectors and violet for acceleration vectors in Active Figure 2.10. The vectors are shown at several instants during the motion of the object. Let us describe the motion of the car in each diagram.

In Active Figure 2.10a, the images of the car are equally spaced, showing us that the car moves through the same displacement in each time interval. This equal spacing is consistent with the car moving with *constant positive velocity* and *zero acceleration*.

ACTIVE FIGURE 2.10

(a) Motion diagram for a car moving at constant velocity (zero acceleration). (b) Motion diagram for a car whose constant acceleration is in the direction of its velocity. The velocity vector at each instant is indicated by a red arrow, and the constant acceleration is indicated by a violet arrow. (c) Motion diagram for a car whose constant acceleration is in the direction *opposite* the velocity at each instant.

Sign in at www.thomsonedu.com and go to ThomsonNOW to select the constant acceleration and initial velocity of the car and observe pictorial and graphical representations of its motion.

We could model the car as a particle and describe it with the particle under constant velocity model.

In Active Figure 2.10b, the images become farther apart as time progresses. In this case, the velocity vector increases in length with time because the car's displacement between adjacent positions increases in time. These features suggest that the car is moving with a *positive velocity* and a *positive acceleration*. The velocity and acceleration are in the same direction. In terms of our earlier force discussion, imagine a force pulling on the car in the same direction it is moving: it speeds up.

In Active Figure 2.10c, we can tell that the car slows as it moves to the right because its displacement between adjacent images decreases with time. This case suggests that the car moves to the right with a negative acceleration. The length of the velocity vector decreases in time and eventually reaches zero. From this diagram we see that the acceleration and velocity vectors are *not* in the same direction. The car is moving with a *positive velocity*, but with a *negative acceleration*. (This type of motion is exhibited by a car that skids to a stop after applying its brakes.) The velocity and acceleration are in opposite directions. In terms of our earlier force discussion, imagine a force pulling on the car opposite to the direction it is moving: it slows down.

The violet acceleration vectors in parts (b) and (c) of Figure 2.10 are all of the same length. Therefore, these diagrams represent motion of a *particle under constant acceleration*. This important analysis model will be discussed in the next section.

Quick Quiz 2.5 Which one of the following statements is true? (a) If a car is traveling eastward, its acceleration must be eastward. (b) If a car is slowing down, its acceleration must be negative. (c) A particle with constant acceleration can never stop and stay stopped.

2.6 The Particle Under Constant Acceleration

If the acceleration of a particle varies in time, its motion can be complex and difficult to analyze. A very common and simple type of one-dimensional motion, however, is that in which the acceleration is constant. In such a case, the average acceleration $a_{x,\,avg}$ over any time interval is numerically equal to the instantaneous acceleration a_x at any instant within the interval, and the velocity changes at the same rate throughout the motion. This situation occurs often enough that we identify it as an analysis model: the **particle under constant acceleration**. In the discussion that follows, we generate several equations that describe the motion of a particle for this model.

If we replace $a_{x,\,avg}$ by a_x in Equation 2.9 and take $t_i = 0$ and t_f to be any later time t, we find that

$$a_x = \frac{v_{xf} - v_{xi}}{t - 0}$$

or

$$v_{xf} = v_{xi} + a_x t \quad \text{(for constant } a_x\text{)} \tag{2.13}$$

This powerful expression enables us to determine an object's velocity at *any* time t if we know the object's initial velocity v_{xi} and its (constant) acceleration a_x. A velocity–time graph for this constant-acceleration motion is shown in Active Figure 2.11b. The graph is a straight line, the slope of which is the acceleration a_x; the (constant) slope is consistent with $a_x = dv_x/dt$ being a constant. Notice that the slope is positive, which indicates a positive acceleration. If the acceleration were negative, the slope of the line in Active Figure 2.11b would be negative. When the acceleration is constant, the graph of acceleration versus time (Active Fig. 2.11c) is a straight line having a slope of zero.

Because velocity at constant acceleration varies linearly in time according to Equation 2.13, we can express the average velocity in any time interval as the arithmetic mean of the initial velocity v_{xi} and the final velocity v_{xf}:

$$v_{x,\,avg} = \frac{v_{xi} + v_{xf}}{2} \quad \text{(for constant } a_x\text{)} \tag{2.14}$$

Notice that this expression for average velocity applies *only* in situations in which the acceleration is constant.

We can now use Equations 2.1, 2.2, and 2.14 to obtain the position of an object as a function of time. Recalling that Δx in Equation 2.2 represents $x_f - x_i$ and recognizing that $\Delta t = t_f - t_i = t - 0 = t$, we find that

$$x_f - x_i = v_{x,\,avg}\,t = \tfrac{1}{2}(v_{xi} + v_{xf})t$$

$$x_f = x_i + \tfrac{1}{2}(v_{xi} + v_{xf})t \quad \text{(for constant } a_x\text{)} \tag{2.15}$$

This equation provides the final position of the particle at time t in terms of the initial and final velocities.

We can obtain another useful expression for the position of a particle under constant acceleration by substituting Equation 2.13 into Equation 2.15:

$$x_f = x_i + \tfrac{1}{2}[v_{xi} + (v_{xi} + a_x t)]t$$

$$x_f = x_i + v_{xi}t + \tfrac{1}{2}a_x t^2 \quad \text{(for constant } a_x\text{)} \tag{2.16}$$

This equation provides the final position of the particle at time t in terms of the initial velocity and the constant acceleration.

The position–time graph for motion at constant (positive) acceleration shown in Active Figure 2.11a is obtained from Equation 2.16. Notice that the curve is a parabola. The slope of the tangent line to this curve at $t = 0$ equals the initial velocity v_{xi}, and the slope of the tangent line at any later time t equals the velocity v_{xf} at that time.

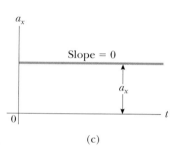

ACTIVE FIGURE 2.11

A particle under constant acceleration a_x moving along the x axis: (a) the position–time graph, (b) the velocity–time graph, and (c) the acceleration–time graph.

Sign in at www.thomsonedu.com and go to ThomsonNOW to adjust the constant acceleration and observe the effect on the position and velocity graphs.

◄ Position as a function of velocity and time

◄ Position as a function of time

Finally, we can obtain an expression for the final velocity that does not contain time as a variable by substituting the value of t from Equation 2.13 into Equation 2.15:

$$x_f = x_i + \tfrac{1}{2}(v_{xi} + v_{xf})\left(\frac{v_{xf} - v_{xi}}{a_x}\right) = x_i + \frac{v_{xf}{}^2 - v_{xi}{}^2}{2a_x}$$

◀ **Velocity as a function of position**

$$v_{xf}{}^2 = v_{xi}{}^2 + 2a_x\,(x_f - x_i) \quad \text{(for constant } a_x\text{)}$$ (2.17)

This equation provides the final velocity in terms of the initial velocity, the constant acceleration, and the position of the particle.

For motion at *zero* acceleration, we see from Equations 2.13 and 2.16 that

$$\left.\begin{array}{c} v_{xf} = v_{xi} = v_x \\ x_f = x_i + v_x t \end{array}\right\} \quad \text{when } a_x = 0$$

That is, when the acceleration of a particle is zero, its velocity is constant and its position changes linearly with time. In terms of models, when the acceleration of a particle is zero, the particle under constant acceleration model reduces to the particle under constant velocity model (Section 2.3).

Quick Quiz 2.6 In Active Figure 2.12, match each v_x–t graph on the top with the a_x–t graph on the bottom that best describes the motion.

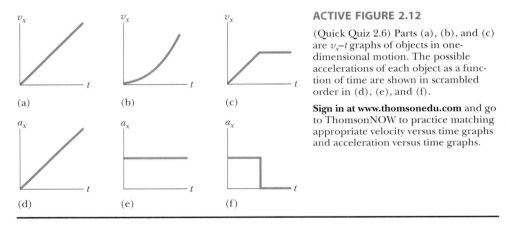

(a) (b) (c)

(d) (e) (f)

ACTIVE FIGURE 2.12

(Quick Quiz 2.6) Parts (a), (b), and (c) are v_x–t graphs of objects in one-dimensional motion. The possible accelerations of each object as a function of time are shown in scrambled order in (d), (e), and (f).

Sign in at www.thomsonedu.com and go to ThomsonNOW to practice matching appropriate velocity versus time graphs and acceleration versus time graphs.

Equations 2.13 through 2.17 are **kinematic equations** that may be used to solve any problem involving a particle under constant acceleration in one dimension. The four kinematic equations used most often are listed for convenience in Table 2.2. The choice of which equation you use in a given situation depends on what you know beforehand. Sometimes it is necessary to use two of these equations to solve for two unknowns. You should recognize that the quantities that vary during the motion are position x_f, velocity v_{xf}, and time t.

You will gain a great deal of experience in the use of these equations by solving a number of exercises and problems. Many times you will discover that more than

TABLE 2.2

Kinematic Equations for Motion of a Particle Under Constant Acceleration

Equation Number	Equation	Information Given by Equation
2.13	$v_{xf} = v_{xi} + a_x t$	Velocity as a function of time
2.15	$x_f = x_i + \tfrac{1}{2}(v_{xi} + v_{xf})t$	Position as a function of velocity and time
2.16	$x_f = x_i + v_{xi}t + \tfrac{1}{2}a_x t^2$	Position as a function of time
2.17	$v_{xf}{}^2 = v_{xi}{}^2 + 2a_x\,(x_f - x_i)$	Velocity as a function of position

Note: Motion is along the x axis.

one method can be used to obtain a solution. Remember that these equations of kinematics *cannot* be used in a situation in which the acceleration varies with time. They can be used only when the acceleration is constant.

EXAMPLE 2.7   **Carrier Landing**

A jet lands on an aircraft carrier at 140 mi/h ($\approx$ 63 m/s).

(A) What is its acceleration (assumed constant) if it stops in 2.0 s due to an arresting cable that snags the jet and brings it to a stop?

SOLUTION

You might have seen movies or television shows in which a jet lands on an aircraft carrier and is brought to rest surprisingly fast by an arresting cable. Because the acceleration of the jet is assumed constant, we model it as a particle under constant acceleration. We define our x axis as the direction of motion of the jet. A careful reading of the problem reveals that in addition to being given the initial speed of 63 m/s, we also know that the final speed is zero. We also notice that we have no information about the change in position of the jet while it is slowing down.

Equation 2.13 is the only equation in Table 2.2 that does not involve position, so we use it to find the acceleration of the jet, modeled as a particle:

$$a_x = \frac{v_{xf} - v_{xi}}{t} \approx \frac{0 - 63 \text{ m/s}}{2.0 \text{ s}}$$

$$= -32 \text{ m/s}^2$$

(B) If the jet touches down at position $x_i = 0$, what is its final position?

SOLUTION

Use Equation 2.15 to solve for the final position: $x_f = x_i + \frac{1}{2}(v_{xi} + v_{xf})t = 0 + \frac{1}{2}(63 \text{ m/s} + 0)(2.0 \text{ s}) = $ 63 m

If the jet travels much farther than 63 m, it might fall into the ocean. The idea of using arresting cables to slow down landing aircraft and enable them to land safely on ships originated at about the time of World War I. The cables are still a vital part of the operation of modern aircraft carriers.

What If? Suppose the jet lands on the deck of the aircraft carrier with a speed higher than 63 m/s but has the same acceleration due to the cable as that calculated in part (A). How will that change the answer to part (B)?

Answer If the jet is traveling faster at the beginning, it will stop farther away from its starting point, so the answer to part (B) should be larger. Mathematically, we see in Equation 2.15 that if v_{xi} is larger, x_f will be larger.

EXAMPLE 2.8   **Watch Out for the Speed Limit!**

A car traveling at a constant speed of 45.0 m/s passes a trooper on a motorcycle hidden behind a billboard. One second after the speeding car passes the billboard, the trooper sets out from the billboard to catch the car, accelerating at a constant rate of 3.00 m/s². How long does it take her to overtake the car?

SOLUTION

A pictorial representation (Fig. 2.13) helps clarify the sequence of events. The car is modeled as a particle under constant velocity, and the trooper is modeled as a particle under constant acceleration.

First, we write expressions for the position of each vehicle as a function of time. It is convenient to choose the position of the billboard as the origin and to set $t_{\text{Ⓑ}} = 0$ as the time the trooper begins moving. At that

$v_{x \text{ car}} = 45.0 \text{ m/s}$
$a_{x \text{ car}} = 0$
$a_{x \text{ trooper}} = 3.00 \text{ m/s}^2$

$t_{\text{Ⓐ}} = -1.00 \text{ s}$ $t_{\text{Ⓑ}} = 0$ $t_{\text{Ⓒ}} = ?$

Ⓐ   Ⓑ   Ⓒ

Figure 2.13   (Example 2.8) A speeding car passes a hidden trooper.

instant, the car has already traveled a distance of 45.0 m from the billboard because it has traveled at a constant speed of $v_x = 45.0$ m/s for 1 s. Therefore, the initial position of the speeding car is $x_\circledB = 45.0$ m.

Apply Equation 2.7 to give the car's position at any time t:

$$x_{car} = x_\circledB + v_{x\,car}t = 45.0 \text{ m} + (45.0 \text{ m/s})t$$

A quick check shows that at $t = 0$, this expression gives the car's correct initial position when the trooper begins to move: $x_{car} = x_\circledB = 45.0$ m.

The trooper starts from rest at $t_\circledB = 0$ and accelerates at 3.00 m/s^2 away from the origin. Use Equation 2.16 to give her position at any time t:

$$x_f = x_i + v_{xi}t + \tfrac{1}{2}a_x t^2$$

$$x_{trooper} = 0 + (0)t + \tfrac{1}{2}a_x t^2 = \tfrac{1}{2}(3.00 \text{ m/s}^2)t^2$$

Set the two positions equal to represent the trooper overtaking the car at position ©:

$$x_{trooper} = x_{car}$$

$$\tfrac{1}{2}(3.00 \text{ m/s}^2)t^2 = 45.0 \text{ m} + (45.0 \text{ m/s})t$$

Simplify to give a quadratic equation:

$$1.50t^2 - 45.0t - 45.0 = 0$$

The positive solution of this equation is $t = \boxed{31.0 \text{ s}}$.
 (For help in solving quadratic equations, see Appendix B.2.)

What If? What if the trooper has a more powerful motorcycle with a larger acceleration? How would that change the time at which the trooper catches the car?

Answer If the motorcycle has a larger acceleration, the trooper will catch up to the car sooner, so the answer for the time will be less than 31 s.

Cast the final quadratic equation above in terms of the parameters in the problem:

$$\tfrac{1}{2}a_x t^2 - v_{x\,car}t - x_\circledB = 0$$

Solve the quadratic equation:

$$t = \frac{v_{x\,car} \pm \sqrt{v_{x\,car}^2 + 2a_x x_\circledB}}{a_x} = \frac{v_{x\,car}}{a_x} + \sqrt{\frac{v_{x\,car}^2}{a_x^2} + \frac{2x_\circledB}{a_x}}$$

where we have chosen the positive sign because that is the only choice consistent with a time $t > 0$. Because all terms on the right side of the equation have the acceleration a_x in the denominator, increasing the acceleration will decrease the time at which the trooper catches the car.

2.7 Freely Falling Objects

It is well known that, in the absence of air resistance, all objects dropped near the Earth's surface fall toward the Earth with the same constant acceleration under the influence of the Earth's gravity. It was not until about 1600 that this conclusion was accepted. Before that time, the teachings of the Greek philosopher Aristotle (384–322 BC) had held that heavier objects fall faster than lighter ones.

The Italian Galileo Galilei (1564–1642) originated our present-day ideas concerning falling objects. There is a legend that he demonstrated the behavior of falling objects by observing that two different weights dropped simultaneously from the Leaning Tower of Pisa hit the ground at approximately the same time. Although there is some doubt that he carried out this particular experiment, it is well established that Galileo performed many experiments on objects moving on inclined planes. In his experiments, he rolled balls down a slight incline and measured the distances they covered in successive time intervals. The purpose of the incline was to reduce the acceleration, which made it possible for him to make accurate measurements of the time intervals. By gradually increasing the slope of the incline, he was finally able to draw conclusions about freely falling objects because a freely falling ball is equivalent to a ball moving down a vertical incline.

You might want to try the following experiment. Simultaneously drop a coin and a crumpled-up piece of paper from the same height. If the effects of air resistance are negligible, both will have the same motion and will hit the floor at the same time. In the idealized case, in which air resistance is absent, such motion is referred to as *free-fall* motion. If this same experiment could be conducted in a vacuum, in which air resistance is truly negligible, the paper and coin would fall with the same acceleration even when the paper is not crumpled. On August 2, 1971, astronaut David Scott conducted such a demonstration on the Moon. He simultaneously released a hammer and a feather, and the two objects fell together to the lunar surface. This simple demonstration surely would have pleased Galileo!

When we use the expression *freely falling object*, we do not necessarily refer to an object dropped from rest. **A freely falling object is any object moving freely under the influence of gravity alone, regardless of its initial motion. Objects thrown upward or downward and those released from rest are all falling freely once they are released. Any freely falling object experiences an acceleration directed** *downward*, **regardless of its initial motion**.

We shall denote the magnitude of the *free-fall acceleration* by the symbol g. The value of g near the Earth's surface decreases with increasing altitude. Furthermore, slight variations in g occur with changes in latitude. At the Earth's surface, the value of g is approximately 9.80 m/s^2. Unless stated otherwise, we shall use this value for g when performing calculations. For making quick estimates, use $g = 10 \text{ m/s}^2$.

If we neglect air resistance and assume the free-fall acceleration does not vary with altitude over short vertical distances, the motion of a freely falling object moving vertically is equivalent to motion of a particle under constant acceleration in one dimension. Therefore, the equations developed in Section 2.6 for objects moving with constant acceleration can be applied. The only modification for freely falling objects that we need to make in these equations is to note that the motion is in the vertical direction (the y direction) rather than in the horizontal direction (x) and that the acceleration is downward and has a magnitude of 9.80 m/s^2. Therefore, we always choose $a_y = -g = -9.80 \text{ m/s}^2$, where the negative sign means that the acceleration of a freely falling object is downward. In Chapter 13, we shall study how to deal with variations in g with altitude.

GALILEO GALILEI
Italian physicist and astronomer
(1564–1642)
Galileo formulated the laws that govern the motion of objects in free fall and made many other significant discoveries in physics and astronomy. Galileo publicly defended Nicolaus Copernicus's assertion that the Sun is at the center of the Universe (the heliocentric system). He published *Dialogue Concerning Two New World Systems* to support the Copernican model, a view that the Catholic Church declared to be heretical.

PITFALL PREVENTION 2.8
Acceleration at the Top of the Motion

A common misconception is that the acceleration of a projectile at the top of its trajectory is zero. Although the velocity at the top of the motion of an object thrown upward momentarily goes to zero, *the acceleration is still that due to gravity* at this point. If the velocity and acceleration were both zero, the projectile would stay at the top.

Quick Quiz 2.7   Consider the following choices: (a) increases, (b) decreases, (c) increases and then decreases, (d) decreases and then increases, (e) remains the same. From these choices, select what happens to **(i)** the acceleration and **(ii)** the speed of a ball after it is thrown upward into the air.

CONCEPTUAL EXAMPLE 2.9   **The Daring Skydivers**

A skydiver jumps out of a hovering helicopter. A few seconds later, another skydiver jumps out, and they both fall along the same vertical line. Ignore air resistance, so that both skydivers fall with the same acceleration. Does the difference in their speeds stay the same throughout the fall? Does the vertical distance between them stay the same throughout the fall?

SOLUTION

At any given instant, the speeds of the skydivers are different because one had a head start. In any time interval

Δt after this instant, however, the two skydivers increase their speeds by the same amount because they have the same acceleration. Therefore, the difference in their speeds remains the same throughout the fall.

The first jumper always has a greater speed than the second. Therefore, in a given time interval, the first skydiver covers a greater distance than the second. Consequently, the separation distance between them increases.

EXAMPLE 2.10 | Not a Bad Throw for a Rookie!

A stone thrown from the top of a building is given an initial velocity of 20.0 m/s straight upward. The building is 50.0 m high, and the stone just misses the edge of the roof on its way down, as shown in Figure 2.14.

(A) Using $t_{\text{Ⓐ}} = 0$ as the time the stone leaves the thrower's hand at position Ⓐ, determine the time at which the stone reaches its maximum height.

SOLUTION

You most likely have experience with dropping objects or throwing them upward and watching them fall, so this problem should describe a familiar experience. Because the stone is in free fall, it is modeled as a particle under constant acceleration due to gravity.

Use Equation 2.13 to calculate the time at which the stone reaches its maximum height:

$$v_{yf} = v_{yi} + a_y t \quad \rightarrow \quad t = \frac{v_{yf} - v_{yi}}{a_y}$$

Substitute numerical values:

$$t = t_{\text{Ⓑ}} = \frac{0 - 20.0 \text{ m/s}}{-9.80 \text{ m/s}^2} = \boxed{2.04 \text{ s}}$$

(B) Find the maximum height of the stone.

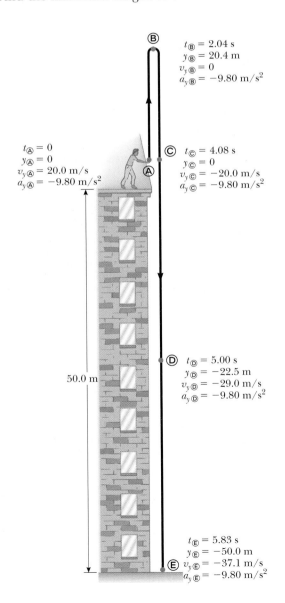

Ⓑ
$t_{\text{Ⓑ}} = 2.04$ s
$y_{\text{Ⓑ}} = 20.4$ m
$v_{y\,\text{Ⓑ}} = 0$
$a_{y\,\text{Ⓑ}} = -9.80$ m/s^2

$t_{\text{Ⓐ}} = 0$
$y_{\text{Ⓐ}} = 0$
$v_{y\,\text{Ⓐ}} = 20.0$ m/s
$a_{y\,\text{Ⓐ}} = -9.80$ m/s^2

Ⓒ $t_{\text{Ⓒ}} = 4.08$ s
$y_{\text{Ⓒ}} = 0$
$v_{y\,\text{Ⓒ}} = -20.0$ m/s
$a_{y\,\text{Ⓒ}} = -9.80$ m/s^2

Ⓓ $t_{\text{Ⓓ}} = 5.00$ s
$y_{\text{Ⓓ}} = -22.5$ m
$v_{y\,\text{Ⓓ}} = -29.0$ m/s
$a_{y\,\text{Ⓓ}} = -9.80$ m/s^2

50.0 m

$t_{\text{Ⓔ}} = 5.83$ s
$y_{\text{Ⓔ}} = -50.0$ m
Ⓔ $v_{y\,\text{Ⓔ}} = -37.1$ m/s
$a_{y\,\text{Ⓔ}} = -9.80$ m/s^2

Figure 2.14   (Example 2.10) Position and velocity versus time for a freely falling stone thrown initially upward with a velocity $v_{yi} = 20.0$ m/s. Many of the quantities in the labels for points in the motion of the stone are calculated in the example. Can you verify the other values that are not?

SOLUTION

Set $y_{Ⓐ} = 0$ and substitute the time from part (A) into Equation 2.16 to find the maximum height:

$$y_{max} = y_{Ⓑ} = y_{Ⓐ} + v_{xⒶ}t + \tfrac{1}{2}a_yt^2$$

$$y_{Ⓑ} = 0 + (20.0 \text{ m/s})(2.04 \text{ s}) + \tfrac{1}{2}(-9.80 \text{ m/s}^2)(2.04 \text{ s})^2 = \boxed{20.4 \text{ m}}$$

(C) Determine the velocity of the stone when it returns to the height from which it was thrown.

Substitute known values into Equation 2.17:

$$v_{yⒸ}^2 = v_{yⒶ}^2 + 2a_y(y_Ⓒ - y_Ⓐ)$$

$$v_{yⒸ}^2 = (20.0 \text{ m/s})^2 + 2(-9.80 \text{ m/s}^2)(0 - 0) = 400 \text{ m}^2/\text{s}^2$$

$$v_{yⒸ} = \boxed{-20.0 \text{ m/s}}$$

When taking the square root, we could choose either a positive or a negative root. We choose the negative root because we know that the stone is moving downward at point Ⓒ. The velocity of the stone when it arrives back at its original height is equal in magnitude to its initial velocity but is opposite in direction.

(D) Find the velocity and position of the stone at $t = 5.00$ s.

Calculate the velocity at Ⓓ from Equation 2.13:

$$v_{yⒹ} = v_{yⒶ} + a_yt = 20.0 \text{ m/s} + (-9.80 \text{ m/s}^2)(5.00 \text{ s}) = \boxed{-29.0 \text{ m/s}}$$

Use Equation 2.16 to find the position of the stone at $t_Ⓓ = 5.00$ s:

$$y_Ⓓ = y_Ⓐ + v_{yⒶ}t + \tfrac{1}{2}a_yt^2$$

$$= 0 + (20.0 \text{ m/s})(5.00 \text{ s}) + \tfrac{1}{2}(-9.80 \text{ m/s}^2)(5.00 \text{ s})^2$$

$$= \boxed{-22.5 \text{ m}}$$

The choice of the time defined as $t = 0$ is arbitrary and up to you to select as the problem-solver. As an example of this arbitrariness, choose $t = 0$ as the time at which the stone is at the highest point in its motion. Then solve parts (C) and (D) again using this new initial instant and note that your answers are the same as those above.

What If? What if the building were 30.0 m tall instead of 50.0 m tall? Which answers in parts (A) to (D) would change?

Answer None of the answers would change. All the motion takes place in the air during the first 5.00 s. (Notice that even for a 30.0-m tall building, the stone is above the ground at $t = 5.00$ s.) Therefore, the height of the building is not an issue. Mathematically, if we look back over our calculations, we see that we never entered the height of the building into any equation.

2.8 Kinematic Equations Derived from Calculus

This section assumes the reader is familiar with the techniques of integral calculus. If you have not yet studied integration in your calculus course, you should skip this section or cover it after you become familiar with integration.

The velocity of a particle moving in a straight line can be obtained if its position as a function of time is known. Mathematically, the velocity equals the derivative of the position with respect to time. It is also possible to find the position of a particle if its velocity is known as a function of time. In calculus, the procedure used to perform this task is referred to either as *integration* or as finding the *antiderivative*. Graphically, it is equivalent to finding the area under a curve.

Suppose the v_x–t graph for a particle moving along the x axis is as shown in Figure 2.15. Let us divide the time interval $t_f - t_i$ into many small intervals, each of duration Δt_n. From the definition of average velocity we see that the displacement of the particle during any small interval, such as the one shaded in Figure 2.15, is

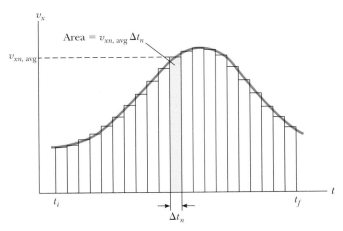

Figure 2.15 Velocity versus time for a particle moving along the x axis. The area of the shaded rectangle is equal to the displacement Δx in the time interval Δt_n, whereas the total area under the curve is the total displacement of the particle.

given by $\Delta x_n = v_{xn,\,avg}\,\Delta t_n$, where $v_{xn,\,avg}$ is the average velocity in that interval. Therefore, the displacement during this small interval is simply the area of the shaded rectangle. The total displacement for the interval $t_f - t_i$ is the sum of the areas of all the rectangles from t_i to t_f:

$$\Delta x = \sum_n v_{xn,\,avg}\,\Delta t_n$$

where the symbol Σ (uppercase Greek sigma) signifies a sum over all terms, that is, over all values of n. Now, as the intervals are made smaller and smaller, the number of terms in the sum increases and the sum approaches a value equal to the area under the velocity–time graph. Therefore, in the limit $n \to \infty$, or $\Delta t_n \to 0$, the displacement is

$$\Delta x = \lim_{\Delta t_n \to 0} \sum_n v_{xn}\,\Delta t_n \qquad (2.18)$$

Notice that we have replaced the average velocity $v_{xn,\,avg}$ with the instantaneous velocity v_{xn} in the sum. As you can see from Figure 2.15, this approximation is valid in the limit of very small intervals. Therefore, if we know the v_x–t graph for motion along a straight line, we can obtain the displacement during any time interval by measuring the area under the curve corresponding to that time interval.

The limit of the sum shown in Equation 2.18 is called a **definite integral** and is written

Definite integral ▶

$$\lim_{\Delta t_n \to 0} \sum_n v_{xn}\,\Delta t_n = \int_{t_i}^{t_f} v_x(t)\,dt \qquad (2.19)$$

where $v_x(t)$ denotes the velocity at any time t. If the explicit functional form of $v_x(t)$ is known and the limits are given, the integral can be evaluated. Sometimes the v_x–t graph for a moving particle has a shape much simpler than that shown in Figure 2.15. For example, suppose a particle moves at a constant velocity v_{xi}. In this case, the v_x–t graph is a horizontal line, as in Figure 2.16, and the displacement of the particle during the time interval Δt is simply the area of the shaded rectangle:

$$\Delta x = v_{xi}\,\Delta t \quad \text{(when } v_x = v_{xi} = \text{constant)}$$

Figure 2.16 The velocity–time curve for a particle moving with constant velocity v_{xi}. The displacement of the particle during the time interval $t_f - t_i$ is equal to the area of the shaded rectangle.

Kinematic Equations

We now use the defining equations for acceleration and velocity to derive two of our kinematic equations, Equations 2.13 and 2.16.

The defining equation for acceleration (Eq. 2.10),

$$a_x = \frac{dv_x}{dt}$$

may be written as $dv_x = a_x \, dt$ or, in terms of an integral (or antiderivative), as

$$v_{xf} - v_{xi} = \int_0^t a_x \, dt$$

For the special case in which the acceleration is constant, a_x can be removed from the integral to give

$$v_{xf} - v_{xi} = a_x \int_0^t dt = a_x(t - 0) = a_x t \qquad \textbf{(2.20)}$$

which is Equation 2.13.

Now let us consider the defining equation for velocity (Eq. 2.5):

$$v_x = \frac{dx}{dt}$$

We can write this equation as $dx = v_x \, dt$, or in integral form as

$$x_f - x_i = \int_0^t v_x \, dt$$

Because $v_x = v_{xf} = v_{xi} + a_x t$, this expression becomes

$$x_f - x_i = \int_0^t (v_{xi} + a_x t) \, dt = \int_0^t v_{xi} \, dt + a_x \int_0^t t \, dt = v_{xi}(t - 0) + a_x \left(\frac{t^2}{2} - 0 \right)$$

$$x_f - x_i = v_{xi} t + \tfrac{1}{2} a_x t^2$$

which is Equation 2.16.

Besides what you might expect to learn about physics concepts, a very valuable skill you should hope to take away from your physics course is the ability to solve complicated problems. The way physicists approach complex situations and break them into manageable pieces is extremely useful. The following is a general problem-solving strategy to guide you through the steps. To help you remember the steps of the strategy, they are *Conceptualize, Categorize, Analyze,* and *Finalize.*

GENERAL PROBLEM-SOLVING STRATEGY

Conceptualize

- The first things to do when approaching a problem are to *think about* and *understand* the situation. Study carefully any representations of the information (e.g., diagrams, graphs, tables, or photographs) that accompany the problem. Imagine a movie, running in your mind, of what happens in the problem.

- If a pictorial representation is not provided, you should almost always make a quick drawing of the situation. Indicate any known values, perhaps in a table or directly on your sketch.

- Now focus on what algebraic or numerical information is given in the problem. Carefully read the problem statement, looking for key phrases such as "starts from rest" ($v_i = 0$), "stops" ($v_f = 0$), or "falls freely" ($a_y = -g = -9.80 \text{ m/s}^2$).

- Now focus on the expected result of solving the problem. Exactly what is the question asking? Will the final result be numerical or algebraic? Do you know what units to expect?

- Don't forget to incorporate information from your own experiences and common sense. What should a reasonable answer look like? For example, you wouldn't expect to calculate the speed of an automobile to be 5×10^6 m/s.

Categorize

- Once you have a good idea of what the problem is about, you need to *simplify* the problem. Remove the details that are not important to the solution. For example, model a moving object as a particle. If appropriate, ignore air resistance or friction between a sliding object and a surface.

- Once the problem is simplified, it is important to *categorize* the problem. Is it a simple *substitution problem* such that numbers can be substituted into an equation? If so, the problem is likely to be finished when this substitution is done. If not, you face what we call an *analysis problem:* the situation must be analyzed more deeply to reach a solution.

- If it is an analysis problem, it needs to be categorized further. Have you seen this type of problem before? Does it fall into the growing list of types of problems that you have solved previously? If so, identify any analysis model(s) appropriate for the problem to prepare for the Analyze step below. We saw the first three analysis models in this chapter: the particle under constant velocity, the particle under constant speed, and the particle under constant acceleration. Being able to classify a problem with an analysis model can make it much easier to lay out a plan to solve it. For example, if your simplification shows that the problem can be treated as a particle under constant acceleration and you have already solved such a problem

(such as the examples in Section 2.6), the solution to the present problem follows a similar pattern.

Analyze

- Now you must analyze the problem and strive for a mathematical solution. Because you have already categorized the problem and identified an analysis model, it should not be too difficult to select relevant equations that apply to the type of situation in the problem. For example, if the problem involves a particle under constant acceleration, Equations 2.13 to 2.17 are relevant.

- Use algebra (and calculus, if necessary) to solve symbolically for the unknown variable in terms of what is given. Substitute in the appropriate numbers, calculate the result, and round it to the proper number of significant figures.

Finalize

- Examine your numerical answer. Does it have the correct units? Does it meet your expectations from your conceptualization of the problem? What about the algebraic form of the result? Does it make sense? Examine the variables in the problem to see whether the answer would change in a physically meaningful way if the variables were drastically increased or decreased or even became zero. Looking at limiting cases to see whether they yield expected values is a very useful way to make sure that you are obtaining reasonable results.

- Think about how this problem compared with others you have solved. How was it similar? In what critical ways did it differ? Why was this problem assigned? Can you figure out what you have learned by doing it? If it is a new category of problem, be sure you understand it so that you can use it as a model for solving similar problems in the future.

When solving complex problems, you may need to identify a series of subproblems and apply the problem-solving strategy to each. For simple problems, you probably don't need this strategy. When you are trying to solve a problem and you don't know what to do next, however, remember the steps in the strategy and use them as a guide.

For practice, it would be useful for you to revisit the worked examples in this chapter and identify the *Conceptualize, Categorize, Analyze,* and *Finalize* steps. In the rest of this book, we will label these steps explicitly in the worked examples. Many chapters in this book include a section labeled Problem-Solving Strategy that should help you through the rough spots. These sections are organized according to the General Problem-Solving Strategy outlined above and are tailored to the specific types of problems addressed in that chapter.

Summary

ThomsonNOW™ Sign in at **www.thomsonedu.com** and go to ThomsonNOW to take a practice test for this chapter.

DEFINITIONS

When a particle moves along the x axis from some initial position x_i to some final position x_f, its **displacement** is

$$\Delta x \equiv x_f - x_i \quad (2.1)$$

The **average velocity** of a particle during some time interval is the displacement Δx divided by the time interval Δt during which that displacement occurs:

$$v_{x,\,avg} \equiv \frac{\Delta x}{\Delta t} \quad (2.2)$$

The **average speed** of a particle is equal to the ratio of the total distance it travels to the total time interval during which it travels that distance:

$$v_{avg} \equiv \frac{d}{\Delta t} \quad (2.3)$$

The **instantaneous velocity** of a particle is defined as the limit of the ratio $\Delta x / \Delta t$ as Δt approaches zero. By definition, this limit equals the derivative of x with respect to t, or the time rate of change of the position:

$$v_x \equiv \lim_{\Delta t \to 0} \frac{\Delta x}{\Delta t} = \frac{dx}{dt} \quad (2.5)$$

The **instantaneous speed** of a particle is equal to the magnitude of its instantaneous velocity.

The **average acceleration** of a particle is defined as the ratio of the change in its velocity Δv_x divided by the time interval Δt during which that change occurs:

$$a_{x,\,avg} \equiv \frac{\Delta v_x}{\Delta t} = \frac{v_{xf} - v_{xi}}{t_f - t_i} \quad (2.9)$$

The **instantaneous acceleration** is equal to the limit of the ratio $\Delta v_x / \Delta t$ as Δt approaches 0. By definition, this limit equals the derivative of v_x with respect to t, or the time rate of change of the velocity:

$$a_x \equiv \lim_{\Delta t \to 0} \frac{\Delta v_x}{\Delta t} = \frac{dv_x}{dt} \quad (2.10)$$

CONCEPTS AND PRINCIPLES

When an object's velocity and acceleration are in the same direction, the object is speeding up. On the other hand, when the object's velocity and acceleration are in opposite directions, the object is slowing down. Remembering that $F_x \propto a_x$ is a useful way to identify the direction of the acceleration by associating it with a force.

An object falling freely in the presence of the Earth's gravity experiences free-fall acceleration directed toward the center of the Earth. If air resistance is neglected, if the motion occurs near the surface of the Earth, and if the range of the motion is small compared with the Earth's radius, the free-fall acceleration g is constant over the range of motion, where g is equal to 9.80 m/s^2.

Complicated problems are best approached in an organized manner. Recall and apply the *Conceptualize, Categorize, Analyze,* and *Finalize* steps of the General Problem-Solving Strategy when you need them.

(continued)

ANALYSIS MODELS FOR PROBLEM-SOLVING

Particle Under Constant Velocity. If a particle moves in a straight line with a constant speed v_x, its constant velocity is given by

$$v_x = \frac{\Delta x}{\Delta t} \qquad (2.6)$$

and its position is given by

$$x_f = x_i + v_x t \qquad (2.7)$$

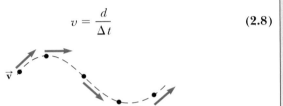

Particle Under Constant Speed. If a particle moves a distance d along a curved or straight path with a constant speed, its constant speed is given by

$$v = \frac{d}{\Delta t} \qquad (2.8)$$

Particle Under Constant Acceleration. If a particle moves in a straight line with a constant acceleration a_x, its motion is described by the kinematic equations:

$$v_{xf} = v_{xi} + a_x t \qquad (2.13)$$

$$v_{x,\,avg} = \frac{v_{xi} + v_{xf}}{2} \qquad (2.14)$$

$$x_f = x_i + \tfrac{1}{2}(v_{xi} + v_{xf})t \qquad (2.15)$$

$$x_f = x_i + v_{xi}t + \tfrac{1}{2}a_x t^2 \qquad (2.16)$$

$$v_{xf}^2 = v_{xi}^2 + 2a_x(x_f - x_i) \qquad (2.17)$$

Questions

☐ denotes answer available in *Student Solutions Manual/Study Guide;* **O** denotes objective question

1. O One drop of oil falls straight down onto the road from the engine of a moving car every 5 s. Figure Q2.1 shows the pattern of the drops left behind on the pavement. What is the average speed of the car over this section of its motion? (a) 20 m/s (b) 24 m/s (c) 30 m/s (d) 100 m/s (e) 120 m/s

Figure Q2.1

2. If the average velocity of an object is zero in some time interval, what can you say about the displacement of the object for that interval?

3. O Can the instantaneous velocity of an object at an instant of time ever be greater in magnitude than the average velocity over a time interval containing the instant? Can it ever be less?

4. O A cart is pushed along a straight horizontal track. (a) In a certain section of its motion, its original velocity is $v_{xi} = +3$ m/s and it undergoes a change in velocity of $\Delta v_x = +4$ m/s. Does it speed up or slow down in this section of its motion? Is its acceleration positive or negative? (b) In another part of its motion, $v_{xi} = -3$ m/s and $\Delta v_x = +4$ m/s. Does it undergo a net increase or decrease in speed? Is its acceleration positive or negative? (c) In a third segment of its motion, $v_{xi} = +3$ m/s and $\Delta v_x =$

-4 m/s. Does it have a net gain or loss in speed? Is its acceleration positive or negative? (d) In a fourth time interval, $v_{xi} = -3$ m/s and $\Delta v_x = -4$ m/s. Does the cart gain or lose speed? Is its acceleration positive or negative?

5. Two cars are moving in the same direction in parallel lanes along a highway. At some instant, the velocity of car A exceeds the velocity of car B. Does that mean that the acceleration of A is greater than that of B? Explain.

6. O When the pilot reverses the propeller in a boat moving north, the boat moves with an acceleration directed south. If the acceleration of the boat remains constant in magnitude and direction, what would happen to the boat (choose one)? (a) It would eventually stop and then remain stopped. (b) It would eventually stop and then start to speed up in the forward direction. (c) It would eventually stop and then start to speed up in the reverse direction. (d) It would never quite stop but lose speed more and more slowly forever. (e) It would never stop but continue to speed up in the forward direction.

7. O Each of the strobe photographs (a), (b), and (c) in Figure Q2.7 was taken of a single disk moving toward the right, which we take as the positive direction. Within each photograph, the time interval between images is constant. **(i)** Which photograph(s), if any, shows constant zero velocity? **(ii)** Which photograph(s), if any, shows constant zero acceleration? **(iii)** Which photograph(s), if any, shows constant positive velocity? **(iv)** Which photograph(s), if any, shows constant positive acceleration? **(v)** Which photograph(s), if any, shows some motion with negative acceleration?

(c)

Figure Q2.7 Question 7 and Problem 17.

8. Try the following experiment away from traffic where you can do it safely. With the car you are driving moving slowly on a straight, level road, shift the transmission into neutral and let the car coast. At the moment the car comes to a complete stop, step hard on the brake and notice what you feel. Now repeat the same experiment on a fairly gentle uphill slope. Explain the difference in what a person riding in the car feels in the two cases. (Brian Popp suggested the idea for this question.)

9. **O** A skateboarder coasts down a long hill, starting from rest and moving with constant acceleration to cover a certain distance in 6 s. In a second trial, he starts from rest and moves with the same acceleration for only 2 s. How is his displacement different in this second trial compared with the first trial? (a) one-third as large   (b) three times larger   (c) one-ninth as large   (d) nine times larger   (e) $1/\sqrt{3}$ times as large   (f) $\sqrt{3}$ times larger   (g) none of these answers

10. **O** Can the equations of kinematics (Eqs. 2.13–2.17) be used in a situation in which the acceleration varies in time? Can they be used when the acceleration is zero?

11. A student at the top of a building of height h throws one ball upward with a speed of v_i and then throws a second ball downward with the same initial speed $|v_i|$. How do the final velocities of the balls compare when they reach the ground?

12. **O** A pebble is released from rest at a certain height and falls freely, reaching an impact speed of 4 m/s at the floor. **(i)** Next, the pebble is thrown down with an initial speed of 3 m/s from the same height. In this trial, what is its speed at the floor? (a) less than 4 m/s   (b) 4 m/s   (c) between 4 m/s and 5 m/s   (d) $\sqrt{3^2 + 4^2}$ m/s = 5 m/s   (e) between 5 m/s and 7 m/s   (f) $(3 + 4)$ m/s = 7 m/s   (g) greater than 7 m/s **(ii)** In a third trial, the pebble is tossed upward with an initial speed of 3 m/s from the same height. What is its speed at the floor in this trial? Choose your answer from the same list (a) through (g).

13. **O** A hard rubber ball, not affected by air resistance in its motion, is tossed upward from shoulder height, falls to the sidewalk, rebounds to a somewhat smaller maximum height, and is caught on its way down again. This motion is represented in Figure Q2.13, where the successive positions of the ball Ⓐ through Ⓖ are not equally spaced in time. At point Ⓔ the center of the ball is at its lowest point in the motion. The motion of the ball is along a straight line, but the diagram shows successive positions offset to the right to avoid overlapping. Choose the positive y direction to be upward. **(i)** Rank the situations Ⓐ through Ⓖ according to the speed of the ball $|v_y|$ at each point, with the largest speed first. **(ii)** Rank the same situations according to the velocity of the ball at each point. **(iii)** Rank the same situations according to the acceleration a_y of the ball at each point. In each ranking, remember that zero is greater than a negative value. If two values are equal, show that they are equal in your ranking.

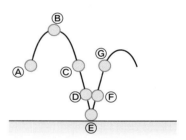

Figure Q2.13

14. **O** You drop a ball from a window located on an upper floor of a building. It strikes the ground with speed v. You now repeat the drop, but you ask a friend down on the ground to throw another ball upward at speed v. Your friend throws the ball upward at the same moment that you drop yours from the window. At some location, the balls pass each other. Is this location (a) *at* the halfway point between window and ground, (b) *above* this point, or (c) *below* this point?

Problems

WebAssign The Problems from this chapter may be assigned online in WebAssign.

ThomsonNOW   Sign in at **www.thomsonedu.com** and go to ThomsonNOW to assess your understanding of this chapter's topics with additional quizzing and conceptual questions.

1, 2, 3 denotes straightforward, intermediate, challenging;   ☐ denotes full solution available in *Student Solutions Manual/Study Guide*;   ▲ denotes coached solution with hints available at **www.thomsonedu.com;**   ▧ denotes developing symbolic reasoning;   ● denotes asking for qualitative reasoning;   ▰ denotes computer useful in solving problem

Section 2.1 Position, Velocity, and Speed

1. The position versus time for a certain particle moving along the x axis is shown in Figure P2.1. Find the average velocity in the following time intervals. (a) 0 to 2 s   (b) 0 to 4 s   (c) 2 s to 4 s   (d) 4 s to 7 s   (e) 0 to 8 s

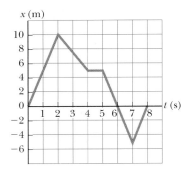

Figure P2.1   Problems 1 and 8.

2. The position of a pinewood derby car was observed at various moments; the results are summarized in the following table. Find the average velocity of the car for (a) the first 1-s time interval, (b) the last 3 s, and (c) the entire period of observation.

t (s)	0	1.0	2.0	3.0	4.0	5.0
x (m)	0	2.3	9.2	20.7	36.8	57.5

3. A person walks first at a constant speed of 5.00 m/s along a straight line from point A to point B and then back along the line from B to A at a constant speed of 3.00 m/s. (a) What is her average speed over the entire trip? (b) What is her average velocity over the entire trip?

4. A particle moves according to the equation $x = 10t^2$, where x is in meters and t is in seconds. (a) Find the average velocity for the time interval from 2.00 s to 3.00 s. (b) Find the average velocity for the time interval from 2.00 s to 2.10 s.

Section 2.2 Instantaneous Velocity and Speed

5. ▲ A position–time graph for a particle moving along the x axis is shown in Figure P2.5. (a) Find the average velocity in the time interval $t = 1.50$ s to $t = 4.00$ s. (b) Determine the instantaneous velocity at $t = 2.00$ s by measuring the slope of the tangent line shown in the graph. (c) At what value of t is the velocity zero?

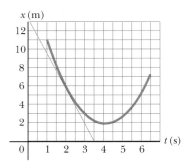

Figure P2.5

6. The position of a particle moving along the x axis varies in time according to the expression $x = 3t^2$, where x is in

meters and t is in seconds. Evaluate its position (a) at $t = 3.00$ s and (b) at 3.00 s + Δt. (c) Evaluate the limit of $\Delta x/\Delta t$ as Δt approaches zero to find the velocity at $t = 3.00$ s.

7. (a) Use the data in Problem 2.2 to construct a smooth graph of position versus time. (b) By constructing tangents to the $x(t)$ curve, find the instantaneous velocity of the car at several instants. (c) Plot the instantaneous velocity versus time and, from the graph, determine the average acceleration of the car. (d) What was the initial velocity of the car?

8. Find the instantaneous velocity of the particle described in Figure P2.1 at the following times: (a) $t = 1.0$ s (b) $t = 3.0$ s (c) $t = 4.5$ s (d) $t = 7.5$ s

Section 2.3 Analysis Models: The Particle Under Constant Velocity

9. A hare and a tortoise compete in a race over a course 1.00 km long. The tortoise crawls straight and steadily at its maximum speed of 0.200 m/s toward the finish line. The hare runs at its maximum speed of 8.00 m/s toward the goal for 0.800 km and then stops to tease the tortoise. How close to the goal can the hare let the tortoise approach before resuming the race, which the tortoise wins in a photo finish? Assume both animals, when moving, move steadily at their respective maximum speeds.

Section 2.4 Acceleration

10. A 50.0-g Super Ball traveling at 25.0 m/s bounces off a brick wall and rebounds at 22.0 m/s. A high-speed camera records this event. If the ball is in contact with the wall for 3.50 ms, what is the magnitude of the average acceleration of the ball during this time interval? *Note:* 1 ms = 10^{-3} s.

11. A particle starts from rest and accelerates as shown in Figure P2.11. Determine (a) the particle's speed at $t = 10.0$ s and at $t = 20.0$ s and (b) the distance traveled in the first 20.0 s.

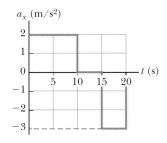

Figure P2.11

12. A velocity–time graph for an object moving along the x axis is shown in Figure P2.12. (a) Plot a graph of the acceleration versus time. (b) Determine the average acceleration of the object in the time intervals $t = 5.00$ s to $t = 15.0$ s and $t = 0$ to $t = 20.0$ s.

13. ▲ A particle moves along the x axis according to the equation $x = 2.00 + 3.00t - 1.00t^2$, where x is in meters and t is in seconds. At $t = 3.00$ s, find (a) the position of the particle, (b) its velocity, and (c) its acceleration.

Figure P2.12

Figure P2.16

14. A child rolls a marble on a bent track that is 100 cm long as shown in Figure P2.14. We use x to represent the position of the marble along the track. On the horizontal sections from $x = 0$ to $x = 20$ cm and from $x = 40$ cm to $x = 60$ cm, the marble rolls with constant speed. On the sloping sections, the speed of the marble changes steadily. At the places where the slope changes, the marble stays on the track and does not undergo any sudden changes in speed. The child gives the marble some initial speed at $x = 0$ and $t = 0$ and then watches it roll to $x = 90$ cm, where it turns around, eventually returning to $x = 0$ with the same speed with which the child initially released it. Prepare graphs of x versus t, v_x versus t, and a_x versus t, vertically aligned with their time axes identical, to show the motion of the marble. You will not be able to place numbers other than zero on the horizontal axis or on the velocity or acceleration axes, but show the correct relative sizes on the graphs.

Figure P2.14

15. An object moves along the x axis according to the equation $x(t) = (3.00t^2 - 2.00t + 3.00)$ m, where t is in seconds. Determine (a) the average speed between $t = 2.00$ s and $t = 3.00$ s, (b) the instantaneous speed at $t = 2.00$ s and at $t = 3.00$ s, (c) the average acceleration between $t = 2.00$ s and $t = 3.00$ s, and (d) the instantaneous acceleration at $t = 2.00$ s and $t = 3.00$ s.

16. Figure P2.16 shows a graph of v_x versus t for the motion of a motorcyclist as he starts from rest and moves along

the road in a straight line. (a) Find the average acceleration for the time interval $t = 0$ to $t = 6.00$ s. (b) Estimate the time at which the acceleration has its greatest positive value and the value of the acceleration at that instant. (c) When is the acceleration zero? (d) Estimate the maximum negative value of the acceleration and the time at which it occurs.

Section 2.5 Motion Diagrams

17. ● Each of the strobe photographs (a), (b), and (c) in Figure Q2.7 was taken of a single disk moving toward the right, which we take as the positive direction. Within each photograph the time interval between images is constant. For each photograph, prepare graphs of x versus t, v_x versus t, and a_x versus t, vertically aligned with their time axes identical, to show the motion of the disk. You will not be able to place numbers other than zero on the axes, but show the correct relative sizes on the graphs.

18. Draw motion diagrams for (a) an object moving to the right at constant speed, (b) an object moving to the right and speeding up at a constant rate, (c) an object moving to the right and slowing down at a constant rate, (d) an object moving to the left and speeding up at a constant rate, and (e) an object moving to the left and slowing down at a constant rate. (f) How would your drawings change if the changes in speed were not uniform; that is, if the speed were not changing at a constant rate?

Section 2.6 The Particle Under Constant Acceleration

19. ● Assume a parcel of air in a straight tube moves with a constant acceleration of -4.00 m/s^2 and has a velocity of 13.0 m/s at 10:05:00 a.m. on a certain date. (a) What is its velocity at 10:05:01 a.m.? (b) At 10:05:02 a.m.? (c) At 10:05:02.5 a.m.? (d) At 10:05:04 a.m.? (e) At 10:04:59 a.m.? (f) Describe the shape of a graph of velocity versus time for this parcel of air. (g) Argue for or against the statement, "Knowing the single value of an object's constant acceleration is like knowing a whole list of values for its velocity."

20. A truck covers 40.0 m in 8.50 s while smoothly slowing down to a final speed of 2.80 m/s. (a) Find its original speed. (b) Find its acceleration.

21. ▲ An object moving with uniform acceleration has a velocity of 12.0 cm/s in the positive x direction when its x coordinate is 3.00 cm. If its x coordinate 2.00 s later is -5.00 cm, what is its acceleration?

22. Figure P2.22 represents part of the performance data of a car owned by a proud physics student. (a) Calculate the total distance traveled by computing the area under the graph line. (b) What distance does the car travel between the times $t = 10$ s and $t = 40$ s? (c) Draw a graph of its acceleration versus time between $t = 0$ and $t = 50$ s. (d) Write an equation for x as a function of time for each phase of the motion, represented by (i) $0a$, (ii) ab, and (iii) bc. (e) What is the average velocity of the car between $t = 0$ and $t = 50$ s?

Figure P2.22

23. ● A jet plane comes in for a landing with a speed of 100 m/s, and its acceleration can have a maximum magnitude of 5.00 m/s^2 as it comes to rest. (a) From the instant the plane touches the runway, what is the minimum time interval needed before it can come to rest? (b) Can this plane land on a small tropical island airport where the runway is 0.800 km long? Explain your answer.

24. ● At $t = 0$, one toy car is set rolling on a straight track with initial position 15.0 cm, initial velocity −3.50 cm/s, and constant acceleration 2.40 cm/s^2. At the same moment, another toy car is set rolling on an adjacent track with initial position 10.0 cm, an initial velocity of +5.50 cm/s, and constant acceleration zero. (a) At what time, if any, do the two cars have equal speeds? (b) What are their speeds at that time? (c) At what time(s), if any, do the cars pass each other? (d) What are their locations at that time? (e) Explain the difference between question (a) and question (c) as clearly as possible. Write (or draw) for a target audience of students who do not immediately understand the conditions are different.

25. The driver of a car slams on the brakes when he sees a tree blocking the road. The car slows uniformly with an acceleration of −5.60 m/s^2 for 4.20 s, making straight skid marks 62.4 m long ending at the tree. With what speed does the car then strike the tree?

26. *Help! One of our equations is missing!* We describe constant-acceleration motion with the variables and parameters v_{xi}, v_{xf}, a_x, t, and $x_f − x_i$. Of the equations in Table 2.2, the first does not involve $x_f − x_i$, the second does not contain a_x, the third omits v_{xf} and the last leaves out t. So, to complete the set there should be an equation *not* involving v_{xi}. Derive it from the others. Use it to solve Problem 25 in one step.

27. For many years Colonel John P. Stapp, USAF, held the world's land speed record. He participated in studying whether a jet pilot could survive emergency ejection. On March 19, 1954, he rode a rocket-propelled sled that moved down a track at a speed of 632 mi/h. He and the

sled were safely brought to rest in 1.40 s (Fig. P2.27). Determine (a) the negative acceleration he experienced and (b) the distance he traveled during this negative acceleration.

Figure P2.27   (*Left*) Col. John Stapp on rocket sled. (*Right*) Stapp's face is contorted by the stress of rapid negative acceleration.

28. A particle moves along the x axis. Its position is given by the equation $x = 2 + 3t − 4t^2$, with x in meters and t in seconds. Determine (a) its position when it changes direction and (b) its velocity when it returns to the position it had at $t = 0$.

29. An electron in a cathode-ray tube accelerates from a speed of 2.00×10^4 m/s to 6.00×10^6 m/s over 1.50 cm. (a) In what time interval does the electron travel this 1.50 cm? (b) What is its acceleration?

30. ● Within a complex machine such as a robotic assembly line, suppose one particular part glides along a straight track. A control system measures the average velocity of the part during each successive time interval $\Delta t_0 = t_0 − 0$, compares it with the value v_c it should be, and switches a servo motor on and off to give the part a correcting pulse of acceleration. The pulse consists of a constant acceleration a_m applied for time interval $\Delta t_m = t_m − 0$ within the next control time interval Δt_0. As shown in Figure P2.30, the part may be modeled as having zero acceleration when the motor is off (between t_m and t_0). A computer in the control system chooses the size of the acceleration so that the final velocity of the part will have the correct value v_c. Assume the part is initially at rest and is to have instantaneous velocity v_c at time t_0. (a) Find the required value of a_m in terms of v_c and t_m. (b) Show that the displacement Δx of the part during the time interval Δt_0 is given by $\Delta x = v_c (t_0 − 0.5t_m)$. For specified values of v_c and t_0, (c) what is the minimum displacement of the part? (d) What is the maximum displacement of the part? (e) Are both the minimum and maximum displacements physically attainable?

Figure P2.30

31. ● A glider on an air track carries a flag of length ℓ through a stationary photogate, which measures the time

interval Δt_d during which the flag blocks a beam of infrared light passing across the photogate. The ratio $v_d = \ell/\Delta t_d$ is the average velocity of the glider over this part of its motion. Suppose the glider moves with constant acceleration. (a) Argue for or against the idea that v_d is equal to the instantaneous velocity of the glider when it is halfway through the photogate in space. (b) Argue for or against the idea that v_d is equal to the instantaneous velocity of the glider when it is halfway through the photogate in time.

32. ● Speedy Sue, driving at 30.0 m/s, enters a one-lane tunnel. She then observes a slow-moving van 155 m ahead traveling at 5.00 m/s. Sue applies her brakes but can accelerate only at -2.00 m/s² because the road is wet. Will there be a collision? State how you decide. If yes, determine how far into the tunnel and at what time the collision occurs. If no, determine the distance of closest approach between Sue's car and the van.

33. *Vroom, vroom!* As soon as a traffic light turns green, a car speeds up from rest to 50.0 mi/h with constant acceleration 9.00 mi/h · s. In the adjoining bike lane, a cyclist speeds up from rest to 20.0 mi/h with constant acceleration 13.0 mi/h · s. Each vehicle maintains constant velocity after reaching its cruising speed. (a) For what time interval is the bicycle ahead of the car? (b) By what maximum distance does the bicycle lead the car?

34. Solve Example 2.8 (Watch Out for the Speed Limit!) by a graphical method. On the same graph plot position versus time for the car and the police officer. From the intersection of the two curves read the time at which the trooper overtakes the car.

35. ● A glider of length 12.4 cm moves on an air track with constant acceleration. A time interval of 0.628 s elapses between the moment when its front end passes a fixed point Ⓐ along the track and the moment when its back end passes this point. Next, a time interval of 1.39 s elapses between the moment when the back end of the glider passes point Ⓐ and the moment when the front end of the glider passes a second point Ⓑ farther down the track. After that, an additional 0.431 s elapses until the back end of the glider passes point Ⓑ. (a) Find the average speed of the glider as it passes point Ⓐ. (b) Find the acceleration of the glider. (c) Explain how you can compute the acceleration without knowing the distance between points Ⓐ and Ⓑ.

Section 2.7 Freely Falling Objects

Note: In all problems in this section, ignore the effects of air resistance.

36. In a classic clip on *America's Funniest Home Videos*, a sleeping cat rolls gently off the top of a warm TV set. Ignoring air resistance, calculate (a) the position and (b) the velocity of the cat after 0.100 s, 0.200 s, and 0.300 s.

37. ● *Every morning at seven o'clock*
    There's twenty terriers drilling on the rock.
    The boss comes around and he says, "Keep still
    And bear down heavy on the cast-iron drill

    And drill, ye terriers, drill." And drill, ye terriers, drill.
    It's work all day for sugar in your tea
    Down beyond the railway. And drill, ye terriers, drill.

The foreman's name was John McAnn.
By God, he was a blamed mean man.
One day a premature blast went off
And a mile in the air went big Jim Goff. And drill . . .

Then when next payday came around
Jim Goff a dollar short was found.
When he asked what for, came this reply:
"You were docked for the time you were up in the sky."
    And drill . . .

—American folksong

What was Goff's hourly wage? State the assumptions you make in computing it.

38. A ball is thrown directly downward, with an initial speed of 8.00 m/s, from a height of 30.0 m. After what time interval does the ball strike the ground?

39. ▲ A student throws a set of keys vertically upward to her sorority sister, who is in a window 4.00 m above. The keys are caught 1.50 s later by the sister's outstretched hand. (a) With what initial velocity were the keys thrown? (b) What was the velocity of the keys just before they were caught?

40. ● Emily challenges her friend David to catch a dollar bill as follows. She holds the bill vertically, as shown in Figure P2.40, with the center of the bill between David's index finger and thumb. David must catch the bill after Emily releases it without moving his hand downward. If his reaction time is 0.2 s, will he succeed? Explain your reasoning.

Figure P2.40

41. A baseball is hit so that it travels straight upward after being struck by the bat. A fan observes that it takes 3.00 s for the ball to reach its maximum height. Find (a) the ball's initial velocity and (b) the height it reaches.

42. ● An attacker at the base of a castle wall 3.65 m high throws a rock straight up with speed 7.40 m/s at a height of 1.55 m above the ground. (a) Will the rock reach the top of the wall? (b) If so, what is its speed at the top? If not, what initial speed must it have to reach the top? (c) Find the change in speed of a rock thrown straight down from the top of the wall at an initial speed of 7.40 m/s and moving between the same two points. (d) Does the change in speed of the downward-moving rock agree with the magnitude of the speed change of the rock moving upward between the same elevations? Explain physically why it does or does not agree.

43. ▲ A daring ranch hand sitting on a tree limb wishes to drop vertically onto a horse galloping under the tree. The constant speed of the horse is 10.0 m/s, and the distance

from the limb to the level of the saddle is 3.00 m. (a) What must the horizontal distance between the saddle and limb be when the ranch hand makes his move? (b) For what time interval is he in the air?

44. The height of a helicopter above the ground is given by $h = 3.00t^3$, where h is in meters and t is in seconds. After 2.00 s, the helicopter releases a small mailbag. How long after its release does the mailbag reach the ground?

45. A freely falling object requires 1.50 s to travel the last 30.0 m before it hits the ground. From what height above the ground did it fall?

Section 2.8 Kinematic Equations Derived from Calculus

46. A student drives a moped along a straight road as described by the velocity-versus-time graph in Figure P2.46. Sketch this graph in the middle of a sheet of graph paper. (a) Directly above your graph, sketch a graph of the position versus time, aligning the time coordinates of the two graphs. (b) Sketch a graph of the acceleration versus time directly below the v_x–t graph, again aligning the time coordinates. On each graph, show the numerical values of x and a_x for all points of inflection. (c) What is the acceleration at $t = 6$ s? (d) Find the position (relative to the starting point) at $t = 6$ s. (e) What is the moped's final position at $t = 9$ s?

Figure P2.46

47. Automotive engineers refer to the time rate of change of acceleration as the "jerk." Assume an object moves in one dimension such that its jerk J is constant. (a) Determine expressions for its acceleration $a_x(t)$, velocity $v_x(t)$, and position $x(t)$, given that its initial acceleration, velocity, and position are a_{xi}, v_{xi}, and x_i, respectively. (b) Show that $a_x^2 = a_{xi}^2 + 2J(v_x - v_{xi})$.

48. The speed of a bullet as it travels down the barrel of a rifle toward the opening is given by $v = (-5.00 \times 10^7)t^2 + (3.00 \times 10^5)t$, where v is in meters per second and t is in seconds. The acceleration of the bullet just as it leaves the barrel is zero. (a) Determine the acceleration and position of the bullet as a function of time when the bullet is in the barrel. (b) Determine the time interval over which the bullet is accelerated. (c) Find the speed at which the bullet leaves the barrel. (d) What is the length of the barrel?

Additional Problems

49. An object is at $x = 0$ at $t = 0$ and moves along the x axis according to the velocity–time graph in Figure P2.49. (a) What is the acceleration of the object between 0 and

4 s? (b) What is the acceleration of the object between 4 s and 9 s? (c) What is the acceleration of the object between 13 s and 18 s? (d) At what time(s) is the object moving with the lowest speed? (e) At what time is the object farthest from $x = 0$? (f) What is the final position x of the object at $t = 18$ s? (g) Through what total distance has the object moved between $t = 0$ and $t = 18$ s?

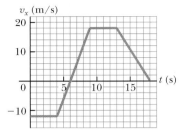

Figure P2.49

50. ● The Acela (pronounced ah-SELL-ah and shown in Fig. P2.50a) is an electric train on the Washington–New York–Boston run, carrying passengers at 170 mi/h. The carriages tilt as much as 6° from the vertical to prevent passengers from feeling pushed to the side as they go around curves. A velocity–time graph for the Acela is shown in Figure P2.50b. (a) Describe the motion of the train in each successive time interval. (b) Find the peak positive acceleration of the train in the motion graphed. (c) Find the train's displacement in miles between $t = 0$ and $t = 200$ s.

(a)

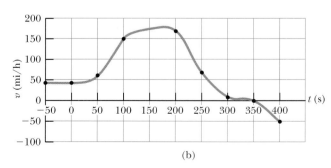

(b)

Figure P2.50 (a) The Acela: 1 171 000 lb of cold steel thundering along with 304 passengers. (b) Velocity-versus-time graph for the Acela.

51. A test rocket is fired vertically upward from a well. A catapult gives it an initial speed of 80.0 m/s at ground level.

Its engines then fire and it accelerates upward at 4.00 m/s² until it reaches an altitude of 1 000 m. At that point its engines fail and the rocket goes into free fall, with an acceleration of −9.80 m/s². (a) For what time interval is the rocket in motion above the ground? (b) What is its maximum altitude? (c) What is its velocity just before it collides with the Earth? (You will need to consider the motion while the engine is operating separate from the free-fall motion.)

52. ● In Active Figure 2.11b, the area under the velocity versus time curve and between the vertical axis and time t (vertical dashed line) represents the displacement. As shown, this area consists of a rectangle and a triangle. Compute their areas and state how the sum of the two areas compares with the expression on the right-hand side of Equation 2.16.

53. Setting a world record in a 100-m race, Maggie and Judy cross the finish line in a dead heat, both taking 10.2 s. Accelerating uniformly, Maggie took 2.00 s and Judy took 3.00 s to attain maximum speed, which they maintained for the rest of the race. (a) What was the acceleration of each sprinter? (b) What were their respective maximum speeds? (c) Which sprinter was ahead at the 6.00-s mark, and by how much?

54. ● *How long should a traffic light stay yellow?* Assume you are driving at the speed limit v_0. As you approach an intersection 22.0 m wide, you see the light turn yellow. During your reaction time of 0.600 s, you travel at constant speed as you recognize the warning, decide whether to stop or to go through the intersection, and move your foot to the brake if you must stop. Your car has good brakes and can accelerate at −2.40 m/s². Before it turns red, the light should stay yellow long enough for you to be able to get to the other side of the intersection without speeding up, if you are too close to the intersection to stop before entering it. (a) Find the required time interval Δt_y that the light should stay yellow in terms of v_0. Evaluate your answer for (b) $v_0 = 8.00$ m/s = 28.8 km/h, (c) $v_0 = 11.0$ m/s = 40.2 km/h, (d) $v_0 = 18.0$ m/s = 64.8 km/h, and (e) $v_0 = 25.0$ m/s = 90.0 km/h. **What If?** Evaluate your answer for (f) v_0 approaching zero, and (g) v_0 approaching infinity. (h) Describe the pattern of variation of Δt_y with v_0. You may wish also to sketch a graph of it. Account for the answers to parts (f) and (g) physically. (i) For what value of v_0 would Δt_y be minimal, and (j) what is this minimum time interval? *Suggestion:* You may find it easier to do part (a) after first doing part (b).

55. A commuter train travels between two downtown stations. Because the stations are only 1.00 km apart, the train never reaches its maximum possible cruising speed. During rush hour the engineer minimizes the time interval Δt between two stations by accelerating for a time interval Δt_1 at a rate $a_1 = 0.100$ m/s² and then immediately braking with acceleration $a_2 = -0.500$ m/s² for a time interval Δt_2. Find the minimum time interval of travel Δt and the time interval Δt_1.

56. A Ferrari F50 of length 4.52 m is moving north on a roadway that intersects another perpendicular roadway. The width of the intersection from near edge to far edge is 28.0 m. The Ferrari has a constant acceleration of magnitude 2.10 m/s² directed south. The time interval required for the nose of the Ferrari to move from the near (south) edge of the intersection to the north edge of the intersection is 3.10 s. (a) How far is the nose of the Ferrari from the south edge of the intersection when it stops? (b) For what time interval is *any* part of the Ferrari within the boundaries of the intersection? (c) A Corvette is at rest on the perpendicular intersecting roadway. As the nose of the Ferrari enters the intersection, the Corvette starts from rest and accelerates east at 5.60 m/s². What is the minimum distance from the near (west) edge of the intersection at which the nose of the Corvette can begin its motion if the Corvette is to enter the intersection after the Ferrari has entirely left the intersection? (d) If the Corvette begins its motion at the position given by your answer to part (c), with what speed does it enter the intersection?

57. An inquisitive physics student and mountain climber climbs a 50.0-m cliff that overhangs a calm pool of water. He throws two stones vertically downward, 1.00 s apart, and observes that they cause a single splash. The first stone has an initial speed of 2.00 m/s. (a) How long after release of the first stone do the two stones hit the water? (b) What initial velocity must the second stone have if they are to hit simultaneously? (c) What is the speed of each stone at the instant the two hit the water?

58. ● A hard rubber ball, released at chest height, falls to the pavement and bounces back to nearly the same height. When it is in contact with the pavement, the lower side of the ball is temporarily flattened. Suppose the maximum depth of the dent is on the order of 1 cm. Compute an order-of-magnitude estimate for the maximum acceleration of the ball while it is in contact with the pavement. State your assumptions, the quantities you estimate, and the values you estimate for them.

59. Kathy Kool buys a sports car that can accelerate at the rate of 4.90 m/s². She decides to test the car by racing with another speedster, Stan Speedy. Both start from rest, but experienced Stan leaves the starting line 1.00 s before Kathy. Stan moves with a constant acceleration of 3.50 m/s² and Kathy maintains an acceleration of 4.90 m/s². Find (a) the time at which Kathy overtakes Stan, (b) the distance she travels before she catches him, and (c) the speeds of both cars at the instant she overtakes him.

60. A rock is dropped from rest into a well. (a) The sound of the splash is heard 2.40 s after the rock is released from rest. How far below the top of the well is the surface of the water? The speed of sound in air (at the ambient temperature) is 336 m/s. (b) **What If?** If the travel time for the sound is ignored, what percentage error is introduced when the depth of the well is calculated?

61. ● In a California driver's handbook, the following data were given about the minimum distance a typical car travels in stopping from various original speeds. The "thinking distance" represents how far the car travels during the driver's reaction time, after a reason to stop can be seen but before the driver can apply the brakes. The "braking distance" is the displacement of the car after the brakes are applied. (a) Is the thinking-distance data

2 = intermediate;   3 = challenging;   □ = SSM/SG;   ▲ = ThomsonNOW;   ▨ = symbolic reasoning;   ● = qualitative reasoning

consistent with the assumption that the car travels with constant speed? Explain. (b) Determine the best value of the reaction time suggested by the data. (c) Is the braking-distance data consistent with the assumption that the car travels with constant acceleration? Explain. (d) Determine the best value for the acceleration suggested by the data.

Speed (mi/h)	Thinking Distance (ft)	Braking Distance (ft)	Total Stopping Distance (ft)
25	27	34	61
35	38	67	105
45	49	110	159
55	60	165	225
65	71	231	302

62. ● ☕ Astronauts on a distant planet toss a rock into the air. With the aid of a camera that takes pictures at a steady rate, they record the height of the rock as a function of time as given in the table in the next column. (a) Find the average velocity of the rock in the time interval between each measurement and the next. (b) Using these average velocities to approximate instantaneous velocities at the midpoints of the time intervals, make a graph of velocity as a function of time. Does the rock move with constant acceleration? If so, plot a straight line of best fit on the graph and calculate its slope to find the acceleration.

Time (s)	Height (m)	Time (s)	Height (m)
0.00	5.00	2.75	7.62
0.25	5.75	3.00	7.25
0.50	6.40	3.25	6.77
0.75	6.94	3.50	6.20
1.00	7.38	3.75	5.52
1.25	7.72	4.00	4.73
1.50	7.96	4.25	3.85
1.75	8.10	4.50	2.86
2.00	8.13	4.75	1.77
2.25	8.07	5.00	0.58
2.50	7.90		

63. Two objects, A and B, are connected by a rigid rod that has length L. The objects slide along perpendicular guide rails as shown in Figure P2.63. Assume A slides to the left with a constant speed v. Find the velocity of B when $\theta = 60.0°$.

Figure P2.63

Answers to Quick Quizzes

2.1 (c). If the particle moves along a line without changing direction, the displacement and distance traveled over any time interval will be the same. As a result, the magnitude of the average velocity and the average speed will be the same. If the particle reverses direction, however, the displacement will be less than the distance traveled. In turn, the magnitude of the average velocity will be smaller than the average speed.

2.2 (b). Regardless of your speeds at all other times, if your instantaneous speed at the instant it is measured is higher than the speed limit, you may receive a speeding ticket.

2.3 (b). If the car is slowing down, a force must be pulling in the direction opposite to its velocity.

2.4 False. Your graph should look something like the following.

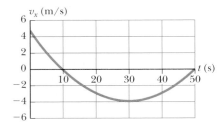

This v_x–t graph shows that the maximum speed is about 5.0 m/s, which is 18 km/h (= 11 mi/h), so the driver was not speeding.

2.5 (c). If a particle with constant acceleration stops and its acceleration remains constant, it must begin to move again in the opposite direction. If it did not, the acceleration would change from its original constant value to zero. Choice (a) is not correct because the direction of acceleration is not specified by the direction of the velocity. Choice (b) is also not correct by counterexample; a car moving in the $-x$ direction and slowing down has a positive acceleration.

2.6 Graph (a) has a constant slope, indicating a constant acceleration; it is represented by graph (e).

Graph (b) represents a speed that is increasing constantly but not at a uniform rate. Therefore, the acceleration must be increasing, and the graph that best indicates that is (d).

Graph (c) depicts a velocity that first increases at a constant rate, indicating constant acceleration. Then the velocity stops increasing and becomes constant, indicating zero acceleration. The best match to this situation is graph (f).

2.7 (i), (e). For the entire time interval that the ball is in free fall, the acceleration is that due to gravity. (ii), (d). While the ball is rising, it is slowing down. After reaching the highest point, the ball begins to fall and its speed increases.

These controls in the cockpit of a commercial aircraft assist the pilot in maintaining control over the velocity of the aircraft—how fast it is traveling and in what direction it is traveling—allowing it to land safely. Quantities that are defined by both a magnitude and a direction, such as velocity, are called *vector quantities*. (Mark Wagner/Getty Images)

3 Vectors

In our study of physics, we often need to work with physical quantities that have both numerical and directional properties. As noted in Section 2.1, quantities of this nature are vector quantities. This chapter is primarily concerned with general properties of vector quantities. We discuss the addition and subtraction of vector quantities, together with some common applications to physical situations.

Vector quantities are used throughout this text. Therefore, it is imperative that you master the techniques discussed in this chapter.

3.1 Coordinate Systems

Many aspects of physics involve a description of a location in space. In Chapter 2, for example, we saw that the mathematical description of an object's motion requires a method for describing the object's position at various times. In two dimensions, this description is accomplished with the use of the Cartesian coordinate system, in which perpendicular axes intersect at a point defined as the origin (Fig. 3.1). Cartesian coordinates are also called *rectangular coordinates*.

Sometimes it is more convenient to represent a point in a plane by its *plane polar coordinates* (r, θ) as shown in Active Figure 3.2a (see page 54). In this *polar coordinate system*, r is the distance from the origin to the point having Cartesian coordinates (x, y) and θ is the angle between a fixed axis and a line drawn from the origin to the point. The fixed axis is often the positive x axis, and θ is usually measured counterclockwise from it. From the right triangle in Active Figure 3.2b,

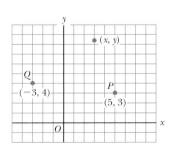

Figure 3.1 Designation of points in a Cartesian coordinate system. Every point is labeled with coordinates (x, y).

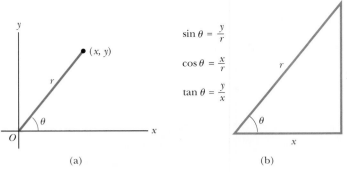

(a)   (b)

ACTIVE FIGURE 3.2

(a) The plane polar coordinates of a point are represented by the distance r and the angle θ, where θ is measured counterclockwise from the positive x axis. (b) The right triangle used to relate (x, y) to (r, θ).

Sign in at www.thomsonedu.com and go to ThomsonNOW to move the point and see the changes to the rectangular and polar coordinates as well as to the sine, cosine, and tangent of angle θ.

we find that $\sin \theta = y/r$ and that $\cos \theta = x/r$. (A review of trigonometric functions is given in Appendix B.4.) Therefore, starting with the plane polar coordinates of any point, we can obtain the Cartesian coordinates by using the equations

$$x = r \cos \theta \tag{3.1}$$

$$y = r \sin \theta \tag{3.2}$$

Furthermore, the definitions of trigonometry tell us that

$$\tan \theta = \frac{y}{x} \tag{3.3}$$

$$r = \sqrt{x^2 + y^2} \tag{3.4}$$

Equation 3.4 is the familiar Pythagorean theorem.

These four expressions relating the coordinates (x, y) to the coordinates (r, θ) apply only when θ is defined as shown in Active Figure 3.2a—in other words, when positive θ is an angle measured counterclockwise from the positive x axis. (Some scientific calculators perform conversions between Cartesian and polar coordinates based on these standard conventions.) If the reference axis for the polar angle θ is chosen to be one other than the positive x axis or if the sense of increasing θ is chosen differently, the expressions relating the two sets of coordinates will change.

EXAMPLE 3.1   **Polar Coordinates**

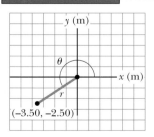

ACTIVE FIGURE 3.3

(Example 3.1) Finding polar coordinates when Cartesian coordinates are given.

Sign in at www.thomsonedu.com and go to ThomsonNOW to move the point in the xy plane and see how its Cartesian and polar coordinates change.

The Cartesian coordinates of a point in the xy plane are $(x, y) = (-3.50, -2.50)$ m as shown in Active Figure 3.3. Find the polar coordinates of this point.

SOLUTION

Conceptualize   The drawing in Active Figure 3.3 helps us conceptualize the problem.

Categorize   Based on the statement of the problem and the Conceptualize step, we recognize that we are simply converting from Cartesian coordinates to polar coordinates. We therefore categorize this example as a substitution problem. Substitution problems generally do not have an extensive Analyze step other than the substitution of numbers into a given equation. Similarly, the Finalize step consists primarily of checking the units and making sure that the answer is reasonable. Therefore, for substitution problems, we will not label Analyze or Finalize steps.

Use Equation 3.4 to find r:

$$r = \sqrt{x^2 + y^2} = \sqrt{(-3.50 \text{ m})^2 + (-2.50 \text{ m})^2} = \boxed{4.30 \text{ m}}$$

Use Equation 3.3 to find θ:

$$\tan \theta = \frac{y}{x} = \frac{-2.50 \text{ m}}{-3.50 \text{ m}} = 0.714$$

$$\theta = \boxed{216°}$$

Notice that you must use the signs of x and y to find that the point lies in the third quadrant of the coordinate system. That is, $\theta = 216°$, not $35.5°$.

3.2 Vector and Scalar Quantities

We now formally describe the difference between scalar quantities and vector quantities. When you want to know the temperature outside so that you will know how to dress, the only information you need is a number and the unit "degrees C" or "degrees F." Temperature is therefore an example of a *scalar quantity*:

> A **scalar quantity** is completely specified by a single value with an appropriate unit and has no direction.

Other examples of scalar quantities are volume, mass, speed, and time intervals. The rules of ordinary arithmetic are used to manipulate scalar quantities.

If you are preparing to pilot a small plane and need to know the wind velocity, you must know both the speed of the wind and its direction. Because direction is important for its complete specification, velocity is a *vector quantity*:

> A **vector quantity** is completely specified by a number and appropriate units plus a direction.

Another example of a vector quantity is displacement, as you know from Chapter 2. Suppose a particle moves from some point Ⓐ to some point Ⓑ along a straight path as shown in Figure 3.4. We represent this displacement by drawing an arrow from Ⓐ to Ⓑ, with the tip of the arrow pointing away from the starting point. The direction of the arrowhead represents the direction of the displacement, and the length of the arrow represents the magnitude of the displacement. If the particle travels along some other path from Ⓐ to Ⓑ, such as shown by the broken line in Figure 3.4, its displacement is still the arrow drawn from Ⓐ to Ⓑ. Displacement depends only on the initial and final positions, so the displacement vector is independent of the path taken by the particle between these two points.

In this text, we use a boldface letter with an arrow over the letter, such as $\vec{\mathbf{A}}$, to represent a vector. Another common notation for vectors with which you should be familiar is a simple boldface character: **A**. The magnitude of the vector $\vec{\mathbf{A}}$ is written either A or $|\vec{\mathbf{A}}|$. The magnitude of a vector has physical units, such as meters for displacement or meters per second for velocity. The magnitude of a vector is *always* a positive number.

Figure 3.4 As a particle moves from Ⓐ to Ⓑ along an arbitrary path represented by the broken line, its displacement is a vector quantity shown by the arrow drawn from Ⓐ to Ⓑ.

Quick Quiz 3.1 Which of the following are vector quantities and which are scalar quantities? (a) your age   (b) acceleration   (c) velocity   (d) speed   (e) mass

3.3 Some Properties of Vectors

In this section, we shall investigate general properties of vectors representing physical quantities. We also discuss how to add and subtract vectors using both algebraic and geometric methods.

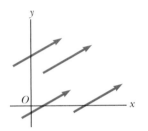

Figure 3.5 These four vectors are equal because they have equal lengths and point in the same direction.

Equality of Two Vectors

For many purposes, two vectors $\vec{A}$ and $\vec{B}$ may be defined to be equal if they have the same magnitude and if they point in the same direction. That is, $\vec{A} = \vec{B}$ only if $A = B$ and if $\vec{A}$ and $\vec{B}$ point in the same direction along parallel lines. For example, all the vectors in Figure 3.5 are equal even though they have different starting points. This property allows us to move a vector to a position parallel to itself in a diagram without affecting the vector.

Adding Vectors

The rules for adding vectors are conveniently described by a graphical method. To add vector $\vec{B}$ to vector $\vec{A}$, first draw vector $\vec{A}$ on graph paper, with its magnitude represented by a convenient length scale, and then draw vector $\vec{B}$ to the same scale, with its tail starting from the tip of $\vec{A}$, as shown in Active Figure 3.6. The **resultant vector** $\vec{R} = \vec{A} + \vec{B}$ is the vector drawn from the tail of $\vec{A}$ to the tip of $\vec{B}$.

A geometric construction can also be used to add more than two vectors as is shown in Figure 3.7 for the case of four vectors. The resultant vector $\vec{R} = \vec{A} + \vec{B} + \vec{C} + \vec{D}$ is the vector that completes the polygon. In other words, $\vec{R}$ is **the vector drawn from the tail of the first vector to the tip of the last vector**. This technique for adding vectors is often called the "head to tail method."

When two vectors are added, the sum is independent of the order of the addition. (This fact may seem trivial, but as you will see in Chapter 11, the order is important when vectors are multiplied. Procedures for multiplying vectors are discussed in Chapters 7 and 11). This property, which can be seen from the geometric construction in Figure 3.8, is known as the **commutative law of addition:**

$$\vec{A} + \vec{B} = \vec{B} + \vec{A} \tag{3.5}$$

When three or more vectors are added, their sum is independent of the way in which the individual vectors are grouped together. A geometric proof of this rule for three vectors is given in Figure 3.9. This property is called the **associative law of addition:**

$$\vec{A} + (\vec{B} + \vec{C}) = (\vec{A} + \vec{B}) + \vec{C} \tag{3.6}$$

In summary, **a vector quantity has both magnitude and direction and also obeys the laws of vector addition** as described in Figures 3.6 to 3.9. When two or more vectors are added together, they must all have the same units and they must all be the same type of quantity. It would be meaningless to add a velocity vector (for example, 60 km/h to the east) to a displacement vector (for example, 200 km to the north) because these vectors represent different physical quantities. The same

PITFALL PREVENTION 3.1
Vector Addition versus Scalar Addition

Notice that $\vec{A} + \vec{B} = \vec{C}$ is very different from $A + B = C$. The first equation is a vector sum, which must be handled carefully, such as with the graphical method. The second equation is a simple algebraic addition of numbers that is handled with the normal rules of arithmetic.

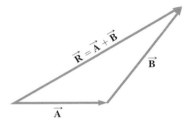

ACTIVE FIGURE 3.6

When vector $\vec{B}$ is added to vector $\vec{A}$, the resultant $\vec{R}$ is the vector that runs from the tail of $\vec{A}$ to the tip of $\vec{B}$.

Sign in at www.thomsonedu.com and go to ThomsonNOW to explore the addition of two vectors.

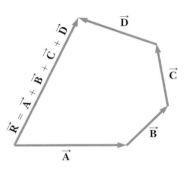

Figure 3.7 Geometric construction for summing four vectors. The resultant vector $\vec{R}$ is by definition the one that completes the polygon.

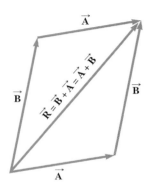

Figure 3.8 This construction shows that $\vec{A} + \vec{B} = \vec{B} + \vec{A}$ or, in other words, that vector addition is commutative.

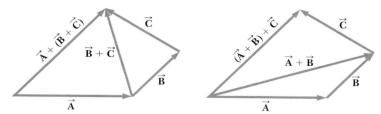

Figure 3.9   Geometric constructions for verifying the associative law of addition.

rule also applies to scalars. For example, it would be meaningless to add time intervals to temperatures.

Negative of a Vector

The negative of the vector $\vec{A}$ is defined as the vector that when added to $\vec{A}$ gives zero for the vector sum. That is, $\vec{A} + (-\vec{A}) = 0$. The vectors $\vec{A}$ and $-\vec{A}$ have the same magnitude but point in opposite directions.

Subtracting Vectors

The operation of vector subtraction makes use of the definition of the negative of a vector. We define the operation $\vec{A} - \vec{B}$ as vector $-\vec{B}$ added to vector $\vec{A}$:

$$\vec{A} - \vec{B} = \vec{A} + (-\vec{B}) \tag{3.7}$$

The geometric construction for subtracting two vectors in this way is illustrated in Figure 3.10a.

Another way of looking at vector subtraction is to notice that the difference $\vec{A} - \vec{B}$ between two vectors $\vec{A}$ and $\vec{B}$ is what you have to add to the second vector to obtain the first. In this case, as Figure 3.10b shows, the vector $\vec{A} - \vec{B}$ points from the tip of the second vector to the tip of the first.

Multiplying a Vector by a Scalar

If vector $\vec{A}$ is multiplied by a positive scalar quantity m, the product $m\vec{A}$ is a vector that has the same direction as $\vec{A}$ and magnitude mA. If vector $\vec{A}$ is multiplied by a negative scalar quantity $-m$, the product $-m\vec{A}$ is directed opposite $\vec{A}$. For example, the vector $5\vec{A}$ is five times as long as $\vec{A}$ and points in the same direction as $\vec{A}$; the vector $-\frac{1}{3}\vec{A}$ is one-third the length of $\vec{A}$ and points in the direction opposite $\vec{A}$.

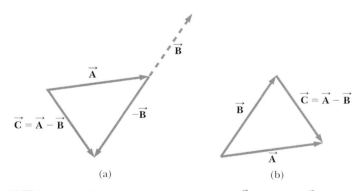

      (a)   (b)

Figure 3.10   (a) This construction shows how to subtract vector $\vec{B}$ from vector $\vec{A}$. The vector $-\vec{B}$ is equal in magnitude to vector $\vec{B}$ and points in the opposite direction. To subtract $\vec{B}$ from $\vec{A}$, apply the rule of vector addition to the combination of $\vec{A}$ and $-\vec{B}$: first draw $\vec{A}$ along some convenient axis and then place the tail of $-\vec{B}$ at the tip of $\vec{A}$, and $\vec{C}$ is the difference $\vec{A} - \vec{B}$. (b) A second way of looking at vector subtraction. The difference vector $\vec{C} = \vec{A} - \vec{B}$ is the vector that we must add to $\vec{B}$ to obtain $\vec{A}$.

Quick Quiz 3.2   The magnitudes of two vectors $\vec{\mathbf{A}}$ and $\vec{\mathbf{B}}$ are $A = 12$ units and $B = 8$ units. Which of the following pairs of numbers represents the *largest* and *smallest* possible values for the magnitude of the resultant vector $\vec{\mathbf{R}} = \vec{\mathbf{A}} + \vec{\mathbf{B}}$? (a) 14.4 units, 4 units   (b) 12 units, 8 units   (c) 20 units, 4 units   (d) none of these answers

Quick Quiz 3.3   If vector $\vec{\mathbf{B}}$ is added to vector $\vec{\mathbf{A}}$, which *two* of the following choices must be true for the resultant vector to be equal to zero? (a) $\vec{\mathbf{A}}$ and $\vec{\mathbf{B}}$ are parallel and in the same direction. (b) $\vec{\mathbf{A}}$ and $\vec{\mathbf{B}}$ are parallel and in opposite directions. (c) $\vec{\mathbf{A}}$ and $\vec{\mathbf{B}}$ have the same magnitude. (d) $\vec{\mathbf{A}}$ and $\vec{\mathbf{B}}$ are perpendicular.

EXAMPLE 3.2   **A Vacation Trip**

A car travels 20.0 km due north and then 35.0 km in a direction 60.0° west of north as shown in Figure 3.11a. Find the magnitude and direction of the car's resultant displacement.

SOLUTION

Conceptualize   The vectors $\vec{\mathbf{A}}$ and $\vec{\mathbf{B}}$ drawn in Figure 3.11a help us conceptualize the problem.

Categorize   We can categorize this example as a simple analysis problem in vector addition. The displacement $\vec{\mathbf{R}}$ is the resultant when the two individual displacements $\vec{\mathbf{A}}$ and $\vec{\mathbf{B}}$ are added. We can further categorize it as a problem about the analysis of triangles, so we appeal to our expertise in geometry and trigonometry.

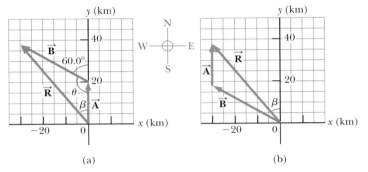

Figure 3.11   (Example 3.2) (a) Graphical method for finding the resultant displacement vector $\vec{\mathbf{R}} = \vec{\mathbf{A}} + \vec{\mathbf{B}}$. (b) Adding the vectors in reverse order ($\vec{\mathbf{B}} + \vec{\mathbf{A}}$) gives the same result for $\vec{\mathbf{R}}$.

Analyze   In this example, we show two ways to analyze the problem of finding the resultant of two vectors. The first way is to solve the problem geometrically, using graph paper and a protractor to measure the magnitude of $\vec{\mathbf{R}}$ and its direction in Figure 3.11a. (In fact, even when you know you are going to be carrying out a calculation, you should sketch the vectors to check your results.) With an ordinary ruler and protractor, a large diagram typically gives answers to two-digit but not to three-digit precision.

The second way to solve the problem is to analyze it algebraically. The magnitude of $\vec{\mathbf{R}}$ can be obtained from the law of cosines as applied to the triangle (see Appendix B.4).

Use $R^2 = A^2 + B^2 - 2AB \cos \theta$ from the law of cosines to find R:

$$R = \sqrt{A^2 + B^2 - 2AB \cos \theta}$$

Substitute numerical values, noting that $\theta = 180° - 60° = 120°$:

$$R = \sqrt{(20.0 \text{ km})^2 + (35.0 \text{ km})^2 - 2(20.0 \text{ km})(35.0 \text{ km}) \cos 120°}$$

$$= \boxed{48.2 \text{ km}}$$

Use the law of sines (Appendix B.4) to find the direction of $\vec{\mathbf{R}}$ measured from the northerly direction:

$$\frac{\sin \beta}{B} = \frac{\sin \theta}{R}$$

$$\sin \beta = \frac{B}{R} \sin \theta = \frac{35.0 \text{ km}}{48.2 \text{ km}} \sin 120° = 0.629$$

$$\beta = \boxed{38.9°}$$

The resultant displacement of the car is 48.2 km in a direction 38.9° west of north.

Finalize Does the angle β that we calculated agree with an estimate made by looking at Figure 3.11a or with an actual angle measured from the diagram using the graphical method? Is it reasonable that the magnitude of $\vec{R}$ is larger than that of both $\vec{A}$ and $\vec{B}$? Are the units of $\vec{R}$ correct?

Although the graphical method of adding vectors works well, it suffers from two disadvantages. First, some people find using the laws of cosines and sines to be awkward. Second, a triangle only results if you are adding two vectors. If you are adding three or more vectors, the resulting geometric shape is usually not a triangle. In Section 3.4, we explore a new method of adding vectors that will address both of these disadvantages.

What If? Suppose the trip were taken with the two vectors in reverse order: 35.0 km at 60.0° west of north first and then 20.0 km due north. How would the magnitude and the direction of the resultant vector change?

Answer They would not change. The commutative law for vector addition tells us that the order of vectors in an addition is irrelevant. Graphically, Figure 3.11b shows that the vectors added in the reverse order give us the same resultant vector.

3.4 Components of a Vector and Unit Vectors

The graphical method of adding vectors is not recommended whenever high accuracy is required or in three-dimensional problems. In this section, we describe a method of adding vectors that makes use of the projections of vectors along coordinate axes. These projections are called the **components** of the vector or its **rectangular components**. Any vector can be completely described by its components.

Consider a vector $\vec{A}$ lying in the xy plane and making an arbitrary angle θ with the positive x axis as shown in Figure 3.12a. This vector can be expressed as the sum of two other *component vectors* $\vec{A}_x$, which is parallel to the x axis, and $\vec{A}_y$, which is parallel to the y axis. From Figure 3.12b, we see that the three vectors form a right triangle and that $\vec{A} = \vec{A}_x + \vec{A}_y$. We shall often refer to the "components of a vector $\vec{A}$," written A_x and A_y (without the boldface notation). The component A_x represents the projection of $\vec{A}$ along the x axis, and the component A_y represents the projection of $\vec{A}$ along the y axis. These components can be positive or negative. The component A_x is positive if the component vector $\vec{A}_x$ points in the positive x direction and is negative if $\vec{A}_x$ points in the negative x direction. The same is true for the component A_y.

From Figure 3.12 and the definition of sine and cosine, we see that $\cos \theta = A_x/A$ and that $\sin \theta = A_y/A$. Hence, the components of $\vec{A}$ are

$$A_x = A \cos \theta \tag{3.8}$$

$$A_y = A \sin \theta \tag{3.9}$$

PITFALL PREVENTION 3.2
Component Vectors versus Components

The vectors $\vec{A}_x$ and $\vec{A}_y$ are the *component vectors* of $\vec{A}$. They should not be confused with the quantities A_x and A_y, which we shall always refer to as the *components* of $\vec{A}$.

◄ Components of the vector $\vec{A}$

PITFALL PREVENTION 3.3
x and y Components

Equations 3.8 and 3.9 associate the cosine of the angle with the x component and the sine of the angle with the y component. This association is true *only* because we measured the angle θ with respect to the x axis, so do not memorize these equations. If θ is measured with respect to the y axis (as in some problems), these equations will be incorrect. Think about which side of the triangle containing the components is adjacent to the angle and which side is opposite and then assign the cosine and sine accordingly.

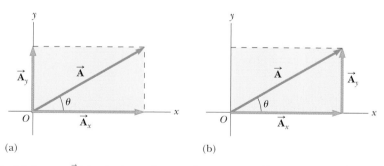

Figure 3.12 (a) A vector $\vec{A}$ lying in the xy plane can be represented by its component vectors $\vec{A}_x$ and $\vec{A}_y$. (b) The y component vector $\vec{A}_y$ can be moved to the right so that it adds to $\vec{A}_x$. The vector sum of the component vectors is $\vec{A}$. These three vectors form a right triangle.

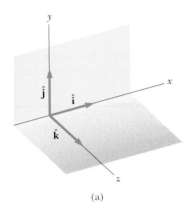

A_x negative	A_x positive
A_y positive	A_y positive
A_x negative	A_x positive
A_y negative	A_y negative

Figure 3.13 The signs of the components of a vector $\vec{A}$ depend on the quadrant in which the vector is located.

(a)

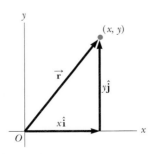

(b)

ACTIVE FIGURE 3.14

(a) The unit vectors $\hat{\mathbf{i}}$, $\hat{\mathbf{j}}$, and $\hat{\mathbf{k}}$ are directed along the x, y, and z axes, respectively. (b) Vector $\vec{A} = A_x\hat{\mathbf{i}} + A_y\hat{\mathbf{j}}$ lying in the xy plane has components A_x and A_y.

Sign in at www.thomsonedu.com and go to ThomsonNOW to rotate the coordinate axes in three-dimensional space and view a representation of vector $\vec{A}$ in three dimensions.

Figure 3.15 The point whose Cartesian coordinates are (x, y) can be represented by the position vector $\vec{r} = x\hat{\mathbf{i}} + y\hat{\mathbf{j}}$.

The magnitudes of these components are the lengths of the two sides of a right triangle with a hypotenuse of length A. Therefore, the magnitude and direction of $\vec{A}$ are related to its components through the expressions

$$A = \sqrt{A_x^2 + A_y^2} \tag{3.10}$$

$$\theta = \tan^{-1}\left(\frac{A_y}{A_x}\right) \tag{3.11}$$

Notice that **the signs of the components A_x and A_y depend on the angle θ**. For example, if $\theta = 120°$, A_x is negative and A_y is positive. If $\theta = 225°$, both A_x and A_y are negative. Figure 3.13 summarizes the signs of the components when $\vec{A}$ lies in the various quadrants.

When solving problems, you can specify a vector $\vec{A}$ either with its components A_x and A_y or with its magnitude and direction A and θ.

Suppose you are working a physics problem that requires resolving a vector into its components. In many applications, it is convenient to express the components in a coordinate system having axes that are not horizontal and vertical but that are still perpendicular to each other. For example, we will consider the motion of objects sliding down inclined planes. For these examples, it is often convenient to orient the x axis parallel to the plane and the y axis perpendicular to the plane.

Quick Quiz 3.4 Choose the correct response to make the sentence true: A component of a vector is (a) always, (b) never, or (c) sometimes larger than the magnitude of the vector.

Unit Vectors

Vector quantities often are expressed in terms of unit vectors. **A unit vector is a dimensionless vector having a magnitude of exactly 1**. Unit vectors are used to specify a given direction and have no other physical significance. They are used solely as a bookkeeping convenience in describing a direction in space. We shall use the symbols $\hat{\mathbf{i}}$, $\hat{\mathbf{j}}$, and $\hat{\mathbf{k}}$ to represent unit vectors pointing in the positive x, y, and z directions, respectively. (The "hats," or circumflexes, on the symbols are a standard notation for unit vectors.) The unit vectors $\hat{\mathbf{i}}$, $\hat{\mathbf{j}}$, and $\hat{\mathbf{k}}$ form a set of mutually perpendicular vectors in a right-handed coordinate system as shown in Active Figure 3.14a. The magnitude of each unit vector equals 1; that is, $|\hat{\mathbf{i}}| = |\hat{\mathbf{j}}| = |\hat{\mathbf{k}}| = 1$.

Consider a vector $\vec{A}$ lying in the xy plane as shown in Active Figure 3.14b. The product of the component A_x and the unit vector $\hat{\mathbf{i}}$ is the component vector $\vec{A}_x = A_x\hat{\mathbf{i}}$, which lies on the x axis and has magnitude $|A_x|$. Likewise, $\vec{A}_y = A_y\hat{\mathbf{j}}$ is the component vector of magnitude $|A_y|$ lying on the y axis. Therefore, the unit–vector notation for the vector $\vec{A}$ is

$$\vec{A} = A_x\hat{\mathbf{i}} + A_y\hat{\mathbf{j}} \tag{3.12}$$

For example, consider a point lying in the xy plane and having Cartesian coordinates (x, y) as in Figure 3.15. The point can be specified by the **position vector $\vec{r}$**, which in unit–vector form is given by

$$\vec{r} = x\hat{\mathbf{i}} + y\hat{\mathbf{j}} \tag{3.13}$$

This notation tells us that the components of $\vec{r}$ are the coordinates x and y.

Now let us see how to use components to add vectors when the graphical method is not sufficiently accurate. Suppose we wish to add vector $\vec{B}$ to vector $\vec{A}$ in Equation 3.12, where vector $\vec{B}$ has components B_x and B_y. Because of the bookkeeping convenience of the unit vectors, all we do is add the x and y components separately. The resultant vector $\vec{R} = \vec{A} + \vec{B}$ is

$$\vec{R} = (A_x\hat{\mathbf{i}} + A_y\hat{\mathbf{j}}) + (B_x\hat{\mathbf{i}} + B_y\hat{\mathbf{j}})$$

or

$$\vec{R} = (A_x + B_x)\hat{i} + (A_y + B_y)\hat{j} \qquad (3.14)$$

Because $\vec{R} = R_x\hat{i} + R_y\hat{j}$, we see that the components of the resultant vector are

$$R_x = A_x + B_x$$
$$R_y = A_y + B_y \qquad (3.15)$$

The magnitude of $\vec{R}$ and the angle it makes with the x axis from its components are obtained using the relationships

$$R = \sqrt{R_x^2 + R_y^2} = \sqrt{(A_x + B_x)^2 + (A_y + B_y)^2} \qquad (3.16)$$

$$\tan\theta = \frac{R_y}{R_x} = \frac{A_y + B_y}{A_x + B_x} \qquad (3.17)$$

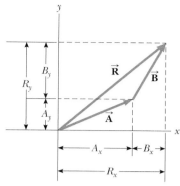

Figure 3.16 This geometric construction for the sum of two vectors shows the relationship between the components of the resultant $\vec{R}$ and the components of the individual vectors.

We can check this addition by components with a geometric construction as shown in Figure 3.16. Remember to note the signs of the components when using either the algebraic or the graphical method.

At times, we need to consider situations involving motion in three component directions. The extension of our methods to three-dimensional vectors is straightforward. If $\vec{A}$ and $\vec{B}$ both have x, y, and z components, they can be expressed in the form

$$\vec{A} = A_x\hat{i} + A_y\hat{j} + A_z\hat{k} \qquad (3.18)$$

$$\vec{B} = B_x\hat{i} + B_y\hat{j} + B_z\hat{k} \qquad (3.19)$$

The sum of $\vec{A}$ and $\vec{B}$ is

$$\vec{R} = (A_x + B_x)\hat{i} + (A_y + B_y)\hat{j} + (A_z + B_z)\hat{k} \qquad (3.20)$$

Notice that Equation 3.20 differs from Equation 3.14: in Equation 3.20, the resultant vector also has a z component $R_z = A_z + B_z$. If a vector $\vec{R}$ has x, y, and z components, the magnitude of the vector is $R = \sqrt{R_x^2 + R_y^2 + R_z^2}$. The angle θ_x that $\vec{R}$ makes with the x axis is found from the expression $\cos\theta_x = R_x/R$, with similar expressions for the angles with respect to the y and z axes.

PITFALL PREVENTION 3.4
Tangents on Calculators

Equation 3.17 involves the calculation of an angle by means of a tangent function. Generally, the inverse tangent function on calculators provides an angle between $-90°$ and $+90°$. As a consequence, if the vector you are studying lies in the second or third quadrant, the angle measured from the positive x axis will be the angle your calculator returns plus $180°$.

Quick Quiz 3.5   For which of the following vectors is the magnitude of the vector equal to one of the components of the vector? (a) $\vec{A} = 2\hat{i} + 5\hat{j}$ (b) $\vec{B} = -3\hat{j}$ (c) $\vec{C} = +5\hat{k}$

EXAMPLE 3.3   **The Sum of Two Vectors**

Find the sum of two vectors $\vec{A}$ and $\vec{B}$ lying in the xy plane and given by

$$\vec{A} = (2.0\hat{i} + 2.0\hat{j})\text{ m} \qquad \text{and} \qquad \vec{B} = (2.0\hat{i} - 4.0\hat{j})\text{ m}$$

SOLUTION

Conceptualize   You can conceptualize the situation by drawing the vectors on graph paper.

Categorize   We categorize this example as a simple substitution problem. Comparing this expression for $\vec{A}$ with the general expression $\vec{A} = A_x\hat{i} + A_y\hat{j} + A_z\hat{k}$, we see that $A_x = 2.0$ m and $A_y = 2.0$ m. Likewise, $B_x = 2.0$ m and $B_y = -4.0$ m.

Use Equation 3.14 to obtain the resultant vector $\vec{R}$: $\qquad \vec{R} = \vec{A} + \vec{B} = (2.0 + 2.0)\hat{i}\text{ m} + (2.0 - 4.0)\hat{j}\text{ m}$

Evaluate the components of $\vec{R}$: $\qquad\qquad\qquad\qquad R_x = 4.0\text{ m} \qquad R_y = -2.0\text{ m}$

Use Equation 3.16 to find the magnitude of $\vec{\mathbf{R}}$: $R = \sqrt{R_x^2 + R_y^2} = \sqrt{(4.0 \text{ m})^2 + (-2.0 \text{ m})^2} = \sqrt{20} \text{ m} = \boxed{4.5 \text{ m}}$

Find the direction of $\vec{\mathbf{R}}$ from Equation 3.17: $\tan \theta = \dfrac{R_y}{R_x} = \dfrac{-2.0 \text{ m}}{4.0 \text{ m}} = -0.50$

Your calculator likely gives the answer $-27°$ for $\theta = \tan^{-1}(-0.50)$. This answer is correct if we interpret it to mean $27°$ clockwise from the x axis. Our standard form has been to quote the angles measured counterclockwise from the $+x$ axis, and that angle for this vector is $\theta = \boxed{333°}$

EXAMPLE 3.4   **The Resultant Displacement**

A particle undergoes three consecutive displacements: $\Delta \vec{\mathbf{r}}_1 = (15\hat{\mathbf{i}} + 30\hat{\mathbf{j}} + 12\hat{\mathbf{k}}) \text{ cm}$, $\Delta \vec{\mathbf{r}}_2 = (23\hat{\mathbf{i}} - 14\hat{\mathbf{j}} - 5.0\hat{\mathbf{k}}) \text{ cm}$, and $\Delta \vec{\mathbf{r}}_3 = (-13\hat{\mathbf{i}} + 15\hat{\mathbf{j}}) \text{ cm}$. Find the components of the resultant displacement and its magnitude.

SOLUTION

Conceptualize   Although x is sufficient to locate a point in one dimension, we need a vector $\vec{\mathbf{r}}$ to locate a point in two or three dimensions. The notation $\Delta \vec{\mathbf{r}}$ is a generalization of the one-dimensional displacement Δx in Equation 2.1. Three-dimensional displacements are more difficult to conceptualize than those in two dimensions because the latter can be drawn on paper.

For this problem, let us imagine that you start with your pencil at the origin of a piece of graph paper on which you have drawn x and y axes. Move your pencil 15 cm to the right along the x axis, then 30 cm upward along the y axis, and then 12 cm *perpendicularly toward you away* from the graph paper. This procedure provides the displacement described by $\Delta \vec{\mathbf{r}}_1$. From this point, move your pencil 23 cm to the right parallel to the x axis, then 14 cm parallel to the graph paper in the $-y$ direction, and then 5.0 cm perpendicularly away from you toward the graph paper. You are now at the displacement from the origin described by $\Delta \vec{\mathbf{r}}_1 + \Delta \vec{\mathbf{r}}_2$. From this point, move your pencil 13 cm to the left in the $-x$ direction, and (finally!) 15 cm parallel to the graph paper along the y axis. Your final position is at a displacement $\Delta \vec{\mathbf{r}}_1 + \Delta \vec{\mathbf{r}}_2 + \Delta \vec{\mathbf{r}}_3$ from the origin.

Categorize   Despite the difficulty in conceptualizing in three dimensions, we can categorize this problem as a substitution problem because of the careful bookkeeping methods that we have developed for vectors. The mathematical manipulation keeps track of this motion along the three perpendicular axes in an organized, compact way, as we see below.

To find the resultant displacement, add the three vectors:

$$\Delta \vec{\mathbf{r}} = \Delta \vec{\mathbf{r}}_1 + \Delta \vec{\mathbf{r}}_2 + \Delta \vec{\mathbf{r}}_3$$

$$= (15 + 23 - 13)\hat{\mathbf{i}} \text{ cm} + (30 - 14 + 15)\hat{\mathbf{j}} \text{ cm} + (12 - 5.0 + 0)\hat{\mathbf{k}} \text{ cm}$$

$$= (25\hat{\mathbf{i}} + 31\hat{\mathbf{j}} + 7.0\hat{\mathbf{k}}) \text{ cm}$$

Find the magnitude of the resultant vector:

$$R = \sqrt{R_x^2 + R_y^2 + R_z^2}$$

$$= \sqrt{(25 \text{ cm})^2 + (31 \text{ cm})^2 + (7.0 \text{ cm})^2} = \boxed{40 \text{ cm}}$$

EXAMPLE 3.5   **Taking a Hike**

A hiker begins a trip by first walking 25.0 km southeast from her car. She stops and sets up her tent for the night. On the second day, she walks 40.0 km in a direction 60.0° north of east, at which point she discovers a forest ranger's tower.

(A) Determine the components of the hiker's displacement for each day.

SOLUTION

Conceptualize   We conceptualize the problem by drawing a sketch as in Figure 3.17. If we denote the displacement vectors on the first and second days by $\vec{\mathbf{A}}$ and $\vec{\mathbf{B}}$, respectively, and use the car as the origin of coordinates, we obtain the vectors shown in Figure 3.17.

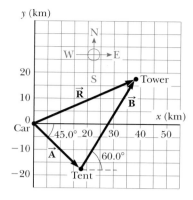

Figure 3.17   (Example 3.5) The total displacement of the hiker is the vector $\vec{\mathbf{R}} = \vec{\mathbf{A}} + \vec{\mathbf{B}}$.

Categorize   Drawing the resultant $\vec{\mathbf{R}}$, we can now categorize this problem as one we've solved before: an addition of two vectors. You should now have a hint of the power of categorization in that many new problems are very similar to problems we have already solved if we are careful to conceptualize them. Once we have drawn the displacement vectors and categorized the problem, this problem is no longer about a hiker, a walk, a car, a tent, or a tower. It is a problem about vector addition, one that we have already solved.

Analyze   Displacement $\vec{\mathbf{A}}$ has a magnitude of 25.0 km and is directed 45.0° below the positive x axis.

Find the components of $\vec{\mathbf{A}}$ using Equations 3.8 and 3.9:

$$A_x = A \cos(-45.0°) = (25.0\ \text{km})(0.707) = \boxed{17.7\ \text{km}}$$

$$A_y = A \sin(-45.0°) = (25.0\ \text{km})(-0.707) = \boxed{-17.7\ \text{km}}$$

The negative value of A_y indicates the hiker walks in the negative y direction on the first day. The signs of A_x and A_y also are evident from Figure 3.17.

Find the components of $\vec{\mathbf{B}}$ using Equations 3.8 and 3.9:

$$B_x = B \cos 60.0° = (40.0\ \text{km})(0.500) = \boxed{20.0\ \text{km}}$$

$$B_y = B \sin 60.0° = (40.0\ \text{km})(0.866) = \boxed{34.6\ \text{km}}$$

(B) Determine the components of the hiker's resultant displacement $\vec{\mathbf{R}}$ for the trip. Find an expression for $\vec{\mathbf{R}}$ in terms of unit vectors.

SOLUTION

Use Equation 3.15 to find the components of the resultant displacement $\vec{\mathbf{R}} = \vec{\mathbf{A}} + \vec{\mathbf{B}}$:

$$R_x = A_x + B_x = 17.7\ \text{km} + 20.0\ \text{km} = \boxed{37.7\ \text{km}}$$

$$R_y = A_y + B_y = -17.7\ \text{km} + 34.6\ \text{km} = \boxed{16.9\ \text{km}}$$

Write the total displacement in unit–vector form:

$$\vec{\mathbf{R}} = (37.7\hat{\mathbf{i}} + 16.9\hat{\mathbf{j}})\ \text{km}$$

Finalize   Looking at the graphical representation in Figure 3.17, we estimate the position of the tower to be about (38 km, 17 km), which is consistent with the components of $\vec{\mathbf{R}}$ in our result for the final position of the hiker. Also, both components of $\vec{\mathbf{R}}$ are positive, putting the final position in the first quadrant of the coordinate system, which is also consistent with Figure 3.17.

What If?   After reaching the tower, the hiker wishes to return to her car along a single straight line. What are the components of the vector representing this hike? What should the direction of the hike be?

Answer   The desired vector $\vec{\mathbf{R}}_{\text{car}}$ is the negative of vector $\vec{\mathbf{R}}$:

$$\vec{\mathbf{R}}_{\text{car}} = -\vec{\mathbf{R}} = (-37.7\hat{\mathbf{i}} - 16.9\hat{\mathbf{j}})\ \text{km}$$

The heading is found by calculating the angle that the vector makes with the x axis:

$$\tan\theta = \frac{R_{\text{car},y}}{R_{\text{car},x}} = \frac{-16.9\ \text{km}}{-37.7\ \text{km}} = 0.448$$

which gives an angle of $\theta = 204.1°$, or 24.1° south of west.

Summary

DEFINITIONS

Scalar quantities are those that have only a numerical value and no associated direction. **Vector quantities** have both magnitude and direction and obey the laws of vector addition. The magnitude of a vector is *always* a positive number.

CONCEPTS AND PRINCIPLES

When two or more vectors are added together, they must all have the same units and all of them must be the same type of quantity. We can add two vectors $\vec{A}$ and $\vec{B}$ graphically. In this method (Active Fig. 3.6), the resultant vector $\vec{R} = \vec{A} + \vec{B}$ runs from the tail of $\vec{A}$ to the tip of $\vec{B}$.

A second method of adding vectors involves **components** of the vectors. The x component A_x of the vector $\vec{A}$ is equal to the projection of $\vec{A}$ along the x axis of a coordinate system, where $A_x = A \cos \theta$. The y component A_y of $\vec{A}$ is the projection of $\vec{A}$ along the y axis, where $A_y = A \sin \theta$.

If a vector $\vec{A}$ has an x component A_x and a y component A_y, the vector can be expressed in unit–vector form as $\vec{A} = A_x \hat{i} + A_y \hat{j}$. In this notation, $\hat{i}$ is a unit vector pointing in the positive x direction and $\hat{j}$ is a unit vector pointing in the positive y direction. Because $\hat{i}$ and $\hat{j}$ are unit vectors, $|\hat{i}| = |\hat{j}| = 1$.

We can find the resultant of two or more vectors by resolving all vectors into their x and y components, adding their resultant x and y components, and then using the Pythagorean theorem to find the magnitude of the resultant vector. We can find the angle that the resultant vector makes with respect to the x axis by using a suitable trigonometric function.

Questions

☐ denotes answer available in *Student Solutions Manual/Study Guide;* **O** denotes objective question

1. **O** Yes or no: Is each of the following quantities a vector? (a) force (b) temperature (c) the volume of water in a can (d) the ratings of a TV show (e) the height of a building (f) the velocity of a sports car (g) the age of the Universe

2. A book is moved once around the perimeter of a tabletop with dimensions 1.0 m × 2.0 m. If the book ends up at its initial position, what is its displacement? What is the distance traveled?

3. **O** Figure Q3.3 shows two vectors, $\vec{D}_1$ and $\vec{D}_2$. Which of the possibilities (a) through (d) is the vector $\vec{D}_2 - 2\vec{D}_1$, or (e) is it none of them?

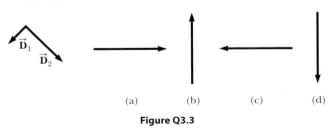

Figure Q3.3

4. **O** The cutting tool on a lathe is given two displacements, one of magnitude 4 cm and one of magnitude 3 cm, in each one of five situations (a) through (e) diagrammed in Figure Q3.4. Rank these situations according to the magnitude of the total displacement of the tool, putting the situation with the greatest resultant magnitude first. If the total displacement is the same size in two situations, give those letters equal ranks.

Figure Q3.4

5. **O** Let $\vec{A}$ represent a velocity vector pointing from the origin into the second quadrant. (a) Is its x component positive, negative, or zero? (b) Is its y component positive, negative, or zero? Let $\vec{B}$ represent a velocity vector point-

ing from the origin into the fourth quadrant. (c) Is its x component positive, negative, or zero? (d) Is its y component positive, negative, or zero? (e) Consider the vector $\vec{A} + \vec{B}$. What, if anything, can you conclude about quadrants it must be in or cannot be in? (f) Now consider the vector $\vec{B} - \vec{A}$. What, if anything, can you conclude about quadrants it must be in or cannot be in?

6. **O** (i) What is the magnitude of the vector $(10\hat{i} - 10\hat{k})$ m/s? (a) 0 (b) 10 m/s (c) -10 m/s (d) 10 (e) -10 (f) 14.1 m/s (g) undefined (ii) What is the y component of this vector? (Choose from among the same answers.)

7. **O** A submarine dives from the water surface at an angle of 30° below the horizontal, following a straight path 50 m long. How far is the submarine then below the water surface? (a) 50 m (b) sin 30° (c) cos 30° (d) tan 30° (e) (50 m)/sin 30° (f) (50 m)/cos 30° (g) (50 m)/tan 30° (h) (50 m)sin 30° (i) (50 m)cos 30° (j) (50 m)tan 30° (k) (sin 30°)/50 m (l) (cos 30°)/50 m (m) (tan 30°)/50 m (n) 30 m (o) 0 (p) none of these answers

8. **O** (i) What is the x component of the vector shown in Figure Q3.8? (a) 1 cm (b) 2 cm (c) 3 cm (d) 4 cm (e) 6 cm (f) -1 cm (g) -2 cm (h) -3 cm (i) -4 cm

(j) -6 cm (k) none of these answers (ii) What is the y component of this vector? (Choose from among the same answers.)

Figure Q3.8

9. **O** Vector $\vec{A}$ lies in the xy plane. (i) Both of its components will be negative if it lies in which quadrant(s)? Choose all that apply. (a) the first quadrant (b) the second quadrant (c) the third quadrant (d) the fourth quadrant (ii) For what orientation(s) will its components have opposite signs? Choose from among the same possibilities.

10. If the component of vector $\vec{A}$ along the direction of vector $\vec{B}$ is zero, what can you conclude about the two vectors?

11. Can the magnitude of a vector have a negative value? Explain.

12. Is it possible to add a vector quantity to a scalar quantity? Explain.

Problems

WebAssign The Problems from this chapter may be assigned online in WebAssign.

ThomsonNOW Sign in at **www.thomsonedu.com** and go to ThomsonNOW to assess your understanding of this chapter's topics with additional quizzing and conceptual questions.

1, 2, 3 denotes straightforward, intermediate, challenging; □ denotes full solution available in *Student Solutions Manual/Study Guide*; ▲ denotes coached solution with hints available at **www.thomsonedu.com;** denotes developing symbolic reasoning; ● denotes asking for qualitative reasoning; ▪ denotes computer useful in solving problem

Section 3.1 Coordinate Systems

1. ▲ The polar coordinates of a point are $r = 5.50$ m and $\theta = 240°$. What are the Cartesian coordinates of this point?

2. Two points in a plane have polar coordinates (2.50 m, 30.0°) and (3.80 m, 120.0°). Determine (a) the Cartesian coordinates of these points and (b) the distance between them.

3. A fly lands on one wall of a room. The lower left-hand corner of the wall is selected as the origin of a two-dimensional Cartesian coordinate system. If the fly is located at the point having coordinates (2.00, 1.00) m, (a) how far is it from the corner of the room? (b) What is its location in polar coordinates?

4. The rectangular coordinates of a point are given by $(2, y)$, and its polar coordinates are $(r, 30°)$. Determine y and r.

5. Let the polar coordinates of the point (x, y) be (r, θ). Determine the polar coordinates for the points (a) $(-x, y)$, (b) $(-2x, -2y)$, and (c) $(3x, -3y)$.

Section 3.2 Vector and Scalar Quantities

Section 3.3 Some Properties of Vectors

6. A plane flies from base camp to lake A, 280 km away in the direction 20.0° north of east. After dropping off supplies it flies to lake B, which is 190 km at 30.0° west of north from lake A. Graphically determine the distance and direction from lake B to the base camp.

7. A surveyor measures the distance across a straight river by the following method: starting directly across from a tree on the opposite bank, she walks 100 m along the riverbank to establish a baseline. Then she sights across to the tree. The angle from her baseline to the tree is 35.0°. How wide is the river?

8. A force $\vec{F}_1$ of magnitude 6.00 units acts on an object at the origin in a direction 30.0° above the positive x axis. A second force $\vec{F}_2$ of magnitude 5.00 units acts on the object in the direction of the positive y axis. Graphically find the magnitude and direction of the resultant force $\vec{F}_1 + \vec{F}_2$.

9. ▲ A skater glides along a circular path of radius 5.00 m. If he coasts around one half of the circle, find (a) the magnitude of the displacement vector and (b) how far he skated. (c) What is the magnitude of the displacement if he skates all the way around the circle?

10. Arbitrarily define the "instantaneous vector height" of a person as the displacement vector from the point halfway between his or her feet to the top of the head. Make an order-of-magnitude estimate of the total vector height of all the people in a city of population 100 000 (a) at 10 o'clock on a Tuesday morning and (b) at 5 o'clock on a Saturday morning. Explain your reasoning.

11. ▲ Each of the displacement vectors $\vec{A}$ and $\vec{B}$ shown in Figure P3.11 has a magnitude of 3.00 m. Graphically find (a) $\vec{A} + \vec{B}$, (b) $\vec{A} - \vec{B}$, (c) $\vec{B} - \vec{A}$, and (d) $\vec{A} - 2\vec{B}$. Report all angles counterclockwise from the positive x axis.

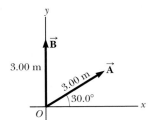

Figure P3.11 Problems 11 and 32.

12. ● Three displacements are $\vec{A} = 200$ m due south, $\vec{B} = 250$ m due west, and $\vec{C} = 150$ m at $30.0°$ east of north. Construct a separate diagram for each of the following possible ways of adding these vectors: $\vec{R}_1 = \vec{A} + \vec{B} + \vec{C}$; $\vec{R}_2 = \vec{B} + \vec{C} + \vec{A}$; $\vec{R}_3 = \vec{C} + \vec{B} + \vec{A}$. Explain what you can conclude from comparing the diagrams.

13. A roller-coaster car moves 200 ft horizontally and then rises 135 ft at an angle of $30.0°$ above the horizontal. It next travels 135 ft at an angle of $40.0°$ downward. What is its displacement from its starting point? Use graphical techniques.

14. ● A shopper pushing a cart through a store moves 40.0 m down one aisle, then makes a $90.0°$ turn and moves 15.0 m. He then makes another $90.0°$ turn and moves 20.0 m. (a) How far is the shopper away from his original position? (b) What angle does his total displacement make with his original direction? Notice that we have not specified whether the shopper turned right or left. Explain how many answers are possible for parts (a) and (b) and give the possible answers.

Section 3.4 Components of a Vector and Unit Vectors

15. ▲ A vector has an x component of -25.0 units and a y component of 40.0 units. Find the magnitude and direction of this vector.

16. A person walks $25.0°$ north of east for 3.10 km. How far would she have to walk due north and due east to arrive at the same location?

17. ● A minivan travels straight north in the right lane of a divided highway at 28.0 m/s. A camper passes the minivan and then changes from the left into the right lane. As it does so, the camper's path on the road is a straight displacement at $8.50°$ east of north. To avoid cutting off the minivan, the north–south distance between the camper's

rear bumper and the minivan's front bumper should not decrease. Can the camper be driven to satisfy this requirement? Explain your answer.

18. A girl delivering newspapers covers her route by traveling 3.00 blocks west, 4.00 blocks north, and then 6.00 blocks east. (a) What is her resultant displacement? (b) What is the total distance she travels?

19. Obtain expressions in component form for the position vectors having the following polar coordinates: (a) 12.8 m, $150°$ (b) 3.30 cm, $60.0°$ (c) 22.0 in., $215°$

20. A displacement vector lying in the xy plane has a magnitude of 50.0 m and is directed at an angle of $120°$ to the positive x axis. What are the rectangular components of this vector?

21. While exploring a cave, a spelunker starts at the entrance and moves the following distances. She goes 75.0 m north, 250 m east, 125 m at an angle $30.0°$ north of east, and 150 m south. Find her resultant displacement from the cave entrance.

22. A map suggests that Atlanta is 730 miles in a direction of $5.00°$ north of east from Dallas. The same map shows that Chicago is 560 miles in a direction of $21.0°$ west of north from Atlanta. Modeling the Earth as flat, use this information to find the displacement from Dallas to Chicago.

23. A man pushing a mop across a floor causes it to undergo two displacements. The first has a magnitude of 150 cm and makes an angle of $120°$ with the positive x axis. The resultant displacement has a magnitude of 140 cm and is directed at an angle of $35.0°$ to the positive x axis. Find the magnitude and direction of the second displacement.

24. Given the vectors $\vec{A} = 2.00\hat{i} + 6.00\hat{j}$ and $\vec{B} = 3.00\hat{i} - 2.00\hat{j}$, (a) draw the vector sum $\vec{C} = \vec{A} + \vec{B}$ and the vector difference $\vec{D} = \vec{A} - \vec{B}$. (b) Calculate $\vec{C}$ and $\vec{D}$, first in terms of unit vectors and then in terms of polar coordinates, with angles measured with respect to the $+x$ axis.

25. Consider the two vectors $\vec{A} = 3\hat{i} - 2\hat{j}$ and $\vec{B} = -\hat{i} - 4\hat{j}$. Calculate (a) $\vec{A} + \vec{B}$, (b) $\vec{A} - \vec{B}$, (c) $|\vec{A} + \vec{B}|$, (d) $|\vec{A} - \vec{B}|$, and (e) the directions of $\vec{A} + \vec{B}$ and $\vec{A} - \vec{B}$.

26. A snow-covered ski slope makes an angle of $35.0°$ with the horizontal. When a ski jumper plummets onto the hill, a parcel of splashed snow projects to a maximum position of 5.00 m at $20.0°$ from the vertical in the uphill direction as shown in Figure P3.26. Find the components of its maximum position (a) parallel to the surface and (b) perpendicular to the surface.

Figure P3.26

27. A particle undergoes the following consecutive displacements: 3.50 m south, 8.20 m northeast, and 15.0 m west. What is the resultant displacement?

28. In a game of American football, a quarterback takes the ball from the line of scrimmage, runs backward a distance of 10.0 yards, and then runs sideways parallel to the line of scrimmage for 15.0 yards. At this point, he throws a forward pass 50.0 yards straight downfield perpendicular to the line of scrimmage. What is the magnitude of the football's resultant displacement?

29. A novice golfer on the green takes three strokes to sink the ball. The successive displacements of the ball are 4.00 m to the north, 2.00 m northeast, and 1.00 m at 30.0° west of south. Starting at the same initial point, an expert golfer could make the hole in what single displacement?

30. Vector $\vec{A}$ has x and y components of -8.70 cm and 15.0 cm, respectively; vector $\vec{B}$ has x and y components of 13.2 cm and -6.60 cm, respectively. If $\vec{A} - \vec{B} + 3\vec{C} = 0$, what are the components of $\vec{C}$?

31. The helicopter view in Figure P3.31 shows two people pulling on a stubborn mule. Find (a) the single force that is equivalent to the two forces shown and (b) the force that a third person would have to exert on the mule to make the resultant force equal to zero. The forces are measured in units of newtons (symbolized N).

Figure P3.31

32. Use the component method to add the vectors $\vec{A}$ and $\vec{B}$ shown in Figure P3.11. Express the resultant $\vec{A} + \vec{B}$ in unit–vector notation.

33. Vector $\vec{B}$ has x, y, and z components of 4.00, 6.00, and 3.00 units, respectively. Calculate the magnitude of $\vec{B}$ and the angles $\vec{B}$ makes with the coordinate axes.

34. Consider the three displacement vectors $\vec{A} = (3\hat{i} - 3\hat{j})$ m, $\vec{B} = (\hat{i} - 4\hat{j})$ m, and $\vec{C} = (-2\hat{i} + 5\hat{j})$ m. Use the component method to determine (a) the magnitude and direction of the vector $\vec{D} = \vec{A} + \vec{B} + \vec{C}$ and (b) the magnitude and direction of $\vec{E} = -\vec{A} - \vec{B} + \vec{C}$.

35. Given the displacement vectors $\vec{A} = (3\hat{i} - 4\hat{j} + 4\hat{k})$ m and $\vec{B} = (2\hat{i} + 3\hat{j} - 7\hat{k})$ m, find the magnitudes of the vectors (a) $\vec{C} = \vec{A} + \vec{B}$ and (b) $\vec{D} = 2\vec{A} - \vec{B}$, also expressing each in terms of its rectangular components.

36. In an assembly operation illustrated in Figure P3.36, a robot moves an object first straight upward and then also to the east, around an arc forming one quarter of a circle of radius 4.80 cm that lies in an east–west vertical plane. The robot then moves the object upward and to the north, through one-quarter of a circle of radius 3.70 cm that lies in a north–south vertical plane. Find (a) the mag-

Figure P3.36

nitude of the total displacement of the object and (b) the angle the total displacement makes with the vertical.

37. The vector $\vec{A}$ has x, y, and z components of 8.00, 12.0, and -4.00 units, respectively. (a) Write a vector expression for $\vec{A}$ in unit–vector notation. (b) Obtain a unit–vector expression for a vector $\vec{B}$ one-fourth the length of $\vec{A}$ pointing in the same direction as $\vec{A}$. (c) Obtain a unit–vector expression for a vector $\vec{C}$ three times the length of $\vec{A}$ pointing in the direction opposite the direction of $\vec{A}$.

38. You are standing on the ground at the origin of a coordinate system. An airplane flies over you with constant velocity parallel to the x axis and at a fixed height of 7.60×10^3 m. At time $t = 0$ the airplane is directly above you so that the vector leading from you to it is $\vec{P}_0 = (7.60 \times 10^3 \text{ m}) \hat{j}$. At $t = 30.0$ s the position vector leading from you to the airplane is $\vec{P}_{30} = (8.04 \times 10^3 \text{ m}) \hat{i} + (7.60 \times 10^3 \text{ m}) \hat{j}$. Determine the magnitude and orientation of the airplane's position vector at $t = 45.0$ s.

39. A radar station locates a sinking ship at range 17.3 km and bearing 136° clockwise from north. From the same station, a rescue plane is at horizontal range 19.6 km, 153° clockwise from north, with elevation 2.20 km. (a) Write the position vector for the ship relative to the plane, letting $\hat{i}$ represent east, $\hat{j}$ north, and $\hat{k}$ up. (b) How far apart are the plane and ship?

40. (a) Vector $\vec{E}$ has magnitude 17.0 cm and is directed 27.0° counterclockwise from the $+x$ axis. Express it in unit–vector notation. (b) Vector $\vec{F}$ has magnitude 17.0 cm and is directed 27.0° counterclockwise from the $+y$ axis. Express it in unit–vector notation. (c) Vector $\vec{G}$ has magnitude 17.0 cm and is directed 27.0° clockwise from the $-y$ axis. Express it in unit–vector notation.

41. Vector $\vec{A}$ has a negative x component 3.00 units in length and a positive y component 2.00 units in length. (a) Determine an expression for $\vec{A}$ in unit–vector notation. (b) Determine the magnitude and direction of $\vec{A}$. (c) What vector $\vec{B}$ when added to $\vec{A}$ gives a resultant vector with no x component and a negative y component 4.00 units in length?

42. As it passes over Grand Bahama Island, the eye of a hurricane is moving in a direction 60.0° north of west with a speed of 41.0 km/h. Three hours later the course of the hurricane suddenly shifts due north, and its speed slows to 25.0 km/h. How far from Grand Bahama is the eye 4.50 h after it passes over the island?

43. ▲ Three displacement vectors of a croquet ball are shown in Figure P3.43, where $|\vec{A}| = 20.0$ units, $|\vec{B}| = 40.0$ units, and $|\vec{C}| = 30.0$ units. Find (a) the resultant in unit–vector

notation and (b) the magnitude and direction of the resultant displacement.

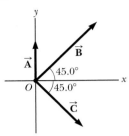

Figure P3.43

44. ● (a) Taking $\vec{A} = (6.00\hat{i} - 8.00\hat{j})$ units, $\vec{B} = (-8.00\hat{i} + 3.00\hat{j})$ units, and $\vec{C} = (26.0\hat{i} + 19.0\hat{j})$ units, determine a and b such that $a\vec{A} + b\vec{B} + \vec{C} = 0$. (b) A student has learned that a single equation cannot be solved to determine values for more than one unknown in it. How would you explain to him that both a and b can be determined from the single equation used in part (a)?

45. ● *Are we there yet?* In Figure P3.45, the line segment represents a path from the point with position vector $(5\hat{i} + 3\hat{j})$ m to the point with location $(16\hat{i} + 12\hat{j})$ m. Point A is along this path, a fraction f of the way to the destination. (a) Find the position vector of point A in terms of f. (b) Evaluate the expression from part (a) in the case $f = 0$. Explain whether the result is reasonable. (c) Evaluate the expression for $f = 1$. Explain whether the result is reasonable.

Figure P3.45   Point A is a fraction f of the distance from the initial point (5, 3) to the final point (16, 12).

Additional Problems

46. On December 1, 1955, Rosa Parks (1913–2005), an icon of the early civil rights movement, stayed seated in her bus seat when a white man demanded it. Police in Montgomery, Alabama, arrested her. On December 5, blacks began refusing to use all city buses. Under the leadership of the Montgomery Improvement Association, an efficient system of alternative transportation sprang up immediately, providing blacks with approximately 35 000 essential trips per day through volunteers, private taxis, carpooling, and ride sharing. The buses remained empty until they were integrated under court order on December 21, 1956. In picking up her riders, suppose a driver in downtown Montgomery traverses four successive displacements represented by the expression

$$(-6.30b)\hat{i} - (4.00b\cos 40°)\hat{i} - (4.00b\sin 40°)\hat{j}$$

$$+ (3.00b\cos 50°)\hat{i} - (3.00b\sin 50°)\hat{j} - (5.00b)\hat{j}$$

Here b represents one city block, a convenient unit of distance of uniform size; $\hat{i}$ is east; and $\hat{j}$ is north. (a) Draw a map of the successive displacements. (b) What total distance did she travel? (c) Compute the magnitude and direction of her total displacement. The logical structure of this problem and of several problems in later chapters was suggested by Alan Van Heuvelen and David Maloney, *American Journal of Physics* **67**(3) 252–256, March 1999.

47. Two vectors $\vec{A}$ and $\vec{B}$ have precisely equal magnitudes. For the magnitude of $\vec{A} + \vec{B}$ to be 100 times larger than the magnitude of $\vec{A} - \vec{B}$, what must be the angle between them?

48. Two vectors $\vec{A}$ and $\vec{B}$ have precisely equal magnitudes. For the magnitude of $\vec{A} + \vec{B}$ to be larger than the magnitude of $\vec{A} - \vec{B}$ by the factor n, what must be the angle between them?

49. An air-traffic controller observes two aircraft on his radar screen. The first is at altitude 800 m, horizontal distance 19.2 km, and 25.0° south of west. The second is at altitude 1 100 m, horizontal distance 17.6 km, and 20.0° south of west. What is the distance between the two aircraft? (Place the x axis west, the y axis south, and the z axis vertical.)

50. The biggest stuffed animal in the world is a snake 420 m long, constructed by Norwegian children. Suppose the snake is laid out in a park as shown in Figure P3.50, forming two straight sides of a 105° angle, with one side 240 m long. Olaf and Inge run a race they invent. Inge runs directly from the tail of the snake to its head, and Olaf starts from the same place at the same moment but runs along the snake. If both children run steadily at 12.0 km/h, Inge reaches the head of the snake how much earlier than Olaf?

Figure P3.50

51. A ferryboat transports tourists among three islands. It sails from the first island to the second island, 4.76 km away, in a direction 37.0° north of east. It then sails from the second island to the third island in a direction 69.0° west of north. Finally, it returns to the first island, sailing in a direction 28.0° east of south. Calculate the distance between (a) the second and third islands and (b) the first and third islands.

52. A vector is given by $\vec{R} = 2\hat{i} + \hat{j} + 3\hat{k}$. Find (a) the magnitudes of the x, y, and z components, (b) the magnitude of $\vec{R}$, and (c) the angles between $\vec{R}$ and the x, y, and z axes.

53. A jet airliner, moving initially at 300 mi/h to the east, suddenly enters a region where the wind is blowing at 100 mi/h toward the direction 30.0° north of east. What are the new speed and direction of the aircraft relative to the ground?

54. ● Let $\vec{A} = 60.0$ cm at 270° measured from the horizontal. Let $\vec{B} = 80.0$ cm at some angle θ. (a) Find the magnitude of $\vec{A} + \vec{B}$ as a function of θ. (b) From the answer to part (a), for what value of θ does $|\vec{A} + \vec{B}|$ take on its maximum

value? What is this maximum value? (c) From the answer to part (a), for what value of θ does $|\vec{A} + \vec{B}|$ take on its minimum value? What is this minimum value? (d) Without reference to the answer to part (a), argue that the answers to each of parts (b) and (c) do or do not make sense.

55. After a ball rolls off the edge of a horizontal table at time $t = 0$, its velocity as a function of time is given by

$$\vec{v} = 1.2\hat{i} \text{ m/s} - 9.8t\hat{j} \text{ m/s}^2$$

The ball's displacement away from the edge of the table, during the time interval of 0.380 s during which it is in flight, is given by

$$\Delta\vec{r} = \int_0^{0.380\text{ s}} \vec{v}\, dt$$

To perform the integral, you can use the calculus theorem

$$\int (A + Bf(x))\, dx = \int A\, dx + B \int f(x)\, dx$$

You can think of the units and unit vectors as constants, represented by A and B. Do the integration to calculate the displacement of the ball.

56. ● Find the sum of these four vector forces: 12.0 N to the right at 35.0° above the horizontal, 31.0 N to the left at 55.0° above the horizontal, 8.40 N to the left at 35.0° below the horizontal, and 24.0 N to the right at 55.0° below the horizontal. Follow these steps. Guided by a sketch of this situation, explain how you can simplify the calculations by making a particular choice for the directions of the x and y axes. What is your choice? Then add the vectors by the component method.

57. A person going for a walk follows the path shown in Figure P3.57. The total trip consists of four straight-line paths. At the end of the walk, what is the person's resultant displacement measured from the starting point?

Figure P3.57

58. ● The instantaneous position of an object is specified by its position vector $\vec{r}$ leading from a fixed origin to the location of the object, modeled as a particle. Suppose for a certain object the position vector is a function of time, given by $\vec{r} = 4\hat{i} + 3\hat{j} - 2t\hat{k}$, where r is in meters and t is in seconds. Evaluate $d\vec{r}/dt$. What does it represent about the object?

59. ● Long John Silver, a pirate, has buried his treasure on an island with five trees, located at the points (30.0 m, −20.0 m), (60.0 m, 80.0 m), (−10.0 m, −10.0 m), (40.0 m, −30.0 m), and (−70.0 m, 60.0 m), all measured relative to some origin as shown in Figure P3.59. His ship's log instructs you to start at tree A and move toward tree B, but to cover only one-half the distance between A and B. Then move toward tree C, covering one-third the distance between your current location and C. Next move toward tree D, covering one-fourth the distance between where you are and D. Finally, move toward tree E, covering one-fifth the distance between you and E, stop, and dig. (a) Assume you have correctly determined the order in which the pirate labeled the trees as A, B, C, D, and E as shown in the figure. What are the coordinates of the point where his treasure is buried? (b) **What If?** What if you do not really know the way the pirate labeled the trees? What would happen to the answer if you rearranged the order of the trees, for instance to B(30 m, −20 m), A(60 m, 80 m), E(−10 m, −10 m), C(40 m, −30 m), and D(−70 m, 60 m)? State reasoning to show the answer does not depend on the order in which the trees are labeled.

Figure P3.59

60. ● Consider a game in which N children position themselves at equal distances around the circumference of a circle. At the center of the circle is a rubber tire. Each child holds a rope attached to the tire and, at a signal, pulls on his or her rope. All children exert forces of the same magnitude F. In the case $N = 2$, it is easy to see that the net force on the tire will be zero because the two oppositely directed force vectors add to zero. Similarly, if $N = 4, 6$, or any even integer, the resultant force on the tire must be zero because the forces exerted by each pair of oppositely positioned children will cancel. When an odd number of children are around the circle, it is not as obvious whether the total force on the central tire will be zero. (a) Calculate the net force on the tire in the case $N = 3$ by adding the components of the three force vectors. Choose the x axis to lie along one of the ropes. (b) **What If?** State reasoning that will determine the net force for the general case where N is any integer, odd or even, greater than one. Proceed as follows. Assume the total force is not zero. Then it must point in some particular direction. Let every child move one position clockwise. Give a reason that the total force must then have a direction turned clockwise by 360°/N. Argue that the total force must nevertheless be the same as before. Explain what the contradiction proves about the magnitude of the force. This problem illustrates a widely useful technique of proving a result "by symmetry," by using a bit of the mathematics of *group theory*. The particular situation is actually encountered in physics and chemistry

when an array of electric charges (ions) exerts electric forces on an atom at a central position in a molecule or in a crystal.

61. Vectors $\vec{A}$ and $\vec{B}$ have equal magnitudes of 5.00. The sum of $\vec{A}$ and $\vec{B}$ is the vector $6.00\hat{j}$. Determine the angle between $\vec{A}$ and $\vec{B}$.

62. A rectangular parallelepiped has dimensions a, b, and c as shown in Figure P3.62. (a) Obtain a vector expression for the face diagonal vector $\vec{R}_1$. What is the magnitude of this vector? (b) Obtain a vector expression for the body diagonal vector $\vec{R}_2$. Notice that $\vec{R}_1$, $c\hat{k}$, and $\vec{R}_2$ make a right triangle. Prove that the magnitude of $\vec{R}_2$ is $\sqrt{a^2 + b^2 + c^2}$.

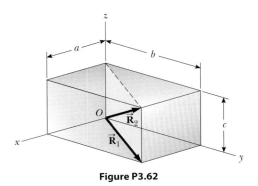

Figure P3.62

Answers to Quick Quizzes

3.1 Scalars: (a), (d), (e). None of these quantities has a direction. Vectors: (b), (c). For these quantities, the direction is necessary to specify the quantity completely.

3.2 (c). The resultant has its maximum magnitude $A + B = 12 + 8 = 20$ units when vector $\vec{A}$ is oriented in the same direction as vector $\vec{B}$. The resultant vector has its minimum magnitude $A - B = 12 - 8 = 4$ units when vector $\vec{A}$ is oriented in the direction opposite vector $\vec{B}$.

3.3 (b) and (c). To add to zero, the vectors must point in opposite directions and have the same magnitude.

3.4 (b). From the Pythagorean theorem, the magnitude of a vector is always larger than the absolute value of each component, unless there is only one nonzero component, in which case the magnitude of the vector is equal to the absolute value of that component.

3.5 (c). The magnitude of $\vec{C}$ is 5 units, the same as the z component. Answer (b) is not correct because the magnitude of any vector is always a positive number, whereas the y component of $\vec{B}$ is negative.

Lava spews from a volcanic eruption. Notice the parabolic paths of embers projected into the air. All projectiles follow a parabolic path in the absence of air resistance. (© Arndt/Premium Stock/PictureQuest)

4 Motion in Two Dimensions

In this chapter, we explore the kinematics of a particle moving in two dimensions. Knowing the basics of two-dimensional motion will allow us—in future chapters— to examine a variety of motions ranging from the motion of satellites in orbit to the motion of electrons in a uniform electric field. We begin by studying in greater detail the vector nature of position, velocity, and acceleration. We then treat projectile motion and uniform circular motion as special cases of motion in two dimensions. We also discuss the concept of relative motion, which shows why observers in different frames of reference may measure different positions and velocities for a given particle.

4.1 The Position, Velocity, and Acceleration Vectors

In Chapter 2, we found that the motion of a particle along a straight line is completely known if its position is known as a function of time. Let us now extend this idea to two-dimensional motion of a particle in the xy plane. We begin by describing the position of the particle by its **position vector $\vec{r}$**, drawn from the origin of some coordinate system to the location of the particle in the xy plane, as in Figure 4.1 (page 72). At time t_i, the particle is at point Ⓐ, described by position vector $\vec{r}_i$. At some later time t_f, it is at point Ⓑ, described by position vector $\vec{r}_f$. The path from

Ⓐ to Ⓑ is not necessarily a straight line. As the particle moves from Ⓐ to Ⓑ in the time interval $\Delta t = t_f - t_i$, its position vector changes from $\vec{\mathbf{r}}_i$ to $\vec{\mathbf{r}}_f$. As we learned in Chapter 2, displacement is a vector, and the displacement of the particle is the difference between its final position and its initial position. We now define the **displacement vector** $\Delta\vec{\mathbf{r}}$ for a particle such as the one in Figure 4.1 as being the difference between its final position vector and its initial position vector:

◀ **Displacement vector**

$$\Delta\vec{\mathbf{r}} \equiv \vec{\mathbf{r}}_f - \vec{\mathbf{r}}_i \tag{4.1}$$

The direction of $\Delta\vec{\mathbf{r}}$ is indicated in Figure 4.1. As we see from the figure, the magnitude of $\Delta\vec{\mathbf{r}}$ is *less* than the distance traveled along the curved path followed by the particle.

As we saw in Chapter 2, it is often useful to quantify motion by looking at the ratio of a displacement divided by the time interval during which that displacement occurs, which gives the rate of change of position. Two-dimensional (or three-dimensional) kinematics is similar to one-dimensional kinematics, but we must now use full vector notation rather than positive and negative signs to indicate the direction of motion.

We define the **average velocity** $\vec{\mathbf{v}}_{\text{avg}}$ of a particle during the time interval Δt as the displacement of the particle divided by the time interval:

◀ **Average velocity**

$$\vec{\mathbf{v}}_{\text{avg}} \equiv \frac{\Delta\vec{\mathbf{r}}}{\Delta t} \tag{4.2}$$

Multiplying or dividing a vector quantity by a positive scalar quantity such as Δt changes only the magnitude of the vector, not its direction. Because displacement is a vector quantity and the time interval is a positive scalar quantity, we conclude that the average velocity is a vector quantity directed along $\Delta\vec{\mathbf{r}}$.

The average velocity between points is *independent of the path* taken. That is because average velocity is proportional to displacement, which depends only on the initial and final position vectors and not on the path taken. As with one-dimensional motion, we conclude that if a particle starts its motion at some point and returns to this point via any path, its average velocity is zero for this trip because its displacement is zero. Consider again our basketball players on the court in Figure 2.2 (page 21). We previously considered only their one-dimensional motion back and forth between the baskets. In reality, however, they move over a two-dimensional surface, running back and forth between the baskets as well as left and right across the width of the court. Starting from one basket, a given player may follow a very complicated two-dimensional path. Upon returning to the original basket, however, a player's average velocity is zero because the player's displacement for the whole trip is zero.

Consider again the motion of a particle between two points in the xy plane as shown in Figure 4.2. As the time interval over which we observe the motion

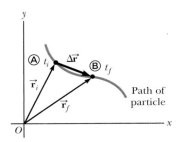

Figure 4.1 A particle moving in the xy plane is located with the position vector $\vec{\mathbf{r}}$ drawn from the origin to the particle. The displacement of the particle as it moves from Ⓐ to Ⓑ in the time interval $\Delta t = t_f - t_i$ is equal to the vector $\Delta\vec{\mathbf{r}} = \vec{\mathbf{r}}_f - \vec{\mathbf{r}}_i$.

Figure 4.2 As a particle moves between two points, its average velocity is in the direction of the displacement vector $\Delta\vec{\mathbf{r}}$. As the end point of the path is moved from Ⓑ to Ⓑ′ to Ⓑ″, the respective displacements and corresponding time intervals become smaller and smaller. In the limit that the end point approaches Ⓐ, Δt approaches zero and the direction of $\Delta\vec{\mathbf{r}}$ approaches that of the line tangent to the curve at Ⓐ. By definition, the instantaneous velocity at Ⓐ is directed along this tangent line.

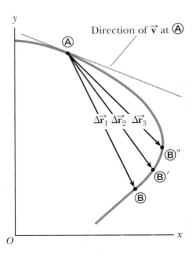

becomes smaller and smaller—that is, as Ⓑ is moved to Ⓑ′ and then to Ⓑ″, and so on—the direction of the displacement approaches that of the line tangent to the path at Ⓐ. The **instantaneous velocity** $\vec{\mathbf{v}}$ is defined as the limit of the average velocity $\Delta\vec{\mathbf{r}}/\Delta t$ as Δt approaches zero:

$$\vec{\mathbf{v}} \equiv \lim_{\Delta t \to 0} \frac{\Delta\vec{\mathbf{r}}}{\Delta t} = \frac{d\vec{\mathbf{r}}}{dt} \qquad (4.3)$$

◀ Instantaneous velocity

That is, the instantaneous velocity equals the derivative of the position vector with respect to time. The direction of the instantaneous velocity vector at any point in a particle's path is along a line tangent to the path at that point and in the direction of motion.

The magnitude of the instantaneous velocity vector $v = |\vec{\mathbf{v}}|$ of a particle is called the *speed* of the particle, which is a scalar quantity.

As a particle moves from one point to another along some path, its instantaneous velocity vector changes from $\vec{\mathbf{v}}_i$ at time t_i to $\vec{\mathbf{v}}_f$ at time t_f. Knowing the velocity at these points allows us to determine the average acceleration of the particle. The **average acceleration** $\vec{\mathbf{a}}_{avg}$ of a particle is defined as the change in its instantaneous velocity vector $\Delta\vec{\mathbf{v}}$ divided by the time interval Δt during which that change occurs:

$$\vec{\mathbf{a}}_{avg} \equiv \frac{\vec{\mathbf{v}}_f - \vec{\mathbf{v}}_i}{t_f - t_i} = \frac{\Delta\vec{\mathbf{v}}}{\Delta t} \qquad (4.4)$$

◀ Average acceleration

Because $\vec{\mathbf{a}}_{avg}$ is the ratio of a vector quantity $\Delta\vec{\mathbf{v}}$ and a positive scalar quantity Δt, we conclude that average acceleration is a vector quantity directed along $\Delta\vec{\mathbf{v}}$. As indicated in Figure 4.3, the direction of $\Delta\vec{\mathbf{v}}$ is found by adding the vector $-\vec{\mathbf{v}}_i$ (the negative of $\vec{\mathbf{v}}_i$) to the vector $\vec{\mathbf{v}}_f$ because, by definition, $\Delta\vec{\mathbf{v}} = \vec{\mathbf{v}}_f - \vec{\mathbf{v}}_i$.

When the average acceleration of a particle changes during different time intervals, it is useful to define its instantaneous acceleration. The **instantaneous acceleration** $\vec{\mathbf{a}}$ is defined as the limiting value of the ratio $\Delta\vec{\mathbf{v}}/\Delta t$ as Δt approaches zero:

$$\vec{\mathbf{a}} \equiv \lim_{\Delta t \to 0} \frac{\Delta\vec{\mathbf{v}}}{\Delta t} = \frac{d\vec{\mathbf{v}}}{dt} \qquad (4.5)$$

◀ Instantaneous acceleration

In other words, the instantaneous acceleration equals the derivative of the velocity vector with respect to time.

Various changes can occur when a particle accelerates. First, the magnitude of the velocity vector (the speed) may change with time as in straight-line (one-dimensional) motion. Second, the direction of the velocity vector may change with time even if its magnitude (speed) remains constant as in two-dimensional motion along a curved path. Finally, both the magnitude and the direction of the velocity vector may change simultaneously.

PITFALL PREVENTION 4.1
Vector Addition

Although the vector addition discussed in Chapter 3 involves *displacement* vectors, vector addition can be applied to *any* type of vector quantity. Figure 4.3, for example, shows the addition of *velocity* vectors using the graphical approach.

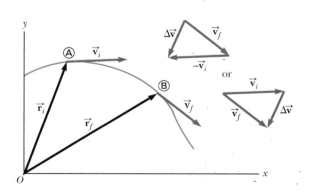

Figure 4.3 A particle moves from position Ⓐ to position Ⓑ. Its velocity vector changes from $\vec{\mathbf{v}}_i$ to $\vec{\mathbf{v}}_f$. The vector diagrams at the upper right show two ways of determining the vector $\Delta\vec{\mathbf{v}}$ from the initial and final velocities.

Quick Quiz 4.1 Consider the following controls in an automobile: gas pedal, brake, steering wheel. What are the controls in this list that cause an acceleration of the car? (a) all three controls (b) the gas pedal and the brake (c) only the brake (d) only the gas pedal

4.2 Two-Dimensional Motion with Constant Acceleration

In Section 2.5, we investigated one-dimensional motion of a particle under constant acceleration. Let us now consider two-dimensional motion during which the acceleration of a particle remains constant in both magnitude and direction. As we shall see, this approach is useful for analyzing some common types of motion.

Before embarking on this investigation, we need to emphasize an important point regarding two-dimensional motion. Imagine an air hockey puck moving in a straight line along a perfectly level, friction-free surface of an air hockey table. Figure 4.4a shows a motion diagram from an overhead point of view of this puck. Recall that in Section 2.4 we related the acceleration of an object to a force on the object. Because there are no forces on the puck in the horizontal plane, it moves with constant velocity in the x direction. Now suppose you blow a puff of air on the puck as it passes your position, with the force from your puff of air *exactly* in the y direction. Because the force from this puff of air has no component in the x direction, it causes no acceleration in the x direction. It only causes a momentary acceleration in the y direction, causing the puck to have a constant y component of velocity once the force from the puff of air is removed. After your puff of air on the puck, its velocity component in the x direction is unchanged, as shown in Figure 4.4b. The generalization of this simple experiment is that **motion in two dimensions can be modeled as two *independent* motions in each of the two perpendicular directions associated with the x and y axes. That is, any influence in the y direction does not affect the motion in the x direction and vice versa.**

The position vector for a particle moving in the xy plane can be written

$$\vec{\mathbf{r}} = x\hat{\mathbf{i}} + y\hat{\mathbf{j}} \qquad (4.6)$$

where x, y, and $\vec{\mathbf{r}}$ change with time as the particle moves while the unit vectors $\hat{\mathbf{i}}$ and $\hat{\mathbf{j}}$ remain constant. If the position vector is known, the velocity of the particle can be obtained from Equations 4.3 and 4.6, which give

$$\vec{\mathbf{v}} = \frac{d\vec{\mathbf{r}}}{dt} = \frac{dx}{dt}\hat{\mathbf{i}} + \frac{dy}{dt}\hat{\mathbf{j}} = v_x\hat{\mathbf{i}} + v_y\hat{\mathbf{j}} \qquad (4.7)$$

(a)

(b)

Figure 4.4 (a) A puck moves across a horizontal air hockey table at constant velocity in the x direction. (b) After a puff of air in the y direction is applied to the puck, the puck has gained a y component of velocity, but the x component is unaffected by the force in the perpendicular direction. Notice that the horizontal red vectors, representing the x component of the velocity, are the same length in both parts of the figure, which demonstrates that motion in two dimensions can be modeled as two independent motions in perpendicular directions.

Because the acceleration $\vec{\mathbf{a}}$ of the particle is assumed constant in this discussion, its components a_x and a_y also are constants. Therefore, we can model the particle as a particle under constant acceleration independently in each of the two directions and apply the equations of kinematics separately to the x and y components of the velocity vector. Substituting, from Equation 2.13, $v_{xf} = v_{xi} + a_x t$ and $v_{yf} = v_{yi} + a_y t$ into Equation 4.7 to determine the final velocity at any time t, we obtain

$$\vec{\mathbf{v}}_f = (v_{xi} + a_x t)\hat{\mathbf{i}} + (v_{yi} + a_y t)\hat{\mathbf{j}} = (v_{xi}\hat{\mathbf{i}} + v_{yi}\hat{\mathbf{j}}) + (a_x\hat{\mathbf{i}} + a_y\hat{\mathbf{j}})t$$

$$\vec{\mathbf{v}}_f = \vec{\mathbf{v}}_i + \vec{\mathbf{a}}t \qquad (4.8)$$

◀ Velocity vector as a function of time

This result states that the velocity of a particle at some time t equals the vector sum of its initial velocity $\vec{\mathbf{v}}_i$ at time $t = 0$ and the additional velocity $\vec{\mathbf{a}}t$ acquired at time t as a result of constant acceleration. Equation 4.8 is the vector version of Equation 2.13.

Similarly, from Equation 2.16 we know that the x and y coordinates of a particle moving with constant acceleration are

$$x_f = x_i + v_{xi}t + \tfrac{1}{2}a_x t^2 \qquad y_f = y_i + v_{yi}t + \tfrac{1}{2}a_y t^2$$

Substituting these expressions into Equation 4.6 (and labeling the final position vector $\vec{\mathbf{r}}_f$) gives

$$\vec{\mathbf{r}}_f = (x_i + v_{xi}t + \tfrac{1}{2}a_x t^2)\hat{\mathbf{i}} + (y_i + v_{yi}t + \tfrac{1}{2}a_y t^2)\hat{\mathbf{j}}$$

$$= (x_i\hat{\mathbf{i}} + y_i\hat{\mathbf{j}}) + (v_{xi}\hat{\mathbf{i}} + v_{yi}\hat{\mathbf{j}})t + \tfrac{1}{2}(a_x\hat{\mathbf{i}} + a_y\hat{\mathbf{j}})t^2$$

$$\vec{\mathbf{r}}_f = \vec{\mathbf{r}}_i + \vec{\mathbf{v}}_i t + \tfrac{1}{2}\vec{\mathbf{a}}t^2 \qquad (4.9)$$

◀ Position vector as a function of time

which is the vector version of Equation 2.16. Equation 4.9 tells us that the position vector $\vec{\mathbf{r}}_f$ of a particle is the vector sum of the original position $\vec{\mathbf{r}}_i$, a displacement $\vec{\mathbf{v}}_i t$ arising from the initial velocity of the particle and a displacement $\tfrac{1}{2}\vec{\mathbf{a}}t^2$ resulting from the constant acceleration of the particle.

Graphical representations of Equations 4.8 and 4.9 are shown in Active Figure 4.5. The components of the position and velocity vectors are also illustrated in the figure. Notice from Active Figure 4.5a that $\vec{\mathbf{v}}_f$ is generally not along the direction of either $\vec{\mathbf{v}}_i$ or $\vec{\mathbf{a}}$ because the relationship between these quantities is a vector expression. For the same reason, from Active Figure 4.5b we see that $\vec{\mathbf{r}}_f$ is generally not along the direction of $\vec{\mathbf{v}}_i$ or $\vec{\mathbf{a}}$. Finally, notice that $\vec{\mathbf{v}}_f$ and $\vec{\mathbf{r}}_f$ are generally not in the same direction.

(a)

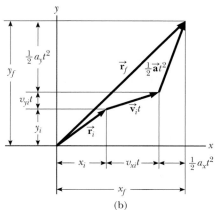
(b)

ACTIVE FIGURE 4.5

Vector representations and components of (a) the velocity and (b) the position of a particle moving with a constant acceleration $\vec{\mathbf{a}}$.

Sign in at www.thomsonedu.com and go to ThomsonNOW to investigate the effect of different initial positions and velocities on the final position and velocity (for constant acceleration).

EXAMPLE 4.1 **Motion in a Plane**

A particle starts from the origin at $t = 0$ with an initial velocity having an x component of 20 m/s and a y component of -15 m/s. The particle moves in the xy plane with an x component of acceleration only, given by $a_x = 4.0$ m/s².

(A) Determine the total velocity vector at any time.

SOLUTION

Conceptualize The components of the initial velocity tell us that the particle starts by moving toward the right and downward. The x component of velocity starts at 20 m/s and increases by 4.0 m/s every second. The y component of velocity never changes from its initial value of -15 m/s. We sketch a motion diagram of the situation in Figure 4.6. Because the particle is accelerating in the $+x$ direction, its velocity component in this direction increases and the path curves as shown in the diagram. Notice that the spacing between successive images

Figure 4.6 (Example 4.1) Motion diagram for the particle.

increases as time goes on because the speed is increasing. The placement of the acceleration and velocity vectors in Figure 4.6 helps us further conceptualize the situation.

Categorize Because the initial velocity has components in both the x and y directions, we categorize this problem as one involving a particle moving in two dimensions. Because the particle only has an x component of acceleration, we model it as a particle under constant acceleration in the x direction and a particle under constant velocity in the y direction.

Analyze To begin the mathematical analysis, we set $v_{xi} = 20$ m/s, $v_{yi} = -15$ m/s, $a_x = 4.0$ m/s², and $a_y = 0$.

Use Equation 4.8 for the velocity vector:

$$\vec{v}_f = \vec{v}_i + \vec{a}t = (v_{xi} + a_x t)\hat{i} + (v_{yi} + a_y t)\hat{j}$$

Substitute numerical values:

$$\vec{v}_f = [20 \text{ m/s} + (4.0 \text{ m/s}^2)t]\hat{i} + [-15 \text{ m/s} + (0)t]\hat{j}$$

$$(1) \quad \vec{v}_f = [(20 + 4.0t)\hat{i} - 15\hat{j}] \text{ m/s}$$

Finalize Notice that the x component of velocity increases in time while the y component remains constant; this result is consistent with what we predicted.

(B) Calculate the velocity and speed of the particle at $t = 5.0$ s.

SOLUTION

Analyze

Evaluate the result from Equation (1) at $t = 5.0$ s:

$$\vec{v}_f = [(20 + 4.0(5.0))\hat{i} - 15\hat{j}] \text{ m/s} = \boxed{(40\hat{i} - 15\hat{j}) \text{ m/s}}$$

Determine the angle θ that $\vec{v}_f$ makes with the x axis at $t = 5.0$ s:

$$\theta = \tan^{-1}\left(\frac{v_{yf}}{v_{xf}}\right) = \tan^{-1}\left(\frac{-15 \text{ m/s}}{40 \text{ m/s}}\right) = \boxed{-21°}$$

Evaluate the speed of the particle as the magnitude of $\vec{v}_f$:

$$v_f = |\vec{v}_f| = \sqrt{v_{xf}^2 + v_{yf}^2} = \sqrt{(40)^2 + (-15)^2} \text{ m/s} = \boxed{43 \text{ m/s}}$$

Finalize The negative sign for the angle θ indicates that the velocity vector is directed at an angle of 21° below the positive x axis. Notice that if we calculate v_i from the x and y components of $\vec{v}_i$, we find that $v_f > v_i$. Is that consistent with our prediction?

(C) Determine the x and y coordinates of the particle at any time t and its position vector at this time.

SOLUTION

Analyze

Use the components of Equation 4.9 with $x_i = y_i = 0$ at $t = 0$:

$$x_f = v_{xi}t + \tfrac{1}{2}a_x t^2 = \boxed{(20t + 2.0t^2) \text{ m}}$$

$$y_f = v_{yi}t = \boxed{(-15t) \text{ m}}$$

Express the position vector of the particle at any time t:

$$\vec{\mathbf{r}}_f = x_f\hat{\mathbf{i}} + y_f\hat{\mathbf{j}} = \left[(20t + 2.0t^2)\hat{\mathbf{i}} - 15t\hat{\mathbf{j}}\right] \text{ m}$$

Finalize   Let us now consider a limiting case for very large values of t.

What If?   What if we wait a very long time and then observe the motion of the particle? How would we describe the motion of the particle for large values of the time?

Answer   Looking at Figure 4.6, we see the path of the particle curving toward the x axis. There is no reason to assume that this tendency will change, which suggests that the path will become more and more parallel to the x axis as time grows large. Mathematically, Equation (1) shows that the y component of the velocity remains constant while the x component grows linearly with t. Therefore, when t is very large, the x component of the velocity will be much larger than the y component, suggesting that the velocity vector becomes more and more parallel to the x axis. Both x_f and y_f continue to grow with time, although x_f grows much faster.

4.3   Projectile Motion

Anyone who has observed a baseball in motion has observed projectile motion. The ball moves in a curved path and returns to the ground. **Projectile motion** of an object is simple to analyze if we make two assumptions: (1) the free-fall acceleration is constant over the range of motion and is directed downward,[1] and (2) the effect of air resistance is negligible.[2] With these assumptions, we find that the path of a projectile, which we call its *trajectory*, is *always* a parabola as shown in Active Figure 4.7. **We use these assumptions throughout this chapter**.

The expression for the position vector of the projectile as a function of time follows directly from Equation 4.9, with $\vec{\mathbf{a}} = \vec{\mathbf{g}}$:

$$\vec{\mathbf{r}}_f = \vec{\mathbf{r}}_i + \vec{\mathbf{v}}_i t + \tfrac{1}{2}\vec{\mathbf{g}}t^2 \tag{4.10}$$

PITFALL PREVENTION 4.2
Acceleration at the Highest Point

As discussed in Pitfall Prevention 2.8, many people claim that the acceleration of a projectile at the topmost point of its trajectory is zero. This mistake arises from confusion between zero vertical velocity and zero acceleration. If the projectile were to experience zero acceleration at the highest point, its velocity at that point would not change; rather, the projectile would move horizontally at constant speed from then on! That does not happen, however, because the acceleration is *not* zero anywhere along the trajectory.

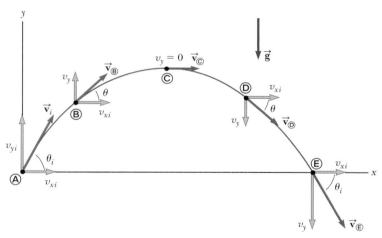

ACTIVE FIGURE 4.7

The parabolic path of a projectile that leaves the origin with a velocity $\vec{\mathbf{v}}_i$. The velocity vector $\vec{\mathbf{v}}$ changes with time in both magnitude and direction. This change is the result of acceleration in the negative y direction. The x component of velocity remains constant in time because there is no acceleration along the horizontal direction. The y component of velocity is zero at the peak of the path.

Sign in at www.thomsonedu.com and go to ThomsonNOW to change launch angle and initial speed. You can also observe the changing components of velocity along the trajectory of the projectile.

[1] This assumption is reasonable as long as the range of motion is small compared with the radius of the Earth (6.4×10^6 m). In effect, this assumption is equivalent to assuming that the Earth is flat over the range of motion considered.

[2] This assumption is generally *not* justified, especially at high velocities. In addition, any spin imparted to a projectile, such as that applied when a pitcher throws a curve ball, can give rise to some very interesting effects associated with aerodynamic forces, which will be discussed in Chapter 14.

A welder cuts holes through a heavy metal construction beam with a hot torch. The sparks generated in the process follow parabolic paths.

where the initial x and y components of the velocity of the projectile are

$$v_{xi} = v_i \cos \theta_i \qquad v_{yi} = v_i \sin \theta_i \qquad (4.11)$$

The expression in Equation 4.10 is plotted in Figure 4.8, for a projectile launched from the origin, so that $\vec{r}_i = 0$. The final position of a particle can be considered to be the superposition of its initial position $\vec{r}_i$; the term $\vec{v}_i t$, which is its displacement if no acceleration were present; and the term $\frac{1}{2}\vec{g}t^2$ that arises from its acceleration due to gravity. In other words, if there were no gravitational acceleration, the particle would continue to move along a straight path in the direction of $\vec{v}_i$. Therefore, the vertical distance $\frac{1}{2}\vec{g}t^2$ through which the particle "falls" off the straight-line path is the same distance that an object dropped from rest would fall during the same time interval.

In Section 4.2, we stated that two-dimensional motion with constant acceleration can be analyzed as a combination of two independent motions in the x and y directions, with accelerations a_x and a_y. Projectile motion can also be handled in this way, with zero acceleration in the x direction and a constant acceleration in the y direction, $a_y = -g$. Therefore, **when analyzing projectile motion, model it to be the superposition of two motions: (1) motion of a particle under constant velocity in the horizontal direction and (2) motion of a particle under constant acceleration (free fall) in the vertical direction**. The horizontal and vertical components of a projectile's motion are completely independent of each other and can be handled separately, with time t as the common variable for both components.

Quick Quiz 4.2 **(i)** As a projectile thrown upward moves in its parabolic path (such as in Fig. 4.8), at what point along its path are the velocity and acceleration vectors for the projectile perpendicular to each other? (a) nowhere   (b) the highest point   (c) the launch point   **(ii)** From the same choices, at what point are the velocity and acceleration vectors for the projectile parallel to each other?

Figure 4.8 The position vector $\vec{r}_f$ of a projectile launched from the origin whose initial velocity at the origin is $\vec{v}_i$. The vector $\vec{v}_i t$ would be the displacement of the projectile if gravity were absent, and the vector $\frac{1}{2}\vec{g}t^2$ is its vertical displacement from a straight-line path due to its downward gravitational acceleration.

Horizontal Range and Maximum Height of a Projectile

Let us assume a projectile is launched from the origin at $t_i = 0$ with a positive v_{yi} component as shown in Figure 4.9 and returns to the same horizontal level. Two points are especially interesting to analyze: the peak point Ⓐ, which has Cartesian coordinates $(R/2, h)$, and the point Ⓑ, which has coordinates $(R, 0)$. The distance R is called the *horizontal range* of the projectile, and the distance h is its *maximum height*. Let us find h and R mathematically in terms of v_i, θ_i, and g.

We can determine h by noting that at the peak $v_{y\text{Ⓐ}} = 0$. Therefore, we can use the y component of Equation 4.8 to determine the time $t_\text{Ⓐ}$ at which the projectile reaches the peak:

$$v_{yf} = v_{yi} + a_y t$$
$$0 = v_i \sin \theta_i - gt_\text{Ⓐ}$$
$$t_\text{Ⓐ} = \frac{v_i \sin \theta_i}{g}$$

Substituting this expression for $t_\text{Ⓐ}$ into the y component of Equation 4.9 and replacing $y = y_\text{Ⓐ}$ with h, we obtain an expression for h in terms of the magnitude and direction of the initial velocity vector:

$$h = (v_i \sin \theta_i)\frac{v_i \sin \theta_i}{g} - \frac{1}{2}g\left(\frac{v_i \sin \theta_i}{g}\right)^2$$
$$h = \frac{v_i^2 \sin^2 \theta_i}{2g} \qquad (4.12)$$

The range R is the horizontal position of the projectile at a time that is twice the time at which it reaches its peak, that is, at time $t_\text{Ⓑ} = 2t_\text{Ⓐ}$. Using the x compo-

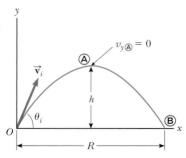

Figure 4.9 A projectile launched over a flat surface from the origin at $t_i = 0$ with an initial velocity $\vec{v}_i$. The maximum height of the projectile is h, and the horizontal range is R. At Ⓐ, the peak of the trajectory, the particle has coordinates $(R/2, h)$.

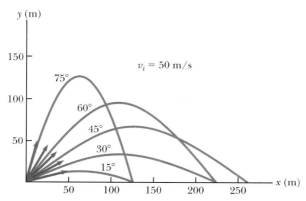

ACTIVE FIGURE 4.10

A projectile launched over a flat surface from the origin with an initial speed of 50 m/s at various angles of projection. Notice that complementary values of θ_i result in the same value of R (range of the projectile).

Sign in at www.thomsonedu.com and go to ThomsonNOW to vary the projection angle, observe the effect on the trajectory, and measure the flight time.

nent of Equation 4.9, noting that $v_{xi} = v_{x\text{\textcircled{B}}} = v_i \cos \theta_i$, and setting $x_{\text{\textcircled{B}}} = R$ at $t = 2t_{\text{\textcircled{A}}}$, we find that

$$R = v_{xi}t_{\text{\textcircled{B}}} = (v_i \cos \theta_i)2t_{\text{\textcircled{A}}}$$

$$= (v_i \cos \theta_i)\frac{2v_i \sin \theta_i}{g} = \frac{2v_i^2 \sin \theta_i \cos \theta_i}{g}$$

Using the identity $\sin 2\theta = 2 \sin \theta \cos \theta$ (see Appendix B.4), we can write R in the more compact form

$$R = \frac{v_i^2 \sin 2\theta_i}{g} \tag{4.13}$$

The maximum value of R from Equation 4.13 is $R_{max} = v_i^2/g$. This result makes sense because the maximum value of $\sin 2\theta_i$ is 1, which occurs when $2\theta_i = 90°$. Therefore, R is a maximum when $\theta_i = 45°$.

Active Figure 4.10 illustrates various trajectories for a projectile having a given initial speed but launched at different angles. As you can see, the range is a maximum for $\theta_i = 45°$. In addition, for any θ_i other than 45°, a point having Cartesian coordinates $(R, 0)$ can be reached by using either one of two complementary values of θ_i, such as 75° and 15°. Of course, the maximum height and time of flight for one of these values of θ_i are different from the maximum height and time of flight for the complementary value.

Quick Quiz 4.3   Rank the launch angles for the five paths in Active Figure 4.10 with respect to time of flight, from the shortest time of flight to the longest.

PITFALL PREVENTION 4.3
The Height and Range Equations

Equation 4.13 is useful for calculating R only for a symmetric path as shown in Active Figure 4.10. If the path is not symmetric, *do not use this equation*. The general expressions given by Equations 4.8 and 4.9 are the *more important* results because they give the position and velocity components of *any* particle moving in two dimensions at *any* time t.

<hr>

PROBLEM-SOLVING STRATEGY   **Projectile Motion**

We suggest you use the following approach when solving projectile motion problems:

1. *Conceptualize.* Think about what is going on physically in the problem. Establish the mental representation by imagining the projectile moving along its trajectory.

2. *Categorize.* Confirm that the problem involves a particle in free fall and that air resistance is neglected. Select a coordinate system with x in the horizontal direction and y in the vertical direction.

3. *Analyze.* If the initial velocity vector is given, resolve it into x and y components. Treat the horizontal motion and the vertical motion independently. Analyze the

horizontal motion of the projectile as a particle under constant velocity. Analyze the vertical motion of the projectile as a particle under constant acceleration.

4. *Finalize.* Once you have determined your result, check to see if your answers are consistent with the mental and pictorial representations and that your results are realistic.

EXAMPLE 4.2 The Long Jump

A long jumper (Fig. 4.11) leaves the ground at an angle of 20.0° above the horizontal and at a speed of 11.0 m/s.

(A) How far does he jump in the horizontal direction?

SOLUTION

Conceptualize   The arms and legs of a long jumper move in a complicated way, but we will ignore this motion. We conceptualize the motion of the long jumper as equivalent to that of a simple projectile.

Categorize   We categorize this example as a projectile motion problem. Because the initial speed and launch angle are given and because the final height is the same as the initial height, we further categorize this problem as satisfying the conditions for which Equations 4.12 and 4.13 can be used. This approach is the most direct way to analyze this problem, although the general methods that have been described will always give the correct answer.

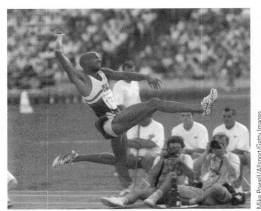

Figure 4.11 (Example 4.2) Mike Powell, current holder of the world long-jump record of 8.95 m.

Mike Powell/Allsport/Getty Images

Analyze

Use Equation 4.13 to find the range of the jumper:

$$R = \frac{v_i^2 \sin 2\theta_i}{g} = \frac{(11.0 \text{ m/s})^2 \sin 2(20.0°)}{9.80 \text{ m/s}^2} = \boxed{7.94 \text{ m}}$$

(B) What is the maximum height reached?

SOLUTION

Analyze

Find the maximum height reached by using Equation 4.12:

$$h = \frac{v_i^2 \sin^2 \theta_i}{2g} = \frac{(11.0 \text{ m/s})^2 (\sin 20.0°)^2}{2(9.80 \text{ m/s}^2)} = \boxed{0.722 \text{ m}}$$

Finalize   Find the answers to parts (A) and (B) using the general method. The results should agree. Treating the long jumper as a particle is an oversimplification. Nevertheless, the values obtained are consistent with experience in sports. We can model a complicated system such as a long jumper as a particle and still obtain results that are reasonable.

EXAMPLE 4.3 A Bull's-Eye Every Time

In a popular lecture demonstration, a projectile is fired at a target in such a way that the projectile leaves the gun at the same time the target is dropped from rest. Show that if the gun is initially aimed at the stationary target, the projectile hits the falling target as shown in Figure 4.12a.

SOLUTION

Conceptualize   We conceptualize the problem by studying Figure 4.12a. Notice that the problem does not ask for numerical values. The expected result must involve an algebraic argument.

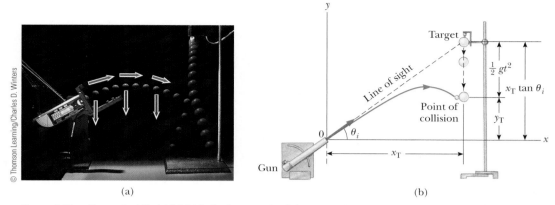

Figure 4.12 (Example 4.3) (a) Multiflash photograph of the projectile–target demonstration. If the gun is aimed directly at the target and is fired at the same instant the target begins to fall, the projectile will hit the target. Notice that the velocity of the projectile (red arrows) changes in direction and magnitude, whereas its downward acceleration (violet arrows) remains constant. (b) Schematic diagram of the projectile–target demonstration.

Categorize Because both objects are subject only to gravity, we categorize this problem as one involving two objects in free fall, the target moving in one dimension and the projectile moving in two.

Analyze The target T is modeled as a particle under constant acceleration in one dimension. Figure 4.12b shows that the initial y coordinate y_{iT} of the target is $x_T \tan \theta_i$ and its initial velocity is zero. It falls with acceleration $a_y = -g$. The projectile P is modeled as a particle under constant acceleration in the y direction and a particle under constant velocity in the x direction.

Write an expression for the y coordinate of the target at any moment after release, noting that its initial velocity is zero:	(1) $y_T = y_{iT} + (0)t - \frac{1}{2}gt^2 = x_T \tan \theta_i - \frac{1}{2}gt^2$
Write an expression for the y coordinate of the projectile at any moment:	(2) $y_P = y_{iP} + v_{yiP}t - \frac{1}{2}gt^2 = 0 + (v_{iP} \sin\theta_i)t - \frac{1}{2}gt^2 = (v_{iP} \sin\theta_i)t - \frac{1}{2}gt^2$
Write an expression for the x coordinate of the projectile at any moment:	$x_P = x_{iP} + v_{xiP}t = 0 + (v_{iP} \cos \theta_i)t = (v_{iP} \cos \theta_i)t$
Solve this expression for time as a function of the horizontal position of the projectile:	$t = \dfrac{x_P}{v_{iP} \cos \theta_i}$
Substitute this expression into Equation (2):	(3) $y_P = (v_{iP} \sin \theta_i)\left(\dfrac{x_P}{v_{iP} \cos \theta_i}\right) - \frac{1}{2}gt^2 = x_P \tan \theta_i - \frac{1}{2}gt^2$

Compare Equations (1) and (3). We see that when the x coordinates of the projectile and target are the same—that is, when $x_T = x_P$—their y coordinates given by Equations (1) and (3) are the same and a collision results.

Finalize Note that a collision can result only when $v_{iP} \sin \theta_i \geq \sqrt{gd/2}$, where d is the initial elevation of the target above the floor. If $v_{iP} \sin \theta_i$ is less than this value, the projectile strikes the floor before reaching the target.

EXAMPLE 4.4   That's Quite an Arm!

A stone is thrown from the top of a building upward at an angle of 30.0° to the horizontal with an initial speed of 20.0 m/s as shown in Figure 4.13. The height of the building is 45.0 m.

(A) How long does it take the stone to reach the ground?

SOLUTION

Conceptualize Study Figure 4.13, in which we have indicated the trajectory and various parameters of the motion of the stone.

Categorize We categorize this problem as a projectile motion problem. The stone is modeled as a particle under constant acceleration in the y direction and a particle under constant velocity in the x direction.

Analyze We have the information $x_i = y_i = 0$, $y_f = -45.0$ m, $a_y = -g$, and $v_i = 20.0$ m/s (the numerical value of y_f is negative because we have chosen the top of the building as the origin).

$v_i = 20.0$ m/s

$(0,0)$

$\theta_i = 30.0°$

45.0 m

Figure 4.13 (Example 4.4) A stone is thrown from the top of a building.

Find the initial x and y components of the stone's velocity:

$$v_{xi} = v_i \cos \theta_i = (20.0 \text{ m/s})\cos 30.0° = 17.3 \text{ m/s}$$

$$v_{yi} = v_i \sin \theta_i = (20.0 \text{ m/s})\sin 30.0° = 10.0 \text{ m/s}$$

Express the vertical position of the stone from the vertical component of Equation 4.9:

$$y_f = y_i + v_{yi}t + \tfrac{1}{2}a_y t^2$$

Substitute numerical values:

$$-45.0 \text{ m} = 0 + (10.0 \text{ m/s})t + \tfrac{1}{2}(-9.80 \text{ m/s}^2)t^2$$

Solve the quadratic equation for t:

$$t = \boxed{4.22 \text{ s}}$$

(B) What is the speed of the stone just before it strikes the ground?

SOLUTION

Use the y component of Equation 4.8 with $t = 4.22$ s to obtain the y component of the velocity of the stone just before it strikes the ground:

$$v_{yf} = v_{yi} + a_y t$$

Substitute numerical values:

$$v_{yf} = 10.0 \text{ m/s} + (-9.80 \text{ m/s}^2)(4.22 \text{ s}) = -31.3 \text{ m/s}$$

Use this component with the horizontal component $v_{xf} = v_{xi} = 17.3$ m/s to find the speed of the stone at $t = 4.22$ s:

$$v_f = \sqrt{v_{xf}^2 + v_{yf}^2} = \sqrt{(17.3 \text{ m/s})^2 + (-31.3 \text{ m/s})^2} = \boxed{35.8 \text{ m/s}}$$

Finalize Is it reasonable that the y component of the final velocity is negative? Is it reasonable that the final speed is larger than the initial speed of 20.0 m/s?

What If? What if a horizontal wind is blowing in the same direction as the stone is thrown and it causes the stone to have a horizontal acceleration component $a_x = 0.500$ m/s^2? Which part of this example, (A) or (B), will have a different answer?

Answer Recall that the motions in the x and y directions are independent. Therefore, the horizontal wind cannot affect the vertical motion. The vertical motion determines the time of the projectile in the air, so the answer to part (A) does not change. The wind causes the horizontal velocity component to increase with time, so the final speed will be larger in part (B). Taking $a_x = 0.500$ m/s^2, we find $v_{xf} = 19.4$ m/s and $v_f = 36.9$ m/s.

EXAMPLE 4.5 **The End of the Ski Jump**

A ski jumper leaves the ski track moving in the horizontal direction with a speed of 25.0 m/s as shown in Figure 4.14. The landing incline below her falls off with a slope of 35.0°. Where does she land on the incline?

SOLUTION

Conceptualize We can conceptualize this problem based on memories of observing winter Olympic ski competitions. We estimate the skier to be airborne for perhaps 4 s and to travel a distance of about 100 m horizontally. We should expect the value of d, the distance traveled along the incline, to be of the same order of magnitude.

Categorize We categorize the problem as one of a particle in projectile motion.

Analyze It is convenient to select the beginning of the jump as the origin. The initial velocity components are $v_{xi} = 25.0$ m/s and $v_{yi} = 0$. From the right triangle in Figure 4.14, we see that the jumper's x and y coordinates at the landing point are given by $x_f = d\cos 35.0°$ and $y_f = -d\sin 35.0°$.

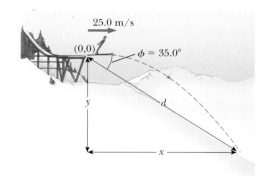

Figure 4.14   (Example 4.5) A ski jumper leaves the track moving in a horizontal direction.

Express the coordinates of the jumper as a function of time:

$$(1) \quad x_f = v_{xi}t = (25.0 \text{ m/s})t$$

$$(2) \quad y_f = v_{yi}t + \tfrac{1}{2}a_y t^2 = -\tfrac{1}{2}(9.80 \text{ m/s}^2)t^2$$

Substitute the values of x_f and y_f at the landing point:

$$(3) \quad d\cos 35.0° = (25.0 \text{ m/s})t$$

$$(4) \quad -d\sin 35.0° = -\tfrac{1}{2}(9.80 \text{ m/s}^2)t^2$$

Solve Equation (3) for t and substitute the result into Equation (4):

$$-d\sin 35.0° = -\tfrac{1}{2}(9.80 \text{ m/s}^2)\left(\frac{d\cos 35.0°}{25.0 \text{ m/s}}\right)^2$$

Solve for d:

$$d = 109 \text{ m}$$

Evaluate the x and y coordinates of the point at which the skier lands:

$$x_f = d\cos 35.0° = (109 \text{ m})\cos 35.0° = \boxed{89.3 \text{ m}}$$

$$y_f = -d\sin 35.0° = -(109 \text{ m})\sin 35.0° = \boxed{-62.5 \text{ m}}$$

Finalize Let us compare these results with our expectations. We expected the horizontal distance to be on the order of 100 m, and our result of 89.3 m is indeed on this order of magnitude. It might be useful to calculate the time interval that the jumper is in the air and compare it with our estimate of about 4 s.

What If? Suppose everything in this example is the same except the ski jump is curved so that the jumper is projected upward at an angle from the end of the track. Is this design better in terms of maximizing the length of the jump?

Answer If the initial velocity has an upward component, the skier will be in the air longer and should therefore travel further. Tilting the initial velocity vector upward, however, will reduce the horizontal component of the initial velocity. Therefore, angling the end of the ski track upward at a *large* angle may actually *reduce* the distance. Consider the extreme case: the skier is projected at 90° to the horizontal and simply goes up and comes back down at the end of the ski track! This argument suggests that there must be an optimal angle between 0° and 90° that represents a balance between making the flight time longer and the horizontal velocity component smaller.

Let us find this optimal angle mathematically. We modify equations (1) through (4) in the following way,

assuming that the skier is projected at an angle θ with respect to the horizontal over a landing incline sloped with an arbitrary angle ϕ:

$$(1) \text{ and } (3) \quad \rightarrow \quad x_f = (v_i\cos\theta)t = d\cos\phi$$

$$(2) \text{ and } (4) \quad \rightarrow \quad y_f = (v_i\sin\theta)t - \tfrac{1}{2}gt^2 = -d\sin\phi$$

By eliminating the time t between these equations and using differentiation to maximize d in terms of θ, we arrive (after several steps; see Problem 62) at the following equation for the angle θ that gives the maximum value of d:

$$\theta = 45° - \frac{\phi}{2}$$

For the slope angle in Figure 4.14, $\phi = 35.0°$; this equation results in an optimal launch angle of $\phi = 27.5°$. For a slope angle of $\phi = 0°$, which represents a horizontal plane, this equation gives an optimal launch angle of $\theta = 45°$, as we would expect (see Active Figure 4.10).

4.4   The Particle in Uniform Circular Motion

Figure 4.15a shows a car moving in a circular path with *constant speed v*. Such motion, called **uniform circular motion**, occurs in many situations. Because it occurs so often, this type of motion is recognized as an analysis model called the **particle in uniform circular motion**. We discuss this model in this section.

It is often surprising to students to find that **even though an object moves at a constant speed in a circular path, it still has an acceleration**. To see why, consider the defining equation for acceleration, $\vec{a} = d\vec{v}/dt$ (Eq. 4.5). Notice that the acceleration depends on the change in the *velocity*. Because velocity is a vector quantity, an acceleration can occur in two ways, as mentioned in Section 4.1: by a change in the *magnitude* of the velocity and by a change in the *direction* of the velocity. The latter situation occurs for an object moving with constant speed in a circular path. The velocity vector is always tangent to the path of the object and perpendicular to the radius of the circular path.

We now show that the acceleration vector in uniform circular motion is always perpendicular to the path and always points toward the center of the circle. If that were not true, there would be a component of the acceleration parallel to the path and therefore parallel to the velocity vector. Such an acceleration component would lead to a change in the speed of the particle along the path. This situation, however, is inconsistent with our setup of the situation: the particle moves with constant speed along the path. Therefore, for *uniform* circular motion, the acceleration vector can only have a component perpendicular to the path, which is toward the center of the circle.

Let us now find the magnitude of the acceleration of the particle. Consider the diagram of the position and velocity vectors in Figure 4.15b. The figure also shows the vector representing the change in position $\Delta \vec{r}$ for an arbitrary time interval. The particle follows a circular path of radius r, part of which is shown by the dashed curve. The particle is at Ⓐ at time t_i, and its velocity at that time is $\vec{v}_i$; it is at Ⓑ at some later time t_f, and its velocity at that time is $\vec{v}_f$. Let us also assume $\vec{v}_i$ and $\vec{v}_f$ differ only in direction; their magnitudes are the same (that is, $v_i = v_f = v$ because it is *uniform* circular motion).

In Figure 4.15c, the velocity vectors in Figure 4.15b have been redrawn tail to tail. The vector $\Delta \vec{v}$ connects the tips of the vectors, representing the vector addition $\vec{v}_f = \vec{v}_i + \Delta \vec{v}$. In both Figures 4.15b and 4.15c, we can identify triangles that help us analyze the motion. The angle $\Delta\theta$ between the two position vectors in Figure 4.15b is the same as the angle between the velocity vectors in Figure 4.15c because the velocity vector $\vec{v}$ is always perpendicular to the position vector $\vec{r}$. Therefore, the two triangles are *similar*. (Two triangles are similar if the angle between any two sides is the same for both triangles and if the ratio of the lengths of these sides is the same.) We can now write a relationship between the lengths of the sides for the two triangles in Figures 4.15b and 4.15c:

$$\frac{|\Delta \vec{v}|}{v} = \frac{|\Delta \vec{r}|}{r}$$

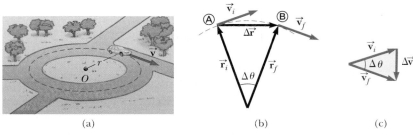

(a)   (b)   (c)

Figure 4.15   (a) A car moving along a circular path at constant speed experiences uniform circular motion. (b) As a particle moves from Ⓐ to Ⓑ, its velocity vector changes from $\vec{v}_i$ to $\vec{v}_f$. (c) The construction for determining the direction of the change in velocity $\Delta \vec{v}$, which is toward the center of the circle for small $\Delta \vec{r}$.

where $v = v_i = v_f$ and $r = r_i = r_f$. This equation can be solved for $|\Delta\vec{v}|$, and the expression obtained can be substituted into Equation 4.4, $\vec{a}_{avg} = \Delta\vec{v}/\Delta t$, to give the magnitude of the average acceleration over the time interval for the particle to move from Ⓐ to Ⓑ:

$$|\vec{a}_{avg}| = \frac{|\Delta\vec{v}|}{|\Delta t|} = \frac{v}{r}\frac{|\Delta\vec{r}|}{\Delta t}$$

Now imagine that points Ⓐ and Ⓑ in Figure 4.15b become extremely close together. As Ⓐ and Ⓑ approach each other, Δt approaches zero, $|\Delta\vec{r}|$ approaches the distance traveled by the particle along the circular path, and the ratio $|\Delta\vec{r}|/\Delta t$ approaches the speed v. In addition, the average acceleration becomes the instantaneous acceleration at point Ⓐ. Hence, in the limit $\Delta t \to 0$, the magnitude of the acceleration is

$$a_c = \frac{v^2}{r} \qquad\qquad (4.14)$$

◀ Centripetal acceleration

An acceleration of this nature is called a **centripetal acceleration** (*centripetal* means *center-seeking*). The subscript on the acceleration symbol reminds us that the acceleration is centripetal.

In many situations, it is convenient to describe the motion of a particle moving with constant speed in a circle of radius r in terms of the **period** T, which is defined as the time interval required for one complete revolution of the particle. In the time interval T, the particle moves a distance of $2\pi r$, which is equal to the circumference of the particle's circular path. Therefore, because its speed is equal to the circumference of the circular path divided by the period, or $v = 2\pi r/T$, it follows that

$$T = \frac{2\pi r}{v} \qquad\qquad (4.15)$$

◀ Period of circular motion

PITFALL PREVENTION 4.5
Centripetal Acceleration Is Not Constant
We derived the magnitude of the centripetal acceleration vector and found it to be constant for uniform circular motion, but *the centripetal acceleration vector is not constant*. It always points toward the center of the circle, but it continuously changes direction as the object moves around the circular path.

Quick Quiz 4.4   A particle moves in a circular path of radius r with speed v. It then increases its speed to $2v$ while traveling along the same circular path. **(i)** The centripetal acceleration of the particle has changed by what factor (choose one)? (a) 0.25 (b) 0.5 (c) 2 (d) 4 (e) impossible to determine **(ii)** From the same choices, by what factor has the period of the particle changed?

EXAMPLE 4.6   **The Centripetal Acceleration of the Earth**

What is the centripetal acceleration of the Earth as it moves in its orbit around the Sun?

SOLUTION

Conceptualize   Think about a mental image of the Earth in a circular orbit around the Sun. We will model the Earth as a particle and approximate the Earth's orbit as circular (it's actually slightly elliptical, as we discuss in Chapter 13).

Categorize   The Conceptualize step allows us to categorize this problem as one of a particle in uniform circular motion.

Analyze   We do not know the orbital speed of the Earth to substitute into Equation 4.14. With the help of Equation 4.15, however, we can recast Equation 4.14 in terms of the period of the Earth's orbit, which we know is one year, and the radius of the Earth's orbit around the Sun, which is 1.496×10^{11} m.

Combine Equations 4.14 and 4.15:

$$a_c = \frac{v^2}{r} = \frac{\left(\dfrac{2\pi r}{T}\right)^2}{r} = \frac{4\pi^2 r}{T^2}$$

Substitute numerical values:

$$a_c = \frac{4\pi^2 (1.496 \times 10^{11}\text{ m})}{(1\text{ yr})^2}\left(\frac{1\text{ yr}}{3.156 \times 10^7\text{ s}}\right)^2 = \boxed{5.93 \times 10^{-3}\text{ m/s}^2}$$

Finalize   This acceleration is much smaller than the free-fall acceleration on the surface of the Earth. An important thing we learned here is the technique of replacing the speed v in Equation 4.14 in terms of the period T of the motion.

4.5   Tangential and Radial Acceleration

Let us consider the motion of a particle along a smooth, curved path where the velocity changes both in direction and in magnitude as described in Active Figure 4.16. In this situation, the velocity vector is always tangent to the path; the acceleration vector $\vec{a}$, however, is at some angle to the path. At each of three points Ⓐ, Ⓑ, and Ⓒ in Active Figure 4.16, we draw dashed circles that represent the curvature of the actual path at each point. The radius of the circles is equal to the path's radius of curvature at each point.

As the particle moves along the curved path in Active Figure 4.16, the direction of the total acceleration vector $\vec{a}$ changes from point to point. At any instant, this vector can be resolved into two components based on an origin at the center of the dashed circle corresponding to that instant: a radial component a_r along the radius of the circle and a tangential component a_t perpendicular to this radius. The *total* acceleration vector $\vec{a}$ can be written as the vector sum of the component vectors:

Total acceleration ▶

$$\vec{a} = \vec{a}_r + \vec{a}_t \tag{4.16}$$

The tangential acceleration component causes a change in the speed v of the particle. This component is parallel to the instantaneous velocity, and its magnitude is given by

Tangential acceleration ▶

$$a_t = \left| \frac{dv}{dt} \right| \tag{4.17}$$

The radial acceleration component arises from a change in direction of the velocity vector and is given by

Radial acceleration ▶

$$a_r = -a_c = -\frac{v^2}{r} \tag{4.18}$$

where r is the radius of curvature of the path at the point in question. We recognize the radial component of the acceleration as the centripetal acceleration discussed in Section 4.4. The negative sign in Equation 4.18 indicates that the direction of the centripetal acceleration is toward the center of the circle representing the radius of curvature. The direction is opposite that of the radial unit vector $\hat{\mathbf{r}}$, which always points away from the origin at the center of the circle.

Because $\vec{a}_r$ and $\vec{a}_t$ are perpendicular component vectors of $\vec{a}$, it follows that the magnitude of $\vec{a}$ is $a = \sqrt{a_r^2 + a_t^2}$. At a given speed, a_r is large when the radius of curvature is small (as at points Ⓐ and Ⓑ in Fig. 4.16) and small when r is large (as at point Ⓒ). The direction of $\vec{a}_t$ is either in the same direction as $\vec{v}$ (if v is increasing) or opposite $\vec{v}$ (if v is decreasing).

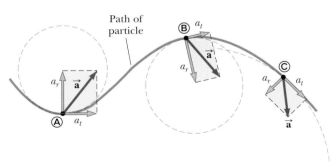

ACTIVE FIGURE 4.16

The motion of a particle along an arbitrary curved path lying in the xy plane. If the velocity vector $\vec{v}$ (always tangent to the path) changes in direction and magnitude, the components of the acceleration $\vec{a}$ are a tangential component a_t and a radial component a_r.

Sign in at www.thomsonedu.com and go to ThomsonNOW to study the acceleration components of a roller-coaster car.

In uniform circular motion, where v is constant, $a_t = 0$ and the acceleration is always completely radial as described in Section 4.4. In other words, uniform circular motion is a special case of motion along a general curved path. Furthermore, if the direction of $\vec{v}$ does not change, there is no radial acceleration and the motion is one dimensional (in this case, $a_r = 0$, but a_t may not be zero).

Quick Quiz 4.5   A particle moves along a path and its speed increases with time. **(i)** In which of the following cases are its acceleration and velocity vectors parallel? **(a)** when the path is circular   **(b)** when the path is straight   **(c)** when the path is a parabola   **(d)** never   **(ii)** From the same choices, in which case are its acceleration and velocity vectors perpendicular everywhere along the path?

| EXAMPLE 4.7 | **Over the Rise** |

A car exhibits a constant acceleration of 0.300 m/s² parallel to the roadway. The car passes over a rise in the roadway such that the top of the rise is shaped like a circle of radius 500 m. At the moment the car is at the top of the rise, its velocity vector is horizontal and has a magnitude of 6.00 m/s. What are the magnitude and direction of the total acceleration vector for the car at this instant?

(a)

SOLUTION

Conceptualize   Conceptualize the situation using Figure 4.17a and any experiences you have had in driving over rises on a roadway.

(b)

Categorize   Because the accelerating car is moving along a curved path, we categorize this problem as one involving a particle experiencing both tangential and radial acceleration. We recognize that it is a relatively simple substitution problem.

Figure 4.17   (Example 4.7) (a) A car passes over a rise that is shaped like a circle. (b) The total acceleration vector $\vec{a}$ is the sum of the tangential and radial acceleration vectors $\vec{a}_t$ and $\vec{a}_r$.

The radial acceleration is given by Equation 4.18, with $v = 6.00$ m/s and $r = 500$ m. The radial acceleration vector is directed straight downward, and the tangential acceleration vector has magnitude 0.300 m/s² and is horizontal.

Evaluate the radial acceleration:

$$a_r = -\frac{v^2}{r} = -\frac{(6.00 \text{ m/s})^2}{500 \text{ m}} = -0.072\,0 \text{ m/s}^2$$

Find the magnitude of $\vec{a}$:

$$\sqrt{a_r^2 + a_t^2} = \sqrt{(-0.072\,0 \text{ m/s}^2)^2 + (0.300 \text{ m/s}^2)^2}$$
$$= 0.309 \text{ m/s}^2$$

Find the angle ϕ (see Fig. 4.17b) between $\vec{a}$ and the horizontal:

$$\phi = \tan^{-1}\frac{a_r}{a_t} = \tan^{-1}\left(\frac{-0.072\,0 \text{ m/s}^2}{0.300 \text{ m/s}^2}\right) = -13.5°$$

4.6   Relative Velocity and Relative Acceleration

In this section, we describe how observations made by different observers in different frames of reference are related to one another. A frame of reference can be described by a Cartesian coordinate system for which an observer is at rest with respect to the origin.

Figure 4.18 Different observers make different measurements. (a) Observer A is located at the origin, and Observer B is at a position of −5. Both observers measure the position of a particle at P. (b) If both observers see themselves at the origin of their own coordinate system, they disagree on the value of the position of the particle at P.

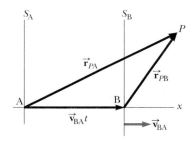

Figure 4.19 Two observers measure the speed of a man walking on a moving beltway. The woman standing on the beltway sees the man moving with a slower speed than does the woman observing from the stationary floor.

Figure 4.20 A particle located at P is described by two observers, one in the fixed frame of reference S_A and the other in the frame S_B, which moves to the right with a constant velocity $\vec{\mathbf{v}}_{BA}$. The vector $\vec{\mathbf{r}}_{PA}$ is the particle's position vector relative to S_A, and $\vec{\mathbf{r}}_{PB}$ is its position vector relative to S_B.

Galilean velocity ▶
transformation

Let us conceptualize a sample situation in which there will be different observations for different observers. Consider the two observers A and B along the number line in Figure 4.18a. Observer A is located at the origin of a one-dimensional x_A axis, while observer B is at the position $x_A = -5$. We denote the position variable as x_A because observer A is at the origin of this axis. Both observers measure the position of point P, which is located at $x_A = +5$. Suppose observer B decides that he is located at the origin of an x_B axis as in Figure 4.18b. Notice that the two observers disagree on the value of the position of point P. Observer A claims point P is located at a position with a value of +5, whereas observer B claims it is located at a position with a value of +10. Both observers are correct, even though they make different measurements. Their measurements differ because they are making the measurement from different frames of reference.

Imagine now that observer B in Figure 4.18b is moving to the right along the x_B axis. Now the two measurements are even more different. Observer A claims point P remains at rest at a position with a value of +5, whereas observer B claims the position of P continuously changes with time, even passing him and moving behind him! Again, both observers are correct, with the difference in their measurements arising from their different frames of reference.

We explore this phenomenon further by considering two observers watching a man walking on a moving beltway at an airport in Figure 4.19. The woman standing on the moving beltway sees the man moving at a normal walking speed. The woman observing from the stationary floor sees the man moving with a higher speed because the beltway speed combines with his walking speed. Both observers look at the same man and arrive at different values for his speed. Both are correct; the difference in their measurements results from the relative velocity of their frames of reference.

In a more general situation, consider a particle located at point P in Figure 4.20. Imagine that the motion of this particle is being described by two observers, observer A in a reference frame S_A fixed relative to Earth and a second observer B in a reference frame S_B moving to the right relative to S_A (and therefore relative to Earth) with a constant velocity $\vec{\mathbf{v}}_{BA}$. In this discussion of relative velocity, we use a double-subscript notation; the first subscript represents what is being observed, and the second represents who is doing the observing. Therefore, the notation $\vec{\mathbf{v}}_{BA}$ means the velocity of observer B (and the attached frame S_B) as measured by observer A. With this notation, observer B measures A to be moving to the left with a velocity $\vec{\mathbf{v}}_{AB} = -\vec{\mathbf{v}}_{BA}$. For purposes of this discussion, let us place each observer at her or his respective origin.

We define the time $t = 0$ as the instant at which the origins of the two reference frames coincide in space. Therefore, at time t, the origins of the reference frames will be separated by a distance $v_{BA}t$. We label the position P of the particle relative to observer A with the position vector $\vec{\mathbf{r}}_{PA}$ and that relative to observer B with the position vector $\vec{\mathbf{r}}_{PB}$, both at time t. From Figure 4.20, we see that the vectors $\vec{\mathbf{r}}_{PA}$ and $\vec{\mathbf{r}}_{PB}$ are related to each other through the expression

$$\vec{\mathbf{r}}_{PA} = \vec{\mathbf{r}}_{PB} + \vec{\mathbf{v}}_{BA}t \tag{4.19}$$

By differentiating Equation 4.19 with respect to time, noting that $\vec{\mathbf{v}}_{BA}$ is constant, we obtain

$$\frac{d\vec{\mathbf{r}}_{PA}}{dt} = \frac{d\vec{\mathbf{r}}_{PB}}{dt} + \vec{\mathbf{v}}_{BA}$$

$$\vec{\mathbf{u}}_{PA} = \vec{\mathbf{u}}_{PB} + \vec{\mathbf{v}}_{BA} \tag{4.20}$$

where $\vec{\mathbf{u}}_{PA}$ is the velocity of the particle at P measured by observer A and $\vec{\mathbf{u}}_{PB}$ is its velocity measured by B. (We use the symbol $\vec{\mathbf{u}}$ for particle velocity rather than $\vec{\mathbf{v}}$, which is used for the relative velocity of two reference frames.) Equations 4.19 and 4.20 are known as **Galilean transformation equations**. They relate the position and velocity of a particle as measured by observers in relative motion. Notice the pattern of the subscripts in Equation 4.20. When relative velocities are added, the inner subscripts (B) are the same and the outer ones (P, A) match the subscripts on the velocity on the left of the equation.

Although observers in two frames measure different velocities for the particle, they measure the *same acceleration* when $\vec{\mathbf{v}}_{BA}$ is constant. We can verify that by taking the time derivative of Equation 4.20:

$$\frac{d\vec{\mathbf{u}}_{PA}}{dt} = \frac{d\vec{\mathbf{u}}_{PB}}{dt} + \frac{d\vec{\mathbf{v}}_{BA}}{dt}$$

Because $\vec{\mathbf{v}}_{BA}$ is constant, $d\vec{\mathbf{v}}_{BA}/dt = 0$. Therefore, we conclude that $\vec{\mathbf{a}}_{PA} = \vec{\mathbf{a}}_{PB}$ because $\vec{\mathbf{a}}_{PA} = d\vec{\mathbf{u}}_{PA}/dt$ and $\vec{\mathbf{a}}_{PB} = d\vec{\mathbf{u}}_{PB}/dt$. That is, **the acceleration of the particle measured by an observer in one frame of reference is the same as that measured by any other observer moving with constant velocity relative to the first frame**.

EXAMPLE 4.8   A Boat Crossing a River

A boat crossing a wide river moves with a speed of 10.0 km/h relative to the water. The water in the river has a uniform speed of 5.00 km/h due east relative to the Earth.

(A) If the boat heads due north, determine the velocity of the boat relative to an observer standing on either bank.

SOLUTION

Conceptualize Imagine moving across a river while the current pushes you down the river. You will not be able to move directly across the river, but will end up downstream as suggested in Figure 4.21a.

Categorize Because of the separate velocities of you and the river, we can categorize this problem as one involving relative velocities.

(a)   (b)

Figure 4.21 (Example 4.8) (a) A boat aims directly across a river and ends up downstream. (b) To move directly across the river, the boat must aim upstream.

Analyze We know $\vec{\mathbf{v}}_{br}$, the velocity of the *boat* relative to the *river*, and $\vec{\mathbf{v}}_{rE}$, the velocity of the *river* relative to the *Earth*. What we must find is $\vec{\mathbf{v}}_{bE}$, the velocity of the *boat* relative to the *Earth*. The relationship between these three quantities is $\vec{\mathbf{v}}_{bE} = \vec{\mathbf{v}}_{br} + \vec{\mathbf{v}}_{rE}$. The terms in the equation must be manipulated as vector quantities; the vectors are shown in Figure 4.21a. The quantity $\vec{\mathbf{v}}_{br}$ is due north; $\vec{\mathbf{v}}_{rE}$ is due east; and the vector sum of the two, $\vec{\mathbf{v}}_{bE}$, is at an angle θ as defined in Figure 4.21a.

Find the speed v_{bE} of the boat relative to the Earth using the Pythagorean theorem:

$$v_{bE} = \sqrt{v_{br}^2 + v_{rE}^2} = \sqrt{(10.0 \text{ km/h})^2 + (5.00 \text{ km/h})^2}$$
$$= \boxed{11.2 \text{ km/h}}$$

Find the direction of $\vec{\mathbf{v}}_{bE}$:

$$\theta = \tan^{-1}\left(\frac{v_{rE}}{v_{br}}\right) = \tan^{-1}\left(\frac{5.00}{10.0}\right) = \boxed{26.6°}$$

Finalize The boat is moving at a speed of 11.2 km/h in the direction 26.6° east of north relative to the Earth. Notice that the speed of 11.2 km/h is faster than your boat speed of 10.0 km/h. The current velocity adds to yours to give you a larger speed. Notice in Figure 4.21a that your resultant velocity is at an angle to the direction straight across the river, so you will end up downstream, as we predicted.

(B) If the boat travels with the same speed of 10.0 km/h relative to the river and is to travel due north as shown in Figure 4.21b, what should its heading be?

SOLUTION

Conceptualize/Categorize   This question is an extension of part (A), so we have already conceptualized and categorized the problem. One new feature of the conceptualization is that we must now aim the boat upstream so as to go straight across the river.

Analyze   The analysis now involves the new triangle shown in Figure 4.21b. As in part (A), we know $\vec{v}_{rE}$ and the magnitude of the vector $\vec{v}_{br}$, and we want $\vec{v}_{bE}$ to be directed across the river. Notice the difference between the triangle in Figure 4.21a and the one in Figure 4.21b: the hypotenuse in Figure 4.21b is no longer $\vec{v}_{bE}$.

Use the Pythagorean theorem to find $\vec{v}_{bE}$:
$$v_{bE} = \sqrt{v_{br}^2 - v_{rE}^2} = \sqrt{(10.0 \text{ km/h})^2 - (5.00 \text{ km/h})^2} = 8.66 \text{ km/h}$$

Find the direction in which the boat is heading:
$$\theta = \tan^{-1}\left(\frac{v_{rE}}{v_{bE}}\right) = \tan^{-1}\left(\frac{5.00}{8.66}\right) = 30.0°$$

Finalize   The boat must head upstream so as to travel directly northward across the river. For the given situation, the boat must steer a course 30.0° west of north. For faster currents, the boat must be aimed upstream at larger angles.

What If?   Imagine that the two boats in parts (A) and (B) are racing across the river. Which boat arrives at the opposite bank first?

Answer   In part (A), the velocity of 10 km/h is aimed directly across the river. In part (B), the velocity that is directed across the river has a magnitude of only 8.66 km/h. Therefore, the boat in part (A) has a larger velocity component directly across the river and arrives first.

Summary

ThomsonNOW   Sign in at **www.thomsonedu.com** and go to ThomsonNOW to take a practice test for this chapter.

DEFINITIONS

The **displacement vector** $\Delta\vec{r}$ for a particle is the difference between its final position vector and its initial position vector:
$$\Delta\vec{r} \equiv \vec{r}_f - \vec{r}_i \tag{4.1}$$

The **average velocity** of a particle during the time interval Δt is defined as the displacement of the particle divided by the time interval:
$$\vec{v}_{avg} \equiv \frac{\Delta\vec{r}}{\Delta t} \tag{4.2}$$

The **instantaneous velocity** of a particle is defined as the limit of the average velocity as Δt approaches zero:
$$\vec{v} \equiv \lim_{\Delta t \to 0}\frac{\Delta\vec{r}}{\Delta t} = \frac{d\vec{r}}{dt} \tag{4.3}$$

The **average acceleration** of a particle is defined as the change in its instantaneous velocity vector divided by the time interval Δt during which that change occurs:
$$\vec{a}_{avg} \equiv \frac{\vec{v}_f - \vec{v}_i}{t_f - t_i} = \frac{\Delta\vec{v}}{\Delta t} \tag{4.4}$$

The **instantaneous acceleration** of a particle is defined as the limiting value of the average acceleration as Δt approaches zero:
$$\vec{a} \equiv \lim_{\Delta t \to 0}\frac{\Delta\vec{v}}{\Delta t} = \frac{d\vec{v}}{dt} \tag{4.5}$$

Projectile motion is one type of two-dimensional motion under constant acceleration, where $a_x = 0$ and $a_y = -g$.
   A particle moving in a circle of radius r with constant speed v is in **uniform circular motion**. For such a particle, the **period** of its motion is
$$T = \frac{2\pi r}{v} \tag{4.15}$$

CONCEPTS AND PRINCIPLES

If a particle moves with *constant* acceleration $\vec{a}$ and has velocity $\vec{v}_i$ and position $\vec{r}_i$ at $t = 0$, its velocity and position vectors at some later time t are

$$\vec{v}_f = \vec{v}_i + \vec{a}t \tag{4.8}$$

$$\vec{r}_f = \vec{r}_i + \vec{v}_i t + \tfrac{1}{2}\vec{a}t^2 \tag{4.9}$$

For two-dimensional motion in the xy plane under constant acceleration, each of these vector expressions is equivalent to two component expressions: one for the motion in the x direction and one for the motion in the y direction.

It is useful to think of projectile motion in terms of a combination of two analysis models: (1) the particle under constant velocity model in the x direction and (2) the particle under constant acceleration model in the vertical direction with a constant downward acceleration of magnitude $g = 9.80 \text{ m/s}^2$.

A particle in uniform circular motion undergoes a radial acceleration $\vec{a}_r$ because the direction of $\vec{v}$ changes in time. This acceleration is called **centripetal acceleration,** and its direction is always toward the center of the circle.

If a particle moves along a curved path in such a way that both the magnitude and the direction of $\vec{v}$ change in time, the particle has an acceleration vector that can be described by two component vectors: (1) a radial component vector $\vec{a}_r$ that causes the change in direction of $\vec{v}$ and (2) a tangential component vector $\vec{a}_t$ that causes the change in magnitude of $\vec{v}$. The magnitude of $\vec{a}_r$ is v^2/r, and the magnitude of $\vec{a}_t$ is $|dv/dt|$.

The velocity $\vec{u}_{PA}$ of a particle measured in a fixed frame of reference S_A can be related to the velocity $\vec{u}_{PB}$ of the same particle measured in a moving frame of reference S_B by

$$\vec{u}_{PA} = \vec{u}_{PB} + \vec{v}_{BA} \tag{4.20}$$

where $\vec{v}_{BA}$ is the velocity of S_B relative to S_A.

ANALYSIS MODEL FOR PROBLEM SOLVING

Particle in Uniform Circular Motion If a particle moves in a circular path of radius r with a constant speed v, the magnitude of its centripetal acceleration is given by

$$a_c = \frac{v^2}{r} \tag{4.14}$$

and the period of the particle's motion is given by Equation 4.15.

Questions

☐ denotes answer available in *Student Solutions Manual/Study Guide;* **O** denotes objective question

1. **O** Figure Q4.1 shows a bird's-eye view of a car going around a highway curve. As the car moves from point 1 to point 2, its speed doubles. Which vector (a) through (g) shows the direction of the car's average acceleration between these two points?

2. If you know the position vectors of a particle at two points along its path and also know the time interval during which it moved from one point to the other, can you determine the particle's instantaneous velocity? Its average velocity? Explain.

3. Construct motion diagrams showing the velocity and acceleration of a projectile at several points along its path, assuming (a) the projectile is launched horizontally

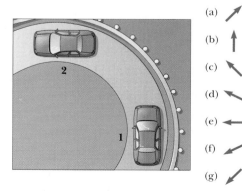

(a) ↗

(b) ↑

(c) ↖

(d) ↘

(e) ←

(f) ↙

(g) ↙

Figure Q4.1

and (b) the projectile is launched at an angle θ with the horizontal.

4. O Entering his dorm room, a student tosses his book bag to the right and upward at an angle of 45° with the horizontal. Air resistance does not affect the bag. It moves through point Ⓐ immediately after it leaves his hand, through point Ⓑ at the top of its flight, and through point Ⓒ immediately before it lands on his top bunk bed. **(i)** Rank the following horizontal and vertical velocity components from the largest to the smallest. Note that zero is larger than a negative number. If two quantities are equal, show them as equal in your list. If any quantity is equal to zero, show that fact in your list. (a) $v_{Ⓐx}$ (b) $v_{Ⓐy}$ (c) $v_{Ⓑx}$ (d) $v_{Ⓑy}$ (e) $v_{Ⓒx}$ (f) $v_{Ⓒy}$ **(ii)** Similarly, rank the following acceleration components. (a) $a_{Ⓐx}$ (b) $a_{Ⓐy}$ (c) $a_{Ⓑx}$ (d) $a_{Ⓑy}$ (e) $a_{Ⓒx}$ (f) $a_{Ⓒy}$

5. A spacecraft drifts through space at a constant velocity. Suddenly a gas leak in the side of the spacecraft gives it a constant acceleration in a direction perpendicular to the initial velocity. The orientation of the spacecraft does not change, so the acceleration remains perpendicular to the original direction of the velocity. What is the shape of the path followed by the spacecraft in this situation?

6. O In which of the following situations is the moving object appropriately modeled as a projectile? Choose all correct answers. (a) A shoe is tossed in an arbitrary direction. (b) A jet airplane crosses the sky with its engines thrusting the plane forward. (c) A rocket leaves the launch pad. (d) A rocket moves through the sky, at much less than the speed of sound, after its fuel has been used up. (e) A diver throws a stone under water.

7. A projectile is launched at some angle to the horizontal with some initial speed v_i, and air resistance is negligible. Is the projectile a freely falling body? What is its acceleration in the vertical direction? What is its acceleration in the horizontal direction?

8. O State which of the following quantities, if any, remain constant as a projectile moves through its parabolic trajectory: (a) speed (b) acceleration (c) horizontal component of velocity (d) vertical component of velocity

9. O A projectile is launched on the Earth with a certain initial velocity and moves without air resistance. Another projectile is launched with the same initial velocity on the Moon, where the acceleration due to gravity is 1/6 as large. **(i)** How does the range of the projectile on the Moon compare with that of the projectile on the Earth? (a) 1/6 as large (b) the same (c) $\sqrt{6}$ times larger (d) 6 times larger (e) 36 times larger **(ii)** How does

the maximum altitude of the projectile on the Moon compare with that of the projectile on the Earth? Choose from the same possibilities (a) through (e).

10. Explain whether or not the following particles have an acceleration: (a) a particle moving in a straight line with constant speed and (b) a particle moving around a curve with constant speed.

11. Describe how a driver can steer a car traveling at constant speed so that (a) the acceleration is zero or (b) the magnitude of the acceleration remains constant.

12. O A rubber stopper on the end of a string is swung steadily in a horizontal circle. In one trial, it moves at speed v in a circle of radius r. In a second trial, it moves at a higher speed $3v$ in a circle of radius $3r$. **(i)** In this second trial, its acceleration is (choose one) (a) the same as in the first trial (b) three times larger (c) one-third as large (d) nine times larger (e) one-ninth as large **(ii)** In the second trial, how does its period compare with its period in the first trial? Choose your answers from the same possibilities (a) through (e).

13. An ice skater is executing a figure eight, consisting of two equal, tangent circular paths. Throughout the first loop she increases her speed uniformly, and during the second loop she moves at a constant speed. Draw a motion diagram showing her velocity and acceleration vectors at several points along the path of motion.

14. O A certain light truck can go around a curve having a radius of 150 m with a maximum speed of 32.0 m/s. To have the same acceleration, at what maximum speed can it go around a curve having a radius of 75.0 m? (a) 64 m/s (b) 45 m/s (c) 32 m/s (d) 23 m/s (e) 16 m/s (f) 8 m/s

15. O Galileo suggested the idea for this question: A sailor drops a wrench from the top of a sailboat's vertical mast while the boat is moving rapidly and steadily straight forward. Where will the wrench hit the deck? (a) ahead of the base of the mast (b) at the base of the mast (c) behind the base of the mast (d) on the windward side of the base of the mast

16. O A girl, moving at 8 m/s on rollerblades, is overtaking a boy moving at 5 m/s as they both skate on a straight path. The boy tosses a ball backward toward the girl, giving it speed 12 m/s relative to him. What is the speed of the ball relative to the girl, who catches it? (a) $(8 + 5 + 12)$ m/s (b) $(8 - 5 - 12)$ m/s (c) $(8 + 5 - 12)$ m/s (d) $(8 - 5 + 12)$ m/s (e) $(-8 + 5 + 12)$ m/s

Problems

WebAssign The Problems from this chapter may be assigned online in WebAssign.

ThomsonNOW™ Sign in at **www.thomsonedu.com** and go to ThomsonNOW to assess your understanding of this chapter's topics with additional quizzing and conceptual questions.

1, 2, 3 denotes straightforward, intermediate, challenging; ☐ denotes full solution available in *Student Solutions Manual/Study Guide*; ▲ denotes coached solution with hints available at **www.thomsonedu.com;** denotes developing symbolic reasoning; ● denotes asking for qualitative reasoning; ▀ denotes computer useful in solving problem

Section 4.1 The Position, Velocity, and Acceleration Vectors

1. ▲ A motorist drives south at 20.0 m/s for 3.00 min, then turns west and travels at 25.0 m/s for 2.00 min, and finally travels northwest at 30.0 m/s for 1.00 min. For this 6.00-min trip, find (a) the total vector displacement, (b) the average speed, and (c) the average velocity. Let the positive x axis point east.

2. A golf ball is hit off a tee at the edge of a cliff. Its x and y coordinates as functions of time are given by the following expressions:

$$x = (18.0 \text{ m/s})t$$

$$y = (4.00 \text{ m/s})t - (4.90 \text{ m/s}^2)t^2$$

(a) Write a vector expression for the ball's position as a function of time, using the unit vectors $\hat{\mathbf{i}}$ and $\hat{\mathbf{j}}$. By taking derivatives, obtain expressions for (b) the velocity vector $\vec{\mathbf{v}}$ as a function of time and (c) the acceleration vector $\vec{\mathbf{a}}$ as a function of time. Next use unit–vector notation to write expressions for (d) the position, (e) the velocity, and (f) the acceleration of the golf ball, all at $t = 3.00$ s.

3. When the Sun is directly overhead, a hawk dives toward the ground with a constant velocity of 5.00 m/s at 60.0° below the horizontal. Calculate the speed of its shadow on the level ground.

4. ● The coordinates of an object moving in the xy plane vary with time according to $x = -(5.00 \text{ m}) \sin(\omega t)$ and $y = (4.00 \text{ m}) - (5.00 \text{ m})\cos(\omega t)$, where ω is a constant and t is in seconds. (a) Determine the components of velocity and components of acceleration of the object at $t = 0$. (b) Write expressions for the position vector, the velocity vector, and the acceleration vector of the object at any time $t > 0$. (c) Describe the path of the object in an xy plot.

Section 4.2 Two-Dimensional Motion with Constant Acceleration

5. A fish swimming in a horizontal plane has velocity $\vec{\mathbf{v}}_i = (4.00\hat{\mathbf{i}} + 1.00\hat{\mathbf{j}})$ m/s at a point in the ocean where the position relative to a certain rock is $\vec{\mathbf{r}}_i = (10.0\hat{\mathbf{i}} - 4.00\hat{\mathbf{j}})$ m. After the fish swims with constant acceleration for 20.0 s, its velocity is $\vec{\mathbf{v}} = (20.0\hat{\mathbf{i}} - 5.00\hat{\mathbf{j}})$ m/s. (a) What are the components of the acceleration? (b) What is the direction of the acceleration with respect to unit vector $\hat{\mathbf{i}}$? (c) If the fish maintains constant acceleration, where is it at $t = 25.0$ s, and in what direction is it moving?

6. The vector position of a particle varies in time according to the expression $\vec{\mathbf{r}} = (3.00\hat{\mathbf{i}} - 6.00t^2\hat{\mathbf{j}})$ m. (a) Find expressions for the velocity and acceleration of the particle as functions of time. (b) Determine the particle's position and velocity at $t = 1.00$ s.

7. *What if the acceleration is not constant?* A particle starts from the origin with velocity $5\hat{\mathbf{i}}$ m/s at $t = 0$ and moves in the xy plane with a varying acceleration given by $\vec{\mathbf{a}} = (6\sqrt{t}\hat{\mathbf{j}})$ m/s², where t is in s. (a) Determine the vector velocity of the particle as a function of time. (b) Determine the position of the particle as a function of time.

8. A particle initially located at the origin has an acceleration of $\vec{\mathbf{a}} = 3.00\hat{\mathbf{j}}$ m/s² and an initial velocity of $\vec{\mathbf{v}}_i = 5.00\hat{\mathbf{i}}$ m/s.

Find (a) the vector position and velocity of the particle at any time t and (b) the coordinates and speed of the particle at $t = 2.00$ s.

Section 4.3 Projectile Motion

Note: Ignore air resistance in all problems. Take $g = 9.80$ m/s² at the Earth's surface.

9. ▲ In a local bar, a customer slides an empty beer mug down the counter for a refill. The bartender is momentarily distracted and does not see the mug, which slides off the counter and strikes the floor 1.40 m from the base of the counter. If the height of the counter is 0.860 m, (a) with what velocity did the mug leave the counter? (b) What was the direction of the mug's velocity just before it hit the floor?

10. In a local bar, a customer slides an empty beer mug down the counter for a refill. The bartender is just deciding to go home and rethink his life, so he does not see the mug. It slides off the counter and strikes the floor at distance d from the base of the counter. The height of the counter is h. (a) With what velocity did the mug leave the counter? (b) What was the direction of the mug's velocity just before it hit the floor?

11. To start an avalanche on a mountain slope, an artillery shell is fired with an initial velocity of 300 m/s at 55.0° above the horizontal. It explodes on the mountainside 42.0 s after firing. What are the x and y coordinates of the shell where it explodes, relative to its firing point?

12. ● A rock is thrown upward from the level ground in such a way that the maximum height of its flight is equal to its horizontal range d. (a) At what angle θ is the rock thrown? (b) **What If?** Would your answer to part (a) be different on a different planet? Explain. (c) What is the range d_{max} the rock can attain if it is launched at the same speed but at the optimal angle for maximum range?

13. A projectile is fired in such a way that its horizontal range is equal to three times its maximum height. What is the angle of projection?

14. A firefighter, a distance d from a burning building, directs a stream of water from a fire hose at angle θ_i above the horizontal as shown in Figure P4.14. If the initial speed of the stream is v_i, at what height h does the water strike the building?

Figure P4.14

15. A ball is tossed from an upper-story window of a building. The ball is given an initial velocity of 8.00 m/s at an angle of 20.0° below the horizontal. It strikes the ground 3.00 s later. (a) How far horizontally from the base of the building does the ball strike the ground? (b) Find the height from which the ball was thrown. (c) How long does it take the ball to reach a point 10.0 m below the level of launching?

16. A landscape architect is planning an artificial waterfall in a city park. Water flowing at 1.70 m/s will leave the end of a horizontal channel at the top of a vertical wall 2.35 m high, and from there the water falls into a pool. (a) Will the space behind the waterfall be wide enough for a pedestrian walkway? (b) To sell her plan to the city council, the architect wants to build a model to standard scale, one-twelfth actual size. How fast should the water flow in the channel in the model?

17. ▲ A placekicker must kick a football from a point 36.0 m (about 40 yards) from the goal, and half the crowd hopes the ball will clear the crossbar, which is 3.05 m high. When kicked, the ball leaves the ground with a speed of 20.0 m/s at an angle of 53.0° to the horizontal. (a) By how much does the ball clear or fall short of clearing the crossbar? (b) Does the ball approach the crossbar while still rising or while falling?

18. A dive-bomber has a velocity of 280 m/s at an angle θ below the horizontal. When the altitude of the aircraft is 2.15 km, it releases a bomb, which subsequently hits a target on the ground. The magnitude of the displacement from the point of release of the bomb to the target is 3.25 km. Find the angle θ.

19. A playground is on the flat roof of a city school, 6.00 m above the street below. The vertical wall of the building is 7.00 m high, forming a 1 m-high railing around the playground. A ball has fallen to the street below, and a passerby returns it by launching it at an angle of 53.0° above the horizontal at a point 24.0 m from the base of the building wall. The ball takes 2.20 s to reach a point vertically above the wall. (a) Find the speed at which the ball was launched. (b) Find the vertical distance by which the ball clears the wall. (c) Find the distance from the wall to the point on the roof where the ball lands.

20. A basketball star covers 2.80 m horizontally in a jump to dunk the ball (Fig. P4.20a). His motion through space can be modeled precisely as that of a particle at his *center of mass*, which we will define in Chapter 9. His center of mass is at elevation 1.02 m when he leaves the floor. It reaches a maximum height of 1.85 m above the floor and is at elevation 0.900 m when he touches down again. Determine (a) his time of flight (his "hang time"), (b) his horizontal and (c) vertical velocity components at the instant of takeoff, and (d) his takeoff angle. (e) For comparison, determine the hang time of a whitetail deer mak-

ing a jump (Fig. P4.20b) with center-of-mass elevations $y_i = 1.20$ m, $y_{max} = 2.50$ m, and $y_f = 0.700$ m.

21. A soccer player kicks a rock horizontally off a 40.0-m-high cliff into a pool of water. If the player hears the sound of the splash 3.00 s later, what was the initial speed given to the rock? Assume the speed of sound in air is 343 m/s.

22. ● The motion of a human body through space can be modeled as the motion of a particle at the body's center of mass, as we will study in Chapter 9. The components of the position of an athlete's center of mass from the beginning to the end of a certain jump are described by the two equations

$$x_f = 0 + (11.2 \text{ m/s})(\cos 18.5°)t$$

$$0.360 \text{ m} =$$
$$0.840 \text{ m} + (11.2 \text{ m/s})(\sin 18.5°)t - \tfrac{1}{2}(9.80 \text{ m/s}^2)t^2$$

where t is the time at which the athlete lands after taking off at $t = 0$. Identify (a) his vector position and (b) his vector velocity at the takeoff point. (c) The world long-jump record is 8.95 m. How far did the athlete jump in this problem? (d) Describe the shape of the trajectory of his center of mass.

23. A fireworks rocket explodes at height h, the peak of its vertical trajectory. It throws out burning fragments in all directions, but all at the same speed v. Pellets of solidified metal fall to the ground without air resistance. Find the smallest angle that the final velocity of an impacting fragment makes with the horizontal.

Section 4.4 The Particle in Uniform Circular Motion

Note: Problems 10 and 12 in Chapter 6 can also be assigned with this section and the next.

24. From information on the endpapers of this book, compute the radial acceleration of a point on the surface of the Earth at the equator, owing to the rotation of the Earth about its axis.

25. ▲ The athlete shown in Figure P4.25 rotates a 1.00-kg discus along a circular path of radius 1.06 m. The maximum speed of the discus is 20.0 m/s. Determine the magnitude of the maximum radial acceleration of the discus.

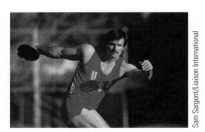

Figure P4.25

26. As their booster rockets separate, space shuttle astronauts typically feel accelerations up to 3g, where $g = 9.80$ m/s^2. In their training, astronauts ride in a device in which they experience such an acceleration as a centripetal acceleration. Specifically, the astronaut is fastened securely at the end of a mechanical arm that then turns at constant

(a)

(b)

Figure P4.20

speed in a horizontal circle. Determine the rotation rate, in revolutions per second, required to give an astronaut a centripetal acceleration of $3.00g$ while in circular motion with radius 9.45 m.

27. Young David who slew Goliath experimented with slings before tackling the giant. He found he could revolve a sling of length 0.600 m at the rate of 8.00 rev/s. If he increased the length to 0.900 m, he could revolve the sling only 6.00 times per second. (a) Which rate of rotation gives the greater speed for the stone at the end of the sling? (b) What is the centripetal acceleration of the stone at 8.00 rev/s? (c) What is the centripetal acceleration at 6.00 rev/s?

Section 4.5 Tangential and Radial Acceleration

28. ● (a) Could a particle moving with instantaneous speed 3.00 m/s on a path with radius of curvature 2.00 m have an acceleration of magnitude 6.00 m/s²? (b) Could it have $|\vec{\mathbf{a}}| = 4.00$ m/s²? In each case, if the answer is yes, explain how it can happen; if the answer is no, explain why not.

29. A train slows down as it rounds a sharp horizontal turn, slowing from 90.0 km/h to 50.0 km/h in the 15.0 s that it takes to round the bend. The radius of the curve is 150 m. Compute the acceleration at the moment the train speed reaches 50.0 km/h. Assume it continues to slow down at this time at the same rate.

30. A ball swings in a vertical circle at the end of a rope 1.50 m long. When the ball is 36.9° past the lowest point on its way up, its total acceleration is $(-22.5\hat{\mathbf{i}} + 20.2\hat{\mathbf{j}})$ m/s². At that instant, (a) sketch a vector diagram showing the components of its acceleration, (b) determine the magnitude of its radial acceleration, and (c) determine the speed and velocity of the ball.

31. Figure P4.31 represents the total acceleration of a particle moving clockwise in a circle of radius 2.50 m at a certain instant of time. At this instant, find (a) the radial acceleration, (b) the speed of the particle, and (c) its tangential acceleration.

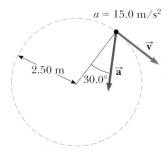

Figure P4.31

32. A race car starts from rest on a circular track. The car increases its speed at a constant rate a_t as it goes once around the track. Find the angle that the total acceleration of the car makes—with the radius connecting the center of the track and the car—at the moment the car completes the circle.

Section 4.6 Relative Velocity and Relative Acceleration

33. A car travels due east with a speed of 50.0 km/h. Raindrops are falling at a constant speed vertically with respect to the Earth. The traces of the rain on the side windows of the car make an angle of 60.0° with the vertical. Find the velocity of the rain with respect to (a) the car and (b) the Earth.

34. Heather in her Corvette accelerates at the rate of $(300\hat{\mathbf{i}} - 2.00\hat{\mathbf{j}})$ m/s², while Jill in her Jaguar accelerates at $(1.00\hat{\mathbf{i}} + 3.00\hat{\mathbf{j}})$ m/s². They both start from rest at the origin of an xy coordinate system. After 5.00 s, (a) what is Heather's speed with respect to Jill, (b) how far apart are they, and (c) what is Heather's acceleration relative to Jill?

35. A river has a steady speed of 0.500 m/s. A student swims upstream a distance of 1.00 km and swims back to the starting point. If the student can swim at a speed of 1.20 m/s in still water, how long does the trip take? Compare this answer with the time interval required for the trip if the water were still.

36. How long does it take an automobile traveling in the left lane at 60.0 km/h to pull alongside a car traveling in the same direction in the right lane at 40.0 km/h if the cars' front bumpers are initially 100 m apart?

37. Two swimmers, Alan and Beth, start together at the same point on the bank of a wide stream that flows with a speed v. Both move at the same speed c (where $c > v$), relative to the water. Alan swims downstream a distance L and then upstream the same distance. Beth swims so that her motion relative to the Earth is perpendicular to the banks of the stream. She swims the distance L and then back the same distance so that both swimmers return to the starting point. Which swimmer returns first? *Note:* First guess the answer.

38. ● A farm truck moves due north with a constant velocity of 9.50 m/s on a limitless horizontal stretch of road. A boy riding on the back of the truck throws a can of soda upward and catches the projectile at the same location on the truck bed, but 16.0 m farther down the road. (a) In the frame of reference of the truck, at what angle to the vertical does the boy throw the can? (b) What is the initial speed of the can relative to the truck? (c) What is the shape of the can's trajectory as seen by the boy? (d) An observer on the ground watches the boy throw the can and catch it. In this observer's ground frame of reference, describe the shape of the can's path and determine the initial velocity of the can.

39. A science student is riding on a flatcar of a train traveling along a straight horizontal track at a constant speed of 10.0 m/s. The student throws a ball into the air along a path that he judges to make an initial angle of 60.0° with the horizontal and to be in line with the track. The student's professor, who is standing on the ground nearby, observes the ball to rise vertically. How high does she see the ball rise?

40. ● A bolt drops from the ceiling of a moving train car that is accelerating northward at a rate of 2.50 m/s². (a) What is the acceleration of the bolt relative to the train car? (b) What is the acceleration of the bolt relative to the Earth? (c) Describe the trajectory of the bolt as seen by

an observer inside the train car. (d) Describe the trajectory of the bolt as seen by an observer fixed on the Earth.

41. A Coast Guard cutter detects an unidentified ship at a distance of 20.0 km in the direction 15.0° east of north. The ship is traveling at 26.0 km/h on a course at 40.0° east of north. The Coast Guard wishes to send a speedboat to intercept the vessel and investigate it. If the speedboat travels 50.0 km/h, in what direction should it head? Express the direction as a compass bearing with respect to due north.

Additional Problems

42. *The "Vomit Comet."* In zero-gravity astronaut training and equipment testing, NASA flies a KC135A aircraft along a parabolic flight path. As shown in Figure P4.42, the aircraft climbs from 24 000 ft to 31 000 ft, where it enters the zero-g parabola with a velocity of 143 m/s nose high at 45.0° and exits with velocity 143 m/s at 45.0° nose low. During this portion of the flight, the aircraft and objects inside its padded cabin are in free fall; they have gone ballistic. The aircraft then pulls out of the dive with an upward acceleration of 0.800g, moving in a vertical circle with radius 4.13 km. (During this portion of the flight, occupants of the aircraft perceive an acceleration of 1.8g.) What are the aircraft's (a) speed and (b) altitude at the top of the maneuver? (c) What is the time interval spent in zero gravity? (d) What is the speed of the aircraft at the bottom of the flight path?

43. An athlete throws a basketball upward from the ground, giving it speed 10.6 m/s at an angle of 55.0° above the horizontal. (a) What is the acceleration of the basketball at the highest point in its trajectory? (b) On its way down, the basketball hits the rim of the basket, 3.05 m above the floor. It bounces straight up with one-half the speed with which it hit the rim. What height above the floor does the basketball reach on this bounce?

44. ● (a) An athlete throws a basketball toward the east, with initial speed 10.6 m/s at an angle of 55.0° above the horizontal. Just as the basketball reaches the highest point of its trajectory, it hits an eagle (the mascot of the opposing team) flying horizontally west. The ball bounces back horizontally west with 1.50 times the speed it had just before their collision. How far behind the player who threw it does the ball land? (b) This situation is not covered in the

rule book, so the officials turn the clock back to repeat this part of the game. The player throws the ball in the same way. The eagle is thoroughly annoyed and this time intercepts the ball so that, at the same point in its trajectory, the ball again bounces from the bird's beak with 1.50 times its impact speed, moving west at some nonzero angle with the horizontal. Now the ball hits the player's head, at the same location where her hands had released it. Is the angle necessarily positive (that is, above the horizontal), necessarily negative (below the horizontal), or could it be either? Give a convincing argument, either mathematical or conceptual, for your answer.

45. Manny Ramírez hits a home run so that the baseball just clears the top row of bleachers, 21.0 m high, located 130 m from home plate. The ball is hit at an angle of 35.0° to the horizontal, and air resistance is negligible. Find (a) the initial speed of the ball, (b) the time interval required for the ball to reach the bleachers, and (c) the velocity components and the speed of the ball when it passes over the top row. Assume the ball is hit at a height of 1.00 m above the ground.

46. As some molten metal splashes, one droplet flies off to the east with initial velocity v_i at angle θ_i above the horizontal and another droplet flies off to the west with the same speed at the same angle above the horizontal as shown in Figure P4.46. In terms of v_i and θ_i, find the distance between the droplets as a function of time.

Figure P4.46

47. A pendulum with a cord of length $r = 1.00$ m swings in a vertical plane (Fig. P4.47). When the pendulum is in the two horizontal positions $\theta = 90.0°$ and $\theta = 270°$, its speed is 5.00 m/s. (a) Find the magnitude of the radial acceleration and tangential acceleration for these positions. (b) Draw vector diagrams to determine the direction of the total acceleration for these two positions. (c) Calculate the magnitude and direction of the total acceleration.

(a)

Figure P4.42

(b)

2 = intermediate;   3 = challenging;   □ = SSM/SG;   ▲ = ThomsonNOW;   ▬ = symbolic reasoning;   ● = qualitative reasoning

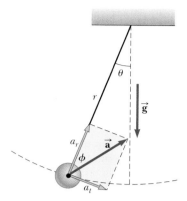

Figure P4.47

no bounce (green path)? (b) Determine the ratio of the time interval for the one-bounce throw to the flight time for the no-bounce throw.

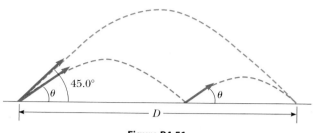

Figure P4.51

48. An astronaut on the surface of the Moon fires a cannon to launch an experiment package, which leaves the barrel moving horizontally. (a) What must be the muzzle speed of the package so that it travels completely around the Moon and returns to its original location? (b) How long does this trip around the Moon take? Assume the free-fall acceleration on the Moon is one-sixth of that on the Earth.

49. ● A projectile is launched from the point $(x = 0, y = 0)$ with velocity $(12.0\hat{\mathbf{i}} + 49.0\hat{\mathbf{j}})$ m/s, at $t = 0$. (a) Make a table listing the projectile's distance $|\vec{\mathbf{r}}|$ from the origin at the end of each second thereafter, for $0 \le t \le 10$ s. Tabulating the x and y coordinates and the components of velocity v_x and v_y may also be useful. (b) Observe that the projectile's distance from its starting point increases with time, goes through a maximum, and starts to decrease. Prove that the distance is a maximum when the position vector is perpendicular to the velocity. *Suggestion:* Argue that if $\vec{\mathbf{v}}$ is not perpendicular to $\vec{\mathbf{r}}$, then $|\vec{\mathbf{r}}|$ must be increasing or decreasing. (c) Determine the magnitude of the maximum distance. Explain your method.

50. ● A spring cannon is located at the edge of a table that is 1.20 m above the floor. A steel ball is launched from the cannon with speed v_0 at 35.0° above the horizontal. (a) Find the horizontal displacement component of the ball to the point where it lands on the floor as a function of v_0. We write this function as $x(v_0)$. Evaluate x for (b) $v_0 = 0.100$ m/s and for (c) $v_0 = 100$ m/s. (d) Assume v_0 is close to zero but not equal to zero. Show that one term in the answer to part (a) dominates so that the function $x(v_0)$ reduces to a simpler form. (e) If v_0 is very large, what is the approximate form of $x(v_0)$? (f) Describe the overall shape of the graph of the function $x(v_0)$. *Suggestion:* As practice, you could do part (b) before doing part (a).

51. When baseball players throw the ball in from the outfield, they usually allow it to take one bounce before it reaches the infield on the theory that the ball arrives sooner that way. Suppose the angle at which a bounced ball leaves the ground is the same as the angle at which the outfielder threw it as shown in Figure P4.51, but the ball's speed after the bounce is one-half of what it was before the bounce. (a) Assume the ball is always thrown with the same initial speed. At what angle θ should the fielder throw the ball to make it go the same distance D with one bounce (blue path) as a ball thrown upward at 45.0° with

52. A truck loaded with cannonball watermelons stops suddenly to avoid running over the edge of a washed-out bridge (Fig. P4.52). The quick stop causes a number of melons to fly off the truck. One melon rolls over the edge with an initial speed $v_i = 10.0$ m/s in the horizontal direction. A cross section of the bank has the shape of the bottom half of a parabola with its vertex at the edge of the road and with the equation $y^2 = 16x$, where x and y are measured in meters. What are the x and y coordinates of the melon when it splatters on the bank?

$v_i = 10$ m/s

Figure P4.52

53. Your grandfather is copilot of a bomber, flying horizontally over level terrain, with a speed of 275 m/s relative to the ground, at an altitude of 3 000 m. (a) The bombardier releases one bomb. How far will the bomb travel horizontally between its release and its impact on the ground? Ignore the effects of air resistance. (b) Firing from the people on the ground suddenly incapacitates the bombardier before he can call, "Bombs away!" Consequently, the pilot maintains the plane's original course, altitude, and speed through a storm of flak. Where will the plane be when the bomb hits the ground? (c) The plane has a telescopic bombsight set so that the bomb hits the target seen in the sight at the moment of release. At what angle from the vertical was the bombsight set?

54. A person standing at the top of a hemispherical rock of radius R kicks a ball (initially at rest on the top of the rock) to give it horizontal velocity $\vec{\mathbf{v}}_i$ as shown in Figure P4.54. (a) What must be its minimum initial speed if the ball is never to hit the rock after it is kicked? (b) With this initial speed, how far from the base of the rock does the ball hit the ground?

2 = intermediate; 3 = challenging; □ = SSM/SG; ▲ = ThomsonNOW;   = symbolic reasoning; ● = qualitative reasoning

Figure P4.54

55. A hawk is flying horizontally at 10.0 m/s in a straight line, 200 m above the ground. A mouse it has been carrying struggles free from its talons. The hawk continues on its path at the same speed for 2.00 s before attempting to retrieve its prey. To accomplish the retrieval, it dives in a straight line at constant speed and recaptures the mouse 3.00 m above the ground. (a) Assuming no air resistance acts on the mouse, find the diving speed of the hawk. (b) What angle did the hawk make with the horizontal during its descent? (c) For how long did the mouse "enjoy" free fall?

56. The determined coyote is out once more in pursuit of the elusive roadrunner. The coyote wears a pair of Acme jet-powered roller skates, which provide a constant horizontal acceleration of 15.0 m/s^2 (Fig. P4.56). The coyote starts at rest 70.0 m from the brink of a cliff at the instant the roadrunner zips past in the direction of the cliff. (a) Assuming the roadrunner moves with constant speed, determine the minimum speed it must have to reach the cliff before the coyote. At the edge of the cliff, the roadrunner escapes by making a sudden turn, while the coyote continues straight ahead. The coyote's skates remain horizontal and continue to operate while the coyote is in flight, so its acceleration while in the air is $(15.0\hat{\mathbf{i}} - 9.80\hat{\mathbf{j}})$ m/s^2. (b) The cliff is 100 m above the flat floor of a canyon. Determine where the coyote lands in the canyon. (c) Determine the components of the coyote's impact velocity.

Coyote   Roadrunner
stupidus   delightus

Figure P4.56

57. ▲ A car is parked on a steep incline overlooking the ocean, where the incline makes an angle of 37.0° below the horizontal. The negligent driver leaves the car in neutral, and the parking brakes are defective. Starting from rest at $t = 0$, the car rolls down the incline with a constant acceleration of 4.00 m/s^2, traveling 50.0 m to the edge of a vertical cliff. The cliff is 30.0 m above the ocean. Find (a) the speed of the car when it reaches the edge of the cliff and the time interval elapsed when it arrives there,

(b) the velocity of the car when it lands in the ocean, (c) the total time interval that the car is in motion, and (d) the position of the car when it lands in the ocean, relative to the base of the cliff.

58. ● Do not hurt yourself; do not strike your hand against anything. Within these limitations, describe what you do to give your hand a large acceleration. Compute an order-of-magnitude estimate of this acceleration, stating the quantities you measure or estimate and their values.

59. ● A skier leaves the ramp of a ski jump with a velocity of 10.0 m/s, 15.0° above the horizontal, as shown in Figure P4.59. The slope is inclined at 50.0°, and air resistance is negligible. Find (a) the distance from the ramp to where the jumper lands and (b) the velocity components just before the landing. (How do you think the results might be affected if air resistance were included? Note that jumpers lean forward in the shape of an airfoil, with their hands at their sides, to increase their distance. Why does this method work?)

10.0 m/s
15.0°

50.0°

Figure P4.59

60. An angler sets out upstream from Metaline Falls on the Pend Oreille River in northwestern Washington State. His small boat, powered by an outboard motor, travels at a constant speed v in still water. The water flows at a lower constant speed v_w. He has traveled upstream for 2.00 km when his ice chest falls out of the boat. He notices that the chest is missing only after he has gone upstream for another 15.0 min. At that point, he turns around and heads back downstream, all the time traveling at the same speed relative to the water. He catches up with the floating ice chest just as it is about to go over the falls at his starting point. How fast is the river flowing? Solve this problem in two ways. (a) First, use the Earth as a reference frame. With respect to the Earth, the boat travels upstream at speed $v - v_w$ and downstream at $v + v_w$. (b) A second much simpler and more elegant solution is obtained by using the water as the reference frame. This approach has important applications in many more complicated problems; examples are calculating the motion of rockets and satellites and analyzing the scattering of subatomic particles from massive targets.

61. An enemy ship is on the east side of a mountainous island as shown in Figure P4.61. The enemy ship has maneuvered to within 2 500 m of the 1 800-m-high mountain peak and can shoot projectiles with an initial speed of 250 m/s. If the western shoreline is horizontally 300 m from the peak, what are the distances from the western shore at which a ship can be safe from the bombardment of the enemy ship?

Figure P4.61

62. In the **What If?** section of Example 4.5, it was claimed that the maximum range of a ski jumper occurs for a launch angle θ given by

$$\theta = 45° - \frac{\phi}{2}$$

where φ is the angle that the hill makes with the horizontal in Figure 4.14. Prove this claim by deriving this equation.

Answers to Quick Quizzes

4.1 (a). Because acceleration occurs whenever the velocity changes in any way—with an increase or decrease in speed, a change in direction, or both—all three controls are accelerators. The gas pedal causes the car to speed up; the brake pedal causes the car to slow down. The steering wheel changes the direction of the velocity vector.

4.2 (i), (b). At only one point—the peak of the trajectory—are the velocity and acceleration vectors perpendicular to each other. The velocity vector is horizontal at that point, and the acceleration vector is downward. (ii), (a). The acceleration vector is always directed downward. The velocity vector is never vertical and parallel to the acceleration vector if the object follows a path such as that in Figure 4.8.

4.3 15°, 30°, 45°, 60°, 75°. The greater the maximum height, the longer it takes the projectile to reach that altitude and then fall back down from it. So, as the launch angle increases, the time of flight increases.

4.4 (i), (d). Because the centripetal acceleration is proportional to the square of the speed of the particle, doubling the speed increases the acceleration by a factor of 4. (ii), (b). The period is inversely proportional to the speed of the particle.

4.5 (i), (b). The velocity vector is tangent to the path. If the acceleration vector is to be parallel to the velocity vector, it must also be tangent to the path, which requires that the acceleration vector have no component perpendicular to the path. If the path were to change direction, the acceleration vector would have a radial component, perpendicular to the path. Therefore, the path must remain straight. (ii), (d). If the acceleration vector is to be perpendicular to the velocity vector, it must have no component tangent to the path. On the other hand, if the speed is changing, there *must* be a component of the acceleration tangent to the path. Therefore, the velocity and acceleration vectors are never perpendicular in this situation. They can only be perpendicular if there is no change in the speed.

A small tugboat exerts a force on a large ship, causing it to move. How can such a small boat move such a large object? (Steve Raymer/CORBIS)

5 The Laws of Motion

In Chapters 2 and 4, we described the motion of an object in terms of its position, velocity, and acceleration without considering what might influence that motion. Now we consider the external influence: What might cause one object to remain at rest and another object to accelerate? The two main factors we need to consider are the forces acting on an object and the mass of the object. In this chapter, we begin our study of *dynamics* by discussing the three basic laws of motion, which deal with forces and masses and were formulated more than three centuries ago by Isaac Newton.

5.1 The Concept of Force

Everyone has a basic understanding of the concept of force from everyday experience. When you push your empty dinner plate away, you exert a force on it. Similarly, you exert a force on a ball when you throw or kick it. In these examples, the word *force* refers to an interaction with an object by means of muscular activity and some change in the object's velocity. Forces do not always cause motion, however. For example, when you are sitting, a gravitational force acts on your body and yet you remain stationary. As a second example, you can push (in other words, exert a force) on a large boulder and not be able to move it.

What force (if any) causes the Moon to orbit the Earth? Newton answered this and related questions by stating that forces are what cause any change in the velocity of an object. The Moon's velocity is not constant because it moves in a nearly circular orbit around the Earth. This change in velocity is caused by the gravitational force exerted by the Earth on the Moon.

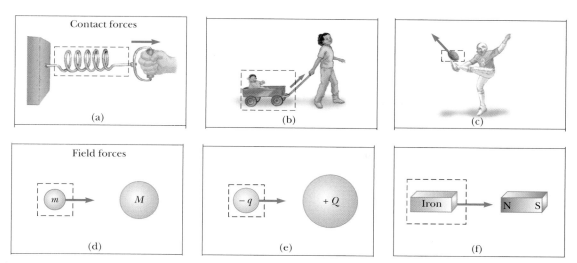

Figure 5.1   Some examples of applied forces. In each case, a force is exerted on the object within the boxed area. Some agent in the environment external to the boxed area exerts a force on the object.

When a coiled spring is pulled, as in Figure 5.1a, the spring stretches. When a stationary cart is pulled, as in Figure 5.1b, the cart moves. When a football is kicked, as in Figure 5.1c, it is both deformed and set in motion. These situations are all examples of a class of forces called *contact forces*. That is, they involve physical contact between two objects. Other examples of contact forces are the force exerted by gas molecules on the walls of a container and the force exerted by your feet on the floor.

Another class of forces, known as *field forces*, does not involve physical contact between two objects. These forces act through empty space. The gravitational force of attraction between two objects with mass, illustrated in Figure 5.1d, is an example of this class of force. The gravitational force keeps objects bound to the Earth and the planets in orbit around the Sun. Another common field force is the electric force that one electric charge exerts on another (Fig. 5.1e). As an example, these charges might be those of the electron and proton that form a hydrogen atom. A third example of a field force is the force a bar magnet exerts on a piece of iron (Fig. 5.1f).

The distinction between contact forces and field forces is not as sharp as you may have been led to believe by the previous discussion. When examined at the atomic level, all the forces we classify as contact forces turn out to be caused by electric (field) forces of the type illustrated in Figure 5.1e. Nevertheless, in developing models for macroscopic phenomena, it is convenient to use both classifications of forces. The only known *fundamental* forces in nature are all field forces: (1) *gravitational forces* between objects, (2) *electromagnetic forces* between electric charges, (3) *strong forces* between subatomic particles, and (4) *weak forces* that arise in certain radioactive decay processes. In classical physics, we are concerned only with gravitational and electromagnetic forces. We will discuss strong and weak forces in Chapter 46.

The Vector Nature of Force

It is possible to use the deformation of a spring to measure force. Suppose a vertical force is applied to a spring scale that has a fixed upper end as shown in Figure 5.2a (page 102). The spring elongates when the force is applied, and a pointer on the scale reads the value of the applied force. We can calibrate the spring by defining a reference force $\vec{F}_1$ as the force that produces a pointer reading of 1.00 cm. If we now apply a different downward force $\vec{F}_2$ whose magnitude is twice that of the reference force $\vec{F}_1$ as seen in Figure 5.2b, the pointer moves to 2.00 cm. Figure 5.2c shows that the combined effect of the two collinear forces is the sum of the effects of the individual forces.

Now suppose the two forces are applied simultaneously with $\vec{F}_1$ downward and $\vec{F}_2$ horizontal as illustrated in Figure 5.2d. In this case, the pointer reads 2.24 cm.

ISAAC NEWTON
English physicist and mathematician
(1642–1727)
Isaac Newton was one of the most brilliant scientists in history. Before the age of 30, he formulated the basic concepts and laws of mechanics, discovered the law of universal gravitation, and invented the mathematical methods of calculus. As a consequence of his theories, Newton was able to explain the motions of the planets, the ebb and flow of the tides, and many special features of the motions of the Moon and the Earth. He also interpreted many fundamental observations concerning the nature of light. His contributions to physical theories dominated scientific thought for two centuries and remain important today.

Figure 5.2   The vector nature of a force is tested with a spring scale. (a) A downward force $\vec{\mathbf{F}}_1$ elongates the spring 1.00 cm. (b) A downward force $\vec{\mathbf{F}}_2$ elongates the spring 2.00 cm. (c) When $\vec{\mathbf{F}}_1$ and $\vec{\mathbf{F}}_2$ are applied simultaneously, the spring elongates by 3.00 cm. (d) When $\vec{\mathbf{F}}_1$ is downward and $\vec{\mathbf{F}}_2$ is horizontal, the combination of the two forces elongates the spring 2.24 cm.

The single force $\vec{\mathbf{F}}$ that would produce this same reading is the sum of the two vectors $\vec{\mathbf{F}}_1$ and $\vec{\mathbf{F}}_2$ as described in Figure 5.2d. That is, $|\vec{\mathbf{F}}| = \sqrt{F_1^2 + F_2^2} = 2.24$ units, and its direction is $\theta = \tan^{-1}(-0.500) = -26.6°$. **Because forces have been experimentally verified to behave as vectors, you must use the rules of vector addition to obtain the net force on an object.**

5.2   Newton's First Law and Inertial Frames

We begin our study of forces by imagining some physical situations involving a puck on a perfectly level air hockey table (Fig. 5.3). You expect that the puck will remain where it is placed. Now imagine your air hockey table is located on a train moving with constant velocity along a perfectly smooth track. If the puck is placed on the table, the puck again remains where it is placed. If the train were to accelerate, however, the puck would start moving along the table opposite the direction of the train's acceleration, just as a set of papers on your dashboard falls onto the front seat of your car when you step on the accelerator.

As we saw in Section 4.6, a moving object can be observed from any number of reference frames. **Newton's first law of motion**, sometimes called the *law of inertia*, defines a special set of reference frames called *inertial frames*. This law can be stated as follows:

Figure 5.3   On an air hockey table, air blown through holes in the surface allows the puck to move almost without friction. If the table is not accelerating, a puck placed on the table will remain at rest.

Newton's first law ▶

> If an object does not interact with other objects, it is possible to identify a reference frame in which the object has zero acceleration.

Inertial frame of reference ▶

Such a reference frame is called an **inertial frame of reference**. When the puck is on the air hockey table located on the ground, you are observing it from an inertial reference frame; there are no horizontal interactions of the puck with any other objects, and you observe it to have zero acceleration in that direction. When you are on the train moving at constant velocity, you are also observing the puck from an inertial reference frame. **Any reference frame that moves with constant velocity relative to an inertial frame is itself an inertial frame.** When you and the train accelerate, however, you are observing the puck from a **noninertial reference frame** because the train is accelerating relative to the inertial reference frame of the Earth's surface. While the puck appears to be accelerating according to your observations, a reference frame can be identified in which the puck has zero acceleration. For example, an observer standing outside the train on the ground sees the puck moving with the same velocity as the train had before it started to accelerate (because there is almost no friction to "tie" the puck and the train together). Therefore, Newton's first law is still satisfied even though your observations as a rider on the train show an apparent acceleration relative to you.

A reference frame that moves with constant velocity relative to the distant stars is the best approximation of an inertial frame, and for our purposes we can consider the Earth as being such a frame. The Earth is not really an inertial frame because of its orbital motion around the Sun and its rotational motion about its own axis, both of which involve centripetal accelerations. These accelerations are small compared with g, however, and can often be neglected. For this reason, we model the Earth as an inertial frame, along with any other frame attached to it.

Let us assume we are observing an object from an inertial reference frame. (We will return to observations made in noninertial reference frames in Section 6.3.) Before about 1600, scientists believed that the natural state of matter was the state of rest. Observations showed that moving objects eventually stopped moving. Galileo was the first to take a different approach to motion and the natural state of matter. He devised thought experiments and concluded that it is not the nature of an object to stop once set in motion: rather, it is its nature to *resist changes in its motion*. In his words, "Any velocity once imparted to a moving body will be rigidly maintained as long as the external causes of retardation are removed." For example, a spacecraft drifting through empty space with its engine turned off will keep moving forever. It would *not* seek a "natural state" of rest.

Given our discussion of observations made from inertial reference frames, we can pose a more practical statement of Newton's first law of motion:

> In the absence of external forces and when viewed from an inertial reference frame, an object at rest remains at rest and an object in motion continues in motion with a constant velocity (that is, with a constant speed in a straight line).

◄   Another statement of Newton's first law

In other words, **when no force acts on an object, the acceleration of the object is zero**. From the first law, we conclude that any *isolated object* (one that does not interact with its environment) is either at rest or moving with constant velocity. The tendency of an object to resist any attempt to change its velocity is called **inertia**. Given the statement of the first law above, we can conclude that an object that is accelerating must be experiencing a force. In turn, from the first law, we can define **force** as **that which causes a change in motion of an object**.

Quick Quiz 5.1 Which of the following statements is correct? (a) It is possible for an object to have motion in the absence of forces on the object. (b) It is possible to have forces on an object in the absence of motion of the object. (c) Neither (a) nor (b) is correct. (d) Both (a) and (b) are correct.

5.3 Mass

Imagine playing catch with either a basketball or a bowling ball. Which ball is more likely to keep moving when you try to catch it? Which ball requires more effort to throw it? The bowling ball requires more effort. In the language of physics, we say that the bowling ball is more resistant to changes in its velocity than the basketball. How can we quantify this concept?

Mass is that property of an object that specifies how much resistance an object exhibits to changes in its velocity, and as we learned in Section 1.1 the SI unit of mass is the kilogram. Experiments show that the greater the mass of an object, the less that object accelerates under the action of a given applied force.

◄   Definition of mass

To describe mass quantitatively, we conduct experiments in which we compare the accelerations a given force produces on different objects. Suppose a force acting on an object of mass m_1 produces an acceleration $\vec{\mathbf{a}}_1$, and the *same force* acting

---

PITFALL PREVENTION 5.1
Newton's First Law

Newton's first law does *not* say what happens for an object with *zero net force*, that is, multiple forces that cancel; it says what happens *in the absence of external forces*. This subtle but important difference allows us to define force as that which causes a change in the motion. The description of an object under the effect of forces that balance is covered by Newton's second law.

on an object of mass m_2 produces an acceleration $\vec{\mathbf{a}}_2$. The ratio of the two masses is defined as the *inverse* ratio of the magnitudes of the accelerations produced by the force:

$$\frac{m_1}{m_2} \equiv \frac{a_2}{a_1} \tag{5.1}$$

For example, if a given force acting on a 3-kg object produces an acceleration of 4 m/s², the same force applied to a 6-kg object produces an acceleration of 2 m/s². According to a huge number of similar observations, we conclude that **the magnitude of the acceleration of an object is inversely proportional to its mass when acted on by a given force**. If one object has a known mass, the mass of the other object can be obtained from acceleration measurements.

Mass is an inherent property of an object and is independent of the object's surroundings and of the method used to measure it. Also, **mass is a scalar quantity** and thus obeys the rules of ordinary arithmetic. For example, if you combine a 3-kg mass with a 5-kg mass, the total mass is 8 kg. This result can be verified experimentally by comparing the acceleration that a known force gives to several objects separately with the acceleration that the same force gives to the same objects combined as one unit.

◀ Mass and weight are different quantities

Mass should not be confused with weight. **Mass and weight are two different quantities**. The weight of an object is equal to the magnitude of the gravitational force exerted on the object and varies with location (see Section 5.5). For example, a person weighing 180 lb on the Earth weighs only about 30 lb on the Moon. On the other hand, the mass of an object is the same everywhere: an object having a mass of 2 kg on the Earth also has a mass of 2 kg on the Moon.

5.4 Newton's Second Law

Newton's first law explains what happens to an object when no forces act on it: it either remains at rest or moves in a straight line with constant speed. Newton's second law answers the question of what happens to an object that has one or more forces acting on it.

Imagine performing an experiment in which you push a block of fixed mass across a frictionless horizontal surface. When you exert some horizontal force $\vec{\mathbf{F}}$ on the block, it moves with some acceleration $\vec{\mathbf{a}}$. If you apply a force twice as great on the same block, the acceleration of the block doubles. If you increase the applied force to $3\vec{\mathbf{F}}$, the acceleration triples, and so on. From such observations, we conclude that **the acceleration of an object is directly proportional to the force acting on it: $\vec{\mathbf{F}} \propto \vec{\mathbf{a}}$**. This idea was first introduced in Section 2.4 when we discussed the direction of the acceleration of an object. The magnitude of the acceleration of an object is inversely proportional to its mass, as stated in the preceding section: $|\vec{\mathbf{a}}| \propto 1/m$.

These experimental observations are summarized in **Newton's second law:**

> When viewed from an inertial reference frame, the acceleration of an object is directly proportional to the net force acting on it and inversely proportional to its mass:
>
> $$\vec{\mathbf{a}} \propto \frac{\sum \vec{\mathbf{F}}}{m}$$

If we choose a proportionality constant of 1, we can relate mass, acceleration, and force through the following mathematical statement of Newton's second law:[1]

Newton's second law ▶

$$\sum \vec{\mathbf{F}} = m\vec{\mathbf{a}} \tag{5.2}$$

PITFALL PREVENTION 5.2
Force Is the Cause of Changes in Motion

Force *does not* cause motion. We can have motion in the absence of forces as described in Newton's first law. Force is the cause of *changes* in motion as measured by acceleration.

---

[1] Equation 5.2 is valid only when the speed of the object is much less than the speed of light. We treat the relativistic situation in Chapter 39.

In both the textual and mathematical statements of Newton's second law, we have indicated that the acceleration is due to the *net force* $\sum \vec{F}$ acting on an object. The **net force** on an object is the vector sum of all forces acting on the object. (We sometimes refer to the net force as the *total force*, the *resultant force*, or the *unbalanced force*.) In solving a problem using Newton's second law, it is imperative to determine the correct net force on an object. Many forces may be acting on an object, but there is only one acceleration.

Equation 5.2 is a vector expression and hence is equivalent to three component equations:

$$\sum F_x = ma_x \qquad \sum F_y = ma_y \qquad \sum F_z = ma_z \qquad (5.3)$$

◀ Newton's second law: component form

Quick Quiz 5.2   An object experiences no acceleration. Which of the following *cannot* be true for the object? (a) A single force acts on the object. (b) No forces act on the object. (c) Forces act on the object, but the forces cancel.

Quick Quiz 5.3   You push an object, initially at rest, across a frictionless floor with a constant force for a time interval Δt, resulting in a final speed of v for the object. You then repeat the experiment, but with a force that is twice as large. What time interval is now required to reach the same final speed v? (a) $4\Delta t$ (b) $2\Delta t$ (c) Δt (d) $\Delta t/2$ (e) $\Delta t/4$

The SI unit of force is the **newton** (N). A force of 1 N is the force that, when acting on an object of mass 1 kg, produces an acceleration of 1 m/s². From this definition and Newton's second law, we see that the newton can be expressed in terms of the following fundamental units of mass, length, and time:

$$1\ \text{N} \equiv 1\ \text{kg} \cdot \text{m/s}^2 \qquad (5.4)$$

◀ Definition of the newton

In the U.S. customary system, the unit of force is the **pound** (lb). A force of 1 lb is the force that, when acting on a 1-slug mass,[2] produces an acceleration of 1 ft/s²:

$$1\ \text{lb} \equiv 1\ \text{slug} \cdot \text{ft/s}^2 \qquad (5.5)$$

A convenient approximation is $1\ \text{N} \approx \frac{1}{4}\ \text{lb}$.

PITFALL PREVENTION 5.3
$m\vec{a}$ Is Not a Force

Equation 5.2 does *not* say that the product $m\vec{a}$ is a force. All forces on an object are added vectorially to generate the net force on the left side of the equation. This net force is then equated to the product of the mass of the object and the acceleration that results from the net force. Do *not* include an "$m\vec{a}$ force" in your analysis of the forces on an object.

| EXAMPLE 5.1 | **An Accelerating Hockey Puck** |

A hockey puck having a mass of 0.30 kg slides on the horizontal, frictionless surface of an ice rink. Two hockey sticks strike the puck simultaneously, exerting the forces on the puck shown in Figure 5.4. The force $\vec{F}_1$ has a magnitude of 5.0 N, and the force $\vec{F}_2$ has a magnitude of 8.0 N. Determine both the magnitude and the direction of the puck's acceleration.

SOLUTION

Conceptualize   Study Figure 5.4. Using your expertise in vector addition from Chapter 3, predict the approximate direction of the net force vector on the puck. The acceleration of the puck will be in the same direction.

Categorize   Because we can determine a net force and we want an acceleration, this problem is categorized as one that may be solved using Newton's second law.

Figure 5.4   (Example 5.1) A hockey puck moving on a frictionless surface is subject to two forces $\vec{F}_1$ and $\vec{F}_2$.

---

[2] The *slug* is the unit of mass in the U.S. customary system and is that system's counterpart of the SI unit the *kilogram*. Because most of the calculations in our study of classical mechanics are in SI units, the slug is seldom used in this text.

Analyze   Find the component of the net force acting on the puck in the x direction:

$$\sum F_x = F_{1x} + F_{2x} = F_1 \cos(-20°) + F_2 \cos 60°$$
$$= (5.0 \text{ N})(0.940) + (8.0 \text{ N})(0.500) = 8.7 \text{ N}$$

Find the component of the net force acting on the puck in the y direction:

$$\sum F_y = F_{1y} + F_{2y} = F_1 \sin(-20°) + F_2 \sin 60°$$
$$= (5.0 \text{ N})(-0.342) + (8.0 \text{ N})(0.866) = 5.2 \text{ N}$$

Use Newton's second law in component form (Eq. 5.3) to find the x and y components of the puck's acceleration:

$$a_x = \frac{\sum F_x}{m} = \frac{8.7 \text{ N}}{0.30 \text{ kg}} = 29 \text{ m/s}^2$$

$$a_y = \frac{\sum F_y}{m} = \frac{5.2 \text{ N}}{0.30 \text{ kg}} = 17 \text{ m/s}^2$$

Find the magnitude of the acceleration:

$$a = \sqrt{(29 \text{ m/s}^2)^2 + (17 \text{ m/s}^2)^2} = \boxed{34 \text{ m/s}^2}$$

Find the direction of the acceleration relative to the positive x axis:

$$\theta = \tan^{-1}\left(\frac{a_y}{a_x}\right) = \tan^{-1}\left(\frac{17}{29}\right) = \boxed{30°}$$

Finalize   The vectors in Figure 5.4 can be added graphically to check the reasonableness of our answer. Because the acceleration vector is along the direction of the resultant force, a drawing showing the resultant force vector helps us check the validity of the answer. (Try it!)

What If?   Suppose three hockey sticks strike the puck simultaneously, with two of them exerting the forces shown in Figure 5.4. The result of the three forces is that the hockey puck shows *no* acceleration. What must be the components of the third force?

Answer   If there is zero acceleration, the net force acting on the puck must be zero. Therefore, the three forces must cancel. We have found the components of the combination of the first two forces. The components of the third force must be of equal magnitude and opposite sign so that all the components add to zero. Therefore, $F_{3x} = -8.7$ N, $F_{3y} = -5.2$ N.

PITFALL PREVENTION 5.4
"Weight of an Object"

We are familiar with the everyday phrase, the "weight of an object." Weight, however, is not an inherent property of an object; rather, it is a measure of the gravitational force between the object and the Earth (or other planet). Therefore, weight is a property of a *system* of items: the object and the Earth.

5.5   The Gravitational Force and Weight

All objects are attracted to the Earth. The attractive force exerted by the Earth on an object is called the **gravitational force** $\vec{F}_g$. This force is directed toward the center of the Earth,[3] and its magnitude is called the **weight** of the object.

We saw in Section 2.6 that a freely falling object experiences an acceleration $\vec{g}$ acting toward the center of the Earth. Applying Newton's second law $\sum \vec{F} = m\vec{a}$ to a freely falling object of mass m, with $\vec{a} = \vec{g}$ and $\sum \vec{F} = \vec{F}_g$, gives

$$\vec{F}_g = m\vec{g}$$

Therefore, the weight of an object, being defined as the magnitude of $\vec{F}_g$, is equal to mg:

$$F_g = mg \qquad (5.6)$$

PITFALL PREVENTION 5.5
Kilogram Is Not a Unit of Weight

You may have seen the "conversion" 1 kg = 2.2 lb. Despite popular statements of weights expressed in kilograms, the kilogram is not a unit of *weight*, it is a unit of *mass*. The conversion statement is not an equality; it is an *equivalence* that is valid only on the Earth's surface.

Because it depends on g, weight varies with geographic location. Because g decreases with increasing distance from the center of the Earth, objects weigh less at higher altitudes than at sea level. For example, a 1 000-kg palette of bricks used in the construction of the Empire State Building in New York City weighed 9 800 N at street level, but weighed about 1 N less by the time it was lifted from sidewalk level to the top of the building. As another example, suppose a student has a mass of 70.0 kg. The student's weight in a location where $g = 9.80$ m/s^2 is 686 N (about 150 lb). At the top of a mountain, however, where $g = 9.77$ m/s^2, the student's

---

[3] This statement ignores that the mass distribution of the Earth is not perfectly spherical.

weight is only 684 N. Therefore, if you want to lose weight without going on a diet, climb a mountain or weigh yourself at 30 000 ft during an airplane flight!

Equation 5.6 quantifies the gravitational force on the object, but notice that this equation does not require the object to be moving. Even for a stationary object or for an object on which several forces act, Equation 5.6 can be used to calculate the magnitude of the gravitational force. The result is a subtle shift in the interpretation of m in the equation. The mass m in Equation 5.6 determines the strength of the gravitational attraction between the object and the Earth. This role is completely different from that previously described for mass, that of measuring the resistance to changes in motion in response to an external force. Therefore, we call m in Equation 5.6 the **gravitational mass**. Even though this quantity is different in behavior from inertial mass, it is one of the experimental conclusions in Newtonian dynamics that gravitational mass and inertial mass have the same value.

Although this discussion has focused on the gravitational force on an object due to the Earth, the concept is generally valid on any planet. The value of g will vary from one planet to the next, but the magnitude of the gravitational force will always be given by the value of mg.

The life-support unit strapped to the back of astronaut Edwin Aldrin weighed 300 lb on the Earth. During his training, a 50-lb mock-up was used. Although this strategy effectively simulated the reduced weight the unit would have on the Moon, it did not correctly mimic the unchanging mass. It was just as difficult to accelerate the unit (perhaps by jumping or twisting suddenly) on the Moon as on the Earth.

Quick Quiz 5.4 Suppose you are talking by interplanetary telephone to a friend, who lives on the Moon. He tells you that he has just won a newton of gold in a contest. Excitedly, you tell him that you entered the Earth version of the same contest and also won a newton of gold! Who is richer? (a) You are. (b) Your friend is. (c) You are equally rich.

| CONCEPTUAL EXAMPLE 5.2 | **How Much Do You Weigh in an Elevator?** |

You have most likely been in an elevator that accelerates upward as it moves toward a higher floor. In this case, you feel heavier. In fact, if you are standing on a bathroom scale at the time, the scale measures a force having a magnitude that is greater than your weight. Therefore, you have tactile and measured evidence that leads you to believe you are heavier in this situation. *Are* you heavier?

SOLUTION

No; your weight is unchanged. Your experiences are due to the fact that you are in a noninertial reference frame. To provide the acceleration upward, the floor or scale must exert on your feet an upward force that is greater in magnitude than your weight. It is this greater force you feel, which you interpret as feeling heavier. The scale reads this upward force, not your weight, and so its reading increases.

5.6   Newton's Third Law

If you press against a corner of this textbook with your fingertip, the book pushes back and makes a small dent in your skin. If you push harder, the book does the same and the dent in your skin is a little larger. This simple activity illustrates that forces are *interactions* between two objects: when your finger pushes on the book, the book pushes back on your finger. This important principle is known as **Newton's third law:**

> If two objects interact, the force $\vec{\mathbf{F}}_{12}$ exerted by object 1 on object 2 is equal in magnitude and opposite in direction to the force $\vec{\mathbf{F}}_{21}$ exerted by object 2 on object 1:
>
> $$\vec{\mathbf{F}}_{12} = -\vec{\mathbf{F}}_{21} \tag{5.7}$$

◀ Newton's third law

When it is important to designate forces as interactions between two objects, we will use this subscript notation, where $\vec{\mathbf{F}}_{ab}$ means "the force exerted *by* a *on* b." The third law is illustrated in Figure 5.5a. The force that object 1 exerts on object 2 is popularly called the *action force,* and the force of object 2 on object 1 is called the

Figure 5.5   Newton's third law. (a) The force $\vec{\mathbf{F}}_{12}$ exerted by object 1 on object 2 is equal in magnitude and opposite in direction to the force $\vec{\mathbf{F}}_{21}$ exerted by object 2 on object 1. (b) The force $\vec{\mathbf{F}}_{hn}$ exerted by the hammer on the nail is equal in magnitude and opposite to the force $\vec{\mathbf{F}}_{nh}$ exerted by the nail on the hammer.

PITFALL PREVENTION 5.6
n Does Not Always Equal mg

In the situation shown in Figure 5.6 and in many others, we find that $n = mg$ (the normal force has the same magnitude as the gravitational force). This result, however, is *not* generally true. If an object is on an incline, if there are applied forces with vertical components, or if there is a vertical acceleration of the system, then $n \neq mg$. *Always* apply Newton's second law to find the relationship between n and mg.

Normal force ▶

PITFALL PREVENTION 5.7
Newton's Third Law

Remember that Newton's third law action and reaction forces act on *different* objects. For example, in Figure 5.6, $\vec{\mathbf{n}} = \vec{\mathbf{F}}_{tm} = -m\vec{\mathbf{g}} = -\vec{\mathbf{F}}_{Em}$. The forces $\vec{\mathbf{n}}$ and $m\vec{\mathbf{g}}$ are equal in magnitude and opposite in direction, but they do not represent an action-reaction pair because both forces act on the *same* object, the monitor.

reaction force. These italicized terms are not scientific terms; furthermore, either force can be labeled the action or reaction force. We will use these terms for convenience. **In all cases, the action and reaction forces act on *different* objects and must be of the same type (gravitational, electrical, etc.).** For example, the force acting on a freely falling projectile is the gravitational force exerted by the Earth on the projectile $\vec{\mathbf{F}}_g = \vec{\mathbf{F}}_{Ep}$ (E = Earth, p = projectile), and the magnitude of this force is mg. The reaction to this force is the gravitational force exerted by the projectile on the Earth $\vec{\mathbf{F}}_{pE} = -\vec{\mathbf{F}}_{Ep}$. The reaction force $\vec{\mathbf{F}}_{pE}$ must accelerate the Earth toward the projectile just as the action force $\vec{\mathbf{F}}_{Ep}$ accelerates the projectile toward the Earth. Because the Earth has such a large mass, however, its acceleration due to this reaction force is negligibly small.

Another example of Newton's third law is shown in Figure 5.5b. The force $\vec{\mathbf{F}}_{hn}$ exerted by the hammer on the nail is equal in magnitude and opposite the force $\vec{\mathbf{F}}_{nh}$ exerted by the nail on the hammer. This latter force stops the forward motion of the hammer when it strikes the nail.

Consider a computer monitor at rest on a table as in Figure 5.6a. The reaction force to the gravitational force $\vec{\mathbf{F}}_g = \vec{\mathbf{F}}_{Em}$ on the monitor is the force $\vec{\mathbf{F}}_{mE} = -\vec{\mathbf{F}}_{Em}$ exerted by the monitor on the Earth. The monitor does not accelerate because it is held up by the table. The table exerts on the monitor an upward force $\vec{\mathbf{n}} = \vec{\mathbf{F}}_{tm}$, called the **normal force**.[4] This force, which prevents the monitor from falling through the table, can have any value needed, up to the point of breaking the table. Because the monitor has zero acceleration, Newton's second law applied to the monitor gives us $\Sigma \vec{\mathbf{F}} = \vec{\mathbf{n}} + m\vec{\mathbf{g}} = 0$, so $n\hat{\mathbf{j}} - mg\hat{\mathbf{j}} = 0$, or $n = mg$. The normal force balances the gravitational force on the monitor, so the net force on the monitor is zero. The reaction force to $\vec{\mathbf{n}}$ is the force exerted by the monitor downward on the table, $\vec{\mathbf{F}}_{mt} = -\vec{\mathbf{F}}_{tm} = -\vec{\mathbf{n}}$.

Notice that the forces acting on the monitor are $\vec{\mathbf{F}}_g$ and $\vec{\mathbf{n}}$ as shown in Figure 5.6b. The two forces $\vec{\mathbf{F}}_{mE}$ and $\vec{\mathbf{F}}_{mt}$ are exerted on objects other than the monitor.

Figure 5.6 illustrates an extremely important step in solving problems involving forces. Figure 5.6a shows many of the forces in the situation: those acting on the monitor, one acting on the table, and one acting on the Earth. Figure 5.6b, by contrast, shows only the forces acting on *one object*, the monitor. This important pictorial representation in Figure 5.6b is called a **free-body diagram**. When analyzing an object subject to forces, we are interested in the net force acting on one object, which we will model as a particle. Therefore, a free-body diagram helps us isolate only those forces on the object and eliminate the other forces from our

[4] *Normal* in this context means *perpendicular*.

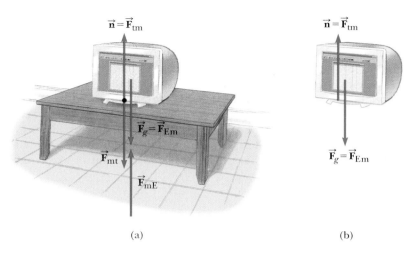

Figure 5.6 (a) When a computer monitor is at rest on a table, the forces acting on the monitor are the normal force $\vec{\mathbf{n}}$ and the gravitational force $\vec{\mathbf{F}}_g$. The reaction to $\vec{\mathbf{n}}$ is the force $\vec{\mathbf{F}}_{mt}$ exerted by the monitor on the table. The reaction to $\vec{\mathbf{F}}_g$ is the force $\vec{\mathbf{F}}_{mE}$ exerted by the monitor on the Earth. (b) The free-body diagram for the monitor.

analysis. This diagram can be simplified further by representing the object (such as the monitor) as a particle simply by drawing a dot.

Quick Quiz 5.5   **(i)** If a fly collides with the windshield of a fast-moving bus, which experiences an impact force with a larger magnitude? (a) The fly. (b) The bus. (c) The same force is experienced by both. **(ii)** Which experiences the greater acceleration? (a) The fly. (b) The bus. (c) The same acceleration is experienced by both.

PITFALL PREVENTION 5.8
Free-Body Diagrams

The *most important* step in solving a problem using Newton's laws is to draw a proper sketch, the free-body diagram. Be sure to draw only those forces that act on the object you are isolating. Be sure to draw *all* forces acting on the object, including any field forces, such as the gravitational force.

CONCEPTUAL EXAMPLE 5.3   **You Push Me and I'll Push You**

A large man and a small boy stand facing each other on frictionless ice. They put their hands together and push against each other so that they move apart.

(A) Who moves away with the higher speed?

SOLUTION

This situation is similar to what we saw in Quick Quiz 5.5. According to Newton's third law, the force exerted by the man on the boy and the force exerted by the boy on the man are a third-law pair of forces, so they must be equal in magnitude. (A bathroom scale placed between their hands would read the same, regardless of which way it faced.) Therefore, the boy, having the

smaller mass, experiences the greater acceleration. Both individuals accelerate for the same amount of time, but the greater acceleration of the boy over this time interval results in his moving away from the interaction with the higher speed.

(B) Who moves farther while their hands are in contact?

SOLUTION

Because the boy has the greater acceleration and therefore the greater average velocity, he moves farther than the man during the time interval during which their hands are in contact.

5.7   Some Applications of Newton's Laws

In this section, we discuss two analysis models for solving problems in which objects are either in equilibrium ($\vec{\mathbf{a}} = 0$) or accelerating along a straight line under the action of constant external forces. Remember that **when Newton's laws are applied to an object, we are interested only in external forces that act on the object**. If the objects are modeled as particles, we need not worry about rotational motion. For now, we also neglect the effects of friction in those problems involving

Rock climbers at rest are in equilibrium and depend on the tension forces in ropes for their safety.

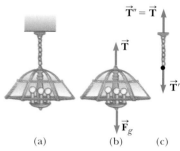

$$\vec{T}'' = \vec{T}$$

$$\vec{T}$$

$$\vec{T}'$$

$$\vec{F}_g$$

(a)   (b)   (c)

Figure 5.7   (a) A lamp suspended from a ceiling by a chain of negligible mass. (b) The forces acting on the lamp are the gravitational force $\vec{F}_g$ and the force $\vec{T}$ exerted by the chain. (c) The forces acting on the chain are the force $\vec{T}'$ exerted by the lamp and the force $\vec{T}''$ exerted by the ceiling.

(a)

$$\vec{n}$$

y

x

$$\vec{T}$$

$$\vec{F}_g$$

(b)

Figure 5.8   (a) A crate being pulled to the right on a frictionless surface. (b) The free-body diagram representing the external forces acting on the crate.

motion, which is equivalent to stating that the surfaces are *frictionless*. (The friction force is discussed in Section 5.8.)

We usually neglect the mass of any ropes, strings, or cables involved. In this approximation, the magnitude of the force exerted by any element of the rope on the adjacent element is the same for all elements along the rope. In problem statements, the synonymous terms *light* and *of negligible mass* are used to indicate that a mass is to be ignored when you work the problems. When a rope attached to an object is pulling on the object, the rope exerts a force $\vec{T}$ on the object in a direction away from the object, parallel to the rope. The magnitude T of that force is called the **tension** in the rope. Because it is the magnitude of a vector quantity, tension is a scalar quantity.

The Particle in Equilibrium

If the acceleration of an object modeled as a particle is zero, the object is treated with the **particle in equilibrium** model. In this model, the net force on the object is zero:

$$\sum \vec{F} = 0 \qquad (5.8)$$

Consider a lamp suspended from a light chain fastened to the ceiling as in Figure 5.7a. The free-body diagram for the lamp (Fig. 5.7b) shows that the forces acting on the lamp are the downward gravitational force $\vec{F}_g$ and the upward force $\vec{T}$ exerted by the chain. Because there are no forces in the x direction, $\sum F_x = 0$ provides no helpful information. The condition $\sum F_y = 0$ gives

$$\sum F_y = T - F_g = 0 \quad \text{or} \quad T = F_g$$

Again, notice that $\vec{T}$ and $\vec{F}_g$ are *not* an action-reaction pair because they act on the same object, the lamp. The reaction force to $\vec{T}$ is $\vec{T}'$, the downward force exerted by the lamp on the chain as shown in Figure 5.7c. Because the chain is a particle in equilibrium, the ceiling must exert on the chain a force $\vec{T}''$ that is equal in magnitude to the magnitude of $\vec{T}'$ and points in the opposite direction.

The Particle Under a Net Force

If an object experiences an acceleration, its motion can be analyzed with the **particle under a net force** model. The appropriate equation for this model is Newton's second law, Equation 5.2. Consider a crate being pulled to the right on a frictionless, horizontal surface as in Figure 5.8a. Suppose you wish to find the acceleration of the crate and the force the floor exerts on it. The forces acting on the crate are illustrated in the free-body diagram in Figure 5.8b. Notice that the horizontal force $\vec{T}$ being applied to the crate acts through the rope. The magnitude of $\vec{T}$ is equal to the tension in the rope. In addition to the force $\vec{T}$, the free-body diagram for the crate includes the gravitational force $\vec{F}_g$ and the normal force $\vec{n}$ exerted by the floor on the crate.

We can now apply Newton's second law in component form to the crate. The only force acting in the x direction is $\vec{T}$. Applying $\sum F_x = ma_x$ to the horizontal motion gives

$$\sum F_x = T = ma_x \quad \text{or} \quad a_x = \frac{T}{m}$$

No acceleration occurs in the y direction because the crate moves only horizontally. Therefore, we use the particle in equilibrium model in the y direction. Applying the y component of Equation 5.8 yields

$$\sum F_y = n + (-F_g) = 0 \quad \text{or} \quad n = F_g$$

That is, the normal force has the same magnitude as the gravitational force but acts in the opposite direction.

If $\vec{\mathbf{T}}$ is a constant force, the acceleration $a_x = T/m$ also is constant. Hence, the crate is also modeled as a particle under constant acceleration in the x direction, and the equations of kinematics from Chapter 2 can be used to obtain the crate's position x and velocity v_x as functions of time.

In the situation just described, the magnitude of the normal force $\vec{\mathbf{n}}$ is equal to the magnitude of $\vec{\mathbf{F}}_g$, but that is not always the case. For example, suppose a book is lying on a table and you push down on the book with a force $\vec{\mathbf{F}}$ as in Figure 5.9. Because the book is at rest and therefore not accelerating, $\Sigma F_y = 0$, which gives $n - F_g - F = 0$, or $n = F_g + F$. In this situation, the normal force is *greater* than the gravitational force. Other examples in which $n \neq F_g$ are presented later.

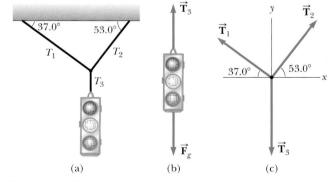

Figure 5.9   When a force $\vec{\mathbf{F}}$ pushes vertically downward on another object, the normal force $\vec{\mathbf{n}}$ on the object is greater than the gravitational force: $n = F_g + F$.

PROBLEM-SOLVING STRATEGY   **Applying Newton's Laws**

The following procedure is recommended when dealing with problems involving Newton's laws:

1. *Conceptualize.* Draw a simple, neat diagram of the system. The diagram helps establish the mental representation. Establish convenient coordinate axes for each object in the system.

2. *Categorize.* If an acceleration component for an object is zero, the object is modeled as a particle in equilibrium in this direction and $\Sigma F = 0$. If not, the object is modeled as a particle under a net force in this direction and $\Sigma F = ma$.

3. *Analyze.* Isolate the object whose motion is being analyzed. Draw a free-body diagram for this object. For systems containing more than one object, draw *separate* free-body diagrams for each object. *Do not* include in the free-body diagram forces exerted by the object on its surroundings.

   Find the components of the forces along the coordinate axes. Apply the appropriate model from the Categorize step for each direction. Check your dimensions to make sure that all terms have units of force.

   Solve the component equations for the unknowns. Remember that you must have as many independent equations as you have unknowns to obtain a complete solution.

4. *Finalize.* Make sure your results are consistent with the free-body diagram. Also check the predictions of your solutions for extreme values of the variables. By doing so, you can often detect errors in your results.

EXAMPLE 5.4   **A Traffic Light at Rest**

A traffic light weighing 122 N hangs from a cable tied to two other cables fastened to a support as in Figure 5.10a. The upper cables make angles of 37.0° and 53.0° with the horizontal. These upper cables are not as strong as the vertical cable and will break if the tension in them exceeds 100 N. Does the traffic light remain hanging in this situation, or will one of the cables break?

SOLUTION

Conceptualize   Inspect the drawing in Figure 5.10a. Let us assume the cables do not break and that nothing is moving.

Figure 5.10   (Example 5.4) (a) A traffic light suspended by cables. (b) The free-body diagram for the traffic light. (c) The free-body diagram for the knot where the three cables are joined.

Categorize If nothing is moving, no part of the system is accelerating. We can now model the light as a particle in equilibrium on which the net force is zero. Similarly, the net force on the knot (Fig. 5.10c) is zero.

Analyze We construct two free-body diagrams: one for the traffic light, shown in Figure 5.10b, and one for the knot that holds the three cables together, shown in Figure 5.10c. This knot is a convenient object to choose because all the forces of interest act along lines passing through the knot.

Apply Equation 5.8 for the traffic light in the y direction:

$$\sum F_y = 0 \quad \rightarrow \quad T_3 - F_g = 0$$

$$T_3 = F_g = 122 \text{ N}$$

Choose the coordinate axes as shown in Figure 5.10c and resolve the forces acting on the knot into their components:

Force	x Component	y Component
$\vec{T}_1$	$-T_1 \cos 37.0°$	$T_1 \sin 37.0°$
$\vec{T}_2$	$T_2 \cos 53.0°$	$T_2 \sin 53.0°$
$\vec{T}_3$	0	-122 N

Apply the particle in equilibrium model to the knot:

$$(1) \quad \sum F_x = -T_1 \cos 37.0° + T_2 \cos 53.0° = 0$$

$$(2) \quad \sum F_y = T_1 \sin 37.0° + T_2 \sin 53.0° + (-122 \text{ N}) = 0$$

Equation (1) shows that the horizontal components of $\vec{T}_1$ and $\vec{T}_2$ must be equal in magnitude, and Equation (2) shows that the sum of the vertical components of $\vec{T}_1$ and $\vec{T}_2$ must balance the downward force $\vec{T}_3$, which is equal in magnitude to the weight of the light.

Solve Equation (1) for T_2 in terms of T_1:

$$(3) \quad T_2 = T_1 \left(\frac{\cos 37.0°}{\cos 53.0°} \right) = 1.33 T_1$$

Substitute this value for T_2 into Equation (2):

$$T_1 \sin 37.0° + (1.33 T_1)(\sin 53.0°) - 122 \text{ N} = 0$$

$$T_1 = 73.4 \text{ N}$$

$$T_2 = 1.33 T_1 = 97.4 \text{ N}$$

Both values are less than 100 N (just barely for T_2), so the cables will not break.

Finalize Let us finalize this problem by imagining a change in the system, as in the following **What If?**

What If? Suppose the two angles in Figure 5.10a are equal. What would be the relationship between T_1 and T_2?

Answer We can argue from the symmetry of the problem that the two tensions T_1 and T_2 would be equal to each other. Mathematically, if the equal angles are called θ, Equation (3) becomes

$$T_2 = T_1 \left(\frac{\cos \theta}{\cos \theta} \right) = T_1$$

which also tells us that the tensions are equal. Without knowing the specific value of θ, we cannot find the values of T_1 and T_2. The tensions will be equal to each other, however, regardless of the value of θ.

CONCEPTUAL EXAMPLE 5.5 **Forces Between Cars in a Train**

Train cars are connected by *couplers*, which are under tension as the locomotive pulls the train. Imagine you are on a train speeding up with a constant acceleration. As you move through the train from the locomotive to the last car, measuring the tension in each set of couplers, does the tension increase, decrease, or stay the same? When the engineer applies the brakes, the couplers are under compression. How does this compression force vary from the locomotive to the last car? (Assume only the brakes on the wheels of the engine are applied.)

SOLUTION

As the train speeds up, tension decreases from the front of the train to the back. The coupler between the locomotive and the first car must apply enough force to accelerate the rest of the cars. As you move back along the train, each coupler is accelerating less mass behind it. The last coupler has to accelerate only the last car, and so it is under the least tension.

When the brakes are applied, the force again decreases from front to back. The coupler connecting the locomotive to the first car must apply a large force to slow down the rest of the cars, but the final coupler must apply a force large enough to slow down only the last car.

| EXAMPLE 5.6 | **The Runaway Car** |

A car of mass m is on an icy driveway inclined at an angle θ as in Figure 5.11a.

(A) Find the acceleration of the car, assuming that the driveway is frictionless.

SOLUTION

Conceptualize   Use Figure 5.11a to conceptualize the situation. From everyday experience, we know that a car on an icy incline will accelerate down the incline. (The same thing happens to a car on a hill with its brakes not set.)

Categorize   We categorize the car as a particle under a net force. Furthermore, this problem belongs to a very common category of problems in which an object moves under the influence of gravity on an inclined plane.

Figure 5.11   (Example 5.6) (a) A car of mass m on a frictionless incline. (b) The free-body diagram for the car.

Analyze   Figure 5.11b shows the free-body diagram for the car. The only forces acting on the car are the normal force $\vec{\mathbf{n}}$ exerted by the inclined plane, which acts perpendicular to the plane, and the gravitational force $\vec{\mathbf{F}}_g = m\vec{\mathbf{g}}$, which acts vertically downward. For problems involving inclined planes, it is convenient to choose the coordinate axes with x along the incline and y perpendicular to it as in Figure 5.11b. (It is possible, although inconvenient, to solve the problem with "standard" horizontal and vertical axes. You may want to try it, just for practice.) With these axes, we represent the gravitational force by a component of magnitude $mg \sin \theta$ along the positive x axis and one of magnitude $mg \cos \theta$ along the negative y axis.

Apply Newton's second law to the car in component form, noting that $a_y = 0$:

$$(1) \quad \sum F_x = mg \sin \theta = ma_x$$

$$(2) \quad \sum F_y = n - mg \cos \theta = 0$$

Solve Equation (1) for a_x:

$$(3) \quad a_x = g \sin \theta$$

Finalize   Our choice of axes results in the car being modeled as a particle under a net force in the x direction and a particle in equilibrium in the y direction. Furthermore, the acceleration component a_x is independent of the mass of the car! It depends only on the angle of inclination and on g.

From Equation (2) we conclude that the component of $\vec{\mathbf{F}}_g$ perpendicular to the incline is balanced by the normal force; that is, $n = mg \cos \theta$. This situation is another case in which the normal force is *not* equal in magnitude to the weight of the object.

(B) Suppose the car is released from rest at the top of the incline and the distance from the car's front bumper to the bottom of the incline is d. How long does it take the front bumper to reach the bottom of the hill, and what is the car's speed as it arrives there?

SOLUTION

Concepualize   Imagine that the car is sliding down the hill and you use a stopwatch to measure the entire time interval until it reaches the bottom.

Categorize   This part of the problem belongs to kinematics rather than to dynamics, and Equation (3) shows that the acceleration a_x is constant. Therefore, you should categorize the car in this part of the problem as a particle under constant acceleration.

Analyze   Defining the initial position of the front bumper as $x_i = 0$ and its final position as $x_f = d$, and recognizing that $v_{xi} = 0$, apply Equation 2.16, $x_f = x_i + v_{xi}t + \frac{1}{2}a_xt^2$:

Solve for t:

$$d = \tfrac{1}{2}a_xt^2$$

$$(4) \quad t = \sqrt{\frac{2d}{a_x}} = \sqrt{\frac{2d}{g\sin\theta}}$$

Use Equation 2.17, with $v_{xi} = 0$, to find the final velocity of the car:

$$v_{xf}^2 = 2a_xd$$

$$(5) \quad v_{xf} = \sqrt{2a_xd} = \sqrt{2gd\sin\theta}$$

Finalize   We see from Equations (4) and (5) that the time t at which the car reaches the bottom and its final speed v_{xf} are independent of the car's mass, as was its acceleration. Notice that we have combined techniques from Chapter 2 with new techniques from this chapter in this example. As we learn more techniques in later chapters, this process of combining information from several parts of the book will occur more often. In these cases, use the General Problem-Solving Strategy to help you identify what analysis models you will need.

What If?   What previously solved problem does this situation become if $\theta = 90°$?

Answer   Imagine θ going to $90°$ in Figure 5.11. The inclined plane becomes vertical, and the car is an object in free-fall! Equation (3) becomes

$$a_x = g\sin\theta = g\sin90° = g$$

which is indeed the free-fall acceleration. (We find $a_x = g$ rather than $a_x = -g$ because we have chosen positive x to be downward in Fig. 5.11.) Notice also that the condition $n = mg\cos\theta$ gives us $n = mg\cos90° = 0$. That is consistent with the car falling downward *next to* the vertical plane, in which case there is no contact force between the car and the plane.

EXAMPLE 5.7   **One Block Pushes Another**

Two blocks of masses m_1 and m_2, with $m_1 > m_2$, are placed in contact with each other on a frictionless, horizontal surface as in Active Figure 5.12a. A constant horizontal force $\vec{F}$ is applied to m_1 as shown.

(A) Find the magnitude of the acceleration of the system.

SOLUTION

Conceptualize   Conceptualize the situation by using Active Figure 5.12a and realize that both blocks must experience the *same* acceleration because they are in contact with each other and remain in contact throughout the motion.

Categorize   We categorize this problem as one involving a particle under a net force because a force is applied to a system of blocks and we are looking for the acceleration of the system.

Analyze   First model the combination of two blocks as a single particle. Apply Newton's second law to the combination:

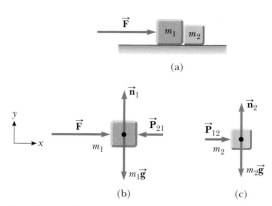

ACTIVE FIGURE 5.12

(Example 5.7) A force is applied to a block of mass m_1, which pushes on a second block of mass m_2. (b) The free-body diagram for m_1. (c) The free-body diagram for m_2.

Sign in at www.thomsonedu.com and go to ThomsonNOW to study the forces involved in this two-block system.

$$\sum F_x = F = (m_1 + m_2)a_x$$

$$(1) \quad a_x = \frac{F}{m_1 + m_2}$$

Finalize   The acceleration given by Equation (1) is the same as that of a single object of mass $m_1 + m_2$ and subject to the same force.

(B) Determine the magnitude of the contact force between the two blocks.

SOLUTION

Conceptualize   The contact force is internal to the system of two blocks. Therefore, we cannot find this force by modeling the whole system (the two blocks) as a single particle.

Categorize   Now consider each of the two blocks individually by categorizing each as a particle under a net force.

Analyze   We first construct a free-body diagram for each block as shown in Active Figures 5.12b and 5.12c, where the contact force is denoted by $\vec{P}$. From Active Figure 5.12c we see that the only horizontal force acting on m_2 is the contact force $\vec{P}_{12}$ (the force exerted by m_1 on m_2), which is directed to the right.

Apply Newton's second law to m_2:

$$(2) \quad \sum F_x = P_{12} = m_2 a_x$$

Substitute the value of the acceleration a_x given by Equation (1) into Equation (2):

$$(3) \quad P_{12} = m_2 a_x = \left(\frac{m_2}{m_1 + m_2} \right) F$$

Finalize   This result shows that the contact force P_{12} is *less* than the applied force F. The force required to accelerate block 2 alone must be less than the force required to produce the same acceleration for the two-block system.

To finalize further, let us check this expression for P_{12} by considering the forces acting on m_1, shown in Active Figure 5.12b. The horizontal forces acting on m_1 are the applied force $\vec{F}$ to the right and the contact force $\vec{P}_{21}$ to the left (the force exerted by m_2 on m_1). From Newton's third law, $\vec{P}_{21}$ is the reaction force to $\vec{P}_{12}$, so $P_{21} = P_{12}$.

Apply Newton's second law to m_1:

$$(4) \quad \sum F_x = F - P_{21} = F - P_{12} = m_1 a_x$$

Solve for P_{12} and substitute the value of a_x from Equation (1):

$$P_{12} = F - m_1 a_x = F - m_1 \left(\frac{F}{m_1 + m_2} \right) = \left(\frac{m_2}{m_1 + m_2} \right) F$$

This result agrees with Equation (3), as it must.

What If?   Imagine that the force $\vec{F}$ in Active Figure 5.12 is applied toward the left on the right-hand block of mass m_2. Is the magnitude of the force $\vec{P}_{12}$ the same as it was when the force was applied toward the right on m_1?

Answer   When the force is applied toward the left on m_2, the contact force must accelerate m_1. In the original situation, the contact force accelerates m_2. Because $m_1 > m_2$, more force is required, so the magnitude of $\vec{P}_{12}$ is greater than in the original situation.

| EXAMPLE 5.8 | **Weighing a Fish in an Elevator** |

A person weighs a fish of mass m on a spring scale attached to the ceiling of an elevator as illustrated in Figure 5.13.

(A) Show that if the elevator accelerates either upward or downward, the spring scale gives a reading that is different from the weight of the fish.

SOLUTION

Conceptualize   The reading on the scale is related to the extension of the spring in the scale, which is related to the force on the end of the spring as in Figure 5.2. Imagine that the fish is hanging on a string attached to the end of the spring. In this case, the magnitude of the force exerted on the spring is equal to the tension T in the string.

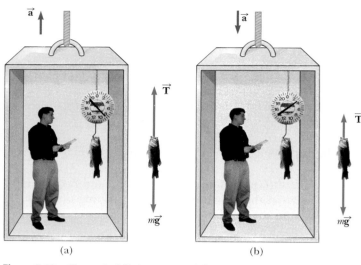

(a)   (b)

Figure 5.13   (Example 5.8) Apparent weight versus true weight. (a) When the elevator accelerates upward, the spring scale reads a value greater than the weight of the fish. (b) When the elevator accelerates downward, the spring scale reads a value less than the weight of the fish.

Therefore, we are looking for T. The force $\vec{\mathbf{T}}$ pulls down on the string and pulls up on the fish.

Categorize   We can categorize this problem by identifying the fish as a particle under a net force.

Analyze   Inspect the free-body diagrams for the fish in Figure 5.13 and notice that the external forces acting on the fish are the downward gravitational force $\vec{\mathbf{F}}_g = m\vec{\mathbf{g}}$ and the force $\vec{\mathbf{T}}$ exerted by the string. If the elevator is either at rest or moving at constant velocity, the fish is a particle in equilibrium, so $\Sigma F_y = T - F_g = 0$ or $T = F_g = mg$. (Remember that the scalar mg is the weight of the fish.)

Now suppose the elevator is moving with an acceleration $\vec{\mathbf{a}}$ relative to an observer standing outside the elevator in an inertial frame (see Fig. 5.13). The fish is now a particle under a net force.

Apply Newton's second law to the fish:

$$\sum F_y = T - mg = ma_y$$

Solve for T:

$$(1) \quad T = ma_y + mg = mg\left(\frac{a_y}{g} + 1\right) = F_g\left(\frac{a_y}{g} + 1\right)$$

where we have chosen upward as the positive y direction. We conclude from Equation (1) that the scale reading T is greater than the fish's weight mg if $\vec{\mathbf{a}}$ is upward, so a_y is positive, and that the reading is less than mg if $\vec{\mathbf{a}}$ is downward, so a_y is negative.

(B) Evaluate the scale readings for a 40.0-N fish if the elevator moves with an acceleration $a_y = \pm 2.00$ m/s².

Evaluate the scale reading from Equation (1) if $\vec{\mathbf{a}}$ is upward:

$$T = (40.0\ \text{N})\left(\frac{2.00\ \text{m/s}^2}{9.80\ \text{m/s}^2} + 1\right) = 48.2\ \text{N}$$

Evaluate the scale reading from Equation (1) if $\vec{\mathbf{a}}$ is downward:

$$T = (40.0\ \text{N})\left(\frac{-2.00\ \text{m/s}^2}{9.80\ \text{m/s}^2} + 1\right) = 31.8\ \text{N}$$

Finalize   Take this advice: if you buy a fish in an elevator, make sure the fish is weighed while the elevator is either at rest or accelerating downward! Furthermore, notice that from the information given here, one cannot determine the direction of motion of the elevator.

What If?   Suppose the elevator cable breaks and the elevator and its contents are in free-fall. What happens to the reading on the scale?

Answer   If the elevator falls freely, its acceleration is $a_y = -g$. We see from Equation (1) that the scale reading T is zero in this case; that is, the fish *appears* to be weightless.

EXAMPLE 5.9   **The Atwood Machine**

When two objects of unequal mass are hung vertically over a frictionless pulley of negligible mass as in Active Figure 5.14a, the arrangement is called an *Atwood machine*. The device is sometimes used in the laboratory to calculate the value of g. Determine the magnitude of the acceleration of the two objects and the tension in the lightweight cord.

SOLUTION

Conceptualize Imagine the situation pictured in Active Figure 5.14a in action: as one object moves upward, the other object moves downward. Because the objects are connected by an inextensible string, their accelerations must be of equal magnitude.

Categorize The objects in the Atwood machine are subject to the gravitational force as well as to the forces exerted by the strings connected to them. Therefore, we can categorize this problem as one involving two particles under a net force.

Analyze The free-body diagrams for the two objects are shown in Active Figure 5.14b. Two forces act on each object: the upward force $\vec{T}$ exerted by the string and the downward gravitational force. In problems such as this one in which the pulley is modeled as massless and frictionless, the tension in the string on both sides of the pulley is the same. If the pulley has mass or is subject to friction, the tensions on either side are not the same and the situation requires techniques we will learn in Chapter 10.

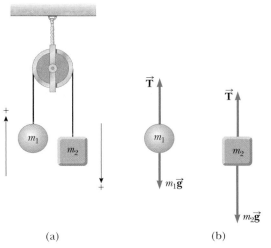

ACTIVE FIGURE 5.14

(Example 5.9) The Atwood machine. (a) Two objects connected by a massless inextensible cord over a frictionless pulley. (b) The free-body diagrams for the two objects.

Sign in at www.thomsonedu.com and go to ThomsonNOW to adjust the masses of the objects on the Atwood machine and observe the motion.

We must be very careful with signs in problems such as this. In Active Figure 5.14a, notice that if object 1 accelerates upward, object 2 accelerates downward. Therefore, for consistency with signs, if we define the upward direction as positive for object 1, we must define the downward direction as positive for object 2. With this sign convention, both objects accelerate in the same direction as defined by the choice of sign. Furthermore, according to this sign convention, the y component of the net force exerted on object 1 is $T - m_1g$, and the y component of the net force exerted on object 2 is $m_2g - T$.

Apply Newton's second law to object 1:

$$(1) \quad \sum F_y = T - m_1g = m_1a_y$$

Apply Newton's second law to object 2:

$$(2) \quad \sum F_y = m_2g - T = m_2a_y$$

Add Equation (2) to Equation (1), noticing that T cancels:

$$-m_1g + m_2g = m_1a_y + m_2a_y$$

Solve for the acceleration:

$$(3) \quad a_y = \left(\frac{m_2 - m_1}{m_1 + m_2}\right)g$$

Substitute Equation (3) into Equation (1) to find T:

$$(4) \quad T = m_1(g + a_y) = \left(\frac{2m_1m_2}{m_1 + m_2}\right)g$$

Finalize The acceleration given by Equation (3) can be interpreted as the ratio of the magnitude of the unbalanced force on the system $(m_2 - m_1)g$ to the total mass of the system $(m_1 + m_2)$, as expected from Newton's second law. Notice that the sign of the acceleration depends on the relative masses of the two objects.

What If? Describe the motion of the system if the objects have equal masses, that is, $m_1 = m_2$.

Answer If we have the same mass on both sides, the system is balanced and should not accelerate. Mathematically, we see that if $m_1 = m_2$, Equation (3) gives us $a_y = 0$.

What If? What if one of the masses is much larger than the other: $m_1 \gg m_2$?

Answer In the case in which one mass is infinitely larger than the other, we can ignore the effect of the smaller mass. Therefore, the larger mass should simply fall as if the smaller mass were not there. We see that if $m_1 \gg m_2$, Equation (3) gives us $a_y = -g$.

EXAMPLE 5.10 **Acceleration of Two Objects Connected by a Cord**

A ball of mass m_1 and a block of mass m_2 are attached by a lightweight cord that passes over a frictionless pulley of negligible mass as in Figure 5.15a. The block lies on a frictionless incline of angle θ. Find the magnitude of the acceleration of the two objects and the tension in the cord.

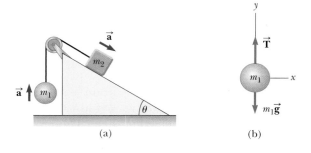

SOLUTION

Conceptualize Imagine the objects in Figure 5.15 in motion. If m_2 moves down the incline, m_1 moves upward. Because the objects are connected by a cord (which we assume does not stretch), their accelerations have the same magnitude.

Categorize We can identify forces on each of the two objects and we are looking for an acceleration, so we categorize the objects as particles under a net force.

Analyze Consider the free-body diagrams shown in Figures 5.15b and 5.15c.

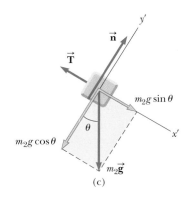

(c)

Figure 5.15 (Example 5.10) (a) Two objects connected by a lightweight cord strung over a frictionless pulley. (b) The free-body diagram for the ball. (c) The free-body diagram for the block. (The incline is frictionless.)

Apply Newton's second law in component form to the ball, choosing the upward direction as positive:

$$(1) \quad \sum F_x = 0$$

$$(2) \quad \sum F_y = T - m_1 g = m_1 a_y = m_1 a$$

For the ball to accelerate upward, it is necessary that $T > m_1 g$. In Equation (2), we replaced a_y with a because the acceleration has only a y component.

For the block it is convenient to choose the positive x' axis along the incline as in Figure 5.15c. For consistency with our choice for the ball, we choose the positive direction to be down the incline.

Apply Newton's second law in component form to the block:

$$(3) \quad \sum F_{x'} = m_2 g \sin \theta - T = m_2 a_{x'} = m_2 a$$

$$(4) \quad \sum F_{y'} = n - m_2 g \cos \theta = 0$$

In Equation (3), we replaced $a_{x'}$ with a because the two objects have accelerations of equal magnitude a.

Solve Equation (2) for T:

$$(5) \quad T = m_1(g + a)$$

Substitute this expression for T into Equation (3):

$$m_2 g \sin \theta - m_1(g + a) = m_2 a$$

Solve for a:

$$(6) \quad a = \frac{m_2 g \sin \theta - m_1 g}{m_1 + m_2}$$

Substitute this expression for a into Equation (5) to find T:

$$(7) \quad T = \frac{m_1 m_2 g (\sin \theta + 1)}{m_1 + m_2}$$

Finalize   The block accelerates down the incline only if $m_2 \sin \theta > m_1$. If $m_1 > m_2 \sin \theta$, the acceleration is up the incline for the block and downward for the ball. Also notice that the result for the acceleration, Equation (6), can be interpreted as the magnitude of the net external force acting on the ball–block system divided by the total mass of the system; this result is consistent with Newton's second law.

What If?   What happens in this situation if $\theta = 90°$?

Answer   If $\theta = 90°$, the inclined plane becomes vertical and there is no interaction between its surface and m_2. Therefore, this problem becomes the Atwood machine of Example 5.9. Letting $\theta \rightarrow 90°$ in Equations (6) and (7) causes them to reduce to Equations (3) and (4) of Example 5.9!

What If?   What if $m_1 = 0$?

Answer   If $m_1 = 0$, then m_2 is simply sliding down an inclined plane without interacting with m_1 through the string. Therefore, this problem becomes the sliding car problem in Example 5.6. Letting $m_1 \rightarrow 0$ in Equation (6) causes it to reduce to Equation (3) of Example 5.6!

5.8   Forces of Friction

When an object is in motion either on a surface or in a viscous medium such as air or water, there is resistance to the motion because the object interacts with its surroundings. We call such resistance a **force of friction**. Forces of friction are very important in our everyday lives. They allow us to walk or run and are necessary for the motion of wheeled vehicles.

Imagine that you are working in your garden and have filled a trash can with yard clippings. You then try to drag the trash can across the surface of your concrete patio as in Active Figure 5.16a. This surface is *real*, not an idealized, friction-

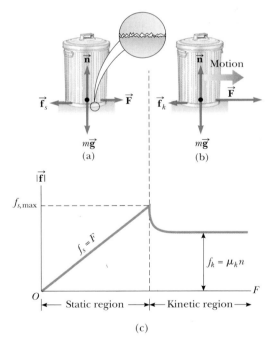

ACTIVE FIGURE 5.16

When pulling on a trash can, the direction of the force of friction $\vec{f}$ between the can and a rough surface is opposite the direction of the applied force $\vec{F}$. Because both surfaces are rough, contact is made only at a few points as illustrated in the "magnified" view. (a) For small applied forces, the magnitude of the force of static friction equals the magnitude of the applied force. (b) When the magnitude of the applied force exceeds the magnitude of the maximum force of static friction, the trash can breaks free. The applied force is now larger than the force of kinetic friction, and the trash can accelerates to the right. (c) A graph of friction force versus applied force. Notice that $f_{s,\,max} > f_k$.

Sign in at www.thomsonedu.com and go to ThomsonNOW to vary the applied force on the trash can and practice sliding it on surfaces of varying roughness. Notice the effect on the trash can's motion and the corresponding behavior of the graph in (c).

Force of static friction ▶

less surface. If we apply an external horizontal force $\vec{\mathbf{F}}$ to the trash can, acting to the right, the trash can remains stationary when $\vec{\mathbf{F}}$ is small. The force on the trash can that counteracts $\vec{\mathbf{F}}$ and keeps it from moving acts toward the left and is called the **force of static friction** $\vec{\mathbf{f}}_s$. As long as the trash can is not moving, $f_s = F$. Therefore, if $\vec{\mathbf{F}}$ is increased, $\vec{\mathbf{f}}_s$ also increases. Likewise, if $\vec{\mathbf{F}}$ decreases, $\vec{\mathbf{f}}_s$ also decreases. Experiments show that the friction force arises from the nature of the two surfaces: because of their roughness, contact is made only at a few locations where peaks of the material touch, as shown in the magnified view of the surface in Active Figure 5.16a.

At these locations, the friction force arises in part because one peak physically blocks the motion of a peak from the opposing surface and in part from chemical bonding ("spot welds") of opposing peaks as they come into contact. Although the details of friction are quite complex at the atomic level, this force ultimately involves an electrical interaction between atoms or molecules.

If we increase the magnitude of $\vec{\mathbf{F}}$ as in Active Figure 5.16b, the trash can eventually slips. When the trash can is on the verge of slipping, f_s has its maximum value $f_{s,\max}$ as shown in Active Figure 5.16c. When F exceeds $f_{s,\max}$, the trash can moves and accelerates to the right. We call the friction force for an object in motion the **force of kinetic friction** $\vec{\mathbf{f}}_k$. When the trash can is in motion, the force of kinetic friction on the can is less than $f_{s,\max}$ (Active Fig. 5.16c). The net force $F - f_k$ in the x direction produces an acceleration to the right, according to Newton's second law. If $F = f_k$, the acceleration is zero and the trash can moves to the right with constant speed. If the applied force $\vec{\mathbf{F}}$ is removed from the moving can, the friction force $\vec{\mathbf{f}}_k$ acting to the left provides an acceleration of the trash can in the $-x$ direction and eventually brings it to rest, again consistent with Newton's second law.

Force of kinetic friction ▶

Experimentally, we find that, to a good approximation, both $f_{s,\max}$ and f_k are proportional to the magnitude of the normal force exerted on an object by the surface. The following descriptions of the force of friction are based on experimental observations and serve as the model we shall use for forces of friction in problem solving:

PITFALL PREVENTION 5.9
The Equal Sign Is Used in Limited Situations

In Equation 5.9, the equal sign is used *only* in the case in which the surfaces are just about to break free and begin sliding. Do not fall into the common trap of using $f_s = \mu_s n$ in *any* static situation.

- The magnitude of the force of static friction between any two surfaces in contact can have the values

$$f_s \leq \mu_s n \tag{5.9}$$

where the dimensionless constant μ_s is called the **coefficient of static friction** and n is the magnitude of the normal force exerted by one surface on the other. The equality in Equation 5.9 holds when the surfaces are on the verge of slipping, that is, when $f_s = f_{s,\max} \equiv \mu_s n$. This situation is called *impending motion*. The inequality holds when the surfaces are not on the verge of slipping.

- The magnitude of the force of kinetic friction acting between two surfaces is

PITFALL PREVENTION 5.10
Friction Equations

Equations 5.9 and 5.10 are *not* vector equations. They are relationships between the *magnitudes* of the vectors representing the friction and normal forces. Because the friction and normal forces are perpendicular to each other, the vectors cannot be related by a multiplicative constant.

$$f_k = \mu_k n \tag{5.10}$$

where μ_k is the **coefficient of kinetic friction**. Although the coefficient of kinetic friction can vary with speed, we shall usually neglect any such variations in this text.

- The values of μ_k and μ_s depend on the nature of the surfaces, but μ_k is generally less than μ_s. Typical values range from around 0.03 to 1.0. Table 5.1 lists some reported values.

- The direction of the friction force on an object is parallel to the surface with which the object is in contact and opposite to the actual motion (kinetic friction) or the impending motion (static friction) of the object relative to the surface.

PITFALL PREVENTION 5.11
The Direction of the Friction Force

Sometimes, an incorrect statement about the friction force between an object and a surface is made—"the friction force on an object is opposite to its motion or impending motion"—rather than the correct phrasing, "the friction force on an object is opposite to its motion or impending motion *relative to the surface*."

- The coefficients of friction are nearly independent of the area of contact between the surfaces. We might expect that placing an object on the side having the most area might increase the friction force. Although this method provides more points in contact as in Active Figure 5.16a, the weight of the

TABLE 5.1
Coefficients of Friction

	μ_s	μ_k
Rubber on concrete	1.0	0.8
Steel on steel	0.74	0.57
Aluminum on steel	0.61	0.47
Glass on glass	0.94	0.4
Copper on steel	0.53	0.36
Wood on wood	0.25–0.5	0.2
Waxed wood on wet snow	0.14	0.1
Waxed wood on dry snow	—	0.04
Metal on metal (lubricated)	0.15	0.06
Teflon on Teflon	0.04	0.04
Ice on ice	0.1	0.03
Synovial joints in humans	0.01	0.003

Note: All values are approximate. In some cases, the coefficient of friction can exceed 1.0.

object is spread out over a larger area and the individual points are not pressed together as tightly. Because these effects approximately compensate for each other, the friction force is independent of the area.

(a)

Quick Quiz 5.6   You press your physics textbook flat against a vertical wall with your hand. What is the direction of the friction force exerted by the wall on the book? (a) downward   (b) upward   (c) out from the wall   (d) into the wall

Quick Quiz 5.7   You are playing with your daughter in the snow. She sits on a sled and asks you to slide her across a flat, horizontal field. You have a choice of (a) pushing her from behind by applying a force downward on her shoulders at 30° below the horizontal (Fig. 5.17a) or (b) attaching a rope to the front of the sled and pulling with a force at 30° above the horizontal (Fig 5.17b). Which would be easier for you and why?

(b)

Figure 5.17   (Quick Quiz 5.7) A father slides his daughter on a sled either by (a) pushing down on her shoulders or (b) pulling up on a rope.

EXAMPLE 5.11	**Experimental Determination of μ_s and μ_k**

The following is a simple method of measuring coefficients of friction. Suppose a block is placed on a rough surface inclined relative to the horizontal as shown in Active Figure 5.18. The incline angle is increased until the block starts to move. Show that you can obtain μ_s by measuring the critical angle θ_c at which this slipping just occurs.

SOLUTION

Conceptualize   Consider the free-body diagram in Active Figure 5.18 and imagine that the block tends to slide down the incline due to the gravitational force. To simulate the situation, place a coin on this book's cover and tilt the book until the coin begins to slide.

Categorize   The block is subject to various forces. Because we are raising the plane to the angle at which the block is just ready to begin to move but is not moving, we categorize the block as a particle in equilibrium.

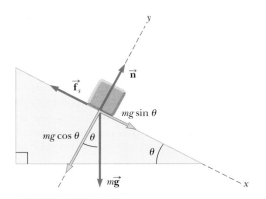

ACTIVE FIGURE 5.18

(Example 5.11) The external forces exerted on a block lying on a rough incline are the gravitational force $m\vec{\mathbf{g}}$, the normal force $\vec{\mathbf{n}}$, and the force of friction $\vec{\mathbf{f}}_s$. For convenience, the gravitational force is resolved into a component $mg \sin \theta$ along the incline and a component $mg \cos \theta$ perpendicular to the incline.

Sign in at www.thomsonedu.com and go to ThomsonNOW to investigate this situation further.

Analyze   The forces acting on the block are the gravitational force $m\vec{g}$, the normal force $\vec{n}$, and the force of static friction $\vec{f}_s$. We choose x to be parallel to the plane and y perpendicular to it.

Apply Equation 5.8 to the block:

(1) $\displaystyle\sum F_x = mg \sin \theta - f_s = 0$

(2) $\displaystyle\sum F_y = n - mg \cos \theta = 0$

Substitute $mg = n/\cos \theta$ from Equation (2) into Equation (1):

(3) $f_s = mg \sin \theta = \left(\dfrac{n}{\cos \theta}\right) \sin \theta = n \tan \theta$

When the incline angle is increased until the block is on the verge of slipping, the force of static friction has reached its maximum value $\mu_s n$. The angle θ in this situation is the critical angle θ_c. Make these substitutions in Equation (3):

$$\mu_s n = n \tan \theta_c$$
$$\mu_s = \tan \theta_c$$

For example, if the block just slips at $\theta_c = 20.0°$, we find that $\mu_s = \tan 20.0° = 0.364$.

Finalize   Once the block starts to move at $\theta \geq \theta_c$, it accelerates down the incline and the force of friction is $f_k = \mu_k n$. If θ is reduced to a value less than θ_c, however, it may be possible to find an angle θ_c' such that the block moves down the incline with constant speed as a particle in equilibrium again ($a_x = 0$). In this case, use Equations (1) and (2) with f_s replaced by f_k to find μ_k: $\mu_k = \tan \theta_c'$ where $\theta_c' < \theta_c$.

EXAMPLE 5.12   **The Sliding Hockey Puck**

A hockey puck on a frozen pond is given an initial speed of 20.0 m/s. If the puck always remains on the ice and slides 115 m before coming to rest, determine the coefficient of kinetic friction between the puck and ice.

SOLUTION

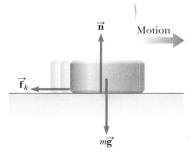

Conceptualize   Imagine that the puck in Figure 5.19 slides to the right and eventually comes to rest due to the force of kinetic friction.

Categorize   The forces acting on the puck are identified in Figure 5.19, but the text of the problem provides kinematic variables. Therefore, we categorize the problem in two ways. First, the problem involves a particle under a net force: kinetic friction causes the puck to accelerate. And, because we model the force of kinetic friction as independent of speed, the acceleration of the puck is constant. So, we can also categorize this problem as one involving a particle under constant acceleration.

Figure 5.19   (Example 5.12) After the puck is given an initial velocity to the right, the only external forces acting on it are the gravitational force $m\vec{g}$, the normal force $\vec{n}$, and the force of kinetic friction $\vec{f}_k$.

Analyze   First, we find the acceleration algebraically in terms of the coefficient of kinetic friction, using Newton's second law. Once we know the acceleration of the puck and the distance it travels, the equations of kinematics can be used to find the numerical value of the coefficient of kinetic friction.

Apply the particle under a net force model in the x direction to the puck:

(1) $\displaystyle\sum F_x = -f_k = ma_x$

Apply the particle in equilibrium model in the y direction to the puck:

(2) $\displaystyle\sum F_y = n - mg = 0$

Substitute $n = mg$ from Equation (2) and $f_k = \mu_k n$ into Equation (1):

$$-\mu_k n = -\mu_k mg = ma_x$$

$$a_x = -\mu_k g$$

The negative sign means the acceleration is to the left in Figure 5.19. Because the velocity of the puck is to the right, the puck is slowing down. The acceleration is independent of the mass of the puck and is constant because we assume that μ_k remains constant.

Apply the particle under constant acceleration model to the puck, using Equation 2.17, $v_{xf}^2 = v_{xi}^2 + 2a_x(x_f - x_i)$, with $x_i = 0$ and $v_f = 0$:

$$0 = v_{xi}^2 + 2a_x x_f = v_{xi}^2 - 2\mu_k g x_f$$

$$\mu_k = \frac{v_{xi}^2}{2g x_f}$$

$$\mu_k = \frac{(20.0 \text{ m/s})^2}{2(9.80 \text{ m/s}^2)(115 \text{ m})} = 0.117$$

Finalize   Notice that μ_k is dimensionless, as it should be, and that it has a low value, consistent with an object sliding on ice.

EXAMPLE 5.13   **Acceleration of Two Connected Objects When Friction Is Present**

A block of mass m_1 on a rough, horizontal surface is connected to a ball of mass m_2 by a lightweight cord over a lightweight, frictionless pulley as shown in Figure 5.20a. A force of magnitude F at an angle θ with the horizontal is applied to the block as shown and the block slides to the right. The coefficient of kinetic friction between the block and surface is μ_k. Determine the magnitude of the acceleration of the two objects.

Figure 5.20   (Example 5.13) (a) The external force $\vec{\mathbf{F}}$ applied as shown can cause the block to accelerate to the right. (b, c) The free-body diagrams assuming the block accelerates to the right and the ball accelerates upward. The magnitude of the force of kinetic friction in this case is given by $f_k = \mu_k n = \mu_k (m_1 g - F \sin \theta)$.

SOLUTION

Conceptualize   Imagine what happens as $\vec{\mathbf{F}}$ is applied to the block. Assuming $\vec{\mathbf{F}}$ is not large enough to lift the block, the block slides to the right and the ball rises.

Categorize   We can identify forces and we want an acceleration, so we categorize this problem as one involving two particles under a net force, the ball and the block.

Analyze   First draw free-body diagrams for the two objects as shown in Figures 5.20b and 5.20c. The applied force $\vec{\mathbf{F}}$ has x and y components $F \cos \theta$ and $F \sin \theta$, respectively. Because the two objects are connected, we can equate the magnitudes of the x component of the acceleration of the block and the y component of the acceleration of the ball and call them both a. Let us assume the motion of the block is to the right.

Apply the particle under a net force model to the block in the horizontal direction:

$$(1) \quad \sum F_x = F \cos \theta - f_k - T = m_1 a_x = m_1 a$$

Apply the particle in equilibrium model to the block in the vertical direction:

$$(2) \quad \sum F_y = n + F \sin \theta - m_1 g = 0$$

Apply the particle under a net force model to the ball in the vertical direction:

$$(3) \quad \sum F_y = T - m_2 g = m_2 a_y = m_2 a$$

Solve Equation (2) for n:

$$n = m_1 g - F \sin \theta$$

Substitute n into $f_k = \mu_k n$ from Equation 5.10:

$$(4) \quad f_k = \mu_k (m_1 g - F \sin \theta)$$

Substitute Equation (4) and the value of T from Equation (3) into Equation (1):

$$F \cos \theta - \mu_k (m_1 g - F \sin \theta) - m_2(a + g) = m_1 a$$

Solve for a:

$$(5) \quad a = \frac{F(\cos \theta + \mu_k \sin \theta) - (m_2 + \mu_k m_1)g}{m_1 + m_2}$$

Finalize   The acceleration of the block can be either to the right or to the left depending on the sign of the numerator in Equation (5). If the motion is to the left, we must reverse the sign of f_k in Equation (1) because the force of kinetic friction must oppose the motion of the block relative to the surface. In this case, the value of a is the same as in Equation (5), with the two plus signs in the numerator changed to minus signs.

Summary

ThomsonNOW™   Sign in at **www.thomsonedu.com** and go to ThomsonNOW to take a practice test for this chapter.

DEFINITIONS

An **inertial frame of reference** is a frame in which an object that does not interact with other objects experiences zero acceleration. Any frame moving with constant velocity relative to an inertial frame is also an inertial frame.	We define **force** as **that which causes a change in motion of an object**.

CONCEPTS AND PRINCIPLES

Newton's first law states that it is possible to find an inertial frame in which an object that does not interact with other objects experiences zero acceleration, or, equivalently, in the absence of an external force, when viewed from an inertial frame, an object at rest remains at rest and an object in uniform motion in a straight line maintains that motion. **Newton's second law** states that the acceleration of an object is directly proportional to the net force acting on it and inversely proportional to its mass. **Newton's third law** states that if two objects interact, the force exerted by object 1 on object 2 is equal in magnitude and opposite in direction to the force exerted by object 2 on object 1.	The **gravitational force** exerted on an object is equal to the product of its mass (a scalar quantity) and the free-fall acceleration: $\vec{F}_g = m\vec{g}$. The **weight** of an object is the magnitude of the gravitational force acting on the object.

The maximum **force of static friction** $\vec{f}_{s,\max}$ between an object and a surface is proportional to the normal force acting on the object. In general, $f_s \leq \mu_s n$, where μ_s is the **coefficient of static friction** and n is the magnitude of the normal force. When an object slides over a surface, the magnitude of the **force of kinetic friction** $\vec{f}_k$ is given by $f_k = \mu_k n$, where μ_k is the **coefficient of kinetic friction**. The direction of the friction force is opposite the direction of motion or impending motion of the object relative to the surface.

ANALYSIS MODELS FOR PROBLEM SOLVING

Particle Under a Net Force   If a particle of mass m experiences a nonzero net force, its acceleration is related to the net force by Newton's second law:

$$\sum \vec{\mathbf{F}} = m\vec{\mathbf{a}} \qquad (5.2)$$

Particle in Equilibrium   If a particle maintains a constant velocity (so that $\vec{\mathbf{a}} = 0$), which could include a velocity of zero, the forces on the particle balance and Newton's second law reduces to

$$\sum \vec{\mathbf{F}} = 0 \qquad (5.8)$$

$\vec{\mathbf{a}} = \mathbf{0}$
m
$\Sigma \vec{\mathbf{F}} = \mathbf{0}$

Questions

☐ denotes answer available in *Student Solutions Manual/Study Guide;* **O** denotes objective question

1. A ball is held in a person's hand. (a) Identify all the external forces acting on the ball and the reaction to each. (b) If the ball is dropped, what force is exerted on it while it is falling? Identify the reaction force in this case. (Ignore air resistance.)

2. If a car is traveling westward with a constant speed of 20 m/s, what is the resultant force acting on it?

3. **O** An experiment is performed on a puck on a level air hockey table, where friction is negligible. A constant horizontal force is applied to the puck and its acceleration is measured. Now the same puck is transported far into outer space, where both friction and gravity are negligible. The same constant force is applied to the puck (through a spring scale that stretches the same amount) and the puck's acceleration (relative to the distant stars) is measured. What is the puck's acceleration in outer space? (a) somewhat greater than its acceleration on the Earth   (b) the same as its acceleration on the Earth   (c) less than its acceleration on the Earth   (d) infinite because neither friction nor gravity constrains it   (e) very large because acceleration is inversely proportional to weight and the puck's weight is very small but not zero

4. In the motion picture *It Happened One Night* (Columbia Pictures, 1934), Clark Gable is standing inside a stationary bus in front of Claudette Colbert, who is seated. The bus suddenly starts moving forward and Clark falls into Claudette's lap. Why did that happen?

5. Your hands are wet and the restroom towel dispenser is empty. What do you do to get drops of water off your hands? How does your action exemplify one of Newton's laws? Which one?

6. A passenger sitting in the rear of a bus claims that she was injured when the driver slammed on the brakes, causing a suitcase to come flying toward her from the front of the bus. If you were the judge in this case, what disposition would you make? Why?

7. A spherical rubber balloon inflated with air is held stationary, and its opening, on the west side, is pinched shut. (a) Describe the forces exerted by the air on sections of the rubber. (b) After the balloon is released, it takes off toward the east, gaining speed rapidly. Explain this motion in terms of the forces now acting on the rubber. (c) Account for the motion of a skyrocket taking off from its launch pad.

8. If you hold a horizontal metal bar several centimeters above the ground and move it through grass, each leaf of grass bends out of the way. If you increase the speed of the bar, each leaf of grass will bend more quickly. How then does a rotary power lawn mower manage to cut grass? How can it exert enough force on a leaf of grass to shear it off?

9. A rubber ball is dropped onto the floor. What force causes the ball to bounce?

10. A child tosses a ball straight up. She says the ball is moving away from her hand because the ball feels an upward "force of the throw" as well as the gravitational force. (a) Can the "force of the throw" exceed the gravitational force? How would the ball move if it did? (b) Can the "force of the throw" be equal in magnitude to the gravitational force? Explain. (c) What strength can accurately be attributed to the force of the throw? Explain. (d) Why does the ball move away from the child's hand?

11. **O** The third graders are on one side of a schoolyard and the fourth graders on the other. The groups are throwing snowballs at each other. Between them, snowballs of various masses are moving with different velocities as shown in Figure Q5.11. Rank the snowballs (a) through (e) according to the magnitude of the total force exerted on each one. Ignore air resistance. If two snowballs rank together, make that fact clear.

Figure Q5.11

12. The mayor of a city decides to fire some city employees because they will not remove the obvious sags from the cables that support the city traffic lights. If you were a lawyer, what defense would you give on behalf of the employees? Which side do you think would win the case in court?

13. A clip from *America's Funniest Home Videos*. Balancing carefully, three boys inch out onto a horizontal tree branch above a pond, each planning to dive in separately. The youngest and cleverest boy notices that the branch is only barely strong enough to support them. He decides to jump straight up and land back on the branch to break it, spilling all three into the pond together. When he starts to carry out his plan, at what precise moment does the branch break? Explain. *Suggestion:* Pretend to be the clever boy and imitate what he does in slow motion. If you are still unsure, stand on a bathroom scale and repeat the suggestion.

14. When you push on a box with a 200-N force instead of a 50-N force, you can feel that you are making a greater effort. When a table exerts a 200-N upward normal force instead of one of smaller magnitude, is the table really doing anything differently?

15. A weightlifter stands on a bathroom scale. He pumps a barbell up and down. What happens to the reading on the scale as he does so? **What If?** What if he is strong enough to actually *throw* the barbell upward? How does the reading on the scale vary now?

16. (a) Can a normal force be horizontal? (b) Can a normal force be directed vertically downward? (c) Consider a tennis ball in contact with a stationary floor and with nothing else. Can the normal force be different in magnitude from the gravitational force exerted on the ball? (d) Can the force exerted by the floor on the ball be different in magnitude from the force the ball exerts on the floor? Explain each of your answers.

17. Suppose a truck loaded with sand accelerates along a highway. If the driving force exerted on the truck remains constant, what happens to the truck's acceleration if its trailer leaks sand at a constant rate through a hole in its bottom?

18. **O** In Figure Q5.18, the light, taut, unstretchable cord B joins block 1 and the larger-mass block 2. Cord A exerts a force on block 1 to make it accelerate forward. (a) How does the magnitude of the force exerted by cord A on block 1 compare with the magnitude of the force exerted by cord B on block 2? Is it larger, smaller, or equal? (b) How does the acceleration of block 1 compare with the acceleration (if any) of block 2? (c) Does cord B exert a force on block 1? If so, is it forward or backward? Is it larger, smaller, or equal in magnitude to the force exerted by cord B on block 2?

Figure Q5.18

19. Identify the action–reaction pairs in the following situations: a man takes a step, a snowball hits a girl in the back, a baseball player catches a ball, a gust of wind strikes a window.

20. **O** In an Atwood machine, illustrated in Figure 5.14, a light string that does not stretch passes over a light, frictionless pulley. On one side, block 1 hangs from the vertical string. On the other side, block 2 of larger mass hangs from the vertical string. (a) The blocks are released from rest. Is the magnitude of the acceleration of the heavier block 2 larger, smaller, or the same as the free-fall acceleration g? (b) Is the magnitude of the acceleration of block 2 larger, smaller, or the same as the acceleration of block 1? (c) Is the magnitude of the force the string exerts on block 2 larger, smaller, or the same as that of the force of the string on block 1?

21. Twenty people participate in a tug-of-war. The two teams of ten people are so evenly matched that neither team wins. After the game, the participants notice that a car is stuck in the mud. They attach the tug-of-war rope to the bumper of the car, and all the people pull on the rope. The heavy car has just moved a couple of decimeters when the rope breaks. Why did the rope break in this situation, but not when the same twenty people pulled on it in a tug-of-war?

22. **O** In Figure Q5.22, a locomotive has broken through the wall of a train station. As it did, what can be said about the force exerted by the locomotive on the wall? (a) The force exerted by the locomotive on the wall was bigger than the force the wall could exert on the locomotive. (b) The force exerted by the locomotive on the wall was the same in magnitude as the force exerted by the wall on the locomotive. (c) The force exerted by the locomotive on the wall was less than the force exerted by the wall on the locomotive. (d) The wall cannot be said to "exert" a force; after all, it broke.

Figure Q5.22

23. An athlete grips a light rope that passes over a low-friction pulley attached to the ceiling of a gym. A sack of sand precisely equal in weight to the athlete is tied to the other end of the rope. Both the sand and the athlete are initially at rest. The athlete climbs the rope, sometimes speeding up and slowing down as he does so. What happens to the sack of sand? Explain.

24. **O** A small bug is nestled between a 1-kg block and a 2-kg block on a frictionless table. A horizontal force can be applied to either of the blocks as shown in Figure Q5.24. **(i)** In which situation illustrated in the figure, (a) or (b), does the bug have a better chance of survival, or (c) does it make no difference? **(ii)** Consider the statement, "The force exerted by the larger block on the smaller one is

larger in magnitude than the force exerted by the smaller block on the larger one." Is this statement true only in situation (a)? Only in situation (b)? Is it true (c) in both situations or (d) in neither? **(iii)** Consider the statement, "As the blocks move, the force exerted by the block in back on the block in front is stronger than the force exerted by the front block on the back one." Is this statement true only in situation (a), only in situation (b), in (c) both situations, or in (d) neither?

(a)   (b)

Figure Q5.24

25. Can an object exert a force on itself? Argue for your answer.

26. **O** The harried manager of a discount department store is pushing horizontally with a force of magnitude 200 N on a box of shirts. The box is sliding across the horizontal floor with a forward acceleration. Nothing else touches the box. What must be true about the magnitude of the force of kinetic friction acting on the box (choose one)? (a) It is greater than 200 N. (b) It is less than 200 N. (c) It is equal to 200 N. (d) None of these statements is necessarily true.

27. A car is moving forward slowly and is speeding up. A student claims "the car exerts a force on itself" or "the car's engine exerts a force on the car." Argue that this idea cannot be accurate and that friction exerted by the road is the propulsive force on the car. Make your evidence and reasoning as persuasive as possible. Is it static or kinetic friction? *Suggestions:* Consider a road covered with light gravel. Consider a sharp print of the tire tread on an asphalt road, obtained by coating the tread with dust.

28. **O** The driver of a speeding empty truck slams on the brakes and skids to a stop through a distance d. **(i)** If the truck now carries a load that doubles its mass, what will be the truck's "skidding distance"? (a) $4d$ (b) $2d$ (c) $\sqrt{2}d$ (d) d (e) $d/\sqrt{2}$ (f) $d/2$ (g) $d/4$ **(ii)** If the initial speed of the empty truck were halved, what would be the truck's skidding distance? Choose from the same possibilities (a) through (g).

29. **O** An object of mass m is sliding with speed v_0 at some instant across a level tabletop, with which its coefficient of kinetic friction is μ. It then moves through a distance d and comes to rest. Which of the following equations for the speed v_0 is reasonable (choose one)? (a) $v_0 = \sqrt{-2\mu mgd}$

(b) $v_0 = \sqrt{2\mu mgd}$ (c) $v_0 = \sqrt{-2\mu gd}$ (d) $v_0 = \sqrt{2\mu gd}$ (e) $v_0 = \sqrt{2gd/\mu}$ (f) $v_0 = \sqrt{2\mu md}$ (g) $v_0 = \sqrt{2\mu d}$

30. **O** A crate remains stationary after it has been placed on a ramp inclined at an angle with the horizontal. Which of the following statements is or are correct about the magnitude of the friction force that acts on the crate? Choose all that are true. (a) It is larger than the weight of the crate. (b) It is at least equal to the weight of the crate. (c) It is equal to $\mu_s n$. (d) It is greater than the component of the gravitational force acting down the ramp. (e) It is equal to the component of the gravitational force acting down the ramp. (f) It is less than the component of the gravitational force acting down the ramp.

31. Suppose you are driving a classic car. Why should you avoid slamming on your brakes when you want to stop in the shortest possible distance? (Many modern cars have antilock brakes that avoid this problem.)

32. Describe a few examples in which the force of friction exerted on an object is in the direction of motion of the object.

33. **O** As shown in Figure Q5.33, student A, a 55-kg girl, sits on one chair with metal runners, at rest on a classroom floor. Student B, an 80-kg boy, sits on an identical chair. Both students keep their feet off the floor. A rope runs from student A's hands around a light pulley to the hands of a teacher standing on the floor next to her. The low-friction axle of the pulley is attached to a second rope held by student B. All ropes run parallel to the chair runners. (a) If student A pulls on her end of the rope, will her chair or will B's chair slide on the floor? (b) If instead the teacher pulls on his rope end, which chair slides? (c) If student B pulls on his rope, which chair slides? (d) Now the teacher ties his rope end to student A's chair. Student A pulls on the end of the rope in her hands. Which chair slides? (Vern Rockcastle suggested the idea for this question.)

Figure Q5.33

Problems

WebAssign The Problems from this chapter may be assigned online in WebAssign.

ThomsonNOW Sign in at **www.thomsonedu.com** and go to ThomsonNOW to assess your understanding of this chapter's topics with additional quizzing and conceptual questions.

1, 2, 3 denotes straightforward, intermediate, challenging; ☐ denotes full solution available in *Student Solutions Manual/Study Guide*; ▲ denotes coached solution with hints available at **www.thomsonedu.com;** denotes developing symbolic reasoning; ● denotes asking for qualitative reasoning; ▪ denotes computer useful in solving problem

Sections 5.1 through 5.6

1. A 3.00-kg object undergoes an acceleration given by $\vec{a} = (2.00\hat{i} + 5.00\hat{j})$ m/s^2. Find the resultant force acting on it and the magnitude of the resultant force.

2. A force $\vec{F}$ applied to an object of mass m_1 produces an acceleration of 3.00 m/s^2. The same force applied to a second object of mass m_2 produces an acceleration of 1.00 m/s^2. (a) What is the value of the ratio m_1/m_2? (b) If m_1 and m_2 are combined into one object, what is its acceleration under the action of the force $\vec{F}$?

3. ▲ To model a spacecraft, a toy rocket engine is securely fastened to a large puck that can glide with negligible friction over a horizontal surface, taken as the xy plane. The 4.00-kg puck has a velocity of $3.00\hat{i}$ m/s at one instant. Eight seconds later, its velocity is to be $(8.00\hat{i} + 10.0\hat{j})$ m/s. Assuming the rocket engine exerts a constant horizontal force, find (a) the components of the force and (b) its magnitude.

4. The average speed of a nitrogen molecule in air is about 6.70×10^2 m/s, and its mass is 4.68×10^{-26} kg. (a) If it takes 3.00×10^{-13} s for a nitrogen molecule to hit a wall and rebound with the same speed but moving in the opposite direction, what is the average acceleration of the molecule during this time interval? (b) What average force does the molecule exert on the wall?

5. An electron of mass 9.11×10^{-31} kg has an initial speed of 3.00×10^5 m/s. It travels in a straight line, and its speed increases to 7.00×10^5 m/s in a distance of 5.00 cm. Assuming its acceleration is constant, (a) determine the force exerted on the electron and (b) compare this force with the weight of the electron, which we ignored.

6. A woman weighs 120 lb. Determine (a) her weight in newtons and (b) her mass in kilograms.

7. The distinction between mass and weight was discovered after Jean Richer transported pendulum clocks from France to French Guiana in 1671. He found that they ran slower there quite systematically. The effect was reversed when the clocks returned to France. How much weight would you personally lose when traveling from Paris, France, where $g = 9.809\ 5$ m/s^2, to Cayenne, French Guiana, where $g = 9.780\ 8$ m/s^2?

8. Besides its weight, a 2.80-kg object is subjected to one other constant force. The object starts from rest and in 1.20 s experiences a displacement of $(4.20\hat{i} - 3.30\hat{j})$ m, where the direction of $\hat{j}$ is the upward vertical direction. Determine the other force.

9. Two forces $\vec{F}_1$ and $\vec{F}_2$ act on a 5.00-kg object. Taking $F_1 = 20.0$ N and $F_2 = 15.0$ N, find the accelerations in (a) and (b) of Figure P5.9.

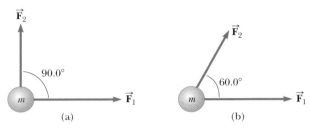

Figure P5.9

10. One or more external forces are exerted on each object enclosed in a dashed box shown in Figure 5.1. Identify the reaction to each of these forces.

11. You stand on the seat of a chair and then hop off. (a) During the time interval you are in flight down to the floor, the Earth is lurching up toward you with an acceleration of what order of magnitude? In your solution, explain your logic. Model the Earth as a perfectly solid object. (b) The Earth moves up through a distance of what order of magnitude?

12. A brick of mass M sits on a rubber pillow of mass m. Together they are sliding to the right at constant velocity on an ice-covered parking lot. (a) Draw a free-body diagram of the brick and identify each force acting on it. (b) Draw a free-body diagram of the pillow and identify each force acting on it. (c) Identify all the action–reaction pairs of forces in the brick–pillow–planet system.

13. A 15.0-lb block rests on the floor. (a) What force does the floor exert on the block? (b) A rope is tied to the block and is run vertically over a pulley. The other end of the rope is attached to a free-hanging 10.0-lb object. What is the force exerted by the floor on the 15.0-lb block? (c) If we replace the 10.0-lb object in part (b) with a 20.0-lb object, what is the force exerted by the floor on the 15.0-lb block?

14. Three forces acting on an object are given by $\vec{F}_1 = (-2.00\hat{i} + 2.00\hat{j})$ N, $\vec{F}_2 = (5.00\hat{i} - 3.00\hat{j})$ N, and $\vec{F}_3 = (-45.0\hat{i})$ N. The object experiences an acceleration of magnitude 3.75 m/s^2. (a) What is the direction of the acceleration? (b) What is the mass of the object? (c) If the object is initially at rest, what is its speed after 10.0 s? (d) What are the velocity components of the object after 10.0 s?

Section 5.7 Some Applications of Newton's Laws

15. Figure P5.15 shows a worker poling a boat—a very efficient mode of transportation—across a shallow lake. He pushes parallel to the length of the light pole, exerting on the bottom of the lake a force of 240 N. Assume the pole lies in the vertical plane containing the boat's keel.

At one moment, the pole makes an angle of 35.0° with the vertical and the water exerts a horizontal drag force of 47.5 N on the boat, opposite to its forward velocity of magnitude 0.857 m/s. The mass of the boat including its cargo and the worker is 370 kg. (a) The water exerts a buoyant force vertically upward on the boat. Find the magnitude of this force. (b) Model the forces as constant over a short interval of time to find the velocity of the boat 0.450 s after the moment described.

Figure P5.15

16. A 3.00-kg object is moving in a plane, with its x and y coordinates given by $x = 5t^2 - 1$ and $y = 3t^3 + 2$, where x and y are in meters and t is in seconds. Find the magnitude of the net force acting on this object at $t = 2.00$ s.

17. The distance between two telephone poles is 50.0 m. When a 1.00-kg bird lands on the telephone wire midway between the poles, the wire sags 0.200 m. Draw a free-body diagram of the bird. How much tension does the bird produce in the wire? Ignore the weight of the wire.

18. An iron bolt of mass 65.0 g hangs from a string 35.7 cm long. The top end of the string is fixed. Without touching it, a magnet attracts the bolt so that it remains stationary, displaced horizontally 28.0 cm to the right from the previously vertical line of the string. (a) Draw a free-body diagram of the bolt. (b) Find the tension in the string. (c) Find the magnetic force on the bolt.

19. ● Figure P5.19 shows the horizontal forces acting on a sailboat moving north at constant velocity, seen from a point straight above its mast. At its particular speed, the water exerts a 220-N drag force on the sailboat's hull. (a) Choose the x direction as east and the y direction as north. Write two component equations representing Newton's second law. Solve the equations for P (the force

exerted by the wind on the sail) and for n (the force exerted by the water on the keel). (b) Choose the x direction as 40.0° north of east and the y direction as 40.0° west of north. Write Newton's second law as two component equations and solve for n and P. (c) Compare your solutions. Do the results agree? Is one calculation significantly easier?

20. A bag of cement of weight 325 N hangs in equilibrium from three wires as shown in Figure P5.20. Two of the wires make angles $\theta_1 = 60.0°$ and $\theta_2 = 25.0°$ with the horizontal. Assuming the system is in equilibrium, find the tensions T_1, T_2, and T_3 in the wires.

Figure P5.20 Problems 20 and 21.

21. A bag of cement of weight F_g hangs in equilibrium from three wires as shown in Figure P5.20. Two of the wires make angles θ_1 and θ_2 with the horizontal. Assuming the system is in equilibrium, show that the tension in the left-hand wire is

$$T_1 = \frac{F_g \cos \theta_2}{\sin (\theta_1 + \theta_2)}$$

22. ● You are a judge in a children's kite-flying contest, and two children will win prizes, one for the kite that pulls the most strongly on its string and one for the kite that pulls the least strongly on its string. To measure string tensions, you borrow a mass hanger, some slotted masses, and a protractor from your physics teacher, and you use the following protocol, illustrated in Figure P5.22. Wait for a child to get her kite well controlled, hook the hanger onto the kite string about 30 cm from her hand, pile on slotted masses until that section of string is horizontal, record the mass required, and record the angle between the horizontal and the string running up to the kite. (a) Explain how this method works. As you construct your explanation, imagine that the children's parents ask you about your method, that they might make false assumptions about your ability

Figure P5.19

Figure P5.22

2 = intermediate;   3 = challenging;   □ = SSM/SG;   ▲ = ThomsonNow;   ░ = symbolic reasoning;   ● = qualitative reasoning

without concrete evidence, and that your explanation is an opportunity to give them confidence in your evaluation technique. (b) Find the string tension if the mass is 132 g and the angle of the kite string is 46.3°.

23. The systems shown in Figure P5.23 are in equilibrium. If the spring scales are calibrated in newtons, what do they read? Ignore the masses of the pulleys and strings, and assume the pulleys and the incline in part (d) are frictionless.

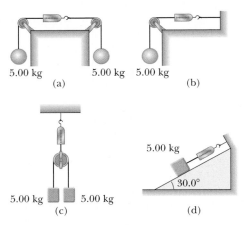

Figure P5.23

24. Draw a free-body diagram of a block that slides down a frictionless plane having an inclination of $\theta = 15.0°$. The block starts from rest at the top, and the length of the incline is 2.00 m. Find (a) the acceleration of the block and (b) its speed when it reaches the bottom of the incline.

25. ▲ A 1.00-kg object is observed to have an acceleration of 10.0 m/s² in a direction 60.0° east of north (Fig. P5.25). The force $\vec{F}_2$ exerted on the object has a magnitude of 5.00 N and is directed north. Determine the magnitude and direction of the force $\vec{F}_1$ acting on the object.

Figure P5.25

26. A 5.00-kg object placed on a frictionless, horizontal table is connected to a string that passes over a pulley and then is fastened to a hanging 9.00-kg object as shown in Figure P5.26. Draw free-body diagrams of both objects. Find the acceleration of the two objects and the tension in the string.

Figure P5.26 Problems 26 and 41.

27. Figure P5.27 shows the speed of a person's body as he does a chin-up. Assume the motion is vertical and the mass of the person's body is 64.0 kg. Determine the force exerted by the chin-up bar on his body at (a) time zero, (b) time 0.5 s, (c) time 1.1 s, and (d) time 1.6 s.

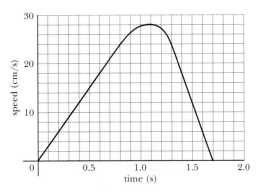

Figure P5.27

28. Two objects are connected by a light string that passes over a frictionless pulley as shown in Figure P5.28. Draw free-body diagrams of both objects. Assuming the incline is frictionless, $m_1 = 2.00$ kg, $m_2 = 6.00$ kg, and $\theta = 55.0°$, find (a) the accelerations of the objects, (b) the tension in the string, and (c) the speed of each object 2.00 s after they are released from rest.

Figure P5.28

29. ▲ A block is given an initial velocity of 5.00 m/s up a frictionless 20.0° incline. How far up the incline does the block slide before coming to rest?

30. In Figure P5.30, the man and the platform together weigh 950 N. The pulley can be modeled as frictionless. Determine how hard the man has to pull on the rope to lift himself steadily upward above the ground. (Or is it impossible? If so, explain why.)

Figure P5.30

2 = intermediate;   3 = challenging;   ☐ = SSM/SG;   ▲ = ThomsonNow;   = symbolic reasoning;   ● = qualitative reasoning

31. In the system shown in Figure P5.31, a horizontal force $\vec{F}_x$ acts on the 8.00-kg object. The horizontal surface is frictionless. Consider the acceleration of the sliding object as a function of F_x. (a) For what values of F_x does the 2.00-kg object accelerate upward? (b) For what values of F_x is the tension in the cord zero? (c) Plot the acceleration of the 8.00-kg object versus F_x. Include values of F_x from -100 N to $+100$ N.

8.00 kg

$\vec{F}_x$

2.00 kg

Figure P5.31

32. An object of mass m_1 on a frictionless horizontal table is connected to an object of mass m_2 through a very light pulley P_1 and a light fixed pulley P_2 as shown in Figure P5.32. (a) If a_1 and a_2 are the accelerations of m_1 and m_2, respectively, what is the relation between these accelerations? Express (b) the tensions in the strings and (c) the accelerations a_1 and a_2 in terms of g and of the masses m_1 and m_2.

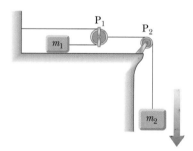

P_1

P_2

m_1

m_2

Figure P5.32

33. A 72.0-kg man stands on a spring scale in an elevator. Starting from rest, the elevator ascends, attaining its maximum speed of 1.20 m/s in 0.800 s. It travels with this constant speed for the next 5.00 s. The elevator then undergoes a uniform acceleration in the negative y direction for 1.50 s and comes to rest. What does the spring scale register (a) before the elevator starts to move, (b) during the first 0.800 s, (c) while the elevator is traveling at constant speed, and (d) during the time interval it is slowing down?

34. In the Atwood machine shown in Figure 5.14a, $m_1 = 2.00$ kg and $m_2 = 7.00$ kg. The masses of the pulley and string are negligible by comparison. The pulley turns without friction and the string does not stretch. The lighter object is released with a sharp push that sets it into motion at $v_i = 2.40$ m/s downward. (a) How far will m_1 descend below its initial level? (b) Find the velocity of m_1 after 1.80 seconds.

Section 5.8 Forces of Friction

35. A car is traveling at 50.0 mi/h on a horizontal highway. (a) If the coefficient of static friction between road and tires on a rainy day is 0.100, what is the minimum distance in which the car will stop? (b) What is the stopping distance when the surface is dry and $\mu_s = 0.600$?

36. A 25.0-kg block is initially at rest on a horizontal surface. A horizontal force of 75.0 N is required to set the block in motion, after which a horizontal force of 60.0 N is required to keep the block moving with constant speed. Find the coefficients of static and kinetic friction from this information.

37. Your 3.80-kg physics book is next to you on the horizontal seat of your car. The coefficient of static friction between the book and the seat is 0.650, and the coefficient of kinetic friction is 0.550. Suppose you are traveling at 72.0 km/h = 20.0 m/s and brake to a stop over a distance of 45.0 m. (a) Will the book start to slide over the seat? (b) What force does the seat exert on the book in this process?

38. ● Before 1960, it was believed that the maximum attainable coefficient of static friction for an automobile tire was less than 1. Then, around 1962, three companies independently developed racing tires with coefficients of 1.6. Since then, tires have improved, as illustrated in this problem. According to the 1990 *Guinness Book of Records*, the fastest time interval for a piston-engine car initially at rest to cover a distance of one-quarter mile is 4.96 s. Shirley Muldowney set this record in September 1989. (a) Assume the rear wheels lifted the front wheels off the pavement as shown in Figure P5.38. What minimum value of μ_s is necessary to achieve the record time interval? (b) Suppose Muldowney were able to double her engine power, keeping other things equal. How would this change affect the time interval?

Jamie Squire/Allsport/Getty Images

Figure P5.38

39. ▲ A 3.00-kg block starts from rest at the top of a 30.0° incline and slides a distance of 2.00 m down the incline in 1.50 s. Find (a) the magnitude of the acceleration of the block, (b) the coefficient of kinetic friction between block and plane, (c) the friction force acting on the block, and (d) the speed of the block after it has slid 2.00 m.

40. A woman at an airport is towing her 20.0-kg suitcase at constant speed by pulling on a strap at an angle θ above the horizontal (Fig. P5.40). She pulls on the strap with a 35.0-N force. The friction force on the suitcase is 20.0 N. Draw a free-body diagram of the suitcase. (a) What angle does the strap make with the horizontal? (b) What normal force does the ground exert on the suitcase?

θ

Figure P5.40

2 = intermediate; 3 = challenging; □ = SSM/SG; ▲ = ThomsonNow; = symbolic reasoning; ● = qualitative reasoning

41. A 9.00-kg hanging object is connected, by a light, inextensible cord over a light, frictionless pulley, to a 5.00-kg block that is sliding on a flat table (Fig. P5.26). Taking the coefficient of kinetic friction as 0.200, find the tension in the string.

42. Three objects are connected on a table as shown in Figure P5.42. The rough table has a coefficient of kinetic friction of 0.350. The objects have masses of 4.00 kg, 1.00 kg, and 2.00 kg, as shown, and the pulleys are frictionless. Draw a free-body diagram for each object. (a) Determine the acceleration of each object and their directions. (b) Determine the tensions in the two cords.

Figure P5.42

43. Two blocks connected by a rope of negligible mass are being dragged by a horizontal force (Fig. P5.43). Suppose $F = 68.0$ N, $m_1 = 12.0$ kg, $m_2 = 18.0$ kg, and the coefficient of kinetic friction between each block and the surface is 0.100. (a) Draw a free-body diagram for each block. (b) Determine the tension T and the magnitude of the acceleration of the system.

Figure P5.43

44. ● A block of mass 3.00 kg is pushed against a wall by a force $\vec{P}$ that makes a $\theta = 50.0°$ angle with the horizontal as shown in Figure P5.44. The coefficient of static friction between the block and the wall is 0.250. (a) Determine the possible values for the magnitude of $\vec{P}$ that allow the block to remain stationary. (b) Describe what happens if $|\vec{P}|$ has a larger value and what happens if it is smaller. (c) Repeat parts (a) and (b) assuming the force makes an angle of $\theta = 13.0°$ with the horizontal.

Figure P5.44

45. ● A 420-g block is at rest on a horizontal surface. The coefficient of static friction between the block and the surface is 0.720, and the coefficient of kinetic friction is 0.340. A force of magnitude P pushes the block forward and downward as shown in Figure P5.45. Assume the force is applied at an angle of 37.0° below the horizontal. (a) Find the acceleration of the block as a function of P. (b) If $P = 5.00$ N, find the acceleration and the friction force exerted on the block. (c) If $P = 10.0$ N, find the acceleration and the friction force exerted on the block. (d) Describe in words how the acceleration depends on P. Is there a definite minimum acceleration for the block? If so, what is it? Is there a definite maximum?

Figure P5.45

46. **Review problem.** One side of the roof of a building slopes up at 37.0°. A student throws a Frisbee onto the roof. It strikes with a speed of 15.0 m/s, does not bounce, and then slides straight up the incline. The coefficient of kinetic friction between the plastic and the roof is 0.400. The Frisbee slides 10.0 m up the roof to its peak, where it goes into free fall, following a parabolic trajectory with negligible air resistance. Determine the maximum height the Frisbee reaches above the point where it struck the roof.

47. The board sandwiched between two other boards in Figure P5.47 weighs 95.5 N. If the coefficient of friction between the boards is 0.663, what must be the magnitude of the compression forces (assumed horizontal) acting on both sides of the center board to keep it from slipping?

Figure P5.47

48. A magician pulls a tablecloth from under a 200-g mug located 30.0 cm from the edge of the cloth. The cloth exerts a friction force of 0.100 N on the mug, and the cloth is pulled with a constant acceleration of 3.00 m/s². How far does the mug move relative to the horizontal tabletop before the cloth is completely out from under it? Note that the cloth must move more than 30 cm relative to the tabletop during the process.

49. ● A package of dishes (mass 60.0 kg) sits on the flatbed of a pickup truck with an open tailgate. The coefficient of static friction between the package and the truck's flatbed is 0.300, and the coefficient of kinetic friction is 0.250. (a) The truck accelerates forward on level ground. What is the maximum acceleration the truck can have so that the package does not slide relative to the truck bed? (b) The truck barely exceeds this acceleration and then moves with constant acceleration, with the package sliding along its bed. What is the acceleration of the package relative to the ground? (c) The driver cleans up the frag-

ments of dishes and starts over again with an identical package at rest in the truck. The truck accelerates up a hill inclined at 10.0° with the horizontal. Now what is the maximum acceleration the truck can have such that the package does not slide relative to the flatbed? (d) When the truck exceeds this acceleration, what is the acceleration of the package relative to the ground? (e) For the truck parked at rest on a hill, what is the maximum slope the hill can have such that the package does not slide? (f) Is any piece of data unnecessary for the solution in all the parts of this problem? Explain.

Additional Problems

50. The following equations describe the motion of a system of two objects:

$$+ n - (6.50 \text{ kg})(9.80 \text{ m/s}^2) \cos 13.0° = 0$$

$$f_k = 0.360n$$

$$+ T + (6.50 \text{ kg})(9.80 \text{ m/s}^2) \sin 13.0° - f_k = (6.50 \text{ kg})a$$

$$- T + (3.80 \text{ kg})(9.80 \text{ m/s}^2) = (3.80 \text{ kg})a$$

(a) Solve the equations for a and T. (b) Describe a situation to which these equations apply. Draw free-body diagrams for both objects.

51. An inventive child named Pat wants to reach an apple in a tree without climbing the tree. Sitting in a chair connected to a rope that passes over a frictionless pulley (Fig. P5.51), Pat pulls on the loose end of the rope with such a force that the spring scale reads 250 N. Pat's true weight is 320 N, and the chair weighs 160 N. (a) Draw free-body diagrams for Pat and the chair considered as separate systems, and another diagram for Pat and the chair considered as one system. (b) Show that the acceleration of the system is *upward* and find its magnitude. (c) Find the force Pat exerts on the chair.

Figure P5.51   Problems 51 and 52.

52. ● In the situation described in Problem 51 and Figure P5.51, the masses of the rope, spring balance, and pulley are negligible. Pat's feet are not touching the ground. (a) Assume Pat is momentarily at rest when he stops pulling down on the rope and passes the end of the rope to another child, of weight 440 N, who is standing on the ground next to him. The rope does not break. Describe the ensuing motion. (b) Instead, assume Pat is momentar-

ily at rest when he ties the end of the rope to a strong hook projecting from the tree trunk. Explain why this action can make the rope break.

53. A time-dependent force, $\vec{F} = (8.00\hat{i} - 4.00t\hat{j})$ N, where t is in seconds, is exerted on a 2.00-kg object initially at rest. (a) At what time will the object be moving with a speed of 15.0 m/s? (b) How far is the object from its initial position when its speed is 15.0 m/s? (c) Through what total displacement has the object traveled at this moment?

54. ● Three blocks are in contact with one another on a frictionless, horizontal surface as shown in Figure P5.54. A horizontal force $\vec{F}$ is applied to m_1. Take $m_1 = 2.00$ kg, $m_2 = 3.00$ kg, $m_3 = 4.00$ kg, and $F = 18.0$ N. Draw a separate free-body diagram for each block and find (a) the acceleration of the blocks, (b) the *resultant* force on each block, and (c) the magnitudes of the contact forces between the blocks. (d) You are working on a construction project. A coworker is nailing plasterboard on one side of a light partition, and you are on the opposite side, providing "backing" by leaning against the wall with your back pushing on it. Every hammer blow makes your back sting. The supervisor helps you to put a heavy block of wood between the wall and your back. Using the situation analyzed in parts (a), (b), and (c) as a model, explain how this change works to make your job more comfortable.

Figure P5.54

55. ● A rope with mass m_1 is attached to the bottom front edge of a block with mass 4.00 kg. Both the rope and the block rest on a horizontal frictionless surface. The rope does not stretch. The free end of the rope is pulled with a horizontal force of 12.0 N. (a) Find the acceleration of the system, as it depends on m_1. (b) Find the magnitude of the force the rope exerts on the block, as it depends on m_1. (c) Evaluate the acceleration and the force on the block for $m_1 = 0.800$ kg. *Suggestion:* You may find it easier to do part (c) before parts (a) and (b).

What If? (d) What happens to the force on the block as the rope's mass grows beyond all bounds? (e) What happens to the force on the block as the rope's mass approaches zero? (f) What theorem can you state about the tension in a *light* cord joining a pair of moving objects?

56. A black aluminum glider floats on a film of air above a level aluminum air track. Aluminum feels essentially no force in a magnetic field, and air resistance is negligible. A strong magnet is attached to the top of the glider, forming a total mass of 240 g. A piece of scrap iron attached to one end stop on the track attracts the magnet with a force of 0.823 N when the iron and the magnet are separated by 2.50 cm. (a) Find the acceleration of the glider at this instant. (b) The scrap iron is now attached to another green glider, forming a total mass of 120 g. Find the acceleration of each glider when they are simultaneously released at 2.50-cm separation.

57. ▲ An object of mass M is held in place by an applied force $\vec{F}$ and a pulley system as shown in Figure P5.57. The pulleys are massless and frictionless. Find (a) the tension in each section of rope, T_1, T_2, T_3, T_4, and T_5 and (b) the magnitude of $\vec{F}$. *Suggestion:* Draw a free-body diagram for each pulley.

Figure P5.57

58. ● A block of mass 2.20 kg is accelerated across a rough surface by a light cord passing over a small pulley as shown in Figure P5.58. The tension T in the cord is maintained at 10.0 N, and the pulley is 0.100 m above the top of the block. The coefficient of kinetic friction is 0.400. (a) Determine the acceleration of the block when $x = 0.400$ m. (b) Describe the general behavior of the acceleration as the block slides from a location where x is large to $x = 0$. (c) Find the maximum value of the acceleration and the position x for which it occurs. (d) Find the value of x for which the acceleration is zero.

Figure P5.58

59. ● Physics students from San Diego have come in first and second in a contest and are down at the docks, watching their prizes being unloaded from a freighter. On a single light vertical cable that does not stretch, a crane is lifting a 1 207-kg Ferrari and, below it, a 1 461-kg red BMW Z8. The Ferrari is moving upward with speed 3.50 m/s and acceleration 1.25 m/s². (a) How do the velocity and acceleration of the BMW compare with those of the Ferrari? (b) Find the tension in the cable between the BMW and the Ferrari. (c) Find the tension in the cable above the Ferrari. (d) In our model, what is the total force exerted

on the section of cable between the cars? What velocity do you predict for it 0.01 s into the future? Explain the motion of this section of cable in cause-and-effect terms.

60. A 2.00-kg aluminum block and a 6.00-kg copper block are connected by a light string over a frictionless pulley. They sit on a steel surface as shown in Figure P5.60, where $\theta = 30.0°$. When they are released from rest, will they start to move? If so, determine (a) their acceleration and (b) the tension in the string. If not, determine the sum of the magnitudes of the forces of friction acting on the blocks.

Figure P5.60

61. A crate of weight F_g is pushed by a force $\vec{P}$ on a horizontal floor. (a) The coefficient of static friction is μ_s, and $\vec{P}$ is directed at angle θ below the horizontal. Show that the minimum value of P that will move the crate is given by

$$P = \frac{\mu_s F_g \sec \theta}{1 - \mu_s \tan \theta}$$

(b) Find the minimum value of P that can produce motion when $\mu_s = 0.400$, $F_g = 100$ N, and $\theta = 0°$, 15.0°, 30.0°, 45.0°, and 60.0°.

62. Review problem. A block of mass $m = 2.00$ kg is released from rest at $h = 0.500$ m above the surface of a table, at the top of a $\theta = 30.0°$ incline as shown in Figure P5.62. The frictionless incline is fixed on a table of height $H = 2.00$ m. (a) Determine the acceleration of the block as it slides down the incline. (b) What is the velocity of the block as it leaves the incline? (c) How far from the table will the block hit the floor? (d) What time interval elapses between when the block is released and when it hits the floor? (e) Does the mass of the block affect any of the above calculations?

Figure P5.62   Problems 62 and 68.

63. ● A couch cushion of mass m is released from rest at the top of a building having height h. A wind blowing along the side of the building exerts a constant horizontal force of magnitude F on the cushion as it drops as shown in Figure P5.63. The air exerts no vertical force. (a) Show that the path of the cushion is a straight line. (b) Does

Figure P5.63

the cushion fall with constant velocity? Explain. (c) If $m =$ 1.20 kg, $h =$ 8.00 m, and $F =$ 2.40 N, how far from the building will the cushion hit the level ground? **What If?** (d) If the cushion is thrown downward with a nonzero speed at the top of the building, what will be the shape of its trajectory? Explain.

64. ⚑ A student is asked to measure the acceleration of a cart on a "frictionless" inclined plane as shown in Figure 5.11, using an air track, a stopwatch, and a meter stick. The height of the incline is measured to be 1.774 cm, and the total length of the incline is measured to be $d =$ 127.1 cm. Hence, the angle of inclination θ is determined from the relation $\sin \theta =$ 1.774/127.1. The cart is released from rest at the top of the incline, and its position x along the incline is measured as a function of time, where $x = 0$ refers to the cart's initial position. For x values of 10.0 cm, 20.0 cm, 35.0 cm, 50.0 cm, 75.0 cm, and 100 cm, the measured times at which these positions are reached (averaged over five runs) are 1.02 s, 1.53 s, 2.01 s, 2.64 s, 3.30 s, and 3.75 s, respectively. Construct a graph of x versus t^2, and perform a linear least-squares fit to the data. Determine the acceleration of the cart from the slope of this graph, and compare it with the value you would get using $a = g \sin \theta$, where $g =$ 9.80 m/s².

65. A 1.30-kg toaster is not plugged in. The coefficient of static friction between the toaster and a horizontal countertop is 0.350. To make the toaster start moving, you carelessly pull on its electric cord. (a) For the cord tension to be as small as possible, you should pull at what angle above the horizontal? (b) With this angle, how large must the tension be?

66. ● In Figure P5.66, the pulleys and the cords are light, all surfaces are frictionless, and the cords do not stretch. (a) How does the acceleration of block 1 compare with the acceleration of block 2? Explain your reasoning. (b) The mass of block 2 is 1.30 kg. Find its acceleration as it depends on the mass m_1 of block 1. (c) Evaluate your

Figure P5.66

answer for $m_1 =$ 0.550 kg. *Suggestion:* You may find it easier to do part (c) before part (b). **What If?** (d) What does the result of part (b) predict if m_1 is very much less than 1.30 kg? (e) What does the result of part (b) predict if m_1 approaches infinity? (f) What is the tension in the long cord in this last case? (g) Could you anticipate the answers (d), (e), and (f) without first doing part (b)? Explain.

67. What horizontal force must be applied to the cart shown in Figure P5.67 so that the blocks remain stationary relative to the cart? Assume all surfaces, wheels, and pulley are frictionless. Notice that the force exerted by the string accelerates m_1.

Figure P5.67

68. In Figure P5.62, the incline has mass M and is fastened to the stationary horizontal tabletop. The block of mass m is placed near the bottom of the incline and is released with a quick push that sets it sliding upward. The block stops near the top of the incline, as shown in the figure, and then slides down again, always without friction. Find the force that the tabletop exerts on the incline throughout this motion.

69. A van accelerates down a hill (Fig. P5.69), going from rest to 30.0 m/s in 6.00 s. During the acceleration, a toy ($m =$ 0.100 kg) hangs by a string from the van's ceiling. The acceleration is such that the string remains perpendicular to the ceiling. Determine (a) the angle θ and (b) the tension in the string.

Figure P5.69

70. ⚑ An 8.40-kg object slides down a fixed, frictionless inclined plane. Use a computer to determine and tabulate the normal force exerted on the object and its acceleration for a series of incline angles (measured from the horizontal) ranging from 0° to 90° in 5° increments. Plot a graph of the normal force and the acceleration as functions of the incline angle. In the limiting cases of 0° and 90°, are your results consistent with the known behavior?

71. A mobile is formed by supporting four metal butterflies of equal mass m from a string of length L. The points of support are evenly spaced a distance ℓ apart as shown in

Figure P5.71. The string forms an angle θ_1 with the ceiling at each endpoint. The center section of string is horizontal. (a) Find the tension in each section of string in terms of θ_1, m, and g. (b) Find the angle θ_2, in terms of θ_1, that the sections of string between the outside butterflies and the inside butterflies form with the horizontal. (c) Show that the distance D between the endpoints of the string is

$$D = \frac{L}{5}\left(2\cos\theta_1 + 2\cos\left[\tan^{-1}(\tfrac{1}{2}\tan\theta_1)\right] + 1\right)$$

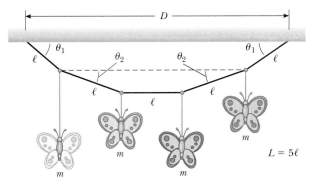

Figure P5.71

Answers to Quick Quizzes

5.1 (d). Choice (a) is true. Newton's first law tells us that motion requires no force: an object in motion continues to move at constant velocity in the absence of external forces. Choice (b) is also true. A stationary object can have several forces acting on it, but if the vector sum of all these external forces is zero, there is no net force and the object remains stationary.

5.2 (a). If a single force acts, this force constitutes the net force and there is an acceleration according to Newton's second law.

5.3 (d). With twice the force, the object will experience twice the acceleration. Because the force is constant, the acceleration is constant, and the speed of the object (starting from rest) is given by $v = at$. With twice the acceleration, the object will arrive at speed v at half the time.

5.4 (b). Because the value of g is smaller on the Moon than on the Earth, more mass of gold would be required to represent 1 newton of weight on the Moon. Therefore, your friend on the Moon is richer, by about a factor of 6!

5.5 (i), (c). In accordance with Newton's third law, the fly and bus experience forces that are equal in magnitude but opposite in direction. (ii), (a). Because the fly has such a small mass, Newton's second law tells us that it undergoes a very large acceleration. The large mass of the bus means that it more effectively resists any change in its motion and exhibits a small acceleration.

5.6 (b). The friction force acts opposite to the gravitational force on the book to keep the book in equilibrium. Because the gravitational force is downward, the friction force must be upward.

5.7 (b). When pulling with the rope, there is a component of your applied force that is upward, which reduces the normal force between the sled and the snow. In turn, the friction force between the sled and the snow is reduced, making the sled easier to move. If you push from behind with a force with a downward component, the normal force is larger, the friction force is larger, and the sled is harder to move.

Passengers on a "corkscrew" roller coaster experience a radial force toward the center of the circular track and a downward force due to gravity. (Robin Smith / Getty Images)

6 Circular Motion and Other Applications of Newton's Laws

In the preceding chapter, we introduced Newton's laws of motion and applied them to situations involving linear motion. Now we discuss motion that is slightly more complicated. For example, we shall apply Newton's laws to objects traveling in circular paths. We shall also discuss motion observed from an accelerating frame of reference and motion of an object through a viscous medium. For the most part, this chapter consists of a series of examples selected to illustrate the application of Newton's laws to a variety of circumstances.

6.1 Newton's Second Law for a Particle in Uniform Circular Motion

In Section 4.4, we discussed the model of a particle in uniform circular motion, in which a particle moves with constant speed v in a circular path of radius r. The particle experiences an acceleration that has a magnitude

$$a_c = \frac{v^2}{r}$$

The acceleration is called *centripetal acceleration* because $\vec{a}_c$ is directed toward the center of the circle. Furthermore, $\vec{a}_c$ is *always* perpendicular to $\vec{v}$. (If there were a component of acceleration parallel to $\vec{v}$, the particle's speed would be changing.)

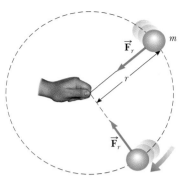

Figure 6.1 An overhead view of a ball moving in a circular path in a horizontal plane. A force $\vec{F}_r$ directed toward the center of the circle keeps the ball moving in its circular path.

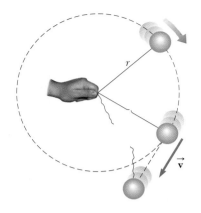

ACTIVE FIGURE 6.2

An overhead view of a ball moving in a circular path in a horizontal plane. When the string breaks, the ball moves in the direction tangent to the circle.

Sign in at www.thomsonedu.com and go to ThomsonNOW to "break" the string yourself and observe the effect on the ball's motion.

Let us now incorporate the concept of force in the particle in uniform circular motion model. Consider a ball of mass m that is tied to a string of length r and is being whirled at constant speed in a horizontal circular path as illustrated in Figure 6.1. Its weight is supported by a frictionless table. Why does the ball move in a circle? According to Newton's first law, the ball would move in a straight line if there were no force on it; the string, however, prevents motion along a straight line by exerting on the ball a radial force $\vec{F}_r$ that makes it follow the circular path. This force is directed along the string toward the center of the circle as shown in Figure 6.1.

If Newton's second law is applied along the radial direction, the net force causing the centripetal acceleration can be related to the acceleration as follows:

▶ Force causing centripetal acceleration

$$\sum F = ma_c = m\,\frac{v^2}{r} \tag{6.1}$$

A force causing a centripetal acceleration acts toward the center of the circular path and causes a change in the direction of the velocity vector. If that force should vanish, the object would no longer move in its circular path; instead, it would move along a straight-line path tangent to the circle. This idea is illustrated in Active Figure 6.2 for the ball whirling at the end of a string in a horizontal plane. If the string breaks at some instant, the ball moves along the straight-line path that is tangent to the circle at the position of the ball at this instant.

PITFALL PREVENTION 6.1
Direction of Travel When the String Is Cut

Study Active Figure 6.2 very carefully. Many students (wrongly) think that the ball will move *radially* away from the center of the circle when the string is cut. The velocity of the ball is *tangent* to the circle. By Newton's first law, the ball continues to move in the same direction in which it is moving just as the force from the string disappears.

Quick Quiz 6.1 You are riding on a Ferris wheel that is rotating with constant speed. The car in which you are riding always maintains its correct upward orientation; it does not invert. **(i)** What is the direction of the normal force on you from the seat when you are at the top of the wheel? (a) upward (b) downward (c) impossible to determine **(ii)** From the same choices, what is the direction of the net force on you when you are at the top of the wheel?

EXAMPLE 6.1 **The Conical Pendulum**

A small ball of mass m is suspended from a string of length L. The ball revolves with constant speed v in a horizontal circle of radius r as shown in Figure 6.3. (Because the string sweeps out the surface of a cone, the system is known as a *conical pendulum*.) Find an expression for v.

SOLUTION

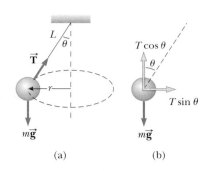

Conceptualize   Imagine the motion of the ball in Figure 6.3a and convince yourself that the string sweeps out a cone and that the ball moves in a circle.

Categorize   The ball in Figure 6.3 does not accelerate vertically. Therefore, we model it as a particle in equilibrium in the vertical direction. It experiences a centripetal acceleration in the horizontal direction, so it is modeled as a particle in uniform circular motion in this direction.

Analyze   Let θ represent the angle between the string and the vertical. In the free-body diagram shown in Figure 6.3b, the force $\vec{T}$ exerted by the string is resolved into a vertical component $T\cos\theta$ and a horizontal component $T\sin\theta$ acting toward the center of the circular path.

Figure 6.3   (Example 6.1) (a) A conical pendulum. The path of the object is a horizontal circle. (b) The free-body diagram for the object.

Apply the particle in equilibrium model in the vertical direction:

$$\sum F_y = T\cos\theta - mg = 0$$

$$(1) \quad T\cos\theta = mg$$

Use Equation 6.1 to express the force providing the centripetal acceleration in the horizontal direction:

$$(2) \quad \sum F_x = T\sin\theta = ma_c = \frac{mv^2}{r}$$

Divide Equation (2) by Equation (1) and use $\sin\theta/\cos\theta = \tan\theta$:

$$\tan\theta = \frac{v^2}{rg}$$

Solve for v:

$$v = \sqrt{rg\tan\theta}$$

Incorporate $r = L\sin\theta$ from the geometry in Figure 6.3a:

$$v = \sqrt{Lg\sin\theta\tan\theta}$$

Finalize   Notice that the speed is independent of the mass of the ball. Consider what happens when θ goes to 90° so that the string is horizontal. Because the tangent of 90° is infinite, the speed v is infinite, which tells us the string cannot possibly be horizontal. If it were, there would be no vertical component of the force $\vec{T}$ to balance the gravitational force on the ball. That is why we mentioned in regard to Figure 6.1 that the ball's weight in the figure is supported by a frictionless table.

    How Fast Can It Spin?

A ball of mass 0.500 kg is attached to the end of a cord 1.50 m long. The ball is whirled in a horizontal circle as shown in Figure 6.1. If the cord can withstand a maximum tension of 50.0 N, what is the maximum speed at which the ball can be whirled before the cord breaks? Assume the string remains horizontal during the motion.

SOLUTION

Conceptualize   It makes sense that the stronger the cord, the faster the ball can whirl before the cord breaks. Also, we expect a more massive ball to break the cord at a lower speed. (Imagine whirling a bowling ball on the cord!)

Categorize   Because the ball moves in a circular path, we model it as a particle in uniform circular motion.

Analyze   Incorporate the tension and the centripetal acceleration into Newton's second law:

$$T = m\frac{v^2}{r}$$

Solve for v:

$$(1) \quad v = \sqrt{\frac{Tr}{m}}$$

Find the maximum speed the ball can have, which corresponds to the maximum tension the string can withstand:

$$v_{max} = \sqrt{\frac{T_{max}r}{m}} = \sqrt{\frac{(50.0\ N)(1.50\ m)}{0.500\ kg}} = \boxed{12.2\ m/s}$$

Finalize   Equation (1) shows that v increases with T and decreases with larger m, as we expected from our conceptualization of the problem.

What If?   Suppose the ball is whirled in a circle of larger radius at the same speed v. Is the cord more likely or less likely to break?

Answer   The larger radius means that the change in the direction of the velocity vector will be smaller in a given time interval. Therefore, the acceleration is smaller and the required tension in the string is smaller. As a result, the string is less likely to break when the ball travels in a circle of larger radius.

EXAMPLE 6.3   What Is the Maximum Speed of the Car?

A 1 500-kg car moving on a flat, horizontal road negotiates a curve as shown in Figure 6.4a. If the radius of the curve is 35.0 m and the coefficient of static friction between the tires and dry pavement is 0.523, find the maximum speed the car can have and still make the turn successfully.

(a)

SOLUTION

Conceptualize   Imagine that the curved roadway is part of a large circle so that the car is moving in a circular path.

Categorize   Based on the conceptualize step of the problem, we model the car as a particle in uniform circular motion in the horizontal direction. The car is not accelerating vertically, so it is modeled as a particle in equilibrium in the vertical direction.

(b)

Analyze   The force that enables the car to remain in its circular path is the force of static friction. (It is *static* because no slipping occurs at the point of contact between road and tires. If this force of static friction were zero—for example, if the car were on an icy road—the car would continue in a straight line and slide off the road.) The maximum speed v_{max} the car can have around the curve is the speed at which it is on the verge of skidding outward. At this point, the friction force has its maximum value $f_{s,max} = \mu_s n$.

Figure 6.4   (Example 6.3) (a) The force of static friction directed toward the center of the curve keeps the car moving in a circular path. (b) The free-body diagram for the car.

Apply Equation 6.1 in the radial direction for the maximum speed condition:

$$(1)\quad f_{s,max} = \mu_s n = m\frac{v_{max}^2}{r}$$

Apply the particle in equilibrium model to the car in the vertical direction:

$$\sum F_y = 0 \quad \rightarrow \quad n - mg = 0 \quad \rightarrow \quad n = mg$$

Solve Equation (1) for the maximum speed and substitute for n:

$$(2)\quad v_{max} = \sqrt{\frac{\mu_s nr}{m}} = \sqrt{\frac{\mu_s mgr}{m}} = \sqrt{\mu_s gr}$$

$$= \sqrt{(0.523)(9.80\ m/s^2)(35.0\ m)} = \boxed{13.4\ m/s}$$

Finalize   This speed is equivalent to 30.0 mi/h. Therefore, this roadway could benefit greatly from some banking, as in the next example! Notice that the maximum speed does not depend on the mass of the car, which is why curved highways do not need multiple speed limits to cover the various masses of vehicles using the road.

What If?   Suppose a car travels this curve on a wet day and begins to skid on the curve when its speed reaches only 8.00 m/s. What can we say about the coefficient of static friction in this case?

Answer   The coefficient of static friction between tires and a wet road should be smaller than that between tires and a dry road. This expectation is consistent with experience with driving because a skid is more likely on a wet road than a dry road.

To check our suspicion, we can solve Equation (2) for the coefficient of static friction:

$$\mu_s = \frac{v_{max}^2}{gr}$$

Substituting the numerical values gives

$$\mu_s = \frac{v_{max}^2}{gr} = \frac{(8.00 \text{ m/s})^2}{(9.80 \text{ m/s}^2)(35.0 \text{ m})} = 0.187$$

which is indeed smaller than the coefficient of 0.523 for the dry road.

EXAMPLE 6.4   The Banked Roadway

A civil engineer wishes to redesign the curved roadway in Example 6.3 in such a way that a car will not have to rely on friction to round the curve without skidding. In other words, a car moving at the designated speed can negotiate the curve even when the road is covered with ice. Such a ramp is usually *banked*, which means that the roadway is tilted toward the inside of the curve. Suppose the designated speed for the ramp is to be 13.4 m/s (30.0 mi/h) and the radius of the curve is 35.0 m. At what angle should the curve be banked?

SOLUTION

Conceptualize   The difference between this example and Example 6.3 is that the car is no longer moving on a flat roadway. Figure 6.5 shows the banked roadway, with the center of the circular path of the car far to the left of the figure. Notice that the horizontal component of the normal force participates in causing the car's centripetal acceleration.

Categorize   As in Example 6.3, the car is modeled as a particle in equilibrium in the vertical direction and a particle in uniform circular motion in the horizontal direction.

Analyze   On a level (unbanked) road, the force that causes the centripetal acceleration is the force of static friction between car and road as we saw in the preceding example. If the road is banked at an angle θ as in Figure 6.5, however, the normal force $\vec{\mathbf{n}}$ has a horizontal component toward the center of the curve. Because the ramp is to be designed so that the force of static friction is zero, only the component $n_x = n \sin \theta$ causes the centripetal acceleration.

Figure 6.5   (Example 6.4) A car rounding a curve on a road banked at an angle θ to the horizontal. When friction is neglected, the force that causes the centripetal acceleration and keeps the car moving in its circular path is the horizontal component of the normal force.

Write Newton's second law for the car in the radial direction, which is the x direction:

$$(1) \quad \sum F_r = n \sin \theta = \frac{mv^2}{r}$$

Apply the particle in equilibrium model to the car in the vertical direction:

$$\sum F_y = n \cos \theta - mg = 0$$

$$(2) \quad n \cos \theta = mg$$

Divide Equation (1) by Equation (2):

$$(3) \quad \tan \theta = \frac{v^2}{rg}$$

Solve for the angle θ:

$$\theta = \tan^{-1} \left(\frac{(13.4 \text{ m/s})^2}{(35.0 \text{ m})(9.80 \text{ m/s}^2)} \right) = \boxed{27.6°}$$

Finalize   Equation (3) shows that the banking angle is independent of the mass of the vehicle negotiating the curve. If a car rounds the curve at a speed less than 13.4 m/s, friction is needed to keep it from sliding down the bank (to the left in Fig. 6.5). A driver attempting to negotiate the curve at a speed greater than 13.4 m/s has to depend on friction to keep from sliding up the bank (to the right in Fig. 6.5).

What If?   Imagine that this same roadway were built on Mars in the future to connect different colony centers. Could it be traveled at the same speed?

Answer   The reduced gravitational force on Mars would mean that the car is not pressed as tightly to the roadway. The reduced normal force results in a smaller component of the normal force toward the center of the circle. This smaller component would not be sufficient to provide the centripetal acceleration associated

with the original speed. The centripetal acceleration must be reduced, which can be done by reducing the speed v.

Mathematically, notice that Equation (3) shows that the speed v is proportional to the square root of g for a roadway of fixed radius r banked at a fixed angle θ. Therefore, if g is smaller, as it is on Mars, the speed v with which the roadway can be safely traveled is also smaller.

EXAMPLE 6.5   Let's Go Loop-the-Loop!

A pilot of mass m in a jet aircraft executes a loop-the-loop, as shown in Figure 6.6a. In this maneuver, the aircraft moves in a vertical circle of radius 2.70 km at a constant speed of 225 m/s.

(A) Determine the force exerted by the seat on the pilot at the bottom of the loop. Express your answer in terms of the weight of the pilot mg.

SOLUTION

Conceptualize   Look carefully at Figure 6.6a. Based on experiences with driving over small hills on a road or riding at the top of a Ferris wheel, you would expect to feel lighter at the top of the path. Similarly, you would expect to feel heavier at the bottom of the path. At the bottom of the loop the normal and gravitational forces on the pilot act in *opposite* directions, whereas at the top of the loop these two forces act in the *same* direction.

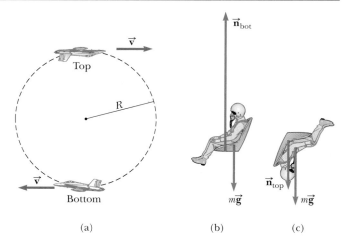

Figure 6.6 (Example 6.5) (a) An aircraft executes a loop-the-loop maneuver as it moves in a vertical circle at constant speed. (b) The free-body diagram for the pilot at the bottom of the loop. In this position the pilot experiences an apparent weight greater than his true weight. (c) The free-body diagram for the pilot at the top of the loop.

The vector sum of these two forces gives a force of constant magnitude that keeps the pilot moving in a circular path at a constant speed. To yield net force vectors with the same magnitude, the normal force at the bottom must be greater than that at the top.

Categorize   Because the speed of the aircraft is constant (how likely is that?), we can categorize this problem as one involving a particle (the pilot) in uniform circular motion, complicated by the gravitational force acting at all times on the aircraft.

Analyze   We draw a free-body diagram for the pilot at the bottom of the loop as shown in Figure 6.6b. The only forces acting on him are the downward gravitational force $\vec{F}_g = m\vec{g}$ and the upward force $\vec{n}_{bot}$ exerted by the seat. The net upward force on the pilot that provides his centripetal acceleration has a magnitude $n_{bot} - mg$.

Apply Newton's second law to the pilot in the radial direction:

$$\sum F = n_{bot} - mg = m\frac{v^2}{r}$$

Solve for the force exerted by the seat on the pilot:

$$n_{bot} = mg + m\frac{v^2}{r} = mg\left(1 + \frac{v^2}{rg}\right)$$

Substitute the values given for the speed and radius:

$$n_{bot} = mg\left(1 + \frac{(225 \text{ m/s})^2}{(2.70 \times 10^3 \text{ m})(9.80 \text{ m/s}^2)}\right)$$

$$= 2.91mg$$

Hence, the magnitude of the force $\vec{n}_{bot}$ exerted by the seat on the pilot is *greater* than the weight of the pilot by a factor of 2.91. So, the pilot experiences an apparent weight that is greater than his true weight by a factor of 2.91.

(B) Determine the force exerted by the seat on the pilot at the top of the loop.

SOLUTION

Analyze   The free-body diagram for the pilot at the top of the loop is shown in Figure 6.6c. As noted earlier, both the gravitational force exerted by the Earth and the force $\vec{\mathbf{n}}_{\text{top}}$ exerted by the seat on the pilot act downward, so the net downward force that provides the centripetal acceleration has a magnitude $n_{\text{top}} + mg$.

Apply Newton's second law to the pilot at this position:

$$\sum F = n_{\text{top}} + mg = m\frac{v^2}{r}$$

$$n_{\text{top}} = m\frac{v^2}{r} - mg = mg\left(\frac{v^2}{rg} - 1\right)$$

$$n_{\text{top}} = mg\left(\frac{(225 \text{ m/s})^2}{(2.70 \times 10^3 \text{ m})(9.80 \text{ m/s}^2)} - 1\right)$$

$$= 0.913\,mg$$

In this case, the magnitude of the force exerted by the seat on the pilot is *less* than his true weight by a factor of 0.913, and the pilot feels lighter.

Finalize   The variations in the normal force are consistent with our prediction in the conceptualize step of the problem.

6.2   Nonuniform Circular Motion

In Chapter 4, we found that if a particle moves with varying speed in a circular path, there is, in addition to the radial component of acceleration, a tangential component having magnitude $|dv/dt|$. Therefore, the force acting on the particle must also have a tangential and a radial component. Because the total acceleration is $\vec{\mathbf{a}} = \vec{\mathbf{a}}_r + \vec{\mathbf{a}}_t$, the total force exerted on the particle is $\sum\vec{\mathbf{F}} = \sum\vec{\mathbf{F}}_r + \sum\vec{\mathbf{F}}_t$ as shown in Active Figure 6.7. (We express the radial and tangential forces as net forces with the summation notation because each force could consist of multiple forces that combine.) The vector $\sum\vec{\mathbf{F}}_r$ is directed toward the center of the circle and is responsible for the centripetal acceleration. The vector $\sum\vec{\mathbf{F}}_t$ tangent to the circle is responsible for the tangential acceleration, which represents a change in the particle's speed with time.

Quick Quiz 6.2   A bead slides freely along a curved wire lying on a horizontal surface at constant speed as shown in Figure 6.8. (a) Draw the vectors representing the force exerted by the wire on the bead at points Ⓐ, Ⓑ, and Ⓒ. (b) Suppose the bead in Figure 6.8 speeds up with constant tangential acceleration as it moves toward the right. Draw the vectors representing the force on the bead at points Ⓐ, Ⓑ, and Ⓒ.

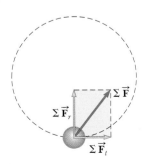

ACTIVE FIGURE 6.7

When the net force acting on a particle moving in a circular path has a tangential component $\sum F_t$, the particle's speed changes. The net force exerted on the particle in this case is the vector sum of the radial force and the tangential force. That is, $\sum\vec{\mathbf{F}} = \sum\vec{\mathbf{F}}_r + \sum\vec{\mathbf{F}}_t$.

Sign in at www.thomsonedu.com and go to ThomsonNOW to adjust the initial position of the particle and compare the component forces acting on the particle with those for a child swinging on a swing set.

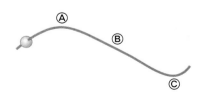

Figure 6.8   (Quick Quiz 6.2) A bead slides along a curved wire.

EXAMPLE 6.6   **Keep Your Eye on the Ball**

A small sphere of mass m is attached to the end of a cord of length R and set into motion in a *vertical* circle about a fixed point O as illustrated in Figure 6.9. Determine the tension in the cord at any instant when the speed of the sphere is v and the cord makes an angle θ with the vertical.

SOLUTION

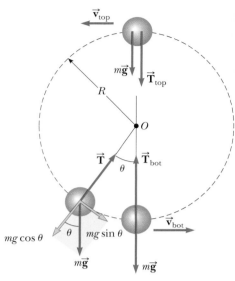

Conceptualize Compare the motion of the sphere in Figure 6.9 to that of the airplane in Figure 6.6a associated with Example 6.5. Both objects travel in a circular path. Unlike the airplane in Example 6.5, however, the speed of the sphere is *not* uniform in this example because, at most points along the path, a tangential component of acceleration arises from the gravitational force exerted on the sphere.

Categorize We model the sphere as a particle under a net force and moving in a circular path, but it is not a particle in *uniform* circular motion. We need to use the techniques discussed in this section on nonuniform circular motion.

Figure 6.9   (Example 6.6) The forces acting on a sphere of mass m connected to a cord of length R and rotating in a vertical circle centered at O. Forces acting on the sphere are shown when the sphere is at the top and bottom of the circle and at an arbitrary location.

Analyze From the free-body diagram in Figure 6.9, we see that the only forces acting on the sphere are the gravitational force $\vec{\mathbf{F}}_g = m\vec{\mathbf{g}}$ exerted by the Earth and the force $\vec{\mathbf{T}}$ exerted by the cord. We resolve $\vec{\mathbf{F}}_g$ into a tangential component $mg \sin \theta$ and a radial component $mg \cos \theta$.

Apply Newton's second law to the sphere in the tangential direction:

$$\sum F_t = mg \sin \theta = ma_t$$
$$a_t = g \sin \theta$$

Apply Newton's second law to the forces acting on the sphere in the radial direction, noting that both $\vec{\mathbf{T}}$ and $\vec{\mathbf{a}}_r$ are directed toward O:

$$\sum F_r = T - mg \cos \theta = \frac{mv^2}{R}$$

$$T = mg\left(\frac{v^2}{Rg} + \cos \theta\right)$$

Finalize Let us evaluate this result at the top and bottom of the circular path (Fig. 6.9):

$$T_{\text{top}} = mg\left(\frac{v_{\text{top}}^2}{Rg} - 1\right) \qquad T_{\text{bot}} = mg\left(\frac{v_{\text{bot}}^2}{Rg} + 1\right)$$

These results have the same mathematical form as those for the normal forces n_{top} and n_{bot} on the pilot in Example 6.5, which is consistent with the normal force on the pilot playing the same physical role in Example 6.5 as the tension in the string plays in this example. Keep in mind, however, that v in the expressions above varies for different positions of the sphere, as indicated by the subscripts, whereas v in Example 6.5 is constant.

What If?   What if the ball is set in motion with a slower speed? (A) What speed would the ball have as it passes over the top of the circle if the tension in the cord goes to zero instantaneously at this point?

Answer Let us set the tension equal to zero in the expression for T_{top}:

$$0 = mg\left(\frac{v_{\text{top}}^2}{Rg} - 1\right) \quad \rightarrow \quad v_{\text{top}} = \sqrt{gR}$$

(B) What if the ball is set in motion such that the speed at the top is less than this value? What happens?

Answer In this case, the ball never reaches the top of the circle. At some point on the way up, the tension in the string goes to zero and the ball becomes a projectile. It follows a segment of a parabolic path over the top of its motion, rejoining the circular path on the other side when the tension becomes nonzero again.

6.3   Motion in Accelerated Frames

Newton's laws of motion, which we introduced in Chapter 5, describe observations that are made in an inertial frame of reference. In this section, we analyze how Newton's laws are applied by an observer in a noninertial frame of reference, that is, one that is accelerating. For example, recall the discussion of the air hockey table on a train in Section 5.2. The train moving at constant velocity represents an inertial frame. An observer on the train sees the puck at rest remain at rest, and Newton's first law appears to be obeyed. The accelerating train is not an inertial frame. According to you as the observer on this train, there appears to be no force on the puck, yet it accelerates from rest toward the back of the train, appearing to violate Newton's first law. This property is a general property of observations made in noninertial frames: there appear to be unexplained accelerations of objects that are not "fastened" to the frame. Newton's first law is not violated, of course. It only *appears* to be violated because of observations made from a noninertial frame. In general, the direction of the unexplained acceleration is opposite the direction of the acceleration of the noninertial frame.

On the accelerating train, as you watch the puck accelerating toward the back of the train, you might conclude based on your belief in Newton's second law that a force has acted on the puck to cause it to accelerate. We call an apparent force such as this one a **fictitious force** because it is due to an accelerated reference frame. A fictitious force appears to act on an object in the same way as a real force. Real forces are always interactions between two objects, however, and you cannot identify a second object for a fictitious force. (What second object is interacting with the puck to cause it to accelerate?)

The train example describes a fictitious force due to a change in the train's speed. Another fictitious force is due to the change in the *direction* of the velocity vector. To understand the motion of a system that is noninertial because of a change in direction, consider a car traveling along a highway at a high speed and approaching a curved exit ramp as shown in Figure 6.10a. As the car takes the sharp left turn onto the ramp, a person sitting in the passenger seat slides to the right and hits the door. At that point the force exerted by the door on the passenger keeps her from being ejected from the car. What causes her to move toward the door? A popular but incorrect explanation is that a force acting toward the right in Figure 6.10b pushes the passenger outward from the center of the circular path. Although often called the "centrifugal force," it is a fictitious force due to the centripetal acceleration associated with the changing direction of the car's velocity vector. (The driver also experiences this effect but wisely holds on to the steering wheel to keep from sliding to the right.)

The phenomenon is correctly explained as follows. Before the car enters the ramp, the passenger is moving in a straight-line path. As the car enters the ramp and travels a curved path, the passenger tends to move along the original straight-line path, which is in accordance with Newton's first law: the natural tendency of an object is to continue moving in a straight line. If a sufficiently large force (toward the center of curvature) acts on the passenger as in Figure 6.10c, however, she moves in a curved path along with the car. This force is the force of friction between her and the car seat. If this friction force is not large enough, the seat follows a curved path while the passenger continues in the straight-line path of the car before the car began the turn. Therefore, from the point of view of an observer in the car, the passenger slides to the right relative to the seat. Eventually, she encounters the door, which provides a force large enough to enable her to follow the same curved path as the car. She slides toward the door not because of an outward force but because **the force of friction is not sufficiently great to allow her to travel along the circular path followed by the car.**

Another interesting fictitious force is the "Coriolis force." It is an apparent force caused by changing the radial position of an object in a rotating coordinate system.

(a)

Fictitious force

(b)

Real force

(c)

Figure 6.10   (a) A car approaching a curved exit ramp. What causes a passenger in the front seat to move toward the right-hand door? (b) From the passenger's frame of reference, a force appears to push her toward the right door, but it is a fictitious force. (c) Relative to the reference frame of the Earth, the car seat applies a real force toward the left on the passenger, causing her to change direction along with the rest of the car.

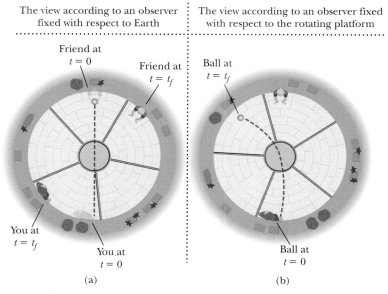

The view according to an observer fixed with respect to Earth

The view according to an observer fixed with respect to the rotating platform

(a)

(b)

ACTIVE FIGURE 6.11

(a) You and your friend sit at the edge of a rotating turntable. In this overhead view observed by someone in an inertial reference frame attached to the Earth, you throw the ball at $t = 0$ in the direction of your friend. By the time t_f that the ball arrives at the other side of the turntable, your friend is no longer there to catch it. According to this observer, the ball follows a straight-line path, consistent with Newton's laws. (b) From your friend's point of view, the ball veers to one side during its flight. Your friend introduces a fictitious force to cause this deviation from the expected path. This fictitious force is called the "Coriolis force."

Sign in at www.thomsonedu.com and go to ThomsonNOW to observe the ball's path simultaneously from the reference frame of an inertial observer and from the reference frame of the rotating turntable.

PITFALL PREVENTION 6.2
Centrifugal Force

The commonly heard phrase "centrifugal force" is described as a force pulling *outward* on an object moving in a circular path. If you are feeling a "centrifugal force" on a rotating carnival ride, what is the other object with which you are interacting? You cannot identify another object because it is a fictitious force that occurs because you are in a noninertial reference frame.

For example, suppose you and a friend are on opposite sides of a rotating circular platform and you decide to throw a baseball to your friend. Active Figure 6.11a represents what an observer would see if the ball is viewed while the observer is hovering at rest above the rotating platform. According to this observer, who is in an inertial frame, the ball follows a straight line as it must according to Newton's first law. At $t = 0$ you throw the ball toward your friend, but by the time t_f when the ball has crossed the platform, your friend has moved to a new position. Now, however, consider the situation from your friend's viewpoint. Your friend is in a noninertial reference frame because he is undergoing a centripetal acceleration relative to the inertial frame of the Earth's surface. He starts off seeing the baseball coming toward him, but as it crosses the platform, it veers to one side as shown in Active Figure 6.11b. Therefore, your friend on the rotating platform states that the ball does not obey Newton's first law and claims that a force is causing the ball to follow a curved path. This fictitious force is called the Coriolis force.

Fictitious forces may not be real forces, but they can have real effects. An object on your dashboard *really* slides off if you press the accelerator of your car. As you ride on a merry-go-round, you feel pushed toward the outside as if due to the fictitious "centrifugal force." You are likely to fall over and injure yourself due to the Coriolis force if you walk along a radial line while a merry-go-round rotates. (One of the authors did so and suffered a separation of the ligaments from his ribs when he fell over.) The Coriolis force due to the rotation of the Earth is responsible for rotations of hurricanes and for large-scale ocean currents.

Quick Quiz 6.3 Consider the passenger in the car making a left turn in Figure 6.10. Which of the following is correct about forces in the horizontal direction if she is making contact with the right-hand door? (a) The passenger is in equilibrium between real forces acting to the right and real forces acting to the left. (b) The passenger is subject only to real forces acting to the right. (c) The passenger is subject only to real forces acting to the left. (d) None of these statements is true.

EXAMPLE 6.7   Fictitious Forces in Linear Motion

A small sphere of mass m hangs by a cord from the ceiling of a boxcar that is accelerating to the right as shown in Figure 6.12. The noninertial observer in Figure 6.12b claims that a force, which we know to be fictitious, causes the observed deviation of the cord from the vertical. How is the magnitude of this force related to the boxcar's acceleration measured by the inertial observer in Figure 6.12a?

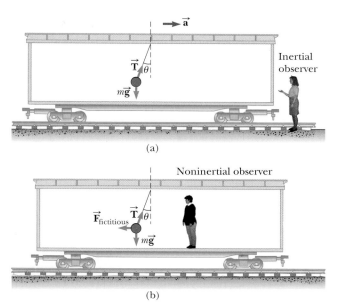

(a)

(b)

Figure 6.12   (Example 6.7) A small sphere suspended from the ceiling of a boxcar accelerating to the right is deflected as shown. (a) An inertial observer at rest outside the car claims that the acceleration of the sphere is provided by the horizontal component of $\vec{\mathbf{T}}$. (b) A noninertial observer riding in the car says that the net force on the sphere is zero and that the deflection of the cord from the vertical is due to a fictitious force $\vec{\mathbf{F}}_{\text{fictitious}}$ that balances the horizontal component of $\vec{\mathbf{T}}$.

SOLUTION

Conceptualize   Place yourself in the role of each of the two observers in Figure 6.12. As the inertial observer on the ground, you see the boxcar accelerating and know that the deviation of the cord is due to this acceleration. As the noninertial observer on the boxcar, imagine that you ignore any effects of the car's motion so that you are not aware of its acceleration. Because you are unaware of this acceleration, you claim that a force is pushing sideways on the sphere to cause the deviation of the cord from the vertical. To make the conceptualization more real, try running from rest while holding a hanging object on a string and notice that the string is at an angle to the vertical while you are accelerating, as if a force is pushing the object backward.

Categorize   For the inertial observer, we model the sphere as a particle under a net force in the horizontal direction and a particle in equilibrium in the vertical direction. For the noninertial observer, the sphere is modeled as a particle in equilibrium for which one of the forces is fictitious.

Analyze   According to the inertial observer at rest (Fig. 6.12a), the forces on the sphere are the force $\vec{\mathbf{T}}$ exerted by the cord and the gravitational force. The inertial observer concludes that the sphere's acceleration is the same as that of the boxcar and that this acceleration is provided by the horizontal component of $\vec{\mathbf{T}}$.

Apply Newton's second law in component form to the sphere according to the inertial observer:

$$\text{Inertial observer}\begin{cases}(1) & \sum F_x = T\sin\theta = ma \\ (2) & \sum F_y = T\cos\theta - mg = 0\end{cases}$$

According to the noninertial observer riding in the car (Fig. 6.12b), the cord also makes an angle θ with the vertical; to that observer, however, the sphere is at rest and so its acceleration is zero. Therefore, the noninertial observer introduces a fictitious force in the horizontal direction to balance the horizontal component of $\vec{\mathbf{T}}$ and claims that the net force on the sphere is zero.

Apply Newton's second law in component form to the sphere according to the noninertial observer:

$$\text{Noninertial observer}\begin{cases}\sum F'_x = T\sin\theta - F_{\text{fictitious}} = 0 \\ \sum F'_y = T\cos\theta - mg = 0\end{cases}$$

These expressions are equivalent to Equations (1) and (2) if $F_{\text{fictitious}} = ma$, where a is the acceleration according to the inertial observer.

Finalize If we were to make this substitution in the equation for F_x' above, the noninertial observer obtains the same mathematical results as the inertial observer. The physical interpretation of the cord's deflection, however, differs in the two frames of reference.

What If? Suppose the inertial observer wants to measure the acceleration of the train by means of the pendulum (the sphere hanging from the cord). How could she do so?

Answer Our intuition tells us that the angle θ the cord makes with the vertical should increase as the acceleration increases. By solving Equations (1) and (2) simultaneously for a, the inertial observer can determine the magnitude of the car's acceleration by measuring the angle θ and using the relationship $a = g \tan \theta$. Because the deflection of the cord from the vertical serves as a measure of acceleration, *a simple pendulum can be used as an accelerometer.*

6.4 Motion in the Presence of Resistive Forces

In Chapter 5, we described the force of kinetic friction exerted on an object moving on some surface. We completely ignored any interaction between the object and the medium through which it moves. Now consider the effect of that medium, which can be either a liquid or a gas. The medium exerts a **resistive force $\vec{R}$** on the object moving through it. Some examples are the air resistance associated with moving vehicles (sometimes called *air drag*) and the viscous forces that act on objects moving through a liquid. The magnitude of $\vec{R}$ depends on factors such as the speed of the object, and the direction of $\vec{R}$ is always opposite the direction of the object's motion relative to the medium.

The magnitude of the resistive force can depend on speed in a complex way, and here we consider only two simplified models. In the first model, we assume the resistive force is proportional to the speed of the moving object; this model is valid for objects falling slowly through a liquid and for very small objects, such as dust particles, moving through air. In the second model, we assume a resistive force that is proportional to the square of the speed of the moving object; large objects, such as a skydiver moving through air in free fall, experience such a force.

Model 1: Resistive Force Proportional to Object Velocity

If we model the resistive force acting on an object moving through a liquid or gas as proportional to the object's velocity, the resistive force can be expressed as

$$\vec{R} = -b\vec{v} \tag{6.2}$$

where b is a constant whose value depends on the properties of the medium and on the shape and dimensions of the object and $\vec{v}$ is the velocity of the object relative to the medium. The negative sign indicates that $\vec{R}$ is in the opposite direction to $\vec{v}$.

Consider a small sphere of mass m released from rest in a liquid as in Active Figure 6.13a. Assuming the only forces acting on the sphere are the resistive force $\vec{R} = -b\vec{v}$ and the gravitational force $\vec{F}_g$, let us describe its motion.[1] Applying Newton's second law to the vertical motion, choosing the downward direction to be positive, and noting that $\Sigma F_y = mg - bv$, we obtain

$$mg - bv = ma = m\frac{dv}{dt} \tag{6.3}$$

where the acceleration of the sphere is downward. Solving this expression for the acceleration dv/dt gives

---

[1] A *buoyant force* is also acting on the submerged object. This force is constant, and its magnitude is equal to the weight of the displaced liquid. This force changes the apparent weight of the sphere by a constant factor, so we will ignore the force here. We discuss buoyant forces in Chapter 14.

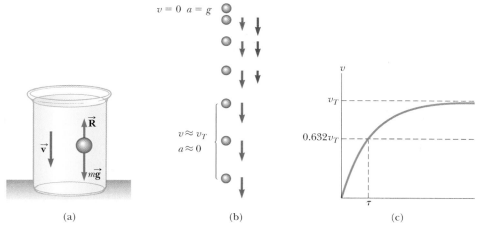

ACTIVE FIGURE 6.13

(a) A small sphere falling through a liquid. (b) A motion diagram of the sphere as it falls. Velocity vectors (red) and acceleration vectors (violet) are shown for each image after the first one. (c) A speed–time graph for the sphere. The sphere approaches a maximum (or terminal) speed v_T, and the time constant τ is the time at which it reaches a speed of $0.632v_T$.

Sign in at www.thomsonedu.com and go to ThomsonNOW to vary the size and mass of the sphere and the viscosity (resistance to flow) of the surrounding medium. Then observe the effects on the sphere's motion and its speed–time graph.

$$\frac{dv}{dt} = g - \frac{b}{m}v \qquad\qquad (6.4)$$

This equation is called a *differential equation*, and the methods of solving it may not be familiar to you as yet. Notice, however, that initially when $v = 0$, the magnitude of the resistive force is also zero and the acceleration of the sphere is simply g. As t increases, the magnitude of the resistive force increases and the acceleration decreases. The acceleration approaches zero when the magnitude of the resistive force approaches the sphere's weight. In this situation, the speed of the sphere approaches its **terminal speed** v_T.

◀ Terminal speed

The terminal speed is obtained from Equation 6.3 by setting $a = dv/dt = 0$. This gives

$$mg - bv_T = 0 \quad \text{or} \quad v_T = \frac{mg}{b}$$

The expression for v that satisfies Equation 6.4 with $v = 0$ at $t = 0$ is

$$v = \frac{mg}{b}(1 - e^{-bt/m}) = v_T(1 - e^{-t/\tau}) \qquad\qquad (6.5)$$

This function is plotted in Active Figure 6.13c. The symbol e represents the base of the natural logarithm and is also called *Euler's number*: $e = 2.718\ 28$. The **time constant** $\tau = m/b$ (Greek letter tau) is the time at which the sphere released from rest at $t = 0$ reaches 63.2% of its terminal speed: when $t = \tau$, Equation 6.5 yields $v = 0.632v_T$.

We can check that Equation 6.5 is a solution to Equation 6.4 by direct differentiation:

$$\frac{dv}{dt} = \frac{d}{dt}\left[\frac{mg}{b}(1 - e^{-bt/m})\right] = \frac{mg}{b}\left(0 + \frac{b}{m}e^{-bt/m}\right) = ge^{-bt/m}$$

(See Appendix Table B.4 for the derivative of e raised to some power.) Substituting into Equation 6.4 both this expression for dv/dt and the expression for v given by Equation 6.5 shows that our solution satisfies the differential equation.

EXAMPLE 6.8   Sphere Falling in Oil

A small sphere of mass 2.00 g is released from rest in a large vessel filled with oil, where it experiences a resistive force proportional to its speed. The sphere reaches a terminal speed of 5.00 cm/s. Determine the time constant τ and the time at which the sphere reaches 90.0% of its terminal speed.

SOLUTION

Conceptualize With the help of Active Figure 6.13, imagine dropping the sphere into the oil and watching it sink to the bottom of the vessel. If you have some thick shampoo, drop a marble in it and observe the motion of the marble.

Categorize We model the sphere as a particle under a net force, with one of the forces being a resistive force that depends on the speed of the sphere.

Analyze From $v_T = mg/b$, evaluate the coefficient b:

$$b = \frac{mg}{v_T} = \frac{(2.00 \text{ g})(980 \text{ cm/s}^2)}{5.00 \text{ cm/s}} = 392 \text{ g/s}$$

Evaluate the time constant τ:

$$\tau = \frac{m}{b} = \frac{2.00 \text{ g}}{392 \text{ g/s}} = \boxed{5.10 \times 10^{-3} \text{ s}}$$

Find the time t at which the sphere reaches a speed of $0.900v_T$ by setting $v = 0.900v_T$ in Equation 6.5 and solving for t:

$$0.900v_T = v_T(1 - e^{-t/\tau})$$

$$1 - e^{-t/\tau} = 0.900$$

$$e^{-t/\tau} = 0.100$$

$$-\frac{t}{\tau} = \ln(0.100) = -2.30$$

$$t = 2.30\tau = 2.30(5.10 \times 10^{-3} \text{ s}) = 11.7 \times 10^{-3} \text{ s}$$

$$= \boxed{11.7 \text{ ms}}$$

Finalize The sphere reaches 90.0% of its terminal speed in a very short time interval. You should have also seen this behavior if you performed the activity with the marble and the shampoo.

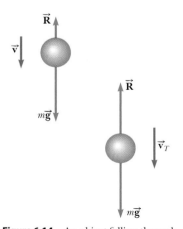

Figure 6.14 An object falling through air experiences a resistive force $\vec{R}$ and a gravitational force $\vec{F}_g = m\vec{g}$. The object reaches terminal speed (on the right) when the net force acting on it is zero, that is, when $\vec{R} = -\vec{F}_g$ or $R = mg$. Before that occurs, the acceleration varies with speed according to Equation 6.8.

Model 2: Resistive Force Proportional to Object Speed Squared

For objects moving at high speeds through air, such as airplanes, skydivers, cars, and baseballs, the resistive force is reasonably well modeled as proportional to the square of the speed. In these situations, the magnitude of the resistive force can be expressed as

$$R = \tfrac{1}{2} D\rho A v^2 \tag{6.6}$$

where D is a dimensionless empirical quantity called the *drag coefficient*, ρ is the density of air, and A is the cross-sectional area of the moving object measured in a plane perpendicular to its velocity. The drag coefficient has a value of about 0.5 for spherical objects but can have a value as great as 2 for irregularly shaped objects.

Let us analyze the motion of an object in free-fall subject to an upward air resistive force of magnitude $R = \tfrac{1}{2} D\rho A v^2$. Suppose an object of mass m is released from rest. As Figure 6.14 shows, the object experiences two external forces:[2] the downward gravitational force $\vec{F}_g = m\vec{g}$ and the upward resistive force $\vec{R}$. Hence, the magnitude of the net force is

$$\sum F = mg - \tfrac{1}{2} D\rho A v^2 \tag{6.7}$$

[2] As with Model 1, there is also an upward buoyant force that we neglect.

TABLE 6.1

Terminal Speed for Various Objects Falling Through Air

Object	Mass (kg)	Cross-Sectional Area (m²)	v_T (m/s)
Skydiver	75	0.70	60
Baseball (radius 3.7 cm)	0.145	4.2×10^{-3}	43
Golf ball (radius 2.1 cm)	0.046	1.4×10^{-3}	44
Hailstone (radius 0.50 cm)	4.8×10^{-4}	7.9×10^{-5}	14
Raindrop (radius 0.20 cm)	3.4×10^{-5}	1.3×10^{-5}	9.0

where we have taken downward to be the positive vertical direction. Using the force in Equation 6.7 in Newton's second law, we find that the object has a downward acceleration of magnitude

$$a = g - \left(\frac{D\rho A}{2m}\right)v^2 \tag{6.8}$$

We can calculate the terminal speed v_T by noticing that when the gravitational force is balanced by the resistive force, the net force on the object is zero and therefore its acceleration is zero. Setting $a = 0$ in Equation 6.8 gives

$$g - \left(\frac{D\rho A}{2m}\right)v_T^2 = 0$$

so

$$v_T = \sqrt{\frac{2mg}{D\rho A}} \tag{6.9}$$

Table 6.1 lists the terminal speeds for several objects falling through air.

Quick Quiz 6.4   A baseball and a basketball, having the same mass, are dropped through air from rest such that their bottoms are initially at the same height above the ground, on the order of 1 m or more. Which one strikes the ground first? (a) The baseball strikes the ground first. (b) The basketball strikes the ground first. (c) Both strike the ground at the same time.

CONCEPTUAL EXAMPLE 6.9   **The Skysurfer**

Consider a skysurfer (Fig. 6.15) who jumps from a plane with her feet attached firmly to her surfboard, does some tricks, and then opens her parachute. Describe the forces acting on her during these maneuvers.

SOLUTION

When the surfer first steps out of the plane, she has no vertical velocity. The downward gravitational force causes her to accelerate toward the ground. As her downward speed increases, so does the upward resistive force exerted by the air on her body and the board. This upward force reduces their acceleration, and so their speed increases more slowly. Eventually, they are going so fast that the upward resistive force matches the downward gravitational force. Now the net force is zero and they no longer accelerate, but instead reach their terminal speed. At some point after reaching terminal speed, she opens her parachute, resulting in a drastic increase in the upward resistive force. The net force (and thus the acceleration) is now upward, in the direction opposite the direction of the velocity. The downward velocity therefore decreases rapidly, and the resistive force on the chute

Figure 6.15   (Conceptual Example 6.9) A skysurfer.

Jump Run Productions/Getty Images

also decreases. Eventually, the upward resistive force and the downward gravitational force balance each other and a much smaller terminal speed is reached, permitting a safe landing.

(Contrary to popular belief, the velocity vector of a skydiver never points upward. You may have seen a videotape in which a skydiver appears to "rocket" upward once the chute opens. In fact, what happens is that the skydiver slows down but the person holding the camera continues falling at high speed.)

EXAMPLE 6.10 | Falling Coffee Filters

The dependence of resistive force on the square of the speed is a model. Let's test the model for a specific situation. Imagine an experiment in which we drop a series of stacked coffee filters and measure their terminal speeds. Table 6.2 presents typical terminal speed data from a real experiment using these coffee filters as they fall through the air. The time constant τ is small, so a dropped filter quickly reaches terminal speed. Each filter has a mass of 1.64 g. When the filters are nested together, they stack in such a way that the front-facing surface area does not increase. Determine the relationship between the resistive force exerted by the air and the speed of the falling filters.

TABLE 6.2

Terminal Speed and Resistive Force for Stacked Coffee Filters

Number of Filters	v_T (m/s)[a]	R (N)
1	1.01	0.016 1
2	1.40	0.032 2
3	1.63	0.048 3
4	2.00	0.064 4
5	2.25	0.080 5
6	2.40	0.096 6
7	2.57	0.112 7
8	2.80	0.128 8
9	3.05	0.144 9
10	3.22	0.161 0

[a] All values of v_T are approximate.

SOLUTION

Conceptualize Imagine dropping the coffee filters through the air. (If you have some coffee filters, try dropping them.) Because of the relatively small mass of the coffee filter, you probably won't notice the time interval during which there is an acceleration. The filters will appear to fall at constant velocity immediately upon leaving your hand.

Categorize Because a filter moves at constant velocity, we model it as a particle in equilibrium.

Analyze At terminal speed, the upward resistive force on the filter balances the downward gravitational force so that $R = mg$.

Evaluate the magnitude of the resistive force:

$$R = mg = (1.64 \text{ g})\left(\frac{1 \text{ kg}}{1\,000 \text{ g}}\right)(9.80 \text{ m/s}^2) = 0.016\ 1 \text{ N}$$

Likewise, two filters nested together experience 0.032 2 N of resistive force, and so forth. These values of resistive force are shown in the rightmost column of Table 6.2. A graph of the resistive force on the filters as a function of terminal speed is shown in Figure 6.16a. A straight line is not a good fit, indicating that the resistive force is *not* proportional to the speed. The behavior is more clearly seen in Figure 6.16b, in which the resistive force is plotted as a function of the square of the terminal speed. This graph indicates that the resistive force is proportional to the *square* of the speed as suggested by Equation 6.6.

Finalize Here is a good opportunity for you to take some actual data at home on real coffee filters and see if you can reproduce the results shown in Figure 6.16. If you have shampoo and a marble as mentioned in Example 6.8, take data on that system too and see if the resistive force is appropriately modeled as being proportional to the speed.

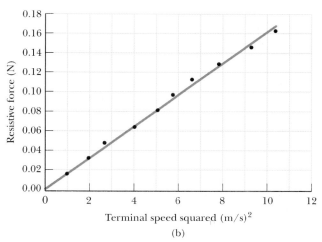

Figure 6.16   (Example 6.10) (a) Relationship between the resistive force acting on falling coffee filters and their terminal speed. The curved line is a second-order polynomial fit. (b) Graph relating the resistive force to the square of the terminal speed. The fit of the straight line to the data points indicates that the resistive force is proportional to the terminal speed squared. Can you find the proportionality constant?

EXAMPLE 6.11   **Resistive Force Exerted on a Baseball**

A pitcher hurls a 0.145-kg baseball past a batter at 40.2 m/s (= 90 mi/h). Find the resistive force acting on the ball at this speed.

SOLUTION

Conceptualize   This example is different from the previous ones in that the object is now moving horizontally through the air instead of moving vertically under the influence of gravity and the resistive force. The resistive force causes the ball to slow down while gravity causes its trajectory to curve downward. We simplify the situation by assuming that the velocity vector is exactly horizontal at the instant it is traveling at 40.2 m/s.

Categorize   In general, the ball is a particle under a net force. Because we are considering only one instant of time, however, we are not concerned about acceleration, so the problem involves only finding the value of one of the forces.

Analyze   To determine the drag coefficient D, imagine we drop the baseball and allow it to reach terminal speed. Solve Equation 6.9 for D and substitute the appropriate values for m, v_T, and A from Table 6.1, taking the density of air as 1.20 kg/m³:

$$D = \frac{2mg}{v_T^2 \rho A} = \frac{2(0.145 \text{ kg})(9.80 \text{ m/s}^2)}{(43 \text{ m/s})^2(1.20 \text{ kg/m}^3)(4.2 \times 10^{-3} \text{ m}^2)}$$

$$= 0.305$$

Use this value for D in Equation 6.6 to find the magnitude of the resistive force:

$$R = \tfrac{1}{2} D\rho A v^2$$

$$= \tfrac{1}{2}(0.305)(1.20 \text{ kg/m}^3)(4.2 \times 10^{-3} \text{ m}^2)(40.2 \text{ m/s})^2$$

$$= \boxed{1.2 \text{ N}}$$

Finalize   The magnitude of the resistive force is similar in magnitude to the weight of the baseball, which is about 1.4 N. Therefore, air resistance plays a major role in the motion of the ball, as evidenced by the variety of curve balls, floaters, sinkers, and the like thrown by baseball pitchers.

Summary

CONCEPTS AND PRINCIPLES

A particle moving in uniform circular motion has a centripetal acceleration; this acceleration must be provided by a net force directed toward the center of the circular path.

An observer in a noninertial (accelerating) frame of reference introduces **fictitious forces** when applying Newton's second law in that frame.

An object moving through a liquid or gas experiences a speed-dependent **resistive force**. This resistive force is in a direction opposite that of the velocity of the object relative to the medium and generally increases with speed. The magnitude of the resistive force depends on the object's size and shape and on the properties of the medium through which the object is moving. In the limiting case for a falling object, when the magnitude of the resistive force equals the object's weight, the object reaches its **terminal speed**.

ANALYSIS MODEL FOR PROBLEM-SOLVING

Particle in Uniform Circular Motion   With our new knowledge of forces, we can add to the model of a particle in uniform circular motion, first introduced in Chapter 4. Newton's second law applied to a particle moving in uniform circular motion states that the net force causing the particle to undergo a centripetal acceleration (Eq. 4.15) is related to the acceleration according to

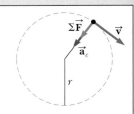

$$\sum F = ma_c = m\frac{v^2}{r} \qquad\qquad \textbf{(6.1)}$$

Questions

□ denotes answer available in *Student Solutions Manual/Study Guide;* **O** denotes objective question

1. **O** A door in a hospital has a pneumatic closer that pulls the door shut such that the doorknob moves with constant speed over most of its path. In this part of its motion, (a) does the doorknob experience a centripetal acceleration? (b) Does it experience a tangential acceleration? Hurrying to an emergency, a nurse gives a sharp push to the closed door. The door swings open against the pneumatic device, slowing down and then reversing its motion. At the moment the door is open the widest, (c) does the doorknob have a centripetal acceleration? (d) Does it have a tangential acceleration?

2. Describe the path of a moving body in the event that its acceleration is constant in magnitude at all times and (a) perpendicular to the velocity; (b) parallel to the velocity.

3. An object executes circular motion with constant speed whenever a net force of constant magnitude acts perpendicular to the velocity. What happens to the speed if the force is not perpendicular to the velocity?

4. **O** A child is practicing for a bicycle motocross race. His speed remains constant as he goes counterclockwise around a level track with two straight sections and two nearly semicircular sections as shown in the helicopter view of Figure Q6.4. (a) Rank the magnitudes of his acceleration at the points *A, B, C, D,* and *E,* from largest to smallest. If his acceleration is the same size at two points, display that fact in your ranking. If his acceleration is zero, display that fact. (b) What are the directions of his

velocity at points *A, B,* and *C*? For each point choose one: north, south, east, west, or nonexistent? (c) What are the directions of his acceleration at points *A, B,* and *C*?

Figure Q6.4

5. **O** A pendulum consists of a small object called a bob hanging from a light cord of fixed length, with the top end of the cord fixed, as represented in Figure Q6.5. The bob moves without friction, swinging equally high on both sides. It moves from its turning point *A* through point *B* and reaches its maximum speed at point *C.* (a) Of these points, is there a point where the bob has nonzero radial acceleration and zero tangential acceleration? If so, which point? What is the direction of its total acceleration at this point? (b) Of these points, is there a point where the bob

has nonzero tangential acceleration and zero radial acceleration? If so, which point? What is the direction of its total acceleration at this point? (c) Is there a point where the bob has no acceleration? If so, which point? (d) Is there a point where the bob has both nonzero tangential and radial acceleration? If so, which point? What is the direction of its total acceleration at this point?

Figure Q6.5

6. If someone told you that astronauts are weightless in orbit because they are beyond the pull of gravity, would you accept the statement? Explain.

7. It has been suggested that rotating cylinders about 20 km in length and 8 km in diameter be placed in space and used as colonies. The purpose of the rotation is to simulate gravity for the inhabitants. Explain this concept for producing an effective imitation of gravity.

8. A pail of water can be whirled in a vertical path such that no water is spilled. Why does the water stay in the pail, even when the pail is above your head?

9. Why does a pilot tend to black out when pulling out of a steep dive?

10. O Before takeoff on an airplane, an inquisitive student on the plane takes out a ring of keys and lets it dangle on a lanyard. It hangs straight down as the plane is at rest waiting to take off. The plane then gains speed rapidly as it moves down the runway. (a) Relative to the student's hand, do the keys shift toward the front of the plane, continue to hang straight down, or shift toward the back of the plane? (b) The speed of the plane increases at a constant rate over a time interval of several seconds. During this interval, does the angle the lanyard makes with the vertical increase, stay constant, or decrease?

11. The observer in the accelerating elevator of Example 5.8 would claim that the "weight" of the fish is T, the scale reading. This answer is obviously wrong. Why does this observation differ from that of a person outside the elevator, at rest with respect to the Earth?

12. A falling skydiver reaches terminal speed with her parachute closed. After the parachute is opened, what parameters change to decrease this terminal speed?

13. What forces cause (a) an automobile, (b) a propeller-driven airplane, and (c) a rowboat to move?

14. Consider a small raindrop and a large raindrop falling through the atmosphere. Compare their terminal speeds. What are their accelerations when they reach terminal speed?

15. O Consider a skydiver who has stepped from a helicopter and is falling through air, before she reaches terminal speed and long before she opens her parachute. (a) Does her speed increase, decrease, or stay constant? (b) Does the magnitude of her acceleration increase, decrease, stay constant at zero, stay constant at 9.80 m/s^2, or stay constant at some other value?

16. "If the current position and velocity of every particle in the Universe were known, together with the laws describing the forces that particles exert on one another, then the whole future of the Universe could be calculated. The future is determinate and preordained. Free will is an illusion." Do you agree with this thesis? Argue for or against it.

Problems

WebAssign The Problems from this chapter may be assigned online in WebAssign.

ThomsonNOW™ Sign in at **www.thomsonedu.com** and go to ThomsonNOW to assess your understanding of this chapter's topics with additional quizzing and conceptual questions.

1, 2, 3 denotes straightforward, intermediate, challenging; □ denotes full solution available in *Student Solutions Manual/Study Guide*; ▲ denotes coached solution with hints available at **www.thomsonedu.com;** denotes developing symbolic reasoning; ● denotes asking for qualitative reasoning; ⬚ denotes computer useful in solving problem

Section 6.1 Newton's Second Law for a Particle in Uniform Circular Motion

1. A light string can support a stationary hanging load of 25.0 kg before breaking. A 3.00-kg object attached to the string rotates on a horizontal, frictionless table in a circle of radius 0.800 m, and the other end of the string is held fixed. What range of speeds can the object have before the string breaks?

2. A curve in a road forms part of a horizontal circle. As a car goes around it at constant speed 14.0 m/s, the total force on the driver has magnitude 130 N. What is the total vector force on the driver if the speed is 18.0 m/s instead?

3. In the Bohr model of the hydrogen atom, the speed of the electron is approximately 2.20×10^6 m/s. Find (a) the force acting on the electron as it revolves in a circular orbit of radius 0.530×10^{-10} m and (b) the centripetal acceleration of the electron.

4. Whenever two *Apollo* astronauts were on the surface of the Moon, a third astronaut orbited the Moon. Assume the orbit to be circular and 100 km above the surface of the Moon, where the acceleration due to gravity is 1.52 m/s^2. The radius of the Moon is 1.70×10^6 m. Determine (a) the astronaut's orbital speed and (b) the period of the orbit.

5. A coin placed 30.0 cm from the center of a rotating horizontal turntable slips when its speed is 50.0 cm/s. (a) What force causes the centripetal acceleration when the coin is stationary relative to the turntable? (b) What is

the coefficient of static friction between the coin and turntable?

6. In a cyclotron (one type of particle accelerator), a deuteron (of mass 2.00 u) reaches a final speed of 10.0% of the speed of light while moving in a circular path of radius 0.480 m. The deuteron is maintained in the circular path by a magnetic force. What magnitude of force is required?

7. A space station, in the form of a wheel 120 m in diameter, rotates to provide an "artificial gravity" of 3.00 m/s² for persons who walk around on the inner wall of the outer rim. Find the rate of rotation of the wheel (in revolutions per minute) that will produce this effect.

8. Consider a conical pendulum (Fig. 6.3) with an 80.0-kg bob on a 10.0-m wire making an angle of $\theta = 5.00°$ with the vertical. Determine (a) the horizontal and vertical components of the force exerted by the wire on the pendulum and (b) the radial acceleration of the bob.

9. A crate of eggs is located in the middle of the flatbed of a pickup truck as the truck negotiates an unbanked curve in the road. The curve may be regarded as an arc of a circle of radius 35.0 m. If the coefficient of static friction between crate and truck is 0.600, how fast can the truck be moving without the crate sliding?

10. A car initially traveling eastward turns north by traveling in a circular path at uniform speed as shown in Figure P6.10. The length of the arc *ABC* is 235 m, and the car completes the turn in 36.0 s. (a) What is the acceleration when the car is at *B* located at an angle of 35.0°? Express your answer in terms of the unit vectors $\hat{\mathbf{i}}$ and $\hat{\mathbf{j}}$. Determine (b) the car's average speed and (c) its average acceleration during the 36.0-s interval.

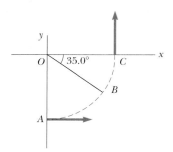

Figure P6.10

11. A 4.00-kg object is attached to a vertical rod by two strings as shown in Figure P6.11. The object rotates in a horizontal circle at constant speed 6.00 m/s. Find the tension in (a) the upper string and (b) the lower string.

Figure P6.11

Section 6.2 Nonuniform Circular Motion

12. A hawk flies in a horizontal arc of radius 12.0 m at a constant speed of 4.00 m/s. (a) Find its centripetal acceleration. (b) It continues to fly along the same horizontal arc but increases its speed at the rate of 1.20 m/s². Find the acceleration (magnitude and direction) under these conditions.

13. A 40.0-kg child swings in a swing supported by two chains, each 3.00 m long. The tension in each chain at the lowest point is 350 N. Find (a) the child's speed at the lowest point and (b) the force exerted by the seat on the child at the lowest point. (Ignore the mass of the seat.)

14. A roller-coaster car (Fig. P6.14) has a mass of 500 kg when fully loaded with passengers. (a) If the vehicle has a speed of 20.0 m/s at point Ⓐ, what is the force exerted by the track on the car at this point? (b) What is the maximum speed the vehicle can have at point Ⓑ and still remain on the track?

Figure P6.14

15. ▲ Tarzan ($m = 85.0$ kg) tries to cross a river by swinging on a vine. The vine is 10.0 m long, and his speed at the bottom of the swing (as he just clears the water) will be 8.00 m/s. Tarzan doesn't know that the vine has a breaking strength of 1 000 N. Does he make it across the river safely?

16. ● One end of a cord is fixed and a small 0.500-kg object is attached to the other end, where it swings in a section of a vertical circle of radius 2.00 m as shown in Figure 6.9. When $\theta = 20.0°$, the speed of the object is 8.00 m/s. At this instant, find (a) the tension in the string, (b) the tangential and radial components of acceleration, and (c) the total acceleration. (d) Is your answer changed if the object is swinging up instead of swinging down? Explain.

17. ▲ A pail of water is rotated in a vertical circle of radius 1.00 m. What is the pail's minimum speed at the top of the circle if no water is to spill out?

18. A roller coaster at Six Flags Great America amusement park in Gurnee, Illinois, incorporates some clever design technology and some basic physics. Each vertical loop, instead of being circular, is shaped like a teardrop (Fig. P6.18). The cars ride on the inside of the loop at the top, and the speeds are fast enough to ensure that the cars remain on the track. The biggest loop is 40.0 m high, with a maximum speed of 31.0 m/s (nearly 70 mi/h) at the bottom. Suppose the speed at the top is 13.0 m/s and the corresponding centripetal acceleration is 2g. (a) What is the radius of the arc of the teardrop at the top? (b) If the total mass of a car plus the riders is *M*, what force does the rail exert on the car at the top? (c) Suppose the roller coaster had a circular loop of radius 20.0 m. If the cars have the same speed, 13.0 m/s at the top, what is the centripetal acceleration at the top? Comment on the normal force at the top in this situation.

Figure P6.18

Section 6.3 Motion in Accelerated Frames

19. ● An object of mass 5.00 kg, attached to a spring scale, rests on a frictionless, horizontal surface as shown in Figure P6.19. The spring scale, attached to the front end of a boxcar, has a constant reading of 18.0 N when the car is in motion. (a) The spring scale reads zero when the car is at rest. Determine the acceleration of the car. (b) What constant reading will the spring scale show if the car moves with constant velocity? (c) Describe the forces on the object as observed by someone in the car and by someone at rest outside the car.

5.00 kg

Figure P6.19

20. A small container of water is placed on a carousel inside a microwave oven at a radius of 12.0 cm from the center. The turntable rotates steadily, turning one revolution each 7.25 s. What angle does the water surface make with the horizontal?

21. A 0.500-kg object is suspended from the ceiling of an accelerating boxcar as shown in Figure 6.12. Taking $a = 3.00$ m/s^2, find (a) the angle that the string makes with the vertical and (b) the tension in the string.

22. A student stands in an elevator that is continuously accelerating upward with acceleration a. Her backpack is sitting on the floor next to the wall. The width of the elevator car is L. The student gives her backpack a quick kick at $t = 0$, imparting to it speed v and making it slide across the elevator floor. At time t, the backpack hits the opposite wall. Find the coefficient of kinetic friction μ_k between the backpack and the elevator floor.

23. A person stands on a scale in an elevator. As the elevator starts, the scale has a constant reading of 591 N. Later, as the elevator stops, the scale reading is 391 N. Assume the magnitude of the acceleration is the same during starting and stopping. Determine (a) the weight of the person, (b) the person's mass, and (c) the acceleration of the elevator.

24. A child on vacation wakes up. She is lying on her back. The tension in the muscles on both sides of her neck is 55.0 N as she raises her head to look past her toes and out the motel window. Finally it is not raining! Ten minutes later she is screaming feet first down a water slide at terminal speed 5.70 m/s, riding high on the outside wall of a horizontal curve of radius 2.40 m (Fig. P6.24). She raises her head to look forward past her toes. Find the tension in the muscles on both sides of her neck.

Figure P6.24

25. A plumb bob does not hang exactly along a line directed to the center of the Earth's rotation. How much does the plumb bob deviate from a radial line at 35.0° north latitude? Assume the Earth is spherical.

Section 6.4 Motion in the Presence of Resistive Forces

26. A skydiver of mass 80.0 kg jumps from a slow-moving aircraft and reaches a terminal speed of 50.0 m/s. (a) What is the acceleration of the skydiver when her speed is 30.0 m/s? What is the drag force on the skydiver when her speed is (b) 50.0 m/s? (c) When it is 30.0 m/s?

27. A small piece of Styrofoam packing material is dropped from a height of 2.00 m above the ground. Until it reaches terminal speed, the magnitude of its acceleration is given by $a = g - bv$. After falling 0.500 m, the Styrofoam effectively reaches terminal speed and then takes 5.00 s more to reach the ground. (a) What is the value of the constant b? (b) What is the acceleration at $t = 0$? (c) What is the acceleration when the speed is 0.150 m/s?

28. (a) Estimate the terminal speed of a wooden sphere (density 0.830 g/cm^3) falling through air, taking its radius as 8.00 cm and its drag coefficient as 0.500. (b) From what height would a freely falling object reach this speed in the absence of air resistance?

29. Calculate the force required to pull a copper ball of radius 2.00 cm upward through a fluid at the constant speed 9.00 cm/s. Take the drag force to be proportional to the speed, with proportionality constant 0.950 kg/s. Ignore the buoyant force.

30. The mass of a sports car is 1 200 kg. The shape of the body is such that the aerodynamic drag coefficient is 0.250 and the frontal area is 2.20 m^2. Ignoring all other sources of friction, calculate the initial acceleration the car has if it has been traveling at 100 km/h and is now shifted into neutral and allowed to coast.

31. A small, spherical bead of mass 3.00 g is released from rest at $t = 0$ in a bottle of liquid shampoo. The terminal speed is observed to be $v_T = 2.00$ cm/s. Find (a) the

value of the constant b in Equation 6.2, (b) the time t at which the bead reaches $0.632v_T$, and (c) the value of the resistive force when the bead reaches terminal speed.

32. **Review problem**. An undercover police agent pulls a rubber squeegee down a very tall vertical window. The squeegee has mass 160 g and is mounted on the end of a light rod. The coefficient of kinetic friction between the squeegee and the dry glass is 0.900. The agent presses it against the window with a force having a horizontal component of 4.00 N. (a) If she pulls the squeegee down the window at constant velocity, what vertical force component must she exert? (b) The agent increases the downward force component by 25.0%, but all other forces remain the same. Find the acceleration of the squeegee in this situation. (c) The squeegee then moves into a wet portion of the window, where its motion is now resisted by a fluid drag force proportional to its velocity according to $R = -(20.0 \text{ N} \cdot \text{s/m})v$. Find the terminal velocity that the squeegee approaches, assuming the agent exerts the same force described in part (b).

33. A 9.00-kg object starting from rest falls through a viscous medium and experiences a resistive force $\vec{R} = -b\vec{v}$, where $\vec{v}$ is the velocity of the object. The object reaches one-half of its terminal speed in 5.54 s. (a) Determine the terminal speed. (b) At what time is the speed of the object three-fourths of the terminal speed? (c) How far has the object traveled in the first 5.54 s of motion?

34. Consider an object on which the net force is a resistive force proportional to the square of its speed. For example, assume the resistive force acting on a speed skater is $f = -kmv^2$, where k is a constant and m is the skater's mass. The skater crosses the finish line of a straight-line race with speed v_0 and then slows down by coasting on his skates. Show that the skater's speed at any time t after crossing the finish line is $v(t) = v_0/(1 + ktv_0)$. This problem also provides the background for the next two problems.

35. (a) Use the result of Problem 34 to find the position x as a function of time for an object of mass m, located at $x = 0$ and moving with velocity $v_0\hat{i}$ at time $t = 0$, and thereafter experiencing a net force $-kmv^2\hat{i}$. (b) Find the object's velocity as a function of position.

36. At major league baseball games it is commonplace to flash on the scoreboard a speed for each pitch. This speed is determined with a radar gun aimed by an operator positioned behind home plate. The gun uses the Doppler shift of microwaves reflected from the baseball, as we will study in Chapter 39. The gun determines the speed at some particular point on the baseball's path, depending on when the operator pulls the trigger. Because the ball is subject to a drag force due to air, it slows as it travels 18.3 m toward the plate. Use the result of Problem 35(b) to find how much its speed decreases. Suppose the ball leaves the pitcher's hand at 90.0 mi/h = 40.2 m/s. Ignore its vertical motion. Use data on baseballs from Example 6.11 to determine the speed of the pitch when it crosses the plate.

37. ▲ The driver of a motorboat cuts its engine when its speed is 10.0 m/s and coasts to rest. The equation describing the motion of the motorboat during this period is $v = v_i e^{-ct}$, where v is the speed at time t, v_i is the initial speed, and c is a constant. At $t = 20.0$ s, the speed is 5.00 m/s. (a) Find the constant c. (b) What is the speed

at $t = 40.0$ s? (c) Differentiate the expression for $v(t)$ and thus show that the acceleration of the boat is proportional to the speed at any time.

38. You can feel a force of air drag on your hand if you stretch your arm out of an open window of a rapidly moving car. *Note:* Do not endanger yourself. What is the order of magnitude of this force? In your solution, state the quantities you measure or estimate and their values.

Additional Problems

39. An object of mass m is projected forward along the x axis with initial speed v_0. The only force on it is a resistive force proportional to its velocity, given by $\vec{R} = -b\vec{v}$. For concreteness, you could visualize an airplane with pontoons landing on a lake. Newton's second law applied to the object is $-bv\hat{i} = m(dv/dt)\hat{i}$. From the fundamental theorem of calculus, this differential equation implies that the speed changes according to

$$\int_{\text{start}}^{\text{a later point}} \frac{dv}{v} = -\frac{b}{m} \int_0^t dt$$

Carry out the integrations to determine the speed of the object as a function of time. Sketch a graph of the speed as a function of time. Does the object come to a complete stop after a finite interval of time? Does the object travel a finite distance in stopping?

40. A 0.400-kg object is swung in a vertical circular path on a string 0.500 m long. If its speed is 4.00 m/s at the top of the circle, what is the tension in the string there?

41. (a) A luggage carousel at an airport has the form of a section of a large cone, steadily rotating about its vertical axis. Its metallic surface slopes downward toward the outside, making an angle of 20.0° with the horizontal. A piece of luggage having mass 30.0 kg is placed on the carousel, 7.46 m from the axis of rotation. The travel bag goes around once in 38.0 s. Calculate the force of static friction exerted by the carousel on the bag. (b) The drive motor is shifted to turn the carousel at a higher constant rate of rotation, and the piece of luggage is bumped to another position, 7.94 m from the axis of rotation. Now going around once in every 34.0 s, the bag is on the verge of slipping. Calculate the coefficient of static friction between the bag and the carousel.

42. In a home laundry dryer, a cylindrical tub containing wet clothes is rotated steadily about a horizontal axis as shown in Figure P6.42. So that the clothes will dry uniformly,

68.0°

Figure P6.42

they are made to tumble. The rate of rotation of the smooth-walled tub is chosen so that a small piece of cloth will lose contact with the tub when the cloth is at an angle of 68.0° above the horizontal. If the radius of the tub is 0.330 m, what rate of revolution is needed?

43. We will study the most important work of Nobel laureate Arthur Compton in Chapter 40. Disturbed by speeding cars outside the physics building at Washington University in St. Louis, Compton designed a speed bump and had it installed. Suppose a 1 800-kg car passes over a bump in a roadway that follows the arc of a circle of radius 20.4 m as shown in Figure P6.43. (a) What force does the road exert on the car as the car passes the highest point of the bump if it travels at 30.0 km/h? (b) **What If?** What is the maximum speed the car can have as it passes this highest point without losing contact with the road?

Figure P6.43   Problems 43 and 44.

44. A car of mass m passes over a bump in a road that follows the arc of a circle of radius R as shown in Figure P6.43. (a) What force does the road exert on the car as the car passes the highest point of the bump if it travels at a speed v? (b) **What If?** What is the maximum speed the car can have as it passes this highest point without losing contact with the road?

45. Interpret the graph in Figure 6.16(b). Proceed as follows. (a) Find the slope of the straight line, including its units. (b) From Equation 6.6, $R = \frac{1}{2} D\rho A v^2$, identify the theoretical slope of a graph of resistive force versus squared speed. (c) Set the experimental and theoretical slopes equal to each other and proceed to calculate the drag coefficient of the filters. Use the value for the density of air listed on the book's endpapers. Model the cross-sectional area of the filters as that of a circle of radius 10.5 cm. (d) Arbitrarily choose the eighth data point on the graph and find its vertical separation from the line of best fit. Express this scatter as a percentage. (e) In a short paragraph, state what the graph demonstrates and compare what it demonstrates to the theoretical prediction. You will need to make reference to the quantities plotted on the axes, to the shape of the graph line, to the data points, and to the results of parts (c) and (d).

46. ● A basin surrounding a drain has the shape of a circular cone opening upward, having everywhere an angle of 35.0° with the horizontal. A 25.0-g ice cube is set sliding around the cone without friction in a horizontal circle of radius R. (a) Find the speed the ice cube must have as it depends on R. (b) Is any piece of data unnecessary for the solution? Suppose R is made two times larger. (c) Will the required speed increase, decrease, or stay constant? If it changes, by what factor? (d) Will the time required for each revolution increase, decrease, or stay constant? If it changes, by what factor? (e) Do the answers to parts (c) and (d) seem contradictory? Explain how they are consistent.

47. Suppose the boxcar of Figure 6.12 is moving with constant acceleration a up a hill that makes an angle ϕ with the horizontal. If the pendulum makes a constant angle θ with the perpendicular to the ceiling, what is a?

48. The pilot of an airplane executes a constant-speed loop-the-loop maneuver in a vertical circle. The speed of the airplane is 300 mi/h; the radius of the circle is 1 200 ft. (a) What is the pilot's apparent weight at the lowest point if his true weight is 160 lb? (b) What is his apparent weight at the highest point? (c) **What If?** Describe how the pilot could experience weightlessness if both the radius and the speed can be varied. *Note:* His apparent weight is equal to the magnitude of the force exerted by the seat on his body.

49. ▲ Because the Earth rotates about its axis, a point on the equator experiences a centripetal acceleration of 0.033 7 m/s², whereas a point at the poles experiences no centripetal acceleration. (a) Show that at the equator the gravitational force on an object must exceed the normal force required to support the object. That is, show that the object's true weight exceeds its apparent weight. (b) What is the apparent weight at the equator and at the poles of a person having a mass of 75.0 kg? Assume the Earth is a uniform sphere and take $g = 9.800$ m/s².

50. ● An air puck of mass m_1 is tied to a string and allowed to revolve in a circle of radius R on a frictionless horizontal table. The other end of the string passes through a small hole in the center of the table, and a load of mass m_2 is tied to the string (Fig. P6.50). The suspended load remains in equilibrium while the puck on the tabletop revolves. What are (a) the tension in the string, (b) the radial force acting on the puck, and (c) the speed of the puck? (d) Qualitatively describe what will happen in the motion of the puck if the value of m_2 is somewhat increased by placing an additional load on it. (e) Qualitatively describe what will happen in the motion of the puck if the value of m_2 is instead decreased by removing a part of the hanging load.

Figure P6.50

51. ● While learning to drive, you are in a 1 200-kg car moving at 20.0 m/s across a large, vacant, level parking lot. Suddenly you realize you are heading straight toward a brick sidewall of a large supermarket and are in danger of running into it. The pavement can exert a maximum horizontal force of 7 000 N on the car. (a) Explain why you should expect the force to have a well-defined maximum value. (b) Suppose you apply the brakes and do not turn the steering wheel. Find the minimum distance you must be from the wall to avoid a collision. (c) If you do not brake but instead maintain constant speed and turn the steering wheel, what is the minimum distance you must be from the wall to avoid a collision? (d) Which method,

(b) or (c), is better for avoiding a collision? Or, should you use both the brakes and the steering wheel, or neither? Explain. (e) Does the conclusion in part (d) depend on the numerical values given in this problem, or is it true in general? Explain.

52. Suppose a Ferris wheel rotates four times each minute. It carries each car around a circle of diameter 18.0 m. (a) What is the centripetal acceleration of a rider? What force does the seat exert on a 40.0-kg rider (b) at the lowest point of the ride and (c) at the highest point of the ride? (d) What force (magnitude and direction) does the seat exert on a rider when the rider is halfway between top and bottom?

53. An amusement park ride consists of a rotating circular platform 8.00 m in diameter from which 10.0-kg seats are suspended at the end of 2.50-m massless chains (Fig. P6.53). When the system rotates, the chains make an angle $\theta = 28.0°$ with the vertical. (a) What is the speed of each seat? (b) Draw a free-body diagram of a 40.0-kg child riding in a seat and find the tension in the chain.

Figure P6.53

54. A piece of putty is initially located at point A on the rim of a grinding wheel rotating about a horizontal axis. The putty is dislodged from point A when the diameter through A is horizontal. It then rises vertically and returns to A at the instant the wheel completes one revolution. (a) Find the speed of a point on the rim of the wheel in terms of the acceleration due to gravity and the radius R of the wheel. (b) If the mass of the putty is m, what is the magnitude of the force that held it to the wheel?

55. ● An amusement park ride consists of a large vertical cylinder that spins about its axis fast enough that any person inside is held up against the wall when the floor drops away (Fig. P6.55). The coefficient of static friction between person and wall is μ_s, and the radius of the cylinder is R. (a) Show that the maximum period of revolution necessary to keep the person from falling is $T = (4\pi^2 R\mu_s/g)^{1/2}$. (b) Obtain a numerical value for T, taking $R = 4.00$ m and $\mu_s = 0.400$. How many revolutions per minute does the cylinder make? (c) If the rate of revolution of the cylinder is made to be somewhat larger, what happens to the magnitude of each one of the forces act-

ing on the person? What happens in the motion of the person? (d) If instead the cylinder's rate of revolution is made to be somewhat smaller, what happens to the magnitude of each one of the forces acting on the person? What happens in the motion of the person?

Figure P6.55

56. *An example of the Coriolis effect.* Suppose air resistance is negligible for a golf ball. A golfer tees off from a location precisely at $\phi_i = 35.0°$ north latitude. He hits the ball due south, with range 285 m. The ball's initial velocity is at 48.0° above the horizontal. (a) For how long is the ball in flight? The cup is due south of the golfer's location, and he would have a hole in one if the Earth were not rotating. The Earth's rotation makes the tee move in a circle of radius $R_E \cos \phi_i = (6.37 \times 10^6 \text{ m}) \cos 35.0°$ as shown in Figure P6.56. The tee completes one revolution each day. (b) Find the eastward speed of the tee, relative to the stars. The hole is also moving east, but it is 285 m farther south and therefore at a slightly lower latitude ϕ_f. Because the hole moves in a slightly larger circle, its speed must be greater than that of the tee. (c) By how much does the hole's speed exceed that of the tee? During the time interval the ball is in flight, it moves upward and downward as well as southward with the projectile motion you studied in Chapter 4, but it also moves eastward with the speed you found in part (b). The hole moves to the east at a faster speed, however, pulling ahead of the ball with the relative speed you found in part (c). (d) How far to the west of the hole does the ball land?

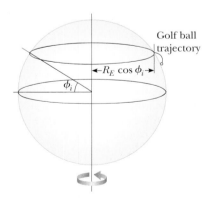

Figure P6.56

57. A car rounds a banked curve as shown in Figure 6.5. The radius of curvature of the road is R, the banking angle is θ, and the coefficient of static friction is μ_s. (a) Determine the range of speeds the car can have without slipping up or down the bank. (b) Find the minimum value for μ_s such that the minimum speed is zero. (c) What is the range of speeds possible if $R = 100$ m, $\theta = 10.0°$, and $\mu_s = 0.100$ (slippery conditions)?

58. ● A single bead can slide with negligible friction on a stiff wire that has been bent into a circular loop of radius 15.0 cm as shown in Figure P6.58. The circle is always in a vertical plane and rotates steadily about its vertical diameter with (a) a period of 0.450 s. The position of the bead is described by the angle θ that the radial line, from the center of the loop to the bead, makes with the vertical. At what angle up from the bottom of the circle can the bead stay motionless relative to the turning circle? (b) **What If?** Repeat the problem, taking the period of the circle's rotation as 0.850 s. (c) Describe how the solution to part (b) is fundamentally different from the solution to part (a). For any period or loop size, is there always an angle at which the bead can stand still relative to the loop? Are there ever more than two angles? Arnold Arons suggested the idea for this problem.

Figure P6.58

59. The expression $F = arv + br^2v^2$ gives the magnitude of the resistive force (in newtons) exerted on a sphere of radius r (in meters) by a stream of air moving at speed v (in meters per second), where a and b are constants with appropriate SI units. Their numerical values are $a = 3.10 \times 10^{-4}$ and $b = 0.870$. Using this expression, find the terminal speed for water droplets falling under their own weight in air, taking the following values for the drop radii: (a) 10.0 μm, (b) 100 μm, (c) 1.00 mm. For (a) and (c), you can obtain accurate answers without solving a quadratic equation by considering which of the two contributions to the air resistance is dominant and ignoring the lesser contribution.

60. ▬ Members of a skydiving club were given the following data to use in planning their jumps. In the table, d is the distance fallen from rest by a skydiver in a "free-fall stable spread position" versus the time of fall t. (a) Convert the distances in feet into meters. (b) Graph d (in meters) ver-

sus t. (c) Determine the value of the terminal speed v_T by finding the slope of the straight portion of the curve. Use a least-squares fit to determine this slope.

t (s)	d (ft)	t (s)	d (ft)	t (s)	d (ft)
0	0	7	652	14	1 831
1	16	8	808	15	2 005
2	62	9	971	16	2 179
3	138	10	1 138	17	2 353
4	242	11	1 309	18	2 527
5	366	12	1 483	19	2 701
6	504	13	1 657	20	2 875

61. A model airplane of mass 0.750 kg flies with a speed of 35.0 m/s in a horizontal circle at the end of a 60.0-m control wire. Compute the tension in the wire, assuming it makes a constant angle of 20.0° with the horizontal. The forces exerted on the airplane are the pull of the control wire, the gravitational force, and aerodynamic lift that acts at 20.0° inward from the vertical as shown in Figure P6.61.

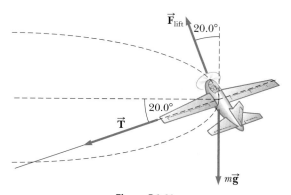

Figure P6.61

62. ● Galileo thought about whether acceleration should be defined as the rate of change of velocity over time or as the rate of change in velocity over distance. He chose the former, so let us use the name "vroomosity" for the rate of change of velocity in space. For motion of a particle on a straight line with constant acceleration, the equation $v = v_i + at$ gives its velocity v as a function of time. Similarly, for a particle's linear motion with constant vroomosity k, the equation $v = v_i + kx$ gives the velocity as a function of the position x if the particle's speed is v_i at $x = 0$. (a) Find the law describing the total force acting on this object, of mass m. Describe an example of such a motion, or explain why such a motion is unrealistic. Consider (b) the possibility of k positive and also (c) the possibility of k negative.

Answers to Quick Quizzes

6.1 (i), (a). The normal force is always perpendicular to the surface that applies the force. Because your car maintains its orientation at all points on the ride, the normal force is always upward. **(ii)**, (b). Your centripetal acceleration is downward toward the center of the circle, so the net force on you must be downward.

6.2 (a) Because the speed is constant, the only direction the force can have is that of the centripetal acceleration. The force is larger at Ⓒ than at Ⓐ because the radius at Ⓒ is smaller. There is no force at Ⓑ because the wire is straight. (b) In addition to the forces in the centripetal direction in (a), there are now tangential forces to provide the tangential acceleration. The tangential force is the same at all three points because the tangential acceleration is constant.

(a)   (b)

QQA 6.2

6.3 (c). The only forces acting on the passenger are the contact force with the door and the friction force from the seat. Both are real forces and both act to the left in Figure 6.10. Fictitious forces should never be drawn in a force diagram.

6.4. (a). The basketball, having a larger cross-sectional area, will have a larger force due to air resistance than the baseball, which will result in a smaller downward acceleration.

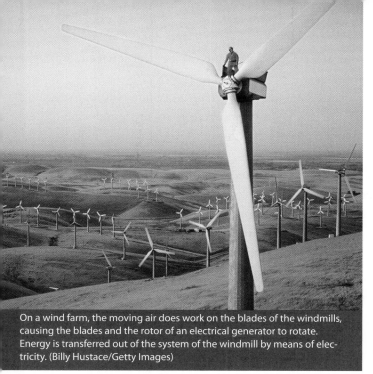

On a wind farm, the moving air does work on the blades of the windmills, causing the blades and the rotor of an electrical generator to rotate. Energy is transferred out of the system of the windmill by means of electricity. (Billy Hustace/Getty Images)

7 Energy of a System

The definitions of quantities such as position, velocity, acceleration, and force and associated principles such as Newton's second law have allowed us to solve a variety of problems. Some problems that could theoretically be solved with Newton's laws, however, are very difficult in practice, but they can be made much simpler with a different approach. Here and in the following chapters, we will investigate this new approach, which will include definitions of quantities that may not be familiar to you. Other quantities may sound familiar, but they may have more specific meanings in physics than in everyday life. We begin this discussion by exploring the notion of *energy*.

The concept of energy is one of the most important topics in science and engineering. In everyday life, we think of energy in terms of fuel for transportation and heating, electricity for lights and appliances, and foods for consumption. These ideas, however, do not truly define energy. They merely tell us that fuels are needed to do a job and that those fuels provide us with something we call energy.

Energy is present in the Universe in various forms. *Every* physical process that occurs in the Universe involves energy and energy transfers or transformations. Unfortunately, despite its extreme importance, energy cannot be easily defined. The variables in previous chapters were relatively concrete; we have everyday experience with velocities and forces, for example. Although we have *experiences* with energy, such as running out of gasoline or losing our electrical service following a violent storm, the *notion* of energy is more abstract.

The concept of energy can be applied to mechanical systems without resorting to Newton's laws. Furthermore, the energy approach allows us to understand thermal and electrical phenomena, for which Newton's laws are of no help, in later chapters of the book.

Our problem-solving techniques presented in earlier chapters were based on the motion of a particle or an object that could be modeled as a particle. These techniques used the *particle model*. We begin our new approach by focusing our attention on a *system* and developing techniques to be used in a *system model*.

7.1 Systems and Environments

PITFALL PREVENTION 7.1
Identify the System

The most important *first* step to take in solving a problem using the energy approach is to identify the appropriate system of interest.

In the system model, we focus our attention on a small portion of the Universe—the **system**—and ignore details of the rest of the Universe outside of the system. A critical skill in applying the system model to problems is *identifying the system*. A valid system

- may be a single object or particle
- may be a collection of objects or particles
- may be a region of space (such as the interior of an automobile engine combustion cylinder)
- may vary in size and shape (such as a rubber ball, which deforms upon striking a wall)

Identifying the need for a system approach to solving a problem (as opposed to a particle approach) is part of the Categorize step in the General Problem-Solving Strategy outlined in Chapter 2. Identifying the particular system is a second part of this step.

No matter what the particular system is in a given problem, we identify a **system boundary**, an imaginary surface (not necessarily coinciding with a physical surface) that divides the Universe into the system and the **environment** surrounding the system.

As an example, imagine a force applied to an object in empty space. We can define the object as the system and its surface as the system boundary. The force applied to it is an influence on the system from the environment that acts across the system boundary. We will see how to analyze this situation from a system approach in a subsequent section of this chapter.

Another example was seen in Example 5.10, where the system can be defined as the combination of the ball, the block, and the cord. The influence from the environment includes the gravitational forces on the ball and the block, the normal and friction forces on the block, and the force exerted by the pulley on the cord. The forces exerted by the cord on the ball and the block are internal to the system and therefore are not included as an influence from the environment.

There are a number of mechanisms by which a system can be influenced by its environment. The first one we shall investigate is *work*.

7.2 Work Done by a Constant Force

Almost all the terms we have used thus far—velocity, acceleration, force, and so on—convey a similar meaning in physics as they do in everyday life. Now, however, we encounter a term whose meaning in physics is distinctly different from its everyday meaning: *work*.

(a)

(b)

(c)

Charles D. Winters

Figure 7.1   An eraser being pushed along a chalkboard tray by a force acting at different angles with respect to the horizontal direction.

To understand what work means to the physicist, consider the situation illustrated in Figure 7.1. A force $\vec{\mathbf{F}}$ is applied to a chalkboard eraser, which we identify as the system, and the eraser slides along the tray. If we want to know how effective the force is in moving the eraser, we must consider not only the magnitude of the force but also its direction. Assuming the magnitude of the applied force is the same in all three photographs, the push applied in Figure 7.1b does more to move the eraser than the push in Figure 7.1a. On the other hand, Figure 7.1c shows a situation in which the applied force does not move the eraser at all, regardless of how hard it is pushed (unless, of course, we apply a force so great that we break the chalkboard tray!). These results suggest that when analyzing forces to determine the work they do, we must consider the vector nature of forces. We must also know the displacement $\Delta \vec{\mathbf{r}}$ of the eraser as it moves along the tray if we want to determine the work done on it by the force. Moving the eraser 3 m along the tray requires more work than moving it 2 cm.

Let us examine the situation in Figure 7.2, where the object (the system) undergoes a displacement along a straight line while acted on by a constant force of magnitude F that makes an angle θ with the direction of the displacement.

The **work** W done on a system by an agent exerting a constant force on the system is the product of the magnitude F of the force, the magnitude Δr of the displacement of the point of application of the force, and $\cos \theta$, where θ is the angle between the force and displacement vectors:

$$W \equiv F \, \Delta r \cos \theta \qquad \textbf{(7.1)}$$

Notice in Equation 7.1 that work is a scalar, even though it is defined in terms of two vectors, a force $\vec{\mathbf{F}}$ and a displacement $\Delta \vec{\mathbf{r}}$. In Section 7.3, we explore how to combine two vectors to generate a scalar quantity.

As an example of the distinction between the definition of work and our everyday understanding of the word, consider holding a heavy chair at arm's length for 3 min. At the end of this time interval, your tired arms may lead you to think you have done a considerable amount of work on the chair. According to our definition, however, you have done no work on it whatsoever. You exert a force to support the chair, but you do not move it. A force does no work on an object if the force does not move through a displacement. If $\Delta r = 0$, Equation 7.1 gives $W = 0$, which is the situation depicted in Figure 7.1c.

Also notice from Equation 7.1 that the work done by a force on a moving object is zero when the force applied is perpendicular to the displacement of its point of application. That is, if $\theta = 90°$, then $W = 0$ because $\cos 90° = 0$. For example, in Figure 7.3, the work done by the normal force on the object and the work done by the gravitational force on the object are both zero because both forces are perpen-

PITFALL PREVENTION 7.2
What Is Being Displaced?

The displacement in Equation 7.1 is that of *the point of application of the force*. If the force is applied to a particle or a nondeformable system, this displacement is the same as the displacement of the particle or system. For deformable systems, however, these two displacements are often not the same.

Figure 7.2   If an object undergoes a displacement $\Delta \vec{\mathbf{r}}$ under the action of a constant force $\vec{\mathbf{F}}$, the work done by the force is $F \Delta r \cos \theta$.

◄   Work done by a constant force

Figure 7.3   An object is displaced on a frictionless, horizontal surface. The normal force $\vec{\mathbf{n}}$ and the gravitational force $m\vec{\mathbf{g}}$ do no work on the object. In the situation shown here, $\vec{\mathbf{F}}$ is the only force doing work on the object.

PITFALL PREVENTION 7.3
Work Is Done by . . . on . . .

Not only must you identify the system, you must also identify what agent in the environment is doing work on the system. When discussing work, always use the phrase, "the work done by . . . on. . . ." After "by," insert the part of the environment that is interacting directly with the system. After "on," insert the system. For example, "the work done by the hammer on the nail" identifies the nail as the system and the force from the hammer represents the interaction with the environment.

PITFALL PREVENTION 7.4
Cause of the Displacement

We can calculate the work done by a force on an object, but that force is *not* necessarily the cause of the object's displacement. For example, if you lift an object, work is done on the object by the gravitational force, although gravity is not the cause of the object moving upward!

dicular to the displacement and have zero components along an axis in the direction of $\Delta\vec{r}$.

The sign of the work also depends on the direction of $\vec{F}$ relative to $\Delta\vec{r}$. The work done by the applied force on a system is positive when the projection of $\vec{F}$ onto $\Delta\vec{r}$ is in the same direction as the displacement. For example, when an object is lifted, the work done by the applied force on the object is positive because the direction of that force is upward, in the same direction as the displacement of its point of application. When the projection of $\vec{F}$ onto $\Delta\vec{r}$ is in the direction opposite the displacement, W is negative. For example, as an object is lifted, the work done by the gravitational force on the object is negative. The factor $\cos\theta$ in the definition of W (Eq. 7.1) automatically takes care of the sign.

If an applied force $\vec{F}$ is in the same direction as the displacement $\Delta\vec{r}$, then $\theta = 0$ and $\cos 0 = 1$. In this case, Equation 7.1 gives

$$W = F\,\Delta r$$

The units of work are those of force multiplied by those of length. Therefore, the SI unit of work is the **newton-meter** (N·m $=$ kg·m²/s²). This combination of units is used so frequently that it has been given a name of its own, the **joule** (J).

An important consideration for a system approach to problems is that **work is an energy transfer**. If W is the work done on a system and W is positive, energy is transferred *to* the system; if W is negative, energy is transferred *from* the system. Therefore, if a system interacts with its environment, this interaction can be described as a transfer of energy across the system boundary. The result is a change in the energy stored in the system. We will learn about the first type of energy storage in Section 7.5, after we investigate more aspects of work.

Quick Quiz 7.1 The gravitational force exerted by the Sun on the Earth holds the Earth in an orbit around the Sun. Let us assume that the orbit is perfectly circular. The work done by this gravitational force during a short time interval in which the Earth moves through a displacement in its orbital path is (a) zero (b) positive (c) negative (d) impossible to determine

Quick Quiz 7.2 Figure 7.4 shows four situations in which a force is applied to an object. In all four cases, the force has the same magnitude, and the displacement of the object is to the right and of the same magnitude. Rank the situations in order of the work done by the force on the object, from most positive to most negative.

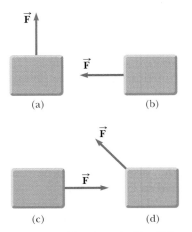

Figure 7.4 (Quick Quiz 7.2) A block is pulled by a force in four different directions. In each case, the displacement of the block is to the right and of the same magnitude.

EXAMPLE 7.1 | **Mr. Clean**

A man cleaning a floor pulls a vacuum cleaner with a force of magnitude $F =$ 50.0 N at an angle of 30.0° with the horizontal (Fig. 7.5). Calculate the work done by the force on the vacuum cleaner as the vacuum cleaner is displaced 3.00 m to the right.

SOLUTION

Conceptualize Figure 7.5 helps conceptualize the situation. Think about an experience in your life in which you pulled an object across the floor with a rope or cord.

Figure 7.5 (Example 7.1) A vacuum cleaner being pulled at an angle of 30.0° from the horizontal.

Categorize We are given a force on an object, a displacement of the object, and the angle between the two vectors, so we categorize this example as a substitution problem. We identify the vacuum cleaner as the system.

Use the definition of work (Eq. 7.1):

$$W = F\,\Delta r\cos\theta = (50.0\ \text{N})(3.00\ \text{m})(\cos 30.0°)$$
$$= \boxed{130\ \text{J}}$$

Notice in this situation that the normal force $\vec{\mathbf{n}}$ and the gravitational $\vec{\mathbf{F}}_g = m\vec{\mathbf{g}}$ do no work on the vacuum cleaner because these forces are perpendicular to its displacement.

7.3 The Scalar Product of Two Vectors

Because of the way the force and displacement vectors are combined in Equation 7.1, it is helpful to use a convenient mathematical tool called the **scalar product** of two vectors. We write this scalar product of vectors $\vec{\mathbf{A}}$ and $\vec{\mathbf{B}}$ as $\vec{\mathbf{A}}\cdot\vec{\mathbf{B}}$. (Because of the dot symbol, the scalar product is often called the **dot product**.)

The scalar product of any two vectors $\vec{\mathbf{A}}$ and $\vec{\mathbf{B}}$ is a scalar quantity equal to the product of the magnitudes of the two vectors and the cosine of the angle θ between them:

$$\vec{\mathbf{A}}\cdot\vec{\mathbf{B}} \equiv AB\cos\theta \qquad (7.2)$$

◄ Scalar product of any two vectors $\vec{\mathbf{A}}$ and $\vec{\mathbf{B}}$

As is the case with any multiplication, $\vec{\mathbf{A}}$ and $\vec{\mathbf{B}}$ need not have the same units.

By comparing this definition with Equation 7.1, we can express Equation 7.1 as a scalar product:

$$W = F\,\Delta r\cos\theta = \vec{\mathbf{F}}\cdot\Delta\vec{\mathbf{r}} \qquad (7.3)$$

In other words, $\vec{\mathbf{F}}\cdot\Delta\vec{\mathbf{r}}$ is a shorthand notation for $F\,\Delta r\cos\theta$.

Before continuing with our discussion of work, let us investigate some properties of the dot product. Figure 7.6 shows two vectors $\vec{\mathbf{A}}$ and $\vec{\mathbf{B}}$ and the angle θ between them used in the definition of the dot product. In Figure 7.6, $B\cos\theta$ is the projection of $\vec{\mathbf{B}}$ onto $\vec{\mathbf{A}}$. Therefore, Equation 7.2 means that $\vec{\mathbf{A}}\cdot\vec{\mathbf{B}}$ is the product of the magnitude of $\vec{\mathbf{A}}$ and the projection of $\vec{\mathbf{B}}$ onto $\vec{\mathbf{A}}$.[1]

From the right-hand side of Equation 7.2, we also see that the scalar product is **commutative**.[2] That is,

$$\vec{\mathbf{A}}\cdot\vec{\mathbf{B}} = \vec{\mathbf{B}}\cdot\vec{\mathbf{A}}$$

Finally, the scalar product obeys the **distributive law of multiplication**, so

$$\vec{\mathbf{A}}\cdot(\vec{\mathbf{B}} + \vec{\mathbf{C}}) = \vec{\mathbf{A}}\cdot\vec{\mathbf{B}} + \vec{\mathbf{A}}\cdot\vec{\mathbf{C}}$$

PITFALL PREVENTION 7.5
Work Is a Scalar

Although Equation 7.3 defines the work in terms of two vectors, *work is a scalar*; there is no direction associated with it. *All* types of energy and energy transfer are scalars. This fact is a major advantage of the energy approach because we don't need vector calculations!

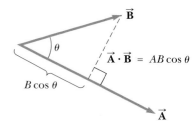

Figure 7.6 The scalar product $\vec{\mathbf{A}}\cdot\vec{\mathbf{B}}$ equals the magnitude of $\vec{\mathbf{A}}$ multiplied by $B\cos\theta$, which is the projection of $\vec{\mathbf{B}}$ onto $\vec{\mathbf{A}}$.

---

[1] This statement is equivalent to stating that $\vec{\mathbf{A}}\cdot\vec{\mathbf{B}}$ equals the product of the magnitude of $\vec{\mathbf{B}}$ and the projection of $\vec{\mathbf{A}}$ onto $\vec{\mathbf{B}}$.

[2] In Chapter 11, you will see another way of combining vectors that proves useful in physics and is not commutative.

The dot product is simple to evaluate from Equation 7.2 when $\vec{A}$ is either perpendicular or parallel to $\vec{B}$. If $\vec{A}$ is perpendicular to $\vec{B}$ ($\theta = 90°$), then $\vec{A} \cdot \vec{B} = 0$. (The equality $\vec{A} \cdot \vec{B} = 0$ also holds in the more trivial case in which either $\vec{A}$ or $\vec{B}$ is zero.) If vector $\vec{A}$ is parallel to vector $\vec{B}$ and the two point in the same direction ($\theta = 0$), then $\vec{A} \cdot \vec{B} = AB$. If vector $\vec{A}$ is parallel to vector $\vec{B}$ but the two point in opposite directions ($\theta = 180°$), then $\vec{A} \cdot \vec{B} = -AB$. The scalar product is negative when $90° < \theta \leq 180°$.

The unit vectors $\hat{i}$, $\hat{j}$, and $\hat{k}$, which were defined in Chapter 3, lie in the positive x, y, and z directions, respectively, of a right-handed coordinate system. Therefore, it follows from the definition of $\vec{A} \cdot \vec{B}$ that the scalar products of these unit vectors are

◀ Dot products of unit vectors

$$\hat{i} \cdot \hat{i} = \hat{j} \cdot \hat{j} = \hat{k} \cdot \hat{k} = 1 \tag{7.4}$$

$$\hat{i} \cdot \hat{j} = \hat{i} \cdot \hat{k} = \hat{j} \cdot \hat{k} = 0 \tag{7.5}$$

Equations 3.18 and 3.19 state that two vectors $\vec{A}$ and $\vec{B}$ can be expressed in unit-vector form as

$$\vec{A} = A_x\hat{i} + A_y\hat{j} + A_z\hat{k}$$

$$\vec{B} = B_x\hat{i} + B_y\hat{j} + B_z\hat{k}$$

Using the information given in Equations 7.4 and 7.5 shows that the scalar product of $\vec{A}$ and $\vec{B}$ reduces to

$$\vec{A} \cdot \vec{B} = A_xB_x + A_yB_y + A_zB_z \tag{7.6}$$

(Details of the derivation are left for you in Problem 5 at the end of the chapter.) In the special case in which $\vec{A} = \vec{B}$, we see that

$$\vec{A} \cdot \vec{A} = A_x^2 + A_y^2 + A_z^2 = A^2$$

Quick Quiz 7.3 Which of the following statements is true about the relationship between the dot product of two vectors and the product of the magnitudes of the vectors? (a) $\vec{A} \cdot \vec{B}$ is larger than AB. (b) $\vec{A} \cdot \vec{B}$ is smaller than AB. (c) $\vec{A} \cdot \vec{B}$ could be larger or smaller than AB, depending on the angle between the vectors. (d) $\vec{A} \cdot \vec{B}$ could be equal to AB.

EXAMPLE 7.2 **The Scalar Product**

The vectors $\vec{A}$ and $\vec{B}$ are given by $\vec{A} = 2\hat{i} + 3\hat{j}$ and $\vec{B} = -\hat{i} + 2\hat{j}$.

(A) Determine the scalar product $\vec{A} \cdot \vec{B}$.

SOLUTION

Conceptualize There is no physical system to imagine here. Rather, it is purely a mathematical exercise involving two vectors.

Categorize Because we have a definition for the scalar product, we categorize this example as a substitution problem.

Substitute the specific vector expressions for $\vec{A}$ and $\vec{B}$:

$$\vec{A} \cdot \vec{B} = (2\hat{i} + 3\hat{j}) \cdot (-\hat{i} + 2\hat{j})$$

$$= -2\hat{i} \cdot \hat{i} + 2\hat{i} \cdot 2\hat{j} - 3\hat{j} \cdot \hat{i} + 3\hat{j} \cdot 2\hat{j}$$

$$= -2(1) + 4(0) - 3(0) + 6(1) = -2 + 6 = \boxed{4}$$

The same result is obtained when we use Equation 7.6 directly, where $A_x = 2$, $A_y = 3$, $B_x = -1$, and $B_y = 2$.

(B) Find the angle θ between $\vec{\mathbf{A}}$ and $\vec{\mathbf{B}}$.

SOLUTION

Evaluate the magnitudes of $\vec{\mathbf{A}}$ and $\vec{\mathbf{B}}$ using the Pythagorean theorem:

$$A = \sqrt{A_x^2 + A_y^2} = \sqrt{(2)^2 + (3)^2} = \sqrt{13}$$

$$B = \sqrt{B_x^2 + B_y^2} = \sqrt{(-1)^2 + (2)^2} = \sqrt{5}$$

Use Equation 7.2 and the result from part (A) to find the angle:

$$\cos\theta = \frac{\vec{\mathbf{A}} \cdot \vec{\mathbf{B}}}{AB} = \frac{4}{\sqrt{13}\sqrt{5}} = \frac{4}{\sqrt{65}}$$

$$\theta = \cos^{-1}\frac{4}{\sqrt{65}} = \boxed{60.3°}$$

EXAMPLE 7.3   **Work Done by a Constant Force**

A particle moving in the xy plane undergoes a displacement given by $\Delta\vec{\mathbf{r}} = (2.0\hat{\mathbf{i}} + 3.0\hat{\mathbf{j}})$ m as a constant force $\vec{\mathbf{F}} = (5.0\hat{\mathbf{i}} + 2.0\hat{\mathbf{j}})$ N acts on the particle.

(A) Calculate the magnitudes of the force and the displacement of the particle.

SOLUTION

Conceptualize   Although this example is a little more physical than the previous one in that it identifies a force and a displacement, it is similar in terms of its mathematical structure.

Categorize   Because we are given two vectors and asked to find their magnitudes, we categorize this example as a substitution problem.

Use the Pythagorean theorem to find the magnitudes of the force and the displacement:

$$F = \sqrt{F_x^2 + F_y^2} = \sqrt{(5.0)^2 + (2.0)^2} = \boxed{5.4\text{ N}}$$

$$\Delta r = \sqrt{(\Delta x)^2 + (\Delta y)^2} = \sqrt{(2.0)^2 + (3.0)^2} = \boxed{3.6\text{ m}}$$

(B) Calculate the work done by $\vec{\mathbf{F}}$ on the particle.

SOLUTION

Substitute the expressions for $\vec{\mathbf{F}}$ and $\Delta\vec{\mathbf{r}}$ into Equation 7.3 and use Equations 4.4 and 7.5:

$$W = \vec{\mathbf{F}} \cdot \Delta\vec{\mathbf{r}} = [(5.0\hat{\mathbf{i}} + 2.0\hat{\mathbf{j}})\text{ N}] \cdot [(2.0\hat{\mathbf{i}} + 3.0\hat{\mathbf{j}})\text{ m}]$$

$$= (5.0\hat{\mathbf{i}} \cdot 2.0\hat{\mathbf{i}} + 5.0\hat{\mathbf{i}} \cdot 3.0\hat{\mathbf{j}} + 2.0\hat{\mathbf{j}} \cdot 2.0\hat{\mathbf{i}} + 2.0\hat{\mathbf{j}} \cdot 3.0\hat{\mathbf{j}})\text{ N} \cdot \text{m}$$

$$= [10 + 0 + 0 + 6]\text{ N} \cdot \text{m} = \boxed{16\text{ J}}$$

7.4   Work Done by a Varying Force

Consider a particle being displaced along the x axis under the action of a force that varies with position. The particle is displaced in the direction of increasing x from $x = x_i$ to $x = x_f$. In such a situation, we cannot use $W = F\,\Delta r \cos\theta$ to calculate the work done by the force because this relationship applies only when $\vec{\mathbf{F}}$ is constant in magnitude and direction. If, however, we imagine that the particle undergoes a very small displacement Δx, shown in Figure 7.7a, the x component F_x of the force is approximately constant over this small interval; for this small displacement, we can approximate the work done on the particle by the force as

$$W \approx F_x\,\Delta x$$

which is the area of the shaded rectangle in Figure 7.7a. If we imagine the F_x versus x curve divided into a large number of such intervals, the total work done for

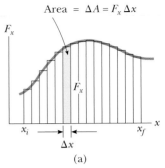

Area $= \Delta A = F_x \Delta x$

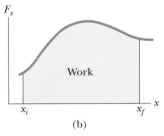

(a)

(b)

Figure 7.7 (a) The work done on a particle by the force component F_x for the small displacement Δx is $F_x \Delta x$, which equals the area of the shaded rectangle. The total work done for the displacement from x_i to x_f is approximately equal to the sum of the areas of all the rectangles. (b) The work done by the component F_x of the varying force as the particle moves from x_i to x_f is *exactly* equal to the area under this curve.

the displacement from x_i to x_f is approximately equal to the sum of a large number of such terms:

$$W \approx \sum_{x_i}^{x_f} F_x \Delta x$$

If the size of the small displacements is allowed to approach zero, the number of terms in the sum increases without limit but the value of the sum approaches a definite value equal to the area bounded by the F_x curve and the x axis:

$$\lim_{\Delta x \to 0} \sum_{x_i}^{x_f} F_x \Delta x = \int_{x_i}^{x_f} F_x \, dx$$

Therefore, we can express the work done by F_x on the particle as it moves from x_i to x_f as

$$W = \int_{x_i}^{x_f} F_x \, dx \qquad (7.7)$$

This equation reduces to Equation 7.1 when the component $F_x = F \cos \theta$ is constant.

If more than one force acts on a system *and the system can be modeled as a particle*, the total work done on the system is just the work done by the net force. If we express the net force in the x direction as ΣF_x, the total work, or *net work*, done as the particle moves from x_i to x_f is

$$\sum W = W_{net} = \int_{x_i}^{x_f} \left(\sum F_x \right) dx$$

For the general case of a net force $\Sigma \vec{F}$ whose magnitude and direction may vary, we use the scalar product,

$$\sum W = W_{net} = \int \left(\sum \vec{F} \right) \cdot d\vec{r} \qquad (7.8)$$

where the integral is calculated over the path that the particle takes through space.

If the system cannot be modeled as a particle (for example, if the system consists of multiple particles that can move with respect to one another), we cannot use Equation 7.8 because different forces on the system may move through different displacements. In this case, we must evaluate the work done by each force separately and then add the works algebraically to find the net work done on the system.

EXAMPLE 7.4 **Calculating Total Work Done from a Graph**

A force acting on a particle varies with x as shown in Figure 7.8. Calculate the work done by the force on the particle as it moves from $x = 0$ to $x = 6.0$ m.

SOLUTION

Conceptualize Imagine a particle subject to the force in Figure 7.8. Notice that the force remains constant as the particle moves through the first 4.0 m and then decreases linearly to zero at 6.0 m.

Categorize Because the force varies during the entire motion of the particle, we must use the techniques for work done by varying forces. In this case, the graphical representation in Figure 7.8 can be used to evaluate the work done.

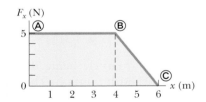

Figure 7.8 (Example 7.4) The force acting on a particle is constant for the first 4.0 m of motion and then decreases linearly with x from $x_{Ⓑ} = 4.0$ m to $x_{Ⓒ} = 6.0$ m. The net work done by this force is the area under the curve.

Analyze The work done by the force is equal to the area under the curve from $x_{Ⓐ} = 0$ to $x_{Ⓒ} = 6.0$ m. This area is equal to the area of the rectangular section from Ⓐ to Ⓑ plus the area of the triangular section from Ⓑ to Ⓒ.

Evaluate the area of the rectangle:

$$W_{\circledA\circledB} = (5.0 \text{ N})(4.0 \text{ m}) = 20 \text{ J}$$

Evaluate the area of the triangle:

$$W_{\circledB\circledC} = \tfrac{1}{2}(5.0 \text{ N})(2.0 \text{ m}) = 5.0 \text{ J}$$

Find the total work done by the force on the particle:

$$W_{\circledA\circledC} = W_{\circledA\circledB} + W_{\circledB\circledC} = 20 \text{ J} + 5.0 \text{ J} = \boxed{25 \text{ J}}$$

Finalize   Because the graph of the force consists of straight lines, we can use rules for finding the areas of simple geometric shapes to evaluate the total work done in this example. In a case in which the force does not vary linearly, such rules cannot be used and the force function must be integrated as in Equation 7.7 or 7.8.

Work Done by a Spring

A model of a common physical system for which the force varies with position is shown in Active Figure 7.9. A block on a horizontal, frictionless surface is connected to a spring. For many springs, if the spring is either stretched or compressed a small distance from its unstretched (equilibrium) configuration, it exerts on the block a force that can be mathematically modeled as

$$F_s = -kx \qquad\qquad (7.9) \qquad \blacktriangleleft \quad \text{Spring force}$$

where x is the position of the block relative to its equilibrium ($x = 0$) position and k is a positive constant called the **force constant** or the **spring constant** of the

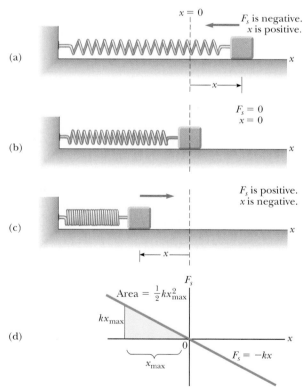

ACTIVE FIGURE 7.9

The force exerted by a spring on a block varies with the block's position x relative to the equilibrium position $x = 0$. (a) When x is positive (stretched spring), the spring force is directed to the left. (b) When x is zero (natural length of the spring), the spring force is zero. (c) When x is negative (compressed spring), the spring force is directed to the right. (d) Graph of F_s versus x for the block–spring system. The work done by the spring force on the block as it moves from $-x_{max}$ to 0 is the area of the shaded triangle, $\tfrac{1}{2}kx_{max}^2$.

Sign in at www.thomsonedu.com and go to ThomsonNOW to observe the block's motion for various spring constants and maximum positions of the block.

spring. In other words, the force required to stretch or compress a spring is proportional to the amount of stretch or compression x. This force law for springs is known as **Hooke's law**. The value of k is a measure of the *stiffness* of the spring. Stiff springs have large k values, and soft springs have small k values. As can be seen from Equation 7.9, the units of k are N/m.

The vector form of Equation 7.9 is

$$\vec{\mathbf{F}}_s = F_s\hat{\mathbf{i}} = -kx\hat{\mathbf{i}} \tag{7.10}$$

where we have chosen the x axis to lie along the direction the spring extends or compresses.

The negative sign in Equations 7.9 and 7.10 signifies that the force exerted by the spring is always directed *opposite* the displacement from equilibrium. When $x > 0$ as in Active Figure 7.9a so that the block is to the right of the equilibrium position, the spring force is directed to the left, in the negative x direction. When $x < 0$ as in Active Figure 7.9c, the block is to the left of equilibrium and the spring force is directed to the right, in the positive x direction. When $x = 0$ as in Active Figure 7.9b, the spring is unstretched and $F_s = 0$. Because the spring force always acts toward the equilibrium position $(x = 0)$, it is sometimes called a *restoring force*.

If the spring is compressed until the block is at the point $-x_{max}$ and is then released, the block moves from $-x_{max}$ through zero to $+x_{max}$. It then reverses direction, returns to $-x_{max}$, and continues oscillating back and forth.

Suppose the block has been pushed to the left to a position $-x_{max}$ and is then released. Let us identify the block as our system and calculate the work W_s done by the spring force on the block as the block moves from $x_i = -x_{max}$ to $x_f = 0$. Applying Equation 7.8 and assuming the block may be modeled as a particle, we obtain

$$W_s = \int \vec{\mathbf{F}}_s \cdot d\vec{\mathbf{r}} = \int_{x_i}^{x_f} (-kx\hat{\mathbf{i}}) \cdot (dx\hat{\mathbf{i}}) = \int_{-x_{max}}^{0} (-kx)\,dx = \tfrac{1}{2}kx_{max}^2 \tag{7.11}$$

where we have used the integral $\int x^n dx = x^{n+1}/(n+1)$ with $n = 1$. The work done by the spring force is positive because the force is in the same direction as its displacement (both are to the right). Because the block arrives at $x = 0$ with some speed, it will continue moving until it reaches a position $+x_{max}$. The work done by the spring force on the block as it moves from $x_i = 0$ to $x_f = x_{max}$ is $W_s = -\tfrac{1}{2}kx_{max}^2$ because for this part of the motion the spring force is to the left and its displacement is to the right. Therefore, the *net* work done by the spring force on the block as it moves from $x_i = -x_{max}$ to $x_f = x_{max}$ is *zero*.

Active Figure 7.9d is a plot of F_s versus x. The work calculated in Equation 7.11 is the area of the shaded triangle, corresponding to the displacement from $-x_{max}$ to 0. Because the triangle has base x_{max} and height kx_{max}, its area is $\tfrac{1}{2}kx_{max}^2$, the work done by the spring as given by Equation 7.11.

If the block undergoes an arbitrary displacement from $x = x_i$ to $x = x_f$, the work done by the spring force on the block is

Work done by a spring ▶

$$W_s = \int_{x_i}^{x_f} (-kx)\,dx = \tfrac{1}{2}kx_i^2 - \tfrac{1}{2}kx_f^2 \tag{7.12}$$

From Equation 7.12, we see that the work done by the spring force is zero for any motion that ends where it began $(x_i = x_f)$. We shall make use of this important result in Chapter 8 when we describe the motion of this system in greater detail.

Equations 7.11 and 7.12 describe the work done by the spring on the block. Now let us consider the work done on the block by an *external agent* as the agent applies a force on the block and the block moves *very slowly* from $x_i = -x_{max}$ to $x_f = 0$ as in Figure 7.10. We can calculate this work by noting that at any value of the position, the *applied force* $\vec{\mathbf{F}}_{app}$ is equal in magnitude and opposite in direction to the spring force $\vec{\mathbf{F}}_s$, so $\vec{\mathbf{F}}_{app} = F_{app}\hat{\mathbf{i}} = -\vec{\mathbf{F}}_s = -(-kx\hat{\mathbf{i}}) = kx\hat{\mathbf{i}}$. Therefore, the work done by this applied force (the external agent) on the block-spring system is

$$W_{\text{app}} = \int \vec{\mathbf{F}}_{\text{app}} \cdot d\vec{\mathbf{r}} = \int_{x_i}^{x_f} (kx\hat{\mathbf{i}}) \cdot (dx\hat{\mathbf{i}}) = \int_{-x_{\text{max}}}^{0} kx \, dx = -\tfrac{1}{2}kx_{\text{max}}^2$$

This work is equal to the negative of the work done by the spring force for this displacement (Eq. 7.11). The work is negative because the external agent must push inward on the spring to prevent it from expanding and this direction is opposite the direction of the displacement of the point of application of the force as the block moves from $-x_{\text{max}}$ to 0.

For an arbitrary displacement of the block, the work done on the system by the external agent is

$$W_{\text{app}} = \int_{x_i}^{x_f} kx \, dx = \tfrac{1}{2}kx_f^2 - \tfrac{1}{2}kx_i^2 \qquad (7.13)$$

Figure 7.10   A block moves from $x_i = -x_{\text{max}}$ to $x_f = 0$ on a frictionless surface as a force $\vec{\mathbf{F}}_{\text{app}}$ is applied to the block. If the process is carried out very slowly, the applied force is equal in magnitude and opposite in direction to the spring force at all times.

Notice that this equation is the negative of Equation 7.12.

Quick Quiz 7.4   A dart is loaded into a spring-loaded toy dart gun by pushing the spring in by a distance x. For the next loading, the spring is compressed a distance $2x$. How much work is required to load the second dart compared with that required to load the first? (a) four times as much   (b) two times as much   (c) the same   (d) half as much   (e) one-fourth as much

---

EXAMPLE 7.5	**Measuring k for a Spring**

A common technique used to measure the force constant of a spring is demonstrated by the setup in Figure 7.11. The spring is hung vertically (Fig. 7.11a), and an object of mass m is attached to its lower end. Under the action of the "load" mg, the spring stretches a distance d from its equilibrium position (Fig. 7.11b).

(A) If a spring is stretched 2.0 cm by a suspended object having a mass of 0.55 kg, what is the force constant of the spring?

SOLUTION

Conceptualize   Consider Figure 7.11b, which shows what happens to the spring when the object is attached to it. Simulate this situation by hanging an object on a rubber band.

Categorize   The object in Figure 7.11b is not accelerating, so it is modeled as a particle in equilibrium.

Figure 7.11   (Example 7.5) Determining the force constant k of a spring. The elongation d is caused by the attached object, which has a weight mg.

Analyze   Because the object is in equilibrium, the net force on it is zero and the upward spring force balances the downward gravitational force $m\vec{\mathbf{g}}$ (Fig. 7.11c).

Apply Hooke's law to give $|\vec{\mathbf{F}}_s| = kd = mg$ and solve for k: $k = \dfrac{mg}{d} = \dfrac{(0.55 \text{ kg})(9.80 \text{ m/s}^2)}{2.0 \times 10^{-2} \text{ m}} = \boxed{2.7 \times 10^2 \text{ N/m}}$

(B) How much work is done by the spring on the object as it stretches through this distance?

SOLUTION

Use Equation 7.12 to find the work done by the spring on the object:

$$W_s = 0 - \tfrac{1}{2}kd^2 = -\tfrac{1}{2}(2.7 \times 10^2 \text{ N/m})(2.0 \times 10^{-2} \text{ m})^2$$

$$= \boxed{-5.4 \times 10^{-2} \text{ J}}$$

Finalize As the object moves through the 2.0-cm distance, the gravitational force also does work on it. This work is positive because the gravitational force is downward and so is the displacement of the point of application of this force. Based on Equation 7.12 and the discussion afterward, would we expect the work done by the gravitational force to be $+5.4 \times 10^{-2}$ J? Let's find out.

Evaluate the work done by the gravitational force on the object:

$$W = \vec{\mathbf{F}} \cdot \Delta \vec{\mathbf{r}} = (mg)(d) \cos 0 = mgd$$

$$= (0.55 \text{ kg})(9.80 \text{ m/s}^2)(2.0 \times 10^{-2} \text{ m}) = 1.1 \times 10^{-1} \text{ J}$$

If you expected the work done by gravity simply to be that done by the spring with a positive sign, you may be surprised by this result! To understand why that is not the case, we need to explore further, as we do in the next section.

7.5 Kinetic Energy and the Work–Kinetic Energy Theorem

We have investigated work and identified it as a mechanism for transferring energy into a system. One possible outcome of doing work on a system is that the system changes its speed. In this section, we investigate this situation and introduce our first type of energy that a system can possess, called *kinetic energy*.

Consider a system consisting of a single object. Figure 7.12 shows a block of mass m moving through a displacement directed to the right under the action of a net force $\Sigma \vec{\mathbf{F}}$, also directed to the right. We know from Newton's second law that the block moves with an acceleration $\vec{\mathbf{a}}$. If the block (and therefore the force) moves through a displacement $\Delta \vec{\mathbf{r}} = \Delta x \hat{\mathbf{i}} = (x_f - x_i) \hat{\mathbf{i}}$, the net work done on the block by the net force $\Sigma \vec{\mathbf{F}}$ is

$$W_{\text{net}} = \int_{x_i}^{x_f} \sum F \, dx \tag{7.14}$$

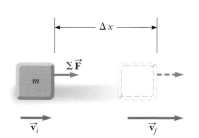

Figure 7.12 An object undergoing a displacement $\Delta \vec{\mathbf{r}} = \Delta x \hat{\mathbf{i}}$ and a change in velocity under the action of a constant net force $\Sigma \vec{\mathbf{F}}$.

Using Newton's second law, we substitute for the magnitude of the net force $\Sigma F = ma$ and then perform the following chain-rule manipulations on the integrand:

$$W_{\text{net}} = \int_{x_i}^{x_f} ma \, dx = \int_{x_i}^{x_f} m \frac{dv}{dt} \, dx = \int_{x_i}^{x_f} m \frac{dv}{dx} \frac{dx}{dt} \, dx = \int_{v_i}^{v_f} mv \, dv$$

$$W_{\text{net}} = \tfrac{1}{2} m v_f^2 - \tfrac{1}{2} m v_i^2 \tag{7.15}$$

where v_i is the speed of the block when it is at $x = x_i$ and v_f is its speed at x_f.

Equation 7.15 was generated for the specific situation of one-dimensional motion, but it is a general result. It tells us that the work done by the net force on a particle of mass m is equal to the difference between the initial and final values of a quantity $\tfrac{1}{2} m v^2$. The quantity $\tfrac{1}{2} m v^2$ represents the energy associated with the motion of the particle. This quantity is so important that it has been given a special name, **kinetic energy**:

Kinetic energy ▶

$$K \equiv \tfrac{1}{2} m v^2 \tag{7.16}$$

Kinetic energy is a scalar quantity and has the same units as work. For example, a 2.0-kg object moving with a speed of 4.0 m/s has a kinetic energy of 16 J. Table 7.1 lists the kinetic energies for various objects.

Equation 7.15 states that the work done on a particle by a net force $\Sigma \vec{\mathbf{F}}$ acting on it equals the change in kinetic energy of the particle. It is often convenient to write Equation 7.15 in the form

$$W_{\text{net}} = K_f - K_i = \Delta K \tag{7.17}$$

Another way to write it is $K_f = K_i + W_{\text{net}}$, which tells us that the final kinetic energy of an object is equal to its initial kinetic energy plus the change due to the net work done on it.

TABLE 7.1

Kinetic Energies for Various Objects

Object	Mass (kg)	Speed (m/s)	Kinetic Energy (J)
Earth orbiting the Sun	5.98×10^{24}	2.98×10^4	2.66×10^{33}
Moon orbiting the Earth	7.35×10^{22}	1.02×10^3	3.82×10^{28}
Rocket moving at escape speed[a]	500	1.12×10^4	3.14×10^{10}
Automobile at 65 mi/h	2 000	29	8.4×10^5
Running athlete	70	10	3 500
Stone dropped from 10 m	1.0	14	98
Golf ball at terminal speed	0.046	44	45
Raindrop at terminal speed	3.5×10^{-5}	9.0	1.4×10^{-3}
Oxygen molecule in air	5.3×10^{-26}	500	6.6×10^{-21}

[a] Escape speed is the minimum speed an object must reach near the Earth's surface to move infinitely far away from the Earth.

We have generated Equation 7.17 by imagining doing work on a particle. We could also do work on a deformable system, in which parts of the system move with respect to one another. In this case, we also find that Equation 7.17 is valid as long as the net work is found by adding up the works done by each force and adding, as discussed earlier with regard to Equation 7.8.

Equation 7.17 is an important result known as the **work–kinetic energy theorem**:

> When work is done on a system and the only change in the system is in its speed, the net work done on the system equals the change in kinetic energy of the system.

◀ Work–kinetic energy theorem

The work–kinetic energy theorem indicates that the speed of a system *increases* if the net work done on it is *positive* because the final kinetic energy is greater than the initial kinetic energy. The speed *decreases* if the net work is *negative* because the final kinetic energy is less than the initial kinetic energy.

Because we have so far only investigated translational motion through space, we arrived at the work–kinetic energy theorem by analyzing situations involving translational motion. Another type of motion is *rotational motion,* in which an object spins about an axis. We will study this type of motion in Chapter 10. The work–kinetic energy theorem is also valid for systems that undergo a change in the rotational speed due to work done on the system. The windmill in the photograph at the beginning of this chapter is an example of work causing rotational motion.

The work–kinetic energy theorem will clarify a result seen earlier in this chapter that may have seemed odd. In Section 7.4, we arrived at a result of zero net work done when we let a spring push a block from $x_i = -x_{max}$ to $x_f = x_{max}$. Notice that because the speed of the block is continually changing, it may seem complicated to analyze this process. The quantity ΔK in the work–kinetic energy theorem, however, only refers to the initial and final points for the speeds; it does not depend on details of the path followed between these points. Therefore, because the speed is zero at both the initial and final points of the motion, the net work done on the block is zero. We will often see this concept of path independence in similar approaches to problems.

Let us also return to the mystery in the Finalize step at the end of Example 7.5. Why was the work done by gravity not just the value of the work done by the spring with a positive sign? Notice that the work done by gravity is larger than the magnitude of the work done by the spring. Therefore, the total work done by all forces on the object is positive. Imagine now how to create the situation in which the *only* forces on the object are the spring force and the gravitational force. You must support the object at the highest point and then *remove* your hand and let the

PITFALL PREVENTION 7.6
Conditions for the Work–Kinetic Energy Theorem

The work–kinetic energy theorem is important but limited in its application; it is not a general principle. In many situations, other changes in the system occur besides its speed, and there are other interactions with the environment besides work. A more general principle involving energy is *conservation of energy* in Section 8.1.

PITFALL PREVENTION 7.7
The Work–Kinetic Energy Theorem: Speed, Not Velocity

The work–kinetic energy theorem relates work to a change in the *speed* of a system, not a change in its velocity. For example, if an object is in uniform circular motion, its speed is constant. Even though its velocity is changing, no work is done on the object by the force causing the circular motion.

object fall. If you do so, you know that when the object reaches a position 2.0 cm below your hand, it will be *moving*, which is consistent with Equation 7.17. Positive net work is done on the object, and the result is that it has a kinetic energy as it passes through the 2.0-cm point. The only way to prevent the object from having a kinetic energy after moving through 2.0 cm is to slowly lower it with your hand. Then, however, there is a third force doing work on the object, the normal force from your hand. If this work is calculated and added to that done by the spring force and the gravitational force, the net work done on the object is zero, which is consistent because it is not moving at the 2.0-cm point.

Earlier, we indicated that work can be considered as a mechanism for transferring energy into a system. Equation 7.17 is a mathematical statement of this concept. When work W_{net} is done on a system, the result is a transfer of energy across the boundary of the system. The result on the system, in the case of Equation 7.17, is a change ΔK in kinetic energy. In the next section, we investigate another type of energy that can be stored in a system as a result of doing work on the system.

Quick Quiz 7.5   A dart is loaded into a spring-loaded toy dart gun by pushing the spring in by a distance x. For the next loading, the spring is compressed a distance $2x$. How much faster does the second dart leave the gun compared with the first? (a) four times as fast   (b) two times as fast   (c) the same   (d) half as fast (e) one-fourth as fast

---

Figure 7.13   (Example 7.6) A block pulled to the right on a frictionless surface by a constant horizontal force.

EXAMPLE 7.6	**A Block Pulled on a Frictionless Surface**

A 6.0-kg block initially at rest is pulled to the right along a horizontal, frictionless surface by a constant horizontal force of 12 N. Find the block's speed after it has moved 3.0 m.

SOLUTION

Conceptualize   Figure 7.13 illustrates this situation. Imagine pulling a toy car across a table with a horizontal rubber band attached to the front of the car. The force is maintained constant by ensuring that the stretched rubber band always has the same length.

Categorize   We could apply the equations of kinematics to determine the answer, but let us practice the energy approach. The block is the system, and three external forces act on the system. The normal force balances the gravitational force on the block, and neither of these vertically acting forces does work on the block because their points of application are horizontally displaced.

Analyze   The net external force acting on the block is the horizontal 12-N force.

Find the work done by this force on the block:

$$W = F\,\Delta x = (12\text{ N})(3.0\text{ m}) = 36\text{ J}$$

Use the work–kinetic energy theorem for the block and note that its initial kinetic energy is zero:

$$W = K_f - K_i = \tfrac{1}{2}mv_f^2 - 0$$

Solve for v_f:

$$v_f = \sqrt{\frac{2W}{m}} = \sqrt{\frac{2(36\text{ J})}{6.0\text{ kg}}} = 3.5\text{ m/s}$$

Finalize   It would be useful for you to solve this problem again by modeling the block as a particle under a net force to find its acceleration and then as a particle under constant acceleration to find its final velocity.

What If?   Suppose the magnitude of the force in this example is doubled to $F' = 2F$. The 6.0-kg block accelerates to 3.5 m/s due to this applied force while moving through a displacement $\Delta x'$. How does the displacement $\Delta x'$ compare with the original displacement Δx?

Answer   If we pull harder, the block should accelerate to a given speed in a shorter distance, so we expect that $\Delta x' < \Delta x$. In both cases, the block experiences the same change in kinetic energy ΔK. Mathematically, from the work-kinetic energy theorem, we find that

$$W = F'\Delta x' = \Delta K = F\Delta x$$

$$\Delta x' = \frac{F}{F'}\,\Delta x = \frac{F}{2F}\,\Delta x = \tfrac{1}{2}\Delta x$$

and the distance is shorter as suggested by our conceptual argument.

CONCEPTUAL EXAMPLE 7.7   **Does the Ramp Lessen the Work Required?**

A man wishes to load a refrigerator onto a truck using a ramp at angle θ as shown in Figure 7.14. He claims that less work would be required to load the truck if the length L of the ramp were increased. Is his claim valid?

SOLUTION

No. Suppose the refrigerator is wheeled on a hand truck up the ramp at constant speed. In this case, for the system of the refrigerator and the hand truck, $\Delta K = 0$. The normal force exerted by the ramp on the system is directed at 90° to the displacement of its point of application and so does no work on the system. Because $\Delta K = 0$, the work-kinetic energy theorem gives

Figure 7.14   (Conceptual Example 7.7) A refrigerator attached to a frictionless, wheeled hand truck is moved up a ramp at constant speed.

$$W_{\text{net}} = W_{\text{by man}} + W_{\text{by gravity}} = 0$$

The work done by the gravitational force equals the product of the weight mg of the system, the distance L through which the refrigerator is displaced, and $\cos(\theta + 90°)$. Therefore,

$$W_{\text{by man}} = -W_{\text{by gravity}} = -(mg)(L)[\cos(\theta + 90°)]$$

$$= mgL \sin\theta = mgh$$

where $h = L\sin\theta$ is the height of the ramp. Therefore, the man must do the same amount of work mgh on the system *regardless* of the length of the ramp. The work depends only on the height of the ramp. Although less force is required with a longer ramp, the point of application of that force moves through a greater displacement.

7.6 Potential Energy of a System

So far in this chapter, we have defined a system in general, but have focused our attention primarily on single particles or objects under the influence of external forces. Let us now consider systems of two or more particles or objects interacting via a force that is *internal* to the system. The kinetic energy of such a system is the algebraic sum of the kinetic energies of all members of the system. There may be systems, however, in which one object is so massive that it can be modeled as stationary and its kinetic energy can be neglected. For example, if we consider a ball–Earth system as the ball falls to the Earth, the kinetic energy of the system can be considered as just the kinetic energy of the ball. The Earth moves so slowly in this process that we can ignore its kinetic energy. On the other hand, the kinetic energy of a system of two electrons must include the kinetic energies of both particles.

Let us imagine a system consisting of a book and the Earth, interacting via the gravitational force. We do some work on the system by lifting the book slowly from rest through a vertical displacement $\Delta\vec{r} = (y_f - y_i)\hat{j}$ as in Active Figure 7.15. According to our discussion of work as an energy transfer, this work done on the system must appear as an increase in energy of the system. The book is at rest

ACTIVE FIGURE 7.15

The work done by an external agent on the system of the book and the Earth as the book is lifted slowly from a height y_i to a height y_f is equal to $mgy_f - mgy_i$.

Sign in at www.thomsonedu.com and go to ThomsonNOW to move the block to various positions and determine the work done by the external agent for a general displacement.

before we perform the work and is at rest after we perform the work. Therefore, there is no change in the kinetic energy of the system.

Because the energy change of the system is not in the form of kinetic energy, it must appear as some other form of energy storage. After lifting the book, we could release it and let it fall back to the position y_i. Notice that the book (and, therefore, the system) now has kinetic energy and that its source is in the work that was done in lifting the book. While the book was at the highest point, the energy of the system had the *potential* to become kinetic energy, but it did not do so until the book was allowed to fall. Therefore, we call the energy storage mechanism before the book is released **potential energy**. We will find that the potential energy of a system can only be associated with specific types of forces acting between members of a system. The amount of potential energy in the system is determined by the *configuration* of the system. Moving members of the system to different positions or rotating them may change the configuration of the system and therefore its potential energy.

Let us now derive an expression for the potential energy associated with an object at a given location above the surface of the Earth. Consider an external agent lifting an object of mass m from an initial height y_i above the ground to a final height y_f as in Active Figure 7.15. We assume the lifting is done slowly, with no acceleration, so the applied force from the agent can be modeled as being equal in magnitude to the gravitational force on the object: the object is modeled as a particle in equilibrium moving at constant velocity. The work done by the external agent on the system (object and the Earth) as the object undergoes this upward displacement is given by the product of the upward applied force $\vec{\mathbf{F}}_{app}$ and the upward displacement of this force, $\Delta\vec{\mathbf{r}} = \Delta y\hat{\mathbf{j}}$:

$$W_{net} = (\vec{\mathbf{F}}_{app}) \cdot \Delta\vec{\mathbf{r}} = (mg\hat{\mathbf{j}}) \cdot [(y_f - y_i)\hat{\mathbf{j}}] = mgy_f - mgy_i \qquad \textbf{(7.18)}$$

where this result is the net work done on the system because the applied force is the only force on the system from the environment. Notice the similarity between Equation 7.18 and Equation 7.15. In each equation, the work done on a system equals a difference between the final and initial values of a quantity. In Equation 7.15, the work represents a transfer of energy into the system and the increase in energy of the system is kinetic in form. In Equation 7.18, the work represents a transfer of energy into the system and the system energy appears in a different form, which we have called potential energy.

Therefore, we can identify the quantity mgy as the **gravitational potential energy** U_g:

Gravitational potential ▶ energy

$$U_g \equiv mgy \qquad \textbf{(7.19)}$$

The units of gravitational potential energy are joules, the same as the units of work and kinetic energy. Potential energy, like work and kinetic energy, is a scalar quantity. Notice that Equation 7.19 is valid only for objects near the surface of the Earth, where g is approximately constant.[3]

Using our definition of gravitational potential energy, Equation 7.18 can now be rewritten as

$$W_{net} = \Delta U_g \qquad \textbf{(7.20)}$$

which mathematically describes that the net work done on the system in this situation appears as a change in the gravitational potential energy of the system.

Gravitational potential energy depends only on the vertical height of the object above the surface of the Earth. The same amount of work must be done on an object–Earth system whether the object is lifted vertically from the Earth or is pushed starting from the same point up a frictionless incline, ending up at the same height. We verified this statement for a specific situation of rolling a refrigerator up a ramp in Conceptual Example 7.7. This statement can be shown to be

---

[3] The assumption that g is constant is valid as long as the vertical displacement of the object is small compared with the Earth's radius.

PITFALL PREVENTION 7.8
Potential Energy

The phrase *potential energy* does not refer to something that has the potential to become energy. Potential energy *is* energy.

PITFALL PREVENTION 7.9
Potential Energy Belongs to a System

Potential energy is always associated with a *system* of two or more interacting objects. When a small object moves near the surface of the Earth under the influence of gravity, we may sometimes refer to the potential energy "associated with the object" rather than the more proper "associated with the system" because the Earth does not move significantly. We will not, however, refer to the potential energy "of the object" because this wording ignores the role of the Earth.

true in general by calculating the work done on an object by an agent moving the object through a displacement having both vertical and horizontal components:

$$W_{net} = (\vec{\mathbf{F}}_{app}) \cdot \Delta \vec{\mathbf{r}} = (mg\hat{\mathbf{j}}) \cdot [(x_f - x_i)\hat{\mathbf{i}} + (y_f - y_i)\hat{\mathbf{j}}] = mgy_f - mgy_i$$

where there is no term involving x in the final result because $\hat{\mathbf{j}} \cdot \hat{\mathbf{i}} = 0$.

In solving problems, you must choose a reference configuration for which the gravitational potential energy of the system is set equal to some reference value, which is normally zero. The choice of reference configuration is completely arbitrary because the important quantity is the *difference* in potential energy, and this difference is independent of the choice of reference configuration.

It is often convenient to choose as the reference configuration for zero gravitational potential energy the configuration in which an object is at the surface of the Earth, but this choice is not essential. Often, the statement of the problem suggests a convenient configuration to use.

Quick Quiz 7.6   Choose the correct answer. The gravitational potential energy of a system (a) is always positive   (b) is always negative   (c) can be negative or positive

---

EXAMPLE 7.8	**The Bowler and the Sore Toe**

A bowling ball held by a careless bowler slips from the bowler's hands and drops on the bowler's toe. Choosing floor level as the $y = 0$ point of your coordinate system, estimate the change in gravitational potential energy of the ball–Earth system as the ball falls. Repeat the calculation, using the top of the bowler's head as the origin of coordinates.

SOLUTION

Conceptualize   The bowling ball changes its vertical position with respect to the surface of the Earth. Associated with this change in position is a change in the gravitational potential energy of the system.

Categorize   We evaluate a change in gravitational potential energy defined in this section, so we categorize this example as a substitution problem.

The problem statement tells us that the reference configuration of the ball–Earth system corresponding to zero potential energy is when the bottom of the ball is at the floor. To find the change in potential energy for the system, we need to estimate a few values. A bowling ball has a mass of approximately 7 kg, and the top of a person's toe is about 0.03 m above the floor. Also, we shall assume the ball falls from a height of 0.5 m.

Calculate the gravitational potential energy of the ball–Earth system just before the bowling ball is released:

$$U_i = mgy_i = (7 \text{ kg})(9.80 \text{ m/s}^2)(0.5 \text{ m}) = 34.3 \text{ J}$$

Calculate the gravitational potential energy of the ball–Earth system when the ball reaches the bowler's toe:

$$U_f = mgy_f = (7 \text{ kg})(9.80 \text{ m/s}^2)(0.03 \text{ m}) = 2.06 \text{ J}$$

Evaluate the change in gravitational potential energy of the ball–Earth system:

$$\Delta U_g = 2.06 \text{ J} - 34.3 \text{ J} = -32.24 \text{ J}$$

We should probably keep only one digit because of the roughness of our estimates; therefore, we estimate that the change in gravitational potential energy is -30 J . The system had 30 J of gravitational potential energy before the ball began its fall and approximately zero potential energy as the ball reaches the top of the toe.

The second case presented indicates that the reference configuration of the system for zero potential energy is chosen to be when the ball is at the bowler's head (even though the ball is never at this position in its motion). We estimate this position to be 1.50 m above the floor).

Calculate the gravitational potential energy of the ball–Earth system just before the bowling ball is released from its position 1 m below the bowler's head:

$$U_i = mgy_i = (7 \text{ kg})(9.80 \text{ m/s}^2)(-1 \text{ m}) = -68.6 \text{ J}$$

Calculate the gravitational potential energy of the ball–Earth system when the ball reaches the bowler's toe located 1.47 m below the bowler's head:

$$U_f = mgy_f = (7 \text{ kg})(9.80 \text{ m/s}^2)(-1.47 \text{ m}) = -100.8 \text{ J}$$

Evaluate the change in gravitational potential energy of the ball–Earth system:

$$\Delta U_g = -100.8 \text{ J} - (-68.6 \text{ J}) = -32.2 \text{ J} \approx \boxed{-30 \text{ J}}$$

This value is the same as before, as it must be.

Elastic Potential Energy

Now that we are familiar with gravitational potential energy of a system, let us explore a second type of potential energy that a system can possess. Consider a system consisting of a block and a spring as shown in Active Figure 7.16. The force that the spring exerts on the block is given by $F_s = -kx$ (Eq. 7.9). The work done by an external applied force F_{app} on a system consisting of a block connected to the spring is given by Equation 7.13:

$$W_{app} = \tfrac{1}{2}kx_f^2 - \tfrac{1}{2}kx_i^2 \tag{7.21}$$

In this situation, the initial and final x coordinates of the block are measured from its equilibrium position, $x = 0$. Again (as in the gravitational case) we see that the work done on the system is equal to the difference between the initial and final values of an expression related to the system's configuration. The **elastic potential energy** function associated with the block-spring system is defined by

Elastic potential energy ▶

$$U_s \equiv \tfrac{1}{2}kx^2 \tag{7.22}$$

The elastic potential energy of the system can be thought of as the energy stored in the deformed spring (one that is either compressed or stretched from its equilibrium position). The elastic potential energy stored in a spring is zero when-

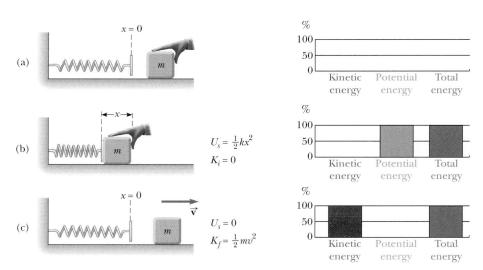

ACTIVE FIGURE 7.16

(a) An undeformed spring on a frictionless, horizontal surface. (b) A block of mass m is pushed against the spring, compressing it a distance x. Elastic potential energy is stored in the spring–block system. (c) When the block is released from rest, the elastic potential energy is transformed to kinetic energy of the block. Energy bar charts on the right of each part of the figure help keep track of the energy in the system.

Sign in at www.thomsonedu.com and go to ThomsonNOW to compress the spring by varying amounts and observe the effect on the block's speed.

ever the spring is undeformed ($x = 0$). Energy is stored in the spring only when the spring is either stretched or compressed. Because the elastic potential energy is proportional to x^2, we see that U_s is always positive in a deformed spring.

Consider Active Figure 7.16, which shows a spring on a frictionless, horizontal surface. When a block is pushed against the spring and the spring is compressed a distance x (Active Fig. 7.16b), the elastic potential energy stored in the spring is $\frac{1}{2}kx^2$. When the block is released from rest, the spring exerts a force on the block and returns to its original length. The stored elastic potential energy is transformed into kinetic energy of the block (Active Fig. 7.16c).

Active Figure 7.16 shows an important graphical representation of information related to energy of systems called an **energy bar chart**. The vertical axis represents the amount of energy of a given type in the system. The horizontal axis shows the types of energy in the system. The bar chart in Active Figure 7.16a shows that the system contains zero energy because the spring is relaxed and the block is not moving. Between Active Figure 7.16a and Active Figure 7.16b, the hand does work on the system, compressing the spring and storing elastic potential energy in the system. In Active Figure 7.16c, the spring has returned to its relaxed length and the system now contains kinetic energy associated with the moving block.

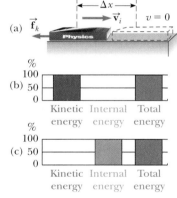

Figure 7.17 (Quick Quiz 7.7) A ball connected to a massless spring suspended vertically. What forms of potential energy are associated with the system when the ball is displaced downward?

Quick Quiz 7.7   A ball is connected to a light spring suspended vertically as shown in Figure 7.17. When pulled downward from its equilibrium position and released, the ball oscillates up and down. **(i)** In the system of *the ball, the spring, and the Earth*, what forms of energy are there during the motion? (a) kinetic and elastic potential   (b) kinetic and gravitational potential   (c) kinetic, elastic potential, and gravitational potential   (d) elastic potential and gravitational potential **(ii)** In the system of *the ball and the spring*, what forms of energy are there during the motion? Choose from the same possibilities (a) through (d).

7.7   Conservative and Nonconservative Forces

We now introduce a third type of energy that a system can possess. Imagine that the book in Active Figure 7.18a has been accelerated by your hand and is now sliding to the right on the surface of a heavy table and slowing down due to the friction force. Suppose the *surface* is the system. Then the friction force from the sliding book does work on the surface. The force on the surface is to the right and the displacement of the point of application of the force is to the right. The work done on the surface is positive, but the surface is not moving after the book has stopped. Positive work has been done on the surface, yet there is no increase in the surface's kinetic energy or the potential energy of any system.

From your everyday experience with sliding over surfaces with friction, you can probably guess that the surface will be *warmer* after the book slides over it. (Rub your hands together briskly to find out!) The work that was done on the surface has gone into warming the surface rather than increasing its speed or changing the configuration of a system. We call the energy associated with the temperature of a system its **internal energy**, symbolized E_{int}. (We will define internal energy more generally in Chapter 20.) In this case, the work done on the surface does indeed represent energy transferred into the system, but it appears in the system as internal energy rather than kinetic or potential energy.

Consider the book and the surface in Active Figure 7.18a together as a system. Initially, the system has kinetic energy because the book is moving. After the book has come to rest, the internal energy of the system has increased: the book and the surface are warmer than before. We can consider the work done by friction

ACTIVE FIGURE 7.18

(a) A book sliding to the right on a horizontal surface slows down in the presence of a force of kinetic friction acting to the left. (b) An energy bar chart showing the energy in the system of the book and the surface at the initial instant of time. The energy of the system is all kinetic energy. (c) After the book has stopped, the energy of the system is all internal energy.

Sign in at www.thomsonedu.com and go to ThomsonNOW to slide the book with varying speeds and watch the energy transformation on an active energy bar chart.

within the system—that is, between the book and the surface—as a *transformation mechanism* for energy. This work transforms the kinetic energy of the system into internal energy. Similarly, when a book falls straight down with no air resistance, the work done by the gravitational force within the book–Earth system transforms gravitational potential energy of the system to kinetic energy.

Active Figures 7.18b and 7.18c show energy bar charts for the situation in Active Figure 7.18a. In Active Figure 7.18b, the bar chart shows that the system contains kinetic energy at the instant the book is released by your hand. We define the reference amount of internal energy in the system as zero at this instant. In Active Figure 7.18c, after the book has stopped sliding, the kinetic energy is zero and the system now contains internal energy. Notice that the amount of internal energy in the system after the book has stopped is equal to the amount of kinetic energy in the system at the initial instant. This equality is described by an important principle called *conservation of energy*. We will explore this principle in Chapter 8.

Now consider in more detail an object moving downward near the surface of the Earth. The work done by the gravitational force on the object does not depend on whether it falls vertically or slides down a sloping incline. All that matters is the change in the object's elevation. The energy transformation to internal energy due to friction on that incline, however, depends on the distance the object slides. In other words, the path makes no difference when we consider the work done by the gravitational force, but it does make a difference when we consider the energy transformation due to friction forces. We can use this varying dependence on path to classify forces as either conservative or nonconservative. Of the two forces just mentioned, the gravitational force is conservative and the friction force is nonconservative.

Conservative Forces

Conservative forces have these two equivalent properties:

◀ Properties of conservative forces

1. The work done by a conservative force on a particle moving between any two points is independent of the path taken by the particle.
2. The work done by a conservative force on a particle moving through any closed path is zero. (A closed path is one for which the beginning point and the endpoint are identical.)

The gravitational force is one example of a conservative force; the force that an ideal spring exerts on any object attached to the spring is another. The work done by the gravitational force on an object moving between any two points near the Earth's surface is $W_g = -mg\hat{\mathbf{j}} \cdot [(y_f - y_i)\hat{\mathbf{j}}] = mgy_i - mgy_f$. From this equation, notice that W_g depends only on the initial and final y coordinates of the object and hence is independent of the path. Furthermore, W_g is zero when the object moves over any closed path (where $y_i = y_f$).

For the case of the object-spring system, the work W_s done by the spring force is given by $W_s = \frac{1}{2}kx_i^2 - \frac{1}{2}kx_f^2$ (Eq. 7.12). We see that the spring force is conservative because W_s depends only on the initial and final x coordinates of the object and is zero for any closed path.

We can associate a potential energy for a system with a force acting between members of the system, but we can do so only for conservative forces. In general, the work W_c done by a conservative force on an object that is a member of a system as the object moves from one position to another is equal to the initial value of the potential energy of the system minus the final value:

$$W_c = U_i - U_f = -\Delta U \tag{7.23}$$

As an example, compare this general equation with the specific equation for the work done by the spring force (Eq. 7.12) as the extension of the spring changes.

PITFALL PREVENTION 7.10
Similar Equation Warning

Compare Equation 7.23 with Equation 7.20. These equations are similar except for the negative sign, which is a common source of confusion. Equation 7.20 tells us that positive work done *by an outside agent* on a system causes an increase in the potential energy of the system (with no change in the kinetic or internal energy). Equation 7.23 states that work done *on a component of a system by a conservative force internal to an isolated system* causes a decrease in the potential energy of the system.

Nonconservative Forces

A force is **nonconservative** if it does not satisfy properties 1 and 2 for conservative forces. We define the sum of the kinetic and potential energies of a system as the **mechanical energy** of the system:

$$E_{mech} \equiv K + U \qquad (7.24)$$

where K includes the kinetic energy of all moving members of the system and U includes all types of potential energy in the system. Nonconservative forces acting within a system cause a *change* in the mechanical energy of the system. For example, for a book sent sliding on a horizontal surface that is not frictionless, the mechanical energy of the book–surface system is transformed to internal energy as we discussed earlier. Only part of the book's kinetic energy is transformed to internal energy in the book. The rest appears as internal energy in the surface. (When you trip and slide across a gymnasium floor, not only does the skin on your knees warm up, so does the floor!) Because the force of kinetic friction transforms the mechanical energy of a system into internal energy, it is a nonconservative force.

As an example of the path dependence of the work for a nonconservative force, consider Figure 7.19. Suppose you displace a book between two points on a table. If the book is displaced in a straight line along the blue path between points Ⓐ and Ⓑ in Figure 7.19, you do a certain amount of work against the kinetic friction force to keep the book moving at a constant speed. Now, imagine that you push the book along the brown semicircular path in Figure 7.19. You perform more work against friction along this curved path than along the straight path because the curved path is longer. The work done on the book depends on the path, so the friction force *cannot* be conservative.

Figure 7.19   The work done against the force of kinetic friction depends on the path taken as the book is moved from Ⓐ to Ⓑ. The work is greater along the brown path than along the blue path.

7.8   Relationship Between Conservative Forces and Potential Energy

In the preceding section, we found that the work done on a member of a system by a conservative force between the members of the system does not depend on the path taken by the moving member. The work depends only on the initial and final coordinates. As a consequence, we can define a **potential energy function** U such that the work done within the system by the conservative force equals the decrease in the potential energy of the system. Let us imagine a system of particles in which the configuration changes due to the motion of one particle along the x axis. The work done by a conservative force $\vec{F}$ as a particle moves along the x axis is[4]

$$W_c = \int_{x_i}^{x_f} F_x\,dx = -\Delta U \qquad (7.25)$$

where F_x is the component of $\vec{F}$ in the direction of the displacement. That is, the work done by a conservative force acting between members of a system equals the negative of the change in the potential energy of the system associated with that force when the system's configuration changes. We can also express Equation 7.25 as

$$\Delta U = U_f - U_i = -\int_{x_i}^{x_f} F_x\,dx \qquad (7.26)$$

---

[4] For a general displacement, the work done in two or three dimensions also equals $-\Delta U$, where $U = U(x, y, z)$. We write this equation formally as $W_c = \int_i^f \vec{F} \cdot d\vec{r} = U_i - U_f$.

Therefore, ΔU is negative when F_x and dx are in the same direction, as when an object is lowered in a gravitational field or when a spring pushes an object toward equilibrium.

It is often convenient to establish some particular location x_i of one member of a system as representing a reference configuration and measure all potential energy differences with respect to it. We can then define the potential energy function as

$$U_f(x) = -\int_{x_i}^{x_f} F_x \, dx + U_i \tag{7.27}$$

The value of U_i is often taken to be zero for the reference configuration. It does not matter what value we assign to U_i because any nonzero value merely shifts $U_f(x)$ by a constant amount and only the *change* in potential energy is physically meaningful.

If the point of application of the force undergoes an infinitesimal displacement dx, we can express the infinitesimal change in the potential energy of the system dU as

$$dU = -F_x \, dx$$

Therefore, the conservative force is related to the potential energy function through the relationship[5]

$$F_x = -\frac{dU}{dx} \tag{7.28}$$

That is, **the x component of a conservative force acting on an object within a system equals the negative derivative of the potential energy of the system with respect to x.**

We can easily check Equation 7.28 for the two examples already discussed. In the case of the deformed spring, $U_s = \frac{1}{2}kx^2$; therefore,

$$F_s = -\frac{dU_s}{dx} = -\frac{d}{dx}(\tfrac{1}{2}kx^2) = -kx$$

which corresponds to the restoring force in the spring (Hooke's law). Because the gravitational potential energy function is $U_g = mgy$, it follows from Equation 7.28 that $F_g = -mg$ when we differentiate U_g with respect to y instead of x.

We now see that U is an important function because a conservative force can be derived from it. Furthermore, Equation 7.28 should clarify that adding a constant to the potential energy is unimportant because the derivative of a constant is zero.

Quick Quiz 7.8   What does the slope of a graph of $U(x)$ versus x represent? (a) the magnitude of the force on the object   (b) the negative of the magnitude of the force on the object   (c) the x component of the force on the object   (d) the negative of the x component of the force on the object

---

[5] In three dimensions, the expression is

$$\vec{F} = -\frac{\partial U}{\partial x}\hat{\mathbf{i}} - \frac{\partial U}{\partial y}\hat{\mathbf{j}} - \frac{\partial U}{\partial z}\hat{\mathbf{k}}$$

where $(\partial U/\partial x)$ and so forth are partial derivatives. In the language of vector calculus, $\vec{F}$ equals the negative of the *gradient* of the scalar quantity $U(x, y, z)$.

7.9 Energy Diagrams and Equilibrium of a System

The motion of a system can often be understood qualitatively through a graph of its potential energy versus the position of a member of the system. Consider the potential energy function for a block–spring system, given by $U_s = \frac{1}{2}kx^2$. This function is plotted versus x in Active Figure 7.20a. The force F_s exerted by the spring on the block is related to U_s through Equation 7.28:

$$F_s = -\frac{dU_s}{dx} = -kx$$

As we saw in Quick Quiz 7.8, the x component of the force is equal to the negative of the slope of the U-versus-x curve. When the block is placed at rest at the equilibrium position of the spring ($x = 0$), where $F_s = 0$, it will remain there unless some external force F_{ext} acts on it. If this external force stretches the spring from equilibrium, x is positive and the slope dU/dx is positive; therefore, the force F_s exerted by the spring is negative and the block accelerates back toward $x = 0$ when released. If the external force compresses the spring, x is negative and the slope is negative; therefore, F_s is positive and again the mass accelerates toward $x = 0$ upon release.

From this analysis, we conclude that the $x = 0$ position for a block-spring system is one of **stable equilibrium**. That is, any movement away from this position results in a force directed back toward $x = 0$. In general, **configurations of a system in stable equilibrium correspond to those for which $U(x)$ for the system is a minimum**.

If the block in Active Figure 7.20 is moved to an initial position x_{max} and then released from rest, its total energy initially is the potential energy $\frac{1}{2}kx_{\text{max}}^2$ stored in the spring. As the block starts to move, the system acquires kinetic energy and loses potential energy. The block oscillates (moves back and forth) between the two points $x = -x_{\text{max}}$ and $x = +x_{\text{max}}$, called the *turning points*. In fact, because no energy is transformed to internal energy due to friction, the block oscillates between $-x_{\text{max}}$ and $+x_{\text{max}}$ forever. (We discuss these oscillations further in Chapter 15.)

Another simple mechanical system with a configuration of stable equilibrium is a ball rolling about in the bottom of a bowl. Anytime the ball is displaced from its lowest position, it tends to return to that position when released.

Now consider a particle moving along the x axis under the influence of a conservative force F_x, where the U-versus-x curve is as shown in Figure 7.21. Once again, $F_x = 0$ at $x = 0$, and so the particle is in equilibrium at this point. This position, however, is one of **unstable equilibrium** for the following reason. Suppose the particle is displaced to the right ($x > 0$). Because the slope is negative for $x > 0$, $F_x = -dU/dx$ is positive and the particle accelerates away from $x = 0$. If instead the particle is at $x = 0$ and is displaced to the left ($x < 0$), the force is negative because the slope is positive for $x < 0$ and the particle again accelerates away from the equilibrium position. The position $x = 0$ in this situation is one of unstable equilibrium because for any displacement from this point, the force pushes the particle farther away from equilibrium and toward a position of lower potential energy. A pencil balanced on its point is in a position of unstable equilibrium. If the pencil is displaced slightly from its absolutely vertical position and is then released, it will surely fall over. In general, **configurations of a system in unstable equilibrium correspond to those for which $U(x)$ for the system is a maximum**.

Finally, a configuration called **neutral equilibrium** arises when U is constant over some region. Small displacements of an object from a position in this region produce neither restoring nor disrupting forces. A ball lying on a flat horizontal surface is an example of an object in neutral equilibrium.

ACTIVE FIGURE 7.20

(a) Potential energy as a function of x for the frictionless block–spring system shown in (b). The block oscillates between the turning points, which have the coordinates $x = \pm x_{\text{max}}$. Notice that the restoring force exerted by the spring always acts toward $x = 0$, the position of stable equilibrium.

PITFALL PREVENTION 7.11
Energy Diagrams

A common mistake is to think that potential energy on the graph in an energy diagram represents height. For example, that is not the case in Active Figure 7.20, where the block is only moving horizontally.

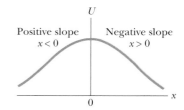

Figure 7.21 A plot of U versus x for a particle that has a position of unstable equilibrium located at $x = 0$. For any finite displacement of the particle, the force on the particle is directed away from $x = 0$.

EXAMPLE 7.9 **Force and Energy on an Atomic Scale**

The potential energy associated with the force between two neutral atoms in a molecule can be modeled by the Lennard–Jones potential energy function:

$$U(x) = 4\epsilon \left[\left(\frac{\sigma}{x} \right)^{12} - \left(\frac{\sigma}{x} \right)^{6} \right]$$

where x is the separation of the atoms. The function $U(x)$ contains two parameters σ and ϵ that are determined from experiments. Sample values for the interaction between two atoms in a molecule are $\sigma = 0.263$ nm and $\epsilon = 1.51 \times 10^{-22}$ J. Using a spreadsheet or similar tool, graph this function and find the most likely distance between the two atoms.

SOLUTION

Conceptualize We identify the two atoms in the molecule as a system. Based on our understanding that stable molecules exist, we expect to find stable equilibrium when the two atoms are separated by some equilibrium distance.

Categorize Because a potential energy function exists, we categorize the force between the atoms as conservative. For a conservative force, Equation 7.28 describes the relationship between the force and the potential energy function.

Analyze Stable equilibrium exists for a separation distance at which the potential energy of the system of two atoms (the molecule) is a minimum.

Take the derivative of the function $U(x)$:

$$\frac{dU(x)}{dx} = 4\epsilon \frac{d}{dx} \left[\left(\frac{\sigma}{x} \right)^{12} - \left(\frac{\sigma}{x} \right)^{6} \right] = 4\epsilon \left[\frac{-12\sigma^{12}}{x^{13}} + \frac{6\sigma^{6}}{x^{7}} \right]$$

Minimize the function $U(x)$ by setting its derivative equal to zero:

$$4\epsilon \left[\frac{-12\sigma^{12}}{x_{eq}^{13}} + \frac{6\sigma^{6}}{x_{eq}^{7}} \right] = 0 \quad \rightarrow \quad x_{eq} = (2)^{1/6}\sigma$$

Evaluate x_{eq}, the equilibrium separation of the two atoms in the molecule:

$$x_{eq} = (2)^{1/6}(0.263 \text{ nm}) = \boxed{2.95 \times 10^{-10} \text{ m}}$$

We graph the Lennard–Jones function on both sides of this critical value to create our energy diagram as shown in Figure 7.22.

Finalize Notice that $U(x)$ is extremely large when the atoms are very close together, is a minimum when the atoms are at their critical separation, and then increases again as the atoms move apart. When $U(x)$ is a minimum, the atoms are in stable equilibrium, indicating that the most likely separation between them occurs at this point.

Figure 7.22 (Example 7.9) Potential energy curve associated with a molecule. The distance x is the separation between the two atoms making up the molecule.

Summary

ThomsonNOW™ Sign in at **www.thomsonedu.com** and go to ThomsonNOW to take a practice test for this chapter.

DEFINITIONS

A **system** is most often a single particle, a collection of particles, or a region of space, and may vary in size and shape. A **system boundary** separates the system from the **environment**.

The **work** W done on a system by an agent exerting a constant force $\vec{F}$ on the system is the product of the magnitude Δr of the displacement of the point of application of the force and the component $F\cos\theta$ of the force along the direction of the displacement $\Delta\vec{r}$:

$$W \equiv F\,\Delta r\cos\theta \tag{7.1}$$

If a varying force does work on a particle as the particle moves along the x axis from x_i to x_f, the work done by the force on the particle is given by

$$W = \int_{x_i}^{x_f} F_x\,dx \tag{7.7}$$

where F_x is the component of force in the x direction.

The **scalar product** (dot product) of two vectors $\vec{A}$ and $\vec{B}$ is defined by the relationship

$$\vec{A}\cdot\vec{B} \equiv AB\cos\theta \tag{7.2}$$

where the result is a scalar quantity and θ is the angle between the two vectors. The scalar product obeys the commutative and distributive laws.

The **kinetic energy** of a particle of mass m moving with a speed v is

$$K \equiv \tfrac{1}{2}mv^2 \tag{7.16}$$

If a particle of mass m is at a distance y above the Earth's surface, the **gravitational potential energy** of the particle–Earth system is

$$U_g \equiv mgy \tag{7.19}$$

The **elastic potential energy** stored in a spring of force constant k is

$$U_s \equiv \tfrac{1}{2}kx^2 \tag{7.22}$$

A force is **conservative** if the work it does on a particle that is a member of the system as the particle moves between two points is independent of the path the particle takes between the two points. Furthermore, a force is conservative if the work it does on a particle is zero when the particle moves through an arbitrary closed path and returns to its initial position. A force that does not meet these criteria is said to be **nonconservative**.

The **total mechanical energy of a system** is defined as the sum of the kinetic energy and the potential energy:

$$E_{\text{mech}} \equiv K + U \tag{7.24}$$

CONCEPTS AND PRINCIPLES

The **work–kinetic energy theorem** states that if work is done on a system by external forces and the only change in the system is in its speed,

$$W_{\text{net}} = K_f - K_i = \Delta K = \tfrac{1}{2}mv_f^2 - \tfrac{1}{2}mv_i^2 \tag{7.15, 7.17}$$

A **potential energy function** U can be associated only with a conservative force. If a conservative force $\vec{F}$ acts between members of a system while one member moves along the x axis from x_i to x_f, the change in the potential energy of the system equals the negative of the work done by that force:

$$U_f - U_i = -\int_{x_i}^{x_f} F_x\,dx \tag{7.26}$$

Systems can be in three types of equilibrium configurations when the net force on a member of the system is zero. Configurations of **stable equilibrium** correspond to those for which $U(x)$ is a minimum. Configurations of **unstable equilibrium** correspond to those for which $U(x)$ is a maximum. **Neutral equilibrium** arises when U is constant as a member of the system moves over some region.

Questions

☐ denotes answer available in *Student Solutions Manual/Study Guide;* **O** denotes objective question

1. Discuss whether any work is being done by each of the following agents and, if so, whether the work is positive or negative: (a) a chicken scratching the ground (b) a person studying (c) a crane lifting a bucket of concrete (d) the gravitational force on the bucket in part (c) (e) the leg muscles of a person in the act of sitting down

2. Cite two examples in which a force is exerted on an object without doing any work on the object.

3. As a simple pendulum swings back and forth, the forces acting on the suspended object are the gravitational force, the tension in the supporting cord, and air resistance. (a) Which of these forces, if any, does no work on the pendulum? (b) Which of these forces does negative work at all times during its motion? (c) Describe the work done by the gravitational force while the pendulum is swinging.

4. **O** Let $\hat{\mathbf{N}}$ represent the direction horizontally north, $\widehat{\mathbf{NE}}$ represent northeast (halfway between north and east), $\widehat{\mathbf{up}}$ represent vertically upward, and so on. Each direction specification can be thought of as a unit vector. Rank from the largest to the smallest the following dot products. Note that zero is larger than a negative number. If two quantities are equal, display that fact in your ranking. (a) $\hat{\mathbf{N}} \cdot \hat{\mathbf{N}}$ (b) $\hat{\mathbf{N}} \cdot \widehat{\mathbf{NE}}$ (c) $\hat{\mathbf{N}} \cdot \hat{\mathbf{S}}$ (d) $\hat{\mathbf{N}} \cdot \hat{\mathbf{E}}$ (e) $\hat{\mathbf{N}} \cdot \widehat{\mathbf{up}}$ (f) $\hat{\mathbf{E}} \cdot \hat{\mathbf{E}}$ (g) $\widehat{\mathbf{SE}} \cdot \hat{\mathbf{S}}$ (h) $\widehat{\mathbf{up}} \cdot \widehat{\mathbf{down}}$

5. For what values of the angle θ between two vectors is their scalar product (a) positive and (b) negative?

6. **O** Figure 7.9a shows a light extended spring exerting a force F_s to the left on a block. **(i)** Does the block exert a force on the spring? Choose every correct answer. (a) No, it does not. (b) Yes, to the left. (c) Yes, to the right. (d) Its magnitude is larger than F_s. (e) Its magnitude is equal to F_s. (f) Its magnitude is smaller than F_s. **(ii)** Does the spring exert a force on the wall? Choose every correct answer from the same list (a) through (f).

7. A certain uniform spring has spring constant k. Now the spring is cut in half. What is the relationship between k and the spring constant k' of each resulting smaller spring? Explain your reasoning.

8. Can kinetic energy be negative? Explain.

9. Discuss the work done by a pitcher throwing a baseball. What is the approximate distance through which the force acts as the ball is thrown?

10. **O** Bullet 2 has twice the mass of bullet 1. Both are fired so that they have the same speed. The kinetic energy of bullet 1 is K. The kinetic energy of bullet 2 is (a) $0.25K$ (b) $0.5K$ (c) $0.71K$ (d) K (e) $2K$ (f) $4K$

11. **O** If the speed of a particle is doubled, what happens to its kinetic energy? (a) It becomes four times larger. (b) It becomes two times larger. (c) It becomes $\sqrt{2}$ times larger. (d) It is unchanged. (e) It becomes half as large.

12. A student has the idea that the total work done on an object is equal to its final kinetic energy. Is this statement true always, sometimes, or never? If sometimes true, under what circumstances? If always or never, explain why.

13. Can a normal force do work? If not, why not? If so, give an example.

14. **O** What can be said about the speed of a particle if the net work done on it is zero? (a) It is zero. (b) It is decreased. (c) It is unchanged. (d) No conclusion can be drawn.

15. **O** A cart is set rolling across a level table, at the same speed on every trial. If it runs into a patch of sand, the cart exerts on the sand an average horizontal force of 6 N and travels a distance of 6 cm through the sand as it comes to a stop. **(i)** If instead the cart runs into a patch of gravel on which the cart exerts an average horizontal force of 9 N, how far into the gravel will the cart roll in stopping? Choose one answer. (a) 9 cm (b) 6 cm (c) 4 cm (d) 3 cm (e) none of these answers **(ii)** If instead the cart runs into a patch of flour, it rolls 18 cm before stopping. What is the average magnitude of the horizontal force that the cart exerts on the flour? (a) 2 N (b) 3 N (c) 6 N (d) 18 N (e) none of these answers **(iii)** If instead the cart runs into no obstacle at all, how far will it travel? (a) 6 cm (b) 18 cm (c) 36 cm (d) an infinite distance

16. The kinetic energy of an object depends on the frame of reference in which its motion is measured. Give an example to illustrate this point.

17. **O** Work in the amount 4 J is required to stretch a spring that is described by Hooke's law by 10 cm from its unstressed length. How much additional work is required to stretch the spring by an additional 10 cm? Choose one: (a) none (b) 2 J (c) 4 J (d) 8 J (e) 12 J (f) 16 J

18. If only one external force acts on a particle, does it necessarily change the particle's (a) kinetic energy? (b) Its velocity?

19. **O (i)** Rank the gravitational accelerations you would measure for (a) a 2-kg object 5 cm above the floor, (b) a 2-kg object 120 cm above the floor, (c) a 3-kg object 120 cm above the floor, and (d) a 3-kg object 80 cm above the floor. List the one with the largest-magnitude acceleration first. If two are equal, show their equality in your list. **(ii)** Rank the gravitational forces on the same four objects, largest magnitude first. **(iii)** Rank the gravitational potential energies (of the object–Earth system) for the same four objects, largest first, taking $y = 0$ at the floor.

20. You are reshelving books in a library. You lift a book from the floor to the top shelf. The kinetic energy of the book on the floor was zero and the kinetic energy of the book on the top shelf is zero, so no change occurs in the kinetic energy yet you did some work in lifting the book. Is the work–kinetic energy theorem violated?

21. Our body muscles exert forces when we lift, push, run, jump, and so forth. Are these forces conservative?

22. What shape would the graph of U versus x have if a particle were in a region of neutral equilibrium?

23. **O** An ice cube has been given a push and slides without friction on a level table. Which is correct? (a) It is in stable equilibrium. (b) It is in unstable equilibrium. (c) It is in neutral equilibrium (d) It is not in equilibrium.

24. Preparing to clean them, you pop all the removable keys off a computer keyboard. Each key has the shape of a tiny box with one side open. By accident, you spill the lot onto the floor. Explain why many more of them land letter-side down than land open-side down.

25. Who first stated the work-kinetic energy theorem? Who showed that it is useful for solving many practical problems? Do some research to answer these questions.

Problems

Web**Assign** The Problems from this chapter may be assigned online in WebAssign.

Thomson**NOW**‾   Sign in at **www.thomsonedu.com** and go to ThomsonNOW to assess your understanding of this chapter's topics with additional quizzing and conceptual questions.

1, 2, 3 denotes straightforward, intermediate, challenging;   ☐ denotes full solution available in *Student Solutions Manual/Study Guide;*   ▲ denotes coached solution with hints available at **www.thomsonedu.com;**   denotes developing symbolic reasoning; ● denotes asking for qualitative reasoning;   ▪ denotes computer useful in solving problem

Section 7.2 Work Done by a Constant Force

1. A block of mass 2.50 kg is pushed 2.20 m along a frictionless horizontal table by a constant 16.0-N force directed 25.0° below the horizontal. Determine the work done on the block by (a) the applied force, (b) the normal force exerted by the table, and (c) the gravitational force. (d) Determine the net work done on the block.

2. A raindrop of mass 3.35×10^{-5} kg falls vertically at constant speed under the influence of gravity and air resistance. Model the drop as a particle. As it falls 100 m, what is the work done on the raindrop (a) by the gravitational force and (b) by air resistance?

3. ▲ Batman, whose mass is 80.0 kg, is dangling on the free end of a 12.0-m rope, the other end of which is fixed to a tree limb above. By repeatedly bending at the waist, he is able to get the rope in motion, eventually making it swing enough that he can reach a ledge when the rope makes a 60.0° angle with the vertical. How much work was done by the gravitational force on Batman in this maneuver?

4. ● Object 1 pushes on object 2 as the objects move together, like a bulldozer pushing a stone. Assume object 1 does 15.0 J of work on object 2. Does object 2 do work on object 1? Explain your answer. If possible, determine how much work, and explain your reasoning.

Section 7.3 The Scalar Product of Two Vectors

5. For any two vectors $\vec{A}$ and $\vec{B}$, show that $\vec{A} \cdot \vec{B} = A_x B_x + A_y B_y + A_z B_z$. *Suggestion:* Write $\vec{A}$ and $\vec{B}$ in unit-vector form and use Equations 7.4 and 7.5.

6. Vector $\vec{A}$ has a magnitude of 5.00 units and $\vec{B}$ has a magnitude of 9.00 units. The two vectors make an angle of 50.0° with each other. Find $\vec{A} \cdot \vec{B}$.

Note: In Problems 7 through 10, calculate numerical answers to three significant figures as usual.

7. ▲ A force $\vec{F} = (6\hat{i} - 2\hat{j})$ N acts on a particle that undergoes a displacement $\Delta\vec{r} = (3\hat{i} + \hat{j})$ m. Find (a) the work done by the force on the particle and (b) the angle between $\vec{F}$ and $\Delta\vec{r}$.

8. Find the scalar product of the vectors in Figure P7.8.

9. Using the definition of the scalar product, find the angles between the following: (a) $\vec{A} = 3\hat{i} - 2\hat{j}$ and $\vec{B} = 4\hat{i} - 4\hat{j}$ (b) $\vec{A} = -2\hat{i} + 4\hat{j}$ and $\vec{B} = 3\hat{i} - 4\hat{j} + 2\hat{k}$ (c) $\vec{A} = \hat{i} - 2\hat{j} + 2\hat{k}$ and $\vec{B} = 3\hat{j} + 4\hat{k}$.

Figure P7.8

10. For the vectors $\vec{A} = 3\hat{i} + \hat{j} - \hat{k}$, $\vec{B} = -\hat{i} + 2\hat{j} + 5\hat{k}$, and $\vec{C} = 2\hat{j} - 3\hat{k}$, find $\vec{C} \cdot (\vec{A} - \vec{B})$.

11. Let $\vec{B} = 5.00$ m at 60.0°. Let $\vec{C}$ have the same magnitude as $\vec{A}$ and a direction angle greater than that of $\vec{A}$ by 25.0°. Let $\vec{A} \cdot \vec{B} = 30.0$ m² and $\vec{B} \cdot \vec{C} = 35.0$ m². Find $\vec{A}$.

Section 7.4 Work Done by a Varying Force

12. The force acting on a particle is $F_x = (8x - 16)$ N, where x is in meters. (a) Make a plot of this force versus x from $x = 0$ to $x = 3.00$ m. (b) From your graph, find the net work done by this force on the particle as it moves from $x = 0$ to $x = 3.00$ m.

13. The force acting on a particle varies as shown in Figure P7.13. Find the work done by the force on the particle as it moves (a) from $x = 0$ to $x = 8.00$ m, (b) from $x = 8.00$ m to $x = 10.0$ m, and (c) from $x = 0$ to $x = 10.0$ m.

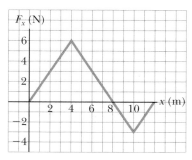

Figure P7.13

14. A force $\vec{F} = (4x\hat{i} + 3y\hat{j})$ N acts on an object as the object moves in the x direction from the origin to $x = 5.00$ m. Find the work $W = \int\vec{F} \cdot d\vec{r}$ done by the force on the object.

15. ▲ A particle is subject to a force F_x that varies with position as shown in Figure P7.15. Find the work done by the force on the particle as it moves (a) from $x = 0$ to $x = 5.00$ m, (b) from $x = 5.00$ m to $x = 10.0$ m, and (c) from $x = 10.0$ m to $x = 15.0$ m. (d) What is the total work done by the force over the distance $x = 0$ to $x = 15.0$ m?

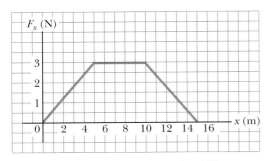

Figure P7.15   Problems 15 and 32.

16. An archer pulls her bowstring back 0.400 m by exerting a force that increases uniformly from zero to 230 N. (a) What is the equivalent spring constant of the bow? (b) How much work does the archer do in drawing the bow?

17. When a 4.00-kg object is hung vertically on a certain light spring described by Hooke's law, the spring stretches 2.50 cm. If the 4.00-kg object is removed, (a) how far will the spring stretch if a 1.50-kg block is hung on it? (b) How much work must an external agent do to stretch the same spring 4.00 cm from its unstretched position?

18. Hooke's law describes a certain light spring of unstressed length 35.0 cm. When one end is attached to the top of a door frame and a 7.50-kg object is hung from the other end, the length of the spring is 41.5 cm. (a) Find its spring constant. (b) The load and the spring are taken down. Two people pull in opposite directions on the ends of the spring, each with a force of 190 N. Find the length of the spring in this situation.

19. In a control system, an accelerometer consists of a 4.70-g object sliding on a horizontal rail. A low-mass spring attaches the object to a flange at one end of the rail. Grease on the rail makes static friction negligible, but rapidly damps out vibrations of the sliding object. When the accelerometer moves with a steady acceleration of $0.800g$, the object is to assume a location 0.500 cm away from its equilibrium position. Find the force constant required for the spring.

20. A light spring with force constant 3.85 N/m is compressed by 8.00 cm as it is held between a 0.250-kg block on the left and a 0.500-kg block on the right, both resting on a horizontal surface. The spring exerts a force on each block, tending to push them apart. The blocks are simultaneously released from rest. Find the acceleration with which each block starts to move, given that the coefficient of kinetic friction between each block and the surface is (a) 0, (b) 0.100, and (c) 0.462.

21. A 6 000-kg freight car rolls along rails with negligible friction. The car is brought to rest by a combination of two coiled springs as illustrated in Figure P7.21. Both springs are described by Hooke's law with $k_1 = 1\ 600$ N/m and $k_2 = 3\ 400$ N/m. After the first spring compresses a distance of 30.0 cm, the second spring acts with the first to increase the force as additional compression occurs as shown in the graph. The car comes to rest 50.0 cm after first contacting the two-spring system. Find the car's initial speed.

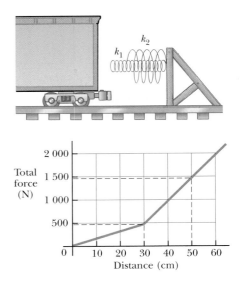

Figure P7.21

22. A 100-g bullet is fired from a rifle having a barrel 0.600 m long. Choose the origin to be at the location where the bullet begins to move. Then the force (in newtons) exerted by the expanding gas on the bullet is 15 000 + $10\ 000x - 25\ 000x^2$, where x is in meters. (a) Determine the work done by the gas on the bullet as the bullet travels the length of the barrel. (b) **What If?** If the barrel is 1.00 m long, how much work is done, and how does this value compare with the work calculated in part (a)?

23. A light spring with spring constant 1 200 N/m hangs from an elevated support. From its lower end hangs a second light spring, which has spring constant 1 800 N/m. An object of mass 1.50 kg hangs at rest from the lower end of the second spring. (a) Find the total extension distance of the pair of springs. (b) Find the effective spring constant of the pair of springs as a system. We describe these springs as *in series*.

24. A light spring with spring constant k_1 hangs from an elevated support. From its lower end hangs a second light spring, which has spring constant k_2. An object of mass m hangs at rest from the lower end of the second spring. (a) Find the total extension distance of the pair of springs. (b) Find the effective spring constant of the pair of springs as a system. We describe these springs as *in series*.

25. A small particle of mass m is pulled to the top of a frictionless half-cylinder (of radius R) by a cord that passes over the top of the cylinder as illustrated in Figure P7.25. (a) Assuming the particle moves at a constant speed, show that $F = mg \cos \theta$. *Note:* If the particle moves at constant speed, the component of its acceleration tangent to the cylinder must be zero at all times. (b) By directly integrating $W = \int \vec{F} \cdot d\vec{r}$, find the work done in moving the particle at constant speed from the bottom to the top of the half-cylinder.

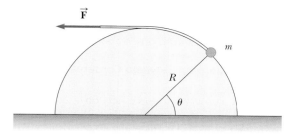

Figure P7.25

26. Express the units of the force constant of a spring in SI fundamental units.

27. **Review problem.** The graph in Figure P7.27 specifies a functional relationship between the two variables u and v.

(a) Find $\int_a^b u\, dv$. (b) Find $\int_b^a u\, dv$. (c) Find $\int_a^b v\, du$.

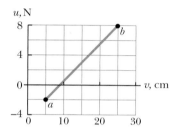

Figure P7.27

28. A cafeteria tray dispenser supports a stack of trays on a shelf that hangs from four identical spiral springs under tension, one near each corner of the shelf. Each tray is rectangular, 45.3 cm by 35.6 cm, 0.450 cm thick, and with mass 580 g. Demonstrate that the top tray in the stack can always be at the same height above the floor, however many trays are in the dispenser. Find the spring constant each spring should have for the dispenser to function in this convenient way. Is any piece of data unnecessary for this determination?

Section 7.5 Kinetic Energy and the Work–Kinetic Energy Theorem

29. A 0.600-kg particle has a speed of 2.00 m/s at point Ⓐ and kinetic energy of 7.50 J at point Ⓑ. What are (a) its kinetic energy at Ⓐ, (b) its speed at Ⓑ, and (c) the net work done on the particle as it moves from Ⓐ to Ⓑ?

30. A 0.300-kg ball has a speed of 15.0 m/s. (a) What is its kinetic energy? (b) **What If?** If its speed were doubled, what would be its kinetic energy?

31. A 3.00-kg object has a velocity of $(6.00\hat{i} - 2.00\hat{j})$ m/s. (a) What is its kinetic energy at this moment? (b) What is the net work done on the object if its velocity changes to $(8.00\hat{i} + 4.00\hat{j})$ m/s? *Note:* From the definition of the dot product, $v^2 = \vec{v}\cdot\vec{v}$.

32. A 4.00-kg particle is subject to a net force that varies with position as shown in Figure P7.15. The particle starts moving at $x = 0$, very nearly from rest. What is its speed at (a) $x = 5.00$ m, (b) $x = 10.0$ m, and (c) $x = 15.0$ m?

33. A 2 100-kg pile driver is used to drive a steel I-beam into the ground. The pile driver falls 5.00 m before coming into contact with the top of the beam. Then it drives the beam 12.0 cm farther into the ground as it comes to rest. Using energy considerations, calculate the average force the beam exerts on the pile driver while the pile driver is brought to rest.

34. ● A 300-g cart is rolling along a straight track with velocity $0.600\hat{i}$ m/s at $x = 0$. A student holds a magnet in front of the cart to temporarily pull forward on it, and then the cart runs into a dusting of sand that turns into a small pile. These effects are represented quantitatively by the graph of the x component of the net force on the cart as a function of position in Figure P7.34. (a) Will the cart roll all the way through the pile of sand? Explain how you can tell. (b) If so, find the speed at which it exits at $x = 7.00$ cm. If not, what maximum x coordinate does it reach?

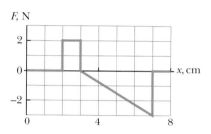

Figure P7.34

35. ● You can think of the work–kinetic energy theorem as a second theory of motion, parallel to Newton's laws in describing how outside influences affect the motion of an object. In this problem, solve parts (a) and (b) separately from parts (c) and (d) so that you can compare the predictions of the two theories. In a rifle barrel, a 15.0-g bullet is accelerated from rest to a speed of 780 m/s. (a) Find the work that is done on the bullet. (b) Assuming the rifle barrel is 72.0 cm long, find the magnitude of the average net force that acted on it, as $\Sigma F = W/(\Delta r \cos\theta)$. (c) Find the constant acceleration of a bullet that starts from rest and gains a speed of 780 m/s over a distance of 72.0 cm. (d) Assuming now the bullet has mass 15.0 g, find the net force that acted on it as $\Sigma F = ma$. (e) What conclusion can you draw from comparing your results?

36. In the neck of the picture tube of a certain black-and-white television set, an electron gun contains two charged metallic plates 2.80 cm apart. An electric force accelerates each electron in the beam from rest to 9.60% of the speed of light over this distance. (a) Determine the kinetic energy of the electron as it leaves the electron gun. Electrons carry this energy to a phosphorescent material on the inner surface of the television screen, making it glow. For an electron passing between the plates in the electron gun, determine (b) the magnitude of the constant electric force acting on the electron, (c) the acceleration, and (d) the time of flight.

Section 7.6 Potential Energy of a System

37. A 1 000-kg roller-coaster car is initially at the top of a rise, at point Ⓐ. It then moves 135 ft, at an angle of 40.0° below the horizontal, to a lower point Ⓑ. (a) Choose the car at point Ⓑ to be the zero configuration for gravitational

potential energy of the roller coaster–Earth system. Find the potential energy of the system when the car is at points Ⓐ and Ⓑ and the change in potential energy as the car moves. (b) Repeat part (a), setting the zero configuration with the car at point Ⓐ.

38. A 400-N child is in a swing that is attached to ropes 2.00 m long. Find the gravitational potential energy of the child–Earth system relative to the child's lowest position when (a) the ropes are horizontal, (b) the ropes make a 30.0° angle with the vertical, and (c) the child is at the bottom of the circular arc.

Section 7.7 Conservative and Nonconservative Forces

39. ● A 4.00-kg particle moves from the origin to position C, having coordinates $x = 5.00$ m and $y = 5.00$ m (Fig. P7.39). One force on the particle is the gravitational force acting in the negative y direction. Using Equation 7.3, calculate the work done by the gravitational force on the particle as it goes from O to C along (a) OAC, (b) OBC, and (c) OC. Your results should all be identical. Why?

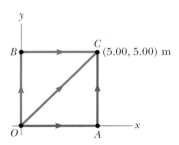

Fig. P7.39   Problems 39 through 42.

40. (a) Suppose a constant force acts on an object. The force does not vary with time or with the position or the velocity of the object. Start with the general definition for work done by a force

$$W = \int_i^f \vec{F} \cdot d\vec{r}$$

and show the force is conservative. (b) As a special case, suppose the force $\vec{F} = (3\hat{i} + 4\hat{j})$ N acts on a particle that moves from O to C in Figure P7.39. Calculate the work done by $\vec{F}$ on the particle as it moves along each one of the three paths OAC, OBC, and OC. Check that your three answers are identical.

41. ● A force acting on a particle moving in the xy plane is given by $\vec{F} = (2y\hat{i} + x^2\hat{j})$ N, where x and y are in meters. The particle moves from the origin to a final position having coordinates $x = 5.00$ m and $y = 5.00$ m as shown in Figure P7.39. Calculate the work done by $\vec{F}$ on the particle as it moves along (a) OAC, (b) OBC, and (c) OC. (d) Is $\vec{F}$ conservative or nonconservative? Explain.

42. ● A particle moves in the xy plane in Figure P7.39 under the influence of a friction force with magnitude 3.00 N and acting in the direction opposite to the particle's displacement. Calculate the work done by the friction force on the particle as it moves along the following closed paths: (a) the path OA followed by the return path AO, (b) the path OA followed by AC and the return path CO,

and (c) the path OC followed by the return path CO. (d) Each of your three answers should be nonzero. What is the significance of this observation?

Section 7.8 Relationship Between Conservative Forces and Potential Energy

43. ▲ A single conservative force acts on a 5.00-kg particle. The equation $F_x = (2x + 4)$ N describes the force, where x is in meters. As the particle moves along the x axis from $x = 1.00$ m to $x = 5.00$ m, calculate (a) the work done by this force on the particle, (b) the change in the potential energy of the system, and (c) the kinetic energy the particle has at $x = 5.00$ m if its speed is 3.00 m/s at $x = 1.00$ m.

44. A single conservative force acting on a particle varies as $\vec{F} = (-Ax + Bx^2)\hat{i}$ N, where A and B are constants and x is in meters. (a) Calculate the potential energy function $U(x)$ associated with this force, taking $U = 0$ at $x = 0$. (b) Find the change in potential energy and the change in kinetic energy of the system as the particle moves from $x = 2.00$ m to $x = 3.00$ m.

45. ▲ The potential energy of a system of two particles separated by a distance r is given by $U(r) = A/r$, where A is a constant. Find the radial force $\vec{F}_r$ that each particle exerts on the other.

46. A potential energy function for a two-dimensional force is of the form $U = 3x^3y - 7x$. Find the force that acts at the point (x, y).

Section 7.9 Energy Diagrams and Equilibrium of a System

47. For the potential energy curve shown in Figure P7.47, (a) determine whether the force F_x is positive, negative, or zero at the five points indicated. (b) Indicate points of stable, unstable, and neutral equilibrium. (c) Sketch the curve for F_x versus x from $x = 0$ to $x = 9.5$ m.

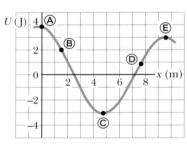

Figure P7.47

48. A right circular cone can be balanced on a horizontal surface in three different ways. Sketch these three equilibrium configurations and identify them as positions of stable, unstable, or neutral equilibrium.

49. A particle of mass 1.18 kg is attached between two identical springs on a horizontal, frictionless tabletop. Both springs have spring constant k and are initially unstressed. (a) The particle is pulled a distance x along a direction perpendicular to the initial configuration of the springs as shown in Figure P7.49. Show that the force exerted by the springs on the particle is

$$\vec{F} = -2kx\left(1 - \frac{L}{\sqrt{x^2 + L^2}}\right)\hat{i}$$

(b) Show that the potential energy of the system is

$$U(x) = kx^2 + 2kL\left(L - \sqrt{x^2 + L^2}\right)$$

(c) Make a plot of $U(x)$ versus x and identify all equilibrium points. Assume $L = 1.20$ m and $k = 40.0$ N/m. (d) If the particle is pulled 0.500 m to the right and then released, what is its speed when it reaches the equilibrium point $x = 0$?

Top View

Figure P7.49

Additional Problems

50. A bead at the bottom of a bowl is one example of an object in a stable equilibrium position. When a physical system is displaced by an amount x from stable equilibrium, a restoring force acts on it, tending to return the system to its equilibrium configuration. The magnitude of the restoring force can be a complicated function of x. For example, when an ion in a crystal is displaced from its lattice site, the restoring force may not be a simple function of x. In such cases, we can generally imagine the function $F(x)$ to be expressed as a power series in x as $F(x) = -(k_1 x + k_2 x^2 + k_3 x^3 + \ldots)$. The first term here is Hooke's law, which describes the force exerted by a simple spring for small displacements. For small excursions from equilibrium we generally ignore the higher-order terms; in some cases, however, it may be desirable to keep the second term as well. If we model the restoring force as $F = -(k_1 x + k_2 x^2)$, how much work is done in displacing the system from $x = 0$ to $x = x_{max}$ by an applied force $-F$?

51. A baseball outfielder throws a 0.150-kg baseball at a speed of 40.0 m/s and an initial angle of 30.0°. What is the kinetic energy of the baseball at the highest point of its trajectory?

52. The spring constant of a car's suspension spring increases with increasing load due to a spring coil that is widest at the bottom, smoothly tapering to a smaller diameter near the top. The result is a softer ride on normal road surfaces from the wider coils, but the car does not bottom out on bumps because when the lower coils collapse, the stiffer coils near the top absorb the load. For a tapered spiral spring that compresses 12.9 cm with a 1 000-N load and 31.5 cm with a 5 000-N load (a) evaluate the constants a and b in the empirical equation $F = ax^b$ and (b) find the work needed to compress the spring 25.0 cm.

53. ● A light spring has an unstressed length of 15.5 cm. It is described by Hooke's law with spring constant 4.30 N/m. One end of the horizontal spring is held on a fixed vertical axle, and the other end is attached to a puck of mass m that can move without friction over a horizontal surface.

The puck is set into motion in a circle with a period of 1.30 s. (a) Find the extension of the spring x as it depends on m. Evaluate x for (b) $m = 0.070\ 0$ kg, (c) $m = 0.140$ kg, (d) $m = 0.180$ kg, and (e) $m = 0.190$ kg. (f) Describe the pattern of variation of x as it depends on m.

54. Two steel balls, each of diameter 25.4 mm, moving in opposite directions at 5 m/s, run into each other head-on and bounce apart. (a) Does their interaction last only for an instant or for a nonzero time interval? State your evidence. One of the balls is squeezed in a vise while precise measurements are made of the resulting amount of compression. The results show that Hooke's law is a fair model of the ball's elastic behavior. For one datum, a force of 16 kN exerted by each jaw of the vise results in a 0.2-mm reduction in the ball's diameter. The diameter returns to its original value when the force is removed. (b) Modeling the ball as a spring, find its spring constant. (c) Compute an estimate for the kinetic energy of each of the balls before they collide. In your solution, explain your logic. (d) Compute an estimate for the maximum amount of compression each ball undergoes when they collide. (e) Compute an order-of-magnitude estimate for the time interval for which the balls are in contact. In your solution, explain your reasoning. (In Chapter 15, you will learn to calculate the contact time precisely in this model.)

55. ● Take $U = 5$ at $x = 0$ and calculate the potential energy, as a function of x, corresponding to the force $(8e^{-2x})\hat{\mathbf{i}}$. Explain whether the force is conservative or nonconservative and how you can tell.

56. The potential energy function for a system is given by $U(x) = -x^3 + 2x^2 + 3x$. (a) Determine the force F_x as a function of x. (b) For what values of x is the force equal to zero? (c) Plot $U(x)$ versus x and F_x versus x and indicate points of stable and unstable equilibrium.

57. The ball launcher in a pinball machine has a spring that has a force constant of 1.20 N/cm (Fig. P7.57). The surface on which the ball moves is inclined 10.0° with respect to the horizontal. The spring is initially compressed 5.00 cm. Find the launching speed of a 100-g ball when the plunger is released. Friction and the mass of the plunger are negligible.

Figure P7.57

58. ● **Review problem.** Two constant forces act on a 5.00-kg object moving in the xy plane as shown in Figure P7.58. Force $\vec{\mathbf{F}}_1$ is 25.0 N at 35.0° and $\vec{\mathbf{F}}_2$ is 42.0 N at 150°. At time $t = 0$, the object is at the origin and has velocity $(4.00\hat{\mathbf{i}} + 2.50\hat{\mathbf{j}})$ m/s. (a) Express the two forces in unit–vector notation. Use unit–vector notation for your other answers. (b) Find the total force exerted on the object. (c) Find the object's acceleration. Now, considering the instant $t = 3.00$ s, (d) find the object's velocity, (e) its position, (f) its kinetic energy from $\frac{1}{2}mv_f^2$, and (g) its kinetic energy from $\frac{1}{2}mv_i^2 + \Sigma \vec{F} \cdot \Delta \vec{r}$. (h) What conclusion can you draw by comparing the answers to parts (f) and (g)?

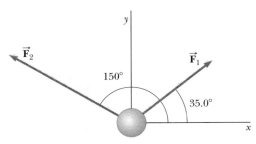

Figure P7.58

59. ⬛ A particle moves along the x axis from $x = 12.8$ m to $x = 23.7$ m under the influence of a force

$$F = \frac{375}{x^3 + 3.75x}$$

where F is in newtons and x is in meters. Using numerical integration, determine the work done by this force on the particle during this displacement. Your result should be accurate to within 2%.

60. ⬛ ● When different loads hang on a spring, the spring stretches to different lengths as shown in the following table. (a) Make a graph of the applied force versus the extension of the spring. By least-squares fitting, determine the straight line that best fits the data. Do you want to use all the data points, or should you ignore some of them? Explain. (b) From the slope of the best-fit line, find the spring constant k. (c) The spring is extended to 105 mm. What force does it exert on the suspended object?

F (N)	2.0	4.0	6.0	8.0	10	12	14	16	18	20	22
L (mm)	15	32	49	64	79	98	112	126	149	175	190

Answers to Quick Quizzes

7.1 (a). The force does no work on the Earth because the force is pointed toward the center of the circle and is therefore perpendicular to the direction of its displacement.

7.2 (c), (a), (d), (b). The work done in (c) is positive and of the largest possible value because the angle between the force and the displacement is zero. The work done in (a) is zero because the force is perpendicular to the displacement. In (d) and (b), negative work is done by the applied force because in neither case is there a component of the force in the direction of the displacement. Situation (b) is the most negative value because the angle between the force and the displacement is 180°.

7.3 (d). Because of the range of values of the cosine function, $\vec{A} \cdot \vec{B}$ has values that range from AB to $-AB$.

7.4 (a). Because the work done in compressing a spring is proportional to the square of the compression distance x, doubling the value of x causes the work to increase four-fold.

7.5 (b). Because the work is proportional to the square of the compression distance x and the kinetic energy is proportional to the square of the speed v, doubling the compression distance doubles the speed.

7.6 (c). The sign of the gravitational potential energy depends on your choice of zero configuration. If the two objects in the system are closer together than in the zero configuration, the potential energy is negative. If they are farther apart, the potential energy is positive.

7.7 (i), (c). This system exhibits changes in kinetic energy as well as in both types of potential energy. (ii), (a). Because the Earth is not included in the system, there is no gravitational potential energy associated with the system.

7.8 (d). The slope of a $U(x)$-versus-x graph is by definition $dU(x)/dx$. From Equation 7.28, we see that this expression is equal to the negative of the x component of the conservative force acting on an object that is part of the system.

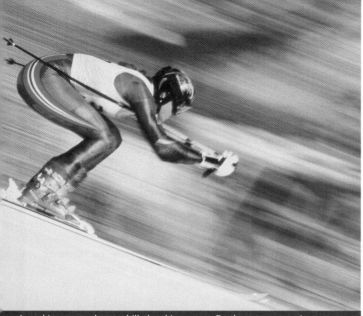

As a skier coasts down a hill, the skier–snow–Earth system experiences changes in kinetic energy, related to the speed of the skier; potential energy, related to the altitude of the skier; and internal energy, related to the temperature of the skis, the snow, and the air. If the total energy of this system were to be evaluated at several instants during this process, the result would be the same at all times. One application of the *conservation of energy principle,* to be discussed in this chapter, is that the total energy of an isolated system remains constant. (Jean Y. Ruszniewski/Getty Images)

8 Conservation of Energy

In Chapter 7, we introduced three methods for storing energy in a system: kinetic energy, associated with movement of members of the system; potential energy, determined by the configuration of the system; and internal energy, which is related to the temperature of the system.

We now consider analyzing physical situations using the energy approach for two types of systems: *nonisolated* and *isolated* systems. For nonisolated systems, we shall investigate ways that energy can cross the boundary of the system, resulting in a change in the system's total energy. This analysis leads to a critically important principle called *conservation of energy*. The conservation of energy principle extends well beyond physics and can be applied to biological organisms, technological systems, and engineering situations.

In isolated systems, energy does not cross the boundary of the system. For these systems, the total energy of the system is constant. If no nonconservative forces act within the system, we can use *conservation of mechanical energy* to solve a variety of problems.

Situations involving the transformation of mechanical energy to internal energy due to nonconservative forces require special handling. We investigate the procedures for these types of problems.

Finally, we recognize that energy can cross the boundary of a system at different rates. We describe the rate of energy transfer with the quantity *power*.

8.1 The Nonisolated System: Conservation of Energy

As we have seen, an object, modeled as a particle, can be acted on by various forces, resulting in a change in its kinetic energy. This very simple situation is the first example of the model of a **nonisolated system**, for which energy crosses the boundary of the system during some time interval due to an interaction with the environment. This scenario is common in physics problems. If a system does not interact with its environment, it is an isolated system, which we will study in Section 8.2.

The work–kinetic energy theorem from Chapter 7 is our first example of an energy equation appropriate for a nonisolated system. In the case of that theorem, the interaction of the system with its environment is the work done by the external force, and the quantity in the system that changes is the kinetic energy.

So far, we have seen only one way to transfer energy into a system: work. We mention below a few other ways to transfer energy into or out of a system. The details of these processes will be studied in other sections of the book. We illustrate mechanisms to transfer energy in Figure 8.1 and summarize them as follows.

Work, as we have learned in Chapter 7, is a method of transferring energy to a system by applying a force to the system and causing a displacement of the point of application of the force (Fig. 8.1a).

Mechanical waves (Chapters 16–18) are a means of transferring energy by allowing a disturbance to propagate through air or another medium. It is the method by which energy (which you detect as sound) leaves your clock radio through the loudspeaker and enters your ears to stimulate the hearing process (Fig. 8.1b). Other examples of mechanical waves are seismic waves and ocean waves.

Heat (Chapter 20) is a mechanism of energy transfer that is driven by a temperature difference between two regions in space. For example, the handle of a metal spoon in a cup of coffee becomes hot because fast-moving electrons and atoms in the submerged portion of the spoon bump into slower ones in the nearby part of the handle (Fig. 8.1c). These particles move faster because of the collisions and bump into the next group of slow particles. Therefore, the internal energy of the spoon handle rises from energy transfer due to this collision process.

Matter transfer (Chapter 20) involves situations in which matter physically crosses the boundary of a system, carrying energy with it. Examples include filling

(a)   (b)   (c)

(d)   (e)   (f)

Figure 8.1 Energy transfer mechanisms. (a) Energy is transferred to the block by *work*; (b) energy leaves the radio from the speaker by *mechanical waves*; (c) energy transfers up the handle of the spoon by *heat*; (d) energy enters the automobile gas tank by *matter transfer*; (e) energy enters the hair dryer by *electrical transmission*; and (f) energy leaves the light bulb by *electromagnetic radiation*.

your automobile tank with gasoline (Fig. 8.1d) and carrying energy to the rooms of your home by circulating warm air from the furnace, a process called *convection*.

Electrical transmission (Chapters 27 and 28) involves energy transfer by means of electric currents. It is how energy transfers into your hair dryer (Fig. 8.1e), stereo system, or any other electrical device.

Electromagnetic radiation (Chapter 34) refers to electromagnetic waves such as light, microwaves, and radio waves (Fig. 8.1f). Examples of this method of transfer include cooking a baked potato in your microwave oven and light energy traveling from the Sun to the Earth through space.[1]

A central feature of the energy approach is the notion that we can neither create nor destroy energy, that energy is always *conserved*. This feature has been tested in countless experiments, and no experiment has ever shown this statement to be incorrect. Therefore, **if the total amount of energy in a system changes, it can *only* be because energy has crossed the boundary of the system by a transfer mechanism such as one of the methods listed above**. This general statement of the principle of **conservation of energy** can be described mathematically with the **conservation of energy equation** as follows:

$$\Delta E_{\text{system}} = \sum T \qquad (8.1)$$

◀ Conservation of energy

where E_{system} is the total energy of the system, including all methods of energy storage (kinetic, potential, and internal) and T (for *transfer*) is the amount of energy transferred across the system boundary by some mechanism. Two of our transfer mechanisms have well-established symbolic notations. For work, $T_{\text{work}} = W$ as discussed in Chapter 7, and for heat, $T_{\text{heat}} = Q$ as defined in Chapter 20. The other four members of our list do not have established symbols, so we will call them T_{MW} (mechanical waves), T_{MT} (matter transfer), T_{ET} (electrical transmission), and T_{ER} (electromagnetic radiation).

The full expansion of Equation 8.1 is

$$\Delta K + \Delta U + \Delta E_{\text{int}} = W + Q + T_{\text{MW}} + T_{\text{MT}} + T_{\text{ET}} + T_{\text{ER}} \qquad (8.2)$$

which is the primary mathematical representation of the energy version of the **nonisolated system model**. (We will see other versions, involving linear momentum and angular momentum, in later chapters.) In most cases, Equation 8.2 reduces to a much simpler one because some of the terms are zero. If, for a given system, all terms on the right side of the conservation of energy equation are zero, the system is an *isolated system*, which we study in the next section.

The conservation of energy equation is no more complicated in theory than the process of balancing your checking account statement. If your account is the system, the change in the account balance for a given month is the sum of all the transfers: deposits, withdrawals, fees, interest, and checks written. You may find it useful to think of energy as the *currency of nature*!

Suppose a force is applied to a nonisolated system and the point of application of the force moves through a displacement. Then suppose the only effect on the system is to change its speed. In this case, the only transfer mechanism is work (so that the right side of Equation 8.2 reduces to just W) and the only kind of energy in the system that changes is the kinetic energy (so that ΔE_{system} reduces to just ΔK). Equation 8.2 then becomes

$$\Delta K = W$$

which is the work–kinetic energy theorem. This theorem is a special case of the more general principle of conservation of energy. We shall see several more special cases in future chapters.

---

[1] Electromagnetic radiation and work done by field forces are the only energy transfer mechanisms that do not require molecules of the environment to be available at the system boundary. Therefore, systems surrounded by a vacuum (such as planets) can only exchange energy with the environment by means of these two possibilities.

8.2   The Isolated System

In this section, we study another very common scenario in physics problems: an **isolated system**, for which no energy crosses the system boundary by any method. We begin by considering a gravitational situation. Think about the book–Earth system in Active Figure 7.15 in the preceding chapter. After we have lifted the book, there is gravitational potential energy stored in the system, which can be calculated from the work done by the external agent on the system, using $W = \Delta U_g$.

Let us now shift our focus to the work done on the book alone by the gravitational force (Fig. 8.2) as the book falls back to its original height. As the book falls from y_i to y_f, the work done by the gravitational force on the book is

$$W_{\text{on book}} = (m\vec{\mathbf{g}}) \cdot \Delta\vec{\mathbf{r}} = (-mg\hat{\mathbf{j}}) \cdot [(y_f - y_i)\hat{\mathbf{j}}] = mgy_i - mgy_f \tag{8.3}$$

From the work–kinetic energy theorem of Chapter 7, the work done on the book is equal to the change in the kinetic energy of the book:

$$W_{\text{on book}} = \Delta K_{\text{book}}$$

We can equate these two expressions for the work done on the book:

$$\Delta K_{\text{book}} = mgy_i - mgy_f \tag{8.4}$$

Let us now relate each side of this equation to the *system* of the book and the Earth. For the right-hand side,

$$mgy_i - mgy_f = -(mgy_f - mgy_i) = -\Delta U_g$$

where $U_g = mgy$ is the gravitational potential energy of the system. For the left-hand side of Equation 8.4, because the book is the only part of the system that is moving, we see that $\Delta K_{\text{book}} = \Delta K$, where K is the kinetic energy of the system. Therefore, with each side of Equation 8.4 replaced with its system equivalent, the equation becomes

$$\Delta K = -\Delta U_g \tag{8.5}$$

This equation can be manipulated to provide a very important general result for solving problems. First, we move the change in potential energy to the left side of the equation:

$$\Delta K + \Delta U_g = 0$$

The left side represents a sum of changes of the energy stored in the system. The right-hand side is zero because there are no transfers of energy across the boundary of the system; the book–Earth system is *isolated* from the environment. We developed this equation for a gravitational system, but it can be shown to be valid for a system with any type of potential energy. Therefore, for an isolated system,

$$\Delta K + \Delta U = 0 \tag{8.6}$$

Figure 8.2   The work done by the gravitational force on the book as the book falls from y_i to a height y_f is equal to $mgy_i - mgy_f$.

We defined in Chapter 7 the sum of the kinetic and potential energies of a system as its mechanical energy:

$$E_{\text{mech}} \equiv K + U \qquad (8.7)$$

◄ Mechanical energy of a system

where U represents the total of *all* types of potential energy. Because the system under consideration is isolated, Equations 8.6 and 8.7 tell us that the mechanical energy of the system is conserved:

$$\Delta E_{\text{mech}} = 0 \qquad (8.8)$$

◄ The mechanical energy of an isolated system with no nonconservative forces acting is conserved.

Equation 8.8 is a statement of **conservation of mechanical energy** for an isolated system with no nonconservative forces acting. The mechanical energy in such a system is conserved: the sum of the kinetic and potential energies remains constant.

If there are nonconservative forces acting within the system, mechanical energy is transformed to internal energy as discussed in Section 7.7. If nonconservative forces act in an isolated system, the total energy of the system is conserved although the mechanical energy is not. In that case, we can express the conservation of energy of the system as

$$\Delta E_{\text{system}} = 0 \qquad (8.9)$$

◄ The total energy of an isolated system is conserved.

where E_{system} includes all kinetic, potential, and internal energies. This equation is the most general statement of the **isolated system model**.

Let us now write the changes in energy in Equation 8.6 explicitly:

$$(K_f - K_i) + (U_f - U_i) = 0$$

$$K_f + U_f = K_i + U_i \qquad (8.10)$$

For the gravitational situation of the falling book, Equation 8.10 can be written as

$$\tfrac{1}{2}mv_f{}^2 + mgy_f = \tfrac{1}{2}mv_i{}^2 + mgy_i$$

As the book falls to the Earth, the book–Earth system loses potential energy and gains kinetic energy such that the total of the two types of energy always remains constant.

PITFALL PREVENTION 8.2
Conditions on Equation 8.10

Equation 8.10 is only true for a system in which conservative forces act. We will see how to handle nonconservative forces in Sections 8.3 and 8.4.

Quick Quiz 8.3 A rock of mass m is dropped to the ground from a height h. A second rock, with mass $2m$, is dropped from the same height. When the second rock strikes the ground, what is its kinetic energy? (a) twice that of the first rock (b) four times that of the first rock (c) the same as that of the first rock (d) half as much as that of the first rock (e) impossible to determine

---

Quick Quiz 8.4 Three identical balls are thrown from the top of a building, all with the same initial speed. As shown in Active Figure 8.3, the first is thrown horizontally, the second at some angle above the horizontal, and the third at some angle below the horizontal. Neglecting air resistance, rank the speeds of the balls at the instant each hits the ground.

ACTIVE FIGURE 8.3

(Quick Quiz 8.4) Three identical balls are thrown with the same initial speed from the top of a building.

Sign in at www.thomsonedu.com and go to ThomsonNOW to throw balls at different angles from the top of the building and compare the trajectories and the speeds as the balls hit the ground.

PROBLEM SOLVING STRATEGY	**Isolated Systems with No Nonconservative Forces: Conservation of Mechanical Energy**

Many problems in physics can be solved using the principle of conservation of energy for an isolated system. The following procedure should be used when you apply this principle:

1. *Conceptualize.* Study the physical situation carefully and form a mental representation of what is happening. As you become more proficient working energy problems, you will begin to be comfortable imagining the types of energy that are changing in the system.

2. *Categorize.* Define your system, which may consist of more than one object and may or may not include springs or other possibilities for storing potential energy. Determine if any energy transfers occur across the boundary of your system. If so, use the nonisolated system model, $\Delta E_{system} = \Sigma\, T$, from Section 8.1. If not, use the isolated system model, $\Delta E_{system} = 0$.

Determine whether any nonconservative forces are present within the system. If so, use the techniques of Sections 8.3 and 8.4. If not, use the principle of conservation of mechanical energy as outlined below.

3. *Analyze.* Choose configurations to represent the initial and final conditions of the system. For each object that changes elevation, select a reference position for the object that defines the zero configuration of gravitational potential energy for the system. For an object on a spring, the zero configuration for elastic potential energy is when the object is at its equilibrium position. If there is more than one conservative force, write an expression for the potential energy associated with each force.

Write the total initial mechanical energy E_i of the system for some configuration as the sum of the kinetic and potential energies associated with the configuration. Then write a similar expression for the total mechanical energy E_f of the system for the final configuration that is of interest. Because mechanical energy is *conserved*, equate the two total energies and solve for the quantity that is unknown.

4. *Finalize.* Make sure your results are consistent with your mental representation. Also make sure the values of your results are reasonable and consistent with connections to everyday experience.

EXAMPLE 8.1 **Ball in Free Fall**

A ball of mass m is dropped from a height h above the ground as shown in Active Figure 8.4.

(A) Neglecting air resistance, determine the speed of the ball when it is at a height y above the ground.

SOLUTION

Conceptualize Active Figure 8.4 and our everyday experience with falling objects allow us to conceptualize the situation. Although we can readily solve this problem with the techniques of Chapter 2, let us practice an energy approach.

Categorize We identify the system as the ball and the Earth. Because there is neither air resistance nor any other interactions between the system and the environment, the system is isolated. The only force between members of the system is the gravitational force, which is conservative.

Analyze Because the system is isolated and there are no nonconservative forces acting within the system, we apply the principle of conservation of mechanical energy to the ball–Earth system. At the instant the ball is released, its kinetic energy is $K_i = 0$ and the gravitational potential energy of the system is $U_{gi} = mgh$. When the ball is at a distance y above the ground, its kinetic energy is $K_f = \frac{1}{2}mv_f^2$ and the potential energy relative to the ground is $U_{gf} = mgy$.

Apply Equation 8.10:

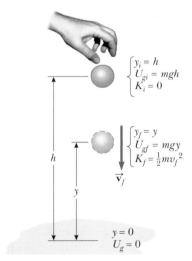

ACTIVE FIGURE 8.4

(Example 8.1) A ball is dropped from a height h above the ground. Initially, the total energy of the ball–Earth system is gravitational potential energy, equal to mgh relative to the ground. At the elevation y, the total energy is the sum of the kinetic and potential energies.

Sign in at www.thomsonedu.com and go to ThomsonNOW to drop the ball and watch energy bar charts for the ball–Earth system.

$$K_f + U_{gf} = K_i + U_{gi}$$

$$\tfrac{1}{2}mv_f^2 + mgy = 0 + mgh$$

Solve for v_f:

$$v_f^2 = 2g(h - y) \quad \rightarrow \quad v_f = \sqrt{2g(h - y)}$$

The speed is always positive. If you had been asked to find the ball's velocity, you would use the negative value of the square root as the y component to indicate the downward motion.

(B) Determine the speed of the ball at y if at the instant of release it already has an initial upward speed v_i at the initial altitude h.

SOLUTION

Analyze　In this case, the initial energy includes kinetic energy equal to $\frac{1}{2}mv_i^2$.

Apply Equation 8.10:

$$\tfrac{1}{2}mv_f^2 + mgy = \tfrac{1}{2}mv_i^2 + mgh$$

Solve for v_f:

$$v_f^2 = v_i^2 + 2g(h - y) \quad \rightarrow \quad v_f = \sqrt{v_i^2 + 2g(h - y)}$$

Finalize　This result for the final speed is consistent with the expression $v_{yf}^2 = v_{yi}^2 - 2g(y_f - y_i)$ from kinematics, where $y_i = h$. Furthermore, this result is valid even if the initial velocity is at an angle to the horizontal (Quick Quiz 8.4) for two reasons: (1) the kinetic energy, a scalar, depends only on the magnitude of the velocity; and (2) the change in the gravitational potential energy of the system depends only on the change in position of the ball in the vertical direction.

What If?　What if the initial velocity $\vec{v}_i$ in part (B) were downward? How would that affect the speed of the ball at position y?

Answer　You might claim that throwing the ball downward would result in it having a higher speed at y than if you threw it upward. Conservation of mechanical energy, however, depends on kinetic and potential energies, which are scalars. Therefore, the direction of the initial velocity vector has no bearing on the final speed.

EXAMPLE 8.2　**A Grand Entrance**

You are designing an apparatus to support an actor of mass 65 kg who is to "fly" down to the stage during the performance of a play. You attach the actor's harness to a 130-kg sandbag by means of a lightweight steel cable running smoothly over two frictionless pulleys as in Figure 8.5a. You need 3.0 m of cable between the harness and the nearest pulley so that the pulley can be hidden behind a curtain. For the apparatus to work successfully, the sandbag must never lift above the floor as the actor swings from above the stage to the floor. Let us call the initial angle that the actor's cable makes with the vertical θ. What is the maximum value θ can have before the sandbag lifts off the floor?

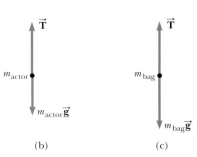

Figure 8.5　(Example 8.2) (a) An actor uses some clever staging to make his entrance. (b) The free-body diagram for the actor at the bottom of the circular path. (c) The free-body diagram for the sandbag if the normal force from the floor goes to zero.

SOLUTION

Conceptualize We must use several concepts to solve this problem. Imagine what happens as the actor approaches the bottom of the swing. At the bottom, the cable is vertical and must support his weight as well as provide centripetal acceleration of his body in the upward direction. At this point, the tension in the cable is the highest and the sandbag is most likely to lift off the floor.

Categorize Looking first at the swinging of the actor from the initial point to the lowest point, we model the actor and the Earth as an isolated system. We ignore air resistance, so there are no nonconservative forces acting. You might initially be tempted to model the system as nonisolated because of the interaction of the system with the cable, which is in the environment. The force applied to the actor by the cable, however, is always perpendicular to each element of the displacement of the actor and hence does no work. Therefore, in terms of energy transfers across the boundary, the system is isolated.

Analyze We use the principle of conservation of mechanical energy for the system to find the actor's speed as he arrives at the floor as a function of the initial angle θ and the radius R of the circular path through which he swings.

Apply conservation of mechanical energy to the actor–Earth system:

$$K_f + U_f = K_i + U_i$$

Let y_i be the initial height of the actor above the floor and v_f be his speed at the instant before he lands. (Notice that $K_i = 0$ because the actor starts from rest and that $U_f = 0$ because we define the configuration of the actor at the floor as having a gravitational potential energy of zero.)

$$(1) \quad \tfrac{1}{2}m_{actor}\,v_f^{\,2} + 0 = 0 + m_{actor}\,gy_i$$

From the geometry in Figure 8.5a, notice that $y_f = 0$, so $y_i = R - R\cos\theta = R(1 - \cos\theta)$. Use this relationship in Equation (1) and solve for $v_f^{\,2}$:

$$(2) \quad v_f^{\,2} = 2gR(1 - \cos\theta)$$

Categorize Next, focus on the instant the actor is at the lowest point. Because the tension in the cable is transferred as a force applied to the sandbag, we model the actor at this instant as a particle under a net force.

Analyze Apply Newton's second law to the actor at the bottom of his path, using the free-body diagram in Figure 8.5b as a guide:

$$\sum F_y = T - m_{actor}\,g = m_{actor}\frac{v_f^{\,2}}{R}$$

$$(3) \quad T = m_{actor}\,g + m_{actor}\frac{v_f^{\,2}}{R}$$

Categorize Finally, notice that the sandbag lifts off the floor when the upward force exerted on it by the cable exceeds the gravitational force acting on it; the normal force is zero when that happens. We do *not*, however, want the sandbag to lift off the floor. The sandbag must remain at rest, so we model it as a particle in equilibrium.

Analyze A force T of the magnitude given by Equation (3) is transmitted by the cable to the sandbag. If the sandbag remains at rest but is just ready to be lifted off the floor if any more force were applied by the cable, the normal force on it becomes zero and Newton's second law with $a = 0$ tells us that $T = m_{bag}g$ as in Figure 8.5c.

Use this condition together with Equations (2) and (3):

$$m_{bag}\,g = m_{actor}\,g + m_{actor}\frac{2gR(1 - \cos\theta)}{R}$$

Solve for $\cos\theta$ and substitute the given parameters:

$$\cos\theta = \frac{3m_{actor} - m_{bag}}{2m_{actor}} = \frac{3(65\text{ kg}) - 130\text{ kg}}{2(65\text{ kg})} = 0.50$$

$$\theta = \boxed{60°}$$

Finalize Here we had to combine techniques from different areas of our study, energy and Newton's second law. Furthermore, notice that the length R of the cable from the actor's harness to the leftmost pulley did not appear in the final algebraic equation. Therefore, the final answer is independent of R.

EXAMPLE 8.3   **The Spring-Loaded Popgun**

The launching mechanism of a popgun consists of a spring of unknown spring constant (Active Fig. 8.6a). When the spring is compressed 0.120 m, the gun, when fired vertically, is able to launch a 35.0-g projectile to a maximum height of 20.0 m above the position of the projectile as it leaves the spring.

(A) Neglecting all resistive forces, determine the spring constant.

SOLUTION

Conceptualize Imagine the process illustrated in Active Figure 8.6. The projectile starts from rest, speeds up as the spring pushes upward on it, leaves the spring, and then slows down as the gravitational force pulls downward on it.

Categorize We identify the system as the projectile, the spring, and the Earth. We ignore air resistance on the projectile and friction in the gun, so we model the system as isolated with no nonconservative forces acting.

Analyze Because the projectile starts from rest, its initial kinetic energy is zero. We choose the zero configuration for the gravitational potential energy of the system to be when the projectile leaves the spring. For this configuration, the elastic potential energy is also zero.

After the gun is fired, the projectile rises to a maximum height $y_\text{©}$. The final kinetic energy of the projectile is zero.

(a)   (b)

ACTIVE FIGURE 8.6

(Example 8.3) A spring-loaded popgun (a) before firing and (b) when the spring extends to its relaxed length.

Sign in at www.thomsonedu.com and go to ThomsonNOW to fire the gun and watch the energy changes in the projectile–spring–Earth system.

Write a conservation of mechanical energy equation for the system between points Ⓐ and ©:

$$K_\text{©} + U_{g\text{©}} + U_{s\text{©}} = K_\text{Ⓐ} + U_{g\text{Ⓐ}} + U_{s\text{Ⓐ}}$$

Substitute for each energy:

$$0 + mgy_\text{©} + 0 = 0 + mgy_\text{Ⓐ} + \tfrac{1}{2}kx^2$$

Solve for k:

$$k = \frac{2mg(y_\text{©} - y_\text{Ⓐ})}{x^2}$$

Substitute numerical values:

$$k = \frac{2(0.035\,0\text{ kg})(9.80\text{ m/s}^2)[20.0\text{ m} - (-0.120\text{ m})]}{(0.120\text{ m})^2} = \boxed{958\text{ N/m}}$$

(B) Find the speed of the projectile as it moves through the equilibrium position of the spring as shown in Active Figure 8.6b.

SOLUTION

Analyze The energy of the system as the projectile moves through the equilibrium position of the spring includes only the kinetic energy of the projectile $\tfrac{1}{2}mv_\text{Ⓑ}^2$.

Write a conservation of mechanical energy equation for the system between points Ⓐ and Ⓑ:

$$K_\text{Ⓑ} + U_{g\text{Ⓑ}} + U_{s\text{Ⓑ}} = K_\text{Ⓐ} + U_{g\text{Ⓐ}} + U_{s\text{Ⓐ}}$$

Substitute for each energy:

$$\tfrac{1}{2}mv_{\circledB}{}^2 + 0 + 0 = 0 + mgy_{\circledA} + \tfrac{1}{2}kx^2$$

Solve for $v_{\circledB}$:

$$v_{\circledB} = \sqrt{\frac{kx^2}{m} + 2gy_{\circledA}}$$

Substitute numerical values:

$$v_{\circledB} = \sqrt{\frac{(958 \text{ N/m})(0.120 \text{ m})^2}{(0.035\,0 \text{ kg})} + 2(9.80 \text{ m/s}^2)(-0.120 \text{ m})} = \boxed{19.8 \text{ m/s}}$$

Finalize This example is the first one we have seen in which we must include two different types of potential energy.

8.3   Situations Involving Kinetic Friction

Consider again the book in Active Figure 7.18 sliding to the right on the surface of a heavy table and slowing down due to the friction force. Work is done by the friction force because there is a force and a displacement. Keep in mind, however, that our equations for work involve the displacement *of the point of application of the force*. A simple model of the friction force between the book and the surface is shown in Figure 8.7a. We have represented the entire friction force between the book and surface as being due to two identical teeth that have been spot-welded together.[2] One tooth projects upward from the surface, the other downward from the book, and they are welded at the points where they touch. The friction force acts at the junction of the two teeth. Imagine that the book slides a small distance d to the right as in Figure 8.7b. Because the teeth are modeled as identical, the junction of the teeth moves to the right by a distance $d/2$. Therefore, the displacement of the point of application of the friction force is $d/2$, but the displacement of the book is d!

In reality, the friction force is spread out over the entire contact area of an object sliding on a surface, so the force is not localized at a point. In addition, because the magnitudes of the friction forces at various points are constantly changing as individual spot welds occur, the surface and the book deform locally, and so on, the displacement of the point of application of the friction force is not at all the same as the displacement of the book. In fact, the displacement of the point of application of the friction force is not calculable and so neither is the work done by the friction force.

The work–kinetic energy theorem is valid for a particle or an object that can be modeled as a particle. When a friction force acts, however, we cannot calculate the work done by friction. For such situations, Newton's second law is still valid for the system even though the work–kinetic energy theorem is not. The case of a nondeformable object like our book sliding on the surface[3] can be handled in a relatively straightforward way.

Starting from a situation in which forces, including friction, are applied to the book, we can follow a similar procedure to that done in developing Equation 7.17. Let us start by writing Equation 7.8 for all forces other than friction:

$$\sum W_{\text{other forces}} = \int \left(\sum \vec{\mathbf{F}}_{\text{other forces}}\right) \cdot d\vec{\mathbf{r}} \tag{8.11}$$

The $d\vec{\mathbf{r}}$ in this equation is the displacement of the object because for forces other than friction, under the assumption that these forces do not deform the object, this displacement is the same as the displacement of the point of application of

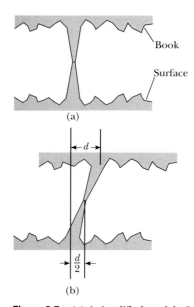

Figure 8.7 (a) A simplified model of friction between a book and a surface. The entire friction force is modeled to be applied at the interface between two identical teeth projecting from the book and the surface. (b) The book is moved to the right by a distance d. The point of application of the friction force moves through a displacement of magnitude $d/2$.

Book

Surface

(a)

(b)

[2] Figure 8.7 and its discussion are inspired by a classic article on friction: B. A. Sherwood and W. H. Bernard, "Work and heat transfer in the presence of sliding friction," *American Journal of Physics*, 52:1001, 1984.

[3] The overall shape of the book remains the same, which is why we say it is nondeformable. On a microscopic level, however, there is deformation of the book's face as it slides over the surface.

the forces. To each side of Equation 8.11 let us add the integral of the scalar product of the force of kinetic friction and $d\vec{\mathbf{r}}$:

$$\sum W_{\text{other forces}} + \int \vec{\mathbf{f}}_k \cdot d\vec{\mathbf{r}} = \int \left(\sum \vec{\mathbf{F}}_{\text{other forces}} \right) \cdot d\vec{\mathbf{r}} + \int \vec{\mathbf{f}}_k \cdot d\vec{\mathbf{r}}$$

$$= \int \left(\sum \vec{\mathbf{F}}_{\text{other forces}} + \vec{\mathbf{f}}_k \right) \cdot d\vec{\mathbf{r}}$$

The integrand on the right side of this equation is the net force $\sum \vec{\mathbf{F}}$, so

$$\sum W_{\text{other forces}} + \int \vec{\mathbf{f}}_k \cdot d\vec{\mathbf{r}} = \int \sum \vec{\mathbf{F}} \cdot d\vec{\mathbf{r}}$$

Incorporating Newton's second law $\sum \vec{\mathbf{F}} = m\vec{\mathbf{a}}$ gives

$$\sum W_{\text{other forces}} + \int \vec{\mathbf{f}}_k \cdot d\vec{\mathbf{r}} = \int m\vec{\mathbf{a}} \cdot d\vec{\mathbf{r}} = \int m \frac{d\vec{\mathbf{v}}}{dt} \cdot d\vec{\mathbf{r}} = \int_{t_i}^{t_f} m \frac{d\vec{\mathbf{v}}}{dt} \cdot \vec{\mathbf{v}}\, dt \quad \textbf{(8.12)}$$

where we have used Equation 4.3 to rewrite $d\vec{\mathbf{r}}$ as $\vec{\mathbf{v}}\, dt$. The scalar product obeys the product rule for differentiation (See Eq. B.30 in Appendix B.6), so the derivative of the scalar product of $\vec{\mathbf{v}}$ with itself can be written

$$\frac{d}{dt} (\vec{\mathbf{v}} \cdot \vec{\mathbf{v}}) = \frac{d\vec{\mathbf{v}}}{dt} \cdot \vec{\mathbf{v}} + \vec{\mathbf{v}} \cdot \frac{d\vec{\mathbf{v}}}{dt} = 2 \frac{d\vec{\mathbf{v}}}{dt} \cdot \vec{\mathbf{v}}$$

where we have used the commutative property of the scalar product to justify the final expression in this equation. Consequently,

$$\frac{d\vec{\mathbf{v}}}{dt} \cdot \vec{\mathbf{v}} = \tfrac{1}{2} \frac{d}{dt} (\vec{\mathbf{v}} \cdot \vec{\mathbf{v}}) = \tfrac{1}{2} \frac{dv^2}{dt}$$

Substituting this result into Equation 8.12 gives

$$\sum W_{\text{other forces}} + \int \vec{\mathbf{f}}_k \cdot d\vec{\mathbf{r}} = \int_{t_i}^{t_f} m \left(\tfrac{1}{2} \frac{dv^2}{dt} \right) dt = \tfrac{1}{2} m \int_{v_i}^{v_f} d(v^2) = \tfrac{1}{2} m v_f^2 - \tfrac{1}{2} m v_i^2 = \Delta K$$

Looking at the left side of this equation, notice that in the inertial frame of the surface, $\vec{\mathbf{f}}_k$ and $d\vec{\mathbf{r}}$ will be in opposite directions for every increment $d\vec{\mathbf{r}}$ of the path followed by the object. Therefore, $\vec{\mathbf{f}}_k \cdot d\vec{\mathbf{r}} = -f_k\, dr$. The previous expression now becomes

$$\sum W_{\text{other forces}} - \int f_k\, dr = \Delta K$$

In our model for friction, the magnitude of the kinetic friction force is constant, so f_k can be brought out of the integral. The remaining integral $\int dr$ is simply the sum of increments of length along the path, which is the total path length d. Therefore,

$$\sum W_{\text{other forces}} - f_k d = \Delta K \qquad \textbf{(8.13)}$$

or

$$K_f = K_i - f_k d + \sum W_{\text{other forces}} \qquad \textbf{(8.14)}$$

Equation 8.13 is a modified form of the work–kinetic energy theorem to be used when a friction force acts on an object. The change in kinetic energy is equal to the work done by all forces other than friction minus a term $f_k d$ associated with the friction force.

Now consider the larger system of the book *and* the surface as the book slows down under the influence of a friction force alone. There is no work done across the boundary of this system because the system does not interact with the environment. There are no other types of energy transfer occurring across the boundary of the system, assuming we ignore the inevitable sound the sliding book makes! In this case, Equation 8.2 becomes

$$\Delta E_{\text{system}} = \Delta K + \Delta E_{\text{int}} = 0$$

The change in kinetic energy of this book–surface system is the same as the change in kinetic energy of the book alone because the book is the only part of the system that is moving. Therefore, incorporating Equation 8.13 gives

$$-f_k d + \Delta E_{int} = 0$$

◄ **Change in internal energy due to friction within the system**

$$\Delta E_{int} = f_k d \qquad (8.15)$$

The increase in internal energy of the system is therefore equal to the product of the friction force and the path length through which the block moves. In summary, **a friction force transforms kinetic energy in a system to internal energy, and the increase in internal energy of the system is equal to its decrease in kinetic energy**.

Quick Quiz 8.5 You are traveling along a freeway at 65 mi/h. Your car has kinetic energy. You suddenly skid to a stop because of congestion in traffic. Where is the kinetic energy your car once had? (a) It is all in internal energy in the road. (b) It is all in internal energy in the tires. (c) Some of it has transformed to internal energy and some of it transferred away by mechanical waves. (d) It is all transferred away from your car by various mechanisms.

EXAMPLE 8.4 A Block Pulled on a Rough Surface

A 6.0-kg block initially at rest is pulled to the right along a horizontal surface by a constant horizontal force of 12 N.

(A) Find the speed of the block after it has moved 3.0 m if the surfaces in contact have a coefficient of kinetic friction of 0.15.

SOLUTION

Conceptualize This example is Example 7.6, modified so that the surface is no longer frictionless. The rough surface applies a friction force on the block opposite to the applied force. As a result, we expect the speed to be lower than that found in Example 7.6.

Categorize The block is pulled by a force and the surface is rough, so we model the block–surface system as nonisolated with a nonconservative force acting.

(a)

ACTIVE FIGURE 8.8

(Example 8.4) (a) A block pulled to the right on a rough surface by a constant horizontal force. (b) The applied force is at an angle θ to the horizontal.

Sign in at www.thomsonedu.com and go to ThomsonNOW to pull the block with a force oriented at different angles.

(b)

Analyze Active Figure 8.8a illustrates this situation. Neither the normal force nor the gravitational force does work on the system because their points of application are displaced horizontally.

Find the work done on the system by the applied force just as in Example 7.6:

$$W = F \,\Delta x = (12\ \text{N})(3.0\ \text{m}) = 36\ \text{J}$$

Apply the particle in equilibrium model to the block in the vertical direction:

$$\Sigma F_y = 0 \quad \rightarrow \quad n - mg = 0 \quad \rightarrow \quad n = mg$$

Find the magnitude of the friction force:

$$f_k = \mu_k n = \mu_k mg = (0.15)(6.0\ \text{kg})(9.80\ \text{m/s}^2) = 8.82\ \text{N}$$

Find the final speed of the block from Equation 8.14:

$$\tfrac{1}{2}mv_f{}^2 = \tfrac{1}{2}mv_i{}^2 - f_k d + \sum W_{\text{other forces}}$$

$$v_f = \sqrt{v_i{}^2 + \frac{2}{m}\left(-f_k d + \sum W_{\text{other forces}}\right)}$$

$$= \sqrt{0 + \frac{2}{6.0\ \text{kg}}\left[-(8.82\ \text{N})(3.0\ \text{m}) + 36\ \text{J}\right]} = \boxed{1.8\ \text{m/s}}$$

Finalize   As expected, this value is less than the 3.5 m/s found in the case of the block sliding on a frictionless surface (see Example 7.6).

(B) Suppose the force $\vec{F}$ is applied at an angle θ as shown in Active Figure 8.8b. At what angle should the force be applied to achieve the largest possible speed after the block has moved 3.0 m to the right?

SOLUTION

Conceptualize   You might guess that $\theta = 0$ would give the largest speed because the force would have the largest component possible in the direction parallel to the surface. Think about an arbitrary nonzero angle, however. Although the horizontal component of the force would be reduced, the vertical component of the force would reduce the normal force, in turn reducing the force of friction, which suggests that the speed could be maximized by pulling at an angle other than $\theta = 0$.

Categorize   As in part (A), we model the block–surface system as nonisolated with a nonconservative force acting.

Analyze   Find the work done by the applied force, noting that $\Delta x = d$ because the path followed by the block is a straight line:

$$W = F \, \Delta x \cos \theta = Fd \cos \theta$$

Apply the particle in equilibrium model to the block in the vertical direction:

$$\sum F_y = n + F \sin \theta - mg = 0$$

Solve for n:

$$n = mg - F \sin \theta$$

Use Equation 8.14 to find the final kinetic energy for this situation:

$$K_f = K_i - f_k d + \sum W_{\text{other forces}}$$

$$= 0 - \mu_k nd + Fd \cos \theta = -\mu_k(mg - F \sin \theta)d + Fd \cos \theta$$

Maximizing the speed is equivalent to maximizing the final kinetic energy. Consequently, differentiate K_f with respect to θ and set the result equal to zero:

$$\frac{d(K_f)}{d\theta} = -\mu_k(0 - F \cos \theta)d - Fd \sin \theta = 0$$

$$\mu_k \cos \theta - \sin \theta = 0$$

$$\tan \theta = \mu_k$$

Evaluate θ for $\mu_k = 0.15$:

$$\theta = \tan^{-1}(\mu_k) = \tan^{-1}(0.15) = \boxed{8.5°}$$

Finalize   Notice that the angle at which the speed of the block is a maximum is indeed not $\theta = 0$. When the angle exceeds 8.5°, the horizontal component of the applied force is too small to be compensated by the reduced friction force and the speed of the block begins to decrease from its maximum value.

CONCEPTUAL EXAMPLE 8.5   **Useful Physics for Safer Driving**

A car traveling at an initial speed v slides a distance d to a halt after its brakes lock. If the car's initial speed is instead $2v$ at the moment the brakes lock, estimate the distance it slides.

SOLUTION

Let us assume the force of kinetic friction between the car and the road surface is constant and the same for both speeds. According to Equation 8.14, the friction force multiplied by the distance d is equal to the initial kinetic energy of the car (because $K_f = 0$ and there is no work done by other forces). If the speed is doubled, as it is in this example, the kinetic energy is quadrupled. For a given friction force, the distance traveled is four times as great when the initial speed is doubled, and so the estimated distance the car slides is $4d$.

| EXAMPLE 8.6 | **A Block–Spring System** |

A block of mass 1.6 kg is attached to a horizontal spring that has a force constant of 1.0×10^3 N/m as shown in Figure 8.9. The spring is compressed 2.0 cm and is then released from rest.

(A) Calculate the speed of the block as it passes through the equilibrium position $x = 0$ if the surface is frictionless.

(a)

(b)

SOLUTION

Conceptualize This situation has been discussed before and it is easy to visualize the block being pushed to the right by the spring and moving off with some speed.

Categorize We identify the system as the block and model the block as a nonisolated system.

Figure 8.9 (Example 8.6) (a) A block is attached to a spring. The spring is compressed by a distance x. (b) The block is then released and the spring pushes it to the right.

Analyze In this situation, the block starts with $v_i = 0$ at $x_i = -2.0$ cm, and we want to find v_f at $x_f = 0$.

Use Equation 7.11 to find the work done by the spring with $x_{max} = x_i = -2.0$ cm $= -2.0 \times 10^{-2}$ m:

$$W_s = \tfrac{1}{2}kx_{max}^2 = \tfrac{1}{2}(1.0 \times 10^3 \,\text{N/m})(-2.0 \times 10^{-2}\,\text{m})^2 = 0.20\,\text{J}$$

Work is done on the block and its speed changes. The conservation of energy equation, Equation 8.2, reduces to the work–kinetic energy theorem. Use that theorem to find the speed at $x = 0$:

$$W_s = \tfrac{1}{2}mv_f^2 - \tfrac{1}{2}mv_i^2$$

$$v_f = \sqrt{v_i^2 + \frac{2}{m}W_s}$$

$$= \sqrt{0 + \frac{2}{1.6\,\text{kg}}(0.20\,\text{J})} = \boxed{0.50\,\text{m/s}}$$

Finalize Although this problem could have been solved in Chapter 7, it is presented here to provide contrast with the following part (B), which requires the techniques of this chapter.

(B) Calculate the speed of the block as it passes through the equilibrium position if a constant friction force of 4.0 N retards its motion from the moment it is released.

SOLUTION

Conceptualize The correct answer must be less than that found in part (A) because the friction force retards the motion.

Categorize We identify the system as the block and the surface. The system is nonisolated because of the work done by the spring and there is a nonconservative force acting: the friction between the block and the surface.

Analyze Write Equation 8.14:

$$(1) \quad K_f = K_i - f_k d + \sum W_{\text{other forces}}$$

Evaluate $f_k d$:

$$f_k d = (4.0\,\text{N})(2.0 \times 10^{-2}\,\text{m}) = 0.080\,\text{J}$$

Evaluate $\sum W_{\text{other forces}}$, the work done by the spring, by recalling that it was found in part (A) to be 0.20 J. Use $K_i = 0$ in Equation (1) and solve for the final speed:

$$K_f = 0 - 0.080\,\text{J} + 0.20\,\text{J} = 0.12\,\text{J} = \tfrac{1}{2}mv_f^2$$

$$v_f = \sqrt{\frac{2K_f}{m}} = \sqrt{\frac{2(0.12\,\text{J})}{1.6\,\text{kg}}} = \boxed{0.39\,\text{m/s}}$$

Finalize As expected, this value is less than the 0.50 m/s found in part (A).

What If? What if the friction force were increased to 10.0 N? What is the block's speed at $x = 0$?

Answer   In this case, the value of $f_k d$ as the block moves to $x = 0$ is

$$f_k d = (10.0\ \text{N})(2.0 \times 10^{-2}\ \text{m}) = 0.20\ \text{J}$$

which is equal in magnitude to the kinetic energy at $x = 0$ without the loss due to friction. Therefore, all the kinetic energy has been transformed by friction when the block arrives at $x = 0$, and its speed at this point is $v = 0$.

In this situation as well as that in part (B), the speed of the block reaches a maximum at some position other than $x = 0$. Problem 47 asks you to locate these positions.

8.4 Changes in Mechanical Energy for Nonconservative Forces

Consider the book sliding across the surface in the preceding section. As the book moves through a distance d, the only force that does work on it is the force of kinetic friction. This force causes a change $-f_k d$ in the kinetic energy of the book as described by Equation 8.13.

Now, however, suppose the book is part of a system that also exhibits a change in potential energy. In this case, $-f_k d$ is the amount by which the *mechanical* energy of the system changes because of the force of kinetic friction. For example, if the book moves on an incline that is not frictionless, there is a change in both the kinetic energy and the gravitational potential energy of the book–Earth system. Consequently,

$$\Delta E_{\text{mech}} = \Delta K + \Delta U_g = -f_k d$$

In general, if a friction force acts within an isolated system,

$$\Delta E_{\text{mech}} = \Delta K + \Delta U = -f_k d \qquad (8.16)$$

◀ Change in mechanical energy of a system due to friction within the system

where ΔU is the change in *all* forms of potential energy. Notice that Equation 8.16 reduces to Equation 8.10 if the friction force is zero.

If the system in which nonconservative forces act is nonisolated, the generalization of Equation 8.13 is

$$\Delta E_{\text{mech}} = -f_k d + \sum W_{\text{other forces}} \qquad (8.17)$$

PROBLEM SOLVING STRATEGY   **Systems with Nonconservative Forces**

The following procedure should be used when you face a problem involving a system in which nonconservative forces act:

1. *Conceptualize.* Study the physical situation carefully and form a mental representation of what is happening.

2. *Categorize.* Define your system, which may consist of more than one object. The system could include springs or other possibilities for storage of potential energy. Determine whether any nonconservative forces are present. If not, use the principle of conservation of mechanical energy as outlined in Section 8.2. If so, use the procedure discussed below.

   Determine if any work is done across the boundary of your system by forces other than friction. If so, use Equation 8.17 to analyze the problem. If not, use Equation 8.16.

3. *Analyze.* Choose configurations to represent the initial and final conditions of the system. For each object that changes elevation, select a reference position for the object that defines the zero configuration of gravitational potential energy for the system. For an object on a spring, the zero configuration for elastic potential energy is when the object is at its equilibrium position. If there is more than one

conservative force, write an expression for the potential energy associated with each force.

Use either Equation 8.16 or Equation 8.17 to establish a mathematical representation of the problem. Solve for the unknown.

4. *Finalize.* Make sure your results are consistent with your mental representation. Also make sure the values of your results are reasonable and consistent with connections to everyday experience.

EXAMPLE 8.7   Crate Sliding Down a Ramp

A 3.00-kg crate slides down a ramp. The ramp is 1.00 m in length and inclined at an angle of 30.0° as shown in Figure 8.10. The crate starts from rest at the top, experiences a constant friction force of magnitude 5.00 N, and continues to move a short distance on the horizontal floor after it leaves the ramp.

(A) Use energy methods to determine the speed of the crate at the bottom of the ramp.

SOLUTION

Conceptualize   Imagine the crate sliding down the ramp in Figure 8.10. The larger the friction force, the more slowly the crate will slide.

Categorize   We identify the crate, the surface, and the Earth as the system. The system is categorized as isolated with a non-conservative force acting.

Figure 8.10   (Example 8.7) A crate slides down a ramp under the influence of gravity. The potential energy of the system decreases, whereas the kinetic energy increases.

Analyze   Because $v_i = 0$, the initial kinetic energy of the system when the crate is at the top of the ramp is zero. If the y coordinate is measured from the bottom of the ramp (the final position of the crate, for which we choose the gravitational potential energy of the system to be zero) with the upward direction being positive, then $y_i = 0.500$ m.

Evaluate the total mechanical energy of the system when the crate is at the top:

$$E_i = K_i + U_i = 0 + U_i = mgy_i$$
$$= (3.00 \text{ kg})(9.80 \text{ m/s}^2)(0.500 \text{ m}) = 14.7 \text{ J}$$

Write an expression for the final mechanical energy:

$$E_f = K_f + U_f = \tfrac{1}{2}mv_f^2 + 0$$

Apply Equation 8.16:

$$\Delta E_{\text{mech}} = E_f - E_i = \tfrac{1}{2}mv_f^2 - mgy_i = -f_k d$$

Solve for v_f^2:

$$(1) \quad v_f^2 = \frac{2}{m}(mgy_i - f_k d)$$

Substitute numerical values and solve for v_f:

$$v_f^2 = \frac{2}{3.00 \text{ kg}}[14.7 \text{ J} - (5.00 \text{ N})(1.00 \text{ m})] = 6.47 \text{ m}^2/\text{s}^2$$

$$v_f = \boxed{2.54 \text{ m/s}}$$

(B) How far does the crate slide on the horizontal floor if it continues to experience a friction force of magnitude 5.00 N?

SOLUTION

Analyze   This part of the problem is handled in exactly the same way as part (A), but in this case we can consider the mechanical energy of the system to consist only of kinetic energy because the potential energy of the system remains fixed.

Evaluate the mechanical energy of the system when the crate leaves the bottom of the ramp:

$$E_i = K_i = \tfrac{1}{2}mv_i^2 = \tfrac{1}{2}(3.00 \text{ kg})(2.54 \text{ m/s})^2 = 9.68 \text{ J}$$

Apply Equation 8.16 with $E_f = 0$:

$$E_f - E_i = 0 - 9.68 \text{ J} = -f_k d$$

Solve for the distance d:

$$d = \frac{9.68 \text{ J}}{f_k} = \frac{9.68 \text{ J}}{5.00 \text{ N}} = \boxed{1.94 \text{ m}}$$

Finalize   For comparison, you may want to calculate the speed of the crate at the bottom of the ramp in the case in which the ramp is frictionless. Also notice that the increase in internal energy of the system as the crate slides down the ramp is 5.00 J. This energy is shared between the crate and the surface, each of which is a bit warmer than before.

   Also notice that the distance d the object slides on the horizontal surface is infinite if the surface is frictionless. Is that consistent with your conceptualization of the situation?

What If?   A cautious worker decides that the speed of the crate when it arrives at the bottom of the ramp may be so large that its contents may be damaged. Therefore, he replaces the ramp with a longer one such that the new ramp makes an angle of 25.0° with the ground. Does this new ramp reduce the speed of the crate as it reaches the ground?

Answer   Because the ramp is longer, the friction force acts over a longer distance and transforms more of the mechanical energy into internal energy. The result is a reduction in the kinetic energy of the crate, and we expect a lower speed as it reaches the ground.

Find the length d of the new ramp:

$$\sin 25.0° = \frac{0.500 \text{ m}}{d} \quad \rightarrow \quad d = \frac{0.500 \text{ m}}{\sin 25.0°} = 1.18 \text{ m}$$

Find v_f^2 from Equation (1) in part (A):

$$v_f^2 = \frac{2}{3.00 \text{ kg}}[14.7 \text{ J} - (5.00 \text{ N})(1.18 \text{ m})] = 5.87 \text{ m}^2/\text{s}^2$$

$$v_f = 2.42 \text{ m/s}$$

The final speed is indeed lower than in the higher-angle case.

EXAMPLE 8.8   **Block–Spring Collision**

A block having a mass of 0.80 kg is given an initial velocity $v_{Ⓐ} = 1.2$ m/s to the right and collides with a spring whose mass is negligible and whose force constant is $k = 50$ N/m as shown in Figure 8.11.

(A) Assuming the surface to be frictionless, calculate the maximum compression of the spring after the collision.

SOLUTION

Conceptualize   The various parts of Figure 8.11 help us imagine what the block will do in this situation. All motion takes place in a horizontal plane, so we do not need to consider changes in gravitational potential energy.

Figure 8.11   (Example 8.8) A block sliding on a smooth, horizontal surface collides with a light spring. (a) Initially, the mechanical energy is all kinetic energy. (b) The mechanical energy is the sum of the kinetic energy of the block and the elastic potential energy in the spring. (c) The energy is entirely potential energy. (d) The energy is transformed back to the kinetic energy of the block. The total energy of the system remains constant throughout the motion.

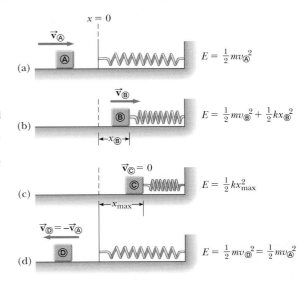

Categorize   We identify the system to be the block and the spring. The block–spring system is isolated with no non-conservative forces acting.

Analyze   Before the collision, when the block is at Ⓐ, it has kinetic energy and the spring is uncompressed, so the elastic potential energy stored in the system is zero. Therefore, the total mechanical energy of the system before the collision is just $\frac{1}{2}mv_Ⓐ^2$. After the collision, when the block is at Ⓒ, the spring is fully compressed; now the block is at rest and so has zero kinetic energy. The elastic potential energy stored in the system, however, has its maximum value $\frac{1}{2}kx^2 = \frac{1}{2}kx_{max}^2$ where the origin of coordinates $x = 0$ is chosen to be the equilibrium position of the spring and x_{max} is the maximum compression of the spring, which in this case happens to be $x_Ⓒ$. The total mechanical energy of the system is conserved because no nonconservative forces act on objects within the isolated system.

Write a conservation of mechanical energy equation:

$$K_Ⓒ + U_{sⓒ} = K_Ⓐ + U_{sⒶ}$$

$$0 + \tfrac{1}{2}kx_{max}^2 = \tfrac{1}{2}mv_Ⓐ^2 + 0$$

Solve for x_{max} and evaluate:

$$x_{max} = \sqrt{\frac{m}{k}}\,v_Ⓐ = \sqrt{\frac{0.80\ \text{kg}}{50\ \text{N/m}}}(1.2\ \text{m/s}) = \boxed{0.15\ \text{m}}$$

(B) Suppose a constant force of kinetic friction acts between the block and the surface, with $\mu_k = 0.50$. If the speed of the block at the moment it collides with the spring is $v_Ⓐ = 1.2$ m/s, what is the maximum compression $x_Ⓒ$ in the spring?

SOLUTION

Conceptualize   Because of the friction force, we expect the compression of the spring to be smaller than in part (A) because some of the block's kinetic energy is transformed to internal energy in the block and the surface.

Categorize   We identify the system as the block, the surface, and the spring. This system is isolated but now involves a nonconservative force.

Analyze   In this case, the mechanical energy $E_{mech} = K + U_s$ of the system is *not* conserved because a friction force acts on the block. From the particle in equilibrium model in the vertical direction, we see that $n = mg$.

Evaluate the magnitude of the friction force:

$$f_k = \mu_k n = \mu_k mg = 0.50(0.80\ \text{kg})(9.80\ \text{m/s}^2) = 3.9\ \text{N}$$

Write the change in the mechanical energy of the system due to friction as the block is displaced from $x = 0$ to $x_Ⓒ$:

$$\Delta E_{mech} = -f_k x_Ⓒ$$

Substitute the initial and final energies:

$$\Delta E_{mech} = E_f - E_i = (0 + \tfrac{1}{2}kx_Ⓒ^2) - (\tfrac{1}{2}mv_Ⓐ^2 + 0) = -f_k x_Ⓒ$$

Substitute numerical values:

$$\tfrac{1}{2}(50)x_Ⓒ^2 - \tfrac{1}{2}(0.80)(1.2)^2 = -3.9x_Ⓒ$$

$$25x_Ⓒ^2 + 3.9x_Ⓒ - 0.58 = 0$$

Solving the quadratic equation for $x_Ⓒ$ gives $x_Ⓒ = 0.093$ m and $x_Ⓒ = -0.25$ m. The physically meaningful root is $x_Ⓒ = \boxed{0.093\ \text{m}}$.

Finalize   The negative root does not apply to this situation because the block must be to the right of the origin (positive value of x) when it comes to rest. Notice that the value of 0.093 m is less than the distance obtained in the frictionless case of part (A) as we expected.

EXAMPLE 8.9   **Connected Blocks in Motion**

Two blocks are connected by a light string that passes over a frictionless pulley as shown in Figure 8.12. The block of mass m_1 lies on a horizontal surface and is connected to a spring of force constant k. The system is released from rest when the spring is unstretched. If the hanging block of mass m_2 falls a distance h before coming to rest, calculate the coefficient of kinetic friction between the block of mass m_1 and the surface.

SOLUTION

Conceptualize   The key word *rest* appears twice in the problem statement. This word suggests that the configurations of the system associated with rest are good candidates for the initial and final configurations because the kinetic energy of the system is zero for these configurations.

Figure 8.12   (Example 8.9) As the hanging block moves from its highest elevation to its lowest, the system loses gravitational potential energy but gains elastic potential energy in the spring. Some mechanical energy is transformed to internal energy because of friction between the sliding block and the surface.

Categorize   In this situation, the system consists of the two blocks, the spring, and the Earth. The system is isolated with a nonconservative force acting. We also model the sliding block as a particle in equilibrium in the vertical direction, leading to $n = m_1 g$.

Analyze   We need to consider two forms of potential energy for the system, gravitational and elastic: $\Delta U_g = U_{gf} - U_{gi}$ is the change in the system's gravitational potential energy, and $\Delta U_s = U_{sf} - U_{si}$ is the change in the system's elastic potential energy. The change in the gravitational potential energy of the system is associated with only the falling block because the vertical coordinate of the horizontally sliding block does not change. The initial and final kinetic energies of the system are zero, so $\Delta K = 0$.

Write the change in mechanical energy for the system:

$$(1) \quad \Delta E_{mech} = \Delta U_g + \Delta U_s$$

Use Equation 8.16 to find the change in mechanical energy in the system due to friction between the horizontally sliding block and the surface, noticing that as the hanging block falls a distance h, the horizontally moving block moves the same distance h to the right:

$$(2) \quad \Delta E_{mech} = -f_k h = -(\mu_k n)h = -\mu_k m_1 g h$$

Evaluate the change in gravitational potential energy of the system, choosing the configuration with the hanging block at the lowest position to represent zero potential energy:

$$(3) \quad \Delta U_g = U_{gf} - U_{gi} = 0 - m_2 g h$$

Evaluate the change in the elastic potential energy of the system:

$$(4) \quad \Delta U_s = U_{sf} - U_{si} = \tfrac{1}{2}kh^2 - 0$$

Substitute Equations (2), (3), and (4) into Equation (1):

$$-\mu_k m_1 g h = -m_2 g h + \tfrac{1}{2}kh^2$$

Solve for μ_k:

$$\mu_k = \frac{m_2 g - \tfrac{1}{2}kh}{m_1 g}$$

Finalize   This setup represents a method of measuring the coefficient of kinetic friction between an object and some surface.

8.5   Power

Consider Conceptual Example 7.7 again, which involved rolling a refrigerator up a ramp into a truck. Suppose the man is not convinced that the work is the same regardless of the ramp's length and sets up a long ramp with a gentle rise. Although he does the same amount of work as someone using a shorter ramp, he takes longer to do the work because he has to move the refrigerator over a greater distance. Although the work done on both ramps is the same, there is *something* different about the tasks: the *time interval* during which the work is done.

The time rate of energy transfer is called the **instantaneous power** $\mathcal{P}$ and is defined as follows:

$$\mathcal{P} \equiv \frac{dE}{dt} \qquad (8.18)$$ ◀ Definition of power

We will focus on work as the energy transfer method in this discussion, but keep in mind that the notion of power is valid for *any* means of energy transfer discussed in Section 8.1. If an external force is applied to an object (which we model as a particle) and if the work done by this force on the object in the time interval Δt is W, the **average power** during this interval is

$$\mathcal{P}_{\text{avg}} = \frac{W}{\Delta t}$$

Therefore, in Example 7.7, although the same work is done in rolling the refrigerator up both ramps, less power is required for the longer ramp.

In a manner similar to the way we approached the definition of velocity and acceleration, the instantaneous power is the limiting value of the average power as Δt approaches zero:

$$\mathcal{P} = \lim_{\Delta t \to 0} \frac{W}{\Delta t} = \frac{dW}{dt}$$

where we have represented the infinitesimal value of the work done by dW. We find from Equation 7.3 that $dW = \vec{\mathbf{F}} \cdot d\vec{\mathbf{r}}$. Therefore, the instantaneous power can be written

$$\mathcal{P} = \frac{dW}{dt} = \vec{\mathbf{F}} \cdot \frac{d\vec{\mathbf{r}}}{dt} = \vec{\mathbf{F}} \cdot \vec{\mathbf{v}} \tag{8.19}$$

where $\vec{\mathbf{v}} = d\vec{\mathbf{r}}/dt$.

The SI unit of power is joules per second (J/s), also called the **watt** (W) after James Watt:

The watt ▶

$$1 \text{ W} = 1 \text{ J/s} = 1 \text{ kg} \cdot \text{m}^2/\text{s}^3$$

A unit of power in the U.S. customary system is the **horsepower** (hp):

$$1 \text{ hp} = 746 \text{ W}$$

A unit of energy (or work) can now be defined in terms of the unit of power. One **kilowatt-hour** (kWh) is the energy transferred in 1 h at the constant rate of $1 \text{ kW} = 1\,000 \text{ J/s}$. The amount of energy represented by 1 kWh is

$$1 \text{ kWh} = (10^3 \text{ W})(3\,600 \text{ s}) = 3.60 \times 10^6 \text{ J}$$

PITFALL PREVENTION 8.3
W, *W*, and watts

Do not confuse the symbol W for the watt with the italic symbol *W* for work. Also, remember that the watt already represents a rate of energy transfer, so "watts per second" does not make sense. The watt is *the same as* a joule per second.

A kilowatt-hour is a unit of energy, not power. When you pay your electric bill, you are buying energy, and the amount of energy transferred by electrical transmission into a home during the period represented by the electric bill is usually expressed in kilowatt-hours. For example, your bill may state that you used 900 kWh of energy during a month and that you are being charged at the rate of 10¢ per kilowatt-hour. Your obligation is then $90 for this amount of energy. As another example, suppose an electric bulb is rated at 100 W. In 1.00 hour of operation, it would have energy transferred to it by electrical transmission in the amount of $(0.100 \text{ kW})(1.00 \text{ h}) = 0.100 \text{ kWh} = 3.60 \times 10^5 \text{ J}$.

EXAMPLE 8.10 **Power Delivered by an Elevator Motor**

An elevator car (Fig. 8.13a) has a mass of 1 600 kg and is carrying passengers having a combined mass of 200 kg. A constant friction force of 4 000 N retards its motion.

(A) How much power must a motor deliver to lift the elevator car and its passengers at a constant speed of 3.00 m/s?

SOLUTION

Conceptualize   The motor must supply the force of magnitude T that pulls the elevator car upward.

Categorize   The friction force increases the power necessary to lift the elevator. The problem states that the speed of the elevator is constant, which tells us that $a = 0$. We model the elevator as a particle in equilibrium.

Figure 8.13   (Example 8.10) (a) The motor exerts an upward force $\vec{\mathbf{T}}$ on the elevator car. The magnitude of this force is the tension T in the cable connecting the car and motor. The downward forces acting on the car are a friction force $\vec{\mathbf{f}}$ and the gravitational force $\vec{\mathbf{F}}_g = M\vec{\mathbf{g}}$. (b) The free-body diagram for the elevator car.

(a)   (b)

Analyze   The free-body diagram in Figure 8.13b specifies the upward direction as positive. The *total* mass M of the system (car plus passengers) is equal to 1 800 kg.

Apply Newton's second law to the car:
$$\sum F_y = T - f - Mg = 0$$

Solve for T:
$$T = f + Mg$$
$$= 4.00 \times 10^3 \text{ N} + (1.80 \times 10^3 \text{ kg})(9.80 \text{ m/s}^2) = 2.16 \times 10^4 \text{ N}$$

Use Equation 8.19 and that $\vec{\mathbf{T}}$ is in the same direction as $\vec{\mathbf{v}}$ to find the power:
$$\mathcal{P} = \vec{\mathbf{T}} \cdot \vec{\mathbf{v}} = Tv$$
$$= (2.16 \times 10^4 \text{ N})(3.00 \text{ m/s}) = \boxed{6.48 \times 10^4 \text{ W}}$$

(B) What power must the motor deliver at the instant the speed of the elevator is v if the motor is designed to provide the elevator car with an upward acceleration of 1.00 m/s²?

SOLUTION

Conceptualize   In this case, the motor must supply the force of magnitude T that pulls the elevator car upward with an increasing speed. We expect that more power will be required to do that than in part (A) because the motor must now perform the additional task of accelerating the car.

Categorize   In this case, we model the elevator car as a particle under a net force because it is accelerating.

Analyze   Apply Newton's second law to the car:
$$\sum F_y = T - f - Mg = Ma$$

Solve for T:
$$T = M(a + g) + f$$
$$= (1.80 \times 10^3 \text{ kg})(1.00 \text{ m/s}^2 + 9.80 \text{ m/s}^2) + 4.00 \times 10^3 \text{ N}$$
$$= 2.34 \times 10^4 \text{ N}$$

Use Equation 8.19 to obtain the required power:
$$\mathcal{P} = Tv = \boxed{(2.34 \times 10^4 \text{ N})v}$$

where v is the instantaneous speed of the car in meters per second.

Finalize   To compare with part (A), let $v = 3.00$ m/s, giving a power of
$$\mathcal{P} = (2.34 \times 10^4 \text{ N})(3.00 \text{ m/s}) = 7.02 \times 10^4 \text{ W}$$

which is larger than the power found in part (A), as expected.

Summary

DEFINITIONS

A **nonisolated system** is one for which energy crosses the boundary of the system. An **isolated system** is one for which no energy crosses the boundary of the system.

The **instantaneous power** $\mathcal{P}$ is defined as the time rate of energy transfer:

$$\mathcal{P} \equiv \frac{dE}{dt} \qquad \textbf{(8.18)}$$

CONCEPTS AND PRINCIPLES

For a nonisolated system, we can equate the change in the total energy stored in the system to the sum of all the transfers of energy across the system boundary, which is a statement of **conservation of energy.** For an isolated system, the total energy is constant.

If a system is isolated and if no nonconservative forces are acting on objects inside the system, the total mechanical energy of the system is constant:

$$K_f + U_f = K_i + U_i \qquad \textbf{(8.10)}$$

If nonconservative forces (such as friction) act between objects inside a system, mechanical energy is not conserved. In these situations, the difference between the total final mechanical energy and the total initial mechanical energy of the system equals the energy transformed to internal energy by the nonconservative forces.

If a friction force acts within an isolated system, the mechanical energy of the system is reduced and the appropriate equation to be applied is

$$\Delta E_{\text{mech}} = \Delta K + \Delta U = -f_k d \qquad \textbf{(8.16)}$$

If a friction force acts within a nonisolated system, the appropriate equation to be applied is

$$\Delta E_{\text{mech}} = -f_k d + \sum W_{\text{other forces}} \qquad \textbf{(8.17)}$$

ANALYSIS MODELS FOR PROBLEM-SOLVING

Nonisolated System (Energy). The most general statement describing the behavior of a nonisolated system is the **conservation of energy equation:**

$$\Delta E_{\text{system}} = \sum T \qquad \textbf{(8.1)}$$

Including the types of energy storage and energy transfer that we have discussed gives

$$\Delta K + \Delta U + \Delta E_{\text{int}} = W + Q + T_{\text{MW}} + T_{\text{MT}} + T_{\text{ET}} + T_{\text{ER}} \quad \textbf{(8.2)}$$

For a specific problem, this equation is generally reduced to a smaller number of terms by eliminating the terms that are not appropriate to the situation.

Isolated System (Energy). The total energy of an isolated system is conserved, so

$$\Delta E_{\text{system}} = 0 \qquad \textbf{(8.9)}$$

If no nonconservative forces act within the isolated system, the mechanical energy of the system is conserved, so

$$\Delta E_{\text{mech}} = 0 \qquad \textbf{(8.8)}$$

Questions

☐ denotes answer available in *Student Solutions Manual/Study Guide;* **O** denotes objective question

1. Does everything have energy? Give reasons for your answer.

2. **O** A pile driver is a device used to drive posts into the Earth by repeatedly dropping a heavy object on them. Assume the object is dropped from the same height each time. By what factor does the energy of the pile driver–Earth system change when the mass of the object being dropped is doubled? (a) $\frac{1}{2}$ (b) 1: the energy is the same (c) 2 (d) 4

3. **O** A curving children's slide is installed next to a backyard swimming pool. Two children climb to a platform at the top of the slide. The smaller child hops off to jump straight down into the pool and the larger child releases herself at the top of the frictionless slide. **(i)** Upon reaching the water, compared with the larger child, is the kinetic energy of the smaller child (a) greater, (b) less, or (c) equal? **(ii)** Upon reaching the water, compared with the larger child, is the speed of the smaller child (a) greater, (b) less, or (c) equal? **(iii)** During the motions from the platform to the water, compared with the larger child, is the average acceleration of the smaller child (a) greater, (b) less, or (c) equal?

4. **O** (a) Can an object–Earth system have kinetic energy and not gravitational potential energy? (b) Can it have gravitational potential energy and not kinetic energy? (c) Can it have both types of energy at the same moment? (d) Can it have neither?

5. **O** A ball of clay falls freely to the hard floor. It does not bounce noticeably, but very quickly comes to rest. What then has happened to the energy the ball had while it was falling? (a) It has been used up in producing the downward motion. (b) It has been transformed back into potential energy. (c) It has been transferred into the ball by heat. (d) It is in the ball and floor (and walls) as energy of invisible molecular motion. (e) Most of it went into sound.

6. **O** You hold a slingshot at arm's length, pull the light elastic band back to your chin, and release it to launch a pebble horizontally with speed 200 cm/s. With the same procedure, you fire a bean with speed 600 cm/s. What is the ratio of the mass of the bean to the mass of the pebble? (a) $\frac{1}{9}$ (b) $\frac{1}{3}$ (c) $1/\sqrt{3}$ (d) 1 (e) $\sqrt{3}$ (f) 3 (g) 9

7. One person drops a ball from the top of a building while another person at the bottom observes its motion. Will these two people agree on the value of the gravitational potential energy of the ball–Earth system? On the change in potential energy? On the kinetic energy?

8. In Chapter 7, the work–kinetic energy theorem, $W_{net} = \Delta K$, was introduced. This equation states that work done on a system appears as a change in kinetic energy. It is a special-case equation, valid if there are no changes in any other type of energy such as potential or internal. Give some examples in which work is done on a system but the change in energy of the system is not a change in kinetic energy.

9. You ride a bicycle. In what sense is your bicycle solar-powered?

10. A bowling ball is suspended from the ceiling of a lecture hall by a strong cord. The ball is drawn away from its equilibrium position and released from rest at the tip of the demonstrator's nose as shown in Figure Q8.10. The demonstrator remains stationary. Explain why the ball does not strike her on its return swing. Would this demonstrator be safe if the ball were given a push from its starting position at her nose?

Figure Q8.10

11. A block is connected to a spring that is suspended from the ceiling. Assuming the block is set into vertical motion and air resistance is ignored, describe the energy transformations that occur within the system consisting of the block, Earth, and spring.

12. **O** In a laboratory model of cars skidding to a stop, data are measured for six trials. Each of three blocks is launched at two different initial speeds v_i and slides across a level table as it comes to rest. The blocks have equal masses but differ in roughness and so have different coefficients of kinetic friction μ_k with the table. Rank the following cases (a) through (f) according to the stopping distance, from largest to smallest. If the stopping distance is the same in two cases, give them equal rank. (a) $v_i = 1$ m/s, $\mu_k = 0.2$ (b) $v_i = 1$ m/s, $\mu_k = 0.4$ (c) $v_i = 1$ m/s, $\mu_k = 0.8$ (d) $v_i = 2$ m/s, $\mu_k = 0.2$ (e) $v_i = 2$ m/s, $\mu_k = 0.4$ (f) $v_i = 2$ m/s, $\mu_k = 0.8$

13. Can a force of static friction do work? If not, why not? If so, give an example.

14. Describe human-made devices designed to produce each of the following energy transfers or transformations. Whenever you can, describe also a natural process in which the energy process occurs. Give details to defend your choices, such as identifying the system and identifying other output energy if the process has limited efficiency. (a) Chemical potential energy transforms into internal energy. (b) Energy transferred by electrical transmission becomes gravitational potential energy. (c) Elastic potential energy transfers out of a system by heat. (d) Energy transferred by mechanical waves does work on a system. (e) Energy carried by electromagnetic waves becomes kinetic energy in a system.

15. In the general conservation of energy equation, state which terms predominate in describing each of the following devices and processes. For a process going on continuously, you may consider what happens in a 10-s time interval. State which terms in the equation represent original and final forms of energy, which would be inputs,

and which would be outputs. (a) a slingshot firing a pebble (b) a fire burning (c) a portable radio operating (d) a car braking to a stop (e) the surface of the sun shining visibly (f) a person jumping up onto a chair

16. O At the bottom of an air track tilted at angle θ, a glider of mass m is given a push to make it coast a distance d up the slope as it slows down and stops. Then the glider comes back down the track to its starting point. Now the experiment is repeated with the same original speed but with a second identical glider set on top of the first. The airflow is strong enough to support the stacked pair of gliders so that they move freely over the track. Static friction holds the second glider stationary relative to the first glider throughout the motion. The coefficient of static friction between the two gliders is μ_s. What is the change in mechanical energy of the two-glider–Earth system in the up- and downslope motion after the pair of gliders is released? Choose one. (a) $-2md$ (b) $-2\mu_s gd$ (c) $-2\mu_s md$ (d) $-2\mu_s mg$ (e) $-2mg$ cos θ (f) $-2mgd$ cos θ (g) $-2\mu_s mgd$ cos θ (h) $-4\mu_s mgd$ cos θ (i) $-\mu_s mgd$ cos θ (j) $-2\mu_s mgd$ sin θ (k) 0 (l) $+2\mu_s mgd$ cos θ

17. A car salesperson claims that a souped-up 300-hp engine is a necessary option in a compact car in place of the conventional 130-hp engine. Suppose you intend to drive the car within speed limits ($\leq$ 65 mi/h) on flat terrain. How would you counter this sales pitch?

Problems

WebAssign The Problems from this chapter may be assigned online in WebAssign.

ThomsonNOW™ Sign in at **www.thomsonedu.com** and go to ThomsonNOW to assess your understanding of this chapter's topics with additional quizzing and conceptual questions.

1, 2, 3 denotes straightforward, intermediate, challenging; ☐ denotes full solution available in *Student Solutions Manual/Study Guide;* ▲ denotes coached solution with hints available at **www.thomsonedu.com;** denotes developing symbolic reasoning; ● denotes asking for qualitative reasoning; ♠ denotes computer useful in solving problem

Section 8.1 The Nonisolated System: Conservation of Energy

1. For each of the following systems and time intervals, write the appropriate reduced version of Equation 8.2, the conservation of energy equation. (a) the heating coils in your toaster during the first five seconds after you turn the toaster on (b) your automobile, from just before you fill it with gas until you pull away from the gas station at 10 mi/h (c) your body while you sit quietly and eat a peanut butter and jelly sandwich for lunch (d) your home during five minutes of a sunny afternoon while the temperature in the home remains fixed.

Section 8.2 The Isolated System

2. At 11:00 a.m. on September 7, 2001, more than one million British schoolchildren jumped up and down for 1 min. The curriculum focus of the "giant jump" was on earthquakes, but it was integrated with many other topics, such as exercise, geography, cooperation, testing hypotheses, and setting world records. Students built their own seismographs that registered local effects. (a) Find the energy converted into mechanical energy in the experiment. Assume 1 050 000 children of average mass 36.0 kg jump 12 times each, raising their centers of mass by 25.0 cm each time and briefly resting between one jump and the next. The free-fall acceleration in Britain is 9.81 m/s^2. (b) Most of the mechanical energy is converted very rapidly into internal energy within the bodies of the students and the floors of the school buildings. Of the energy that propagates into the ground, most produces high-frequency "microtremor" vibrations that are rapidly damped and cannot travel far. Assume 0.01% of the energy is carried away by a long-range seismic wave. The magnitude of an earthquake on the Richter scale is given by

$$M = \frac{\log E - 4.8}{1.5}$$

where E is the seismic wave energy in joules. According to this model, what is the magnitude of the demonstration quake? It did not register above background noise overseas or on the seismograph of the Wolverton Seismic Vault, Hampshire.

3. A bead slides without friction around a loop-the-loop (Fig. P8.3). The bead is released from a height $h = 3.50R$. (a) What is the bead's speed at point Ⓐ? (b) How large is the normal force on the bead if its mass is 5.00 g?

Figure P8.3

4. A particle of mass $m = 5.00$ kg is released from point Ⓐ and slides on the frictionless track shown in Figure P8.4. Determine (a) the particle's speed at points Ⓑ and Ⓒ and (b) the net work done by the gravitational force as the particle moves from Ⓐ to Ⓒ.

Figure P8.4

5. A block of mass 0.250 kg is placed on top of a light vertical spring of force constant 5 000 N/m and pushed downward so that the spring is compressed by 0.100 m. After the block is released from rest, it travels upward and then leaves the spring. To what maximum height above the point of release does it rise?

6. A circus trapeze consists of a bar suspended by two parallel ropes, each of length ℓ, allowing performers to swing in a vertical circular arc (Figure P8.6). Suppose a performer with mass m holds the bar and steps off an elevated platform, starting from rest with the ropes at an angle θ_i with respect to the vertical. Assume the size of the performer's body is small compared to the length ℓ, she does not pump the trapeze to swing higher, and air resistance is negligible. (a) Show that when the ropes make an angle θ with the vertical, the performer must exert a force

$$mg(3 \cos \theta - 2 \cos \theta_i)$$

so as to hang on. (b) Determine the angle θ_i for which the force needed to hang on at the bottom of the swing is twice as large as the gravitational force exerted on the performer.

Figure P8.6

7. Two objects are connected by a light string passing over a light, frictionless pulley as shown in Figure P8.7. The object of mass 5.00 kg is released from rest. Using the isolated system model, (a) determine the speed of the 3.00-kg object just as the 5.00-kg object hits the ground. (b) Find the maximum height to which the 3.00-kg object rises.

Figure P8.7 Problems 7 and 8.

8. Two objects are connected by a light string passing over a light, frictionless pulley as shown in Figure P8.7. The object of mass m_1 is released from rest at height h. Using the isolated system model, (a) determine the speed of m_2 just as m_1 hits the ground. (b) Find the maximum height to which m_2 rises.

9. A light, rigid rod is 77.0 cm long. Its top end is pivoted on a low-friction horizontal axle. The rod hangs straight down at rest with a small massive ball attached to its bot-

tom end. You strike the ball, suddenly giving it a horizontal velocity so that it swings around in a full circle. What minimum speed at the bottom is required to make the ball go over the top of the circle?

10. A 20.0-kg cannonball is fired from a cannon with muzzle speed of 1 000 m/s at an angle of 37.0° with the horizontal. A second cannonball is fired at an angle of 90.0°. Use the isolated system model to find (a) the maximum height reached by each ball and (b) the total mechanical energy of the ball–Earth system at the maximum height for each ball. Let $y = 0$ at the cannon.

11. A daredevil plans to bungee-jump from a hot-air balloon 65.0 m above a carnival midway (Fig. P8.11). He will use a uniform elastic cord, tied to a harness around his body, to stop his fall at a point 10.0 m above the ground. Model his body as a particle and the cord as having negligible mass and obeying Hooke's law. In a preliminary test, hanging at rest from a 5.00-m length of the cord, the daredevil finds his body weight stretches the cord by 1.50 m. He intends to drop from rest at the point where the top end of a longer section of the cord is attached to the stationary hot-air balloon. (a) What length of cord should he use? (b) What maximum acceleration will he experience?

Figure P8.11 Problems 11 and 46.

12. **Review problem**. The system shown in Figure P8.12 consists of a light, inextensible cord; light, frictionless pulleys; and blocks of equal mass. It is initially held at rest so that the blocks are at the same height above the ground. The blocks are then released. Find the speed of block A at the moment when the vertical separation of the blocks is h.

Figure P8.12

Section 8.3 Situations Involving Kinetic Friction

13. A 40.0-kg box initially at rest is pushed 5.00 m along a rough, horizontal floor with a constant applied horizontal force of 130 N. The coefficient of friction between box and floor is 0.300. Find (a) the work done by the applied force, (b) the increase in internal energy in the box–floor system as a result of friction, (c) the work done by the

normal force, (d) the work done by the gravitational force, (e) the change in kinetic energy of the box, and (f) the final speed of the box.

14. A 2.00-kg block is attached to a spring of force constant 500 N/m as shown in Active Figure 7.9. The block is pulled 5.00 cm to the right of equilibrium and released from rest. Find the speed the block has as it passes through equilibrium if (a) the horizontal surface is frictionless and (b) the coefficient of friction between block and surface is 0.350.

15. A crate of mass 10.0 kg is pulled up a rough incline with an initial speed of 1.50 m/s. The pulling force is 100 N parallel to the incline, which makes an angle of 20.0° with the horizontal. The coefficient of kinetic friction is 0.400, and the crate is pulled 5.00 m. (a) How much work is done by the gravitational force on the crate? (b) Determine the increase in internal energy of the crate–incline system owing to friction. (c) How much work is done by the 100-N force on the crate? (d) What is the change in kinetic energy of the crate? (e) What is the speed of the crate after being pulled 5.00 m?

16. ● A block of mass m is on a horizontal surface with which its coefficient of kinetic friction is μ_k. The block is pushed against the free end of a light spring with force constant k, compressing the spring by distance d. Then the block is released from rest so that the spring fires the block across the surface. Of the possible expressions (a) through (k) listed below for the speed of the block after it has slid over distance d, (i) which cannot be true because they are dimensionally incorrect? (ii) Of those remaining, which give(s) an incorrect result in the limit as k becomes very large? (iii) Of those remaining, which give(s) an incorrect result in the limit as μ_k goes to zero? (iv) Of those remaining, which can you rule out for other reasons you specify? (v) Which expression is correct? (vi) Evaluate the speed in the case $m = 250$ g, $\mu_k = 0.600$, $k = 18.0$ N/m, and $d = 12.0$ cm. You will need to explain your answer. (a) $(kd^2 - \mu_k mgd)^{1/2}$ (b) $(kd^2/m - \mu_k g)^{1/2}$ (c) $(kd/m - 2\mu_k gd)^{1/2}$ (d) $(kd^2/m - gd)^{1/2}$ (e) $(kd^2/m - \mu_k^2 gd)^{1/2}$ (f) $kd^2/m - \mu_k gd$ (g) $(\mu_k kd^2/m - gd)^{1/2}$ (h) $(kd^2/m - 2\mu_k gd)^{1/2}$ (i) $(\mu_k gd - kd^2/m)^{1/2}$ (j) $(gd - \mu_k gd)^{1/2}$ (k) $(kd^2/m + \mu_k gd)^{1/2}$

17. ▲ A sled of mass m is given a kick on a frozen pond. The kick imparts to it an initial speed of 2.00 m/s. The coefficient of kinetic friction between sled and ice is 0.100. Use energy considerations to find the distance the sled moves before it stops.

Section 8.4 Changes in Mechanical Energy for Nonconservative Forces

18. ● At time t_i, the kinetic energy of a particle is 30.0 J and the potential energy of the system to which it belongs is 10.0 J. At some later time t_f, the kinetic energy of the particle is 18.0 J. (a) If only conservative forces act on the particle, what are the potential energy and the total energy at time t_f? (b) If the potential energy of the system at time t_f is 5.00 J, are any nonconservative forces acting on the particle? Explain.

19. ▲ The coefficient of friction between the 3.00-kg block and the surface in Figure P8.19 is 0.400. The system starts from rest. What is the speed of the 5.00-kg ball when it has fallen 1.50 m?

3.00 kg

5.00 kg

Figure P8.19

20. In her hand, a softball pitcher swings a ball of mass 0.250 kg around a vertical circular path of radius 60.0 cm before releasing it from her hand. The pitcher maintains a component of force on the ball of constant magnitude 30.0 N in the direction of motion around the complete path. The speed of the ball at the top of the circle is 15.0 m/s. If the pitcher releases the ball at the bottom of the circle, what is its speed upon release?

21. A 5.00-kg block is set into motion up an inclined plane with an initial speed of 8.00 m/s (Fig. P8.21). The block comes to rest after traveling 3.00 m along the plane, which is inclined at an angle of 30.0° to the horizontal. For this motion, determine (a) the change in the block's kinetic energy, (b) the change in the potential energy of the block–Earth system, and (c) the friction force exerted on the block (assumed to be constant). (d) What is the coefficient of kinetic friction?

$v_i = 8.00$ m/s

3.00 m

30.0°

Figure P8.21

22. ● An 80.0-kg skydiver jumps out of a balloon at an altitude of 1 000 m and opens the parachute at an altitude of 200 m. (a) Assuming the total retarding force on the diver is constant at 50.0 N with the parachute closed and constant at 3 600 N with the parachute open, find the skydiver's speed when he lands on the ground. (b) Do you think the skydiver will be injured? Explain. (c) At what height should the parachute be opened so that the final speed of the skydiver when he hits the ground is 5.00 m/s? (d) How realistic is the assumption that the total retarding force is constant? Explain.

23. A toy cannon uses a spring to project a 5.30-g soft rubber ball. The spring is originally compressed by 5.00 cm and has a force constant of 8.00 N/m. When the cannon is fired, the ball moves 15.0 cm through the horizontal barrel of the cannon and the barrel exerts a constant friction force of 0.032 0 N on the ball. (a) With what speed does the projectile leave the barrel of the cannon? (b) At what point does the ball have maximum speed? (c) What is this maximum speed?

24. A particle moves along a line where the potential energy of its system depends on its position r as graphed in Figure P8.24. In the limit as r increases without bound, $U(r)$ approaches +1 J. (a) Identify each equilibrium position for this particle. Indicate whether each is a point of stable, unstable, or neutral equilibrium. (b) The particle will

be bound if the total energy of the system is in what range? Now suppose the system has energy −3 J. Determine (c) the range of positions where the particle can be found, (d) its maximum kinetic energy, (e) the location where it has maximum kinetic energy, and (f) the *binding energy* of the system, that is, the additional energy it would have to be given for the particle to move out to $r \rightarrow \infty$.

Figure P8.24

25. A 1.50-kg object is held 1.20 m above a relaxed, massless vertical spring with a force constant of 320 N/m. The object is dropped onto the spring. (a) How far does the object compress the spring? (b) **What If?** How far does the object compress the spring if the same experiment is performed on the Moon, where $g = 1.63$ m/s²? (c) **What If?** Repeat part (a), but this time assume a constant air-resistance force of 0.700 N acts on the object during its motion.

26. A boy in a wheelchair (total mass 47.0 kg) wins a race with a skateboarder. The boy has speed 1.40 m/s at the crest of a slope 2.60 m high and 12.4 m long. At the bottom of the slope his speed is 6.20 m/s. Assume air resistance and rolling resistance can be modeled as a constant friction force of 41.0 N. Find the work he did in pushing forward on his wheels during the downhill ride.

27. A uniform board of length L is sliding along a smooth (frictionless) horizontal plane as shown in Figure P8.27a. The board then slides across the boundary with a rough horizontal surface. The coefficient of kinetic friction between the board and the second surface is μ_k. (a) Find the acceleration of the board at the moment its front end has traveled a distance x beyond the boundary. (b) The board stops at the moment its back end reaches the boundary as shown in Figure P8.27b. Find the initial speed v of the board.

(a)

(b)

Figure P8.27

Section 8.5 Power

28. The electric motor of a model train accelerates the train from rest to 0.620 m/s in 21.0 ms. The total mass of the train is 875 g. Find the average power delivered to the train during the acceleration.

29. ▲ A 700-N Marine in basic training climbs a 10.0-m vertical rope at a constant speed in 8.00 s. What is his power output?

30. Columnist Dave Barry poked fun at the name "The Grand Cities" adopted by Grand Forks, North Dakota, and East Grand Forks, Minnesota. Residents of the prairie towns then named their next municipal building for him. At the Dave Barry Lift Station No. 16, untreated sewage is raised vertically by 5.49 m, at the rate of 1 890 000 liters each day. The waste, of density 1 050 kg/m³, enters and leaves the pump at atmospheric pressure, through pipes of equal diameter. (a) Find the output mechanical power of the lift station. (b) Assume an electric motor continuously operating with average power 5.90 kW runs the pump. Find its efficiency.

31. Make an order-of-magnitude estimate of the power a car engine contributes to speeding the car up to highway speed. For concreteness, consider your own car if you use one. In your solution, state the physical quantities you take as data and the values you measure or estimate for them. The mass of the vehicle is given in the owner's manual. If you do not wish to estimate for a car, consider a bus or truck that you specify.

32. A 650-kg elevator starts from rest. It moves upward for 3.00 s with constant acceleration until it reaches its cruising speed of 1.75 m/s. (a) What is the average power of the elevator motor during this time interval? (b) How does this power compare with the motor power when the elevator moves at its cruising speed?

33. An energy-efficient lightbulb, taking in 28.0 W of power, can produce the same level of brightness as a conventional lightbulb operating at power 100 W. The lifetime of the energy-efficient lightbulb is 10 000 h and its purchase price is $17.0, whereas the conventional lightbulb has lifetime 750 h and costs $0.420 per bulb. Determine the total savings obtained by using one energy-efficient lightbulb over its lifetime as opposed to using conventional lightbulbs over the same time interval. Assume an energy cost of $0.080 0 per kilowatt-hour.

34. An electric scooter has a battery capable of supplying 120 Wh of energy. If friction forces and other losses account for 60.0% of the energy usage, what altitude change can a rider achieve when driving in hilly terrain if the rider and scooter have a combined weight of 890 N?

35. A loaded ore car has a mass of 950 kg and rolls on rails with negligible friction. It starts from rest and is pulled up a mine shaft by a cable connected to a winch. The shaft is inclined at 30.0° above the horizontal. The car accelerates uniformly to a speed of 2.20 m/s in 12.0 s and then continues at constant speed. (a) What power must the winch motor provide when the car is moving at constant speed? (b) What maximum power must the winch motor provide? (c) What total energy has transferred out of the motor by work by the time the car moves off the end of the track, which is of length 1 250 m?

36. Energy is conventionally measured in Calories as well as in joules. One Calorie in nutrition is one kilocalorie, defined as 1 kcal = 4 186 J. Metabolizing 1 g of fat can release 9.00 kcal. A student decides to try to lose weight by exercising. She plans to run up and down the stairs in a football stadium as fast as she can and as many times as necessary. Is this activity in itself a practical way to lose weight? To evaluate the program, suppose she runs up a flight of 80 steps, each 0.150 m high, in 65.0 s. For simplicity, ignore the energy she uses in coming down (which is small). Assume a typical efficiency for human muscles is 20.0%. This statement means that when your body converts 100 J from metabolizing fat, 20 J goes into doing mechanical work (here, climbing stairs). The remainder goes into extra internal energy. Assume the student's mass is 50.0 kg. (a) How many times must she run the flight of stairs to lose 1 lb of fat? (b) What is her average power output, in watts and in horsepower, as she is running up the stairs?

Additional Problems

37. A skateboarder with his board can be modeled as a particle of mass 76.0 kg, located at his center of mass (which we will study in Chapter 9). As shown in Figure P8.37, the skateboarder starts from rest in a crouching position at one lip of a half-pipe (point Ⓐ). The half-pipe is a dry water channel, forming one half of a cylinder of radius 6.80 m with its axis horizontal. On his descent, the skateboarder moves without friction so that his center of mass moves through one quarter of a circle of radius 6.30 m. (a) Find his speed at the bottom of the half-pipe (point Ⓑ). (b) Find his centripetal acceleration. (c) Find the normal force $n_Ⓑ$ acting on the skateboarder at point Ⓑ. Immediately after passing point Ⓑ, he stands up and raises his arms, lifting his center of mass from 0.500 m to 0.950 m above the concrete (point Ⓒ). To account for the conversion of chemical into mechanical energy, model his legs as doing work by pushing him vertically up, with a constant force equal to the normal force $n_Ⓑ$, over a distance of 0.450 m. (You will be able to solve this problem with a more accurate model in Chapter 11.) (d) What is the work done on the skateboarder's body in this process? Next, the skateboarder glides upward with his center of mass moving in a quarter circle of radius 5.85 m. His body is horizontal when he passes point Ⓓ, the far lip of the half-pipe. (e) Find his speed at this location. At last he goes ballistic, twisting around while his center of mass moves vertically. (f) How high above point Ⓓ does he rise? (g) Over what time interval is he airborne before he touches down, 2.34 m below the level of point Ⓓ? *Caution:* Do not try this stunt yourself without the required skill and protective equipment or in a drainage channel to which you do not have legal access.

Figure P8.37

38. ● **Review problem**. As shown in Figure P8.38, a light string that does not stretch changes from horizontal to vertical as it passes over the edge of a table. The string connects a 3.50-kg block, originally at rest on the horizontal table, 1.20 m above the floor, to a hanging 1.90-kg block, originally 0.900 m above the floor. Neither the surface of the table nor its edge exerts a force of kinetic friction. The blocks start to move with negligible speed. Consider the two blocks plus the Earth as the system. (a) Does the mechanical energy of the system remain constant between the instant of release and the instant before the hanging block hits the floor? (b) Find the speed at which the sliding block leaves the edge of the table. (c) Now suppose the hanging block stops permanently as soon as it reaches the sticky floor. Does the mechanical energy of the system remain constant between the instant of release and the instant before the sliding block hits the floor? (d) Find the impact speed of the sliding block. (e) How long must the string be if it does not go taut while the sliding block is in flight? (f) Would it invalidate your speed calculation if the string does go taut? (g) Even with negligible kinetic friction, the coefficient of static friction between the heavier block and the table is 0.560. Evaluate the force of friction acting on this block before the motion begins. (h) Will the motion begin by itself, or must the experimenter give a little tap to the sliding block to get it started? Are the speed calculations still valid?

Figure P8.38

39. A 4.00-kg particle moves along the x axis. Its position varies with time according to $x = t + 2.0t^3$, where x is in meters and t is in seconds. Find (a) the kinetic energy at any time t, (b) the acceleration of the particle and the force acting on it at time t, (c) the power being delivered to the particle at time t, and (d) the work done on the particle in the interval $t = 0$ to $t = 2.00$ s.

40. ● Heedless of danger, a child leaps onto a pile of old mattresses to use them as a trampoline. His motion between two particular points is described by the energy conservation equation

$$\tfrac{1}{2}(46.0 \text{ kg})(2.40 \text{ m/s})^2 + (46.0 \text{ kg})(9.80 \text{ m/s}^2)(2.80 \text{ m} + x)$$
$$= \tfrac{1}{2}(1.94 \times 10^4 \text{ N/m})x^2$$

(a) Solve the equation for x. (b) Compose the statement of a problem, including data, for which this equation gives the solution. Identify the physical meaning of the value of x.

41. As the driver steps on the gas pedal, a car of mass 1 160 kg accelerates from rest. During the first few seconds of motion, the car's acceleration increases with time according to the expression

$$a = (1.16 \text{ m/s}^3)t - (0.210 \text{ m/s}^4)t^2 + (0.240 \text{ m/s}^5)t^3$$

(a) What work is done on the car by the wheels during the interval from $t = 0$ to $t = 2.50$ s? (b) What is the wheels' output power at the instant $t = 2.50$ s?

42. A 0.400-kg particle slides around a horizontal track. The track has a smooth vertical outer wall forming a circle with a radius of 1.50 m. The particle is given an initial speed of 8.00 m/s. After one revolution, its speed has dropped to 6.00 m/s because of friction with the rough floor of the track. (a) Find the energy transformed from mechanical to internal in the system as a result of friction in one revolution. (b) Calculate the coefficient of kinetic friction. (c) What is the total number of revolutions the particle makes before stopping?

43. A 200-g block is pressed against a spring of force constant 1.40 kN/m until the block compresses the spring 10.0 cm. The spring rests at the bottom of a ramp inclined at 60.0° to the horizontal. Using energy considerations, determine how far up the incline the block moves before it stops (a) if the ramp exerts no friction force on the block and (b) if the coefficient of kinetic friction is 0.400.

44. ● As it plows a parking lot, a snowplow pushes an ever-growing pile of snow in front of it. Suppose a car moving through the air is similarly modeled as a cylinder pushing a growing plug of air in front of it. The originally stationary air is set into motion at the constant speed v of the cylinder as shown in Figure P8.44. In a time interval Δt, a new disk of air of mass Δm must be moved a distance $v \Delta t$ and hence must be given a kinetic energy $\frac{1}{2}(\Delta m)v^2$. Using this model, show that the car's power loss owing to air resistance is $\frac{1}{2}\rho A v^3$ and that the resistive force acting on the car is $\frac{1}{2}\rho A v^2$, where ρ is the density of air. Compare this result with the empirical expression $\frac{1}{2}D\rho A v^2$ for the resistive force.

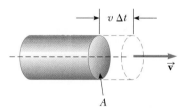

Figure P8.44

45. A windmill such as that shown in the opening photograph for Chapter 7 turns in response to a force of high-speed air resistance, $R = \frac{1}{2}D\rho A v^2$. The power available is $\mathcal{P} = Rv = \frac{1}{2}D\rho\pi r^2 v^3$, where v is the wind speed and we have assumed a circular face for the windmill, of radius r. Take the drag coefficient as $D = 1.00$ and the density of air from the front endpaper of this book. For a home windmill having $r = 1.50$ m, calculate the power available with (a) $v = 8.00$ m/s and (b) $v = 24.0$ m/s. The power delivered to the generator is limited by the efficiency of the system, about 25%. For comparison, a typical U.S. home uses about 3 kW of electric power.

46. ● Starting from rest, a 64.0-kg person bungee jumps from a tethered balloon 65.0 m above the ground (Fig. P8.11). The bungee cord has negligible mass and unstretched length 25.8 m. One end is tied to the basket of the hot-air balloon and the other end to a harness around the person's body. The cord is modeled as a spring that obeys Hooke's law with a spring constant of 81.0 N/m, and the person's body is modeled as a particle. The hot-air balloon does not move. (a) Express the gravitational potential energy of the person–Earth system as a function of the person's variable height y above the ground. (b) Express the elastic potential energy of the cord as a function of y. (c) Express the total potential energy of the person–cord–Earth system as a function of y. (d) Plot a graph of the gravitational, elastic, and total potential energies as functions of y. (e) Assume air resistance is negligible. Determine the minimum height of the person above the ground during his plunge. (f) Does the potential energy graph show any equilibrium position or positions? If so, at what elevations? Are they stable or unstable? (g) Determine the jumper's maximum speed.

47. Consider the block–spring–surface system in part (B) of Example 8.6. (a) At what position x of the block is its speed a maximum? (b) In the **What If?** section of that example, we explored the effects of an increased friction force of 10.0 N. At what position of the block does its maximum speed occur in this situation?

48. ● More than 2 300 years ago the Greek teacher Aristotle wrote the first book called *Physics*. Put into more precise terminology, this passage is from the end of its Section Eta:

> Let $\mathcal{P}$ be the power of an agent causing motion; w, the load moved; d, the distance covered; and Δt, the time interval required. Then (1) a power equal to $\mathcal{P}$ will in an interval of time equal to Δt move $w/2$ a distance $2d$, or (2) it will move $w/2$ the given distance d in the time interval $\Delta t/2$. Also, if (3) the given power $\mathcal{P}$ moves the given load w a distance $d/2$ in time interval $\Delta t/2$, then (4) $\mathcal{P}/2$ will move $w/2$ the given distance d in the given time interval Δt.

(a) Show that Aristotle's proportions are included in the equation $\mathcal{P}\Delta t = bwd$, where b is a proportionality constant. (b) Show that our theory of motion includes this part of Aristotle's theory as one special case. In particular, describe a situation in which it is true, derive the equation representing Aristotle's proportions, and determine the proportionality constant.

49. **Review problem**. The mass of a car is 1 500 kg. The shape of the car's body is such that its aerodynamic drag coefficient is $D = 0.330$ and the frontal area is 2.50 m². Assuming the drag force is proportional to v^2 and ignoring other sources of friction, calculate the power required to maintain a speed of 100 km/h as the car climbs a long hill sloping at 3.20°.

50. A 200-g particle is released from rest at point Ⓐ along the horizontal diameter on the inside of a frictionless, hemispherical bowl of radius $R = 30.0$ cm (Fig. P8.50). Calculate (a) the gravitational potential energy of the particle–Earth system when the particle is at point Ⓐ relative to

Figure P8.50 Problems 50 and 51.

point Ⓑ, (b) the kinetic energy of the particle at point Ⓑ, (c) its speed at point Ⓑ, and (d) its kinetic energy and the potential energy when the particle is at point Ⓒ.

51. ● ▲ **What If?** The particle described in Problem 50 (Fig. P8.50) is released from rest at Ⓐ, and the surface of the bowl is rough. The speed of the particle at Ⓑ is 1.50 m/s. (a) What is its kinetic energy at Ⓑ? (b) How much mechanical energy is transformed into internal energy as the particle moves from Ⓐ to Ⓑ? (c) Is it possible to determine the coefficient of friction from these results in any simple manner? Explain.

52. Assume you attend a state university that was founded as an agricultural college. Close to the center of the campus is a tall silo topped with a hemispherical cap. The cap is frictionless when wet. Someone has balanced a pumpkin at the silo's highest point. The line from the center of curvature of the cap to the pumpkin makes an angle $\theta_i = 0°$ with the vertical. While you happen to be standing nearby in the middle of a rainy night, a breath of wind makes the pumpkin start sliding downward from rest. The pumpkin loses contact with the cap when the line from the center of the hemisphere to the pumpkin makes a certain angle with the vertical. What is this angle?

53. A child's pogo stick (Fig. P8.53) stores energy in a spring with a force constant of 2.50×10^4 N/m. At position Ⓐ ($x_Ⓐ = -0.100$ m), the spring compression is a maximum and the child is momentarily at rest. At position Ⓑ ($x_Ⓑ = 0$), the spring is relaxed and the child is moving upward. At position Ⓒ, the child is again momentarily at rest at the top of the jump. The combined mass of child and pogo stick is 25.0 kg. (a) Calculate the total energy of the child–stick–Earth system, taking both gravitational and elastic potential energies as zero for $x = 0$. (b) Determine $x_Ⓒ$. (c) Calculate the speed of the child at $x = 0$. (d) Determine the value of x for which the kinetic energy of the system is a maximum. (e) Calculate the child's maximum upward speed.

Figure P8.53

54. A 1.00-kg object slides to the right on a surface having a coefficient of kinetic friction 0.250 (Fig. P8.54). The object has a speed of $v_i = 3.00$ m/s when it makes contact with a light spring that has a force constant of 50.0 N/m. The object comes to rest after the spring has been compressed a distance d. The object is then forced toward the left by the spring and continues to move in that direction beyond the spring's unstretched position. Finally, the object comes to rest a distance D to the left of the

unstretched spring. Find (a) the distance of compression d, (b) the speed v at the unstretched position when the object is moving to the left, and (c) the distance D where the object comes to rest.

Figure P8.54

55. A 10.0-kg block is released from point Ⓐ in Figure P8.55. The track is frictionless except for the portion between points Ⓑ and Ⓒ, which has a length of 6.00 m. The block travels down the track, hits a spring of force constant 2 250 N/m, and compresses the spring 0.300 m from its equilibrium position before coming to rest momentarily. Determine the coefficient of kinetic friction between the block and the rough surface between Ⓑ and Ⓒ.

Figure P8.55

56. A uniform chain of length 8.00 m initially lies stretched out on a horizontal table. (a) Assuming the coefficient of static friction between chain and table is 0.600, show that the chain will begin to slide off the table if at least 3.00 m of it hangs over the edge of the table. (b) Determine the speed of the chain as its last link leaves the table, given that the coefficient of kinetic friction between the chain and the table is 0.400.

57. A 20.0-kg block is connected to a 30.0-kg block by a string that passes over a light, frictionless pulley. The 30.0-kg block is connected to a spring that has negligible mass and a force constant of 250 N/m as shown in Figure P8.57. The spring is unstretched when the system is as shown in the figure, and the incline is frictionless. The 20.0-kg block is pulled 20.0 cm down the incline (so that the 30.0-kg block is 40.0 cm above the floor) and released from rest. Find the speed of each block when the 30.0-kg block is 20.0 cm above the floor (that is, when the spring is unstretched).

2 = intermediate;   3 = challenging;   □ = SSM/SG;   ▲ = ThomsonNOW;   ▨ = symbolic reasoning;   ● = qualitative reasoning

Figure P8.57

58. Jane, whose mass is 50.0 kg, needs to swing across a river (having width D) filled with person-eating crocodiles to save Tarzan from danger. She must swing into a wind exerting constant horizontal force $\vec{F}$, on a vine having length L and initially making an angle θ with the vertical (Fig. P8.58). Take $D = 50.0$ m, $F = 110$ N, $L = 40.0$ m, and $\theta = 50.0°$. (a) With what minimum speed must Jane begin her swing to just make it to the other side? (b) Once the rescue is complete, Tarzan and Jane must swing back across the river. With what minimum speed must they begin their swing? Assume Tarzan has a mass of 80.0 kg.

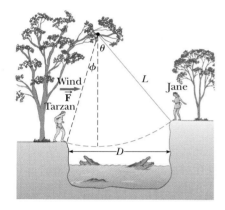

Figure P8.58

59. ● ▲ A block of mass 0.500 kg is pushed against a horizontal spring of negligible mass until the spring is compressed a distance x (Fig. P8.59). The force constant of the spring is 450 N/m. When it is released, the block travels along a frictionless, horizontal surface to point B, the bottom of a vertical circular track of radius $R = 1.00$ m, and continues to move along the track. The speed of the block at the bottom of the track is $v_B = 12.0$ m/s, and the block experiences an average friction force of 7.00 N while sliding up the track. (a) What is x? (b) What speed do you predict for the block at the top of the track? (c) Does the block actually reach the top of the track, or does it fall off before reaching the top?

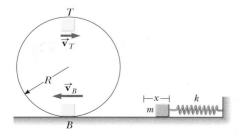

Figure P8.59

60. A ball of mass $m = 300$ g is connected by a strong string of length $L = 80.0$ cm to a pivot and held in place with the string vertical. A wind exerts constant force F to the right on the ball as shown in Figure P8.60. The ball is released from rest. The wind makes it swing up to attain maximum height H above its starting point before it swings down again. (a) Find H as a function of F. Evaluate H (b) for $F = 1.00$ N and (c) for $F = 10.0$ N. How does H behave (d) as F approaches zero (e) and as F approaches infinity? (f) Now consider the equilibrium height of the ball with the wind blowing. Determine it as a function of F. Evaluate the equilibrium height (g) for $F = 10$ N and (h) for F going to infinity.

Figure P8.60

61. A block of mass M rests on a table. It is fastened to the lower end of a light, vertical spring. The upper end of the spring is fastened to a block of mass m. The upper block is pushed down by an additional force $3mg$, so the spring compression is $4mg/k$. In this configuration, the upper block is released from rest. The spring lifts the lower block off the table. In terms of m, what is the greatest possible value for M?

62. A pendulum, comprising a light string of length L and a small sphere, swings in the vertical plane. The string hits a peg located a distance d below the point of suspension (Fig. P8.62). (a) Show that if the sphere is released from a height below that of the peg, it will return to this height after the string strikes the peg. (b) Show that if the pendulum is released from the horizontal position ($\theta = 90°$) and is to swing in a complete circle centered on the peg, the minimum value of d must be $3L/5$.

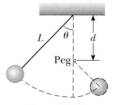

Figure P8.62

63. A ball whirls around in a vertical circle at the end of a string. The other end of the string is fixed at the center of the circle. Assuming the total energy of the ball–Earth system remains constant, show that the tension in the string at the bottom is greater than the tension at the top by six times the weight of the ball.

64. A roller-coaster car is released from rest at the top of the first rise and then moves freely with negligible friction. The roller coaster shown in Figure P8.64 has a circular loop of radius R in a vertical plane. (a) First suppose the

car barely makes it around the loop; at the top of the loop, the riders are upside down and feel weightless. Find the required height of the release point above the bottom of the loop in terms of R. (b) Now assume the release point is at or above the minimum required height. Show that the normal force on the car at the bottom of the loop exceeds the normal force at the top of the loop by six times the weight of the car. The normal force on each rider follows the same rule. Because such a large normal force is dangerous and very uncomfortable for the riders, roller coasters are not built with circular loops in vertical planes. Figure P6.18 and the photograph on page 137 show two actual designs.

Figure P8.64

65. **Review problem**. In 1887 in Bridgeport, Connecticut, C. J. Belknap built the water slide shown in Figure P8.65. A rider on a small sled, of total mass 80.0 kg, pushed off to start at the top of the slide (point Ⓐ) with a speed of 2.50 m/s. The chute was 9.76 m high at the top, 54.3 m long, and 0.51 m wide. Along its length, 725 small wheels made friction negligible. Upon leaving the chute horizontally at its bottom end (point Ⓒ), the rider skimmed across the water of Long Island Sound for as much as 50 m, "skipping along like a flat pebble," before at last coming to rest and swimming ashore, pulling his sled after him. According to *Scientific American*, "The facial expression of novices taking their first adventurous slide is quite remarkable, and the sensations felt are corre-

spondingly novel and peculiar." (a) Find the speed of the sled and rider at point Ⓒ. (b) Model the force of water friction as a constant retarding force acting on a particle. Find the work done by water friction in stopping the sled and rider. (c) Find the magnitude of the force the water exerts on the sled. (d) Find the magnitude of the force the chute exerts on the sled at point Ⓑ. (e) At point Ⓒ, the chute is horizontal but curving in the vertical plane. Assume its radius of curvature is 20.0 m. Find the force the chute exerts on the sled at point Ⓒ.

Figure P8.65

66. Consider the block–spring collision discussed in Example 8.8. (a) For the situation in part (B), in which the surface exerts a friction force on the block, show that the block never arrives back at $x = 0$. (b) What is the maximum value of the coefficient of friction that would allow the block to return to $x = 0$?

Answers to Quick Quizzes

8.1 (a) For the television set, energy enters by electrical transmission (through the power cord). Energy leaves by heat (from hot surfaces into the air), mechanical waves (sound from the speaker), and electromagnetic radiation (from the screen). (b) For the gasoline-powered lawn mower, energy enters by matter transfer (gasoline). Energy leaves by work (on the blades of grass), mechanical waves (sound), and heat (from hot surfaces into the air). (c) For the hand-cranked pencil sharpener, energy enters by work (from your hand turning the crank). Energy leaves by work (done on the pencil), mechanical waves (sound), and heat due to the temperature increase from friction.

8.2 **(i)**, (b). For the block, the friction force from the surface represents an interaction with the environment. **(ii)**, (b). For the surface, the friction force from the block represents an interaction with the environment. **(iii)**, (a). For the block and the surface, the friction force is internal to the system, so there are no interactions with the environment.

8.3 (a). The more massive rock has twice as much gravitational potential energy associated with it compared with that of the lighter rock. Because mechanical energy of an isolated system is conserved, the more massive rock will arrive at the ground with twice as much kinetic energy as the lighter rock.

8.4 $v_1 = v_2 = v_3$. The first and third balls speed up after they are thrown, whereas the second ball initially slows down but then speeds up after reaching its peak. The paths of all three balls are parabolas, and the balls take different time intervals to reach the ground because they have different initial velocities. All three balls, however, have the same speed at the moment they hit the ground because all start with the same kinetic energy and because the ball–Earth system undergoes the same change in gravitational potential energy in all three cases.

8.5 (c). The brakes and the roadway are warmer, so their internal energy has increased. In addition, the sound of the skid represents transfer of energy away by mechanical waves.

A moving bowling ball carries momentum, the topic of this chapter. In the collision between the ball and the pins, momentum is transferred to the pins. (Mark Cooper/Corbis Stock Market)

9 Linear Momentum and Collisions

Consider what happens when a bowling ball strikes a pin, as in the photograph above. The pin is given a large velocity as a result of the collision; consequently, it flies away and hits other pins or is projected toward the backstop. Because the average force exerted on the pin during the collision is large (resulting in a large acceleration), the pin achieves its large velocity very rapidly and experiences the force for a very short time interval.

Although the force and acceleration are large for the pin, they vary in time, making for a complicated situation! One of the main objectives of this chapter is to enable you to understand and analyze such events in a simple way. First, we introduce the concept of *momentum*, which is useful for describing objects in motion. The momentum of an object is related to both its mass and its velocity. The concept of momentum leads us to a second conservation law for an isolated system, that of conservation of momentum. This law is especially useful for treating problems that involve collisions between objects and for analyzing rocket propulsion. This chapter also introduces the concept of the center of mass of a system of particles. We find that the motion of a system of particles can be described by the motion of one representative particle located at the center of mass.

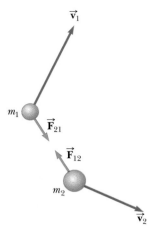

Figure 9.1 Two particles interact with each other. According to Newton's third law, we must have $\vec{\mathbf{F}}_{12} = -\vec{\mathbf{F}}_{21}$.

9.1   Linear Momentum and Its Conservation

In Chapter 8, we studied situations that are difficult to analyze with Newton's laws. We were able to solve problems involving these situations by identifying a system and applying a conservation principle, conservation of energy. Consider another situation in which a 60-kg archer stands on frictionless ice and fires a 0.50-kg arrow horizontally at 50 m/s. From Newton's third law, we know that the force that the bow exerts on the arrow is matched by a force in the opposite direction on the bow (and the archer). This force causes the archer to slide backward on the ice, but with what speed? We cannot answer this question directly using *either* Newton's second law or an energy approach because we do not have enough information.

Despite our inability to solve the archer problem using techniques learned so far, this problem is very simple to solve if we introduce a new quantity that describes motion, *linear momentum*. Let us apply the General Problem-Solving Strategy and *conceptualize* an isolated system of two particles (Fig. 9.1) with masses m_1 and m_2 moving with velocities $\vec{\mathbf{v}}_1$ and $\vec{\mathbf{v}}_2$ at an instant of time. Because the system is isolated, the only force on one particle is that from the other particle, and we can *categorize* this situation as one in which Newton's laws are useful. If a force from particle 1 (for example, a gravitational force) acts on particle 2, there must be a second force—equal in magnitude but opposite in direction—that particle 2 exerts on particle 1. That is, the forces on the particles form a Newton's third law action–reaction pair, and $\vec{\mathbf{F}}_{12} = -\vec{\mathbf{F}}_{21}$. We can express this condition as

$$\vec{\mathbf{F}}_{21} + \vec{\mathbf{F}}_{12} = 0$$

Let us further *analyze* this situation by incorporating Newton's second law. Over some time interval, the interacting particles in the system accelerate in response to the force. Therefore, replacing the force on each particle with $m\vec{\mathbf{a}}$ for the particle gives

$$m_1 \vec{\mathbf{a}}_1 + m_2 \vec{\mathbf{a}}_2 = 0$$

Now we replace each acceleration with its definition from Equation 4.5:

$$m_1 \frac{d\vec{\mathbf{v}}_1}{dt} + m_2 \frac{d\vec{\mathbf{v}}_2}{dt} = 0$$

If the masses m_1 and m_2 are constant, we can bring them inside the derivative operation, which gives

$$\frac{d(m_1\vec{\mathbf{v}}_1)}{dt} + \frac{d(m_2\vec{\mathbf{v}}_2)}{dt} = 0$$

$$\frac{d}{dt}(m_1\vec{\mathbf{v}}_1 + m_2\vec{\mathbf{v}}_2) = 0 \tag{9.1}$$

To *finalize* this discussion, notice that the derivative of the sum $m_1\vec{\mathbf{v}}_1 + m_2\vec{\mathbf{v}}_2$ with respect to time is zero. Consequently, this sum must be constant. We learn from this discussion that the quantity $m\vec{\mathbf{v}}$ for a particle is important in that the sum of these quantities for an isolated system of particles is conserved. We call this quantity *linear momentum*:

◄ **Definition of linear momentum of a particle**

The **linear momentum** of a particle or an object that can be modeled as a particle of mass m moving with a velocity $\vec{\mathbf{v}}$ is defined to be the product of the mass and velocity of the particle:

$$\vec{\mathbf{p}} \equiv m\vec{\mathbf{v}} \tag{9.2}$$

Linear momentum is a vector quantity because it equals the product of a scalar quantity m and a vector quantity $\vec{\mathbf{v}}$. Its direction is along $\vec{\mathbf{v}}$, it has dimensions ML/T, and its SI unit is kg·m/s.

If a particle is moving in an arbitrary direction, $\vec{\mathbf{p}}$ has three components, and Equation 9.2 is equivalent to the component equations

$$p_x = mv_x \qquad p_y = mv_y \qquad p_z = mv_z$$

As you can see from its definition, the concept of momentum[1] provides a quantitative distinction between heavy and light particles moving at the same velocity. For example, the momentum of a bowling ball is much greater than that of a tennis ball moving at the same speed. Newton called the product $m\vec{\mathbf{v}}$ *quantity of motion*; this term is perhaps a more graphic description than our present-day word *momentum*, which comes from the Latin word for movement.

Using Newton's second law of motion, we can relate the linear momentum of a particle to the resultant force acting on the particle. We start with Newton's second law and substitute the definition of acceleration:

$$\sum \vec{\mathbf{F}} = m\vec{\mathbf{a}} = m\,\frac{d\vec{\mathbf{v}}}{dt}$$

In Newton's second law, the mass m is assumed to be constant. Therefore, we can bring m inside the derivative operation to give us

$$\sum \vec{\mathbf{F}} = \frac{d(m\vec{\mathbf{v}})}{dt} = \frac{d\vec{\mathbf{p}}}{dt} \qquad (9.3)$$

◀ Newton's second law for a particle

This equation shows that **the time rate of change of the linear momentum of a particle is equal to the net force acting on the particle.**

This alternative form of Newton's second law is the form in which Newton presented the law, and it is actually more general than the form introduced in Chapter 5. In addition to situations in which the velocity vector varies with time, we can use Equation 9.3 to study phenomena in which the mass changes. For example, the mass of a rocket changes as fuel is burned and ejected from the rocket. We cannot use $\sum \vec{\mathbf{F}} = m\vec{\mathbf{a}}$ to analyze rocket propulsion; we must use Equation 9.3, as we will show in Section 9.8.

Quick Quiz 9.1 Two objects have equal kinetic energies. How do the magnitudes of their momenta compare? (a) $p_1 < p_2$ (b) $p_1 = p_2$ (c) $p_1 > p_2$ (d) not enough information to tell

---

Quick Quiz 9.2 Your physical education teacher throws a baseball to you at a certain speed and you catch it. The teacher is next going to throw you a medicine ball whose mass is ten times the mass of the baseball. You are given the following choices: You can have the medicine ball thrown with (a) the same speed as the baseball, (b) the same momentum, or (c) the same kinetic energy. Rank these choices from easiest to hardest to catch.

Using the definition of momentum, Equation 9.1 can be written

$$\frac{d}{dt}(\vec{\mathbf{p}}_1 + \vec{\mathbf{p}}_2) = 0$$

Because the time derivative of the total momentum $\vec{\mathbf{p}}_{tot} = \vec{\mathbf{p}}_1 + \vec{\mathbf{p}}_2$ is *zero*, we conclude that the *total* momentum of the isolated system of the two particles in Figure 9.1 must remain constant:

$$\vec{\mathbf{p}}_{tot} = \text{constant} \qquad (9.4)$$

or, equivalently,

$$\vec{\mathbf{p}}_{1i} + \vec{\mathbf{p}}_{2i} = \vec{\mathbf{p}}_{1f} + \vec{\mathbf{p}}_{2f} \qquad (9.5)$$

PITFALL PREVENTION 9.1
Momentum of an Isolated *System* Is Conserved

Although the momentum of an isolated *system* is conserved, the momentum of one particle within an isolated system is not necessarily conserved because other particles in the system may be interacting with it. Always apply conservation of momentum to an isolated *system*.

---

[1] In this chapter, the terms *momentum* and *linear momentum* have the same meaning. Later, in Chapter 11, we shall use the term *angular momentum* for a different quantity when dealing with rotational motion.

where $\vec{\mathbf{p}}_{1i}$ and $\vec{\mathbf{p}}_{2i}$ are the initial values and $\vec{\mathbf{p}}_{1f}$ and $\vec{\mathbf{p}}_{2f}$ are the final values of the momenta for the two particles for the time interval during which the particles interact. Equation 9.5 in component form demonstrates that the total momenta in the x, y, and z directions are all independently conserved:

$$p_{1ix} + p_{2ix} = p_{1fx} + p_{2fx} \qquad p_{1iy} + p_{2iy} = p_{1fy} + p_{2fy} \qquad p_{1iz} + p_{2iz} = p_{1fz} + p_{2fz} \qquad (9.6)$$

This result, known as the **law of conservation of linear momentum**, can be extended to any number of particles in an isolated system. It is considered one of the most important laws of mechanics. We can state it as follows:

Conservation of ▶
momentum

> Whenever two or more particles in an isolated system interact, the total momentum of the system remains constant.

This law tells us that **the total momentum of an isolated system at all times equals its initial momentum.** The law is the mathematical representation of the momentum version of the **isolated system model.** We studied the energy version of the isolated system model in Chapter 8.

Notice that we have made no statement concerning the type of forces acting on the particles of the system. Furthermore, we have not specified whether the forces are conservative or nonconservative. The only requirement is that the forces must be *internal* to the system.

EXAMPLE 9.1 | **The Archer**

Let us consider the situation proposed at the beginning of this section. A 60-kg archer stands at rest on frictionless ice and fires a 0.50-kg arrow horizontally at 50 m/s (Fig. 9.2). With what velocity does the archer move across the ice after firing the arrow?

SOLUTION

Conceptualize You may have conceptualized this problem already when it was introduced at the beginning of the section. Imagine the arrow being fired one way and the archer recoiling in the opposite direction.

Categorize We *cannot* solve this problem by modeling the arrow as a particle under a net force because we have no information about the force on the arrow or its acceleration. We *cannot* solve this problem by using a system model and applying an energy approach because we do not know how much work is done in pulling the bow back or how much potential energy is stored in the bow. Nonetheless, we *can* solve this problem very easily with an approach involving momentum.

Let us take the system to consist of the archer (including the bow) and the arrow. The system is not isolated because the gravitational force and the normal force from the ice act on the system. These forces, however, are vertical and perpendicular to the motion of the system. Therefore, there are no external forces in the horizontal direction, and we can consider the system to be isolated in terms of momentum components in this direction.

Figure 9.2 (Example 9.1) An archer fires an arrow horizontally to the right. Because he is standing on frictionless ice, he will begin to slide to the left across the ice.

Analyze The total horizontal momentum of the system before the arrow is fired is zero because nothing in the system is moving. Therefore, the total horizontal momentum of the system after the arrow is fired must also be zero. We choose the direction of firing of the arrow as the positive x direction. Identifying the archer as particle 1 and the arrow as particle 2, we have $m_1 = 60$ kg, $m_2 = 0.50$ kg, and $\vec{\mathbf{v}}_{2f} = 50\hat{\mathbf{i}}$ m/s.

Set the final momentum of the system equal to zero: $\qquad\qquad\qquad m_1\vec{\mathbf{v}}_{1f} + m_2\vec{\mathbf{v}}_{2f} = 0$

Solve this equation for $\vec{v}_{1f}$ and substitute numerical values:

$$\vec{v}_{1f} = -\frac{m_2}{m_1}\vec{v}_{2f} = -\left(\frac{0.50 \text{ kg}}{60 \text{ kg}}\right)(50\,\hat{i} \text{ m/s}) = \boxed{-0.42\,\hat{i} \text{ m/s}}$$

Finalize   The negative sign for $\vec{v}_{1f}$ indicates that the archer is moving to the left in Figure 9.2 after the arrow is fired, in the direction opposite the direction of motion of the arrow, in accordance with Newton's third law. Because the archer is much more massive than the arrow, his acceleration and consequent velocity are much smaller than the acceleration and velocity of the arrow.

What If?   What if the arrow were fired in a direction that makes an angle θ with the horizontal? How will that change the recoil velocity of the archer?

Answer   The recoil velocity should decrease in magnitude because only a component of the velocity of the arrow is in the x direction. Conservation of momentum in the x direction gives

$$m_1 v_{1f} + m_2 v_{2f}\cos\theta = 0$$

leading to

$$v_{1f} = -\frac{m_2}{m_1} v_{2f}\cos\theta$$

For $\theta = 0$, $\cos\theta = 1$, and the final velocity of the archer reduces to the value when the arrow is fired horizontally. For nonzero values of θ, the cosine function is less than 1 and the recoil velocity is less than the value calculated for $\theta = 0$. If $\theta = 90°$, then $\cos\theta = 0$ and $v_{1f} = 0$, so there is no recoil velocity.

EXAMPLE 9.2   **Can We Really Ignore the Kinetic Energy of the Earth?**

In Section 7.6, we claimed that we can ignore the kinetic energy of the Earth when considering the energy of a system consisting of the Earth and a dropped ball. Verify this claim.

SOLUTION

Conceptualize   Imagine dropping a ball at the surface of the Earth. From your point of view, the ball falls while the Earth remains stationary. By Newton's third law, however, the Earth experiences an upward force and therefore an upward acceleration while the ball falls. In the calculation below, we will show that this motion can be ignored.

Categorize   We identify the system as the ball and the Earth. Let us ignore air resistance and any other forces on the system, so the system is isolated in terms of momentum.

Analyze   We will verify this claim by setting up a ratio of the kinetic energy of the Earth to that of the ball. We identify v_E and v_b as the speeds of the Earth and the ball, respectively, after the ball has fallen through some distance.

Use the definition of kinetic energy to set up a ratio:

$$(1)\quad \frac{K_E}{K_b} = \frac{\frac{1}{2}m_E v_E^2}{\frac{1}{2}m_b v_b^2} = \left(\frac{m_E}{m_b}\right)\left(\frac{v_E}{v_b}\right)^2$$

The initial momentum of the system is zero, so set the final momentum equal to zero:

$$p_i = p_f \quad\rightarrow\quad 0 = m_b v_b + m_E v_E$$

Solve the equation for the ratio of speeds:

$$\frac{v_E}{v_b} = -\frac{m_b}{m_E}$$

Substitute this expression for v_E/v_b in Equation (1):

$$\frac{K_E}{K_b} = \left(\frac{m_E}{m_b}\right)\left(-\frac{m_b}{m_E}\right)^2 = \frac{m_b}{m_E}$$

Substitute order-of-magnitude numbers for the masses:

$$\frac{K_E}{K_b} = \frac{m_b}{m_E} \sim \frac{1 \text{ kg}}{10^{24} \text{ kg}} \sim 10^{-24}$$

Finalize The kinetic energy of the Earth is a very small fraction of the kinetic energy of the ball, so we are justified in ignoring it in the kinetic energy of the system.

9.2 Impulse and Momentum

Air bags in automobiles have saved countless lives in accidents. The air bag increases the time interval during which the passenger is brought to rest, thereby decreasing the force on (and resultant injury to) the passenger.

According to Equation 9.3, the momentum of a particle changes if a net force acts on the particle. Knowing the change in momentum caused by a force is useful in solving some types of problems. To build a better understanding of this important concept, let us assume that a net force $\Sigma \vec{F}$ acts on a particle and that this force may vary with time. According to Newton's second law, $\Sigma \vec{F} = d\vec{p}/dt$, or

$$d\vec{p} = \sum \vec{F} \, dt \tag{9.7}$$

We can integrate[2] this expression to find the change in the momentum of a particle when the force acts over some time interval. If the momentum of the particle changes from $\vec{p}_i$ at time t_i to $\vec{p}_f$ at time t_f, integrating Equation 9.7 gives

$$\Delta \vec{p} = \vec{p}_f - \vec{p}_i = \int_{t_i}^{t_f} \sum \vec{F} \, dt \tag{9.8}$$

To evaluate the integral, we need to know how the net force varies with time. The quantity on the right side of this equation is a vector called the **impulse** of the net force $\Sigma \vec{F}$ acting on a particle over the time interval $\Delta t = t_f - t_i$:

◀ Impulse of a force

$$\vec{I} \equiv \int_{t_i}^{t_f} \sum \vec{F} \, dt \tag{9.9}$$

From its definition, we see that impulse $\vec{I}$ is a vector quantity having a magnitude equal to the area under the force–time curve as described in Figure 9.3a. It is assumed the force varies in time in the general manner shown in the figure and is nonzero in the time interval $\Delta t = t_f - t_i$. The direction of the impulse vector is the same as the direction of the change in momentum. Impulse has the dimensions of momentum, that is, ML/T. Impulse is *not* a property of a particle; rather, it is a measure of the degree to which an external force changes the particle's momentum.

Equation 9.8 is an important statement known as the **impulse–momentum theorem:**

◀ Impulse–momentum theorem

> The change in the momentum of a particle is equal to the impulse of the net force acting on the particle:
>
> $$\Delta \vec{p} = \vec{I} \tag{9.10}$$

This statement is equivalent to Newton's second law. When we say that an impulse is given to a particle, we mean that momentum is transferred from an external agent to that particle. Equation 9.10 is identical in form to the conservation of energy equation, Equation 8.1. The left side of Equation 9.10 represents the change in the momentum of the system, which in this case is a single particle. The right side is a measure of how much momentum crosses the boundary of the system due to the net force being applied to the system.

Because the net force imparting an impulse to a particle can generally vary in time, it is convenient to define a time-averaged net force:

---

[2] Here we are integrating force with respect to time. Compare this strategy with our efforts in Chapter 7, where we integrated force with respect to position to find the work done by the force.

$$\left(\sum \vec{F}\right)_{\text{avg}} \equiv \frac{1}{\Delta t} \int_{t_i}^{t_f} \sum \vec{F}\, dt \qquad (9.11)$$

where $\Delta t = t_f - t_i$. (This equation is an application of the mean value theorem of calculus.) Therefore, we can express Equation 9.9 as

$$\vec{I} = \left(\sum \vec{F}\right)_{\text{avg}} \Delta t \qquad (9.12)$$

This time-averaged force, shown in Figure 9.3b, can be interpreted as the constant force that would give to the particle in the time interval Δt the same impulse that the time-varying force gives over this same interval.

In principle, if $\sum \vec{F}$ is known as a function of time, the impulse can be calculated from Equation 9.9. The calculation becomes especially simple if the force acting on the particle is constant. In this case, $\left(\sum \vec{F}\right)_{\text{avg}} = \sum \vec{F}$, where $\sum \vec{F}$ is the constant net force, and Equation 9.12 becomes

$$\vec{I} = \sum \vec{F}\, \Delta t \qquad (9.13)$$

In many physical situations, we shall use what is called the **impulse approximation, in which we assume one of the forces exerted on a particle acts for a short time but is much greater than any other force present.** In this case, the net force $\sum \vec{F}$ in Equation 9.9 is replaced with a single force $\vec{F}$ to find the impulse on the particle. This approximation is especially useful in treating collisions in which the duration of the collision is very short. When this approximation is made, the single force is referred to as an *impulsive force*. For example, when a baseball is struck with a bat, the time of the collision is about 0.01 s and the average force that the bat exerts on the ball in this time is typically several thousand newtons. Because this contact force is much greater than the magnitude of the gravitational force, the impulse approximation justifies our ignoring the gravitational forces exerted on the ball and bat. When we use this approximation, it is important to remember that $\vec{p}_i$ and $\vec{p}_f$ represent the momenta *immediately* before and after the collision, respectively. Therefore, in any situation in which it is proper to use the impulse approximation, the particle moves very little during the collision.

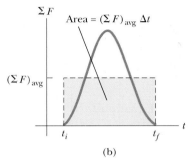

Figure 9.3   (a) A net force acting on a particle may vary in time. The impulse imparted to the particle by the force is the area under the force-versus-time curve. (b) In the time interval Δt, the time-averaged net force (horizontal dashed line) gives the same impulse to a particle as does the time-varying force described in (a).

Quick Quiz 9.3   Two objects are at rest on a frictionless surface. Object 1 has a greater mass than object 2. **(i)** When a constant force is applied to object 1, it accelerates through a distance d in a straight line. The force is removed from object 1 and is applied to object 2. At the moment when object 2 has accelerated through the same distance d, which statements are true? (a) $p_1 < p_2$ (b) $p_1 = p_2$ (c) $p_1 > p_2$ (d) $K_1 < K_2$ (e) $K_1 = K_2$ (f) $K_1 > K_2$ **(ii)** When a force is applied to object 1, it accelerates for a time interval Δt. The force is removed from object 1 and is applied to object 2. From the same list of choices, which statements are true after object 2 has accelerated for the same time interval Δt?

Quick Quiz 9.4   Rank an automobile dashboard, seat belt, and air bag in terms of (a) the impulse and (b) the average force each delivers to a front-seat passenger during a collision, from greatest to least.

EXAMPLE 9.3   **How Good Are the Bumpers?**

In a particular crash test, a car of mass 1 500 kg collides with a wall as shown in Figure 9.4. The initial and final velocities of the car are $\vec{v}_i = -15.0\hat{\imath}$ m/s and $\vec{v}_f = 2.60\hat{\imath}$ m/s, respectively. If the collision lasts 0.150 s, find the impulse caused by the collision and the average force exerted on the car.

SOLUTION

Conceptualize   The collision time is short, so we can imagine the car being brought to rest very rapidly and then moving back in the opposite direction with a reduced speed.

Categorize Let us assume that the force exerted by the wall on the car is large compared with other forces on the car (such as friction and air resistance). Furthermore, the gravitational force and the normal force exerted by the road on the car are perpendicular to the motion and therefore do not affect the horizontal momentum. Therefore, we categorize the problem as one in which we can apply the impulse approximation in the horizontal direction.

Before

−15.0 m/s

After

+2.60 m/s

(a)

(b)

Tim Wright/CORBIS

Figure 9.4 (Example 9.3) (a) This car's momentum changes as a result of its collision with the wall. (b) In a crash test, much of the car's initial kinetic energy is transformed into energy associated with the damage to the car.

Analyze

Evaluate the initial and final momenta of the car:

$$\vec{\mathbf{p}}_i = m\vec{\mathbf{v}}_i = (1\ 500\ \text{kg})(-15.0\hat{\mathbf{i}}\ \text{m/s}) = -2.25 \times 10^4 \hat{\mathbf{i}}\ \text{kg} \cdot \text{m/s}$$

$$\vec{\mathbf{p}}_f = m\vec{\mathbf{v}}_f = (1\ 500\ \text{kg})(2.60\hat{\mathbf{i}}\ \text{m/s}) = 0.39 \times 10^4 \hat{\mathbf{i}}\ \text{kg} \cdot \text{m/s}$$

Use Equation 9.10 to find the impulse on the car:

$$\vec{\mathbf{I}} = \Delta\vec{\mathbf{p}} = \vec{\mathbf{p}}_f - \vec{\mathbf{p}}_i = 0.39 \times 10^4 \hat{\mathbf{i}}\ \text{kg} \cdot \text{m/s} - (-2.25 \times 10^4 \hat{\mathbf{i}}\ \text{kg} \cdot \text{m/s})$$

$$= \boxed{2.64 \times 10^4 \hat{\mathbf{i}}\ \text{kg} \cdot \text{m/s}}$$

Use Equation 9.3 to evaluate the average force exerted by the wall on the car:

$$\vec{\mathbf{F}}_{\text{avg}} = \frac{\Delta\vec{\mathbf{p}}}{\Delta t} = \frac{2.64 \times 10^4 \hat{\mathbf{i}}\ \text{kg} \cdot \text{m/s}}{0.150\ \text{s}} = \boxed{1.76 \times 10^5 \hat{\mathbf{i}}\ \text{N}}$$

Finalize Notice that the signs of the velocities in this example indicate the reversal of directions. What would the mathematics be describing if both the initial and final velocities had the same sign?

What If? What if the car did not rebound from the wall? Suppose the final velocity of the car is zero and the time interval of the collision remains at 0.150 s. Would that represent a larger or a smaller force by the wall on the car?

Answer In the original situation in which the car rebounds, the force by the wall on the car does two things during the time interval: (1) it stops the car, and (2) it causes the car to move away from the wall at 2.60 m/s after the collision. If the car does not rebound, the force is only doing the first of these steps—stopping the car—which requires a *smaller* force.

Mathematically, in the case of the car that does not rebound, the impulse is

$$\vec{\mathbf{I}} = \Delta\vec{\mathbf{p}} = \vec{\mathbf{p}}_f - \vec{\mathbf{p}}_i = 0 - (-2.25 \times 10^4 \hat{\mathbf{i}}\ \text{kg} \cdot \text{m/s}) = 2.25 \times 10^4 \hat{\mathbf{i}}\ \text{kg} \cdot \text{m/s}$$

The average force exerted by the wall on the car is

$$\vec{\mathbf{F}}_{\text{avg}} = \frac{\Delta\vec{\mathbf{p}}}{\Delta t} = \frac{2.25 \times 10^4 \hat{\mathbf{i}}\ \text{kg} \cdot \text{m/s}}{0.150\ \text{s}} = 1.50 \times 10^5 \hat{\mathbf{i}}\ \text{N}$$

which is indeed smaller than the previously calculated value, as was argued conceptually.

9.3 Collisions in One Dimension

In this section, we use the law of conservation of linear momentum to describe what happens when two particles collide. The term **collision** represents an event during which two particles come close to each other and interact by means of forces. The interaction forces are assumed to be much greater than any external forces present, so we can use the impulse approximation.

A collision may involve physical contact between two macroscopic objects as described in Active Figure 9.5a, but the notion of what is meant by a collision must be generalized because "physical contact" on a submicroscopic scale is ill-defined and hence meaningless. To understand this concept, consider a collision on an atomic scale (Active Fig. 9.5b) such as the collision of a proton with an alpha particle (the nucleus of a helium atom). Because the particles are both positively charged, they repel each other due to the strong electrostatic force between them at close separations and never come into "physical contact."

When two particles of masses m_1 and m_2 collide as shown in Active Figure 9.5, the impulsive forces may vary in time in complicated ways, such as that shown in Figure 9.3. Regardless of the complexity of the time behavior of the impulsive force, however, this force is internal to the system of two particles. Therefore, the two particles form an isolated system and the momentum of the system must be conserved.

In contrast, the total kinetic energy of the system of particles may or may not be conserved, depending on the type of collision. In fact, collisions are categorized as being either *elastic* or *inelastic* depending on whether or not kinetic energy is conserved.

An **elastic collision** between two objects is one in which **the total kinetic energy (as well as total momentum) of the system is the same before and after the collision.** Collisions between certain objects in the macroscopic world, such as billiard balls, are only *approximately* elastic because some deformation and loss of kinetic energy take place. For example, you can hear a billiard ball collision, so you know that some of the energy is being transferred away from the system by sound. An elastic collision must be perfectly silent! *Truly* elastic collisions occur between atomic and subatomic particles.

An **inelastic collision** is one in which **the total kinetic energy of the system is not the same before and after the collision (even though the momentum of the system is conserved).** Inelastic collisions are of two types. When the objects stick together after they collide, as happens when a meteorite collides with the Earth, the collision is called **perfectly inelastic.** When the colliding objects do not stick together but some kinetic energy is lost, as in the case of a rubber ball colliding with a hard surface, the collision is called **inelastic** (with no modifying adverb). When the rubber ball collides with the hard surface, some of the ball's kinetic energy is lost when the ball is deformed while it is in contact with the surface.

In the remainder of this section, we treat collisions in one dimension and consider the two extreme cases, perfectly inelastic and elastic collisions.

Perfectly Inelastic Collisions

Consider two particles of masses m_1 and m_2 moving with initial velocities $\vec{\mathbf{v}}_{1i}$ and $\vec{\mathbf{v}}_{2i}$ along the same straight line as shown in Active Figure 9.6. The two particles collide head-on, stick together, and then move with some common velocity $\vec{\mathbf{v}}_f$ after the collision. Because the momentum of an isolated system is conserved in *any* collision, we can say that the total momentum before the collision equals the total momentum of the composite system after the collision:

$$m_1\vec{\mathbf{v}}_{1i} + m_2\vec{\mathbf{v}}_{2i} = (m_1 + m_2)\vec{\mathbf{v}}_f \qquad (9.14)$$

Solving for the final velocity gives

$$\vec{\mathbf{v}}_f = \frac{m_1\vec{\mathbf{v}}_{1i} + m_2\vec{\mathbf{v}}_{2i}}{m_1 + m_2} \qquad (9.15)$$

Elastic Collisions

Consider two particles of masses m_1 and m_2 moving with initial velocities $\vec{\mathbf{v}}_{1i}$ and $\vec{\mathbf{v}}_{2i}$ along the same straight line as shown in Active Figure 9.7. The two particles collide head-on and then leave the collision site with different velocities, $\vec{\mathbf{v}}_{1f}$ and $\vec{\mathbf{v}}_{2f}$. In an elastic collision, both the momentum and kinetic energy of the system are

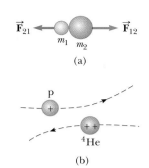

ACTIVE FIGURE 9.5

(a) The collision between two objects as the result of direct contact. (b) The "collision" between two charged particles.

Sign in at www.thomsonedu.com and go to ThomsonNOW to observe these collisions and watch the time variation of the forces on each particle.

PITFALL PREVENTION 9.2
Inelastic Collisions

Generally, inelastic collisions are hard to analyze without additional information. Lack of this information appears in the mathematical representation as having more unknowns than equations.

Before collision

(a)

After collision

(b)

ACTIVE FIGURE 9.6

Schematic representation of a perfectly inelastic head-on collision between two particles: (a) before and (b) after collision.

Sign in at www.thomsonedu.com and go to ThomsonNOW to adjust the masses and velocities of the colliding objects and see the effect on the final velocity.

Before collision

(a)

After collision

(b)

ACTIVE FIGURE 9.7

Schematic representation of an elastic head-on collision between two particles: (a) before and (b) after collision.

Sign in at www.thomsonedu.com and go to ThomsonNOW to adjust the masses and velocities of the colliding objects and see the effect on the final velocities.

conserved. Therefore, considering velocities along the horizontal direction in Active Figure 9.7, we have

$$m_1 v_{1i} + m_2 v_{2i} = m_1 v_{1f} + m_2 v_{2f} \qquad (9.16)$$

$$\tfrac{1}{2} m_1 v_{1i}^2 + \tfrac{1}{2} m_2 v_{2i}^2 = \tfrac{1}{2} m_1 v_{1f}^2 + \tfrac{1}{2} m_2 v_{2f}^2 \qquad (9.17)$$

Because all velocities in Active Figure 9.7 are either to the left or the right, they can be represented by the corresponding speeds along with algebraic signs indicating direction. We shall indicate v as positive if a particle moves to the right and negative if it moves to the left.

In a typical problem involving elastic collisions, there are two unknown quantities, and Equations 9.16 and 9.17 can be solved simultaneously to find them. An alternative approach, however—one that involves a little mathematical manipulation of Equation 9.17—often simplifies this process. To see how, let us cancel the factor $\tfrac{1}{2}$ in Equation 9.17 and rewrite it as

$$m_1(v_{1i}^2 - v_{1f}^2) = m_2(v_{2f}^2 - v_{2i}^2)$$

Factoring both sides of this equation gives

$$m_1(v_{1i} - v_{1f})(v_{1i} + v_{1f}) = m_2(v_{2f} - v_{2i})(v_{2f} + v_{2i}) \qquad (9.18)$$

Next, let us separate the terms containing m_1 and m_2 in Equation 9.16 to obtain

$$m_1(v_{1i} - v_{1f}) = m_2(v_{2f} - v_{2i}) \qquad (9.19)$$

To obtain our final result, we divide Equation 9.18 by Equation 9.19 and obtain

$$v_{1i} + v_{1f} = v_{2f} + v_{2i}$$

$$v_{1i} - v_{2i} = -(v_{1f} - v_{2f}) \qquad (9.20)$$

PITFALL PREVENTION 9.3

Not a General Equation

Equation 9.20 can only be used in a very *specific* situation, a one-dimensional, elastic collision between two objects. The *general* concept is conservation of momentum (and conservation of kinetic energy if the collision is elastic) for an isolated system.

This equation, in combination with Equation 9.16, can be used to solve problems dealing with elastic collisions. According to Equation 9.20, the *relative* velocity of the two particles before the collision, $v_{1i} - v_{2i}$, equals the negative of their relative velocity after the collision, $-(v_{1f} - v_{2f})$.

Suppose the masses and initial velocities of both particles are known. Equations 9.16 and 9.20 can be solved for the final velocities in terms of the initial velocities because there are two equations and two unknowns:

$$v_{1f} = \left(\frac{m_1 - m_2}{m_1 + m_2}\right) v_{1i} + \left(\frac{2 m_2}{m_1 + m_2}\right) v_{2i} \qquad (9.21)$$

$$v_{2f} = \left(\frac{2 m_1}{m_1 + m_2}\right) v_{1i} + \left(\frac{m_2 - m_1}{m_1 + m_2}\right) v_{2i} \qquad (9.22)$$

It is important to use the appropriate signs for v_{1i} and v_{2i} in Equations 9.21 and 9.22.

Let us consider some special cases. If $m_1 = m_2$, Equations 9.21 and 9.22 show that $v_{1f} = v_{2i}$ and $v_{2f} = v_{1i}$, which means that the particles exchange velocities if they have equal masses. That is approximately what one observes in head-on billiard ball collisions: the cue ball stops and the struck ball moves away from the collision with the same velocity the cue ball had.

If particle 2 is initially at rest, then $v_{2i} = 0$, and Equations 9.21 and 9.22 become

◀ Elastic collision: particle 2 initially at rest

$$v_{1f} = \left(\frac{m_1 - m_2}{m_1 + m_2}\right) v_{1i} \qquad (9.23)$$

$$v_{2f} = \left(\frac{2 m_1}{m_1 + m_2}\right) v_{1i} \qquad (9.24)$$

If m_1 is much greater than m_2 and $v_{2i} = 0$, we see from Equations 9.23 and 9.24 that $v_{1f} \approx v_{1i}$ and $v_{2f} \approx 2 v_{1i}$. That is, when a very heavy particle collides head-on with a very light one that is initially at rest, the heavy particle continues its motion unaltered after the collision and the light particle rebounds with a speed equal to about twice the initial speed of the heavy particle. An example of such a collision is that of a moving heavy atom, such as uranium, striking a light atom, such as hydrogen.

If m_2 is much greater than m_1 and particle 2 is initially at rest, then $v_{1f} \approx -v_{1i}$ and $v_{2f} \approx 0$. That is, when a very light particle collides head-on with a very heavy particle that is initially at rest, the light particle has its velocity reversed and the heavy one remains approximately at rest.

Quick Quiz 9.5 In a perfectly inelastic one-dimensional collision between two moving objects, what condition alone is necessary so that the final kinetic energy of the system is zero after the collision? (a) The objects must have momenta with the same magnitude but opposite directions. (b) The objects must have the same mass. (c) The objects must have the same velocity. (d) The objects must have the same speed, with velocity vectors in opposite directions.

Quick Quiz 9.6 A table-tennis ball is thrown at a stationary bowling ball. The table-tennis ball makes a one-dimensional elastic collision and bounces back along the same line. Compared with the bowling ball after the collision, does the table-tennis ball have (a) a larger magnitude of momentum and more kinetic energy, (b) a smaller magnitude of momentum and more kinetic energy, (c) a larger magnitude of momentum and less kinetic energy, (d) a smaller magnitude of momentum and less kinetic energy, or (e) the same magnitude of momentum and the same kinetic energy?

PROBLEM-SOLVING STRATEGY   **One-Dimensional Collisions**

You should use the following approach when solving collision problems in one dimension:

1. *Conceptualize.* Imagine the collision occurring in your mind. Draw simple diagrams of the particles before and after the collision and include appropriate velocity vectors. At first, you may have to guess at the directions of the final velocity vectors.

2. *Categorize.* Is the system of particles isolated? If so, categorize the collision as elastic, inelastic, or perfectly inelastic.

3. *Analyze.* Set up the appropriate mathematical representation for the problem. If the collision is perfectly inelastic, use Equation 9.15. If the collision is elastic, use Equations 9.16 and 9.20. If the collision is inelastic, use Equation 9.16. To find the final velocities in this case, you will need some additional information.

4. *Finalize.* Once you have determined your result, check to see if your answers are consistent with the mental and pictorial representations and that your results are realistic.

EXAMPLE 9.4   **The Executive Stress Reliever**

An ingenious device that illustrates conservation of momentum and kinetic energy is shown in Figure 9.8 (page 238). It consists of five identical hard balls supported by strings of equal lengths. When ball 1 is pulled out and released, after the almost-elastic collision between it and ball 2, ball 1 stops and ball 5 moves out as shown in Figure 9.8b. If balls 1 and 2 are pulled out and released, they stop after the collision and balls 4 and 5 swing out, and so forth. Is it ever possible that when ball 1 is released, it stops after the collision and balls 4 and 5 will swing out on the opposite side and travel with half the speed of ball 1 as in Figure 9.8c?

SOLUTION

Conceptualize With the help of Figure 9.8c, imagine one ball coming in from the left and two balls exiting the collision on the right. That is the phenomenon we want to test to see if it could ever happen.

Categorize Because of the very short time interval between the arrival of the ball from the left and the departure of the ball(s) from the right, we can use the impulse approximation to ignore the gravitational forces on the balls and categorize the system of five balls as isolated in terms of momentum and energy. Because the balls are hard, we can categorize the collisions between them as elastic for purposes of calculation.

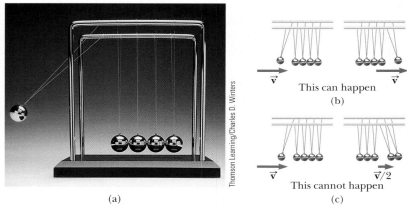

Thomson Learning/Charles D. Winters

Figure 9.8 (Example 9.4) (a) An executive stress reliever. (b) If one ball swings down, we see one ball swing out at the other end. (c) Is it possible for one ball to swing down and two balls to leave the other end with half the speed of the first ball? In (b) and (c), the velocity vectors shown represent those of the balls immediately before and immediately after the collision.

Analyze The momentum of the system before the collision is mv, where m is the mass of ball 1 and v is its speed immediately before the collision. After the collision, we imagine that ball 1 stops and balls 4 and 5 swing out, each moving with speed $v/2$. The total momentum of the system after the collision would be $m(v/2) + m(v/2) = mv$. Therefore, the momentum of the system is conserved.

The kinetic energy of the system immediately before the collision is $K_i = \frac{1}{2}mv^2$ and that after the collision is $K_f = \frac{1}{2}m(v/2)^2 + \frac{1}{2}m(v/2)^2 = \frac{1}{4}mv^2$. That shows that the kinetic energy of the system is *not* conserved, which is inconsistent with our assumption that the collisions are elastic.

Finalize Our analysis shows that it is *not* possible for balls 4 and 5 to swing out when only ball 1 is released. The only way to conserve both momentum and kinetic energy of the system is for one ball to move out when one ball is released, two balls to move out when two are released, and so on.

What If? Consider what would happen if balls 4 and 5 are glued together. Now what happens when ball 1 is pulled out and released?

Answer In this situation, balls 4 and 5 must move together as a single object after the collision. We have argued that both momentum and energy of the system cannot be conserved in this case. We assumed, however, ball 1 stopped after striking ball 2. What if we do not make this assumption? Consider the conservation equations with the assumption that ball 1 moves after the collision. For conservation of momentum,

$$p_i = p_f$$

$$mv_{1i} = mv_{1f} + 2mv_{4,5}$$

where $v_{4,5}$ refers to the final speed of the ball 4–ball 5 combination. Conservation of kinetic energy gives us

$$K_i = K_f$$

$$\tfrac{1}{2}mv_{1i}^2 = \tfrac{1}{2}mv_{1f}^2 + \tfrac{1}{2}(2m)v_{4,5}^2$$

Combining these equations gives

$$v_{4,5} = \tfrac{2}{3}v_{1i} \qquad v_{1f} = -\tfrac{1}{3}v_{1i}$$

Therefore, balls 4 and 5 move together as one object after the collision while ball 1 bounces back from the collision with one third of its original speed.

EXAMPLE 9.5   **Carry Collision Insurance!**

An 1 800-kg car stopped at a traffic light is struck from the rear by a 900-kg car. The two cars become entangled, moving along the same path as that of the originally moving car. If the smaller car were moving at 20.0 m/s before the collision, what is the velocity of the entangled cars after the collision?

SOLUTION

Conceptualize   This kind of collision is easily visualized, and one can predict that after the collision both cars will be moving in the same direction as that of the initially moving car. Because the initially moving car has only half the mass of the stationary car, we expect the final velocity of the cars to be relatively small.

Categorize   We identify the system of two cars as isolated and apply the impulse approximation during the short time interval of the collision. The phrase "become entangled" tells us to categorize the collision as perfectly inelastic.

Analyze   The magnitude of the total momentum of the system before the collision is equal to that of the smaller car because the larger car is initially at rest.

Evaluate the initial momentum of the system:

$$p_i = m_1 v_i = (900 \text{ kg})(20.0 \text{ m/s}) = 1.80 \times 10^4 \text{ kg} \cdot \text{m/s}$$

Evaluate the final momentum of the system:

$$p_f = (m_1 + m_2)v_f = (2\,700 \text{ kg})v_f$$

Equate the initial and final momenta and solve for v_f:

$$v_f = \frac{p_i}{m_1 + m_2} = \frac{1.80 \times 10^4 \text{ kg} \cdot \text{m/s}}{2\,700 \text{ kg}} = \boxed{6.67 \text{ m/s}}$$

Finalize   Because the final velocity is positive, the direction of the final velocity of the combination is the same as the velocity of the initially moving car as predicted. The speed of the combination is also much lower than the initial speed of the moving car.

What If?   Suppose we reverse the masses of the cars. What if a stationary 900-kg car is struck by a moving 1 800-kg car? Is the final speed the same as before?

Answer   Intuitively, we can guess that the final speed of the combination is higher than 6.67 m/s if the initially moving car is the more massive car. Mathematically, that should be the case because the system has a larger momentum if the initially moving car is the more massive one. Solving for the new final velocity, we find

$$v_f = \frac{p_i}{m_1 + m_2} = \frac{(1\,800 \text{ kg})(20.0 \text{ m/s})}{2\,700 \text{ kg}} = 13.3 \text{ m/s}$$

which is two times greater than the previous final velocity.

EXAMPLE 9.6   **The Ballistic Pendulum**

The ballistic pendulum (Fig. 9.9) is an apparatus used to measure the speed of a fast-moving projectile such as a bullet. A projectile of mass m_1 is fired into a large block of wood of mass m_2 suspended from some light wires. The projectile embeds in the block, and the entire system swings through a height h. How can we determine the speed of the projectile from a measurement of h?

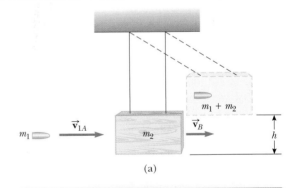

(a)

SOLUTION

Conceptualize   Figure 9.9a helps conceptualize the situation. Run the animation in your mind: the projectile enters the pendulum, which swings up to some height at which it comes to rest.

Categorize   The projectile and the block form an isolated system. Identify configuration A as immediately before the collision and configuration B as immediately after the collision. Because the projectile imbeds in the block, we can categorize the collision between them as perfectly inelastic.

Figure 9.9   (Example 9.6) (a) Diagram of a ballistic pendulum. Notice that $\vec{\mathbf{v}}_{1A}$ is the velocity of the projectile immediately before the collision and $\vec{\mathbf{v}}_B$ is the velocity of the projectile–block system immediately after the perfectly inelastic collision. (b) Multiflash photograph of a ballistic pendulum used in the laboratory.

Thomson Learning/Charles D. Winters

(b)

Analyze To analyze the collision, we use Equation 9.15, which gives the speed of the system immediately after the collision when we assume the impulse approximation.

Noting that $v_{2A} = 0$, solve Equation 9.15 for v_B:

$$(1) \quad v_B = \frac{m_1 v_{1A}}{m_1 + m_2}$$

Categorize For the process during which the projectile–block combination swings upward to height h (ending at configuration C), we focus on a *different* system, that of the projectile, the block, and the Earth. We categorize this part of the problem as one involving an isolated system for energy with no nonconservative forces acting.

Analyze Write an expression for the total kinetic energy of the system immediately after the collision:

$$(2) \quad K_B = \tfrac{1}{2}(m_1 + m_2)v_B^2$$

Substitute the value of v_B from Equation (1) into Equation (2):

$$K_B = \frac{m_1^2 v_{1A}^2}{2(m_1 + m_2)}$$

This kinetic energy of the system immediately after the collision is *less* than the initial kinetic energy of the projectile as is expected in an inelastic collision.

We define the gravitational potential energy of the system for configuration B to be zero. Therefore, $U_B = 0$, whereas $U_C = (m_1 + m_2)gh$.

Apply the conservation of mechanical energy principle to the system:

$$K_B + U_B = K_C + U_C$$

$$\frac{m_1^2 v_{1A}^2}{2(m_1 + m_2)} + 0 = 0 + (m_1 + m_2)gh$$

Solve for v_{1A}:

$$v_{1A} = \left(\frac{m_1 + m_2}{m_1}\right)\sqrt{2gh}$$

Finalize We had to solve this problem in two steps. Each step involved a different system and a different conservation principle. Because the collision was assumed to be perfectly inelastic, some mechanical energy was transformed to internal energy. It would have been *incorrect* to equate the initial kinetic energy of the incoming projectile with the final gravitational potential energy of the projectile–block–Earth combination.

EXAMPLE 9.7 A Two-Body Collision with a Spring

A block of mass $m_1 = 1.60$ kg initially moving to the right with a speed of 4.00 m/s on a frictionless, horizontal track collides with a spring attached to a second block of mass $m_2 = 2.10$ kg initially moving to the left with a speed of 2.50 m/s as shown in Figure 9.10a. The spring constant is 600 N/m.

(A) Find the velocities of the two blocks after the collision.

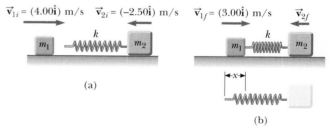

(a)

(b)

Figure 9.10 (Example 9.7) A moving block approaches a second moving block that is attached to a spring.

SOLUTION

Conceptualize With the help of Figure 9.10a, run an animation of the collision in your mind. Figure 9.10b shows an instant during the collision when the spring is compressed. Eventually, block 1 and the spring will again separate, so the system will look like Figure 9.10a again but with different velocity vectors for the two blocks.

Categorize Because the spring force is conservative, kinetic energy in the system is not transformed to internal energy during the compression of the spring. Ignoring any sound made when the block hits the spring, we can categorize the collision as being elastic.

Analyze Because momentum of the system is conserved, apply Equation 9.16:

$$m_1 v_{1i} + m_2 v_{2i} = m_1 v_{1f} + m_2 v_{2f}$$

Substitute the known values:	$(1.60 \text{ kg})(4.00 \text{ m/s}) + (2.10 \text{ kg})(-2.50 \text{ m/s}) = (1.60 \text{ kg})v_{1f} + (2.10 \text{ kg})v_{2f}$
	(1) $1.15 \text{ kg} \cdot \text{m/s} = (1.60 \text{ kg})v_{1f} + (2.10 \text{ kg})v_{2f}$

Because the collision is elastic, apply Equation 9.20:	$v_{1i} - v_{2i} = -(v_{1f} - v_{2f})$

Substitute the known values:	(2) $4.00 \text{ m/s} - (-2.50 \text{ m/s}) = 6.50 \text{ m/s} = -v_{1f} + v_{2f}$

Multiply Equation (2) by 1.60 kg:	(3) $10.4 \text{ kg} \cdot \text{m/s} = -(1.60 \text{ kg})v_{1f} + (1.60 \text{ kg})v_{2f}$

Add Equations (1) and (3):	$11.55 \text{ kg} \cdot \text{m/s} = (3.70 \text{ kg})v_{2f}$

Solve for v_{2f}:	$v_{2f} = \dfrac{11.55 \text{ kg} \cdot \text{m/s}}{3.70 \text{ kg}} = \boxed{3.12 \text{ m/s}}$

Use Equation (2) to find v_{1f}:	$6.50 \text{ m/s} = -v_{1f} + 3.12 \text{ m/s}$
	$v_{1f} = \boxed{-3.38 \text{ m/s}}$

(B) During the collision, at the instant block 1 is moving to the right with a velocity of $+3.00$ m/s as in Figure 9.10b, determine the velocity of block 2.

SOLUTION

Conceptualize   Focus your attention now on Figure 9.10b, which represents the final configuration of the system for the time interval of interest.

Categorize   Because the momentum and mechanical energy of the system of two blocks are conserved *throughout* the collision for the system of two blocks, the collision can be categorized as elastic for *any* final instant of time. Let us now choose the final instant to be when block 1 is moving with a velocity of $+3.00$ m/s.

Analyze Apply Equation 9.16:	$m_1 v_{1i} + m_2 v_{2i} = m_1 v_{1f} + m_2 v_{2f}$

Substitute the known values:	$(1.60 \text{ kg})(4.00 \text{ m/s}) + (2.10 \text{ kg})(-2.50 \text{ m/s}) = (1.60 \text{ kg})(3.00 \text{ m/s}) + (2.10 \text{ kg})v_{2f}$

Solve for v_{2f}:	$v_{2f} = \boxed{-1.74 \text{ m/s}}$

Finalize   The negative value for v_{2f} means that block 2 is still moving to the left at the instant we are considering.

(C) Determine the distance the spring is compressed at that instant.

SOLUTION

Conceptualize   Once again, focus on the configuration of the system shown in Figure 9.10b.

Categorize   For the system of the spring and two blocks, no friction or other nonconservative forces act within the system. Therefore, we categorize the system as isolated with no nonconservative forces acting.

Analyze   We choose the initial configuration of the system to be that existing immediately before block 1 strikes the spring and the final configuration to be that when block 1 is moving to the right at 3.00 m/s.

Write a conservation of mechanical energy equation for the system:	$K_i + U_i = K_f + U_f$
	$\frac{1}{2} m_1 v_{1i}^2 + \frac{1}{2} m_2 v_{2i}^2 + 0 = \frac{1}{2} m_1 v_{1f}^2 + \frac{1}{2} m_2 v_{2f}^2 + \frac{1}{2} kx^2$

Substitute the known values and the result of part (B):

$$\tfrac{1}{2}(1.60 \text{ kg})(4.00 \text{ m/s})^2 + \tfrac{1}{2}(2.10 \text{ kg})(2.50 \text{ m/s})^2 + 0$$

$$= \tfrac{1}{2}(1.60 \text{ kg})(3.00 \text{ m/s})^2 + \tfrac{1}{2}(2.10 \text{ kg})(1.74 \text{ m/s})^2 + \tfrac{1}{2}(600 \text{ N/m})x^2$$

Solve for x:

$$x = \boxed{0.173 \text{ m}}$$

Finalize This answer is not the maximum compression of the spring because the two blocks are still moving toward each other at the instant shown in Figure 9.10b. Can you determine the maximum compression of the spring?

(a) Before the collision

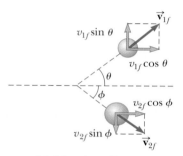

(b) After the collision

ACTIVE FIGURE 9.11

An elastic, glancing collision between two particles.

Sign in at www.thomsonedu.com and go to ThomsonNOW to adjust the speed and position of the blue particle and the masses of both particles and see the effects.

PITFALL PREVENTION 9.4
Don't Use Equation 9.20

Equation 9.20, relating the initial and final relative velocities of two colliding objects, is only valid for one-dimensional elastic collisions. Do not use this equation when analyzing two-dimensional collisions.

9.4 Collisions in Two Dimensions

In Section 9.1, we showed that the momentum of a system of two particles is conserved when the system is isolated. For any collision of two particles, this result implies that the momentum in each of the directions x, y, and z is conserved. An important subset of collisions takes place in a plane. The game of billiards is a familiar example involving multiple collisions of objects moving on a two-dimensional surface. For such two-dimensional collisions, we obtain two component equations for conservation of momentum:

$$m_1 v_{1ix} + m_2 v_{2ix} = m_1 v_{1fx} + m_2 v_{2fx}$$

$$m_1 v_{1iy} + m_2 v_{2iy} = m_1 v_{1fy} + m_2 v_{2fy}$$

where three subscripts on the velocity components in these equations represent, respectively, the identification of the object (1, 2), initial and final values (i, f), and the velocity component (x, y).

Let us consider a specific two-dimensional problem in which particle 1 of mass m_1 collides with particle 2 of mass m_2 initially at rest as in Active Figure 9.11. After the collision (Active Fig. 9.11b), particle 1 moves at an angle θ with respect to the horizontal and particle 2 moves at an angle ϕ with respect to the horizontal. This event is called a *glancing* collision. Applying the law of conservation of momentum in component form and noting that the initial y component of the momentum of the two-particle system is zero gives

$$m_1 v_{1i} = m_1 v_{1f} \cos \theta + m_2 v_{2f} \cos \phi \qquad (9.25)$$

$$0 = m_1 v_{1f} \sin \theta - m_2 v_{2f} \sin \phi \qquad (9.26)$$

where the minus sign in Equation 9.26 is included because after the collision particle 2 has a y component of velocity that is downward. (The symbols v in these particular equations are speeds, not velocity components. The direction of the component vector is indicated explicitly with plus or minus signs.) We now have two independent equations. As long as no more than two of the seven quantities in Equations 9.25 and 9.26 are unknown, we can solve the problem.

If the collision is elastic, we can also use Equation 9.17 (conservation of kinetic energy) with $v_{2i} = 0$:

$$\tfrac{1}{2} m_1 v_{1i}{}^2 = \tfrac{1}{2} m_1 v_{1f}{}^2 + \tfrac{1}{2} m_2 v_{2f}{}^2 \qquad (9.27)$$

Knowing the initial speed of particle 1 and both masses, we are left with four unknowns (v_{1f}, v_{2f}, θ, and ϕ). Because we have only three equations, one of the four remaining quantities must be given to determine the motion after the elastic collision from conservation principles alone.

If the collision is inelastic, kinetic energy is *not* conserved and Equation 9.27 does *not* apply.

Two-Dimensional Collisions

The following procedure is recommended when dealing with problems involving collisions between two particles in two dimensions.

1. *Conceptualize.* Imagine the collisions occurring and predict the approximate directions in which the particles will move after the collision. Set up a coordinate system and define your velocities in terms of that system. It is convenient to have the *x* axis coincide with one of the initial velocities. Sketch the coordinate system, draw and label all velocity vectors, and include all the given information.

2. *Categorize.* Is the system of particles truly isolated? If so, categorize the collision as elastic, inelastic, or perfectly inelastic.

3. *Analyze.* Write expressions for the *x* and *y* components of the momentum of each object before and after the collision. Remember to include the appropriate signs for the components of the velocity vectors and pay careful attention to signs.

    Write expressions for the *total* momentum in the *x* direction *before* and *after* the collision, and equate the two. Repeat this procedure for the total momentum in the *y* direction.

    Proceed to solve the momentum equations for the unknown quantities. If the collision is inelastic, kinetic energy is *not* conserved and additional information is probably required. If the collision is perfectly inelastic, the final velocities of the two objects are equal.

    If the collision is elastic, kinetic energy is conserved and you can equate the total kinetic energy of the system before the collision to the total kinetic energy after the collision, providing an additional relationship between the velocity magnitudes.

4. *Finalize.* Once you have determined your result, check to see if your answers are consistent with the mental and pictorial representations and that your results are realistic.

EXAMPLE 9.8   **Collision at an Intersection**

A 1 500-kg car traveling east with a speed of 25.0 m/s collides at an intersection with a 2 500-kg van traveling north at a speed of 20.0 m/s as shown in Figure 9.12. Find the direction and magnitude of the velocity of the wreckage after the collision, assuming the vehicles stick together after the collision.

SOLUTION

Conceptualize   Figure 9.12 should help you conceptualize the situation before and after the collision. Let us choose east to be along the positive *x* direction and north to be along the positive *y* direction.

Categorize   Because we consider moments immediately before and immediately after the collision as defining our time interval, we ignore the small effect that friction would have on the wheels of the car and model the system of two cars as isolated. We also ignore the cars' sizes and model them as particles. The collision is perfectly inelastic because the two cars stick together after the collision.

Figure 9.12   (Example 9.8) An east-bound car colliding with a north-bound van.

Analyze   Before the collision, the only object having momentum in the *x* direction is the car. Therefore, the magnitude of the total initial momentum of the system (car plus van) in the *x* direction is that of only the car. Similarly, the total initial momentum of the system in the *y* direction is that of the van. After the collision, let us assume that the wreckage moves at an angle θ and speed v_f.

Evaluate the initial momentum of the system in the x direction:

$$\sum p_{xi} = (1\,500 \text{ kg})(25.0 \text{ m/s}) = 3.75 \times 10^4 \text{ kg} \cdot \text{m/s}$$

Write an expression for the final momentum in the x direction:

$$\sum p_{xf} = (4\,000 \text{ kg})v_f \cos\theta$$

Equate the initial and final momenta in the x direction:

$$(1) \quad 3.75 \times 10^4 \text{ kg} \cdot \text{m/s} = (4\,000 \text{ kg})v_f \cos\theta$$

Evaluate the initial momentum of the system in the y direction:

$$\sum p_{yi} = (2\,500 \text{ kg})(20.0 \text{ m/s}) = 5.00 \times 10^4 \text{ kg} \cdot \text{m/s}$$

Write an expression for the final momentum in the y direction:

$$\sum p_{yf} = (4\,000 \text{ kg})v_f \sin\theta$$

Equate the initial and final momenta in the y direction:

$$(2) \quad 5.00 \times 10^4 \text{ kg} \cdot \text{m/s} = (4\,000 \text{ kg})v_f \sin\theta$$

Divide Equation (2) by Equation (1) and solve for θ:

$$\frac{(4\,000 \text{ kg})v_f \sin\theta}{(4\,000 \text{ kg})v_f \cos\theta} = \tan\theta = \frac{5.00 \times 10^4}{3.75 \times 10^4} = 1.33$$

$$\theta = \boxed{53.1°}$$

Use Equation (2) to find the value of v_f:

$$v_f = \frac{5.00 \times 10^4 \text{ kg} \cdot \text{m/s}}{(4\,000 \text{ kg}) \sin 53.1°} = \boxed{15.6 \text{ m/s}}$$

Finalize Notice that the angle θ is qualitatively in agreement with Figure 9.12. Also notice that the final speed of the combination is less than the initial speeds of the two cars. This result is consistent with the kinetic energy of the system being reduced in an inelastic collision. It might help if you draw the momentum vectors of each vehicle before the collision and the two vehicles together after the collision.

EXAMPLE 9.9   **Proton–Proton Collision**

A proton collides elastically with another proton that is initially at rest. The incoming proton has an initial speed of 3.50×10^5 m/s and makes a glancing collision with the second proton as in Active Figure 9.11. (At close separations, the protons exert a repulsive electrostatic force on each other.) After the collision, one proton moves off at an angle of 37.0° to the original direction of motion and the second deflects at an angle of ϕ to the same axis. Find the final speeds of the two protons and the angle ϕ.

SOLUTION

Conceptualize This collision is like that shown in Active Figure 9.11, which will help you conceptualize the behavior of the system. We define the x axis to be along the direction of the velocity vector of the initially moving proton.

Categorize The pair of protons form an isolated system. Both momentum and kinetic energy of the system are conserved in this glancing elastic collision.

Analyze We know that $m_1 = m_2$ and $\theta = 37.0°$, and we are given that $v_{1i} = 3.50 \times 10^5$ m/s.

Enter the known values into Equations 9.25, 9.26, and 9.27:

$$(1) \quad v_{1f} \cos 37° + v_{2f} \cos\phi = 3.50 \times 10^5 \text{ m/s}$$

$$(2) \quad v_{1f} \sin 37.0° - v_{2f} \sin\phi = 0$$

$$(3) \quad v_{1f}^2 + v_{2f}^2 = (3.50 \times 10^5 \text{ m/s})^2 = 1.23 \times 10^{11} \text{ m}^2/\text{s}^2$$

Rearrange Equations (1) and (2):

$$v_{2f} \cos\phi = 3.50 \times 10^5 \text{ m/s} - v_{1f} \cos 37.0°$$

$$v_{2f} \sin\phi = v_{1f} \sin 37.0°$$

Square these two equations and add them:

$$v_{2f}^2 \cos^2 \phi + v_{2f}^2 \sin^2 \phi$$

$$= 1.23 \times 10^{11} \text{ m}^2/\text{s}^2 - (7.00 \times 10^5 \text{ m/s})v_{1f} \cos 37.0° + v_{1f}^2 \cos^2 37.0°$$

$$+ v_{1f}^2 \sin^2 37.0°$$

$$(4) \quad v_{2f}^2 = 1.23 \times 10^{11} - (5.59 \times 10^5)v_{1f} + v_{1f}^2$$

Substitute Equation (4) into Equation (3):

$$v_{1f}^2 + [1.23 \times 10^{11} - (5.59 \times 10^5)v_{1f} + v_{1f}^2] = 1.23 \times 10^{11}$$

$$2v_{1f}^2 - (5.59 \times 10^5)v_{1f} = (2v_{1f} - 5.59 \times 10^5)v_{1f} = 0$$

One possible solution of this equation is $v_{1f} = 0$, which corresponds to a head-on collision in which the first proton stops and the second continues with the same speed in the same direction. That is not the solution we want.

Set the other factor equal to zero:

$$2v_{1f} - 5.59 \times 10^5 = 0 \quad \rightarrow \quad v_{1f} = \boxed{2.80 \times 10^5 \text{ m/s}}$$

Use Equation (3) to find v_{2f}:

$$v_{2f} = \sqrt{1.23 \times 10^{11} - v_{1f}^2} = \sqrt{1.23 \times 10^{11} - (2.80 \times 10^5)^2}$$

$$= \boxed{2.11 \times 10^5 \text{ m/s}}$$

Use Equation (2) to find ϕ:

$$\phi = \sin^{-1}\left(\frac{v_{1f} \sin 37.0°}{v_{2f}}\right) = \sin^{-1}\left(\frac{(2.80 \times 10^5) \sin 37.0°}{2.11 \times 10^5}\right) = \boxed{53.0°}$$

Finalize   It is interesting that $\theta + \phi = 90°$. This result is *not* accidental. Whenever two objects of equal mass collide elastically in a glancing collision and one of them is initially at rest, their final velocities are perpendicular to each other.

9.5   The Center of Mass

In this section, we describe the overall motion of a system in terms of a special point called the **center of mass** of the system. The system can be either a group of particles, such as a collection of atoms in a container, or an extended object, such as a gymnast leaping through the air. We shall see that the translational motion of the center of mass of the system is the same as if all the mass of the system were concentrated at that point. That is, the system moves as if the net external force were applied to a single particle located at the center of mass. This behavior is independent of other motion, such as rotation or vibration of the system. This model, the *particle model*, was introduced in Chapter 2.

Consider a system consisting of a pair of particles that have different masses and are connected by a light, rigid rod (Active Fig. 9.13). The position of the center of mass of a system can be described as being the *average position* of the system's mass. The center of mass of the system is located somewhere on the line joining the two particles and is closer to the particle having the larger mass. If a single force is applied at a point on the rod above the center of mass, the system rotates clockwise (see Active Fig. 9.13a). If the force is applied at a point on the rod below the center of mass, the system rotates counterclockwise (see Active Fig. 9.13b). If the force is applied at the center of mass, the system moves in the direction of the force without rotating (see Active Fig. 9.13c). The center of mass of an object can be located with this procedure.

The center of mass of the pair of particles described in Active Figure 9.14 (page 246) is located on the x axis and lies somewhere between the particles. Its x coordinate is given by

$$x_{CM} \equiv \frac{m_1 x_1 + m_2 x_2}{m_1 + m_2} \tag{9.28}$$

ACTIVE FIGURE 9.13

Two particles of unequal mass are connected by a light, rigid rod. (a) The system rotates clockwise when a force is applied above the center of mass. (b) The system rotates counterclockwise when a force is applied below the center of mass. (c) The system moves in the direction of the force without rotating when a force is applied at the center of mass.

Sign in at www.thomsonedu.com and go to ThomsonNOW to choose the point at which to apply the force.

For example, if $x_1 = 0$, $x_2 = d$, and $m_2 = 2m_1$, we find that $x_{CM} = \frac{2}{3}d$. That is, the center of mass lies closer to the more massive particle. If the two masses are equal, the center of mass lies midway between the particles.

We can extend this concept to a system of many particles with masses m_i in three dimensions. The x coordinate of the center of mass of n particles is defined to be

$$x_{CM} \equiv \frac{m_1x_1 + m_2x_2 + m_3x_3 + \cdots + m_nx_n}{m_1 + m_2 + m_3 + \cdots + m_n} = \frac{\sum\limits_i m_ix_i}{\sum\limits_i m_i} = \frac{\sum\limits_i m_ix_i}{M} = \frac{1}{M}\sum\limits_i m_ix_i \quad (9.29)$$

where x_i is the x coordinate of the ith particle and the total mass is $M \equiv \sum\limits_i m_i$ where the sum runs over all n particles. The y and z coordinates of the center of mass are similarly defined by the equations

$$y_{CM} \equiv \frac{1}{M}\sum\limits_i m_iy_i \quad \text{and} \quad z_{CM} \equiv \frac{1}{M}\sum\limits_i m_iz_i \quad (9.30)$$

The center of mass can be located in three dimensions by its position vector $\vec{r}_{CM}$. The components of this vector are x_{CM}, y_{CM}, and z_{CM}, defined in Equations 9.29 and 9.30. Therefore,

$$\vec{r}_{CM} = x_{CM}\hat{i} + y_{CM}\hat{j} + z_{CM}\hat{k} = \frac{1}{M}\sum\limits_i m_ix_i\hat{i} + \frac{1}{M}\sum\limits_i m_iy_i\hat{j} + \frac{1}{M}\sum\limits_i m_iz_i\hat{k}$$

$$\vec{r}_{CM} \equiv \frac{1}{M}\sum\limits_i m_i\vec{r}_i \quad (9.31)$$

where $\vec{r}_i$ is the position vector of the ith particle, defined by

$$\vec{r}_i \equiv x_i\hat{i} + y_i\hat{j} + z_i\hat{k}$$

Although locating the center of mass for an extended object is somewhat more cumbersome than locating the center of mass of a system of particles, the basic ideas we have discussed still apply. Think of an extended object as a system containing a large number of particles (Fig. 9.15). Because the particle separation is very small, the object can be considered to have a continuous mass distribution. By dividing the object into elements of mass Δm_i with coordinates x_i, y_i, z_i, we see that the x coordinate of the center of mass is approximately

$$x_{CM} \approx \frac{1}{M}\sum\limits_i x_i\,\Delta m_i$$

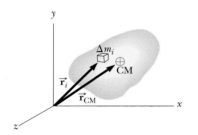

Figure 9.15 An extended object can be considered to be a distribution of small elements of mass Δm_i. The center of mass is located at the vector position $\vec{r}_{CM}$, which has coordinates x_{CM}, y_{CM}, and z_{CM}.

with similar expressions for y_{CM} and z_{CM}. If we let the number of elements n approach infinity, the size of each element approaches zero and x_{CM} is given precisely. In this limit, we replace the sum by an integral and Δm_i by the differential element dm:

$$x_{CM} = \lim_{\Delta m_i \to 0} \frac{1}{M}\sum\limits_i x_i\,\Delta m_i = \frac{1}{M}\int x\,dm \quad (9.32)$$

Likewise, for y_{CM} and z_{CM} we obtain

$$y_{CM} = \frac{1}{M}\int y\,dm \quad \text{and} \quad z_{CM} = \frac{1}{M}\int z\,dm \quad (9.33)$$

We can express the vector position of the center of mass of an extended object in the form

$$\vec{r}_{CM} = \frac{1}{M}\int \vec{r}\,dm \quad (9.34)$$

which is equivalent to the three expressions given by Equations 9.32 and 9.33.

The center of mass of any symmetric object lies on an axis of symmetry and on any plane of symmetry.[3] For example, the center of mass of a uniform rod lies in the rod, midway between its ends. The center of mass of a sphere or a cube lies at its geometric center.

The center of mass of an irregularly shaped object such as a wrench can be determined by suspending the object first from one point and then from another. In Figure 9.16, a wrench is hung from point A and a vertical line AB (which can be established with a plumb bob) is drawn when the wrench has stopped swinging. The wrench is then hung from point C, and a second vertical line CD is drawn. The center of mass is halfway through the thickness of the wrench, under the intersection of these two lines. In general, if the wrench is hung freely from any point, the vertical line through this point must pass through the center of mass.

Because an extended object is a continuous distribution of mass, each small mass element is acted upon by the gravitational force. The net effect of all these forces is equivalent to the effect of a single force $M\vec{g}$ acting through a special point, called the **center of gravity.** If $\vec{g}$ is constant over the mass distribution, the center of gravity coincides with the center of mass. If an extended object is pivoted at its center of gravity, it balances in any orientation.

Figure 9.16 An experimental technique for determining the center of mass of a wrench. The wrench is hung freely first from point A and then from point C. The intersection of the two lines AB and CD locates the center of mass.

Quick Quiz 9.7 A baseball bat of uniform density is cut at the location of its center of mass as shown in Figure 9.17. Which piece has the smaller mass? (a) the piece on the right   (b) the piece on the left   (c) both pieces have the same mass   (d) impossible to determine

Figure 9.17 (Quick Quiz 9.7) A baseball bat cut at the location of its center of mass.

EXAMPLE 9.10   **The Center of Mass of Three Particles**

A system consists of three particles located as shown in Figure 9.18. Find the center of mass of the system.

SOLUTION

Conceptualize Figure 9.18 shows the three masses. Your intuition should tell you that the center of mass is located somewhere in the region between the orange particle and the pair of particles colored blue and green as shown in the figure.

Categorize We categorize this example as a substitution problem because we will be using the equations for the center of mass developed in this section.

We set up the problem by labeling the masses of the particles as shown in the figure, with $m_1 = m_2 = 1.0$ kg and $m_3 = 2.0$ kg.

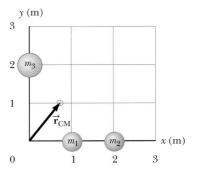

Figure 9.18 (Example 9.10) Two 1.0-kg particles are located on the x axis, and a single 2.0-kg particle is located on the y axis as shown. The vector indicates the location of the system's center of mass.

---

[3] This statement is valid only for objects that have a uniform density.

Use the defining equations for the coordinates of the center of mass and notice that $z_{CM} = 0$:

$$x_{CM} = \frac{1}{M} \sum_i m_i x_i = \frac{m_1 x_1 + m_2 x_2 + m_3 x_3}{m_1 + m_2 + m_3}$$

$$= \frac{(1.0 \text{ kg})(1.0 \text{ m}) + (1.0 \text{ kg})(2.0 \text{ m}) + (2.0 \text{ kg})(0)}{1.0 \text{ kg} + 1.0 \text{ kg} + 2.0 \text{ kg}}$$

$$= \frac{3.0 \text{ kg} \cdot \text{m}}{4.0 \text{ kg}} = 0.75 \text{ m}$$

$$y_{CM} = \frac{1}{M} \sum_i m_i y_i = \frac{m_1 y_1 + m_2 y_2 + m_3 y_3}{m_1 + m_2 + m_3}$$

$$= \frac{(1.0 \text{ kg})(0) + (1.0 \text{ kg})(0) + (2.0 \text{ kg})(2.0 \text{ m})}{4.0 \text{ kg}} = \frac{4.0 \text{ kg} \cdot \text{m}}{4.0 \text{ kg}} = 1.0 \text{ m}$$

Write the position vector of the center of mass:

$$\vec{r}_{CM} \equiv x_{CM}\hat{i} + y_{CM}\hat{j} = (0.75\hat{i} + 1.0\hat{j}) \text{ m}$$

EXAMPLE 9.11 | **The Center of Mass of a Rod**

(A) Show that the center of mass of a rod of mass M and length L lies midway between its ends, assuming the rod has a uniform mass per unit length.

SOLUTION

Conceptualize The rod is shown aligned along the x axis in Figure 9.19, so $y_{CM} = z_{CM} = 0$.

Figure 9.19 (Example 9.11) The geometry used to find the center of mass of a uniform rod.

Categorize We categorize this example as an analysis problem because we need to divide the rod up into elements to perform the integration in Equation 9.32.

Analyze The mass per unit length (this quantity is called the *linear mass density*) can be written as $\lambda = M/L$ for the uniform rod. If the rod is divided into elements of length dx, the mass of each element is $dm = \lambda\, dx$.

Use Equation 9.32 to find an expression for x_{CM}:

$$x_{CM} = \frac{1}{M} \int x\, dm = \frac{1}{M} \int_0^L x\lambda\, dx = \frac{\lambda}{M} \frac{x^2}{2}\Big|_0^L = \frac{\lambda L^2}{2M}$$

Substitute $\lambda = M/L$:

$$x_{CM} = \frac{L^2}{2M}\left(\frac{M}{L}\right) = \frac{L}{2}$$

One can also use symmetry arguments to obtain the same result.

(B) Suppose a rod is *nonuniform* such that its mass per unit length varies linearly with x according to the expression $\lambda = \alpha x$, where α is a constant. Find the x coordinate of the center of mass as a fraction of L.

SOLUTION

Conceptualize Because the mass per unit length is not constant but is proportional to x, elements of the rod to the right are more massive than elements near the left end of the rod.

Categorize This problem is categorized similarly to part (A), with the added twist that the linear mass density is not constant.

Analyze In this case, we replace dm in Equation 9.32 by $\lambda\, dx$, where $\lambda = \alpha x$.

Use Equation 9.32 to find an expression for x_{CM}:

$$x_{CM} = \frac{1}{M}\int x\,dm = \frac{1}{M}\int_0^L x\lambda\,dx = \frac{1}{M}\int_0^L x\alpha x\,dx$$

$$= \frac{\alpha}{M}\int_0^L x^2\,dx = \frac{\alpha L^3}{3M}$$

Find the total mass of the rod:

$$M = \int dm = \int_0^L \lambda\,dx = \int_0^L \alpha x\,dx = \frac{\alpha L^2}{2}$$

Substitute M into the expression for x_{CM}:

$$x_{CM} = \frac{\alpha L^3}{3\alpha L^2/2} = \tfrac{2}{3}L$$

Finalize   Notice that the center of mass in part (B) is farther to the right than that in part (A). That result is reasonable because the elements of the rod become more massive as one moves to the right along the rod in part (B).

EXAMPLE 9.12   **The Center of Mass of a Right Triangle**

You have been asked to hang a metal sign from a single vertical wire. The sign has the triangular shape shown in Figure 9.20a. The bottom of the sign is to be parallel to the ground. At what distance from the left end of the sign should you attach the support wire?

SOLUTION

Conceptualize   Figure 9.20a shows the sign hanging from the wire. The wire must be attached at a point directly above the center of gravity of the sign, which is the same as its center of mass because it is in a uniform gravitational field.

Categorize   As in the case of Example 9.11, we categorize this example as an analysis problem because it is necessary to identify infinitesimal elements of the sign to perform the integration in Equation 9.32.

Analyze   We assume the triangular sign has a uniform density and total mass M. Because the sign is a continuous distribution of mass, we must use the integral expression in Equation 9.32 to find the x coordinate of the center of mass.

We divide the triangle into narrow strips of width dx and height y as shown in Figure 9.20b, where y is the height of the hypotenuse of the triangle above the x axis for a given value of x. The mass of each strip is the product of the volume of the strip and the density ρ of the material from which the sign is made: $dm = \rho yt\,dx$, where t is the thickness of the metal sign. The density of the material is the total mass of the sign divided by its total volume (area of the triangle times thickness).

Figure 9.20   (Example 9.12) (a) A triangular sign to be hung from a single wire. (b) Geometric construction for locating the center of mass.

Evaluate dm:

$$dm = \rho yt\,dx = \left(\frac{M}{\frac{1}{2}abt}\right)yt\,dx = \frac{2My}{ab}\,dx$$

Use Equation 9.32 to find the x coordinate of the center of mass:

$$(1)\quad x_{CM} = \frac{1}{M}\int x\,dm = \frac{1}{M}\int_0^a x\frac{2My}{ab}\,dx = \frac{2}{ab}\int_0^a xy\,dx$$

To proceed further and evaluate the integral, we must express y in terms of x. The line representing the hypotenuse of the triangle in Figure 9.20b has a slope of b/a and passes through the origin, so the equation of this line is $y = (b/a)x$.

Substitute for y in Equation (1):

$$x_{CM} = \frac{2}{ab}\int_0^a x\left(\frac{b}{a}x\right)dx = \frac{2}{a^2}\int_0^a x^2 dx = \frac{2}{a^2}\left[\frac{x^3}{3}\right]_0^a$$

$$= \tfrac{2}{3}a$$

Therefore, the wire must be attached to the sign at a distance two-thirds of the length of the bottom edge from the left end.

Finalize   This answer is identical to that in part (B) of Example 9.11. For the triangular sign, the linear increase in height y with position x means that elements in the sign increase in mass linearly, reflecting the linear increase in mass density in Example 9.11. We could also find the y coordinate of the center of mass of the sign, but that is not needed to determine where the wire should be attached. You might try cutting a right triangle out of cardboard and hanging it from a string so that the long base is horizontal. Does the string need to be attached at $\tfrac{2}{3}a$?

9.6   Motion of a System of Particles

We can begin to understand the physical significance and utility of the center of mass concept by taking the time derivative of the position vector for the center of mass given by Equation 9.31. From Section 4.1 we know that the time derivative of a position vector is by definition the velocity vector. Assuming M remains constant for a system of particles—that is, no particles enter or leave the system—we obtain the following expression for the **velocity of the center of mass** of the system:

◀ Velocity of the center of mass

$$\vec{\mathbf{v}}_{CM} = \frac{d\vec{\mathbf{r}}_{CM}}{dt} = \frac{1}{M}\sum_i m_i\frac{d\vec{\mathbf{r}}_i}{dt} = \frac{1}{M}\sum_i m_i\vec{\mathbf{v}}_i \tag{9.35}$$

where $\vec{\mathbf{v}}_i$ is the velocity of the ith particle. Rearranging Equation 9.35 gives

◀ Total momentum of a system of particles

$$M\vec{\mathbf{v}}_{CM} = \sum_i m_i\vec{\mathbf{v}}_i = \sum_i \vec{\mathbf{p}}_i = \vec{\mathbf{p}}_{tot} \tag{9.36}$$

Therefore, the **total linear momentum of the system equals the total mass multiplied by the velocity of the center of mass.** In other words, the total linear momentum of the system is equal to that of a single particle of mass M moving with a velocity $\vec{\mathbf{v}}_{CM}$.

Differentiating Equation 9.35 with respect to time, we obtain the **acceleration of the center of mass** of the system:

◀ Acceleration of the center of mass

$$\vec{\mathbf{a}}_{CM} = \frac{d\vec{\mathbf{v}}_{CM}}{dt} = \frac{1}{M}\sum_i m_i\frac{d\vec{\mathbf{v}}_i}{dt} = \frac{1}{M}\sum_i m_i\vec{\mathbf{a}}_i \tag{9.37}$$

Rearranging this expression and using Newton's second law gives

$$M\vec{\mathbf{a}}_{CM} = \sum_i m_i\vec{\mathbf{a}}_i = \sum_i \vec{\mathbf{F}}_i \tag{9.38}$$

where $\vec{\mathbf{F}}_i$ is the net force on particle i.

The forces on any particle in the system may include both external forces (from outside the system) and internal forces (from within the system). By Newton's third law, however, the internal force exerted by particle 1 on particle 2, for example, is equal in magnitude and opposite in direction to the internal force exerted by particle 2 on particle 1. Therefore, when we sum over all internal forces in Equation 9.38, they cancel in pairs and we find that the net force on the system is caused *only* by external forces. We can then write Equation 9.38 in the form

◀ Newton's second law for a system of particles

$$\sum \vec{\mathbf{F}}_{ext} = M\vec{\mathbf{a}}_{CM} \tag{9.39}$$

That is, **the net external force on a system of particles equals the total mass of the system multiplied by the acceleration of the center of mass.** Comparing Equation 9.39 with Newton's second law for a single particle, we see that the particle model we have used in several chapters can be described in terms of the center of mass:

The center of mass of a system of particles having combined mass M moves like an equivalent particle of mass M would move under the influence of the net external force on the system.

Let us integrate Equation 9.39 over a finite time interval:

$$\int \sum \vec{F}_{ext}\, dt = \int M\vec{a}_{CM}\, dt = \int M\frac{d\vec{v}_{CM}}{dt}\, dt = M\int d\vec{v}_{CM} = M\,\Delta\vec{v}_{CM}$$

Notice that this equation can be written as

$$\vec{I} = \Delta\vec{p}_{tot} \tag{9.40}$$

where $\vec{I}$ is the impulse imparted to the system by external forces and $\vec{p}_{tot}$ is the momentum of the system. Equation 9.40 is the generalization of the impulse-momentum theorem for a particle (Eq. 9.10) to a system of particles.

Finally, if the net external force on a system is zero, it follows from Equation 9.39 that

$$M\vec{a}_{CM} = M\frac{d\vec{v}_{CM}}{dt} = 0$$

so

$$M\vec{v}_{CM} = \vec{p}_{tot} = \text{constant} \quad (\text{when } \sum \vec{F}_{ext} = 0) \tag{9.41}$$

That is, the total linear momentum of a system of particles is conserved if no net external force is acting on the system. It follows that for an isolated system of particles, both the total momentum and the velocity of the center of mass are constant in time. This statement is a generalization of the law of conservation of momentum for a many-particle system.

Suppose an isolated system consisting of two or more members is at rest. The center of mass of such a system remains at rest unless acted upon by an external force. For example, consider a system of a swimmer standing on a raft, with the system initially at rest. When the swimmer dives horizontally off the raft, the raft moves in the direction opposite that of the swimmer and the center of mass of the system remains at rest (if we neglect friction between raft and water). Furthermore, the linear momentum of the diver is equal in magnitude to that of the raft, but opposite in direction.

Quick Quiz 9.8 A cruise ship is moving at constant speed through the water. The vacationers on the ship are eager to arrive at their next destination. They decide to try to speed up the cruise ship by gathering at the bow (the front) and running together toward the stern (the back) of the ship. **(i)** While they are running toward the stern, is the speed of the ship (a) higher than it was before, (b) unchanged, (c) lower than it was before, or (d) impossible to determine? **(ii)** The vacationers stop running when they reach the stern of the ship. After they have all stopped running, is the speed of the ship (a) higher than it was before they started running, (b) unchanged from what it was before they started running, (c) lower than it was before they started running, or (d) impossible to determine?

CONCEPTUAL EXAMPLE 9.13 | **Exploding Projectile**

A projectile fired into the air suddenly explodes into several fragments (Active Fig. 9.21).

(A) What can be said about the motion of the center of mass of the system made up of all the fragments after the explosion?

SOLUTION

Neglecting air resistance, the only external force on the projectile is the gravitational force. Therefore, if the projectile did not explode, it would continue to move along the parabolic path indicated by the dashed line in Active Figure 9.21. Because the forces caused by the explosion are internal, they do not affect the motion of the center of mass of the system (the fragments). Therefore, after the explosion, the center of mass of the fragments follows the same parabolic path the projectile would have followed if no explosion had occurred.

(B) If the projectile did not explode, it would land at a distance R from its launch point. Suppose the projectile explodes and splits into two pieces of equal mass. One piece lands at a distance $2R$ from the launch point. Where does the other piece land?

ACTIVE FIGURE 9.21

(Conceptual Example 9.13) When a projectile explodes into several fragments, the center of mass of the system made up of all the fragments follows the same parabolic path the projectile would have taken had there been no explosion.

Sign in at www.thomsonedu.com and go to ThomsonNOW to observe a variety of explosions and follow the trajectory of the center of mass.

SOLUTION

As discussed in part (A), the center of mass of the two-piece system lands at a distance R from the launch point. One of the pieces lands at a further distance R from the landing point (or a distance $2R$ from the launch point), to the right in Active Figure 9.21. Because the two pieces have the same mass, the other piece must land a distance R to the left of the landing point in Active Figure 9.21, which places this piece right back at the launch point!

EXAMPLE 9.14 | **The Exploding Rocket**

A rocket is fired vertically upward. At the instant it reaches an altitude of 1 000 m and a speed of 300 m/s, it explodes into three fragments having equal mass. One fragment moves upward with a speed of 450 m/s following the explosion. The second fragment has a speed of 240 m/s and is moving east right after the explosion. What is the velocity of the third fragment immediately after the explosion?

SOLUTION

Conceptualize Picture the explosion in your mind, with one piece going upward and a second piece moving horizontally toward the east. Do you have an intuitive feeling about the direction in which the third piece moves?

Categorize This example is a two-dimensional problem because we have two fragments moving in perpendicular directions after the explosion as well as a third fragment moving in an unknown direction in the plane defined by the velocity vectors of the other two fragments. We assume the time interval of the explosion is very short, so we use the impulse approximation in which we ignore the gravitational force and air resistance. Because the forces of the explosion are internal to the system (the rocket), the system is modeled as isolated and the total momentum $\vec{\mathbf{p}}_i$ of the rocket immediately before the explosion must equal the total momentum $\vec{\mathbf{p}}_f$ of the fragments immediately after the explosion.

Analyze Because the three fragments have equal mass, the mass of each fragment is $M/3$, where M is the total mass of the rocket. We will let $\vec{\mathbf{v}}_f$ represent the unknown velocity of the third fragment.

Write an expression for the momentum of the system before the explosion:

$$\vec{\mathbf{p}}_i = M\vec{\mathbf{v}}_i = M(300\,\hat{\mathbf{j}}\,\text{m/s})$$

Write an expression for the momentum of the system after the explosion:

$$\vec{\mathbf{p}}_f = \frac{M}{3}(240\,\hat{\mathbf{i}}\,\text{m/s}) + \frac{M}{3}(450\,\hat{\mathbf{j}}\,\text{m/s}) + \frac{M}{3}\vec{\mathbf{v}}_f$$

Equate these two expressions:
$$\frac{M}{3}\vec{v}_f + \frac{M}{3}(240\,\hat{i}\,\text{m/s}) + \frac{M}{3}(450\,\hat{j}\,\text{m/s}) = M(300\,\hat{j}\,\text{m/s})$$

Solve for $\vec{v}_f$:
$$\vec{v}_f = (-240\,\hat{i} + 450\,\hat{j})\,\text{m/s}$$

Finalize   Notice that this event is the reverse of a perfectly inelastic collision. There is one object before the collision and three objects afterward. Imagine running a movie of the event backward: the three objects would come together and become a single object. In a perfectly inelastic collision, the kinetic energy of the system decreases. If you were to calculate the kinetic energy before and after the event in this example, you would find that the kinetic energy of the system increases. (Try it!) This increase in kinetic energy comes from the potential energy stored in whatever fuel exploded to cause the breakup of the rocket.

9.7   Deformable Systems

So far in our discussion of mechanics, we have analyzed the motion of particles or nondeformable systems that can be modeled as particles. The discussion in Section 9.6 can be applied to an analysis of the motion of deformable systems. For example, suppose you stand on a skateboard and push off a wall, setting yourself in motion away from the wall. How would we describe this event?

The force from the wall on your hands moves through no displacement; the force is always located at the interface between the wall and your hands. Therefore, the force does no work on the system, which is you and your skateboard. Pushing off the wall, however, does indeed result in a change in the kinetic energy of the system. If you try to use the work–kinetic energy theorem, $W = \Delta K$, to describe this event, notice that the left side of the equation is zero but the right side is not zero. The work–kinetic energy theorem is not valid for this event and is often not valid for systems that are deformable. Your body has deformed during this event: your arms were bent before the event, and they straightened out while you pushed off the wall.

To analyze the motion of deformable systems, we appeal to Equation 8.2, the conservation of energy equation, and Equation 9.40, the impulse–momentum theorem for a system. For the example of you pushing off the wall on your skateboard, Equation 8.2 gives

$$\Delta E_{\text{system}} = \sum T$$

$$\Delta K + \Delta U = 0$$

where ΔK is the change in kinetic energy due to the increased speed of the system and ΔU is the decrease in potential energy stored in the body from previous meals. This equation tells us that the system transformed potential energy into kinetic energy by virtue of the muscular exertion necessary to push off the wall.

Applying Equation 9.40 to this situation gives us

$$\vec{I} = \Delta\vec{p}_{\text{tot}}$$

$$\int \vec{F}_{\text{wall}}\,dt = m\,\Delta\vec{v}$$

where $\vec{F}_{\text{wall}}$ is the force exerted by the wall on your hands, m is the mass of you and the skateboard, and $\Delta\vec{v}$ is the change in the velocity of the system during the event. To evaluate the left side of this equation, we would need to know how the force from the wall varies in time. In general, this process might be complicated. In the case of constant forces, or well-behaved forces, however, the integral on the left side of the equation can be evaluated.

Pushing on a Spring[4]

As shown in Figure 9.22a, two blocks are at rest on a level, frictionless table. Both blocks have the same mass m, and they are connected by a spring of negligible mass. The separation distance of the blocks when the spring is relaxed is L. During a time interval Δt, a constant force F is applied horizontally to the left block, moving it through a distance x_1 as shown in Figure 9.22b. During this time interval, the right block moves through a distance x_2. At the end of this time interval, the force F is removed.

(A) Find the resulting speed $\vec{v}_{CM}$ of the center of mass of the system.

SOLUTION

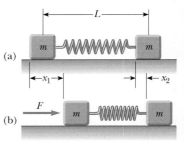

Conceptualize Imagine what happens as you push on the left block. It begins to move to the right in Figure 9.22, and the spring begins to compress. As a result, the spring pushes to the right on the right block, which begins to move to the right. At any given time, the blocks are generally moving with different velocities. As the center of mass of the system moves to the right, the two blocks oscillate back and forth with respect to the center of mass.

Figure 9.22 (Example 9.15) (a) Two blocks of equal mass are connected by a spring. (b) The left block is pushed with a constant force of magnitude F and moves a distance x_1 during some time interval. During this same time interval, the right block moves through a distance x_2.

Categorize The system of two blocks and a spring is a nonisolated system because work is being done on it by the applied force. It is also a deformable system. During the time interval Δt, the center of mass of the system moves a distance $\frac{1}{2}(x_1 + x_2)$. Because the applied force on the system is constant, the acceleration of its center of mass is constant and the center of mass is modeled as a particle under constant acceleration.

Analyze We apply the impulse–momentum theorem to the system of two blocks, recognizing that the force F is constant during the time interval Δt while the force is applied.

Write Equation 9.40 for the system:

$$(1) \quad F\,\Delta t = (2m)(v_{CM} - 0) = 2mv_{CM}$$

Because the center of mass is modeled as a particle under constant acceleration, the average velocity of the center of mass is the average of the initial velocity, which is zero, and the final velocity v_{CM}.

Express the time interval in terms of v_{CM}:

$$\Delta t = \frac{\frac{1}{2}(x_1 + x_2)}{v_{CM,\,avg}} = \frac{\frac{1}{2}(x_1 + x_2)}{\frac{1}{2}(0 + v_{CM})} = \frac{(x_1 + x_2)}{v_{CM}}$$

Substitute this expression into Equation (1):

$$F\frac{(x_1 + x_2)}{v_{CM}} = 2mv_{CM}$$

Solve for v_{CM}:

$$v_{CM} = \sqrt{F\frac{(x_1 + x_2)}{2m}}$$

(B) Find the total energy of the system associated with vibration relative to its center of mass after the force F is removed.

SOLUTION

Analyze The vibrational energy is all the energy of the system other than the kinetic energy associated with translational motion of the center of mass. To find the vibrational energy, we apply the conservation of energy equation. The kinetic energy of the system can be expressed as $K = K_{CM} + K_{vib}$, where K_{vib} is the kinetic energy of the blocks relative to the center of mass due to their vibration. The potential energy of the system is U_{vib}, which is the potential energy stored in the spring when the separation of the blocks is some value other than L.

Express Equation 8.2 for this system:

$$(2) \quad \Delta K_{CM} + \Delta K_{vib} + \Delta U_{vib} = W$$

[4] Example 9.15 was inspired in part by C. E. Mungan, "A primer on work–energy relationships for introductory physics," *The Physics Teacher,* 43:10, 2005.

Express Equation (2) in an alternate form, noting that $K_{vib} + U_{vib} = E_{vib}$:

$$\Delta K_{CM} + \Delta E_{vib} = W$$

The initial values of the kinetic energy of the center of mass and the vibrational energy of the system are zero:

$$K_{CM} + E_{vib} = W = Fx_1$$

Solve for the vibrational energy and use the result to part (A):

$$E_{vib} = Fx_1 - K_{CM} = Fx_1 - \tfrac{1}{2}(2m)v_{CM}^2 = \boxed{F\frac{(x_1 - x_2)}{2}}$$

Finalize   Neither of the two answers in this example depends on the spring length, the spring constant, or the time interval. Notice also that the magnitude x_1 of the displacement of the point of application of the applied force is different from the magnitude $\tfrac{1}{2}(x_1 + x_2)$ of the displacement of the center of mass of the system. This difference reminds us that the displacement in the definition of work is that of the point of application of the force.

9.8 Rocket Propulsion

When ordinary vehicles such as cars are propelled, the driving force for the motion is friction. In the case of the car, the driving force is the force exerted by the road on the car. A rocket moving in space, however, has no road to push against. Therefore, the source of the propulsion of a rocket must be something other than friction. **The operation of a rocket depends on the law of conservation of linear momentum as applied to a system of particles, where the system is the rocket plus its ejected fuel.**

Rocket propulsion can be understood by first considering our archer standing on frictionless ice in Example 9.1. Imagine that the archer fires several arrows horizontally. For each arrow fired, the archer receives a compensating momentum in the opposite direction. As more arrows are fired, the archer moves faster and faster across the ice.

In a similar manner, as a rocket moves in free space, its linear momentum changes when some of its mass is ejected in the form of exhaust gases. **Because the gases are given momentum when they are ejected out of the engine, the rocket receives a compensating momentum in the opposite direction.** Therefore, the rocket is accelerated as a result of the "push," or thrust, from the exhaust gases. In free space, the center of mass of the system (rocket plus expelled gases) moves uniformly, independent of the propulsion process.[5]

Suppose at some time t that the magnitude of the momentum of a rocket plus its fuel is $(M + \Delta m)v$, where v is the speed of the rocket relative to the Earth (Fig. 9.23a). Over a short time interval Δt, the rocket ejects fuel of mass Δm. At the end of this interval, the rocket's mass is M and its speed is $v + \Delta v$, where Δv is the change in speed of the rocket (Fig. 9.23b). If the fuel is ejected with a speed v_e relative to the rocket (the subscript e stands for *exhaust*, and v_e is usually called the *exhaust speed*), the velocity of the fuel relative to the Earth is $v - v_e$. If we equate the total initial momentum of the system to the total final momentum, we obtain

$$(M + \Delta m)v = M(v + \Delta v) + \Delta m(v - v_e)$$

Simplifying this expression gives

$$M\Delta v = v_e\,\Delta m$$

If we now take the limit as Δt goes to zero, we let $\Delta v \rightarrow dv$ and $\Delta m \rightarrow dm$. Furthermore, the increase in the exhaust mass dm corresponds to an equal decrease

Figure 9.23   Rocket propulsion. (a) The initial mass of the rocket plus all its fuel is $M + \Delta m$ at a time t, and its speed is v. (b) At a time $t + \Delta t$, the rocket's mass has been reduced to M and an amount of fuel Δm has been ejected. The rocket's speed increases by an amount Δv.

The force from a nitrogen-propelled hand-controlled device allows an astronaut to move about freely in space without restrictive tethers, using the thrust force from the expelled nitrogen.

[5] The rocket and the archer represent cases of the reverse of a perfectly inelastic collision: momentum is conserved, but the kinetic energy of the rocket-exhaust gas system increases (at the expense of chemical potential energy in the fuel), as does the kinetic energy of the archer-arrow system (at the expense of potential energy from the archer's previous meals).

in the rocket mass, so $dm = -dM$. Notice that dM is negative because it represents a decrease in mass, so $-dM$ is a positive number. Using this fact gives

$$M \, dv = v_e \, dm = -v_e \, dM \tag{9.42}$$

Now divide the equation by M and integrate, taking the initial mass of the rocket plus fuel to be M_i and the final mass of the rocket plus its remaining fuel to be M_f. The result is

$$\int_{v_i}^{v_f} dv = -v_e \int_{M_i}^{M_f} \frac{dM}{M}$$

Expression for rocket propulsion ▶

$$v_f - v_i = v_e \ln\!\left(\frac{M_i}{M_f}\right) \tag{9.43}$$

which is the basic expression for rocket propulsion. First, Equation 9.43 tells us that the increase in rocket speed is proportional to the exhaust speed v_e of the ejected gases. Therefore, the exhaust speed should be very high. Second, the increase in rocket speed is proportional to the natural logarithm of the ratio M_i/M_f. Therefore, this ratio should be as large as possible, that is, the mass of the rocket without its fuel should be as small as possible and the rocket should carry as much fuel as possible.

The **thrust** on the rocket is the force exerted on it by the ejected exhaust gases. We obtain the following expression for the thrust from Newton's second law and Equation 9.42:

$$\text{Thrust} = M\frac{dv}{dt} = \left| v_e \frac{dM}{dt} \right| \tag{9.44}$$

This expression shows that the thrust increases as the exhaust speed increases and as the rate of change of mass (called the *burn rate*) increases.

EXAMPLE 9.16 | Fighting a Fire

Two firefighters must apply a total force of 600 N to steady a hose that is discharging water at the rate of 3 600 L/min. Estimate the speed of the water as it exits the nozzle.

SOLUTION

Conceptualize As the water leaves the hose, it acts in a way similar to the gases being ejected from a rocket engine. As a result, a force (thrust) acts on the firefighters in a direction opposite the direction of motion of the water. In this case, we want the end of the hose to be a particle in equilibrium rather than to accelerate as in the case of the rocket. Consequently, the firefighters must apply a force of magnitude equal to the thrust in the opposite direction to keep the end of the hose stationary.

Categorize This example is a substitution problem in which we use given values in an equation derived in this section. The water exits at 3 600 L/min, which is 60 L/s. Knowing that 1 L of water has a mass of 1 kg, we estimate that about 60 kg of water leaves the nozzle each second.

Use Equation 9.44 for the thrust:

$$\text{Thrust} = \left| v_e \frac{dM}{dt} \right|$$

Substitute the known values:

$$600\text{ N} = \left| v_e (60 \text{ kg/s}) \right|$$

Solve for the exhaust speed:

$$v_e = \boxed{10 \text{ m/s}}$$

EXAMPLE 9.17   **A Rocket in Space**

A rocket moving in space, far from all other objects, has a speed of 3.0×10^3 m/s relative to the Earth. Its engines are turned on, and fuel is ejected in a direction opposite the rocket's motion at a speed of 5.0×10^3 m/s relative to the rocket.

(A) What is the speed of the rocket relative to the Earth once the rocket's mass is reduced to half its mass before ignition?

SOLUTION

Conceptualize   From the discussion in this section and scenes from science fiction movies, we can easily imagine the rocket accelerating to a higher speed as the engine operates.

Categorize   This problem is a substitution problem in which we use given values in the equations derived in this section.

Solve Equation 9.43 for the final velocity and substitute the known values:

$$v_f = v_i + v_e \ln\left(\frac{M_i}{M_f}\right)$$

$$= 3.0 \times 10^3 \text{ m/s} + (5.0 \times 10^3 \text{ m/s})\ln\left(\frac{M_i}{0.5M_i}\right)$$

$$= \boxed{6.5 \times 10^3 \text{ m/s}}$$

(B) What is the thrust on the rocket if it burns fuel at the rate of 50 kg/s?

SOLUTION

Use Equation 9.44 and the result to part (A), noting that $dM/dt = 50$ kg/s:

$$\text{Thrust} = \left|v_e \frac{dM}{dt}\right| = (5.0 \times 10^3 \text{ m/s})(50 \text{ kg/s}) = \boxed{2.5 \times 10^5 \text{ N}}$$

Summary

ThomsonNOW Sign in at **www.thomsonedu.com** and go to ThomsonNOW to take a practice test for this chapter.

DEFINITIONS

The **linear momentum** $\vec{\mathbf{p}}$ of a particle of mass m moving with a velocity $\vec{\mathbf{v}}$ is

$$\vec{\mathbf{p}} \equiv m\vec{\mathbf{v}} \tag{9.2}$$

The **impulse** imparted to a particle by a net force $\sum \vec{\mathbf{F}}$ is equal to the time integral of the force:

$$\vec{\mathbf{I}} \equiv \int_{t_i}^{t_f} \sum \vec{\mathbf{F}} \, dt \tag{9.9}$$

An **inelastic collision** is one for which the total kinetic energy of the system of colliding particles is not conserved. A **perfectly inelastic collision** is one in which the colliding particles stick together after the collision. An **elastic collision** is one in which the kinetic energy of the system is conserved.

The position vector of the **center of mass** of a system of particles is defined as

$$\vec{\mathbf{r}}_{CM} \equiv \frac{1}{M} \sum_i m_i \vec{\mathbf{r}}_i \tag{9.31}$$

where $M = \sum_i m_i$ is the total mass of the system and $\vec{\mathbf{r}}_i$ is the position vector of the ith particle.

CONCEPTS AND PRINCIPLES

The position vector of the center of mass of an extended object can be obtained from the integral expression

$$\vec{\mathbf{r}}_{CM} = \frac{1}{M} \int \vec{\mathbf{r}} \, dm \tag{9.34}$$

The velocity of the center of mass for a system of particles is

$$\vec{\mathbf{v}}_{CM} = \frac{\sum_i m_i \vec{\mathbf{v}}_i}{M} \tag{9.35}$$

The total momentum of a system of particles equals the total mass multiplied by the velocity of the center of mass.

Newton's second law applied to a system of particles is

$$\sum \vec{\mathbf{F}}_{ext} = M\vec{\mathbf{a}}_{CM} \tag{9.39}$$

where $\vec{\mathbf{a}}_{CM}$ is the acceleration of the center of mass and the sum is over all external forces. The center of mass moves like an imaginary particle of mass M under the influence of the resultant external force on the system.

ANALYSIS MODELS FOR PROBLEM SOLVING

Nonisolated System (Momentum). If a system interacts with its environment in the sense that there is an external force on the system, the behavior of the system is described by the **impulse-momentum theorem:**

$$\vec{\mathbf{I}} = \Delta\vec{\mathbf{p}}_{tot} \tag{9.40}$$

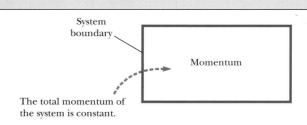

The total momentum of the system is constant.

Isolated System (Momentum). The principle of **conservation of linear momentum** indicates that the total momentum of an isolated system (no external forces) is conserved regardless of the nature of the forces between the members of the system:

$$M\vec{\mathbf{v}}_{CM} = \vec{\mathbf{p}}_{tot} = \text{constant} \left(\text{when } \sum \vec{\mathbf{F}}_{ext} = 0\right) \tag{9.41}$$

In the case of a two-particle system, this principle can be expressed as

$$\vec{\mathbf{p}}_{1i} + \vec{\mathbf{p}}_{2i} = \vec{\mathbf{p}}_{1f} + \vec{\mathbf{p}}_{2f} \tag{9.5}$$

The system may be isolated in terms of momentum but nonisolated in terms of energy, as in the case of inelastic collisions.

Questions

☐ denotes answer available in *Student Solutions Manual/Study Guide;* **O** denotes objective question

1. (a) Does a larger net force exerted on an object always produce a larger change in the momentum of the object compared with a smaller net force? Explain. (b) Does a larger net force always produce a larger change in kinetic energy than a smaller net force? Explain.

2. **O** (i) The momentum of a certain object is made four times larger in magnitude. By what factor is its kinetic energy changed? (a) 16 (b) 8 (c) 4 (d) 2 (e) 1 **(ii)** The kinetic energy of an object is made four times larger. By what factor is the magnitude of its momentum changed? (a) 16 (b) 8 (c) 4 (d) 2 (e) 1

3. **O (i)** If two particles have equal momenta, are their kinetic energies equal? (a) yes (b) no (c) if and only if their masses are equal **(ii)** If two particles have equal kinetic energies, are their momenta equal? (a) yes (b) no (c) if and only if their masses are equal (d) if and only if their masses and directions of motion are the same

4. **O** Two particles of different mass start from rest. The same net force acts on both of them as they move over equal distances. **(i)** How do their final kinetic energies compare? (a) The particle of larger mass has more kinetic energy. (b) The particle of smaller mass has more kinetic energy. (c) The particles have equal kinetic energies. (d) Either particle might have more kinetic energy. **(ii)** How do the magnitudes of their momentum compare? (a) The particle of larger mass has more momentum. (b) The particle of smaller mass has more momentum. (c) The particles have equal momenta. (d) Either particle might have more momentum.

5. While in motion, a pitched baseball carries kinetic energy and momentum. (a) Can we say that it carries a force that it can exert on any object it strikes? (b) Can the baseball deliver more kinetic energy to the object it strikes than the ball carries initially? (c) Can the baseball deliver to the object it strikes more momentum than the ball carries initially? Explain your answers.

6. **O** A basketball is tossed up into the air, falls freely, and bounces from the wooden floor. From the moment after the player releases it until the ball reaches the top of its bounce, what is the smallest system for which momentum is conserved? (a) the ball (b) the ball plus player (c) the ball plus floor (d) the ball plus Earth (e) momentum is not conserved

7. A bomb, initially at rest, explodes into several pieces. (a) Is linear momentum of the system conserved? (b) Is kinetic energy of the system conserved? Explain.

8. You are standing perfectly still and then you take a step forward. Before the step your momentum was zero, but afterward you have some momentum. Is the principle of conservation of momentum violated in this case?

9. **O** A massive manure spreader rolls down a country road. In a perfectly inelastic collision, a small sports car runs into the machine from behind. **(i)** Which vehicle experiences a change in momentum of larger magnitude? (a) The car does. (b) The manure spreader does. (c) Their momentum changes are the same size. (d) It could be either. **(ii)** Which vehicle experiences a larger change in kinetic energy? (a) The car does. (b) The manure spreader does. (c) Their kinetic energy changes are the same size. (d) It could be either vehicle.

10. A sharpshooter fires a rifle while standing with the butt of the gun against her shoulder. If the forward momentum of a bullet is the same as the backward momentum of the gun, why isn't it as dangerous to be hit by the gun as by the bullet?

11. **O** A ball is suspended by a string that is tied to a fixed point above a wooden block standing on end. The ball is pulled back as shown in Figure Q9.11 and released. In trial (a), the ball rebounds elastically from the block. In trial (b), two-sided tape causes the ball to stick to the block. **(i)** In which case, (a) or (b), is the ball more likely to knock the block over? Or (c) does it make no difference? Or (d) could it be either case depending on other factors? **(ii)** In which case, (a) or (b), is there a larger momentary temperature increase in the ball and the adjacent bit of wood? Or (c) is it the same for both? Or (d) is there no temperature increase anyway?

Figure Q9.11

12. A pole-vaulter falls from a height of 6.0 m onto a foam rubber pad. Can you calculate his speed immediately before he reaches the pad? Can you calculate the force exerted on him by the pad? Explain.

13. Two students hold a large bedsheet vertically between them. A third student, who happens to be the star pitcher on the school baseball team, throws a raw egg at the sheet. Explain why the egg does not break when it hits the sheet, regardless of its initial speed. (If you try this demonstration, make sure the pitcher hits the sheet near its center, and do not allow the egg to fall on the floor after it is caught.)

14. **O** You are standing on a saucer-shaped sled at rest in the middle of a frictionless ice rink. Your lab partner throws you a heavy Frisbee. You take different actions in successive experimental trials. Rank the following situations in order according to your final speed, from largest to smallest. If your final speed is the same in two cases, give them equal rank. (a) You catch the Frisbee and hold onto it. (b) You catch the Frisbee and throw it back to your partner. (c) You catch the Frisbee and throw it to a third person off to the side at a right angle. (d) You bobble the catch, just touching the Frisbee so that it continues in its original direction more slowly. (e) You catch the Frisbee and throw it so that it moves vertically upward above your

head. (f) You catch the Frisbee as it comes from the south, spin around, and throw it north several times faster. (g) You catch the Frisbee and set it down at rest on the ice.

15. A person balances a meterstick in a horizontal position on the extended index fingers of her right and left hands. She slowly brings the two fingers together. The stick remains balanced and the two fingers always meet at the 50-cm mark regardless of their original positions. (Try it!) Explain.

16. **O** As a railroad train is assembled, a yard engine releases one boxcar in motion at the top of a hump. The car rolls down quietly and without friction. Switches are set to shunt it onto a straight, level track where it couples with a flatcar of smaller mass, originally at rest, so that the two cars then roll together without friction. Consider the two cars as a system from the moment of release of the boxcar until both are rolling together. (a) Is mechanical energy of the system conserved? (b) Is momentum conserved? Next, consider the process of the boxcar gaining speed as it rolls down the hump. For the boxcar and the Earth as a system, (c) is mechanical energy conserved? (d) Is momentum conserved? Finally, consider the two cars as a system as the boxcar is slowing down in the coupling process. (e) Is mechanical energy of this system conserved? (f) Is momentum conserved?

17. A juggler juggles three balls in a continuous cycle. Any one ball is in contact with his hands for one-fifth of the time. Describe the motion of the center of mass of the three balls. What average force does the juggler exert on one ball while he is touching it?

18. Does the center of mass of a rocket in free space accelerate? Explain. Can the speed of a rocket exceed the exhaust speed of the fuel? Explain.

19. On the subject of the following positions, state your own view and argue to support it. (a) The best theory of motion is that force causes acceleration. (b) The true measure of a force's effectiveness is the work it does, and the best theory of motion is that work done on an object changes its energy. (c) The true measure of a force's effect is impulse, and the best theory of motion is that impulse imparted to an object changes its momentum.

Problems

WebAssign The Problems from this chapter may be assigned online in WebAssign.

ThomsonNOW™ Sign in at **www.thomsonedu.com** and go to ThomsonNOW to assess your understanding of this chapter's topics with additional quizzing and conceptual questions.

1, 2, 3 denotes straightforward, intermediate, challenging; ☐ denotes full solution available in *Student Solutions Manual/Study Guide;* ▲ denotes coached solution with hints available at **www.thomsonedu.com;** ▮ denotes developing symbolic reasoning; ● denotes asking for qualitative reasoning; ▮ denotes computer useful in solving problem

Section 9.1 Linear Momentum and Its Conservation

1. A 3.00-kg particle has a velocity of $(3.00\hat{i} - 4.00\hat{j})$ m/s. (a) Find its x and y components of momentum. (b) Find the magnitude and direction of its momentum.

2. ● A 65.0-kg boy and his 40.0-kg sister, both wearing roller blades, face each other at rest. The girl pushes the boy hard, sending him backward with velocity 2.90 m/s toward the west. Ignore friction. (a) Describe the subsequent motion of the girl. (b) How much chemical energy is converted into mechanical energy in the girl's muscles? (c) Is the momentum of the boy-girl system conserved in the pushing-apart process? How can it be, with large forces acting? How can it be, with no motion beforehand and plenty of motion afterward?

3. How fast can you set the Earth moving? In particular, when you jump straight up as high as you can, what is the order of magnitude of the maximum recoil speed that you give to the Earth? Model the Earth as a perfectly solid object. In your solution, state the physical quantities you take as data and the values you measure or estimate for them.

4. ● Two blocks of masses M and $3M$ are placed on a horizontal, frictionless surface. A light spring is attached to one of them, and the blocks are pushed together with the spring between them (Fig. P9.4). A cord initially holding the blocks together is burned; after that happens, the block of mass $3M$ moves to the right with a speed of 2.00 m/s. (a) What is the velocity of the block of mass M?

(b) Find the system's original elastic potential energy, taking $M = 0.350$ kg. (c) Is the original energy in the spring or in the cord? Explain your answer. (d) Is momentum of the system conserved in the bursting-apart process? How can it be, with large forces acting? How can it be, with no motion beforehand and plenty of motion afterward?

Figure P9.4

5. (a) A particle of mass m moves with momentum of magnitude p. Show that the kinetic energy of the particle is given by $K = p^2/2m$. (b) Express the magnitude of the particle's momentum in terms of its kinetic energy and mass.

Section 9.2 Impulse and Momentum

6. ● A friend claims that as long as he has his seat belt on, he can hold on to a 12.0-kg child in a 60.0 mi/h head-on

collision with a brick wall in which the car passenger compartment comes to a stop in 0.050 0 s. Is his claim true? Explain why he will experience a violent force during the collision, tearing the child from his arms. Evaluate the size of this force. (A child should always be in a toddler seat secured with a seat belt in the back seat of a car.)

7. An estimated force–time curve for a baseball struck by a bat is shown in Figure P9.7. From this curve, determine (a) the impulse delivered to the ball, (b) the average force exerted on the ball, and (c) the peak force exerted on the ball.

Figure P9.7

8. A ball of mass 0.150 kg is dropped from rest from a height of 1.25 m. It rebounds from the floor to reach a height of 0.960 m. What impulse was given to the ball by the floor?

9. ▲ A 3.00-kg steel ball strikes a wall with a speed of 10.0 m/s at an angle of 60.0° with the surface. It bounces off with the same speed and angle (Fig. P9.9). If the ball is in contact with the wall for 0.200 s, what is the average force exerted by the wall on the ball?

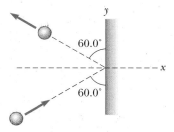

Figure P9.9

10. A tennis player receives a shot with the ball (0.060 0 kg) traveling horizontally at 50.0 m/s and returns the shot with the ball traveling horizontally at 40.0 m/s in the opposite direction. (a) What is the impulse delivered to the ball by the tennis racquet? (b) What work does the racquet do on the ball?

11. The magnitude of the net force exerted in the x direction on a 2.50-kg particle varies in time as shown in Figure P9.11. Find (a) the impulse of the force, (b) the final velocity the particle attains if it is originally at rest, (c) its

Figure P9.11

final velocity if its original velocity is −2.00 m/s, and (d) the average force exerted on the particle for the time interval between 0 and 5.00 s.

12. A *force platform* is a tool used to analyze the performance of athletes by measuring the vertical force that the athlete exerts on the ground as a function of time. Starting from rest, a 65.0-kg athlete jumps down onto the platform from a height of 0.600 m. While she is in contact with the platform during the time interval $0 < t < 0.800$ s, the force she exerts on it is described by the function

$$F = (9\,200\text{ N/s})t - (11\,500\text{ N/s}^2)t^2$$

(a) What impulse did the athlete receive from the platform? (b) With what speed did she reach the platform? (c) With what speed did she leave it? (d) To what height did she jump upon leaving the platform?

13. ● A glider of mass m is free to slide along a horizontal air track. It is pushed against a launcher at one end of the track. Model the launcher as a light spring of force constant k compressed by a distance x. The glider is released from rest. (a) Show that the glider attains a speed of $v = x(k/m)^{1/2}$. (b) Does a glider of large or of small mass attain a greater speed? (c) Show that the impulse imparted to the glider is given by the expression $x(km)^{1/2}$. (d) Is a greater impulse imparted to a large or a small mass? (e) Is more work done on a large or a small mass?

14. Water falls without splashing at a rate of 0.250 L/s from a height of 2.60 m into a 0.750-kg bucket on a scale. If the bucket is originally empty, what does the scale read 3.00 s after water starts to accumulate in it?

Section 9.3 Collisions in One Dimension

15. A 10.0-g bullet is fired into a stationary block of wood ($m = 5.00$ kg). The bullet imbeds into the block. The speed of the bullet-plus-wood combination immediately after the collision is 0.600 m/s. What was the original speed of the bullet?

16. A railroad car of mass 2.50×10^4 kg is moving with a speed of 4.00 m/s. It collides and couples with three other coupled railroad cars, each of the same mass as the single car and moving in the same direction with an initial speed of 2.00 m/s. (a) What is the speed of the four cars immediately after the collision? (b) How much energy is transformed into internal energy in the collision?

17. ● Four railroad cars, each of mass 2.50×10^4 kg, are coupled together and coasting along horizontal tracks at speed v_i toward the south. A very strong movie actor, riding on the second car, uncouples the front car and gives it a big push, increasing its speed to 4.00 m/s southward. The remaining three cars continue moving south, now at 2.00 m/s. (a) Find the initial speed of the cars. (b) How much work did the actor do? (c) State the relationship between the process described here and the process in Problem 16.

18. As shown in Figure P9.18 (page 262), a bullet of mass m and speed v passes completely through a pendulum bob of mass M. The bullet emerges with a speed of $v/2$. The pendulum bob is suspended by a stiff rod of length ℓ and negligible mass. What is the minimum value of v such that the pendulum bob will barely swing through a complete vertical circle?

2 = intermediate;   3 = challenging;   ☐ = SSM/SG;   ▲ = ThomsonNOW;   ▨ = symbolic reasoning;   ● = qualitative reasoning

Figure P9.18

19. Two blocks are free to slide along the frictionless wooden track ABC shown in Figure P9.19. The block of mass $m_1 = 5.00$ kg is released from A. Protruding from its front end is the north pole of a strong magnet, which is repelling the north pole of an identical magnet embedded in the back end of the block of mass $m_2 = 10.0$ kg, initially at rest. The two blocks never touch. Calculate the maximum height to which m_1 rises after the elastic collision.

Figure P9.19

20. A tennis ball of mass 57.0 g is held just above a basketball of mass 590 g. With their centers vertically aligned, both are released from rest at the same moment, to fall through a distance of 1.20 m, as shown in Figure P9.20. (a) Find the magnitude of the downward velocity with which the basketball reaches the ground. Assume an elastic collision with the ground instantaneously reverses the velocity of the basketball while the tennis ball is still moving down. Next, the two balls meet in an elastic collision. (b) To what height does the tennis ball rebound?

Figure P9.20

21. A 45.0-kg girl is standing on a plank that has a mass of 150 kg. The plank, originally at rest, is free to slide on a frozen lake that constitutes a flat, frictionless supporting surface. The girl begins to walk along the plank at a constant velocity of $1.50\hat{\mathbf{i}}$ m/s relative to the plank. (a) What is her velocity relative to the ice surface? (b) What is the velocity of the plank relative to the ice surface?

22. A 7.00-g bullet, when fired from a gun into a 1.00-kg block of wood held in a vise, penetrates the block to a depth of 8.00 cm. This block of wood is placed on a frictionless horizontal surface, and a second 7.00-g bullet is fired from the gun into the block. To what depth does the bullet penetrate the block in this case?

23. ▲ A neutron in a nuclear reactor makes an elastic head-on collision with the nucleus of a carbon atom initially at rest. (a) What fraction of the neutron's kinetic energy is transferred to the carbon nucleus? (b) The initial kinetic energy of the neutron is 1.60×10^{-13} J. Find its final kinetic energy and the kinetic energy of the carbon nucleus after the collision. (The mass of the carbon nucleus is nearly 12.0 times the mass of the neutron.)

24. ● (a) Three carts of masses 4.00 kg, 10.0 kg, and 3.00 kg move on a frictionless, horizontal track with speeds of 5.00 m/s, 3.00 m/s, and 4.00 m/s as shown in Figure P9.24. Velcro couplers make the carts stick together after colliding. Find the final velocity of the train of three carts. (b) **What If?** Does your answer require that all the carts collide and stick together at the same moment? What if they collide in a different order?

Figure P9.24

25. ▲ A 12.0-g wad of sticky clay is hurled horizontally at a 100-g wooden block initially at rest on a horizontal surface. The clay sticks to the block. After impact, the block slides 7.50 m before coming to rest. If the coefficient of friction between the block and the surface is 0.650, what was the speed of the clay immediately before impact?

Section 9.4 Collisions in Two Dimensions

26. ● In an American football game, a 90.0-kg fullback running east with a speed of 5.00 m/s is tackled by a 95.0-kg opponent running north with a speed of 3.00 m/s. (a) Explain why the successful tackle constitutes a perfectly inelastic collision. (b) Calculate the velocity of the players immediately after the tackle. (c) Determine the mechanical energy that disappears as a result of the collision. Account for the missing energy.

27. A billiard ball moving at 5.00 m/s strikes a stationary ball of the same mass. After the collision, the first ball moves, at 4.33 m/s, at an angle of 30.0° with respect to the original line of motion. Assuming an elastic collision (and ignoring friction and rotational motion), find the struck ball's velocity after the collision.

28. ● Two automobiles of equal mass approach an intersection. One vehicle is traveling with velocity 13.0 m/s toward the east, and the other is traveling north with speed v_{2i}. Neither driver sees the other. The vehicles collide in the intersection and stick together, leaving parallel skid marks at an angle of 55.0° north of east. The speed limit for both roads is 35 mi/h, and the driver of the northward-moving vehicle claims he was within the speed limit when the collision occurred. Is he telling the truth? Explain your reasoning.

29. Two shuffleboard disks of equal mass, one orange and the other yellow, are involved in an elastic, glancing collision. The yellow disk is initially at rest and is struck by the orange disk moving with a speed of 5.00 m/s. After the collision, the orange disk moves along a direction that

makes an angle of 37.0° with its initial direction of motion. The velocities of the two disks are perpendicular after the collision. Determine the final speed of each disk.

30. Two shuffleboard disks of equal mass, one orange and the other yellow, are involved in an elastic, glancing collision. The yellow disk is initially at rest and is struck by the orange disk moving with a speed v_i. After the collision, the orange disk moves along a direction that makes an angle θ with its initial direction of motion. The velocities of the two disks are perpendicular after the collision. Determine the final speed of each disk.

31. An object of mass 3.00 kg, moving with an initial velocity of $5.00\hat{i}$ m/s, collides with and sticks to an object of mass 2.00 kg with an initial velocity of $-3.00\hat{j}$ m/s. Find the final velocity of the composite object.

32. Two particles with masses m and $3m$ are moving toward each other along the x axis with the same initial speeds v_i. Particle m is traveling to the left, and particle $3m$ is traveling to the right. They undergo an elastic, glancing collision such that particle m is moving downward after the collision at a right angle from its initial direction. (a) Find the final speeds of the two particles. (b) What is the angle θ at which the particle $3m$ is scattered?

33. ▲ An unstable atomic nucleus of mass 17.0×10^{-27} kg initially at rest disintegrates into three particles. One of the particles, of mass 5.00×10^{-27} kg, moves in the y direction with a speed of 6.00×10^6 m/s. Another particle, of mass 8.40×10^{-27} kg, moves in the x direction with a speed of 4.00×10^6 m/s. Find (a) the velocity of the third particle and (b) the total kinetic energy increase in the process.

34. The mass of the blue puck in Figure P9.34 is 20.0% greater than the mass of the green puck. Before colliding, the pucks approach each other with momenta of equal magnitudes and opposite directions, and the green puck has an initial speed of 10.0 m/s. Find the speed each puck has after the collision if half the kinetic energy of the system becomes internal energy during the collision.

Figure P9.34

Section 9.5 The Center of Mass

35. Four objects are situated along the y axis as follows: a 2.00-kg object is located at $+3.00$ m, a 3.00-kg object is at $+2.50$ m, a 2.50-kg object is at the origin, and a 4.00-kg object is at -0.500 m. Where is the center of mass of these objects?

36. The mass of the Earth is 5.98×10^{24} kg, and the mass of the Moon is 7.36×10^{22} kg. The distance of separation, measured between their centers, is 3.84×10^8 m. Locate the center of mass of the Earth–Moon system as measured from the center of the Earth.

37. A uniform piece of sheet steel is shaped as shown in Figure P9.37. Compute the x and y coordinates of the center of mass of the piece.

Figure P9.37

38. (a) Consider an extended object whose different portions have different elevations. Assume the free-fall acceleration is uniform over the object. Prove that the gravitational potential energy of the object–Earth system is given by $U_g = Mgy_{CM}$, where M is the total mass of the object and y_{CM} is the elevation of its center of mass above the chosen reference level. (b) Calculate the gravitational potential energy associated with a ramp constructed on level ground with stone with density 3 800 kg/m³ and everywhere 3.60 m wide. In a side view, the ramp appears as a right triangle with height 15.7 m at the top end and base 64.8 m (Fig. P9.38).

Figure P9.38

39. A rod of length 30.0 cm has linear density (mass-per-length) given by

$$\lambda = 50.0 \text{ g/m} + 20.0x \text{ g/m}^2$$

where x is the distance from one end, measured in meters. (a) What is the mass of the rod? (b) How far from the $x = 0$ end is its center of mass?

40. In the 1968 Summer Olympic Games, University of Oregon high jumper Dick Fosbury introduced a new technique of high jumping called the "Fosbury flop." It contributed to raising the world record by about 30 cm and is presently used by nearly every world-class jumper. In this technique, the jumper goes over the bar face up while arching his back as much as possible as shown in Figure P9.40a. This action places his center of mass outside his body, below his back. As his body goes over the bar, his center of mass passes below the bar. Because a given energy input implies a certain elevation for his center of mass, the action of arching his back means his body is

(a)   (b)

Figure P9.40

higher than if his back were straight. As a model, consider the jumper as a thin, uniform rod of length L. When the rod is straight, its center of mass is at its center. Now bend the rod in a circular arc so that it subtends an angle of $90.0°$ at the center of the arc as shown in Figure P9.40b. In this configuration, how far outside the rod is the center of mass?

Section 9.6 Motion of a System of Particles

41. A 2.00-kg particle has a velocity $(2.00\hat{\mathbf{i}} - 3.00\hat{\mathbf{j}})$ m/s, and a 3.00-kg particle has a velocity $(1.00\hat{\mathbf{i}} + 6.00\hat{\mathbf{j}})$ m/s. Find (a) the velocity of the center of mass and (b) the total momentum of the system.

42. The vector position of a 3.50-g particle moving in the xy plane varies in time according to $\vec{\mathbf{r}}_1 = (3\hat{\mathbf{i}} + 3\hat{\mathbf{j}})t + 2\hat{\mathbf{j}}t^2$. At the same time, the vector position of a 5.50-g particle varies as $\vec{\mathbf{r}}_2 = 3\hat{\mathbf{i}} - 2\hat{\mathbf{i}}t^2 - 6\hat{\mathbf{j}}t$, where t is in s and r is in cm. At $t = 2.50$ s, determine (a) the vector position of the center of mass, (b) the linear momentum of the system, (c) the velocity of the center of mass, (d) the acceleration of the center of mass, and (e) the net force exerted on the two-particle system.

43. Romeo (77.0 kg) entertains Juliet (55.0 kg) by playing his guitar from the rear of their boat at rest in still water, 2.70 m away from Juliet, who is in the front of the boat. After the serenade, Juliet carefully moves to the rear of the boat (away from shore) to plant a kiss on Romeo's cheek. How far does the 80.0-kg boat move toward the shore it is facing?

44. A ball of mass 0.200 kg has a velocity of $1.50\hat{\mathbf{i}}$ m/s; a ball of mass 0.300 kg has a velocity of $-0.400\hat{\mathbf{i}}$ m/s. They meet in a head-on elastic collision. (a) Find their velocities after the collision. (b) Find the velocity of their center of mass before and after the collision.

Section 9.7 Deformable Systems

45. ● For a technology project, a student has built a vehicle, of total mass 6.00 kg, that moves itself. As shown in Figure P9.45, it runs on two light caterpillar tracks that pass around four light wheels. A reel is attached to one of the axles, and a cord originally wound on the reel passes over a pulley attached to the vehicle to support an elevated load. After the vehicle is released from rest, the load descends slowly, unwinding the cord to turn the axle and make the vehicle move forward. Friction is negligible in the pulley and axle bearings. The caterpillar tread does not slip on the wheels or the floor. The reel has a conical shape so that the load descends at a constant low speed

Figure P9.45

while the vehicle moves horizontally across the floor with constant acceleration, reaching final velocity $3.00\hat{\mathbf{i}}$ m/s. (a) Does the floor impart impulse to the vehicle? If so, how much? (b) Does the floor do work on the vehicle? If so, how much? (c) Does it make sense to say that the final momentum of the vehicle came from the floor? If not, from where? (d) Does it make sense to say that the final kinetic energy of the vehicle came from the floor? If not, from where? (e) Can we say that one particular force causes the forward acceleration of the vehicle? What does cause it?

46. ● A 60.0-kg person bends his knees and then jumps straight up. After his feet leave the floor his motion is unaffected by air resistance and his center of mass rises by a maximum of 15.0 cm. Model the floor as completely solid and motionless. (a) Does the floor impart impulse to the person? (b) Does the floor do work on the person? (c) With what momentum does the person leave the floor? (d) Does it make sense to say that this momentum came from the floor? Explain. (e) With what kinetic energy does the person leave the floor? (f) Does it make sense to say that this energy came from the floor? Explain.

47. ● A particle is suspended from a post on top of a cart by a light string of length L as shown in Figure P9.47a. The cart and particle are initially moving to the right at constant speed v_i, with the string vertical. The cart suddenly comes to rest when it runs into and sticks to a bumper as shown in Figure P9.47b. The suspended particle swings through an angle θ. (a) Show that the original speed of the cart can be computed from $v_i = \sqrt{2gL(1 - \cos\theta)}$. (b) Find the initial speed implied by $L = 1.20$ m and $\theta = 35.0°$. (c) Is the bumper still exerting a horizontal force on the cart when the hanging particle is at its maximum angle from the vertical? At what moment in the observable motion does the bumper stop exerting a horizontal force on the cart?

(a)   (b)

Figure P9.47

48. On a horizontal air track, a glider of mass m carries a Γ-shaped post. The post supports a small dense sphere, also of mass m, hanging just above the top of the glider on a cord of length L. The glider and sphere are initially at rest with the cord vertical. (Fig. P9.47a shows a cart and a sphere similarly connected.) A constant horizontal force of magnitude F is applied to the glider, moving it through displacement x_1; then the force is removed. During the time interval when the force is applied, the sphere moves through a displacement with horizontal component x_2. (a) Find the horizontal component of the velocity of the center of mass of the glider-sphere system when the force is removed. (b) After the force is removed, the glider continues to move on the track and the sphere swings back and forth, both without friction. Find an expression for the largest angle the cord makes with the vertical.

49. ● Sand from a stationary hopper falls onto a moving conveyor belt at the rate of 5.00 kg/s as shown in Figure P9.49. The conveyor belt is supported by frictionless rollers. It moves at a constant speed of 0.750 m/s under the action of a constant horizontal external force $\vec{F}_{ext}$ supplied by the motor that drives the belt. Find (a) the sand's rate of change of momentum in the horizontal direction, (b) the force of friction exerted by the belt on the sand, (c) the external force $\vec{F}_{ext}$, (d) the work done by $\vec{F}_{ext}$ in 1 s, and (e) the kinetic energy acquired by the falling sand each second due to the change in its horizontal motion. (f) Why are the answers to (d) and (e) different?

0.750 m/s

$\vec{F}_{ext}$

Figure P9.49

Section 9.8 Rocket Propulsion

50. Model rocket engines are sized by thrust, thrust duration, and total impulse, among other characteristics. A size C5 model rocket engine has an average thrust of 5.26 N, a fuel mass of 12.7 g, and an initial mass of 25.5 g. The duration of its burn is 1.90 s. (a) What is the average exhaust speed of the engine? (b) This engine is placed in a rocket body of mass 53.5 g. What is the final velocity of the rocket if it is fired in outer space? Assume the fuel burns at a constant rate.

51. ▲ The first stage of a Saturn V space vehicle consumed fuel and oxidizer at the rate of 1.50×10^4 kg/s, with an exhaust speed of 2.60×10^3 m/s. (a) Calculate the thrust produced by this engine. (b) Find the acceleration the vehicle had just as it lifted off the launch pad on the Earth, taking the vehicle's initial mass as 3.00×10^6 kg. *Note:* You must include the gravitational force to solve part (b).

52. *Rocket science.* A rocket has total mass $M_i = 360$ kg, including 330 kg of fuel and oxidizer. In interstellar space, it starts from rest at the position $x = 0$, turns on its engine at time $t = 0$, and puts out exhaust with relative speed $v_e = 1\,500$ m/s at the constant rate $k = 2.50$ kg/s. The fuel will last for an actual burn time of 330 kg/(2.5 kg/s) = 132 s, but define a "projected depletion time" as $T_p = M_i/k = 360$ kg/(2.5 kg/s) = 144 s (which would be the burn time if the rocket could use its payload and fuel tanks, and even the walls of the combustion chamber as fuel). (a) Show that during the burn the velocity of the rocket as a function of time is given by

$$v(t) = -v_e \ln\left(1 - \frac{t}{T_p}\right)$$

(b) Make a graph of the velocity of the rocket as a function of time for times running from 0 to 132 s. (c) Show that the acceleration of the rocket is

$$a(t) = \frac{v_e}{T_p - t}$$

(d) Graph the acceleration as a function of time. (e) Show that the position of the rocket is

$$x(t) = v_e(T_p - t)\ln\left(1 - \frac{t}{T_p}\right) + v_e t$$

(f) Graph the position during the burn as a function of time.

53. ● A rocket for use in deep space is to be capable of boosting a total load (payload plus rocket frame and engine) of 3.00 metric tons to a speed of 10 000 m/s. (a) It has an engine and fuel designed to produce an exhaust speed of 2 000 m/s. How much fuel plus oxidizer is required? (b) If a different fuel and engine design could give an exhaust speed of 5 000 m/s, what amount of fuel and oxidizer would be required for the same task? This exhaust speed is 2.50 times higher than that in part (a). Explain why the required fuel mass is 2.50 times smaller, or larger than that, or still smaller.

Additional Problems

54. Two gliders are set in motion on an air track. A spring of force constant k is attached to the back end of the second glider. The first glider, of mass m_1, has velocity $\vec{v}_1$, and the second glider, of mass m_2, moves more slowly, with velocity $\vec{v}_2$, as shown in Figure P9.54. When m_1 collides with the spring attached to m_2 and compresses the spring to its maximum compression x_{max}, the velocity of the gliders is $\vec{v}$. In terms of $\vec{v}_1$, $\vec{v}_2$, m_1, m_2, and k, find (a) the velocity $\vec{v}$ at maximum compression, (b) the maximum compression x_{max}, and (c) the velocity of each glider after m_1 has lost contact with the spring.

$\vec{v}_2$

k

m_2

$\vec{v}_1$

m_1

Figure P9.54

55. An 80.0-kg astronaut is taking a space walk to work on the engines of his ship, which is drifting through space with a constant velocity. The astronaut, wishing to get a better view of the Universe, pushes against the ship and much later finds himself 30.0 m behind the ship. Without a thruster or tether, the only way to return to the ship is to throw his 0.500-kg wrench directly away from the ship. If he throws the wrench with a speed of 20.0 m/s relative to the ship, after what time interval does the astronaut reach the ship?

56. ● An aging Hollywood actor (mass 80.0 kg) has been cloned, but the genetic replica is far from perfect. The clone has a different mass m, his stage presence is poor,

and he uses foul language. The clone, serving as the actor's stunt double, stands on the brink of a cliff 36.0 m high, next to a sturdy tree. The actor stands on top of a Humvee, 1.80 m above the level ground, holding a taut rope tied to a tree branch directly above the clone. When the director calls "action," the actor starts from rest and swings down on the rope without friction. The actor is momentarily hidden from the camera at the bottom of the arc, where he undergoes an elastic head-on collision with the clone, sending him over the cliff. Cursing vilely, the clone falls freely into the ocean below. The actor is prosecuted for making an obscene clone fall, and you are called as an expert witness at the sensational trial. (a) Find the horizontal component R of the clone's displacement as it depends on m. Evaluate R (b) for $m = 79.0$ kg and (c) for $m = 81.0$ kg. (d) What value of m gives a range of 30.0 m? (e) What is the maximum possible value for R, and (f) to what value of m does it correspond? What are (g) the minimum values of R and (h) the corresponding value of m? (i) For the actor–clone–Earth system, is mechanical energy conserved throughout the action sequence? Is this principle sufficient to solve the problem? Explain. (j) For the same system, is momentum conserved? Explain how this principle is used. (k) **What If?** Show that R does not depend on the value of the gravitational acceleration. Is this result remarkable? State how one might make sense of it.

57. A bullet of mass m is fired into a block of mass M initially at rest at the edge of a frictionless table of height h (Fig. P9.57). The bullet remains in the block, and after impact the block lands a distance d from the bottom of the table. Determine the initial speed of the bullet.

Figure P9.57

58. A small block of mass $m_1 = 0.500$ kg is released from rest at the top of a curve-shaped, frictionless wedge of mass $m_2 = 3.00$ kg, which sits on a frictionless horizontal surface as shown in Figure P9.58a. When the block leaves the wedge, its velocity is measured to be 4.00 m/s to the right as shown in the figure. (a) What is the velocity of the

Figure P9.58

wedge after the block reaches the horizontal surface? (b) What is the height h of the wedge?

59. ● A 0.500-kg sphere moving with a velocity given by $(2.00\hat{i} - 3.00\hat{j} + 1.00\hat{k})$ m/s strikes another sphere of mass 1.50 kg that is moving with an initial velocity of $(-1.00\hat{i} + 2.00\hat{j} - 3.00\hat{k})$ m/s. (a) The velocity of the 0.500-kg sphere after the collision is given by $(-1.00\hat{i} + 3.00\hat{j} - 8.00\hat{k})$ m/s. Find the final velocity of the 1.50-kg sphere and identify the kind of collision (elastic, inelastic, or perfectly inelastic). (b) Now assume the velocity of the 0.500-kg sphere after the collision is $(-0.250\hat{i} + 0.750\hat{j} - 2.00\hat{k})$ m/s. Find the final velocity of the 1.50-kg sphere and identify the kind of collision. (c) **What If?** Take the velocity of the 0.500-kg sphere after the collision as $(-1.00\hat{i} + 3.00\hat{j} + a\hat{k})$ m/s. Find the value of a and the velocity of the 1.50-kg sphere after an elastic collision.

60. A 75.0-kg firefighter slides down a pole while a constant friction force of 300 N retards her motion. A horizontal 20.0-kg platform is supported by a spring at the bottom of the pole to cushion the fall. The firefighter starts from rest 4.00 m above the platform, and the spring constant is 4 000 N/m. Find (a) the firefighter's speed immediately before she collides with the platform and (b) the maximum distance the spring is compressed. Assume the friction force acts during the entire motion.

61. ● George of the Jungle, with mass m, swings on a light vine hanging from a stationary tree branch. A second vine of equal length hangs from the same point, and a gorilla of larger mass M swings in the opposite direction on it. Both vines are horizontal when the primates start from rest at the same moment. George and the gorilla meet at the lowest point of their swings. Each is afraid that one vine will break, so they grab each other and hang on. They swing upward together, reaching a point where the vines make an angle of 35.0° with the vertical. (a) Find the value of the ratio m/M. (b) **What If?** Try the following experiment at home. Tie a small magnet and a steel screw to opposite ends of a string. Hold the center of the string fixed to represent the tree branch, and reproduce a model of the motions of George and the gorilla. What changes in your analysis will make it apply to this situation? **What If?** Next assume the magnet is strong so that it noticeably attracts the screw over a distance of a few centimeters. Then the screw will be moving faster immediately before it sticks to the magnet. Does this extra magnet strength make a difference?

62. ● A student performs a ballistic pendulum experiment using an apparatus similar to that shown in Figure 9.9b. She obtains the following average data: $h = 8.68$ cm, $m_1 = 68.8$ g, and $m_2 = 263$ g. The symbols refer to the quantities in Figure 9.9a. (a) Determine the initial speed v_{1A} of the projectile. (b) The second part of her experiment is to obtain v_{1A} by firing the same projectile horizontally (with the pendulum removed from the path) and measuring its final horizontal position x and distance of fall y (Fig. P9.62). Show that the initial speed of the projectile is related to x and y by the equation

$$v_{1A} = \frac{x}{\sqrt{2y/g}}$$

Figure P9.62

What numerical value does she obtain for v_{1A} based on her measured values of $x = 257$ cm and $y = 85.3$ cm? What factors might account for the difference in this value compared with that obtained in part (a)?

63. ● Lazarus Carnot, an artillery general, managed the military draft for Napoleon. Carnot used a ballistic pendulum to measure the firing speeds of cannonballs. In the symbols defined in Example 9.6, he proved that the ratio of the kinetic energy immediately after the collision to the kinetic energy immediately before is $m_1/(m_1 + m_2)$. (a) Carry out the proof yourself. (b) If the cannonball has mass 9.60 kg and the block (a tree trunk) has mass 214 kg, what fraction of the original energy remains mechanical after the collision? (c) What is the ratio of the momentum immediately after the collision to the momentum immediately before? (d) A student believes that such a large loss of mechanical energy must be accompanied by at least a small loss of momentum. How would you convince this student of the truth? General Carnot's son Sadi was the second most important engineer in the history of ideas; we will study his work in Chapter 22.

64. ● Pursued by ferocious wolves, you are in a sleigh with no horses, gliding without friction across an ice-covered lake. You take an action described by these equations:

$$(270 \text{ kg})(7.50 \text{ m/s})\hat{\mathbf{i}} = (15.0 \text{ kg})(-v_{1f}\hat{\mathbf{i}}) + (255 \text{ kg})(v_{2f}\hat{\mathbf{i}})$$

$$v_{1f} + v_{2f} = 8.00 \text{ m/s}$$

(a) Complete the statement of the problem, giving the data and identifying the unknowns. (b) Find the values of v_{1f} and v_{2f}. (c) Find the work you do.

65. **Review problem.** A light spring of force constant 3.85 N/m is compressed by 8.00 cm and held between a 0.250-kg block on the left and a 0.500-kg block on the right. Both blocks are at rest on a horizontal surface. The blocks are released simultaneously so that the spring tends to push them apart. Find the maximum velocity each block attains if the coefficient of kinetic friction between each block and the surface is (a) 0, (b) 0.100, and (c) 0.462. Assume the coefficient of static friction is greater than the coefficient of kinetic friction in every case.

66. Consider as a system the Sun with the Earth in a circular orbit around it. Find the magnitude of the change in the velocity of the Sun relative to the center of mass of the system over a 6-month period. Ignore the influence of other celestial objects. You may obtain the necessary astronomical data from the endpapers of the book.

67. A 5.00-g bullet moving with an initial speed of 400 m/s is fired into and passes through a 1.00-kg block as shown in Figure P9.67. The block, initially at rest on a frictionless, horizontal surface, is connected to a spring with force constant 900 N/m. The block moves 5.00 cm to the right after impact. Find (a) the speed at which the bullet emerges from the block and (b) the mechanical energy converted into internal energy in the collision.

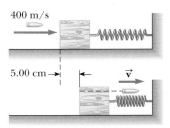

Figure P9.67

68. ● **Review problem.** There are (one can say) three coequal theories of motion: Newton's second law, stating that the total force on a particle causes its acceleration; the work–kinetic energy theorem, stating that the total work on a particle causes its change in kinetic energy; and the impulse–momentum theorem, stating that the total impulse on a particle causes its change in momentum. In this problem, you compare predictions of the three theories in one particular case. A 3.00-kg object has velocity $7.00\hat{\mathbf{j}}$ m/s. Then, a total force $12.0\hat{\mathbf{i}}$ N acts on the object for 5.00 s. (a) Calculate the object's final velocity, using the impulse–momentum theorem. (b) Calculate its acceleration from $\vec{\mathbf{a}} = (\vec{\mathbf{v}}_f - \vec{\mathbf{v}}_i)/\Delta t$. (c) Calculate its acceleration from $\vec{\mathbf{a}} = \Sigma \vec{\mathbf{F}}/m$. (d) Find the object's vector displacement from $\Delta \vec{\mathbf{r}} = \vec{\mathbf{v}}_i t + \frac{1}{2}\vec{\mathbf{a}}t^2$. (e) Find the work done on the object from $W = \vec{\mathbf{F}} \cdot \Delta\vec{\mathbf{r}}$. (f) Find the final kinetic energy from $\frac{1}{2}mv_f^2 = \frac{1}{2}m\vec{\mathbf{v}}_f \cdot \vec{\mathbf{v}}_f$. (g) Find the final kinetic energy from $\frac{1}{2}mv_i^2 + W$. (h) State the result of comparing the answers to parts b and c, and the answers to parts f and g.

69. A chain of length L and total mass M is released from rest with its lower end just touching the top of a table as shown in Figure P9.69a. Find the force exerted by the table on the chain after the chain has fallen through a distance x as shown in Figure P9.69b. (Assume each link comes to rest the instant it reaches the table.)

(a)   (b)

Figure P9.69

Answers to Quick Quizzes

9.1 (d). Two identical objects ($m_1 = m_2$) traveling at the same speed ($v_1 = v_2$) have the same kinetic energies and the same magnitudes of momentum. It also is possible, however, for particular combinations of masses and velocities to satisfy $K_1 = K_2$ but not $p_1 = p_2$. For example, a 1-kg object moving at 2 m/s has the same kinetic energy as a 4-kg object moving at 1 m/s, but the two clearly do not have the same momenta. Because we have no information about masses and speeds, we cannot choose among (a), (b), or (c).

9.2 (b), (c), (a). The slower the ball, the easier it is to catch. If the momentum of the medicine ball is the same as the momentum of the baseball, the speed of the medicine ball must be 1/10 the speed of the baseball because the medicine ball has 10 times the mass. If the kinetic energies are the same, the speed of the medicine ball must be $1/\sqrt{10}$ the speed of the baseball because of the squared speed term in the equation for K. The medicine ball is hardest to catch when it has the same speed as the baseball.

9.3 **(i)**, (c), (e). Object 2 has a greater acceleration because of its smaller mass. Therefore, it travels the distance d in a shorter time interval. Even though the force applied to objects 1 and 2 is the same, the change in momentum is less for object 2 because Δt is smaller. The work $W = Fd$ done on both objects is the same because both F and d are the same in the two cases. Therefore, $K_1 = K_2$. **(ii)**, (b), (d). The same impulse is applied to both objects, so they experience the same change in momentum. Object 2 has a larger acceleration due to its smaller mass. Therefore, the distance that object 2 covers in the time interval is larger than that for object 1. As a result, more work is done on object 2 and $K_2 > K_1$.

9.4 (a) All three are the same. Because the passenger is brought from the car's initial speed to a full stop, the change in momentum (equal to the impulse) is the same regardless of what stops the passenger. (b) Dashboard, seat belt, air bag. The dashboard stops the passenger very quickly in a front-end collision, resulting in a very large force. The seat belt takes somewhat more time, so the force is smaller. Used along with the seat belt, the air bag can extend the passenger's stopping time further, notably for his head, which would otherwise snap forward.

9.5 (a). If all the initial kinetic energy is transformed or transferred away from the system, nothing is moving after the collision. Consequently, the final momentum of the system is necessarily zero and the initial momentum of the system must therefore be zero. Although (b) and (d) *together* would satisfy the conditions, neither one *alone* does.

9.6 (b). Because momentum of the two-ball system is conserved, $\vec{p}_{Ti} + 0 = \vec{p}_{Tf} + \vec{p}_B$. Because the table-tennis ball bounces back from the much more massive bowling ball with approximately the same speed, $\vec{p}_{Tf} = -\vec{p}_{Ti}$. As a consequence, $\vec{p}_B = 2\vec{p}_{Ti}$. Kinetic energy can be expressed as $K = p^2/2m$. Because of the much larger mass of the bowling ball, its kinetic energy is much smaller than that of the table-tennis ball.

9.7 (b). The piece with the handle will have less mass than the piece made up of the end of the bat. To see why, take the origin of coordinates as the center of mass before the bat was cut. Replace each cut piece by a small sphere located at each piece's center of mass. The sphere representing the handle piece is farther from the origin, but the product of less mass and greater distance balances the product of greater mass and less distance for the end piece as shown.

9.8 **(i)**, (a). This effect is the same one as the swimmer diving off the raft that we just discussed. The vessel–passengers system is isolated. If the passengers all start running one way, the speed of the vessel increases (a small amount!) the other way. **(ii)**, (b). Once they stop running, the momentum of the system is the same as it was before they started running; you cannot change the momentum of an isolated system by means of internal forces. In case you are thinking that the passengers could run to the stern repeatedly to take advantage of the speed increase *while* they are running, remember that they will slow the ship down every time they return to the bow!

The Malaysian pastime of *gasing* involves the spinning of tops that can have masses up to 5 kg. Professional spinners can spin their tops so that they might rotate for more than an hour before stopping. We will study the rotational motion of objects such as these tops in this chapter. (Courtesy Tourism Malaysia)

10 Rotation of a Rigid Object About a Fixed Axis

When an extended object such as a wheel rotates about its axis, the motion cannot be analyzed by modeling the object as a particle because at any given time different parts of the object have different linear velocities and linear accelerations. We can, however, analyze the motion of an extended object by modeling it as a collection of particles, each of which has its own linear velocity and linear acceleration.

In dealing with a rotating object, analysis is greatly simplified by assuming the object is rigid. A **rigid object** is one that is nondeformable; that is, the relative locations of all particles of which the object is composed remain constant. All real objects are deformable to some extent; our rigid-object model, however, is useful in many situations in which deformation is negligible.

10.1 Angular Position, Velocity, and Acceleration

Figure 10.1 illustrates an overhead view of a rotating compact disc, or CD. The disc rotates about a fixed axis perpendicular to the plane of the figure and passing through the center of the disc at O. A small element of the disc modeled as a particle at P is at a fixed distance r from the origin and rotates about it in a circle of radius r. (In fact, *every* particle on the disc undergoes circular motion about O.) It is convenient to represent the position of P with its polar coordinates (r, θ), where

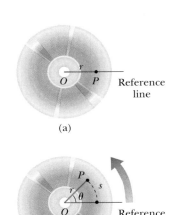

Figure 10.1 A compact disc rotating about a fixed axis through O perpendicular to the plane of the figure. (a) To define angular position for the disc, a fixed reference line is chosen. A particle at P is located at a distance r from the rotation axis at O. (b) As the disc rotates, a particle at P moves through an arc length s on a circular path of radius r.

269

r is the distance from the origin to P and θ is measured *counterclockwise* from some reference line fixed in space as shown in Figure 10.1a. In this representation, the angle θ changes in time while r remains constant. As the particle moves along the circle from the reference line, which is at angle $\theta = 0$, it moves through an arc of length s as in Figure 10.1b. The arc length s is related to the angle θ through the relationship

$$s = r\theta \tag{10.1a}$$

$$\theta = \frac{s}{r} \tag{10.1b}$$

PITFALL PREVENTION 10.1
Remember the Radian

In rotational equations, you *must* use angles expressed in radians. Don't fall into the trap of using angles measured in degrees in rotational equations.

Because θ is the ratio of an arc length and the radius of the circle, it is a pure number. Usually, however, we give θ the artificial unit **radian** (rad), where **one radian is the angle subtended by an arc length equal to the radius of the arc.** Because the circumference of a circle is $2\pi r$, it follows from Equation 10.1b that 360° corresponds to an angle of $(2\pi r/r)$ rad $= 2\pi$ rad. Hence, 1 rad $= 360°/2\pi \approx 57.3°$. To convert an angle in degrees to an angle in radians, we use that π rad $= 180°$, so

$$\theta(\text{rad}) = \frac{\pi}{180°}\,\theta(\text{deg})$$

For example, 60° equals $\pi/3$ rad and 45° equals $\pi/4$ rad.

Because the disc in Figure 10.1 is a rigid object, as the particle moves through an angle θ from the reference line, every other particle on the object rotates through the same angle θ. Therefore, **we can associate the angle θ with the entire rigid object as well as with an individual particle,** which allows us to define the *angular position* of a rigid object in its rotational motion. We choose a reference line on the object, such as a line connecting O and a chosen particle on the object. The **angular position** of the rigid object is the angle θ between this reference line on the object and the fixed reference line in space, which is often chosen as the x axis. Such identification is similar to the way we define the position of an object in translational motion as the distance x between the object and the reference position, which is the origin, $x = 0$.

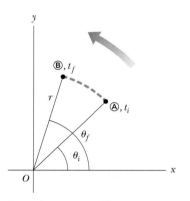

Figure 10.2 A particle on a rotating rigid object moves from Ⓐ to Ⓑ along the arc of a circle. In the time interval $\Delta t = t_f - t_i$, the radial line of length r moves through an angular displacement $\Delta\theta = \theta_f - \theta_i$.

As the particle in question on our rigid object travels from position Ⓐ to position Ⓑ in a time interval Δt as in Figure 10.2, the reference line fixed to the object sweeps out an angle $\Delta\theta = \theta_f - \theta_i$. This quantity $\Delta\theta$ is defined as the **angular displacement** of the rigid object:

$$\Delta\theta \equiv \theta_f - \theta_i$$

The rate at which this angular displacement occurs can vary. If the rigid object spins rapidly, this displacement can occur in a short time interval. If it rotates slowly, this displacement occurs in a longer time interval. These different rotation rates can be quantified by defining the **average angular speed** ω_{avg} (Greek letter omega) as the ratio of the angular displacement of a rigid object to the time interval Δt during which the displacement occurs:

Average angular speed ▶

$$\omega_{\text{avg}} \equiv \frac{\theta_f - \theta_i}{t_f - t_i} = \frac{\Delta\theta}{\Delta t} \tag{10.2}$$

In analogy to linear speed, the **instantaneous angular speed** ω is defined as the limit of the average angular speed as Δt approaches zero:

Instantaneous angular speed ▶

$$\omega \equiv \lim_{\Delta t \to 0}\frac{\Delta\theta}{\Delta t} = \frac{d\theta}{dt} \tag{10.3}$$

Angular speed has units of radians per second (rad/s), which can be written as s^{-1} because radians are not dimensional. We take ω to be positive when θ is increasing (counterclockwise motion in Figure 10.2) and negative when θ is decreasing (clockwise motion in Figure 10.2).

Quick Quiz 10.1   A rigid object rotates in a counterclockwise sense around a fixed axis. Each of the following pairs of quantities represents an initial angular position and a final angular position of the rigid object. **(i)** Which of the sets can *only* occur if the rigid object rotates through more than 180°? (a) 3 rad, 6 rad (b) −1 rad, 1 rad (c) 1 rad, 5 rad **(ii)** Suppose the change in angular position for each of these pairs of values occurs in 1 s. Which choice represents the lowest average angular speed?

If the instantaneous angular speed of an object changes from ω_i to ω_f in the time interval Δt, the object has an angular acceleration. The **average angular acceleration** α_{avg} (Greek letter alpha) of a rotating rigid object is defined as the ratio of the change in the angular speed to the time interval Δt during which the change in the angular speed occurs:

$$\alpha_{avg} \equiv \frac{\omega_f - \omega_i}{t_f - t_i} = \frac{\Delta\omega}{\Delta t} \tag{10.4}$$

◀ Average angular acceleration

In analogy to linear acceleration, the **instantaneous angular acceleration** is defined as the limit of the average angular acceleration as Δt approaches zero:

$$\alpha \equiv \lim_{\Delta t \to 0} \frac{\Delta\omega}{\Delta t} = \frac{d\omega}{dt} \tag{10.5}$$

◀ Instantaneous angular acceleration

Angular acceleration has units of radians per second squared (rad/s^2), or simply s^{-2}. Notice that α is positive when a rigid object rotating counterclockwise is speeding up or when a rigid object rotating clockwise is slowing down during some time interval.

When a rigid object is rotating about a *fixed* axis, **every particle on the object rotates through the same angle in a given time interval and has the same angular speed and the same angular acceleration.** That is, the quantities θ, ω, and α characterize the rotational motion of the entire rigid object as well as individual particles in the object.

Angular position (θ), angular speed (ω), and angular acceleration (α) are analogous to translational position (x), translational speed (v), and translational acceleration (a). The variables θ, ω, and α differ dimensionally from the variables x, v, and a only by a factor having the unit of length. (See Section 10.3.)

We have not specified any direction for angular speed and angular acceleration. Strictly speaking, ω and α are the magnitudes of the angular velocity and the angular acceleration vectors[1] $\vec{\omega}$ and $\vec{\alpha}$, respectively, and they should always be positive. Because we are considering rotation about a fixed axis, however, we can use nonvector notation and indicate the vectors' directions by assigning a positive or negative sign to ω and α as discussed earlier with regard to Equations 10.3 and 10.5. For rotation about a fixed axis, the only direction that uniquely specifies the rotational motion is the direction along the axis of rotation. Therefore, the directions of $\vec{\omega}$ and $\vec{\alpha}$ are along this axis. If a particle rotates in the xy plane as in Figure 10.2, the direction of $\vec{\omega}$ for the particle is out of the plane of the diagram when the rotation is counterclockwise and into the plane of the diagram when the rotation is clockwise. To illustrate this convention, it is convenient to use the *right-hand rule* demonstrated in Figure 10.3. When the four fingers of the right hand are wrapped in the direction of rotation, the extended right thumb points in the direction of $\vec{\omega}$. The direction of $\vec{\alpha}$ follows from its definition $\vec{\alpha} \equiv d\vec{\omega}/dt$. It is in the same direction as $\vec{\omega}$ if the angular speed is increasing in time, and it is antiparallel to $\vec{\omega}$ if the angular speed is decreasing in time.

PITFALL PREVENTION 10.2
Specify Your Axis

In solving rotation problems, you must specify an axis of rotation. This new feature does not exist in our study of translational motion. The choice is arbitrary, but once you make it, you must maintain that choice consistently throughout the problem. In some problems, the physical situation suggests a natural axis, such as the center of an automobile wheel. In other problems, there may not be an obvious choice, and you must exercise judgment.

Figure 10.3 The right-hand rule for determining the direction of the angular velocity vector.

---

[1] Although we do not verify it here, the instantaneous angular velocity and instantaneous angular acceleration are vector quantities, but the corresponding average values are not because angular displacements do not add as vector quantities for finite rotations.

10.2 Rotational Kinematics: The Rigid Object Under Constant Angular Acceleration

When a rigid object rotates about a fixed axis, it often undergoes a constant angular acceleration. Therefore, we generate a new analysis model for rotational motion called the **rigid object under constant angular acceleration**. This model is the rotational analog to the particle under constant acceleration model. We develop kinematic relationships for this model in this section. Writing Equation 10.5 in the form $d\omega = \alpha\, dt$ and integrating from $t_i = 0$ to $t_f = t$ gives

◀ Rotational kinematic equations

$$\omega_f = \omega_i + \alpha t \quad \text{(for constant } \alpha\text{)} \tag{10.6}$$

where ω_i is the angular speed of the rigid object at time $t = 0$. Equation 10.6 allows us to find the angular speed ω_f of the object at any later time t. Substituting Equation 10.6 into Equation 10.3 and integrating once more, we obtain

$$\theta_f = \theta_i + \omega_i t + \tfrac{1}{2}\alpha t^2 \quad \text{(for constant } \alpha\text{)} \tag{10.7}$$

where θ_i is the angular position of the rigid object at time $t = 0$. Equation 10.7 allows us to find the angular position θ_f of the object at any later time t. Eliminating t from Equations 10.6 and 10.7 gives

$$\omega_f^{\,2} = \omega_i^{\,2} + 2\alpha(\theta_f - \theta_i) \quad \text{(for constant } \alpha\text{)} \tag{10.8}$$

This equation allows us to find the angular speed ω_f of the rigid object for any value of its angular position θ_f. If we eliminate α between Equations 10.6 and 10.7, we obtain

$$\theta_f = \theta_i + \tfrac{1}{2}(\omega_i + \omega_f)t \quad \text{(for constant } \alpha\text{)} \tag{10.9}$$

Notice that these kinematic expressions for the rigid object under constant angular acceleration are of the same mathematical form as those for a particle under constant acceleration (Chapter 2). They can be generated from the equations for translational motion by making the substitutions $x \to \theta$, $v \to \omega$, and $a \to \alpha$. Table 10.1 compares the kinematic equations for rotational and translational motion.

PITFALL PREVENTION 10.3
Just Like Translation?

Equations 10.6 to 10.9 and Table 10.1 suggest that rotational kinematics is just like translational kinematics. That is almost true, with two key differences. (1) In rotational kinematics, you must specify a rotation axis (per Pitfall Prevention 10.2). (2) In rotational motion, the object keeps returning to its original orientation; therefore, you may be asked for the number of revolutions made by a rigid object. This concept has no meaning in translational motion.

Quick Quiz 10.2 Consider again the pairs of angular positions for the rigid object in Quick Quiz 10.1. If the object starts from rest at the initial angular position, moves counterclockwise with constant angular acceleration, and arrives at the final angular position with the same angular speed in all three cases, for which choice is the angular acceleration the highest?

TABLE 10.1

Kinematic Equations for Rotational and Translational Motion Under Constant Acceleration

Rotational Motion About a Fixed Axis	Translational Motion
$\omega_f = \omega_i + \alpha t$	$v_f = v_i + at$
$\theta_f = \theta_i + \omega_i t + \tfrac{1}{2}\alpha t^2$	$x_f = x_i + v_i t + \tfrac{1}{2}at^2$
$\omega_f^{\,2} = \omega_i^{\,2} + 2\alpha(\theta_f - \theta_i)$	$v_f^{\,2} = v_i^{\,2} + 2a(x_f - x_i)$
$\theta_f = \theta_i + \tfrac{1}{2}(\omega_i + \omega_f)t$	$x_f = x_i + \tfrac{1}{2}(v_i + v_f)t$

EXAMPLE 10.1	**Rotating Wheel**

A wheel rotates with a constant angular acceleration of 3.50 rad/s^2.

(A) If the angular speed of the wheel is 2.00 rad/s at $t_i = 0$, through what angular displacement does the wheel rotate in 2.00 s?

SOLUTION

Conceptualize   Look again at Figure 10.1. Imagine that the compact disc rotates with its angular speed increasing at a constant rate. You start your stopwatch when the disc is rotating at 2.00 rad/s. This mental image is a model for the motion of the wheel in this example.

Categorize   The phrase "with a constant angular acceleration" tells us to use the rigid object under constant angular acceleration model.

Analyze   Arrange Equation 10.7 so that it expresses the angular displacement of the object:

$$\Delta\theta = \theta_f - \theta_i = \omega_i t + \tfrac{1}{2}\alpha t^2$$

Substitute the known values to find the angular displacement at $t = 2.00$ s:

$$\Delta\theta = (2.00 \text{ rad/s})(2.00 \text{ s}) + \tfrac{1}{2}(3.50 \text{ rad/s}^2)(2.00 \text{ s})^2$$

$$= \boxed{11.0 \text{ rad}} = (11.0 \text{ rad})(57.3°/\text{rad}) = \boxed{630°}$$

(B) Through how many revolutions has the wheel turned during this time interval?

SOLUTION

Multiply the angular displacement found in part (A) by a conversion factor to find the number of revolutions:

$$\Delta\theta = 630°\left(\frac{1 \text{ rev}}{360°}\right) = \boxed{1.75 \text{ rev}}$$

(C) What is the angular speed of the wheel at $t = 2.00$ s?

SOLUTION

Use Equation 10.6 to find the angular speed at $t = 2.00$ s:

$$\omega_f = \omega_i + \alpha t = 2.00 \text{ rad/s} + (3.50 \text{ rad/s}^2)(2.00 \text{ s})$$

$$= \boxed{9.00 \text{ rad/s}}$$

Finalize   We could also obtain this result using Equation 10.8 and the results of part (A). (Try it!)

What If?   Suppose a particle moves along a straight line with a constant acceleration of 3.50 m/s^2. If the velocity of the particle is 2.00 m/s at $t_i = 0$, through what displacement does the particle move in 2.00 s? What is the velocity of the particle at $t = 2.00$ s?

Answer   Notice that these questions are translational analogs to parts (A) and (C) of the original problem. The mathematical solution follows exactly the same form. For the displacement,

$$\Delta x = x_f - x_i = v_i t + \tfrac{1}{2}at^2$$

$$= (2.00 \text{ m/s})(2.00 \text{ s}) + \tfrac{1}{2}(3.50 \text{ m/s}^2)(2.00 \text{ s})^2 = 11.0 \text{ m}$$

and for the velocity,

$$v_f = v_i + at = 2.00 \text{ m/s} + (3.50 \text{ m/s}^2)(2.00 \text{ s}) = 9.00 \text{ m/s}$$

There is no translational analog to part (B) because translational motion under constant acceleration is not repetitive.

10.3   Angular and Translational Quantities

In this section, we derive some useful relationships between the angular speed and acceleration of a rotating rigid object and the translational speed and acceleration of a point in the object. To do so, we must keep in mind that when a rigid object

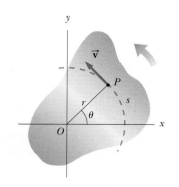

ACTIVE FIGURE 10.4

As a rigid object rotates about the fixed axis through O, the point P has a tangential velocity $\vec{v}$ that is always tangent to the circular path of radius r.

Sign in at www.thomsonedu.com and go to ThomsonNOW to move point P and observe the tangential velocity as the object rotates.

rotates about a fixed axis as in Active Figure 10.4, **every particle of the object moves in a circle whose center is on the axis of rotation.**

Because point P in Active Figure 10.4 moves in a circle, the translational velocity vector $\vec{v}$ is always tangent to the circular path and hence is called *tangential velocity*. The magnitude of the tangential velocity of the point P is by definition the tangential speed $v = ds/dt$, where s is the distance traveled by this point measured along the circular path. Recalling that $s = r\theta$ (Eq. 10.1a) and noting that r is constant, we obtain

$$v = \frac{ds}{dt} = r\frac{d\theta}{dt}$$

Because $d\theta/dt = \omega$ (see Eq. 10.3), it follows that

$$v = r\omega \qquad (10.10)$$

That is, the tangential speed of a point on a rotating rigid object equals the perpendicular distance of that point from the axis of rotation multiplied by the angular speed. Therefore, although every point on the rigid object has the same *angular* speed, not every point has the same *tangential* speed because r is not the same for all points on the object. Equation 10.10 shows that the tangential speed of a point on the rotating object increases as one moves outward from the center of rotation, as we would intuitively expect. For example, the outer end of a swinging golf club moves much faster than the handle.

We can relate the angular acceleration of the rotating rigid object to the tangential acceleration of the point P by taking the time derivative of v:

$$a_t = \frac{dv}{dt} = r\frac{d\omega}{dt}$$

◀ **Relation between tangential and angular acceleration**

$$a_t = r\alpha \qquad (10.11)$$

That is, the tangential component of the translational acceleration of a point on a rotating rigid object equals the point's perpendicular distance from the axis of rotation multiplied by the angular acceleration.

In Section 4.4, we found that a point moving in a circular path undergoes a radial acceleration a_r directed toward the center of rotation and whose magnitude is that of the centripetal acceleration v^2/r (Fig. 10.5). Because $v = r\omega$ for a point P on a rotating object, we can express the centripetal acceleration at that point in terms of angular speed as

$$a_c = \frac{v^2}{r} = r\omega^2 \qquad (10.12)$$

The total acceleration vector at the point is $\vec{a} = \vec{a}_t + \vec{a}_r$, where the magnitude of $\vec{a}_r$ is the centripetal acceleration a_c. Because $\vec{a}$ is a vector having a radial and a tangential component, the magnitude of $\vec{a}$ at the point P on the rotating rigid object is

$$a = \sqrt{a_t^2 + a_r^2} = \sqrt{r^2\alpha^2 + r^2\omega^4} = r\sqrt{\alpha^2 + \omega^4} \qquad (10.13)$$

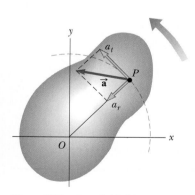

Figure 10.5   As a rigid object rotates about a fixed axis through O, the point P experiences a tangential component of translational acceleration a_t and a radial component of translational acceleration a_r. The total acceleration of this point is $\vec{a} = \vec{a}_t + \vec{a}_r$.

Quick Quiz 10.3   Alex and Brian are riding on a merry-go-round. Alex rides on a horse at the outer rim of the circular platform, twice as far from the center of the circular platform as Brian, who rides on an inner horse. **(i)** When the merry-go-round is rotating at a constant angular speed, what is Alex's angular speed? (a) twice Brian's   (b) the same as Brian's   (c) half of Brian's   (d) impossible to determine   **(ii)** When the merry-go-round is rotating at a constant angular speed, describe Alex's tangential speed from the same list of choices.

EXAMPLE 10.2

EXAMPLE 10.2   **CD Player**

On a compact disc (Fig. 10.6), audio information is stored digitally in a series of pits and flat areas on the surface of the disc. The alternations between pits and flat areas on the surface represent binary ones and zeroes to be read by the CD player and converted back to sound waves. The pits and flat areas are detected by a system consisting of a laser and lenses. The length of a string of ones and zeroes representing one piece of information is the same everywhere on the disc, whether the information is near the center of the disc or near its outer edge. So that this length of ones and zeroes always passes by the laser–lens system in the same time interval, the tangential speed of the disc surface at the location of the lens must be constant. According to Equation 10.10, the angular speed must therefore vary as the laser–lens system moves radially along the disc. In a typical CD player, the constant speed of the surface at the point of the laser–lens system is 1.3 m/s.

Figure 10.6   (Example 10.2) A compact disc.

(A) Find the angular speed of the disc in revolutions per minute when information is being read from the innermost first track ($r = 23$ mm) and the outermost final track ($r = 58$ mm).

SOLUTION

Conceptualize   Figure 10.6 shows a photograph of a compact disc. Trace your finger around the circle marked "23 mm" in a time interval of about 3 s. Now trace your finger around the circle marked "58 mm" in the same time interval. Notice how much faster your finger is moving relative to the page around the larger circle. If your finger represents the laser reading the disc, it is moving over the surface of the disc much faster for the outer circle than for the inner circle.

Categorize   This part of the example is categorized as a simple substitution problem. In later parts, we will need to identify analysis models.

Use Equation 10.10 to find the angular speed that gives the required tangential speed at the position of the inner track:

$$\omega_i = \frac{v}{r_i} = \frac{1.3 \text{ m/s}}{2.3 \times 10^{-2} \text{ m}} = 57 \text{ rad/s}$$

$$= (57 \text{ rad/s})\left(\frac{1 \text{ rev}}{2\pi \text{ rad}}\right)\left(\frac{60 \text{ s}}{1 \text{ min}}\right) = \boxed{5.4 \times 10^2 \text{ rev/min}}$$

Do the same for the outer track:

$$\omega_f = \frac{v}{r_f} = \frac{1.3 \text{ m/s}}{5.8 \times 10^{-2} \text{ m}} = 22 \text{ rad/s} = \boxed{2.1 \times 10^2 \text{ rev/min}}$$

The CD player adjusts the angular speed ω of the disc within this range so that information moves past the objective lens at a constant rate.

(B) The maximum playing time of a standard music disc is 74 min and 33 s. How many revolutions does the disc make during that time?

SOLUTION

Categorize   From part (A), the angular speed decreases as the disc plays. Let us assume it decreases steadily, with α constant. We can then use the rigid object under constant angular acceleration model.

Analyze   If $t = 0$ is the instant the disc begins rotating, with angular speed of 57 rad/s, the final value of the time t is (74 min)(60 s/min) + 33 s = 4 473 s. We are looking for the angular displacement $\Delta\theta$ during this time interval.

Use Equation 10.9 to find the angular displacement of the disc at $t = 4$ 473 s:

$$\Delta\theta = \theta_f - \theta_i = \tfrac{1}{2}(\omega_i + \omega_f)t$$

$$= \tfrac{1}{2}(57 \text{ rad/s} + 22 \text{ rad/s})(4 \text{ 473 s}) = 1.8 \times 10^5 \text{ rad}$$

Convert this angular displacement to revolutions:

$$\Delta\theta = (1.8 \times 10^5 \text{ rad})\left(\frac{1 \text{ rev}}{2\pi \text{ rad}}\right) = \boxed{2.8 \times 10^4 \text{ rev}}$$

(C) What is the angular acceleration of the compact disc over the 4 473-s time interval?

SOLUTION

Categorize We again model the disc as a rigid object under constant angular acceleration. In this case, Equation 10.6 gives the value of the constant angular acceleration. Another approach is to use Equation 10.4 to find the average angular acceleration. In this case, we are not assuming that the angular acceleration is constant. The answer is the same from both equations; only the interpretation of the result is different.

Analyze Use Equation 10.6 to find the angular acceleration:

$$\alpha = \frac{\omega_f - \omega_i}{t} = \frac{22 \text{ rad/s} - 57 \text{ rad/s}}{4\ 473 \text{ s}} = \boxed{-7.8 \times 10^{-3} \text{ rad/s}^2}$$

Finalize The disc experiences a very gradual decrease in its rotation rate, as expected from the long time interval required for the angular speed to change from the initial value to the final value. In reality, the angular acceleration of the disc is not constant. Problem 20 allows you to explore the actual time behavior of the angular acceleration.

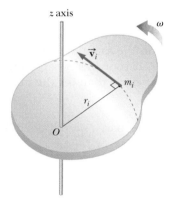

Figure 10.7 A rigid object rotating about the z axis with angular speed ω. The kinetic energy of the particle of mass m_i is $\frac{1}{2}m_iv_i^2$. The total kinetic energy of the object is called its rotational kinetic energy.

10.4 Rotational Kinetic Energy

In Chapter 7, we defined the kinetic energy of an object as the energy associated with its motion through space. An object rotating about a fixed axis remains stationary in space, so there is no kinetic energy associated with translational motion. The individual particles making up the rotating object, however, are moving through space; they follow circular paths. Consequently, there is kinetic energy associated with rotational motion.

Let us consider an object as a collection of particles and assume it rotates about a fixed z axis with an angular speed ω. Figure 10.7 shows the rotating object and identifies one particle on the object located at a distance r_i from the rotation axis. If the mass of the ith particle is m_i and its tangential speed is v_i, its kinetic energy is

$$K_i = \tfrac{1}{2}m_iv_i^2$$

To proceed further, recall that although every particle in the rigid object has the same angular speed ω, the individual tangential speeds depend on the distance r_i from the axis of rotation according to Equation 10.10. The *total* kinetic energy of the rotating rigid object is the sum of the kinetic energies of the individual particles:

$$K_R = \sum_i K_i = \sum_i \tfrac{1}{2}m_iv_i^2 = \tfrac{1}{2}\sum_i m_ir_i^2\omega^2$$

We can write this expression in the form

$$K_R = \tfrac{1}{2}\left(\sum_i m_ir_i^2\right)\omega^2 \tag{10.14}$$

where we have factored ω^2 from the sum because it is common to every particle. We simplify this expression by defining the quantity in parentheses as the **moment of inertia** I:

Moment of inertia ▶

$$I \equiv \sum_i m_ir_i^2 \tag{10.15}$$

From the definition of moment of inertia,[2] we see that it has dimensions of ML^2 (kg·m^2 in SI units). With this notation, Equation 10.14 becomes

Rotational kinetic energy ▶

$$K_R = \tfrac{1}{2}I\omega^2 \tag{10.16}$$

Although we commonly refer to the quantity $\frac{1}{2}I\omega^2$ as **rotational kinetic energy,** it is not a new form of energy. It is ordinary kinetic energy because it is derived from a

[2] Civil engineers use moment of inertia to characterize the elastic properties (rigidity) of such structures as loaded beams. Hence, it is often useful even in a nonrotational context.

sum over individual kinetic energies of the particles contained in the rigid object. The mathematical form of the kinetic energy given by Equation 10.16 is convenient when we are dealing with rotational motion, provided we know how to calculate I.

It is important to recognize the analogy between kinetic energy $\frac{1}{2}mv^2$ associated with translational motion and rotational kinetic energy $\frac{1}{2}I\omega^2$. The quantities I and ω in rotational motion are analogous to m and v in translational motion, respectively. (In fact, I takes the place of m and ω takes the place of v every time we compare a translational motion equation with its rotational counterpart.) Moment of inertia is a measure of the resistance of an object to changes in its rotational motion, just as mass is a measure of the tendency of an object to resist changes in its translational motion.

EXAMPLE 10.3   Four Rotating Objects

Four tiny spheres are fastened to the ends of two rods of negligible mass lying in the xy plane (Fig. 10.8). We shall assume the radii of the spheres are small compared with the dimensions of the rods.

(A) If the system rotates about the y axis (Fig. 10.8a) with an angular speed ω, find the moment of inertia and the rotational kinetic energy of the system about this axis.

SOLUTION

Conceptualize   Figure 10.8 is a pictorial representation that helps conceptualize the system of spheres and how it spins.

Categorize   This example is a substitution problem because it is a straightforward application of the definitions discussed in this section.

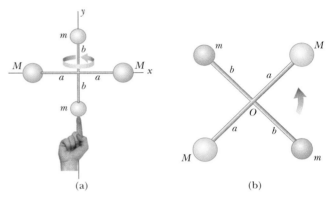

Figure 10.8   (Example 10.3) Four spheres form an unusual baton. (a) The baton is rotated about the y axis. (b) The baton is rotated about the z axis.

Apply Equation 10.15 to the system:

$$I_y = \sum_i m_i r_i^2 = Ma^2 + Ma^2 = \boxed{2Ma^2}$$

Evaluate the rotational kinetic energy using Equation 10.16:

$$K_R = \tfrac{1}{2}I_y\omega^2 = \tfrac{1}{2}(2Ma^2)\omega^2 = \boxed{Ma^2\omega^2}$$

That the two spheres of mass m do not enter into this result makes sense because they have no motion about the axis of rotation; hence, they have no rotational kinetic energy. By similar logic, we expect the moment of inertia about the x axis to be $I_x = 2mb^2$ with a rotational kinetic energy about that axis of $K_R = mb^2\omega^2$.

(B) Suppose the system rotates in the xy plane about an axis (the z axis) through O (Fig. 10.8b). Calculate the moment of inertia and rotational kinetic energy about this axis.

SOLUTION
Apply Equation 10.15 for this new rotation axis:

$$I_z = \sum_i m_i r_i^2 = Ma^2 + Ma^2 + mb^2 + mb^2 = \boxed{2Ma^2 + 2mb^2}$$

Evaluate the rotational kinetic energy using Equation 10.16:

$$K_R = \tfrac{1}{2}I_z\omega^2 = \tfrac{1}{2}(2Ma^2 + 2mb^2)\omega^2 = \boxed{(Ma^2 + mb^2)\omega^2}$$

Comparing the results for parts (A) and (B), we conclude that the moment of inertia and therefore the rotational kinetic energy associated with a given angular speed depend on the axis of rotation. In part (B), we expect the result to include all four spheres and distances because all four spheres are rotating in the xy plane. Based on the work–kinetic energy theorem, that the rotational kinetic energy in part (A) is smaller than that in part (B) indicates it would require less work to set the system into rotation about the y axis than about the z axis.

What If? What if the mass M is much larger than m? How do the answers to parts (A) and (B) compare?

Answer If $M \gg m$, then m can be neglected and the moment of inertia and the rotational kinetic energy in part (B) become

$$I_z = 2Ma^2 \quad \text{and} \quad K_R = Ma^2\omega^2$$

which are the same as the answers in part (A). If the masses m of the two orange spheres in Figure 10.8 are negligible, these spheres can be removed from the figure and rotations about the y and z axes are equivalent.

10.5 Calculation of Moments of Inertia

We can evaluate the moment of inertia of an extended rigid object by imagining the object to be divided into many small elements, each of which has mass Δm_i. We use the definition $I = \sum_i r_i^2 \Delta m_i$ and take the limit of this sum as $\Delta m_i \to 0$. In this limit, the sum becomes an integral over the volume of the object:

◄ Moment of inertia of a rigid object

$$I = \lim_{\Delta m_i \to 0} \sum_i r_i^2 \Delta m_i = \int r^2 dm \qquad (10.17)$$

It is usually easier to calculate moments of inertia in terms of the volume of the elements rather than their mass, and we can easily make that change by using

TABLE 10.2

Moments of Inertia of Homogeneous Rigid Objects with Different Geometries

Hoop or thin cylindrical shell
$I_{CM} = MR^2$

Hollow cylinder
$I_{CM} = \frac{1}{2}M(R_1{}^2 + R_2{}^2)$

Solid cylinder or disk
$I_{CM} = \frac{1}{2}MR^2$

Rectangular plate
$I_{CM} = \frac{1}{12}M(a^2 + b^2)$

Long, thin rod with rotation axis through center
$I_{CM} = \frac{1}{12}ML^2$

Long, thin rod with rotation axis through end
$I = \frac{1}{3}ML^2$

Solid sphere
$I_{CM} = \frac{2}{5}MR^2$

Thin spherical shell
$I_{CM} = \frac{2}{3}MR^2$

Equation 1.1, $\rho \equiv m/V$, where ρ is the density of the object and V is its volume. From this equation, the mass of a small element is $dm = \rho \, dV$. Substituting this result into Equation 10.17 gives

$$I = \int \rho r^2 \, dV$$

If the object is homogeneous, ρ is constant and the integral can be evaluated for a known geometry. If ρ is not constant, its variation with position must be known to complete the integration.

The density given by $\rho = m/V$ sometimes is referred to as *volumetric mass density* because it represents mass per unit volume. Often we use other ways of expressing density. For instance, when dealing with a sheet of uniform thickness t, we can define a *surface mass density* $\sigma = \rho t$, which represents *mass per unit area*. Finally, when mass is distributed along a rod of uniform cross-sectional area A, we sometimes use *linear mass density* $\lambda = M/L = \rho A$, which is the *mass per unit length*.

Table 10.2 gives the moments of inertia for a number of objects about specific axes. The moments of inertia of rigid objects with simple geometry (high symmetry) are relatively easy to calculate provided the rotation axis coincides with an axis of symmetry, as in the examples below.

Quick Quiz 10.4 A section of hollow pipe and a solid cylinder have the same radius, mass, and length. They both rotate about their long central axes with the same angular speed. Which object has the higher rotational kinetic energy? (a) The hollow pipe does. (b) The solid cylinder does. (c) They have the same rotational kinetic energy. (d) It is impossible to determine.

EXAMPLE 10.4	**Uniform Rigid Rod**

Calculate the moment of inertia of a uniform rigid rod of length L and mass M (Fig. 10.9) about an axis perpendicular to the rod (the y axis) and passing through its center of mass.

SOLUTION

Conceptualize Imagine twirling the rod in Figure 10.9 with your fingers around its midpoint. If you have a meterstick handy, use it to simulate the spinning of a thin rod.

Categorize This example is a substitution problem, using the definition of moment of inertia in Equation 10.17. As with any calculus problem, the solution involves reducing the integrand to a single variable.

The shaded length element dx in Figure 10.9 has a mass dm equal to the mass per unit length λ multiplied by dx.

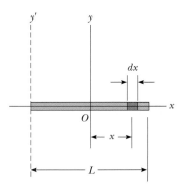

Figure 10.9 (Example 10.4) A uniform rigid rod of length L. The moment of inertia about the y axis is less than that about the y' axis. The latter axis is examined in Example 10.6.

Express dm in terms of dx:

$$dm = \lambda \, dx = \frac{M}{L} \, dx$$

Substitute this expression into Equation 10.17, with $r^2 = x^2$:

$$I_y = \int r^2 \, dm = \int_{-L/2}^{L/2} x^2 \frac{M}{L} \, dx = \frac{M}{L} \int_{-L/2}^{L/2} x^2 \, dx$$

$$= \frac{M}{L} \left[\frac{x^3}{3} \right]_{-L/2}^{L/2} = \tfrac{1}{12} ML^2$$

Check this result in Table 10.2.

EXAMPLE 10.5   Uniform Solid Cylinder

A uniform solid cylinder has a radius R, mass M, and length L. Calculate its moment of inertia about its central axis (the z axis in Fig. 10.10).

SOLUTION

Conceptualize   To simulate this situation, imagine twirling a can of frozen juice around its central axis.

Categorize   This example is a substitution problem, using the definition of moment of inertia. As with Example 10.4, we must reduce the integrand to a single variable.

It is convenient to divide the cylinder into many cylindrical shells, each having radius r, thickness dr, and length L as shown in Figure 10.10. The density of the cylinder is ρ. The volume dV of each shell is its cross-sectional area multiplied by its length: $dV = L\, dA = L(2\pi r)\, dr$.

Figure 10.10   (Example 10.5) Calculating I about the z axis for a uniform solid cylinder.

Express dm in terms of dr:

$$dm = \rho\, dV = 2\pi\rho Lr\, dr$$

Substitute this expression into Equation 10.17:

$$I_z = \int r^2\, dm = \int r^2(2\pi\rho Lr\, dr) = 2\pi\rho L \int_0^R r^3\, dr = \tfrac{1}{2}\pi\rho LR^4$$

Use the total volume $\pi R^2 L$ of the cylinder to express its density:

$$\rho = \frac{M}{V} = \frac{M}{\pi R^2 L}$$

Substitute this value into the expression for I_z:

$$I_z = \tfrac{1}{2}\pi\left(\frac{M}{\pi R^2 L}\right)LR^4 = \boxed{\tfrac{1}{2}MR^2}$$

Check this result in Table 10.2.

What If?   What if the length of the cylinder in Figure 10.10 is increased to $2L$, while the mass M and radius R are held fixed? How does that change the moment of inertia of the cylinder?

Answer   Notice that the result for the moment of inertia of a cylinder does not depend on L, the length of the cylinder. It applies equally well to a long cylinder and a flat disk having the same mass M and radius R. Therefore, the moment of inertia of the cylinder would not be affected by changing its length.

The calculation of moments of inertia of an object about an arbitrary axis can be cumbersome, even for a highly symmetric object. Fortunately, use of an important theorem, called the **parallel-axis theorem,** often simplifies the calculation.

To generate the parallel-axis theorem, suppose an object rotates about the z axis as shown in Figure 10.11. The moment of inertia does not depend on how the mass is distributed along the z axis; as we found in Example 10.5, the moment of inertia of a cylinder is independent of its length. Imagine collapsing the three-dimensional object into a planar object as in Figure 10.11b. In this imaginary process, all mass moves parallel to the z axis until it lies in the xy plane. The coordinates of the object's center of mass are now x_{CM}, y_{CM}, and $z_{CM} = 0$. Let the mass element dm have coordinates $(x, y, 0)$. Because this element is a distance $r = \sqrt{x^2 + y^2}$ from the z axis, the moment of inertia about the z axis is

$$I = \int r^2\, dm = \int (x^2 + y^2)\, dm$$

We can relate the coordinates x, y of the mass element dm to the coordinates of this same element located in a coordinate system having the object's center of mass as its origin. If the coordinates of the center of mass are x_{CM}, y_{CM}, and $z_{CM} = 0$

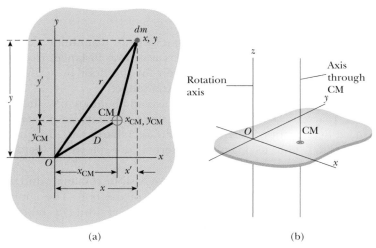

Figure 10.11   (a) The parallel-axis theorem. If the moment of inertia about an axis perpendicular to the figure through the center of mass is I_{CM}, the moment of inertia about the z axis is $I_z = I_{CM} + MD^2$. (b) Perspective drawing showing the z axis (the axis of rotation) and the parallel axis through the center of mass.

in the original coordinate system centered on O, we see from Figure 10.11a that the relationships between the unprimed and primed coordinates are $x = x' + x_{CM}$, $y = y' + y_{CM}$, and $z = z' = 0$. Therefore,

$$I = \int \left[(x' + x_{CM})^2 + (y' + y_{CM})^2 \right] dm$$

$$= \int \left[(x')^2 + (y')^2 \right] dm + 2x_{CM} \int x'\, dm + 2y_{CM} \int y'\, dm + (x_{CM}^{\,2} + y_{CM}^{\,2}) \int dm$$

The first integral is, by definition, the moment of inertia I_{CM} about an axis that is parallel to the z axis and passes through the center of mass. The second two integrals are zero because, by definition of the center of mass, $\int x'\, dm = \int y'\, dm = 0$. The last integral is simply MD^2 because $\int dm = M$ and $D^2 = x_{CM}^{\,2} + y_{CM}^{\,2}$. Therefore, we conclude that

$$I = I_{CM} + MD^2 \qquad\qquad (10.18) \qquad \blacktriangleleft \;\; \text{Parallel-axis theorem}$$

EXAMPLE 10.6   **Applying the Parallel-Axis Theorem**

Consider once again the uniform rigid rod of mass M and length L shown in Figure 10.9. Find the moment of inertia of the rod about an axis perpendicular to the rod through one end (the y' axis in Fig. 10.9).

SOLUTION

Conceptualize   Imagine twirling the rod around an endpoint rather than the midpoint. If you have a meterstick handy, try it and notice the degree of difficulty in rotating it around the end compared with rotating it around the center.

Categorize   This example is a substitution problem, involving the parallel-axis theorem.

Intuitively, we expect the moment of inertia to be greater than the result $I_{CM} = \frac{1}{12}ML^2$ from Example 10.4 because there is mass up to a distance of L away from the rotation axis, whereas the farthest distance in Example 10.4 was only $L/2$. The distance between the center-of-mass axis and the y' axis is $D = L/2$.

Use the parallel-axis theorem:
$$I = I_{CM} + MD^2 = \tfrac{1}{12}ML^2 + M\left(\frac{L}{2}\right)^2 = \boxed{\tfrac{1}{3}ML^2}$$

Check this result in Table 10.2.

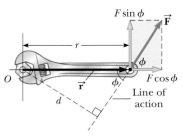

Figure 10.12 The force $\vec{F}$ has a greater rotating tendency about an axis through O as F increases and as the moment arm d increases. The component $F \sin \phi$ tends to rotate the wrench about O.

PITFALL PREVENTION 10.5

Torque Depends on Your Choice of Axis

Like moment of inertia, there is no unique value of the torque on an object. Its value depends on your choice of rotation axis.

Moment arm ▶

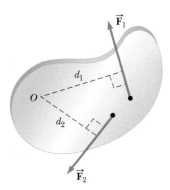

ACTIVE FIGURE 10.13

The force $\vec{F}_1$ tends to rotate the object counterclockwise about an axis through O, and $\vec{F}_2$ tends to rotate it clockwise.

Sign in at www.thomsonedu.com and go to ThomsonNOW to change the magnitudes, directions, and points of application of forces $\vec{F}_1$ and $\vec{F}_2$ and see how the object accelerates under the action of the two forces.

10.6   Torque

Imagine trying to rotate a door by applying a force of magnitude F perpendicular to the door surface near the hinges and then at various distances from the hinges. You will achieve a more rapid rate of rotation for the door by applying the force near the doorknob than by applying it near the hinges.

When a force is exerted on a rigid object pivoted about an axis, the object tends to rotate about that axis. The tendency of a force to rotate an object about some axis is measured by a quantity called **torque** $\vec{\tau}$ (Greek letter tau). Torque is a vector, but we will consider only its magnitude here and explore its vector nature in Chapter 11.

Consider the wrench in Figure 10.12 that we wish to rotate around an axis perpendicular to the page and through the center of the bolt. The applied force $\vec{F}$ acts at an angle ϕ to the horizontal. We define the magnitude of the torque associated with the force $\vec{F}$ by the expression

$$\tau \equiv rF \sin \phi = Fd \tag{10.19}$$

where r is the distance between the rotation axis and the point of application of $\vec{F}$, and d is the perpendicular distance from the rotation axis to the line of action of $\vec{F}$. (The *line of action* of a force is an imaginary line extending out both ends of the vector representing the force. The dashed line extending from the tail of $\vec{F}$ in Figure 10.12 is part of the line of action of $\vec{F}$.) From the right triangle in Figure 10.12 that has the wrench as its hypotenuse, we see that $d = r \sin \phi$. The quantity d is called the **moment arm** (or *lever arm*) of $\vec{F}$.

In Figure 10.12, the only component of $\vec{F}$ that tends to cause rotation of the wrench around an axis through O is $F \sin \phi$, the component perpendicular to a line drawn from the rotation axis to the point of application of the force. The horizontal component $F \cos \phi$, because its line of action passes through O, has no tendency to produce rotation about an axis passing through O. From the definition of torque, the rotating tendency increases as F increases and as d increases, which explains why it is easier to rotate a door if we push at the doorknob rather than at a point close to the hinges. We also want to apply our push as closely perpendicular to the door as we can so that ϕ is close to $90°$. Pushing sideways on the doorknob ($\phi = 0$) will not cause the door to rotate.

If two or more forces act on a rigid object as in Active Figure 10.13, each tends to produce rotation about the axis at O. In this example, $\vec{F}_2$ tends to rotate the object clockwise and $\vec{F}_1$ tends to rotate it counterclockwise. We use the convention that the sign of the torque resulting from a force is positive if the turning tendency of the force is counterclockwise and negative if the turning tendency is clockwise. For example, in Active Figure 10.13, the torque resulting from $\vec{F}_1$, which has a moment arm d_1, is positive and equal to $+F_1 d_1$; the torque from $\vec{F}_2$ is negative and equal to $-F_2 d_2$. Hence, the *net* torque about an axis through O is

$$\sum \tau = \tau_1 + \tau_2 = F_1 d_1 - F_2 d_2$$

Torque should not be confused with force. Forces can cause a change in translational motion as described by Newton's second law. Forces can also cause a change in rotational motion, but the effectiveness of the forces in causing this change depends on both the magnitudes of the forces and the moment arms of the forces, in the combination we call *torque*. Torque has units of force times length—newton meters in SI units—and should be reported in these units. Do not confuse torque and work, which have the same units but are very different concepts.

Quick Quiz 10.5 **(i)** If you are trying to loosen a stubborn screw from a piece of wood with a screwdriver and fail, should you find a screwdriver for which the handle is (a) longer or (b) fatter? **(ii)** If you are trying to loosen a stubborn bolt from a piece of metal with a wrench and fail, should you find a wrench for which the handle is (a) longer or (b) fatter?

EXAMPLE 10.7   **The Net Torque on a Cylinder**

A one-piece cylinder is shaped as shown in Figure 10.14, with a core section protruding from the larger drum. The cylinder is free to rotate about the central axis shown in the drawing. A rope wrapped around the drum, which has radius R_1, exerts a force $\vec{\mathbf{T}}_1$ to the right on the cylinder. A rope wrapped around the core, which has radius R_2, exerts a force $\vec{\mathbf{T}}_2$ downward on the cylinder.

(A) What is the net torque acting on the cylinder about the rotation axis (which is the z axis in Fig. 10.14)?

SOLUTION

Conceptualize   Imagine that the cylinder in Figure 10.14 is a shaft in a machine. The force $\vec{\mathbf{T}}_2$ could be applied by a drive belt wrapped around the drum. The force $\vec{\mathbf{T}}_1$ could be applied by a friction brake at the surface of the core.

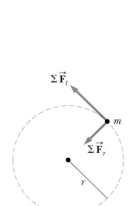

Figure 10.14   (Example 10.7) A solid cylinder pivoted about the z axis through O. The moment arm of $\vec{\mathbf{T}}_1$ is R_1, and the moment arm of $\vec{\mathbf{T}}_2$ is R_2.

Categorize   This example is a substitution problem in which we evaluate the net torque using Equation 10.19.

The torque due to $\vec{\mathbf{T}}_1$ about the rotation axis is $-R_1 T_1$. (The sign is negative because the torque tends to produce clockwise rotation.) The torque due to $\vec{\mathbf{T}}_2$ is $+R_2 T_2$. (The sign is positive because the torque tends to produce counterclockwise rotation of the cylinder.)

Evaluate the net torque about the rotation axis:
$$\sum \tau = \tau_1 + \tau_2 = \boxed{R_2 T_2 - R_1 T_1}$$

As a quick check, notice that if the two forces are of equal magnitude, the net torque is negative because $R_1 > R_2$. Starting from rest with both forces of equal magnitude acting on it, the cylinder would rotate clockwise because $\vec{\mathbf{T}}_1$ would be more effective at turning it than would $\vec{\mathbf{T}}_2$.

(B) Suppose $T_1 = 5.0$ N, $R_1 = 1.0$ m, $T_2 = 15.0$ N, and $R_2 = 0.50$ m. What is the net torque about the rotation axis, and which way does the cylinder rotate starting from rest?

SOLUTION

Substitute the given values:
$$\sum \tau = (0.50 \text{ m})(15 \text{ N}) - (1.0 \text{ m})(5.0 \text{ N}) = \boxed{2.5 \text{ N} \cdot \text{m}}$$

Because this net torque is positive, the cylinder begins to rotate in the counterclockwise direction.

10.7   The Rigid Object Under a Net Torque

In Chapter 5, we learned that a net force on an object causes an acceleration of the object and that the acceleration is proportional to the net force. These facts are the basis of the particle under a net force model whose mathematical representation is Newton's second law. In this section, we show the rotational analog of Newton's second law: the angular acceleration of a rigid object rotating about a fixed axis is proportional to the net torque acting about that axis. Before discussing the more complex case of rigid-object rotation, however, it is instructive first to discuss the case of a particle moving in a circular path about some fixed point under the influence of an external force.

Consider a particle of mass m rotating in a circle of radius r under the influence of a tangential net force $\sum \vec{\mathbf{F}}_t$ and a radial net force $\sum \vec{\mathbf{F}}_r$ as shown in Figure 10.15. The radial net force causes the particle to move in the circular path with a centripetal acceleration. The tangential force provides a tangential acceleration $\vec{\mathbf{a}}_t$, and

$$\sum F_t = m a_t$$

Figure 10.15   A particle rotating in a circle under the influence of a net tangential force $\sum \vec{\mathbf{F}}_t$. A net force $\sum \vec{\mathbf{F}}_r$ in the radial direction also must be present to maintain the circular motion.

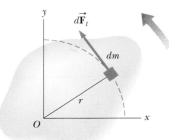

Figure 10.16 A rigid object rotating about an axis through O. Each mass element dm rotates about the axis with the same angular acceleration α.

The magnitude of the net torque due to $\Sigma\,\vec{\mathbf{F}}_t$ on the particle about an axis through the center of the circle is

$$\sum \tau = \sum F_t r = (ma_t)r$$

Because the tangential acceleration is related to the angular acceleration through the relationship $a_t = r\alpha$ (Eq. 10.11), the net torque can be expressed as

$$\sum \tau = (mr\alpha)r = (mr^2)\alpha$$

Recall from Equation 10.15 that mr^2 is the moment of inertia of the particle about the z axis passing through the origin, so that

$$\sum \tau = I\alpha \qquad \text{(10.20)}$$

That is, **the net torque acting on the particle is proportional to its angular acceleration,** and the proportionality constant is the moment of inertia. Notice that $\Sigma\,\tau = I\alpha$ has the same mathematical form as Newton's second law of motion, $\Sigma\,F = ma$.

Now let us extend this discussion to a rigid object of arbitrary shape rotating about a fixed axis as in Figure 10.16. The object can be regarded as an infinite number of mass elements dm of infinitesimal size. If we impose a Cartesian coordinate system on the object, each mass element rotates in a circle about the origin and each has a tangential acceleration $\vec{\mathbf{a}}_t$ produced by an external tangential force $d\vec{\mathbf{F}}_t$. For any given element, we know from Newton's second law that

$$dF_t = (dm)a_t$$

The torque $d\tau$ associated with the force $d\vec{\mathbf{F}}_t$ acts about the origin and is given by

$$d\tau = r\,dF_t = a_t r\,dm$$

Because $a_t = r\alpha$, the expression for $d\tau$ becomes

$$d\tau = \alpha r^2\,dm$$

Although each mass element of the rigid object may have a different translational acceleration $\vec{\mathbf{a}}_t$, they all have the *same* angular acceleration α. With this in mind, we can integrate the above expression to obtain the net torque $\Sigma\tau$ about an axis through O due to the external forces:

$$\sum \tau = \int \alpha r^2\,dm = \alpha \int r^2\,dm$$

where α can be taken outside the integral because it is common to all mass elements. From Equation 10.17, we know that $\int r^2\,dm$ is the moment of inertia of the object about the rotation axis through O, and so the expression for $\Sigma\,\tau$ becomes

▶ Torque is proportional to angular acceleration

$$\sum \tau = I\alpha \qquad \text{(10.21)}$$

This equation for a rigid object is the same as that found for a particle moving in a circular path (Eq. 10.20). The net torque about the rotation axis is proportional to the angular acceleration of the object, with the proportionality factor being I, a quantity that depends on the axis of rotation and on the size and shape of the object. Equation 10.21 is the mathematical representation of the analysis model of a **rigid object under a net torque**, the rotational analog to the particle under a net force.

Finally, notice that the result $\Sigma\,\tau = I\alpha$ also applies when the forces acting on the mass elements have radial components as well as tangential components. That is because the line of action of all radial components must pass through the axis of rotation; hence, all radial components produce zero torque about that axis.

Quick Quiz 10.6 You turn off your electric drill and find that the time interval for the rotating bit to come to rest due to frictional torque in the drill is Δt. You replace the bit with a larger one that results in a doubling of the moment of inertia of the drill's entire rotating mechanism. When this larger bit is rotated at the same angular speed as the first and the drill is turned off, the frictional torque remains the same as that for the previous situation. What is the time interval for this second bit to come to rest? (a) $4\,\Delta t$ (b) $2\,\Delta t$ (c) Δt (d) $0.5\,\Delta t$ (e) $0.25\,\Delta t$ (f) impossible to determine.

EXAMPLE 10.8   Rotating Rod

A uniform rod of length L and mass M is attached at one end to a frictionless pivot and is free to rotate about the pivot in the vertical plane as in Figure 10.17. The rod is released from rest in the horizontal position. What are the initial angular acceleration of the rod and the initial translational acceleration of its right end?

Figure 10.17   (Example 10.8) A rod is free to rotate around a pivot at the left end. The gravitational force on the rod acts at its center of mass.

SOLUTION

Conceptualize   Imagine what happens to the rod in Figure 10.17 when it is released. It rotates clockwise around the pivot at the left end.

Categorize   The rod is categorized as a rigid object under a net torque. The torque is due only to the gravitational force on the rod if the rotation axis is chosen to pass through the pivot in Figure 10.17. We *cannot* categorize the rod as a rigid object under constant angular acceleration because the torque exerted on the rod and therefore the angular acceleration of the rod vary with its angular position.

Analyze   The only force contributing to the torque about an axis through the pivot is the gravitational force $M\vec{\mathbf{g}}$ exerted on the rod. (The force exerted by the pivot on the rod has zero torque about the pivot because its moment arm is zero.) To compute the torque on the rod, we assume the gravitational force acts at the center of mass of the rod as shown in Figure 10.17.

Write an expression for the magnitude of the torque due to the gravitational force about an axis through the pivot:

$$\tau = Mg\left(\frac{L}{2}\right)$$

Use Equation 10.21 to obtain the angular acceleration of the rod:

$$(1)\quad \alpha = \frac{\tau}{I} = \frac{Mg\,(L/2)}{\frac{1}{3}ML^2} = \frac{3g}{2L}$$

Use Equation 10.11 with $r = L$ to find the initial translational acceleration of the right end of the rod:

$$a_t = L\alpha = \tfrac{3}{2}g$$

Finalize   These values are the *initial* values of the angular and translational accelerations. Once the rod begins to rotate, the gravitational force is no longer perpendicular to the rod and the values of the two accelerations decrease, going to zero at the moment the rod passes through the vertical orientation.

What If?   What if we were to place a penny on the end of the rod and then release the rod? Would the penny stay in contact with the rod?

Answer   The result for the initial acceleration of a point on the end of the rod shows that $a_t > g$. An unsupported penny falls at acceleration g. So, if we place a penny at the end of the rod and then release the rod, the end of the rod falls faster than the penny does! The penny does not stay in contact with the rod. (Try this with a penny and a meterstick!)

The question now is to find the location on the rod at which we can place a penny that *will* stay in contact as both begin to fall. To find the translational acceleration of an arbitrary point on the rod at a distance $r < L$ from the pivot point, we combine Equation (1) with Equation 10.11:

$$a_t = r\alpha = \frac{3g}{2L}\,r$$

For the penny to stay in contact with the rod, the limiting case is that the translational acceleration must be equal to that due to gravity:

$$a_t = g = \frac{3g}{2L}\, r$$

$$r = \tfrac{2}{3}L$$

Therefore, a penny placed closer to the pivot than two-thirds of the length of the rod stays in contact with the falling rod, but a penny farther out than this point loses contact.

CONCEPTUAL EXAMPLE 10.9   Falling Smokestacks and Tumbling Blocks

When a tall smokestack falls over, it often breaks somewhere along its length before it hits the ground as shown in Figure 10.18. Why?

SOLUTION

As the smokestack rotates around its base, each higher portion of the smokestack falls with a larger tangential acceleration than the portion below it according to Equation 10.11. The angular acceleration increases as the smokestack tips farther. Eventually, higher portions of the smokestack experience an acceleration greater than the acceleration that could result from gravity alone; this situation is similar to that described in Example 10.8. It can happen only if these portions are being pulled downward by a force in addition to the gravitational force. The force that causes that to occur is the shear force from lower portions of the smokestack. Eventually, the shear force that provides this acceleration is greater than the smokestack can withstand, and the smokestack breaks. The same thing happens

Figure 10.18 (Conceptual Example 10.9) A falling smokestack breaks at some point along its length.

with a tall tower of children's toy blocks. Borrow some blocks from a child and build such a tower. Push it over and watch it come apart at some point before it strikes the floor.

EXAMPLE 10.10   Angular Acceleration of a Wheel

A wheel of radius R, mass M, and moment of inertia I is mounted on a frictionless, horizontal axle as in Figure 10.19. A light cord wrapped around the wheel supports an object of mass m. Calculate the angular acceleration of the wheel, the linear acceleration of the object, and the tension in the cord.

SOLUTION

Conceptualize Imagine that the object is a bucket in an old-fashioned wishing well. It is tied to a cord that passes around a cylinder equipped with a crank for raising the bucket. After the bucket has been raised, the system is released and the bucket accelerates downward while the cord unwinds off the cylinder.

Categorize The object is modeled as a particle under a net force. The wheel is modeled as a rigid object under a net torque.

Analyze The magnitude of the torque acting on the wheel about its axis of rotation is $\tau = TR$, where T is the force exerted by the cord on the rim of the wheel. (The gravitational force exerted by the Earth on the wheel and the normal force exerted by the axle on the wheel both pass through the axis of rotation and therefore produce no torque.)

Figure 10.19 (Example 10.10) An object hangs from a cord wrapped around a wheel.

Write Equation 10.21:

$$\sum \tau = I\alpha$$

Solve for α and substitute the net torque:

$$(1) \quad \alpha = \frac{\sum \tau}{I} = \frac{TR}{I}$$

Apply Newton's second law to the motion of the object, taking the downward direction to be positive:

$$\sum F_y = mg - T = ma$$

Solve for the acceleration a:

$$(2) \quad a = \frac{mg - T}{m}$$

Equations (1) and (2) have three unknowns: α, a, and T. Because the object and wheel are connected by a cord that does not slip, the translational acceleration of the suspended object is equal to the tangential acceleration of a point on the wheel's rim. Therefore, the angular acceleration α of the wheel and the translational acceleration of the object are related by $a = R\alpha$.

Use this fact together with Equations (1) and (2):

$$(3) \quad a = R\alpha = \frac{TR^2}{I} = \frac{mg - T}{m}$$

Solve for the tension T:

$$(4) \quad T = \frac{mg}{1 + (mR^2/I)}$$

Substitute Equation (4) into Equation (2) and solve for a:

$$(5) \quad a = \frac{g}{1 + (I/mR^2)}$$

Use $a = R\alpha$ and Equation (5) to solve for α:

$$\alpha = \frac{a}{R} = \frac{g}{R + (I/mR)}$$

Finalize   We finalize this problem by imagining the behavior of the system in some extreme limits.

What If?   What if the wheel were to become very massive so that I becomes very large? What happens to the acceleration a of the object and the tension T?

Answer   If the wheel becomes infinitely massive, we can imagine that the object of mass m will simply hang from the cord without causing the wheel to rotate.

We can show that mathematically by taking the limit $I \to \infty$. Equation (5) then becomes

$$a = \frac{g}{1 + (I/mR^2)} \quad \to \quad 0$$

which agrees with our conceptual conclusion that the object will hang at rest. Also, Equation (4) becomes

$$T = \frac{mg}{1 + (mR^2/I)} \quad \to \quad \frac{mg}{1 + 0} = mg$$

which is consistent because the object simply hangs at rest in equilibrium between the gravitational force and the tension in the string.

10.8   Energy Considerations in Rotational Motion

Up to this point in our discussion of rotational motion in this chapter, we focused primarily on an approach involving force, leading to a description of torque on a rigid object. In Section 10.4, we discussed the rotational kinetic energy of a rigid

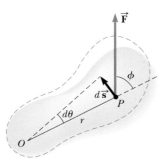

Figure 10.20 A rigid object rotates about an axis through O under the action of an external force $\vec{F}$ applied at P.

object. Let us now extend that initial energy discussion and see how an energy approach can be useful in solving rotational problems.

We begin by considering the relationship between the torque acting on a rigid object and its resulting rotational motion so as to generate expressions for power and a rotational analog to the work–kinetic energy theorem. Consider the rigid object pivoted at O in Figure 10.20. Suppose a single external force $\vec{F}$ is applied at P, where $\vec{F}$ lies in the plane of the page. The work done on the object by $\vec{F}$ as its point of application rotates through an infinitesimal distance $ds = r\, d\theta$ is

$$dW = \vec{F} \cdot d\vec{s} = (F \sin \phi)\, r\, d\theta$$

where $F \sin \phi$ is the tangential component of $\vec{F}$, or, in other words, the component of the force along the displacement. Notice that the radial component vector of $\vec{F}$ does no work on the object because it is perpendicular to the displacement of the point of application of $\vec{F}$.

Because the magnitude of the torque due to $\vec{F}$ about an axis through O is defined as $rF \sin \phi$ by Equation 10.19, we can write the work done for the infinitesimal rotation as

$$dW = \tau\, d\theta \tag{10.22}$$

The rate at which work is being done by $\vec{F}$ as the object rotates about the fixed axis through the angle $d\theta$ in a time interval dt is

$$\frac{dW}{dt} = \tau \frac{d\theta}{dt}$$

Because dW/dt is the instantaneous power $\mathcal{P}$ (see Section 8.5) delivered by the force and $d\theta/dt = \omega$, this expression reduces to

◀ Power delivered to a rotating rigid object

$$\mathcal{P} = \frac{dW}{dt} = \tau \omega \tag{10.23}$$

This equation is analogous to $\mathcal{P} = Fv$ in the case of translational motion, and Equation 10.22 is analogous to $dW = F_x\, dx$.

In studying translational motion, models based on an energy approach can be extremely useful in describing a system's behavior. From what we learned of translational motion, we expect that when a symmetric object rotates about a fixed axis, the work done by external forces equals the change in the rotational energy of the object.

To prove that fact, let us begin with $\sum \tau = I\alpha$. Using the chain rule from calculus, we can express the net torque as

$$\sum \tau = I\alpha = I\frac{d\omega}{dt} = I\frac{d\omega}{d\theta}\frac{d\theta}{dt} = I\frac{d\omega}{d\theta}\omega$$

Rearranging this expression and noting that $\sum \tau\, d\theta = dW$ gives

$$\sum \tau\, d\theta = dW = I\omega\, d\omega$$

Integrating this expression, we obtain for the total work done by the net external force acting on a rotating system

◀ Work–kinetic energy theorem for rotational motion

$$\sum W = \int_{\omega_i}^{\omega_f} I\omega\, d\omega = \tfrac{1}{2}I\omega_f^2 - \tfrac{1}{2}I\omega_i^2 \tag{10.24}$$

where the angular speed changes from ω_i to ω_f. Equation 10.24 is the **work–kinetic energy theorem for rotational motion.** Similar to the work–kinetic energy theorem in translational motion (Section 7.5), this theorem states that the net work done by external forces in rotating a symmetric rigid object about a fixed axis equals the change in the object's rotational energy.

This theorem is a form of the nonisolated system model discussed in Chapter 8. Work is done on the system of the rigid object, which represents a transfer of energy across the boundary of the system that appears as an increase in the object's rotational kinetic energy.

TABLE 10.3

Useful Equations in Rotational and Translational Motion

Rotational Motion About a Fixed Axis	Translational Motion
Angular speed $\omega = d\theta/dt$	Translational speed $v = dx/dt$
Angular acceleration $\alpha = d\omega/dt$	Translational acceleration $a = dv/dt$
Net torque $\Sigma \tau = I\alpha$	Net force $\Sigma F = ma$
If $\alpha = $ constant $\begin{cases} \omega_f = \omega_i + \alpha t \\ \theta_f = \theta_i + \omega_i t + \frac{1}{2}\alpha t^2 \\ \omega_f^2 = \omega_i^2 + 2\alpha(\theta_f - \theta_i) \end{cases}$	If $a = $ constant $\begin{cases} v_f = v_i + at \\ x_f = x_i + v_i t + \frac{1}{2}at^2 \\ v_f^2 = v_i^2 + 2a(x_f - x_i) \end{cases}$
Work $W = \displaystyle\int_{\theta_i}^{\theta_f} \tau\, d\theta$	Work $W = \displaystyle\int_{x_i}^{x_f} F_x\, dx$
Rotational kinetic energy $K_R = \frac{1}{2}I\omega^2$	Kinetic energy $K = \frac{1}{2}mv^2$
Power $\mathcal{P} = \tau\omega$	Power $\mathcal{P} = Fv$
Angular momentum $L = I\omega$	Linear momentum $p = mv$
Net torque $\Sigma\tau = dL/dt$	Net force $\Sigma F = dp/dt$

In general, we can combine this theorem with the translational form of the work–kinetic energy theorem from Chapter 7. Therefore, the net work done by external forces on an object is the change in its *total* kinetic energy, which is the sum of the translational and rotational kinetic energies. For example, when a pitcher throws a baseball, the work done by the pitcher's hands appears as kinetic energy associated with the ball moving through space as well as rotational kinetic energy associated with the spinning of the ball.

In addition to the work–kinetic energy theorem, other energy principles can also be applied to rotational situations. For example, if a system involving rotating objects is isolated and no nonconservative forces act within the system, the isolated system model and the principle of conservation of mechanical energy can be used to analyze the system as in Example 10.11 below.

Finally, in some situations an energy approach does not provide enough information to solve the problem and it must be combined with a momentum approach. Such a case is illustrated in Example 10.14 in Section 10.9.

Table 10.3 lists the various equations we have discussed pertaining to rotational motion together with the analogous expressions for translational motion. The last two equations in Table 10.3, involving angular momentum L, are discussed in Chapter 11 and are included here only for the sake of completeness.

EXAMPLE 10.11 | Rotating Rod Revisited

A uniform rod of length L and mass M is free to rotate on a frictionless pin passing through one end (Fig 10.21). The rod is released from rest in the horizontal position.

(A) What is its angular speed when the rod reaches its lowest position?

SOLUTION

Conceptualize   Consider Figure 10.21 and imagine the rod rotating downward through a quarter turn about the pivot at the left end. Also look back at Example 10.8. This physical situation is the same.

Categorize   As mentioned in Example 10.8, the angular acceleration of the rod is not constant. Therefore, the kinematic equations for rotation (Section 10.2) cannot be used to solve this example. We categorize the system of the rod and the Earth as an isolated system with no nonconservative forces acting and use the principle of conservation of mechanical energy.

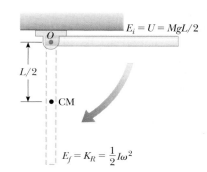

Figure 10.21   (Example 10.11) A uniform rigid rod pivoted at O rotates in a vertical plane under the action of the gravitational force.

Analyze We choose the configuration in which the rod is hanging straight down as the reference configuration for gravitational potential energy and assign a value of zero for this configuration. When the rod is in the horizontal position, it has no rotational kinetic energy. The potential energy of the system in this configuration relative to the reference configuration is $MgL/2$ because the center of mass of the rod is at a height $L/2$ higher than its position in the reference configuration. When the rod reaches its lowest position, the energy of the system is entirely rotational energy $\frac{1}{2}I\omega^2$, where I is the moment of inertia of the rod about an axis passing through the pivot.

Write a conservation of mechanical energy equation for the system:

$$K_f + U_f = K_i + U_i$$

Substitute for each of the energies:

$$\tfrac{1}{2}I\omega^2 + 0 = 0 + \tfrac{1}{2}MgL$$

Solve for ω and use $I = \frac{1}{3}ML^2$ (see Table 10.2) for the rod:

$$\omega = \sqrt{\frac{MgL}{I}} = \sqrt{\frac{MgL}{\frac{1}{3}ML^2}} = \boxed{\sqrt{\frac{3g}{L}}}$$

(B) Determine the tangential speed of the center of mass and the tangential speed of the lowest point on the rod when it is in the vertical position.

SOLUTION

Use Equation 10.10 and the result from part (A):

$$v_{CM} = r\omega = \frac{L}{2}\omega = \boxed{\tfrac{1}{2}\sqrt{3gL}}$$

Because r for the lowest point on the rod is twice what it is for the center of mass, the lowest point has a tangential speed twice that of the center of mass:

$$v = 2v_{CM} = \boxed{\sqrt{3gL}}$$

Finalize The initial configuration in this example is the same as that in Example 10.8. In Example 10.8, however, we could only find the initial angular acceleration of the rod. Applying an energy approach in the current example allows us to find additional information, the angular speed of the rod at another instant of time.

EXAMPLE 10.12 | **Energy and the Atwood Machine**

Two cylinders having different masses m_1 and m_2 are connected by a string passing over a pulley, as shown in Active Figure 10.22. The pulley has a radius R and moment of inertia I about its axis of rotation. The string does not slip on the pulley, and the system is released from rest. Find the translational speeds of the cylinders after cylinder 2 descends through a distance h, and find the angular speed of the pulley at this time.

SOLUTION

Conceptualize We have already seen examples involving the Atwood machine, so the motion of the objects in Active Figure 10.22 should be easy to visualize.

Categorize Because the string does not slip, the pulley rotates about the axle. We can neglect friction in the axle because the axle's radius is small relative to that of the pulley. Hence, the frictional torque is much smaller than the net torque applied by the two cylinders provided that their masses are significantly different. Consequently, the system consisting of the two cylinders, the pulley, and the Earth is an isolated system with no nonconservative forces acting; therefore, the mechanical energy of the system is conserved.

Analyze We define the zero configuration for gravitational potential energy as that which exists when the system is released. From Active Figure 10.22, we see

ACTIVE FIGURE 10.22

(Example 10.12) An Atwood machine with a massive pulley.

Sign in at www.thomsonedu.com and go to ThomsonNOW to change the masses of the hanging cylinders and the mass and radius of the pulley and see how the cylinders move.

that the descent of cylinder 2 is associated with a decrease in system potential energy and that the rise of cylinder 1 represents an increase in potential energy.

Write a conservation of energy equation for the system:

$$K_f + U_f = K_i + U_i$$

Substitute for each of the energies:

$$(\tfrac{1}{2}m_1v_f^{\,2} + \tfrac{1}{2}m_2v_f^{\,2} + \tfrac{1}{2}I\omega_f^{\,2}) + (m_1gh - m_2gh) = 0 + 0$$

Use $v_f = R\omega_f$ to substitute for ω_f:

$$\tfrac{1}{2}m_1v_f^{\,2} + \tfrac{1}{2}m_2v_f^{\,2} + \tfrac{1}{2}\frac{I}{R^2}v_f^{\,2} = m_2gh - m_1gh$$

$$\tfrac{1}{2}\left(m_1 + m_2 + \frac{I}{R^2}\right)v_f^{\,2} = m_2gh - m_1gh$$

Solve for v_f:

$$(1) \quad v_f = \left[\frac{2(m_2 - m_1)gh}{m_1 + m_2 + I/R^2}\right]^{1/2}$$

Use $v_f = R\omega_f$ to solve for ω_f:

$$\omega_f = \frac{v_f}{R} = \frac{1}{R}\left[\frac{2(m_2 - m_1)gh}{m_1 + m_2 + I/R^2}\right]^{1/2}$$

Finalize   Each cylinder can be modeled as a particle under constant acceleration because it experiences a constant net force. Think about what you would need to do to use Equation (1) to find the acceleration of one of the cylinders and reduce the result so that it matches the result of Example 5.9. Then do it and see if it works!

10.9   Rolling Motion of a Rigid Object

In this section, we treat the motion of a rigid object rolling along a flat surface. In general, such motion is complex. For example, suppose a cylinder is rolling on a straight path such that the axis of rotation remains parallel to its initial orientation in space. As Figure 10.23 shows, a point on the rim of the cylinder moves in a complex path called a *cycloid*. We can simplify matters, however, by focusing on the center of mass rather than on a point on the rim of the rolling object. As shown in Figure 10.23, the center of mass moves in a straight line. If an object such as a cylinder rolls without slipping on the surface (called *pure rolling motion*), a simple relationship exists between its rotational and translational motions.

Consider a uniform cylinder of radius R rolling without slipping on a horizontal surface (Fig. 10.24). As the cylinder rotates through an angle θ, its center of mass

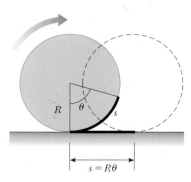

Figure 10.24   For pure rolling motion, as the cylinder rotates through an angle θ its center moves a linear distance $s = R\theta$.

Figure 10.23   One light source at the center of a rolling cylinder and another at one point on the rim illustrate the different paths these two points take. The center moves in a straight line (green line), whereas the point on the rim moves in the path called a cycloid (red curve).

PITFALL PREVENTION 10.6
Equation 10.25 Looks Familiar

Equation 10.25 looks very similar to Equation 10.10, so be sure to be clear on the difference. Equation 10.10 gives the *tangential* speed of a point on a *rotating* object located a distance *r* from a fixed rotation axis if the object is rotating with angular speed *ω*. Equation 10.25 gives the *translational* speed of the center of mass of a *rolling* object of radius *R* rotating with angular speed *ω*.

moves a linear distance $s = R\theta$ (see Eq. 10.1a). Therefore, the translational speed of the center of mass for pure rolling motion is given by

$$v_{CM} = \frac{ds}{dt} = R\frac{d\theta}{dt} = R\omega \qquad (10.25)$$

where ω is the angular speed of the cylinder. Equation 10.25 holds whenever a cylinder or sphere rolls without slipping and is the **condition for pure rolling motion.** The magnitude of the linear acceleration of the center of mass for pure rolling motion is

$$a_{CM} = \frac{dv_{CM}}{dt} = R\frac{d\omega}{dt} = R\alpha \qquad (10.26)$$

where α is the angular acceleration of the cylinder.

Imagine that you are moving along with a rolling object at speed v_{CM}, staying in a frame of reference at rest with respect to the center of mass of the object. As you observe the object, you will see the object in pure rotation around its center of mass. Figure 10.25a shows the velocities of points at the top, center, and bottom of the object as observed by you. In addition to these velocities, every point on the object moves in the same direction with speed v_{CM} relative to the surface on which it rolls. Figure 10.25b shows these velocities for a nonrotating object. In the reference frame at rest with respect to the surface, the velocity of a given point on the object is the sum of the velocities shown in Figures 10.25a and 10.25b. Figure 10.25c shows the results of adding these velocities.

Notice that the contact point between the surface and cylinder in Figure 10.25c has a translational speed of zero. At this instant, the rolling object is moving in exactly the same way as if the surface were removed and the object were pivoted at point *P* and spun about an axis passing through *P*. We can express the total kinetic energy of this imagined spinning object as

$$K = \tfrac{1}{2}I_P\omega^2 \qquad (10.27)$$

where I_P is the moment of inertia about a rotation axis through *P*.

Because the motion of the imagined spinning object is the same at this instant as our actual rolling object, Equation 10.27 also gives the kinetic energy of the rolling object. Applying the parallel-axis theorem, we can substitute $I_P = I_{CM} + MR^2$ into Equation 10.27 to obtain

$$K = \tfrac{1}{2}I_{CM}\omega^2 + \tfrac{1}{2}MR^2\omega^2$$

Using $v_{CM} = R\omega$, this equation can be expressed as

Total kinetic energy of ▶
a rolling object

$$\boxed{K = \tfrac{1}{2}I_{CM}\omega^2 + \tfrac{1}{2}Mv_{CM}^2} \qquad (10.28)$$

The term $\tfrac{1}{2}I_{CM}\omega^2$ represents the rotational kinetic energy of the cylinder about its center of mass, and the term $\tfrac{1}{2}Mv_{CM}^2$ represents the kinetic energy the cylinder

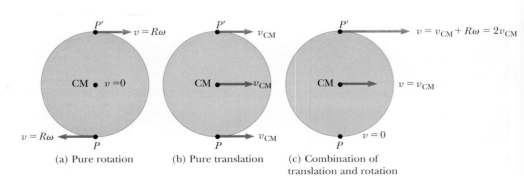

(a) Pure rotation   (b) Pure translation   (c) Combination of translation and rotation

Figure 10.25   The motion of a rolling object can be modeled as a combination of pure translation and pure rotation.

would have if it were just translating through space without rotating. Therefore, the **total kinetic energy of a rolling object is the sum of the rotational kinetic energy about the center of mass and the translational kinetic energy of the center of mass.** This statement is consistent with the situation illustrated in Figure 10.25, which shows that the velocity of a point on the object is the sum of the velocity of the center of mass and the tangential velocity around the center of mass.

Energy methods can be used to treat a class of problems concerning the rolling motion of an object on a rough incline. For example, consider Active Figure 10.26, which shows a sphere rolling without slipping after being released from rest at the top of the incline. Accelerated rolling motion is possible only if a friction force is present between the sphere and the incline to produce a net torque about the center of mass. Despite the presence of friction, no loss of mechanical energy occurs because the contact point is at rest relative to the surface at any instant. (On the other hand, if the sphere were to slip, mechanical energy of the sphere–incline–Earth system would be lost due to the nonconservative force of kinetic friction.)

In reality, *rolling friction* causes mechanical energy to transform to internal energy. Rolling friction is due to deformations of the surface and the rolling object. For example, automobile tires flex as they roll on a roadway, representing a transformation of mechanical energy to internal energy. The roadway also deforms a small amount, representing additional rolling friction. In our problem-solving models, we ignore rolling friction unless stated otherwise.

Using $v_{CM} = R\omega$ for pure rolling motion, we can express Equation 10.28 as

$$K = \tfrac{1}{2}I_{CM}\left(\frac{v_{CM}}{R}\right)^2 + \tfrac{1}{2}Mv_{CM}^2$$

$$K = \tfrac{1}{2}\left(\frac{I_{CM}}{R^2} + M\right)v_{CM}^2 \qquad (10.29)$$

For the sphere–Earth system, we define the zero configuration of gravitational potential energy to be when the sphere is at the bottom of the incline. Therefore, conservation of mechanical energy gives

$$K_f + U_f = K_i + U_i$$

$$\tfrac{1}{2}\left(\frac{I_{CM}}{R^2} + M\right)v_{CM}^2 + 0 = 0 + Mgh$$

$$v_{CM} = \left[\frac{2gh}{1 + (I_{CM}/MR^2)}\right]^{1/2} \qquad (10.30)$$

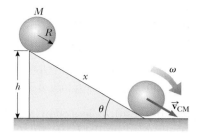

ACTIVE FIGURE 10.26

A sphere rolling down an incline. Mechanical energy of the sphere–Earth system is conserved if no slipping occurs.

Sign in at www.thomsonedu.com and go to ThomsonNOW to roll several objects down the hill and see how the final speed depends on the type of object.

Quick Quiz 10.7   A ball rolls without slipping down incline A, starting from rest. At the same time, a box starts from rest and slides down incline B, which is identical to incline A except that it is frictionless. Which arrives at the bottom first? (a) The ball arrives first. (b) The box arrives first. (c) Both arrive at the same time. (d) It is impossible to determine.

EXAMPLE 10.13   **Sphere Rolling Down an Incline**

For the solid sphere shown in Active Figure 10.26, calculate the translational speed of the center of mass at the bottom of the incline and the magnitude of the translational acceleration of the center of mass.

SOLUTION

Conceptualize   Imagine rolling the sphere down the incline. Compare it in your mind to a book sliding down a frictionless incline. You probably have experience with objects rolling down inclines and may be tempted to think that the sphere would move down the incline faster than the book. You do *not*, however, have experience with objects sliding down *frictionless* inclines! So, which object will reach the bottom first? (See Quick Quiz 10.7.)

Categorize   We model the sphere and the Earth as an isolated system with no nonconservative forces acting. This model is the one that led to Equation 10.30, so we can use that result.

Analyze   Evaluate the speed of the center of mass of the sphere from Equation 10.30:

$$(1) \quad v_{CM} = \left[\frac{2gh}{1 + \left(\frac{2}{5}MR^2/MR^2\right)} \right]^{1/2} = \left(\tfrac{10}{7}gh\right)^{1/2}$$

This result is less than $\sqrt{2gh}$, which is the speed an object would have if it simply slid down the incline without rotating. (Eliminate the rotation by setting $I_{CM} = 0$ in Equation 10.30.)

To calculate the translational acceleration of the center of mass, notice that the vertical displacement of the sphere is related to the distance x it moves along the incline through the relationship $h = x \sin \theta$.

Use this relationship to rewrite Equation (1):

$$v_{CM}{}^2 = \tfrac{10}{7}gx \sin \theta$$

Write Equation 2.17 for an object starting from rest and moving through a distance x:

$$v_{CM}{}^2 = 2a_{CM}x$$

Equate the preceding two expressions to find a_{CM}:

$$a_{CM} = \tfrac{5}{7}g \sin \theta$$

Finalize   Both the speed and the acceleration of the center of mass are *independent* of the mass and the radius of the sphere. That is, **all homogeneous solid spheres experience the same speed and acceleration on a given incline.** Try to verify this statement experimentally with balls of different sizes, such as a marble and a croquet ball.

If we were to repeat the acceleration calculation for a hollow sphere, a solid cylinder, or a hoop, we would obtain similar results in which only the factor in front of $g \sin \theta$ would differ. The constant factors that appear in the expressions for v_{CM} and a_{CM} depend only on the moment of inertia about the center of mass for the specific object. In all cases, the acceleration of the center of mass is *less* than $g \sin \theta$, the value the acceleration would have if the incline were frictionless and no rolling occurred.

EXAMPLE 10.14   **Pulling on a Spool[3]**

A cylindrically symmetric spool of mass m and radius R sits at rest on a horizontal table with friction (Fig. 10.27). With your hand on a massless string wrapped around the axle of radius r, you pull on the spool with a constant horizontal force of magnitude T to the right. As a result, the spool rolls without slipping a distance L along the table with no rolling friction.

(A) Find the final translational speed of the center of mass of the spool.

SOLUTION

Conceptualize   Use Figure 10.27 to visualize the motion of the spool when you pull the string. For the spool to roll through a distance L, notice that your hand on the string must pull through a distance *different* from L.

Figure 10.27   (Example 10.14) A spool rests on a horizontal table. A string is wrapped around the axle and is pulled to the right by a hand.

Categorize   The spool is a rigid object under a net torque, but the net torque includes that due to the friction force, about which we know nothing. Therefore, an approach based on the rigid object under a net torque model will not be successful. Work is done by your hand on the spool and string, which form a nonisolated system. Let's see if an approach based on the nonisolated system model is fruitful.

---

[3] Example 10.14 was inspired in part by C. E. Mungan, "A primer on work–energy relationships for introductory physics," *The Physics Teacher*, 43:10, 2005.

Analyze The only type of energy that changes in the system is the kinetic energy of the spool. There is no rolling friction, so there is no change in internal energy. The only way that energy crosses the system's boundary is by the work done by your hand on the string. No work is done by the static force of friction on the bottom of the spool because the point of application of the force moves through no displacement.

Write the appropriate reduction of the conservation of energy equation, Equation 8.2:

$$(1) \quad W = \Delta K = \Delta K_{\text{trans}} + \Delta K_{\text{rot}}$$

where W is the work done on the string by your hand. To find this work, we need to find the displacement of your hand during the process.

We first find the length of string that has unwound off the spool. If the spool rolls through a distance L, the total angle through which it rotates is $\theta = L/R$. The axle also rotates through this angle.

Use Equation 10.1a to find the total arc length through which the axle turns:

$$\ell = r\theta = \frac{r}{R} L$$

This result also gives the length of string pulled off the axle. Your hand will move through this distance *plus* the distance L through which the spool moves. Therefore, the magnitude of the displacement of the point of application of the force applied by your hand is $\ell + L = L(1 + r/R)$.

Evaluate the work done by your hand on the string:

$$(2) \quad W = TL\left(1 + \frac{r}{R}\right)$$

Substitute Equation (2) into Equation (1):

$$TL\left(1 + \frac{r}{R}\right) = \tfrac{1}{2}mv_{\text{CM}}^2 + \tfrac{1}{2}I\omega^2$$

where I is the moment of inertia of the spool about its center of mass and v_{CM} and ω are the final values after the wheel rolls through the distance L.

Apply the nonslip rolling condition $\omega = v_{\text{CM}}/R$:

$$TL\left(1 + \frac{r}{R}\right) = \tfrac{1}{2}mv_{\text{CM}}^2 + \tfrac{1}{2}I\frac{v_{\text{CM}}^2}{R^2}$$

Solve for v_{CM}:

$$(3) \quad v_{\text{CM}} = \sqrt{\frac{2TL(1 + r/R)}{m(1 + I/mR^2)}}$$

(B) Find the value of the friction force f.

SOLUTION

Categorize Because the friction force does no work, we cannot evaluate it from an energy approach. We model the spool as a nonisolated system, but this time in terms of momentum. The string applies a force across the boundary of the system, resulting in an impulse on the system. Because the forces on the spool are constant, we can model the spool's center of mass as a particle under constant acceleration.

Analyze Write the impulse–momentum theorem (Eq. 9.40) for the spool:

$$(4) \quad (T - f)\Delta t = m(v_{\text{CM}} - 0) = mv_{\text{CM}}$$

For a particle under constant acceleration starting from rest, Equation 2.14 tells us that the average velocity of the center of mass is half the final velocity.

Use Equation 2.2 to find the time interval for the center of mass of the spool to move a distance L from rest to a final speed v_{CM}:

$$(5) \quad \Delta t = \frac{L}{v_{CM,\,avg}} = \frac{2L}{v_{CM}}$$

Substitute Equation (5) into Equation (4):

$$(T - f)\frac{2L}{v_{CM}} = mv_{CM}$$

Solve for the friction force f:

$$f = T - \frac{mv_{CM}^2}{2L}$$

Substitute v_{CM} from Equation (3):

$$f = T - \frac{m}{2L}\left[\frac{2TL(1 + r/R)}{m(1 + I/mR^2)}\right]$$

$$= T - T\frac{(1 + r/R)}{(1 + I/mR^2)} = \boxed{T\left[1 - \frac{(1 + r/R)}{(1 + I/mR^2)}\right]}$$

Finalize Notice that we could use the impulse-momentum theorem for the translational motion of the spool while ignoring that the spool is rotating! This fact demonstrates the power of our growing list of approaches to solving problems.

Summary

ThomsonNOW™ Sign in at **www.thomsonedu.com** and go to ThomsonNOW to take a practice test for this chapter.

DEFINITIONS

The **angular position** of a rigid object is defined as the angle θ between a reference line attached to the object and a reference line fixed in space. The **angular displacement** of a particle moving in a circular path or a rigid object rotating about a fixed axis is $\Delta\theta \equiv \theta_f - \theta_i$.

The **instantaneous angular speed** of a particle moving in a circular path or of a rigid object rotating about a fixed axis is

$$\omega \equiv \frac{d\theta}{dt} \qquad (10.3)$$

The **instantaneous angular acceleration** of a particle moving in a circular path or of a rigid object rotating about a fixed axis is

$$\alpha \equiv \frac{d\omega}{dt} \qquad (10.5)$$

When a rigid object rotates about a fixed axis, every part of the object has the same angular speed and the same angular acceleration.

The **moment of inertia of a system of particles** is defined as

$$I \equiv \sum_i m_i r_i^2 \qquad (10.15)$$

where m_i is the mass of the ith particle and r_i is its distance from the rotation axis.

The magnitude of the **torque** associated with a force $\vec{F}$ acting on an object at a distance r from the rotation axis is

$$\tau \equiv rF\sin\phi = Fd \qquad (10.19)$$

where ϕ is the angle between the position vector of the point of application of the force and the force vector, and d is the moment arm of the force, which is the perpendicular distance from the rotation axis to the line of action of the force.

CONCEPTS AND PRINCIPLES

When a rigid object rotates about a fixed axis, the angular position, angular speed, and angular acceleration are related to the translational position, translational speed, and translational acceleration through the relationships

$$s = r\theta \qquad \textbf{(10.1a)}$$

$$v = r\omega \qquad \textbf{(10.10)}$$

$$a_t = r\alpha \qquad \textbf{(10.11)}$$

If a rigid object rotates about a fixed axis with angular speed ω, its **rotational kinetic energy** can be written

$$K_R = \tfrac{1}{2}I\omega^2 \qquad \textbf{(10.16)}$$

where I is the moment of inertia about the axis of rotation.

The **moment of inertia of a rigid object** is

$$I = \int r^2 \, dm \qquad \textbf{(10.17)}$$

where r is the distance from the mass element dm to the axis of rotation.

The rate at which work is done by an external force in rotating a rigid object about a fixed axis, or the **power** delivered, is

$$\mathcal{P} = \tau\omega \qquad \textbf{(10.23)}$$

If work is done on a rigid object and the only result of the work is rotation about a fixed axis, the net work done by external forces in rotating the object equals the change in the rotational kinetic energy of the object:

$$\sum W = \tfrac{1}{2}I\omega_f^2 - \tfrac{1}{2}I\omega_i^2 \qquad \textbf{(10.24)}$$

The **total kinetic energy** of a rigid object rolling on a rough surface without slipping equals the rotational kinetic energy about its center of mass plus the translational kinetic energy of the center of mass:

$$K = \tfrac{1}{2}I_{CM}\omega^2 + \tfrac{1}{2}Mv_{CM}^2 \qquad \textbf{(10.28)}$$

ANALYSIS MODELS FOR PROBLEM SOLVING

α = constant

Rigid Object Under Constant Angular Acceleration. If a rigid object rotates about a fixed axis under constant angular acceleration, one can apply equations of kinematics that are analogous to those for translational motion of a particle under constant acceleration:

$$\omega_f = \omega_i + \alpha t \qquad \textbf{(10.6)}$$

$$\theta_f = \theta_i + \omega_i t + \tfrac{1}{2}\alpha t^2 \qquad \textbf{(10.7)}$$

$$\omega_f^2 = \omega_i^2 + 2\alpha(\theta_f - \theta_i) \qquad \textbf{(10.8)}$$

$$\theta_f = \theta_i + \tfrac{1}{2}(\omega_i + \omega_f)t \qquad \textbf{(10.9)}$$

α

Rigid Object Under a Net Torque. If a rigid object free to rotate about a fixed axis has a net external torque acting on it, the object undergoes an angular acceleration α, where

$$\sum \tau = I\alpha \qquad \textbf{(10.21)}$$

This equation is the rotational analog to Newton's second law in the particle under a net force model.

Questions

☐ denotes answer available in *Student Solutions Manual/Study Guide;* **O** denotes objective question

1. What is the angular speed of the second hand of a clock? What is the direction of $\vec{\omega}$ as you view a clock hanging on a vertical wall? What is the magnitude of the angular acceleration vector $\vec{\alpha}$ of the second hand?

2. One blade of a pair of scissors rotates counterclockwise in the *xy* plane. What is the direction of $\vec{\omega}$? What is the direction of $\vec{\alpha}$ if the magnitude of the angular velocity is decreasing in time?

3. **O** A wheel is moving with constant angular acceleration 3 rad/s². At different moments its angular speed is −2 rad/s, 0, and +2 rad/s. At these moments, analyze the magnitude of the tangential component of acceleration and the magnitude of the radial component of acceleration for a point on the rim of the wheel. Rank the following six items from largest to smallest: (a) $|a_t|$ when ω = −2 rad/s (b) $|a_r|$ when ω = −2 rad/s (c) $|a_t|$ when ω = 0 (d) $|a_r|$ when ω = 0 (e) $|a_t|$ when ω = 2 rad/s (f) $|a_r|$ when ω = 2 rad/s If two items are equal, show them as equal in your ranking. If a quantity is equal to zero, show that in your ranking.

4. **O** (i) Suppose a car's standard tires are replaced with tires 1.30 times larger in diameter. Then what will the speedometer reading be? (a) 1.69 times too high (b) 1.30 times too high (c) accurate (d) 1.30 times too low (e) 1.69 times too low (e) inaccurate by an unpredictable factor (ii) What will be the car's fuel economy in miles per gallon or km/L? (a) 1.69 times better (b) 1.30 times better (c) essentially the same (d) 1.30 times worse (e) 1.69 times worse

5. **O** Figure 10.8 shows a system of four particles joined by light, rigid rods. Assume $a = b$ and M is somewhat larger than m. (i) About which of the coordinate axes does the system have the smallest moment of inertia? (a) the *x* axis (b) the *y* axis (c) the *z* axis (d) The moment of inertia has the same small value for two axes. (e) The moment of inertia is the same for all axes. (ii) About which axis does the system have the largest moment of inertia? (a) the *x* axis (b) the *y* axis (c) the *z* axis (d) The moment of inertia has the same large value for two axes. (e) The moment of inertia is the same for all axes.

6. Suppose just two external forces act on a stationary rigid object and the two forces are equal in magnitude and opposite in direction. Under what condition does the object start to rotate?

7. **O** As shown in Figure 10.19, a cord is wrapped onto a cylindrical reel mounted on a fixed, frictionless, horizontal axle. Two experiments are conducted. (a) The cord is pulled down with a constant force of 50 N. (b) An object of weight 50 N is hung from the cord and released. Are the angular accelerations equal in the two experiments? If not, in which experiment is the angular acceleration greater in magnitude?

8. Explain how you might use the apparatus described in Example 10.10 to determine the moment of inertia of the wheel. (If the wheel does not have a uniform mass density, the moment of inertia is not necessarily equal to $\frac{1}{2}MR^2$.)

9. **O** A constant nonzero net torque is exerted on an object. Which of the following can *not* be constant? Choose all that apply. (a) angular position (b) angular velocity (c) angular acceleration (d) moment of inertia (e) kinetic energy (f) location of center of mass

10. Using the results from Example 10.10, how would you calculate the angular speed of the wheel and the linear speed of the suspended counterweight at t = 2 s, assuming the system is released from rest at t = 0? Is the expression $v = R\omega$ valid in this situation?

11. If a small sphere of mass M were placed at the end of the rod in Figure 10.21, would the result for ω be greater than, less than, or equal to the value obtained in Example 10.11?

12. **O** A solid aluminum sphere of radius R has moment of inertia I about an axis through its center. What is the moment of inertia about a central axis of a solid aluminum sphere of radius $2R$? (a) I (b) $2I$ (c) $4I$ (d) $8I$ (e) $16I$ (f) $32I$

13. Explain why changing the axis of rotation of an object changes its moment of inertia.

14. Suppose you remove two eggs from the refrigerator, one hard-boiled and the other uncooked. You wish to determine which is the hard-boiled egg without breaking the eggs. This determination can be made by spinning the two eggs on the floor and comparing the rotational motions. Which egg spins faster? Which egg rotates more uniformly? Explain.

15. Which of the entries in Table 10.2 applies to finding the moment of inertia of a long, straight sewer pipe rotating about its axis of symmetry? Of an embroidery hoop rotating about an axis through its center and perpendicular to its plane? Of a uniform door turning on its hinges? Of a coin turning about an axis through its center and perpendicular to its faces?

16. Is it possible to change the translational kinetic energy of an object without changing its rotational energy?

17. Must an object be rotating to have a nonzero moment of inertia?

18. If you see an object rotating, is there necessarily a net torque acting on it?

19. **O** A decoration hangs from the ceiling of your room at the bottom end of a string. Your bored roommate turns the decoration clockwise several times to wind up the string. When your roommate releases it, the decoration starts to spin counterclockwise, slowly at first and then faster and faster. Take counterclockwise as the positive sense and assume friction is negligible. When the string is entirely unwound, the ornament has its maximum rate of rotation. (i) At this moment, is its angular acceleration (a) positive, (b) negative, or (c) zero? (ii) The decoration continues to spin, winding the string counterclockwise as it slows down. At the moment it finally stops, is its angular acceleration (a) positive, (b) negative, or (c) zero?

20. The polar diameter of the Earth is slightly less than the equatorial diameter. How would the moment of inertia of

the Earth about its axis of rotation change if some material from near the equator were removed and transferred to the polar regions to make the Earth a perfect sphere?

21. **O** A basketball rolls across a floor without slipping, with its center of mass moving at a certain velocity. A block of ice of the same mass is set sliding across the floor with the same speed along a parallel line. **(i)** How do their energies compare? (a) The basketball has more kinetic energy. (b) The ice has more kinetic energy. (c) They have equal kinetic energies. **(ii)** How do their momenta compare? (a) The basketball has more momentum. (b) The ice has more momentum. (c) They have equal momenta. (d) Their momenta have equal magnitudes but are different vectors. **(iii)** The two objects encounter a ramp sloping upward. (a) The basketball will travel farther up the ramp. (b) The ice will travel farther up the ramp. (c) They will travel equally far up the ramp.

22. Suppose you set your textbook sliding across a gymnasium floor with a certain initial speed. It quickly stops moving because of a friction force exerted on it by the floor. Next, you start a basketball rolling with the same initial speed. It keeps rolling from one end of the gym to the other. Why does the basketball roll so far? Does friction significantly affect its motion?

23. Three objects of uniform density—a solid sphere, a solid cylinder, and a hollow cylinder—are placed at the top of an incline (Fig. Q10.23). They are all released from rest

at the same elevation and roll without slipping. Which object reaches the bottom first? Which reaches it last? Try this experiment at home and notice that the result is independent of the masses and the radii of the objects.

24. Figure Q10.24 shows a side view of a child's tricycle with rubber tires on a horizontal concrete sidewalk. If a string is attached to the upper pedal on the far side and pulled forward horizontally, the tricycle rolls forward. Instead, assume a string is attached to the lower pedal on the near side and pulled forward horizontally as shown by A. Does the tricycle start to roll? If so, which way? Answer the same questions if (b) the string is pulled forward and upward as shown by B, (c) the string is pulled straight down as shown by C, and (d) the string is pulled forward and downward as shown by D. **(e) What if** the string is instead attached to the rim of the front wheel and pulled upward and backward as shown by E? (f) Explain a pattern of reasoning, based on the diagram, that makes it easy to answer questions such as all of these. What physical quantity must you evaluate?

Figure Q10.24

Figure Q10.23

Problems

WebAssign The Problems from this chapter may be assigned online in WebAssign.

ThomsonNOW™ Sign in at **www.thomsonedu.com** and go to ThomsonNOW to assess your understanding of this chapter's topics with additional quizzing and conceptual questions.

1, 2, 3 denotes straightforward, intermediate, challenging; ☐ denotes full solution available in *Student Solutions Manual/Study Guide;* ▲ denotes coached solution with hints available at **www.thomsonedu.com;** ▨ denotes developing symbolic reasoning; ● denotes asking for qualitative reasoning; ☖ denotes computer useful in solving problem

Section 10.1 Angular Position, Velocity, and Acceleration

1. During a certain period of time, the angular position of a swinging door is described by $\theta = 5.00 + 10.0t + 2.00t^2$, where θ is in radians and t is in seconds. Determine the angular position, angular speed, and angular acceleration of the door (a) at $t = 0$ and (b) at $t = 3.00$ s.

2. A bar on a hinge starts from rest and rotates with an angular acceleration $\alpha = (10 + 6t)$ rad/s², where t is in seconds. Determine the angle in radians through which the bar turns in the first 4.00 s.

Section 10.2 Rotational Kinematics: The Rigid Object Under Constant Angular Acceleration

3. A wheel starts from rest and rotates with constant angular acceleration to reach an angular speed of 12.0 rad/s in 3.00 s. Find (a) the magnitude of the angular acceleration of the wheel and (b) the angle in radians through which it rotates in this time interval.

4. A centrifuge in a medical laboratory rotates at an angular speed of 3 600 rev/min. When switched off, it rotates

through 50.0 revolutions before coming to rest. Find the constant angular acceleration of the centrifuge.

5. ▲ An electric motor rotating a grinding wheel at 100 rev/min is switched off. The wheel then moves with constant negative angular acceleration of magnitude 2.00 rad/s². (a) During what time interval does the wheel come to rest? (b) Through how many radians does it turn while it is slowing down?

6. A rotating wheel requires 3.00 s to rotate through 37.0 revolutions. Its angular speed at the end of the 3.00-s interval is 98.0 rad/s. What is the constant angular acceleration of the wheel?

7. (a) Find the angular speed of the Earth's rotation on its axis. As the Earth turns toward the east, we see the sky turning toward the west at this same rate.

(b) *The rainy Pleiads wester*
  And seek beyond the sea
  The head that I shall dream of
  That shall not dream of me.

  —A. E. Housman (© Robert E. Symons)

Cambridge, England is at longitude 0°, and Saskatoon, Saskatchewan, Canada is at longitude 107° west. How much time elapses after the Pleiades set in Cambridge until these stars fall below the western horizon in Saskatoon?

8. A merry-go-round is stationary. A dog is running on the ground just outside the merry-go-round's circumference, moving with a constant angular speed of 0.750 rad/s. The dog does not change his pace when he sees what he has been looking for: a bone resting on the edge of the merry-go-round one third of a revolution in front of him. At the instant the dog sees the bone ($t = 0$), the merry-go-round begins to move in the direction the dog is running, with a constant angular acceleration equal to 0.015 0 rad/s². (a) At what time will the dog reach the bone? (b) The confused dog keeps running and passes the bone. How long after the merry-go-round starts to turn do the dog and the bone draw even with each other for the second time?

9. The tub of a washing machine goes into its spin cycle, starting from rest and gaining angular speed steadily for 8.00 s, at which time it is turning at 5.00 rev/s. At this point, the person doing the laundry opens the lid and a safety switch turns off the machine. The tub smoothly slows to rest in 12.0 s. Through how many revolutions does the tub turn while it is in motion?

Section 10.3 Angular and Translational Quantities

10. A racing car travels on a circular track of radius 250 m. Assuming the car moves with a constant speed of 45.0 m/s, find (a) its angular speed and (b) the magnitude and direction of its acceleration.

11. Make an order-of-magnitude estimate of the number of revolutions through which a typical automobile tire turns in 1 yr. State the quantities you measure or estimate and their values.

12. ● Figure P10.12 shows the drive train of a bicycle that has wheels 67.3 cm in diameter and pedal cranks 17.5 cm long. The cyclist pedals at a steady cadence of 76.0 rev/min. The chain engages with a front sprocket 15.2 cm in diameter and a rear sprocket 7.00 cm in diameter. (a) Calculate the

speed of a link of the chain relative to the bicycle frame. (b) Calculate the angular speed of the bicycle wheels. (c) Calculate the speed of the bicycle relative to the road. (d) What pieces of data, if any, are not necessary for the calculations?

Crank
Sprocket
Chain

Figure P10.12

13. A wheel 2.00 m in diameter lies in a vertical plane and rotates with a constant angular acceleration of 4.00 rad/s². The wheel starts at rest at $t = 0$, and the radius vector of a certain point P on the rim makes an angle of 57.3° with the horizontal at this time. At $t = 2.00$ s, find (a) the angular speed of the wheel, (b) the tangential speed and the total acceleration of the point P, and (c) the angular position of the point P.

14. A discus thrower (Fig. P10.14) accelerates a discus from rest to a speed of 25.0 m/s by whirling it through 1.25 rev. Assume the discus moves on the arc of a circle 1.00 m in radius. (a) Calculate the final angular speed of the discus. (b) Determine the magnitude of the angular acceleration of the discus, assuming it to be constant. (c) Calculate the time interval required for the discus to accelerate from rest to 25.0 m/s.

Figure P10.14

15. A small object with mass 4.00 kg moves counterclockwise with constant speed 4.50 m/s in a circle of radius 3.00 m centered at the origin. It starts at the point with position vector $(3.00\hat{\mathbf{i}} + 0\hat{\mathbf{j}})$ m. Then it undergoes an angular displacement of 9.00 rad. (a) What it its position vector? Use unit–vector notation for all vector answers. (b) In what quadrant is the particle located, and what angle does its position vector make with the positive x axis? (c) What is its velocity? (d) In what direction is it moving? Make a sketch of its position, velocity, and acceleration vectors. (e) What is its acceleration? (f) What total force is exerted on the object?

16. A car accelerates uniformly from rest and reaches a speed of 22.0 m/s in 9.00 s. The tires have diameter 58.0 cm and do not slip on the pavement. (a) Find the number of revolutions each tire makes during this motion. (b) What is the final angular speed of a tire in revolutions per second?

17. ▲ A disk 8.00 cm in radius rotates at a constant rate of 1 200 rev/min about its central axis. Determine (a) its angular speed, (b) the tangential speed at a point 3.00 cm from its center, (c) the radial acceleration of a point on the rim, and (d) the total distance a point on the rim moves in 2.00 s.

18. ● A straight ladder is leaning against the wall of a house. The ladder has rails 4.90 m long, joined by rungs 0.410 m long. Its bottom end is on solid but sloping ground so that the top of the ladder is 0.690 m to the left of where it should be, and the ladder is unsafe to climb. You want to put a rock under one foot of the ladder to compensate for the slope of the ground. (a) What should be the thickness of the flat rock? (b) Does using ideas from this chapter make it easier to explain the solution to part (a)? Explain your answer.

19. A car traveling on a flat (unbanked) circular track accelerates uniformly from rest with a tangential acceleration of 1.70 m/s². The car makes it one-quarter of the way around the circle before it skids off the track. Determine the coefficient of static friction between the car and track from these data.

20. In part (B) of Example 10.2, the compact disc was modeled as a rigid object under constant angular acceleration to find the total angular displacement during the playing time of the disc. In reality, the angular acceleration of a disc is not constant. In this problem, let us explore the actual time dependence of the angular acceleration. (a) Assume the track on the disc is a spiral such that adjacent loops of the track are separated by a small distance h. Show that the radius r of a given portion of the track is given by

$$r = r_i + \frac{h}{2\pi}\theta$$

where r_i is the radius of the innermost portion of the track and θ is the angle through which the disc turns to arrive at the location of the track of radius r. (b) Show that the rate of change of the angle θ is given by

$$\frac{d\theta}{dt} = \frac{v}{r_i + (h/2\pi)\theta}$$

where v is the constant speed with which the disc surface passes the laser. (c) From the result in part (b), use integration to find an expression for the angle θ as a function of time. (d) From the result in part (c), use differentiation to find the angular acceleration of the disc as a function of time.

Section 10.4 Rotational Kinetic Energy

21. ▲ The four particles in Figure P10.21 are connected by rigid rods of negligible mass. The origin is at the center of the rectangle. The system rotates in the xy plane about the z axis with an angular speed of 6.00 rad/s. Calculate (a) the moment of inertia of the system about the z axis and (b) the rotational kinetic energy of the system.

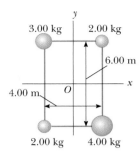

Figure P10.21

22. ● Rigid rods of negligible mass lying along the y axis connect three particles (Fig. P10.22). The system rotates about the x axis with an angular speed of 2.00 rad/s. Find (a) the moment of inertia about the x axis and the total rotational kinetic energy evaluated from $\frac{1}{2}I\omega^2$ and (b) the tangential speed of each particle and the total kinetic energy evaluated from $\Sigma \frac{1}{2}m_iv_i^2$. (c) Compare the answers for kinetic energy in parts (a) and (b).

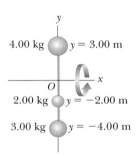

Figure P10.22

23. Two balls with masses M and m are connected by a rigid rod of length L and negligible mass as shown in Figure P10.23. For an axis perpendicular to the rod, show that the system has the minimum moment of inertia when the axis passes through the center of mass. Show that this moment of inertia is $I = \mu L^2$, where $\mu = mM/(m + M)$.

Figure P10.23

24. As a gasoline engine operates, a flywheel turning with the crankshaft stores energy after each fuel explosion to provide the energy required to compress the next charge of fuel and air. In the engine of a certain lawn tractor, suppose a flywheel must be no more than 18.0 cm in diameter. Its thickness, measured along its axis of rotation, must be no larger than 8.00 cm. The flywheel must release 60.0 J of energy when its angular speed drops from 800 rev/min to 600 rev/min. Design a sturdy steel flywheel to meet these requirements with the smallest mass you can reasonably attain. Assume the material has the density listed for iron in Table 14.1. Specify the shape and mass of the flywheel.

25. ● A *war-wolf* or *trebuchet* is a device used during the Middle Ages to throw rocks at castles and now sometimes used to fling large vegetables and pianos as a sport. A simple trebuchet is shown in Figure P10.25. Model it as a stiff rod of negligible mass, 3.00 m long, joining particles of mass 60.0 kg and 0.120 kg at its ends. It can turn on a frictionless, horizontal axle perpendicular to the rod and 14.0 cm from the large-mass particle. The rod is released from rest in a horizontal orientation. (a) Find the maximum speed that the 0.120-kg object attains. (b) While the 0.120-kg object is gaining speed, does it move with constant acceleration? Does it move with constant tangential acceleration? Does the trebuchet move with constant angular acceleration? Does it have constant momentum? Does the trebuchet-Earth system have constant mechanical energy?

Figure P10.25

Section 10.5 Calculation of Moments of Inertia

26. Three identical thin rods, each of length L and mass m, are welded perpendicular to one another as shown in Figure P10.26. The assembly is rotated about an axis that passes through the end of one rod and is parallel to another. Determine the moment of inertia of this structure.

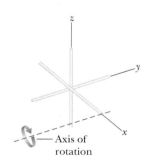

Figure P10.26

27. Figure P10.27 shows a side view of a car tire. Model it as having two sidewalls of uniform thickness 0.635 cm and a

Figure P10.27

tread wall of uniform thickness 2.50 cm and width 20.0 cm. Assume the rubber has uniform density equal to 1.10×10^3 kg/m³. Find its moment of inertia about an axis through its center.

28. ● A uniform, thin solid door has height 2.20 m, width 0.870 m, and mass 23.0 kg. Find its moment of inertia for rotation on its hinges. Is any piece of data unnecessary?

29. *Attention! About face!* Compute an order-of-magnitude estimate for the moment of inertia of your body as you stand tall and turn about a vertical axis through the top of your head and the point halfway between your ankles. In your solution, state the quantities you measure or estimate and their values.

30. Many machines employ cams for various purposes such as opening and closing valves. In Figure P10.30, the cam is a circular disk rotating on a shaft that does not pass through the center of the disk. In the manufacture of the cam, a uniform solid cylinder of radius R is first machined. Then an off-center hole of radius $R/2$ is drilled, parallel to the axis of the cylinder, and centered at a point a distance $R/2$ from the cylinder's center. The cam, of mass M, is then slipped onto the circular shaft and welded into place. What is the kinetic energy of the cam when it is rotating with angular speed ω about the axis of the shaft?

Figure P10.30

31. Following the procedure used in Example 10.4, prove that the moment of inertia about the y' axis of the rigid rod in Figure 10.9 is $\frac{1}{3}ML^2$.

Section 10.6 Torque

32. The fishing pole in Figure P10.32 makes an angle of 20.0° with the horizontal. What is the torque exerted by the fish about an axis perpendicular to the page and passing through the angler's hand?

Figure P10.32

33. ▲ Find the net torque on the wheel in Figure P10.33 about the axle through O, taking $a = 10.0$ cm and $b = 25.0$ cm.

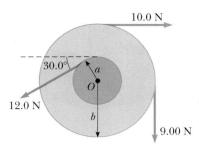

Figure P10.33

Section 10.7 The Rigid Object Under a Net Torque

34. A grinding wheel is in the form of a uniform solid disk of radius 7.00 cm and mass 2.00 kg. It starts from rest and accelerates uniformly under the action of the constant torque of 0.600 N·m that the motor exerts on the wheel. (a) How long does the wheel take to reach its final operating speed of 1 200 rev/min? (b) Through how many revolutions does it turn while accelerating?

35. ▲ A model airplane with mass 0.750 kg is tethered by a wire so that it flies in a circle 30.0 m in radius. The airplane engine provides a net thrust of 0.800 N perpendicular to the tethering wire. (a) Find the torque the net thrust produces about the center of the circle. (b) Find the angular acceleration of the airplane when it is in level flight. (c) Find the translational acceleration of the airplane tangent to its flight path.

36. The combination of an applied force and a friction force produces a constant total torque of 36.0 N·m on a wheel rotating about a fixed axis. The applied force acts for 6.00 s. During this time, the angular speed of the wheel increases from 0 to 10.0 rad/s. The applied force is then removed, and the wheel comes to rest in 60.0 s. Find (a) the moment of inertia of the wheel, (b) the magnitude of the frictional torque, and (c) the total number of revolutions of the wheel.

37. A block of mass m_1 = 2.00 kg and a block of mass m_2 = 6.00 kg are connected by a massless string over a pulley in the shape of a solid disk having radius R = 0.250 m and mass M = 10.0 kg. These blocks are allowed to move on a fixed wedge of angle θ = 30.0° as shown in Figure P10.37. The coefficient of kinetic friction is 0.360 for both blocks. Draw free-body diagrams of both blocks and of the pulley. Determine (a) the acceleration of the two blocks and (b) the tensions in the string on both sides of the pulley.

Figure P10.37

38. A potter's wheel—a thick stone disk of radius 0.500 m and mass 100 kg—is freely rotating at 50.0 rev/min. The potter can stop the wheel in 6.00 s by pressing a wet rag against the rim and exerting a radially inward force of 70.0 N. Find the effective coefficient of kinetic friction between wheel and rag.

39. An electric motor turns a flywheel through a drive belt that joins a pulley on the motor and a pulley that is rigidly attached to the flywheel as shown in Figure P10.39. The flywheel is a solid disk with a mass of 80.0 kg and a diameter of 1.25 m. It turns on a frictionless axle. Its pulley has much smaller mass and a radius of 0.230 m. The tension in the upper (taut) segment of the belt is 135 N, and the flywheel has a clockwise angular acceleration of 1.67 rad/s². Find the tension in the lower (slack) segment of the belt.

Figure P10.39

40. ● A disk having moment of inertia 100 kg·m² is free to rotate without friction, starting from rest, about a fixed axis through its center as shown at the top of Figure 10.19. A tangential force whose magnitude can range from T = 0 to T = 50.0 N can be applied at any distance ranging from R = 0 to R = 3.00 m from the axis of rotation. Find a pair of values of T and R that cause the disk to complete 2.00 revolutions in 10.0 s. Does one answer exist, or no answer, or two answers, or more than two, or many, or an infinite number?

Section 10.8 Energy Considerations in Rotational Motion

41. In a city with an air-pollution problem, a bus has no combustion engine. It runs on energy drawn from a large, rapidly rotating flywheel under the floor of the bus. At the bus terminal, the flywheel is spun up to its maximum rotation rate of 4 000 rev/min by an electric motor. Every time the bus speeds up, the flywheel slows down slightly. The bus is equipped with regenerative braking so that the flywheel can speed up when the bus slows down. The flywheel is a uniform solid cylinder with mass 1 600 kg and radius 0.650 m. The bus body does work against air resistance and rolling resistance at the average rate of 18.0 hp as it travels with an average speed of 40.0 km/h. How far can the bus travel before the flywheel has to be spun up to speed again?

42. Big Ben, the Parliament tower clock in London, has an hour hand 2.70 m long with a mass of 60.0 kg and a minute hand 4.50 m long with a mass of 100 kg (Fig.

Figure P10.42 Problem 42 and 76.

2 = intermediate; 3 = challenging; □ = SSM/SG; ▲ = ThomsonNOW; = symbolic reasoning; ● = qualitative reasoning

P10.42). Calculate the total rotational kinetic energy of the two hands about the axis of rotation. (You may model the hands as long, thin rods.)

43. The top in Figure P10.43 has a moment of inertia equal to 4.00×10^{-4} kg·m^2 and is initially at rest. It is free to rotate about the stationary axis AA'. A string, wrapped around a peg along the axis of the top, is pulled in such a manner as to maintain a constant tension of 5.57 N. If the string does not slip while it is unwound from the peg, what is the angular speed of the top after 80.0 cm of string has been pulled off the peg?

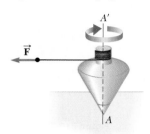

Figure P10.43

44. ● Consider the system shown in Figure P10.44 with $m_1 = 20.0$ kg, $m_2 = 12.5$ kg, $R = 0.200$ m, and the mass of the uniform pulley $M = 5.00$ kg. Object m_2 is resting on the floor, and object m_1 is 4.00 m above the floor when it is released from rest. The pulley axis is frictionless. The cord is light, does not stretch, and does not slip on the pulley. Calculate the time interval required for m_1 to hit the floor. How would your answer change if the pulley were massless?

Figure P10.44

45. In Figure P10.45, the sliding block has a mass of 0.850 kg, the counterweight has a mass of 0.420 kg, and the pulley is a hollow cylinder with a mass of 0.350 kg, an inner radius of 0.020 0 m, and an outer radius of 0.030 0 m. The coefficient of kinetic friction between the block and the horizontal surface is 0.250. The pulley turns without friction on its axle. The light cord does not stretch and does not slip on the pulley. The block has a velocity of 0.820 m/s toward the pulley when it passes through a photogate. (a) Use energy methods to predict its speed after it has moved to a second photogate, 0.700 m away. (b) Find the angular speed of the pulley at the same moment.

Figure P10.45

46. A cylindrical rod 24.0 cm long with mass 1.20 kg and radius 1.50 cm has a ball of diameter 8.00 cm and mass 2.00 kg attached to one end. The arrangement is originally vertical and stationary, with the ball at the top. The system is free to pivot about the bottom end of the rod after being given a slight nudge. (a) After the rod rotates through 90°, what is its rotational kinetic energy? (b) What is the angular speed of the rod and ball? (c) What is the linear speed of the ball? (d) How does this speed compare with the speed if the ball had fallen freely through the same distance of 28 cm?

47. An object with a weight of 50.0 N is attached to the free end of a light string wrapped around a reel of radius 0.250 m and mass 3.00 kg. The reel is a solid disk, free to rotate in a vertical plane about the horizontal axis passing through its center. The suspended object is released 6.00 m above the floor. (a) Determine the tension in the string, the acceleration of the object, and the speed with which the object hits the floor. (b) Verify your last answer by using the principle of conservation of energy to find the speed with which the object hits the floor.

48. A horizontal 800-N merry-go-round is a solid disk of radius 1.50 m, started from rest by a constant horizontal force of 50.0 N applied tangentially to the edge of the disk. Find the kinetic energy of the disk after 3.00 s.

49. This problem describes one experimental method for determining the moment of inertia of an irregularly shaped object such as the payload for a satellite. Figure P10.49 shows a counterweight of mass m suspended by a cord wound around a spool of radius r, forming part of a turntable supporting the object. The turntable can rotate without friction. When the counterweight is released from rest, it descends through a distance h, acquiring a speed v. Show that the moment of inertia I of the rotating apparatus (including the turntable) is $mr^2(2gh/v^2 - 1)$.

Figure P10.49

50. The head of a grass string trimmer has 100 g of cord wound in a light cylindrical spool with inside diameter 3.00 cm and outside diameter 18.0 cm, as shown in Figure P10.50. The cord has a linear density of 10.0 g/m. A single strand of the cord extends 16.0 cm from the outer edge of the spool. (a) When switched on, the trimmer speeds up from 0 to 2 500 rev/min in 0.215 s. (a) What average power is delivered to the head by the trimmer motor while it is accelerating? (b) When the trimmer is cutting grass, it spins at 2 000 rev/min and the grass exerts an average tangential force of 7.65 N on the outer end of the cord, which is still at a radial distance of 16.0 cm from the outer edge of the spool. What is the power delivered to the head under load?

Figure P10.50

51. (a) A uniform solid disk of radius R and mass M is free to rotate on a frictionless pivot through a point on its rim (Fig. P10.51). If the disk is released from rest in the position shown by the blue circle, what is the speed of its center of mass when the disk reaches the position indicated by the dashed circle? (b) What is the speed of the lowest point on the disk in the dashed position? (c) **What If?** Repeat part (a) using a uniform hoop.

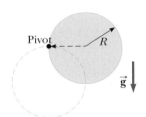

Figure P10.51

Section 10.9 Rolling Motion of a Rigid Object

52. ● A solid sphere is released from height h from the top of an incline making an angle θ with the horizontal. Calculate the speed of the sphere when it reaches the bottom of the incline (a) in the case that it rolls without slipping and (b) in the case that it slides frictionlessly without rolling. (c) Compare the time intervals required to reach the bottom in cases (a) and (b).

53. ▲ A cylinder of mass 10.0 kg rolls without slipping on a horizontal surface. At a certain instant its center of mass has a speed of 10.0 m/s. Determine (a) the translational kinetic energy of its center of mass, (b) the rotational kinetic energy about its center of mass, and (c) its total energy.

54. ● A smooth cube of mass m and edge length r slides with speed v on a horizontal surface with negligible friction.

The cube then moves up a smooth incline that makes an angle θ with the horizontal. A cylinder of mass m and radius r rolls without slipping with its center of mass moving with speed v and encounters an incline of the same angle of inclination but with sufficient friction that the cylinder continues to roll without slipping. (a) Which object will go the greater distance up the incline? (b) Find the difference between the maximum distances the objects travel up the incline. (c) Explain what accounts for this difference in distances traveled.

55. (a) Determine the acceleration of the center of mass of a uniform solid disk rolling down an incline making angle θ with the horizontal. Compare this acceleration with that of a uniform hoop. (b) What is the minimum coefficient of friction required to maintain pure rolling motion for the disk?

56. A uniform solid disk and a uniform hoop are placed side by side at the top of an incline of height h. If they are released from rest at the same time and roll without slipping, which object reaches the bottom first? Verify your answer by calculating their speeds when they reach the bottom in terms of h.

57. ● A metal can containing condensed mushroom soup has mass 215 g, height 10.8 cm, and diameter 6.38 cm. It is placed at rest on its side at the top of a 3.00-m-long incline that is at 25.0° to the horizontal and is then released to roll straight down. It reaches the bottom of the incline after 1.50 s. Assuming mechanical energy conservation, calculate the moment of inertia of the can. Which pieces of data, if any, are unnecessary for calculating the solution?

58. ● A tennis ball is a hollow sphere with a thin wall. It is set rolling without slipping at 4.03 m/s on a horizontal section of a track as shown in Figure P10.58. It rolls around the inside of a vertical circular loop 90.0 cm in diameter and finally leaves the track at a point 20.0 cm below the horizontal section. (a) Find the speed of the ball at the top of the loop. Demonstrate that it will not fall from the track. (b) Find its speed as it leaves the track. **What If?** (c) Suppose static friction between ball and track were negligible so that the ball slid instead of rolling. Would its speed then be higher, lower, or the same at the top of the loop? Explain.

Figure P10.58

Additional Problems

59. As shown in Figure P10.59, toppling chimneys often break apart in midfall because the mortar between the bricks cannot withstand much shear stress. As the chimney begins to fall, shear forces must act on the topmost sections to accelerate them tangentially so that they can keep up with the rotation of the lower part of the stack. For simplicity, let us model the chimney as a uniform rod of

---

2 = intermediate;   3 = challenging;   □ = SSM/SG;   ▲ = ThomsonNOW;   ▓ = symbolic reasoning;   ● = qualitative reasoning

length ℓ pivoted at the lower end. The rod starts at rest in a vertical position (with the frictionless pivot at the bottom) and falls over under the influence of gravity. What fraction of the length of the rod has a tangential acceleration greater than $g \sin \theta$, where θ is the angle the chimney makes with the vertical axis?

Figure P10.59 A building demolition site in Baltimore, Maryland. At the left is a chimney, mostly concealed by the building, that has broken apart on its way down. Compare with Figure 10.18.

60. **Review problem.** A mixing beater consists of three thin rods, each 10.0 cm long. The rods diverge from a central hub, separated from one another by 120°, and all turn in the same plane. A ball is attached to the end of each rod. Each ball has cross-sectional area 4.00 cm² and is so shaped that it has a drag coefficient of 0.600. Calculate the power input required to spin the beater at 1 000 rev/min (a) in air and (b) in water.

61. A 4.00-m length of light nylon cord is wound around a uniform cylindrical spool of radius 0.500 m and mass 1.00 kg. The spool is mounted on a frictionless axle and is initially at rest. The cord is pulled from the spool with a constant acceleration of magnitude 2.50 m/s². (a) How much work has been done on the spool when it reaches an angular speed of 8.00 rad/s? (b) Assuming there is enough cord on the spool, how long does it take the spool to reach this angular speed? (c) Is there enough cord on the spool?

62. ● An elevator system in a tall building consists of an 800-kg car and a 950-kg counterweight, joined by a cable that passes over a pulley of mass 280 kg. The pulley, called a sheave, is a solid cylinder of radius 0.700 m turning on a horizontal axle. The cable has comparatively small mass and constant length. It does not slip on the sheave. The car and the counterweight move vertically, next to each other inside the same shaft. A number n of people, each of mass 80.0 kg, are riding in the elevator car, moving upward at 3.00 m/s and approaching the floor where the car should stop. As an energy-conservation measure, a computer disconnects the electric elevator motor at just the right moment so that the sheave-car-counterweight system then coasts freely without friction and comes to rest at the floor desired. There it is caught by a simple latch rather than by a massive brake. (a) Determine the distance d the car coasts upward as a function of n. Evaluate the distance for (b) $n = 2$, (c) $n = 12$, and (d) $n = 0$.

(e) Does the expression in part (a) apply for all integer values of n or only for what values? Explain. (f) Describe the shape of a graph of d versus n. (g) Is any piece of data unnecessary for the solution? Explain. (h) Contrast the meaning of energy conservation as it is used in the statement of this problem and as it is used in Chapter 8. (i) Find the magnitude of the acceleration of the coasting elevator car, as it depends on n.

63. ● Figure P10.63 is a photograph of a lawn sprinkler. Its rotor consists of three metal tubes that fill with water when a hose is connected to the base. As water sprays out of the holes at the ends of the arms and the hole near the center of each arm, the assembly with the three arms rotates. To analyze this situation, let us make the following assumptions: (1) The arms can be modeled as thin, straight rods, each of length L. (2) The water coming from the hole at distance ℓ from the center sprays out horizontally, parallel to the ground and perpendicular to the arm. (3) The water emitted from the holes at the ends of the arms sprays out radially away from the center of the rotor. When filled with water, each arm has mass m. The center of the assembly is massless. The water ejected from a hole at distance ℓ from the center causes a thrust force F on the arm containing the hole. The mounting for the three-arm rotor assembly exerts a frictional torque that is described by $\tau = -b\omega$, where ω is the angular speed of the assembly. (a) Imagine that the sprinkler is in operation. Find an expression for the constant angular speed with which the assembly rotates *after* it completes an initial period of angular acceleration. Your expression should be in terms of F, ℓ, and b. (b) Imagine that the sprinkler has been at rest and is just turned on. Find an expression for the *initial* angular acceleration of the rotor, that is, the angular acceleration when the arms are filled with water and the assembly just begins to move from rest. Your expression should be in terms of F, ℓ, m, and L. (c) Now, take a step toward reality from the simplified model. The arms are actually bent as shown in the photograph. Therefore, the water from the ends of the arms is not actually sprayed radially. How will this fact affect the constant angular speed with which the assembly rotates in part (a)? In reality, will it be larger, smaller, or unchanged? Provide a convincing argument for your response. (d) How will the bend in the arms, described in part (c), affect the angular acceleration in part (b)? In reality, will it be larger, smaller, or unchanged? Provide a convincing argument for your response.

Figure P10.63

64. A shaft is turning at 65.0 rad/s at time $t = 0$. Thereafter, its angular acceleration is given by

$$\alpha = -10.0 \text{ rad/s}^2 - 5.00t \text{ rad/s}^3$$

where t is the elapsed time. (a) Find its angular speed at $t = 3.00$ s. (b) How far does it turn in these 3 s?

65. A long, uniform rod of length L and mass M is pivoted about a horizontal, frictionless pin through one end. The rod is released, almost from rest in a vertical position as shown in Figure P10.65. At the instant the rod is horizontal, find (a) its angular speed, (b) the magnitude of its angular acceleration, (c) the x and y components of the acceleration of its center of mass, and (d) the components of the reaction force at the pivot.

Figure P10.65

66. A cord is wrapped around a pulley of mass m and radius r. The free end of the cord is connected to a block of mass M. The block starts from rest and then slides down an incline that makes an angle θ with the horizontal. The coefficient of kinetic friction between block and incline is μ. (a) Use energy methods to show that the block's speed as a function of position d down the incline is

$$v = \sqrt{\frac{4gdM(\sin\theta - \mu\cos\theta)}{m + 2M}}$$

(b) Find the magnitude of the acceleration of the block in terms of μ, m, M, g, and θ.

67. A bicycle is turned upside down while its owner repairs a flat tire. A friend spins the other wheel, of radius 0.381 m, and observes that drops of water fly off tangentially. She measures the height reached by drops moving vertically (Fig. P10.67). A drop that breaks loose from the tire on one turn rises $h = 54.0$ cm above the tangent point. A drop that breaks loose on the next turn rises 51.0 cm above the tangent point. The height to which the drops rise decreases because the angular speed of the wheel decreases. From this information, determine the magnitude of the average angular acceleration of the wheel.

Figure P10.67   Problems 67 and 68.

68. A bicycle is turned upside down while its owner repairs a flat tire. A friend spins the other wheel, of radius R, and

observes that drops of water fly off tangentially. She measures the height reached by drops moving vertically (Fig. P10.67). A drop that breaks loose from the tire on one turn rises a distance h_1 above the tangent point. A drop that breaks loose on the next turn rises a distance $h_2 < h_1$ above the tangent point. The height to which the drops rise decreases because the angular speed of the wheel decreases. From this information, determine the magnitude of the average angular acceleration of the wheel.

69. A uniform, hollow, cylindrical spool has inside radius $R/2$, outside radius R, and mass M (Fig. P10.69). It is mounted so that it rotates on a fixed, horizontal axle. A counterweight of mass m is connected to the end of a string wound around the spool. The counterweight falls from rest at $t = 0$ to a position y at time t. Show that the torque due to the friction forces between spool and axle is

$$\tau_f = R\left[m\left(g - \frac{2y}{t^2}\right) - M\frac{5y}{4t^2}\right]$$

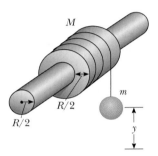

Figure P10.69

70. (a) What is the rotational kinetic energy of the Earth about its spin axis? Model the Earth as a uniform sphere and use data from the endpapers. (b) The rotational kinetic energy of the Earth is decreasing steadily because of tidal friction. Find the change in one day, assuming the rotational period increases by 10.0 μs each year.

71. Two blocks as shown in Figure P10.71 are connected by a string of negligible mass passing over a pulley of radius 0.250 m and moment of inertia I. The block on the frictionless incline is moving up with a constant acceleration of 2.00 m/s^2. (a) Determine T_1 and T_2, the tensions in the two parts of the string. (b) Find the moment of inertia of the pulley.

Figure P10.71

72. The reel shown in Figure P10.72 has radius R and moment of inertia I. One end of the block of mass m is connected to a spring of force constant k, and the other end is fastened to a cord wrapped around the reel. The reel axle and the incline are frictionless. The reel is wound counterclockwise so that the spring stretches a distance d from its unstretched position and the reel is then released from rest. (a) Find the angular speed of the reel when the spring is again unstretched. (b) Evaluate the angular speed numerically at this point, taking $I = 1.00$ kg · m², $R = 0.300$ m, $k = 50.0$ N/m, $m = 0.500$ kg, $d = 0.200$ m, and $\theta = 37.0°$.

Figure P10.72

73. As a result of friction, the angular speed of a wheel changes with time according to

$$\frac{d\theta}{dt} = \omega_0 e^{-\sigma t}$$

where ω_0 and σ are constants. The angular speed changes from 3.50 rad/s at $t = 0$ to 2.00 rad/s at $t = 9.30$ s. Use this information to determine σ and ω_0. Then determine (a) the magnitude of the angular acceleration at $t = 3.00$ s, (b) the number of revolutions the wheel makes in the first 2.50 s, and (c) the number of revolutions it makes before coming to rest.

74. A common demonstration, illustrated in Figure P10.74, consists of a ball resting at one end of a uniform board of length ℓ, hinged at the other end, and elevated at an angle θ. A light cup is attached to the board at r_c so that it will catch the ball when the support stick is suddenly removed. (a) Show that the ball will lag behind the falling board when θ is less than 35.3°. (b) Assuming the board is 1.00 m long and is supported at this limiting angle, show that the cup must be 18.4 cm from the moving end.

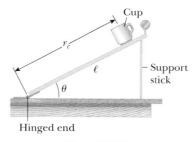

Figure P10.74

75. ● A tall building is located on the Earth's equator. As the Earth rotates, a person on the top floor of the building moves faster than someone on the ground with respect to an inertial reference frame because the latter person is closer to the Earth's axis. Consequently, if an object is dropped from the top floor to the ground a distance h below, it lands east of the point vertically below where it was dropped. (a) How far to the east will the object land?

Express your answer in terms of h, g, and the angular speed ω of the Earth. Ignore air resistance, and assume the free-fall acceleration is constant over this range of heights. (b) Evaluate the eastward displacement for $h = 50.0$ m. (c) In your judgment, were we justified in ignoring this aspect of the *Coriolis effect* in our previous study of free fall?

76. ▼ The hour hand and the minute hand of Big Ben, the Parliament tower clock in London, are 2.70 m and 4.50 m long and have masses of 60.0 kg and 100 kg, respectively (see Figure P10.42). (i) Determine the total torque due to the weight of these hands about the axis of rotation when the time reads (a) 3:00, (b) 5:15, (c) 6:00, (d) 8:20, and (e) 9:45. (You may model the hands as long, thin uniform rods.) (ii) Determine all times when the total torque about the axis of rotation is zero. Determine the times to the nearest second, solving a transcendental equation numerically.

77. A string is wound around a uniform disk of radius R and mass M. The disk is released from rest with the string vertical and its top end tied to a fixed bar (Fig. P10.77). Show that (a) the tension in the string is one-third of the weight of the disk, (b) the magnitude of the acceleration of the center of mass is $2g/3$, and (c) the speed of the center of mass is $(4gh/3)^{1/2}$ after the disk has descended through distance h. Verify your answer to part (c) using the energy approach.

Figure P10.77

78. A uniform solid sphere of radius r is placed on the inside surface of a hemispherical bowl with much larger radius R. The sphere is released from rest at an angle θ to the vertical and rolls without slipping (Fig. P10.78). Determine the angular speed of the sphere when it reaches the bottom of the bowl.

Figure P10.78

79. A solid sphere of mass m and radius r rolls without slipping along the track shown in Figure P10.79. It starts from rest with the lowest point of the sphere at height h

above the bottom of the loop of radius R, much larger than r. (a) What is the minimum value of h (in terms of R) such that the sphere completes the loop? (b) What are the components of the net force on the sphere at the point P if $h = 3R$?

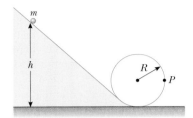

Figure P10.79

80. A thin rod of mass 0.630 kg and length 1.24 m is at rest, hanging vertically from a strong fixed hinge at its top end. Suddenly a horizontal impulsive force $(14.7\hat{\mathbf{i}})$ N is applied to it. (a) Suppose the force acts at the bottom end of the rod. Find the acceleration of its center of mass and the horizontal force the hinge exerts. (b) Suppose the force acts at the midpoint of the rod. Find the acceleration of this point and the horizontal hinge reaction. (c) Where can the impulse be applied so that the hinge will exert no horizontal force? This point is called the *center of percussion*.

81. (a) A thin rod of length h and mass M is held vertically with its lower end resting on a frictionless horizontal surface. The rod is then released to fall freely. Determine the speed of its center of mass just before it hits the horizontal surface. (b) **What If?** Now suppose the rod has a fixed pivot at its lower end. Determine the speed of the rod's center of mass just before it hits the surface.

82. Following Thanksgiving dinner your uncle falls into a deep sleep, sitting straight up facing the television set. A naughty grandchild balances a small spherical grape at the top of his bald head, which itself has the shape of a sphere. After all the children have had time to giggle, the grape starts from rest and rolls down without slipping. The grape loses contact with your uncle's scalp when the radial line joining it to the center of curvature makes what angle with the vertical?

83. A spool of wire of mass M and radius R is unwound under a constant force $\vec{\mathbf{F}}$ (Fig. P10.83). Assuming the spool is a uniform solid cylinder that doesn't slip, show that (a) the acceleration of the center of mass is $4\vec{\mathbf{F}}/3M$ and (b) the

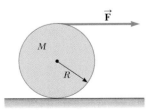

Figure P10.83

force of friction is to the *right* and equal in magnitude to $F/3$. (c) If the cylinder starts from rest and rolls without slipping, what is the speed of its center of mass after it has rolled through a distance d?

84. A plank with a mass $M = 6.00$ kg rides on top of two identical solid cylindrical rollers that have $R = 5.00$ cm and $m = 2.00$ kg (Fig. P10.84). The plank is pulled by a constant horizontal force $\vec{\mathbf{F}}$ of magnitude 6.00 N applied to the end of the plank and perpendicular to the axes of the cylinders (which are parallel). The cylinders roll without slipping on a flat surface. There is also no slipping between the cylinders and the plank. (a) Find the acceleration of the plank and of the rollers. (b) What friction forces are acting?

Figure P10.84

85. A spool of thread consists of a cylinder of radius R_1 with end caps of radius R_2 as shown in the end view illustrated in Figure P10.85. The mass of the spool, including the thread, is m, and its moment of inertia about an axis through its center is I. The spool is placed on a rough horizontal surface so that it rolls without slipping when a force $\vec{\mathbf{T}}$ acting to the right is applied to the free end of the thread. Show that the magnitude of the friction force exerted by the surface on the spool is given by

$$f = \left(\frac{I + mR_1 R_2}{I + mR_2^2} \right) T$$

Determine the direction of the force of friction.

Figure P10.85

86. ● A large, cylindrical roll of tissue paper of initial radius R lies on a long, horizontal surface with the outside end of the paper nailed to the surface. The roll is given a slight shove ($v_i \approx 0$) and commences to unroll. Assume the roll has a uniform density and that mechanical energy is conserved in the process. (a) Determine the speed of the center of mass of the roll when its radius has diminished to r. (b) Calculate a numerical value for this speed at $r = 1.00$ mm, assuming $R = 6.00$ m. (c) **What If?** What happens to the energy of the system when the paper is completely unrolled?

Answers to Quick Quizzes

10.1 **(i),** (c). For a rotation of more than 180°, the angular displacement must be larger than $\pi = 3.14$ rad. The angular displacements in the three choices are (a) 6 rad − 3 rad = 3 rad, (b) 1 rad − (−1) rad = 2 rad, and (c) 5 rad − 1 rad = 4 rad. **(ii),** (b). Because all angular displacements occur in the same time interval, the displacement with the lowest value will be associated with the lowest average angular speed.

10.2 (b). In Equation 10.8, both the initial and final angular speeds are the same in all three cases. As a result, the angular acceleration is inversely proportional to the angular displacement. Therefore, the highest angular acceleration is associated with the lowest angular displacement.

10.3 **(i),** (b). The system of the platform, Alex, and Brian is a rigid object, so all points on the rigid object have the same angular speed. **(ii),** (a). The tangential speed is proportional to the radial distance from the rotation axis.

10.4 (a). Almost all the mass of the pipe is at the same distance from the rotation axis, so it has a larger moment of inertia than the solid cylinder.

10.5 **(i),** (b). The fatter handle of the screwdriver gives you a larger moment arm and increases the torque you can apply with a given force from your hand. **(ii),** (a). The longer handle of the wrench gives you a larger moment arm and increases the torque you can apply with a given force from your hand.

10.6 (b). With twice the moment of inertia and the same frictional torque, there is half the angular acceleration. With half the angular acceleration, it will require twice as long to change the speed to zero.

10.7 (b). All the gravitational potential energy of the box–Earth system is transformed to kinetic energy of translation. For the ball, some of the gravitational potential energy of the ball–Earth system is transformed to rotational kinetic energy, leaving less for translational kinetic energy, so the ball moves downhill more slowly than the box does.

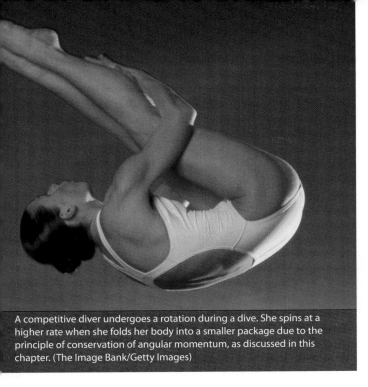

A competitive diver undergoes a rotation during a dive. She spins at a higher rate when she folds her body into a smaller package due to the principle of conservation of angular momentum, as discussed in this chapter. (The Image Bank/Getty Images)

11 Angular Momentum

The central topic of this chapter is angular momentum, a quantity that plays a key role in rotational dynamics. In analogy to the principle of conservation of linear momentum for an isolated system, the angular momentum of a system is conserved if no external torques act on the system. Like the law of conservation of linear momentum, the law of conservation of angular momentum is a fundamental law of physics, equally valid for relativistic and quantum systems.

11.1 The Vector Product and Torque

An important consideration in defining angular momentum is the process of multiplying two vectors by means of the operation called the *vector product*. We will introduce the vector product by considering the vector nature of torque.

Consider a force $\vec{\mathbf{F}}$ acting on a rigid object at the vector position $\vec{\mathbf{r}}$ (Active Fig. 11.1). As we saw in Section 10.6, the *magnitude* of the torque due to this force about an axis through the origin is $rF \sin \phi$, where ϕ is the angle between $\vec{\mathbf{r}}$ and $\vec{\mathbf{F}}$. The axis about which $\vec{\mathbf{F}}$ tends to produce rotation is perpendicular to the plane formed by $\vec{\mathbf{r}}$ and $\vec{\mathbf{F}}$.

The torque vector $\vec{\boldsymbol{\tau}}$ is related to the two vectors $\vec{\mathbf{r}}$ and $\vec{\mathbf{F}}$. We can establish a mathematical relationship between $\vec{\boldsymbol{\tau}}$, $\vec{\mathbf{r}}$, and $\vec{\mathbf{F}}$ using a mathematical operation called the **vector product**, or **cross product**:

$$\vec{\boldsymbol{\tau}} \equiv \vec{\mathbf{r}} \times \vec{\mathbf{F}} \tag{11.1}$$

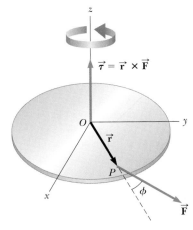

ACTIVE FIGURE 11.1

The torque vector $\vec{\boldsymbol{\tau}}$ lies in a direction perpendicular to the plane formed by the position vector $\vec{\mathbf{r}}$ and the applied force vector $\vec{\mathbf{F}}$.

Sign in at www.thomsonedu.com and go to ThomsonNOW to move point P and change the force vector $\vec{\mathbf{F}}$ to see the effect on the torque vector.

311

PITFALL PREVENTION 11.1
The Cross Product Is a Vector

Remember that the result of taking a cross product between two vectors is *a third vector*. Equation 11.3 gives only the magnitude of this vector.

We now give a formal definition of the vector product. Given any two vectors $\vec{A}$ and $\vec{B}$, the **vector product** $\vec{A} \times \vec{B}$ is defined as a third vector $\vec{C}$, which has a magnitude of $AB \sin \theta$, where θ is the angle between $\vec{A}$ and $\vec{B}$. That is, if $\vec{C}$ is given by

$$\vec{C} = \vec{A} \times \vec{B} \tag{11.2}$$

its magnitude is

$$C = AB \sin \theta \tag{11.3}$$

The quantity $AB \sin \theta$ is equal to the area of the parallelogram formed by $\vec{A}$ and $\vec{B}$ as shown in Figure 11.2. The *direction* of $\vec{C}$ is perpendicular to the plane formed by $\vec{A}$ and $\vec{B}$, and the best way to determine this direction is to use the right-hand rule illustrated in Figure 11.2. The four fingers of the right hand are pointed along $\vec{A}$ and then "wrapped" into $\vec{B}$ through the angle θ. The direction of the upright thumb is the direction of $\vec{A} \times \vec{B} = \vec{C}$. Because of the notation, $\vec{A} \times \vec{B}$ is often read "$\vec{A}$ cross $\vec{B}$," hence the term *cross product*.

Some properties of the vector product that follow from its definition are as follows:

◄ **Properties of the vector product**

1. Unlike the scalar product, the vector product is *not* commutative. Instead, the order in which the two vectors are multiplied in a cross product is important:

$$\vec{A} \times \vec{B} = -\vec{B} \times \vec{A} \tag{11.4}$$

   Therefore, if you change the order of the vectors in a cross product, you must change the sign. You can easily verify this relationship with the right-hand rule.
2. If $\vec{A}$ is parallel to $\vec{B}$ ($\theta = 0$ or $180°$), then $\vec{A} \times \vec{B} = 0$; therefore, it follows that $\vec{A} \times \vec{A} = 0$.
3. If $\vec{A}$ is perpendicular to $\vec{B}$, then $|\vec{A} \times \vec{B}| = AB$.
4. The vector product obeys the distributive law:

$$\vec{A} \times (\vec{B} + \vec{C}) = \vec{A} \times \vec{B} + \vec{A} \times \vec{C} \tag{11.5}$$

5. The derivative of the cross product with respect to some variable such as t is

$$\frac{d}{dt}(\vec{A} \times \vec{B}) = \frac{d\vec{A}}{dt} \times \vec{B} + \vec{A} \times \frac{d\vec{B}}{dt} \tag{11.6}$$

   where it is important to preserve the multiplicative order of the terms on the right side in view of Equation 11.4.

It is left as an exercise (Problem 10) to show from Equations 11.3 and 11.4 and from the definition of unit vectors that the cross products of the unit vectors $\hat{i}$, $\hat{j}$, and $\hat{k}$ obey the following rules:

◄ **Cross products of unit vectors**

$$\hat{i} \times \hat{i} = \hat{j} \times \hat{j} = \hat{k} \times \hat{k} = 0 \tag{11.7a}$$

$$\hat{i} \times \hat{j} = -\hat{j} \times \hat{i} = \hat{k} \tag{11.7b}$$

Right-hand rule

Figure 11.2 The vector product $\vec{A} \times \vec{B}$ is a third vector $\vec{C}$ having a magnitude $AB \sin \theta$ equal to the area of the parallelogram shown. The direction of $\vec{C}$ is perpendicular to the plane formed by $\vec{A}$ and $\vec{B}$, and this direction is determined by the right-hand rule.

$$\hat{\mathbf{j}} \times \hat{\mathbf{k}} = -\hat{\mathbf{k}} \times \hat{\mathbf{j}} = \hat{\mathbf{i}} \qquad \textbf{(11.7c)}$$

$$\hat{\mathbf{k}} \times \hat{\mathbf{i}} = -\hat{\mathbf{i}} \times \hat{\mathbf{k}} = \hat{\mathbf{j}} \qquad \textbf{(11.7d)}$$

Signs are interchangeable in cross products. For example, $\vec{\mathbf{A}} \times (-\vec{\mathbf{B}}) = -\vec{\mathbf{A}} \times \vec{\mathbf{B}}$ and $\hat{\mathbf{i}} \times (-\hat{\mathbf{j}}) = -\hat{\mathbf{i}} \times \hat{\mathbf{j}}$.

The cross product of any two vectors $\vec{\mathbf{A}}$ and $\vec{\mathbf{B}}$ can be expressed in the following determinant form:

$$\vec{\mathbf{A}} \times \vec{\mathbf{B}} = \begin{vmatrix} \hat{\mathbf{i}} & \hat{\mathbf{j}} & \hat{\mathbf{k}} \\ A_x & A_y & A_z \\ B_x & B_y & B_z \end{vmatrix} = \begin{vmatrix} A_y & A_z \\ B_y & B_z \end{vmatrix} \hat{\mathbf{i}} + \begin{vmatrix} A_z & A_x \\ B_z & B_x \end{vmatrix} \hat{\mathbf{j}} + \begin{vmatrix} A_x & A_y \\ B_x & B_y \end{vmatrix} \hat{\mathbf{k}}$$

Expanding these determinants gives the result

$$\vec{\mathbf{A}} \times \vec{\mathbf{B}} = (A_y B_z - A_z B_y)\hat{\mathbf{i}} + (A_z B_x - A_x B_z)\hat{\mathbf{j}} + (A_x B_y - A_y B_x)\hat{\mathbf{k}} \qquad \textbf{(11.8)}$$

Given the definition of the cross product, we can now assign a direction to the torque vector. If the force lies in the xy plane, as in Active Figure 11.1, the torque $\vec{\boldsymbol{\tau}}$ is represented by a vector parallel to the z axis. The force in Active Figure 11.1 creates a torque that tends to rotate the object counterclockwise about the z axis; the direction of $\vec{\boldsymbol{\tau}}$ is toward increasing z, and $\vec{\boldsymbol{\tau}}$ is therefore in the positive z direction. If we reversed the direction of $\vec{\mathbf{F}}$ in Active Figure 11.1, $\vec{\boldsymbol{\tau}}$ would be in the negative z direction.

Quick Quiz 11.1 Which of the following statements about the relationship between the magnitude of the cross product of two vectors and the product of the magnitudes of the vectors is true? (a) $|\vec{\mathbf{A}} \times \vec{\mathbf{B}}|$ is larger than AB. (b) $|\vec{\mathbf{A}} \times \vec{\mathbf{B}}|$ is smaller than AB. (c) $|\vec{\mathbf{A}} \times \vec{\mathbf{B}}|$ could be larger or smaller than AB, depending on the angle between the vectors. (d) $|\vec{\mathbf{A}} \times \vec{\mathbf{B}}|$ could be equal to AB.

EXAMPLE 11.1   The Vector Product

Two vectors lying in the xy plane are given by the equations $\vec{\mathbf{A}} = 2\hat{\mathbf{i}} + 3\hat{\mathbf{j}}$ and $\vec{\mathbf{B}} = -\hat{\mathbf{i}} + 2\hat{\mathbf{j}}$. Find $\vec{\mathbf{A}} \times \vec{\mathbf{B}}$ and verify that $\vec{\mathbf{A}} \times \vec{\mathbf{B}} = -\vec{\mathbf{B}} \times \vec{\mathbf{A}}$.

SOLUTION

Conceptualize Given the unit–vector notations of the vectors, think about the directions the vectors point in space. Imagine the parallelogram shown in Figure 11.2 for these vectors.

Categorize Because we use the definition of the cross product discussed in this section, we categorize this example as a substitution problem.

Write the cross product of the two vectors:

$$\vec{\mathbf{A}} \times \vec{\mathbf{B}} = (2\hat{\mathbf{i}} + 3\hat{\mathbf{j}}) \times (-\hat{\mathbf{i}} + 2\hat{\mathbf{j}})$$

Perform the multiplication:

$$\vec{\mathbf{A}} \times \vec{\mathbf{B}} = 2\hat{\mathbf{i}} \times (-\hat{\mathbf{i}}) + 2\hat{\mathbf{i}} \times 2\hat{\mathbf{j}} + 3\hat{\mathbf{j}} \times (-\hat{\mathbf{i}}) + 3\hat{\mathbf{j}} \times 2\hat{\mathbf{j}}$$

Use Equations 11.7a through 11.7d to evaluate the various terms:

$$\vec{\mathbf{A}} \times \vec{\mathbf{B}} = 0 + 4\hat{\mathbf{k}} + 3\hat{\mathbf{k}} + 0 = \boxed{7\hat{\mathbf{k}}}$$

To verify that $\vec{\mathbf{A}} \times \vec{\mathbf{B}} = -\vec{\mathbf{B}} \times \vec{\mathbf{A}}$, evaluate $\vec{\mathbf{B}} \times \vec{\mathbf{A}}$:

$$\vec{\mathbf{B}} \times \vec{\mathbf{A}} = (-\hat{\mathbf{i}} + 2\hat{\mathbf{j}}) \times (2\hat{\mathbf{i}} + 3\hat{\mathbf{j}})$$

Perform the multiplication:

$$\vec{\mathbf{B}} \times \vec{\mathbf{A}} = (-\hat{\mathbf{i}}) \times 2\hat{\mathbf{i}} + (-\hat{\mathbf{i}}) \times 3\hat{\mathbf{j}} + 2\hat{\mathbf{j}} \times 2\hat{\mathbf{i}} + 2\hat{\mathbf{j}} \times 3\hat{\mathbf{j}}$$

Use Equations 11.7a through 11.7d to evaluate the various terms:

$$\vec{\mathbf{B}} \times \vec{\mathbf{A}} = 0 - 3\hat{\mathbf{k}} - 4\hat{\mathbf{k}} + 0 = \boxed{-7\hat{\mathbf{k}}}$$

Therefore, $\vec{\mathbf{A}} \times \vec{\mathbf{B}} = -\vec{\mathbf{B}} \times \vec{\mathbf{A}}$. As an alternative method for finding $\vec{\mathbf{A}} \times \vec{\mathbf{B}}$, you could use Equation 11.8. Try it!

EXAMPLE 11.2   **The Torque Vector**

A force of $\vec{\mathbf{F}} = (2.00\hat{\mathbf{i}} + 3.00\hat{\mathbf{j}})$ N is applied to an object that is pivoted about a fixed axis aligned along the z coordinate axis. The force is applied at a point located at $\vec{\mathbf{r}} = (4.00\hat{\mathbf{i}} + 5.00\hat{\mathbf{j}})$ m. Find the torque vector $\vec{\boldsymbol{\tau}}$.

SOLUTION

Conceptualize   Given the unit–vector notations, think about the directions of the force and position vectors. If this force were applied at this position, in what direction would an object pivoted at the origin turn?

Categorize   Because we use the definition of the cross product discussed in this section, we categorize this example as a substitution problem.

Set up the torque vector using Equation 11.1:

$$\vec{\boldsymbol{\tau}} = \vec{\mathbf{r}} \times \vec{\mathbf{F}} = [(4.00\hat{\mathbf{i}} + 5.00\hat{\mathbf{j}})\text{ m}] \times [(2.00\hat{\mathbf{i}} + 3.00\hat{\mathbf{j}})\text{ N}]$$

Perform the multiplication:

$$\vec{\boldsymbol{\tau}} = [(4.00)(2.00)\hat{\mathbf{i}} \times \hat{\mathbf{i}} + (4.00)(3.00)\hat{\mathbf{i}} \times \hat{\mathbf{j}}$$
$$+ (5.00)(2.00)\hat{\mathbf{j}} \times \hat{\mathbf{i}} + (5.00)(3.00)\hat{\mathbf{j}} \times \hat{\mathbf{j}}]\text{ N} \cdot \text{m}$$

Use Equations 11.7a through 11.7d to evaluate the various terms:

$$\vec{\boldsymbol{\tau}} = [0 + 12.0\hat{\mathbf{k}} - 10.0\hat{\mathbf{k}} + 0]\text{ N} \cdot \text{m} = \boxed{2.0\hat{\mathbf{k}}\text{ N} \cdot \text{m}}$$

Notice that both $\vec{\mathbf{r}}$ and $\vec{\mathbf{F}}$ are in the xy plane. As expected, the torque vector is perpendicular to this plane, having only a z component. We have followed the rules for significant figures discussed in Section 1.6, which lead to an answer with two significant figures. We have lost some precision because we ended up subtracting two numbers that are close.

11.2 Angular Momentum: The Nonisolated System

ACTIVE FIGURE 11.3

As the skater passes the pole, she grabs hold of it, which causes her to swing around the pole rapidly in a circular path.

Sign in at www.thomsonedu.com and go to ThomsonNOW to change the speed of the skater and her distance to the pole and watch her spin when she grabs the pole.

Imagine a rigid pole sticking up through the ice on a frozen pond (Active Fig. 11.3). A skater glides rapidly toward the pole, aiming a little to the side so that she does not hit it. As she passes the pole, she reaches out to her side and grabs it, an action that causes her to move in a circular path around the pole. Just as the idea of linear momentum helps us analyze translational motion, a rotational analog—*angular momentum*—helps us analyze the motion of this skater and other objects undergoing rotational motion.

In Chapter 9, we developed the mathematical form of linear momentum and then proceeded to show how this new quantity was valuable in problem solving. We will follow a similar procedure for angular momentum.

Consider a particle of mass m located at the vector position $\vec{\mathbf{r}}$ and moving with linear momentum $\vec{\mathbf{p}}$ as in Active Figure 11.4. In describing translational motion, we found that the net force on the particle equals the time rate of change of its linear momentum, $\Sigma\,\vec{\mathbf{F}} = d\vec{\mathbf{p}}/dt$ (see Eq. 9.3). Let us take the cross product of each side of Equation 9.3 with $\vec{\mathbf{r}}$, which gives the net torque on the particle on the left side of the equation:

$$\vec{\mathbf{r}} \times \sum \vec{\mathbf{F}} = \sum \vec{\boldsymbol{\tau}} = \vec{\mathbf{r}} \times \frac{d\vec{\mathbf{p}}}{dt}$$

Now let's add to the right side the term $(d\vec{\mathbf{r}}/dt) \times \vec{\mathbf{p}}$, which is zero because $d\vec{\mathbf{r}}/dt = \vec{\mathbf{v}}$ and $\vec{\mathbf{v}}$ and $\vec{\mathbf{p}}$ are parallel. Therefore,

$$\sum \vec{\boldsymbol{\tau}} = \vec{\mathbf{r}} \times \frac{d\vec{\mathbf{p}}}{dt} + \frac{d\vec{\mathbf{r}}}{dt} \times \vec{\mathbf{p}}$$

We recognize the right side of this equation as the derivative of $\vec{\mathbf{r}} \times \vec{\mathbf{p}}$ (see Eq. 11.6). Therefore,

$$\sum \vec{\boldsymbol{\tau}} = \frac{d(\vec{\mathbf{r}} \times \vec{\mathbf{p}})}{dt} \tag{11.9}$$

which looks very similar in form to Equation 9.3, $\sum \vec{\mathbf{F}} = d\vec{\mathbf{p}}/dt$. This result suggests that the combination $\vec{\mathbf{r}} \times \vec{\mathbf{p}}$ should play the same role in rotational motion that $\vec{\mathbf{p}}$ plays in translational motion. We call this combination the *angular momentum* of the particle:

> The instantaneous **angular momentum** $\vec{\mathbf{L}}$ of a particle relative to an axis through the origin O is defined by the cross product of the particle's instantaneous position vector $\vec{\mathbf{r}}$ and its instantaneous linear momentum $\vec{\mathbf{p}}$:
>
> $$\vec{\mathbf{L}} \equiv \vec{\mathbf{r}} \times \vec{\mathbf{p}} \tag{11.10}$$

◄ Angular momentum of a particle

We can now write Equation 11.9 as

$$\sum \vec{\boldsymbol{\tau}} = \frac{d\vec{\mathbf{L}}}{dt} \tag{11.11}$$

which is the rotational analog of Newton's second law, $\sum \vec{\mathbf{F}} = d\vec{\mathbf{p}}/dt$. Torque causes the angular momentum $\vec{\mathbf{L}}$ to change just as force causes linear momentum $\vec{\mathbf{p}}$ to change. Equation 11.11 states that **the torque acting on a particle is equal to the time rate of change of the particle's angular momentum.**

Notice that Equation 11.11 is valid only if $\sum \vec{\boldsymbol{\tau}}$ and $\vec{\mathbf{L}}$ are measured about the same axis. Furthermore, **the expression is valid for any axis fixed in an inertial frame.**

The SI unit of angular momentum is $\text{kg} \cdot \text{m}^2/\text{s}$. Notice also that both the magnitude and the direction of $\vec{\mathbf{L}}$ depend on the choice of axis. Following the right-hand rule, we see that the direction of $\vec{\mathbf{L}}$ is perpendicular to the plane formed by $\vec{\mathbf{r}}$ and $\vec{\mathbf{p}}$. In Active Figure 11.4, $\vec{\mathbf{r}}$ and $\vec{\mathbf{p}}$ are in the xy plane, so $\vec{\mathbf{L}}$ points in the z direction. Because $\vec{\mathbf{p}} = m\vec{\mathbf{v}}$, the magnitude of $\vec{\mathbf{L}}$ is

$$L = mvr \sin \phi \tag{11.12}$$

where ϕ is the angle between $\vec{\mathbf{r}}$ and $\vec{\mathbf{p}}$. It follows that L is zero when $\vec{\mathbf{r}}$ is parallel to $\vec{\mathbf{p}}$ ($\phi = 0$ or $180°$). In other words, when the translational velocity of the particle is along a line that passes through the axis, the particle has zero angular momentum with respect to the axis. On the other hand, if $\vec{\mathbf{r}}$ is perpendicular to $\vec{\mathbf{p}}$ ($\phi = 90°$), then $L = mvr$. At that instant, the particle moves exactly as if it were on the rim of a wheel rotating about the axis in a plane defined by $\vec{\mathbf{r}}$ and $\vec{\mathbf{p}}$.

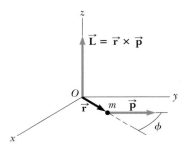

ACTIVE FIGURE 11.4

The angular momentum $\vec{\mathbf{L}}$ of a particle with linear momentum $\vec{\mathbf{p}}$ located at the vector position $\vec{\mathbf{r}}$ is a vector given by $\vec{\mathbf{L}} = \vec{\mathbf{r}} \times \vec{\mathbf{p}}$. The value of $\vec{\mathbf{L}}$ depends on the axis about which it is measured and is a vector perpendicular to both $\vec{\mathbf{r}}$ and $\vec{\mathbf{p}}$.

Sign in at www.thomsonedu.com and go to ThomsonNOW to change the position vector $\vec{\mathbf{r}}$ and the momentum vector $\vec{\mathbf{p}}$ and see the effect on the angular momentum vector.

PITFALL PREVENTION 11.2
Is Rotation Necessary for Angular Momentum?

We can define angular momentum even if the particle is not moving in a circular path. Even a particle moving in a straight line has angular momentum about any axis displaced from the path of the particle.

Quick Quiz 11.2   Recall the skater described at the beginning of this section. Let her mass be m. **(i)** What would be her angular momentum relative to the pole at the instant she is a distance d from the pole if she were skating directly toward it at speed v? (a) zero   (b) mvd (c) impossible to determine   **(ii)** What would be her angular momentum relative to the pole at the instant she is a distance d from the pole if she were skating at speed v along a straight path that is a perpendicular distance a from the pole? (a) zero   (b) mvd (c) mva (d) impossible to determine

EXAMPLE 11.3 | **Angular Momentum of a Particle in Circular Motion**

A particle moves in the xy plane in a circular path of radius r as shown in Figure 11.5. Find the magnitude and direction of its angular momentum relative to an axis through O when its velocity is $\vec{v}$.

SOLUTION

Conceptualize The linear momentum of the particle is changing in direction (but not in magnitude). You might therefore be tempted to conclude that the angular momentum of the particle is always changing. In this situation, however, that is not the case. Let's see why.

Categorize We use the definition of the angular momentum of a particle discussed in this section, so we categorize this example as a substitution problem.

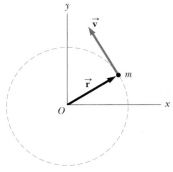

Figure 11.5 (Example 11.3) A particle moving in a circle of radius r has an angular momentum about an axis through O that has magnitude mvr. The vector $\vec{L} = \vec{r} \times \vec{p}$ points *out* of the page.

Use Equation 11.12 to evaluate the magnitude of $\vec{L}$:

$$L = mvr \sin 90° = \boxed{mvr}$$

This value of L is constant because all three factors on the right are constant. The direction of $\vec{L}$ also is constant, even though the direction of $\vec{p} = m\vec{v}$ keeps changing. To verify this statement, apply the right-hand rule to find the direction of $\vec{L} = \vec{r} \times \vec{p} = m\vec{r} \times \vec{v}$ in Figure 11.5. Your thumb points upward and away from the page, so that is the direction of $\vec{L}$. Hence, we can write the vector expression $\vec{L} = (mvr)\hat{k}$. If the particle were to move clockwise, $\vec{L}$ would point downward and into the page and $\vec{L} = -(mvr)\hat{k}$. **A particle in uniform circular motion has a constant angular momentum about an axis through the center of its path.**

Angular Momentum of a System of Particles

In Section 9.6, we showed that Newton's second law for a particle could be extended to a system of particles, resulting in

$$\sum \vec{F}_{ext} = \frac{d\vec{p}_{tot}}{dt}$$

This equation states that the net external force on a system of particles is equal to the time rate of change of the total linear momentum of the system. Let's see if a similar statement can be made for rotational motion. The total angular momentum of a system of particles about some axis is defined as the vector sum of the angular momenta of the individual particles:

$$\vec{L}_{tot} = \vec{L}_1 + \vec{L}_2 + \cdots + \vec{L}_n = \sum_i \vec{L}_i$$

where the vector sum is over all n particles in the system.

Differentiating this equation with respect to time gives

$$\frac{d\vec{L}_{tot}}{dt} = \sum_i \frac{d\vec{L}_i}{dt} = \sum_i \vec{\tau}_i$$

where we have used Equation 11.11 to replace the time rate of change of the angular momentum of each particle with the net torque on the particle.

The torques acting on the particles of the system are those associated with internal forces between particles and those associated with external forces. The net torque associated with all internal forces, however, is zero. Recall that Newton's third law tells us that internal forces between particles of the system are equal in magnitude and opposite in direction. If we assume these forces lie along the line of separation of each pair of particles, the total torque around some axis passing through an origin O due to each action–reaction force pair is zero (that is, the moment arm d from O to the line of action of the forces is equal for both particles and the forces are in opposite directions). In the summation, therefore, the net internal torque is zero. We conclude that the total angular momentum of a system can vary with time only if a net external torque is acting on the system:

$$\sum \vec{\tau}_{ext} = \frac{d\vec{L}_{tot}}{dt} \qquad (11.13)$$

◄ The net external torque on a system equals the time rate of change of angular momentum of the system

This equation is indeed the rotational analog of $\sum \vec{F}_{ext} = d\vec{p}_{tot}/dt$ for a system of particles. Equation 11.13 is the mathematical representation of the **angular momentum version of the nonisolated system model. If a system is nonisolated in the sense that there is a net torque on it, the torque is equal to the time rate of change of angular momentum.**

Although we do not prove it here, this statement is true regardless of the motion of the center of mass. It applies even if the center of mass is accelerating, provided that the torque and angular momentum are evaluated relative to an axis through the center of mass.

EXAMPLE 11.4 | A System of Objects

A sphere of mass m_1 and a block of mass m_2 are connected by a light cord that passes over a pulley as shown in Figure 11.6. The radius of the pulley is R, and the mass of the thin rim is M. The spokes of the pulley have negligible mass. The block slides on a frictionless, horizontal surface. Find an expression for the linear acceleration of the two objects, using the concepts of angular momentum and torque.

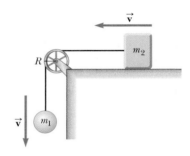

SOLUTION

Conceptualize When the system is released, the block slides to the left, the sphere drops downward, and the pulley rotates counterclockwise. This situation is similar to problems we have solved earlier except that now we want to use an angular momentum approach.

Figure 11.6 (Example 11.4) When the system is released, the sphere moves downward and the block moves to the left.

Categorize We identify the block, pulley, and sphere as a nonisolated system, subject to the external torque due to the gravitational force on the sphere. We shall calculate the angular momentum about an axis that coincides with the axle of the pulley. The angular momentum of the system includes that of two objects moving translationally (the sphere and the block) and one object undergoing pure rotation (the pulley).

Analyze At any instant of time, the sphere and the block have a common speed v, so the angular momentum of the sphere is $m_1 vR$ and that of the block is $m_2 vR$. At the same instant, all points on the rim of the pulley also move with speed v, so the angular momentum of the pulley is MvR.

Now let's address the total external torque acting on the system about the pulley axle. Because it has a moment arm of zero, the force exerted by the axle on the pulley does not contribute to the torque. Furthermore, the normal force acting on the block is balanced by the gravitational force $m_2\vec{g}$, so these forces do not contribute to the torque. The gravitational force $m_1\vec{g}$ acting on the sphere produces a torque about the axle equal in magnitude to $m_1 gR$, where R is the moment arm of the force about the axle. This result is the total external torque about the pulley axle; that is, $\sum \tau_{ext} = m_1 gR$.

Write an expression for the total angular momentum of the system:

$$(1) \quad L = m_1 vR + m_2 vR + MvR = (m_1 + m_2 + M)vR$$

Substitute this expression and the total external torque into Equation 11.13:

$$\sum \tau_{ext} = \frac{dL}{dt}$$

$$m_1 gR = \frac{d}{dt}\left[(m_1 + m_2 + M)vR\right]$$

$$(2) \quad m_1 gR = (m_1 + m_2 + M)R\frac{dv}{dt}$$

Recognizing that $dv/dt = a$, solve Equation (2) for a:

$$a = \frac{m_1 g}{m_1 + m_2 + M}$$

Finalize Evaluating the net torque about the axle, we did not include the forces that the cord exerts on the objects because these forces are internal to the system under consideration. Instead we analyzed the system as a whole. Only *external* torques contribute to the change in the system's angular momentum.

11.3 Angular Momentum of a Rotating Rigid Object

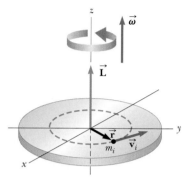

Figure 11.7 When a rigid object rotates about an axis, the angular momentum $\vec{L}$ is in the same direction as the angular velocity $\vec{\omega}$ according to the expression $\vec{L} = I\vec{\omega}$.

In Example 11.4, we considered the angular momentum of a deformable system. Let us now restrict our attention to a nondeformable system, a rigid object. Consider a rigid object rotating about a fixed axis that coincides with the z axis of a coordinate system as shown in Figure 11.7. Let's determine the angular momentum of this object. Each *particle* of the object rotates in the xy plane about the z axis with an angular speed ω. The magnitude of the angular momentum of a particle of mass m_i about the z axis is $m_i v_i r_i$. Because $v_i = r_i \omega$ (Eq. 10.10), we can express the magnitude of the angular momentum of this particle as

$$L_i = m_i r_i^2 \omega$$

The vector $\vec{L}_i$ is directed along the z axis, as is the vector $\vec{\omega}$.

We can now find the angular momentum (which in this situation has only a z component) of the whole object by taking the sum of L_i over all particles:

$$L_z = \sum_i L_i = \sum_i m_i r_i^2 \omega = \left(\sum_i m_i r_i^2 \right) \omega$$

$$L_z = I\omega \tag{11.14}$$

where $\sum_i m_i r_i^2$ is the moment of inertia I of the object about the z axis (Eq. 10.15).

Now let's differentiate Equation 11.14 with respect to time, noting that I is constant for a rigid object:

$$\frac{dL_z}{dt} = I\frac{d\omega}{dt} = I\alpha \tag{11.15}$$

where α is the angular acceleration relative to the axis of rotation. Because dL_z/dt is equal to the net external torque (see Eq. 11.13), we can express Equation 11.15 as

◀ Rotational form of Newton's second law

$$\sum \tau_{\text{ext}} = I\alpha \tag{11.16}$$

That is, the net external torque acting on a rigid object rotating about a fixed axis equals the moment of inertia about the rotation axis multiplied by the object's angular acceleration relative to that axis. This result is the same as Equation 10.21, which was derived using a force approach, but we derived Equation 11.16 using the concept of angular momentum. This equation is also valid for a rigid object rotating about a moving axis provided the moving axis (1) passes through the center of mass and (2) is a symmetry axis.

If a symmetrical object rotates about a fixed axis passing through its center of mass, you can write Equation 11.14 in vector form as $\vec{L} = I\vec{\omega}$, where $\vec{L}$ is the total angular momentum of the object measured with respect to the axis of rotation. Furthermore, the expression is valid for any object, regardless of its symmetry, if $\vec{L}$ stands for the component of angular momentum along the axis of rotation.[1]

[1] In general, the expression $\vec{L} = I\vec{\omega}$ is not always valid. If a rigid object rotates about an *arbitrary* axis, then $\vec{L}$ and $\vec{\omega}$ may point in different directions. In this case, the moment of inertia cannot be treated as a scalar. Strictly speaking, $\vec{L} = I\vec{\omega}$ applies only to rigid objects of any shape that rotate about one of three mutually perpendicular axes (called *principal axes*) through the center of mass. This concept is discussed in more advanced texts on mechanics.

EXAMPLE 11.5	**Bowling Ball**

Estimate the magnitude of the angular momentum of a bowling ball spinning at 10 rev/s as shown in Figure 11.8.

SOLUTION

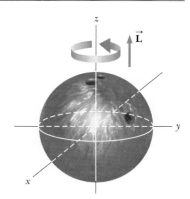

Conceptualize   Imagine spinning a bowling ball on the smooth floor of a bowling alley. Because a bowling ball is relatively heavy, the angular momentum should be relatively large.

Categorize   We evaluate the angular momentum using Equation 11.14, so we categorize this example as a substitution problem.
  We start by making some estimates of the relevant physical parameters and model the ball as a uniform solid sphere. A typical bowling ball might have a mass of 7.0 kg and a radius of 12 cm.

Figure 11.8   (Example 11.5) A bowling ball that rotates about the z axis in the direction shown has an angular momentum $\vec{L}$ in the positive z direction. If the direction of rotation is reversed, $\vec{L}$ points in the negative z direction.

Evaluate the moment of inertia of the ball about an axis through its center from Table 10.2:

$$I = \tfrac{2}{5}MR^2 = \tfrac{2}{5}(7.0 \text{ kg})(0.12 \text{ m})^2 = 0.040 \text{ kg} \cdot \text{m}^2$$

Evaluate the magnitude of the angular momentum from Equation 11.14:

$$L_z = I\omega = (0.040 \text{ kg} \cdot \text{m}^2)(10 \text{ rev/s})(2\pi \text{ rad/rev}) = 2.53 \text{ kg} \cdot \text{m}^2/\text{s}$$

Because of the roughness of our estimates, we should keep only one significant figure, so $L_z = $ 3 kg $\cdot$ m²/s

---

EXAMPLE 11.6	**The Seesaw**

A father of mass m_f and his daughter of mass m_d sit on opposite ends of a seesaw at equal distances from the pivot at the center (Fig. 11.9). The seesaw is modeled as a rigid rod of mass M and length ℓ and is pivoted without friction. At a given moment, the combination rotates in a vertical plane with an angular speed ω.

(A) Find an expression for the magnitude of the system's angular momentum.

SOLUTION

Conceptualize   Imagine an axis of rotation passing through the pivot at O in Figure 11.9. The rotating system has angular momentum about that axis.

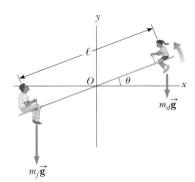

Categorize   Ignore any movement of arms or legs of the father and daughter and model them both as particles. The system is therefore modeled as a rigid object. This first part of the example is categorized as a substitution problem.

Figure 11.9   (Example 11.6) A father and daughter demonstrate angular momentum on a seesaw.

  The moment of inertia of the system equals the sum of the moments of inertia of the three components: the seesaw and the two individuals. We can refer to Table 10.2 to obtain the expression for the moment of inertia of the rod and use the particle expression $I = mr^2$ for each person.

Find the total moment of inertia of the system about the z axis through O:

$$I = \tfrac{1}{12}M\ell^2 + m_f\left(\frac{\ell}{2}\right)^2 + m_d\left(\frac{\ell}{2}\right)^2 = \frac{\ell^2}{4}\left(\frac{M}{3} + m_f + m_d\right)$$

Find the magnitude of the angular momentum of the system:

$$L = I\omega = \frac{\ell^2}{4}\left(\frac{M}{3} + m_f + m_d\right)\omega$$

(B) Find an expression for the magnitude of the angular acceleration of the system when the seesaw makes an angle θ with the horizontal.

SOLUTION

Conceptualize Generally, fathers are more massive than daughters, so the system is not in equilibrium and has an angular acceleration. We expect the angular acceleration to be positive in Figure 11.9.

Categorize We identify the system as nonisolated because of the external torque associated with the gravitational force. We again identify an axis of rotation passing through the pivot at O in Figure 11.9.

Analyze To find the angular acceleration of the system at any angle θ, we first calculate the net torque on the system and then use $\Sigma \tau_{\text{ext}} = I\alpha$ to obtain an expression for α.

Evaluate the torque due to the gravitational force on the father:

$$\tau_f = m_f g\frac{\ell}{2}\cos\theta \quad (\vec{\tau}_f \text{ out of page})$$

Evaluate the torque due to the gravitational force on the daughter:

$$\tau_d = -m_d g\frac{\ell}{2}\cos\theta \quad (\vec{\tau}_d \text{ into page})$$

Evaluate the net torque exerted on the system:

$$\sum \tau_{\text{ext}} = \tau_f + \tau_d = \tfrac{1}{2}(m_f - m_d)g\ell\cos\theta$$

Use Equation 11.16 and I from part (A) to find α:

$$\alpha = \frac{\sum \tau_{\text{ext}}}{I} = \frac{2(m_f - m_d)g\cos\theta}{\ell\,[(M/3) + m_f + m_d]}$$

Finalize For a father more massive than his daughter, the angular acceleration is positive as expected. If the seesaw begins in a horizontal orientation ($\theta = 0$) and is released, the rotation is counterclockwise in Figure 11.9 and the father's end of the seesaw drops, which is consistent with everyday experience.

What If? Imagine the father moves inward on the seesaw to a distance d from the pivot to try to balance the two sides. What is the angular acceleration of the system in this case when it is released from an arbitrary angle θ?

Answer The angular acceleration of the system should decrease if the system is more balanced.

Find the total moment of inertia about the z axis through O for the modified system:

$$I = \tfrac{1}{12}M\ell^2 + m_f d^2 + m_d\left(\frac{\ell}{2}\right)^2 = \frac{\ell^2}{4}\left(\frac{M}{3} + m_d\right) + m_f d^2$$

Find the net torque exerted on the system about an axis through O:

$$\sum \tau_{\text{ext}} = \tau_f + \tau_d = m_f g d\cos\theta - \tfrac{1}{2}m_d g\ell\cos\theta$$

Find the new angular acceleration of the system:

$$\alpha = \frac{\sum \tau_{\text{ext}}}{I} = \frac{m_f g d\cos\theta - \tfrac{1}{2}m_d g\ell\cos\theta}{(\ell^2/4)\,[(M/3) + m_d] + m_f d^2}$$

The seesaw is balanced when the angular acceleration is zero. In this situation, both father and daughter can push off the ground and rise to the highest possible point.

Find the required position of the father by setting $\alpha = 0$:

$$\alpha = \frac{m_f g d \cos \theta - \frac{1}{2} m_d g \ell \cos \theta}{(\ell^2/4)[(M/3) + m_d] + m_f d^2} = 0$$

$$m_f g d \cos \theta - \tfrac{1}{2} m_d g \ell \cos \theta = 0 \quad \rightarrow \quad d = \left(\frac{m_d}{m_f}\right) \frac{1}{2} \ell$$

In the rare case that the father and daughter have the same mass, the father is located at the end of the seesaw, $d = \ell/2$.

11.4 The Isolated System: Conservation of Angular Momentum

In Chapter 9, we found that the total linear momentum of a system of particles remains constant if the system is isolated, that is, if the net external force acting on the system is zero. We have an analogous conservation law in rotational motion:

> The total angular momentum of a system is constant in both magnitude and direction if the net external torque acting on the system is zero, that is, if the system is isolated.

◀ Conservation of angular momentum

This statement is the principle of **conservation of angular momentum** and is the basis of the **angular momentum version of the isolated system model.** This principle follows directly from Equation 11.13, which indicates that if

$$\sum \vec{\tau}_{\text{ext}} = \frac{d\vec{L}_{\text{tot}}}{dt} = 0 \tag{11.17}$$

then

$$\vec{L}_{\text{tot}} = \text{constant} \quad \text{or} \quad \vec{L}_i = \vec{L}_f \tag{11.18}$$

For an isolated system consisting of a number of particles, we write this conservation law as $\vec{L}_{\text{tot}} = \sum \vec{L}_n = \text{constant}$, where the index n denotes the nth particle in the system.

If an isolated rotating system is deformable so that its mass undergoes redistribution in some way, the system's moment of inertia changes. Because the magnitude of the angular momentum of the system is $L = I\omega$ (Eq. 11.14), conservation of angular momentum requires that the product of I and ω must remain constant. Therefore, a change in I for an isolated system requires a change in ω. In this case, we can express the principle of conservation of angular momentum as

$$I_i \omega_i = I_f \omega_f = \text{constant} \tag{11.19}$$

This expression is valid both for rotation about a fixed axis and for rotation about an axis through the center of mass of a moving system as long as that axis remains fixed in direction. We require only that the net external torque be zero.

Many examples demonstrate conservation of angular momentum for a deformable system. You may have observed a figure skater spinning in the finale of a program (Fig. 11.10). The angular speed of the skater is large when his hands and feet are close to the trunk of his body. Ignoring friction between skater and ice, there are no external torques on the skater. The moment of inertia of his body increases as his hands and feet are moved away from his body at the finish of the spin. According to the principle of conservation of angular momentum, his angular speed must decrease. In a similar way, when divers or acrobats wish to make

Figure 11.10 Angular momentum is conserved as Russian figure skater Evgeni Plushenko performs during the 2004 World Figure Skating Championships. When his arms and legs are close to his body, his moment of inertia is small and his angular speed is large. To slow down for the finish of his spin, he moves his arms and legs outward, increasing his moment of inertia.

several somersaults, they pull their hands and feet close to their bodies to rotate at a higher rate, as in the opening photograph of this chapter. In these cases, the external force due to gravity acts through the center of mass and hence exerts no torque about an axis through this point. Therefore, the angular momentum about the center of mass must be conserved; that is, $I_i \omega_i = I_f \omega_f$. For example, when divers wish to double their angular speed, they must reduce their moment of inertia to half its initial value.

In Equation 11.18, we have a third version of the isolated system model. We can now state that the energy, linear momentum, and angular momentum of an isolated system are all conserved:

$$\text{For an isolated system} \begin{cases} E_i = E_f & \text{(if there are no energy transfers)} \\ \vec{\mathbf{p}}_i = \vec{\mathbf{p}}_f & \text{(if the net external force is zero)} \\ \vec{\mathbf{L}}_i = \vec{\mathbf{L}}_f & \text{(if the net external torque is zero)} \end{cases}$$

Quick Quiz 11.4 A competitive diver leaves the diving board and falls toward the water with her body straight and rotating slowly. She pulls her arms and legs into a tight tuck position. **(i)** What happens to her angular speed? (a) It increases. (b) It decreases. (c) It stays the same. (d) It is impossible to determine. **(ii)** From the same list of choices, what happens to the rotational kinetic energy of her body?

EXAMPLE 11.7	**Formation of a Neutron Star**

A star rotates with a period of 30 days about an axis through its center. After the star undergoes a supernova explosion, the stellar core, which had a radius of 1.0×10^4 km, collapses into a neutron star of radius 3.0 km. Determine the period of rotation of the neutron star.

SOLUTION

Conceptualize The change in the neutron star's motion is similar to that of the skater described above, but in the reverse direction. As the mass of the star moves closer to the rotation axis, we expect the star to spin faster.

Categorize Let us assume that during the collapse of the stellar core, (1) no external torque acts on it, (2) it remains spherical with the same relative mass distribution, and (3) its mass remains constant. We categorize the star as an isolated system. We do not know the mass distribution of the star, but we have assumed the distribution is symmetric, so the moment of inertia can be expressed as kMR^2, where k is some numerical constant. (From Table 10.2, for example, we see that $k = \frac{2}{5}$ for a solid sphere and $k = \frac{2}{3}$ for a spherical shell.)

Analyze Let's use the symbol T for the period, with T_i being the initial period of the star and T_f being the period of the neutron star. The period is the time interval required for a point on the star's equator to make one complete revolution around the axis of rotation. The star's angular speed is given by $\omega = 2\pi/T$.

Write Equation 11.19 for the star:
$$I_i \omega_i = I_f \omega_f$$

Use $\omega = 2\pi/T$ to rewrite this equation in terms of the initial and final periods:
$$I_i \left(\frac{2\pi}{T_i} \right) = I_f \left(\frac{2\pi}{T_f} \right)$$

Substitute the moments of inertia in the preceding equation:
$$kMR_i^2 \left(\frac{2\pi}{T_i} \right) = kMR_f^2 \left(\frac{2\pi}{T_f} \right)$$

Solve for the final period of the star:
$$T_f = \left(\frac{R_f}{R_i} \right)^2 T_i$$

Substitute numerical values:

$$T_f = \left(\frac{3.0 \text{ km}}{1.0 \times 10^4 \text{ km}}\right)^2 (30 \text{ days}) = 2.7 \times 10^{-6} \text{ days} = \boxed{0.23 \text{ s}}$$

Finalize   The neutron star does indeed rotate faster after it collapses, as predicted. It moves very fast, in fact, rotating about four times each second.

EXAMPLE 11.8   The Merry-Go-Round

A horizontal platform in the shape of a circular disk rotates freely in a horizontal plane about a frictionless vertical axle (Fig. 11.11). The platform has a mass $M = 100$ kg and a radius $R = 2.0$ m. A student whose mass is $m = 60$ kg walks slowly from the rim of the disk toward its center. If the angular speed of the system is 2.0 rad/s when the student is at the rim, what is the angular speed when she reaches a point $r = 0.50$ m from the center?

SOLUTION

Conceptualize   The speed change here is similar to those of the spinning skater and the neutron star in preceding discussions. This problem is different because part of the moment of inertia of the system changes (that of the student) while part remains fixed (that of the platform).

Figure 11.11   (Example 11.8) As the student walks toward the center of the rotating platform, the angular speed of the system increases because the angular momentum of the system remains constant.

Categorize   Because the platform rotates on a frictionless axle, we identify the system of the student and the platform as an isolated system.

Analyze   Let us denote the moment of inertia of the platform as I_p and that of the student as I_s. We model the student as a particle.

Find the initial moment of inertia I_i of the system (student plus platform) about the axis of rotation:

$$I_i = I_{pi} + I_{si} = \tfrac{1}{2}MR^2 + mR^2$$

Find the moment of inertia of the system when the student walks to the position $r < R$:

$$I_f = I_{pf} + I_{sf} = \tfrac{1}{2}MR^2 + mr^2$$

Apply the law of conservation of angular momentum to the system:

$$I_i\omega_i = I_f\omega_f$$

Substitute the moments of inertia:

$$(\tfrac{1}{2}MR^2 + mR^2)\omega_i = (\tfrac{1}{2}MR^2 + mr^2)\omega_f$$

Solve for the final angular speed:

$$\omega_f = \left(\frac{\tfrac{1}{2}MR^2 + mR^2}{\tfrac{1}{2}MR^2 + mr^2}\right)\omega_i$$

Substitute numerical values:

$$\omega_f = \left[\frac{\tfrac{1}{2}(100 \text{ kg})(2.0 \text{ m})^2 + (60 \text{ kg})(2.0 \text{ m})^2}{\tfrac{1}{2}(100 \text{ kg})(2.0 \text{ m})^2 + (60 \text{ kg})(0.50 \text{ m})^2}\right](2.0 \text{ rad/s})$$

$$\omega_f = \left(\frac{440 \text{ kg} \cdot \text{m}^2}{215 \text{ kg} \cdot \text{m}^2}\right)(2.0 \text{ rad/s}) = \boxed{4.1 \text{ rad/s}}$$

Finalize   As expected, the angular speed increases. The fastest that this system could spin would be when the student moves to the center of the platform. Do this calculation to show that this maximum angular speed is 4.4 rad/s. Notice that the activity described in this problem is dangerous as discussed with regard to the Coriolis force in Section 6.3.

What If? What if you measured the kinetic energy of the system before and after the student walks inward? Are the initial kinetic energy and the final kinetic energy the same?

Answer You may be tempted to say yes because the system is isolated. Remember, however, that energy can be transformed among several forms, so we have to handle an energy question carefully.

Find the initial kinetic energy:

$$K_i = \tfrac{1}{2}I_i\omega_i^{\,2} = \tfrac{1}{2}(440 \text{ kg} \cdot \text{m}^2)(2.0 \text{ rad/s})^2 = 880 \text{ J}$$

Find the final kinetic energy:

$$K_f = \tfrac{1}{2}I_f\omega_f^{\,2} = \tfrac{1}{2}(215 \text{ kg} \cdot \text{m}^2)(4.1 \text{ rad/s})^2 = 1.81 \times 10^3 \text{ J}$$

Therefore, the kinetic energy of the system *increases*. The student must do work to move herself closer to the center of rotation, so this extra kinetic energy comes from chemical potential energy in the student's body.

EXAMPLE 11.9 | Disk and Stick Collision

A 2.0-kg disk traveling at 3.0 m/s strikes a 1.0-kg stick of length 4.0 m that is lying flat on nearly frictionless ice as shown in the overhead view of Figure 11.12a. Assume the collision is elastic and the disk does not deviate from its original line of motion. Find the translational speed of the disk, the translational speed of the stick, and the angular speed of the stick after the collision. The moment of inertia of the stick about its center of mass is 1.33 kg · m².

(a)

(b)

Figure 11.12 (Example 11.9) Overhead view of a disk striking a stick in an elastic collision. (a) Before the collision, the disk moves toward the stick. (b) The collision causes the stick to rotate and move to the right.

SOLUTION

Conceptualize Examine Figure 11.12a and imagine what happens after the disk hits the stick. Figure 11.12b shows what you might expect: the disk continues to move at a slower speed and the stick is in both translational and rotational motion. We assume the disk does not deviate from its original line of motion because the force exerted by the stick on the disk is parallel to the original path of the disk.

Categorize Because the ice is frictionless, the disk and stick form an isolated system. Also, because the collision is assumed to be elastic, the energy, linear momentum, and angular momentum of the system are all conserved.

Analyze First notice that we have three unknowns, so we need three equations to solve simultaneously.

Apply the law of the conservation of linear momentum to the system:

$$m_d v_{di} = m_d v_{df} + m_s v_s$$

Substitute the known values:

$$(2.0 \text{ kg})(3.0 \text{ m/s}) = (2.0 \text{ kg})v_{df} + (1.0 \text{ kg})v_s$$

Rearrange the equation:

$$(1) \quad 6.0 \text{ kg} \cdot \text{m/s} - (2.0 \text{ kg})v_{df} = (1.0 \text{ kg})v_s$$

Now we apply the law of conservation of angular momentum for the system, using an axis passing through the center of the stick as our rotation axis. The component of angular momentum of the disk along the axis perpendicular to the plane of the ice is negative. (The right-hand rule shows that $\vec{L}_d$ points into the ice.)

Apply conservation of angular momentum to the system:

$$-rm_d v_{di} = -rm_d v_{df} + I\omega$$

Substitute the known values:

$$-(2.0\text{ m})(2.0\text{ kg})(3.0\text{ m/s}) = -(2.0\text{ m})(2.0\text{ kg})v_{df} + (1.33\text{ kg}\cdot\text{m}^2)\omega$$

$$-12\text{ kg}\cdot\text{m}^2/\text{s} = -(4.0\text{ kg}\cdot\text{m})v_{df} + (1.33\text{ kg}\cdot\text{m}^2)\omega$$

Divide the equation by
1.33 kg · m² and rearrange:

$$(2)\quad -9.0\text{ rad/s} + (3.0\text{ rad/m})v_{df} = \omega$$

Finally, the elastic nature of the collision tells us that the kinetic energy of the system is conserved; in this case, the kinetic energy consists of translational and rotational forms.

Apply conservation of kinetic
energy to the system:

$$\tfrac{1}{2}m_d v_{di}^2 = \tfrac{1}{2}m_d v_{df}^2 + \tfrac{1}{2}m_s v_s^2 + \tfrac{1}{2}I\omega^2$$

Substitute the known values:

$$\tfrac{1}{2}(2.0\text{ kg})(3.0\text{ m/s})^2 = \tfrac{1}{2}(2.0\text{ kg})v_{df}^2 + \tfrac{1}{2}(1.0\text{ kg})v_s^2 + \tfrac{1}{2}(1.33\text{ kg}\cdot\text{m}^2)\omega^2$$

$$(3)\quad 18\text{ m}^2/\text{s}^2 = 2.0v_{df}^2 + v_s^2 + (1.33\text{ m}^2)\omega^2$$

Solving Equations (1), (2), and (3) simultaneously, we find that $v_d =$ 2.3 m/s, $v_s =$ 1.3 m/s, and $\omega =$ −2.0 rad/s.

Finalize   These values seem reasonable. The disk is moving more slowly after the collision than it was before the collision, and the stick has a small translational speed. Table 11.1 summarizes the initial and final values of variables for the disk and the stick, and verifies the conservation of linear momentum, angular momentum, and kinetic energy for the system.

TABLE 11.1

Comparison of Values in Example 11.9 Before and After the Collision

	v (m/s)	ω (rad/s)	p (kg·m/s)	L (kg·m²/s)	K_{trans} (J)	K_{rot} (J)
Before						
Disk	3.0	—	6.0	−12	9.0	—
Stick	0	0	0	0	0	0
Total for system	—	—	6.0	−12	9.0	0
After						
Disk	2.3	—	4.7	−9.3	5.4	—
Stick	1.3	−2.0	1.3	−2.7	0.9	2.7
Total for system	—	—	6.0	−12	6.3	2.7

Note: Linear momentum, angular momentum, and total kinetic energy of the system are all conserved.

What If?   What if the collision between the disk and the stick is perfectly inelastic? How does that change the analysis?

Answer   In this case, the disk adheres to the end of the stick upon collision.

Alter the conservation of linear momentum principle
leading to Equation (1):

$$m_d v_{di} = (m_d + m_s)v_{\text{CM}}$$

$$(2.0\text{ kg})(3.0\text{ m/s}) = (2.0\text{ kg} + 1.0\text{ kg})v_{\text{CM}}$$

$$v_{\text{CM}} = 2.0\text{ m/s}$$

Choose the center of the stick as the origin and find
the y position of the center of mass along the vertical
stick:

$$y_{\text{CM}} = \frac{(2.0\text{ kg})(2.0\text{ m}) + (1.0\text{ kg})(0)}{(2.0\text{ kg} + 1.0\text{ kg})} = 1.33\text{ m}$$

Therefore, the center of mass of the system is 2.0 m − 1.33 m = 0.67 m from the upper end of the stick.

Alter the conservation of angular momentum principle leading to Equation (2), evaluating angular momenta around an axis passing through the center of mass of the system:

$$-rm_d v_{di} = I_d \omega + I_s \omega$$

$$(4) \quad -(0.67 \text{ m}) m_d v_{di} = [m_d (0.67 \text{ m})^2] \omega + I_s \omega$$

Find the moment of inertia of the stick around the center of mass *of the system* from the parallel-axis theorem:

$$I_s = I_{CM} + MD^2$$

$$= 1.33 \text{ kg} \cdot \text{m}^2 + (1.0 \text{ kg})(1.33 \text{ m})^2 = 3.1 \text{ kg} \cdot \text{m}^2$$

Use these results in Equation (4):

$$-(0.67 \text{ m})(2.0 \text{ kg})(3.0 \text{ m/s}) = [(2.0 \text{ kg})(0.67 \text{ m})^2]\omega + (3.1 \text{ kg} \cdot \text{m}^2)\omega$$

$$-4.0 \text{ kg} \cdot \text{m}^2/\text{s} = (4.0 \text{ kg} \cdot \text{m}^2)\omega$$

$$\omega = \frac{-4.0 \text{ kg} \cdot \text{m}^2/\text{s}}{4.0 \text{ kg} \cdot \text{m}^2} = -1.0 \text{ rad/s}$$

Evaluating the total kinetic energy of the system after the collision shows that it is less than that before the collision because kinetic energy is not conserved in an inelastic collision.

11.5 The Motion of Gyroscopes and Tops

An unusual and fascinating type of motion you have probably observed is that of a top spinning about its axis of symmetry as shown in Figure 11.13a. If the top spins rapidly, the symmetry axis rotates about the z axis, sweeping out a cone (see Fig. 11.13b). The motion of the symmetry axis about the vertical—known as **precessional motion**—is usually slow relative to the spinning motion of the top.

It is quite natural to wonder why the top does not fall over. Because the center of mass is not directly above the pivot point O, a net torque is acting on the top about an axis passing through O, a torque resulting from the gravitational force $M\vec{g}$. The top would certainly fall over if it were not spinning. Because it is spinning, however, it has an angular momentum $\vec{L}$ directed along its symmetry axis. We shall show that this symmetry axis moves about the z axis (precessional motion occurs) because the torque produces a change in the *direction* of the symmetry axis. This illustration is an excellent example of the importance of the directional nature of angular momentum.

The essential features of precessional motion can be illustrated by considering the simple gyroscope shown in Figure 11.14a. The two forces acting on the gyroscope are the downward gravitational force $M\vec{g}$ and the normal force $\vec{n}$ acting upward at the pivot point O. The normal force produces no torque about an axis passing through the pivot because its moment arm through that point is zero. The gravitational force, however, produces a torque $\vec{\tau} = \vec{r} \times M\vec{g}$ about an axis passing through O, where the direction of $\vec{\tau}$ is perpendicular to the plane formed by $\vec{r}$ and $M\vec{g}$. By necessity, the vector $\vec{\tau}$ lies in a horizontal xy plane perpendicular to the angular momentum vector. The net torque and angular momentum of the gyroscope are related through Equation 11.13:

$$\vec{\tau} = \frac{d\vec{L}}{dt}$$

This expression shows that in the infinitesimal time interval dt, the nonzero torque produces a change in angular momentum $d\vec{L}$, a change that is in the same direction as $\vec{\tau}$. Therefore, like the torque vector, $d\vec{L}$ must also be perpendicular to $\vec{L}$. Figure 11.14b illustrates the resulting precessional motion of the symmetry axis of the gyroscope. In a time interval dt, the change in angular momentum is $d\vec{L} = \vec{L}_f - \vec{L}_i = \vec{\tau}\,dt$. Because $d\vec{L}$ is perpendicular to $\vec{L}$, the magnitude of $\vec{L}$ does not change ($|\vec{L}_i| = |\vec{L}_f|$). Rather, what is changing is the *direction* of $\vec{L}$. Because the

◀ Precessional motion

Figure 11.13 Precessional motion of a top spinning about its symmetry axis. (a) The only external forces acting on the top are the normal force $\vec{n}$ and the gravitational force $M\vec{g}$. The direction of the angular momentum $\vec{L}$ is along the axis of symmetry. The right-hand rule indicates that $\vec{\tau} = \vec{r} \times \vec{F} = \vec{r} \times M\vec{g}$ is in the xy plane. (b). The direction of $\Delta\vec{L}$ is parallel to that of $\vec{\tau}$ in (a). Because $\vec{L}_f = \Delta\vec{L} + \vec{L}_i$, the top precesses about the z axis.

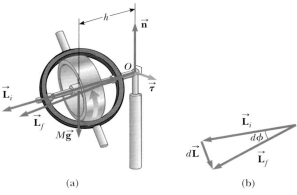

(a)   (b)

Figure 11.14   (a) The motion of a simple gyroscope pivoted a distance h from its center of mass. The gravitational force $M\vec{g}$ produces a torque about the pivot, and this torque is perpendicular to the axle. (b) Overhead view of the initial and final angular momentum vectors. The torque results in a change in angular momentum $d\vec{L}$ in a direction perpendicular to the axle. The axle sweeps out an angle $d\phi$ in a time interval dt.

change in angular momentum $d\vec{L}$ is in the direction of $\vec{\tau}$, which lies in the xy plane, the gyroscope undergoes precessional motion.

To simplify the description of the system, we assume that the total angular momentum of the precessing wheel is the sum of the angular momentum $I\vec{\omega}$ due to the spinning and the angular momentum due to the motion of the center of mass about the pivot. In our treatment, we shall neglect the contribution from the center-of-mass motion and take the total angular momentum to be simply $I\vec{\omega}$. In practice, this approximation is good if $\vec{\omega}$ is made very large.

The vector diagram in Figure 11.14b shows that in the time interval dt, the angular momentum vector rotates through an angle $d\phi$, which is also the angle through which the axle rotates. From the vector triangle formed by the vectors $\vec{L}_i$, $\vec{L}_f$, and $d\vec{L}$, we see that

$$\sin(d\phi) \approx d\phi = \frac{dL}{L} = \frac{\tau\, dt}{L} = \frac{(Mgh)\, dt}{L}$$

where we have used that, for small values of any angle θ, $\sin\theta \approx \theta$. Dividing through by dt and using the relationship $L = I\omega$, we find that the rate at which the axle rotates about the vertical axis is

$$\omega_p = \frac{d\phi}{dt} = \frac{Mgh}{I\omega} \qquad\qquad \textbf{(11.20)}$$

The angular speed ω_p is called the **precessional frequency.** This result is valid only when $\omega_p \ll \omega$. Otherwise, a much more complicated motion is involved. As you can see from Equation 11.20, the condition $\omega_p \ll \omega$ is met when ω is large, that is, when the wheel spins rapidly. Furthermore, notice that the precessional frequency decreases as ω increases, that is, as the wheel spins faster about its axis of symmetry.

As an example of the usefulness of gyroscopes, suppose you are in a spacecraft in deep space and you need to alter your trajectory. To fire the engines in the correct direction, you need to turn the spacecraft around. How, though, do you turn a spacecraft around in empty space? One way is to have small rocket engines that fire perpendicularly out the side of the spacecraft, providing a torque around its center of mass. Such a setup is desirable, and many spacecraft have such rockets.

Let us consider another method, however, that is related to angular momentum and does not require the consumption of rocket fuel. Suppose the spacecraft carries a gyroscope that is not rotating as in Figure 11.15a. In this case, the angular momentum of the spacecraft about its center of mass is zero. Suppose the gyroscope is set into rotation, giving the gyroscope a nonzero angular momentum. There is no external torque on the isolated system (spacecraft and gyroscope), so the angular momentum of this system must remain zero according to the principle of conservation of angular momentum. This principle can be satisfied if the

(a)

Spacecraft rotates clockwise

Gyroscope rotates counterclockwise

(b)

Figure 11.15   (a) A spacecraft carries a gyroscope that is not spinning. (b) When the gyroscope is set into rotation, the spacecraft turns the other way so that the angular momentum of the system is conserved.

spacecraft rotates in the direction opposite that of the gyroscope so that the angular momentum vectors of the gyroscope and the spacecraft cancel, resulting in no angular momentum of the system. The result of rotating the gyroscope, as in Figure 11.15b, is that the spacecraft turns around! By including three gyroscopes with mutually perpendicular axles, any desired rotation in space can be achieved.

This effect created an undesirable situation with the *Voyager 2* spacecraft during its flight. The spacecraft carried a tape recorder whose reels rotated at high speeds. Each time the tape recorder was turned on, the reels acted as gyroscopes and the spacecraft started an undesirable rotation in the opposite direction. This rotation had to be counteracted by Mission Control by using the sideward-firing jets to stop the rotation!

Summary

ThomsonNOW™ Sign in at **www.thomsonedu.com** and go to ThomsonNOW to take a practice test for this chapter.

DEFINITIONS

Given two vectors $\vec{\mathbf{A}}$ and $\vec{\mathbf{B}}$, the cross product $\vec{\mathbf{A}} \times \vec{\mathbf{B}}$ is a vector $\vec{\mathbf{C}}$ having a magnitude

$$C = AB \sin \theta \qquad (11.3)$$

where θ is the angle between $\vec{\mathbf{A}}$ and $\vec{\mathbf{B}}$. The direction of the vector $\vec{\mathbf{C}} = \vec{\mathbf{A}} \times \vec{\mathbf{B}}$ is perpendicular to the plane formed by $\vec{\mathbf{A}}$ and $\vec{\mathbf{B}}$, and this direction is determined by the right-hand rule.

The **torque** $\vec{\boldsymbol{\tau}}$ due to a force $\vec{\mathbf{F}}$ about an axis through the origin in an inertial frame is defined to be

$$\vec{\boldsymbol{\tau}} \equiv \vec{\mathbf{r}} \times \vec{\mathbf{F}} \qquad (11.1)$$

The **angular momentum** $\vec{\mathbf{L}}$ of a particle having linear momentum $\vec{\mathbf{p}} = m\vec{\mathbf{v}}$ about an axis through the origin is

$$\vec{\mathbf{L}} \equiv \vec{\mathbf{r}} \times \vec{\mathbf{p}} \qquad (11.10)$$

where $\vec{\mathbf{r}}$ is the vector position of the particle relative to the origin.

CONCEPTS AND PRINCIPLES

The z component of angular momentum of a rigid object rotating about a fixed z axis is

$$L_z = I\omega \qquad (11.14)$$

where I is the moment of inertia of the object about the axis of rotation and ω is its angular speed.

ANALYSIS MODELS FOR PROBLEM SOLVING

The rate of change in the angular momentum of the system is equal to the net external torque on the system.

Nonisolated System (Angular Momentum). If a system interacts with its environment in the sense that there is an external torque on the system, the net external torque acting on a system is equal to the time rate of change of its angular momentum:

$$\sum \vec{\boldsymbol{\tau}}_{\text{ext}} = \frac{d\vec{\mathbf{L}}_{\text{tot}}}{dt} \qquad (11.13)$$

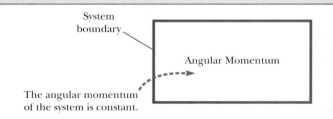

The angular momentum of the system is constant.

Isolated System (Angular Momentum). If a system experiences no external torque from the environment, the total angular momentum of the system is conserved:

$$\vec{\mathbf{L}}_i = \vec{\mathbf{L}}_f \qquad (11.18)$$

Applying this law of conservation of angular momentum to a system whose moment of inertia changes gives

$$I_i \omega_i = I_f \omega_f = \text{constant} \qquad (11.19)$$

Questions

☐ denotes answer available in *Student Solutions Manual/Study Guide;* **O** denotes objective question

1. **O** Is it possible to calculate the torque acting on a rigid object without specifying an axis of rotation? Is the torque independent of the location of the axis of rotation?

2. **O** Vector $\vec{A}$ is in the negative y direction and vector $\vec{B}$ is in the negative x direction. **(i)** What is the direction of $\vec{A} \times \vec{B}$? (a) y (b) $-y$ (c) x (d) $-x$ (e) z (f) $-z$ (g) no direction because it is zero (h) no direction because it is a scalar **(ii)** What is the direction of $\vec{B} \times \vec{A}$? Choose from the same possibilities (a) through (h).

3. **O** Let us name three perpendicular directions as right, up, and toward you, as you might name them when you are facing a television screen that lies in a vertical plane. Unit vectors for these directions are $\hat{r}$, $\hat{u}$, and $\hat{t}$, respectively. For the quantity $(-3\hat{u} \text{ m} \times 2\hat{t} \text{ N})$, identify the magnitude, unit, and direction, if any. **(i)** The magnitude is (a) 6 (b) 3 (c) 2 (d) 0 **(ii)** The unit is (a) newton meters (b) newtons (c) meters (d) no unit **(iii)** The direction is (a) down (b) toward you (c) no direction (d) up (e) away from you (f) left (g) right

4. **O** Let the four horizontal compass directions north, east, south, and west be represented by units vectors $\hat{n}$, $\hat{e}$, $\hat{s}$, and $\hat{w}$, respectively. Vertically up and down are represented as $\hat{u}$ and $\hat{d}$. Let us also identify unit vectors that are halfway between these directions, such as $\widehat{ne}$ for northeast. Rank the magnitudes of the following cross products from the largest to the smallest. If any are equal in magnitude, or equal to zero, show that in your ranking. (a) $\hat{n} \times \hat{n}$ (b) $\hat{w} \times \widehat{ne}$ (c) $\hat{u} \times \widehat{ne}$ (d) $\hat{n} \times \widehat{nw}$ (e) $\hat{n} \times \hat{e}$

5. If the torque acting on a particle about a certain origin is zero, what can you say about its angular momentum about that origin?

6. A ball is thrown in such a way that it does not spin about its own axis. Does this statement imply that the angular momentum is zero about an arbitrary origin? Explain.

7. **O** Compound terms can sometimes be confusing. For example, an ant lion is not a kind of lion but rather a different kind of insect. (a) Is rotational kinetic energy a kind of kinetic energy? (b) Is torque a kind of force? (c) Is angular momentum a kind of momentum?

8. Why does a long pole help a tightrope walker stay balanced?

9. **O** An ice skater starts a spin with her arms stretched out to the sides. She balances on the tip of one skate to turn without friction. She then pulls her arms in so that her moment of inertia decreases by a factor of two. In the process of her doing so, what happens to her kinetic energy? (a) It increases by a factor of four. (b) It increases by a factor of two. (c) It remains constant. (d) It decreases by a factor of two. (e) It decreases by a factor of four. (f) It is zero because her center of mass is stationary. (g) It undergoes a change by an amount that obviously depends on how fast the skater pulls her arms in.

10. In a tape recorder, the tape is pulled past the read-and-write heads at a constant speed by the drive mechanism. Consider the reel from which the tape is pulled. As the tape is pulled from it, the radius of the roll of remaining tape decreases. How does the torque on the reel change with time? How does the angular speed of the reel change in time? If the drive mechanism is switched on so that the tape is suddenly jerked with a large force, is the tape more likely to break when it is being pulled from a nearly full reel or from a nearly empty reel?

11. **O** A pet mouse sleeps near the eastern edge of a stationary, horizontal turntable that is supported by a frictionless, vertical axle through its center. The mouse wakes up and starts to walk north on the turntable. **(i)** As it takes its first steps, what is the mouse's displacement relative to the stationary ground below? (A) north (B) south (C) none **(ii)** In this process, the spot on the turntable where the mouse had been snoozing undergoes what displacement relative to the ground below? (A) north (B) south (C) none **(iii)** In this process for the mouse-turntable system, is mechanical energy conserved? **(iv)** Is momentum conserved? **(v)** Is angular momentum conserved?

12. **O** An employee party for a very successful company features a merry-go-round with real animals. The horizontal turntable has no motor, but is turning freely on a vertical, frictionless axle through its center. Two ponies of equal mass are tethered at diametrically opposite points on the rim. Children untie them, and the placid beasts simultaneously start plodding toward each other across the turntable. **(i)** As they walk, what happens to the angular speed of the carousel? (a) It increases. (b) It stays constant. (c) It decreases. Consider the ponies–turntable system in this process. **(ii)** Is its mechanical energy conserved? **(iii)** Is its momentum conserved? **(iv)** Is its angular momentum conserved?

13. **O** A horizontal disk with moment of inertia I_1 rotates with angular velocity ω_0 on a vertical, frictionless axle. A second horizontal disk, having moment of inertia I_2 and initially not rotating, drops onto the first. Because of friction between the surfaces of the disks, the two reach the same angular velocity. What is it? (a) $I_1\omega_0/I_2$ (b) $I_2\omega_0/I_1$ (c) $I_1\omega_0/(I_1 + I_2)$ (d) $I_2\omega_0/(I_1 + I_2)$ (e) $(I_1 + I_2)\omega_0/I_1$ (f) $(I_1 + I_2)\omega_0/I_2$

14. In some motorcycle races, the riders drive over small hills and the motorcycle becomes airborne for a short time interval. If the motorcycle racer keeps the throttle open while leaving the hill and going into the air, the motorcycle tends to nose upward. Why?

15. If global warming continues over the next one hundred years, it is likely that some polar ice will melt and the water will be distributed closer to the Equator. How would that change the moment of inertia of the Earth? Would the duration of the day (one revolution) increase or decrease?

16. A scientist arriving at a hotel asks a bellhop to carry a heavy suitcase. When the bellhop rounds a corner, the suitcase suddenly swings away from him for some unknown reason. The alarmed bellhop drops the suitcase and runs away. What might be in the suitcase?

Problems

WebAssign The Problems from this chapter may be assigned online in WebAssign.

ThomsonNOW™ Sign in at **www.thomsonedu.com** and go to ThomsonNOW to assess your understanding of this chapter's topics with additional quizzing and conceptual questions.

1, 2, 3 denotes straightforward, intermediate, challenging; □ denotes full solution available in *Student Solutions Manual/Study Guide*; ▲ denotes coached solution with hints available at **www.thomsonedu.com;** denotes developing symbolic reasoning; ● denotes asking for qualitative reasoning; ⬚ denotes computer useful in solving problem

Section 11.1 The Vector Product and Torque

1. Given $\vec{\mathbf{M}} = 6\hat{\mathbf{i}} + 2\hat{\mathbf{j}} - \hat{\mathbf{k}}$ and $\vec{\mathbf{N}} = 2\hat{\mathbf{i}} - \hat{\mathbf{j}} - 3\hat{\mathbf{k}}$, calculate the vector product $\vec{\mathbf{M}} \times \vec{\mathbf{N}}$.

2. The vectors 42.0 cm at 15.0° and 23.0 cm at 65.0° both start from the origin. Both angles are measured counterclockwise from the *x* axis. The vectors form two sides of a parallelogram. (a) Find the area of the parallelogram. (b) Find the length of its longer diagonal.

3. ▲ Two vectors are given by $\vec{\mathbf{A}} = -3\hat{\mathbf{i}} + 4\hat{\mathbf{j}}$ and $\vec{\mathbf{B}} = 2\hat{\mathbf{i}} + 3\hat{\mathbf{j}}$. Find (a) $\vec{\mathbf{A}} \times \vec{\mathbf{B}}$ and (b) the angle between $\vec{\mathbf{A}}$ and $\vec{\mathbf{B}}$.

4. Two vectors are given by $\vec{\mathbf{A}} = -3\hat{\mathbf{i}} + 7\hat{\mathbf{j}} - 4\hat{\mathbf{k}}$ and $\vec{\mathbf{B}} = 6\hat{\mathbf{i}} - 10\hat{\mathbf{j}} + 9\hat{\mathbf{k}}$. Evaluate the quantities (a) $\cos^{-1}[\vec{\mathbf{A}} \cdot \vec{\mathbf{B}}/AB]$ and (b) $\sin^{-1}[|\vec{\mathbf{A}} \times \vec{\mathbf{B}}|/AB]$. (c) Which give(s) the angle between the vectors?

5. The wind exerts on a flower the force 0.785 N horizontally to the east. The stem of the flower is 0.450 m long and tilts toward the east, making an angle of 14.0° with the vertical. Find the vector torque of the wind force about the base of the stem.

6. ● A student claims that he has found a vector $\vec{\mathbf{A}}$ such that $(2\hat{\mathbf{i}} - 3\hat{\mathbf{j}} + 4\hat{\mathbf{k}}) \times \vec{\mathbf{A}} = (4\hat{\mathbf{i}} + 3\hat{\mathbf{j}} - \hat{\mathbf{k}})$. Do you believe this claim? Explain.

7. Assume $|\vec{\mathbf{A}} \times \vec{\mathbf{B}}| = \vec{\mathbf{A}} \cdot \vec{\mathbf{B}}$. What is the angle between $\vec{\mathbf{A}}$ and $\vec{\mathbf{B}}$?

8. ● A particle is located at the vector position $\vec{\mathbf{r}} = (4.00\hat{\mathbf{i}} + 6.00\hat{\mathbf{j}})$ m and a force exerted on it is given by $\vec{\mathbf{F}} = (3.00\hat{\mathbf{i}} + 2.00\hat{\mathbf{j}})$ N. (a) What is the torque acting on the particle about the origin? (b) Can there be another point about which the torque caused by this force on this particle will be in the opposite direction and half as large in magnitude? Can there be more than one such point? Can such a point lie on the *y* axis? Can more than one such point lie on the *y* axis? Determine the position vector of such a point.

9. Two forces $\vec{\mathbf{F}}_1$ and $\vec{\mathbf{F}}_2$ act along the two sides of an equilateral triangle as shown in Figure P11.9. Point *O* is the intersection of the altitudes of the triangle. Find a third force $\vec{\mathbf{F}}_3$ to be applied at *B* and along *BC* that will make the total torque zero about the point *O*. **What If?** Will the total torque change if $\vec{\mathbf{F}}_3$ is applied not at *B* but at any other point along *BC*?

Figure P11.9

10. Use the definition of the vector product and the definitions of the unit vectors $\hat{\mathbf{i}}$, $\hat{\mathbf{j}}$, and $\hat{\mathbf{k}}$ to prove Equations 11.7. You may assume the *x* axis points to the right, the *y* axis up, and the *z* axis horizontally toward you (not away from you). This choice is said to make the coordinate system a *right-handed* system.

Section 11.2 Angular Momentum: The Nonisolated System

11. A light, rigid rod 1.00 m in length joins two particles, with masses 4.00 kg and 3.00 kg, at its ends. The combination rotates in the *xy* plane about a pivot through the center of the rod (Fig. P11.11). Determine the angular momentum of the system about the origin when the speed of each particle is 5.00 m/s.

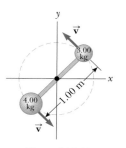

Figure P11.11

12. A 1.50-kg particle moves in the *xy* plane with a velocity of $\vec{\mathbf{v}} = (4.20\hat{\mathbf{i}} - 3.60\hat{\mathbf{j}})$ m/s. Determine the angular momentum of the particle about the origin when its position vector is $\vec{\mathbf{r}} = (1.50\hat{\mathbf{i}} + 2.20\hat{\mathbf{j}})$ m.

13. ▲ The position vector of a particle of mass 2.00 kg as a function of time is given by $\vec{\mathbf{r}} = (6.00\hat{\mathbf{i}} + 5.00t\hat{\mathbf{j}})$ m. Determine the angular momentum of the particle about the origin as a function of time.

14. A conical pendulum consists of a bob of mass *m* in motion in a circular path in a horizontal plane as shown in Figure P11.14. During the motion, the supporting wire of length ℓ maintains the constant angle θ with the vertical. Show that the magnitude of the angular momentum of the bob about the circle's center is

$$L = \left(\frac{m^2 g \ell^3 \sin^4 \theta}{\cos \theta} \right)^{1/2}$$

Figure P11.14

15. A particle of mass m moves in a circle of radius R at a constant speed v as shown in Figure P11.15. The motion begins at point Q at time $t = 0$. Determine the angular momentum of the particle about point P as a function of time.

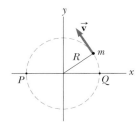

Figure P11.15 Problems 15 and 30.

16. A 4.00-kg counterweight is attached to a light cord that is wound around a reel (refer to Fig. 10.19). The reel is a uniform solid cylinder of radius 8.00 cm and mass 2.00 kg. (a) What is the net torque on the system about the point O? (b) When the counterweight has a speed v, the reel has an angular speed $\omega = v/R$. Determine the total angular momentum of the system about O. (c) Using that $\vec{\tau} = d\vec{L}/dt$ and your result from part (b), calculate the acceleration of the counterweight.

17. ● A particle of mass m is shot with an initial velocity $\vec{v}_i$ making an angle θ with the horizontal as shown in Figure P11.17. The particle moves in the gravitational field of the Earth. Find the angular momentum of the particle about the origin when the particle is (a) at the origin, (b) at the highest point of its trajectory, and (c) just before it hits the ground. (d) What torque causes its angular momentum to change?

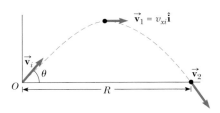

Figure P11.17

18. Heading straight toward the summit of Pikes Peak, an airplane of mass 12 000 kg flies over the plains of Kansas at nearly constant altitude 4.30 km with constant velocity 175 m/s west. (a) What is the airplane's vector angular momentum relative to a wheat farmer on the ground directly below the airplane? (b) Does this value change as the airplane continues its motion along a straight line? (c) **What If?** What is its angular momentum relative to the summit of Pikes Peak?

19. ● A ball having mass m is fastened at the end of a flagpole that is connected to the side of a tall building at point P shown in Figure P11.19. The length of the flagpole is ℓ, and it makes an angle θ with the x axis. The ball becomes loose and starts to fall with acceleration $-g\hat{j}$. (a) Determine the angular momentum of the ball about point P as a function of time. (b) For what physical reason does the angular momentum change? (c) What is its rate of change?

Figure P11.19

20. ● A 5.00-kg particle starts from the origin at time zero. Its velocity as a function of time is given by

$$\vec{v} = (6 \text{ m/s}^3)t^2\hat{i} + (2 \text{ m/s}^2)t\hat{j}$$

(a) Find its position as a function of time. (b) Describe its motion qualitatively. (c) Find its acceleration as a function of time. (d) Find the net force exerted on the particle as a function of time. (e) Find the net torque about the origin exerted on the particle as a function of time. (f) Find the angular momentum of the particle as a function of time. (g) Find the kinetic energy of the particle as a function of time. (h) Find the power injected into the particle as a function of time.

Section 11.3 Angular Momentum of a Rotating Rigid Object

21. Show that the kinetic energy of an object rotating about a fixed axis with angular momentum $L = I\omega$ can be written as $K = L^2/2I$.

22. A uniform solid sphere of radius 0.500 m and mass 15.0 kg turns counterclockwise about a vertical axis through its center. Find its vector angular momentum when its angular speed is 3.00 rad/s.

23. A uniform solid disk of mass 3.00 kg and radius 0.200 m rotates about a fixed axis perpendicular to its face with angular frequency 6.00 rad/s. Calculate the angular momentum of the disk when the axis of rotation (a) passes through its center of mass and (b) passes through a point midway between the center and the rim.

24. ● (a) Model the Earth as a uniform sphere. Calculate the angular momentum of the Earth due to its spinning motion about its axis. (b) Calculate the angular momentum of the Earth due to its orbital motion about the Sun. (c) Are the two quantities of angular momentum nearly equal or quite different? Which is larger in magnitude? By what factor?

25. A particle of mass 0.400 kg is attached to the 100-cm mark of a meterstick of mass 0.100 kg. The meterstick rotates on a horizontal, frictionless table with an angular speed of 4.00 rad/s. Calculate the angular momentum of the system when the meterstick is pivoted about an axis (a) perpendicular to the table through the 50.0-cm mark and (b) perpendicular to the table through the 0-cm mark.

26. Big Ben (Fig. P10.42), the Parliament tower clock in London, has hour and minute hands with lengths of 2.70 m and 4.50 m and masses of 60.0 kg and 100 kg, respectively. Calculate the total angular momentum of these hands about the center point. Treat the hands as long, thin, uniform rods.

2 = intermediate;　3 = challenging;　□ = SSM/SG;　▲ = ThomsonNOW;　▨ = symbolic reasoning;　● = qualitative reasoning

27. A space station is constructed in the shape of a hollow ring of mass 5.00×10^4 kg. Members of the crew walk on a deck formed by the inner surface of the outer cylindrical wall of the ring with radius 100 m. At rest when constructed, the ring is set rotating about its axis so that the people inside experience an effective free-fall acceleration equal to g. (Fig. P11.27 shows the ring together with some other parts that make a negligible contribution to the total moment of inertia.) The rotation is achieved by firing two small rockets attached tangentially to opposite points on the outside of the ring. (a) What angular momentum does the space station acquire? (b) For what time interval must the rockets be fired if each exerts a thrust of 125 N? (c) Prove that the total torque on the ring, multiplied by the time interval found in part (b), is equal to the change in angular momentum, found in part (a). This equality represents the *angular impulse–angular momentum theorem.*

Figure P11.27 Problems 27 and 38.

28. The distance between the centers of the wheels of a motorcycle is 155 cm. The center of mass of the motorcycle, including the biker, is 88.0 cm above the ground and halfway between the wheels. Assume the mass of each wheel is small compared with the body of the motorcycle. The engine drives the rear wheel only. What horizontal acceleration of the motorcycle will make the front wheel rise off the ground?

Section 11.4 The Isolated System: Conservation of Angular Momentum

29. A cylinder with moment of inertia I_1 rotates about a vertical, frictionless axle with angular speed ω_i. A second cylinder, this one having moment of inertia I_2 and initially not rotating, drops onto the first cylinder (Fig. P11.29). Because of friction between the surfaces, the two eventually reach the same angular speed ω_f. (a) Calculate ω_f. (b) Show that the kinetic energy of the system decreases in this interaction, and calculate the ratio of the final to the initial rotational energy.

Figure P11.29

30. ● Figure P11.15 represents a small, flat puck with mass $m = 2.40$ kg sliding on a frictionless, horizontal surface. It is held in a circular orbit about a fixed axis by a rod with negligible mass and length $R = 1.50$ m, pivoted at one end. Initially, the puck has a speed of $v = 5.00$ m/s. A 1.30-kg ball of putty is dropped vertically onto the puck from a small distance above it and immediately sticks to the puck. (a) What is the new period of rotation? (b) Is angular momentum of the puck-putty system about the axis of rotation conserved in this process? (c) Is momentum of the system conserved in the process of the putty sticking to the puck? (d) Is mechanical energy of the system conserved in the process?

31. ● A uniform cylindrical turntable of radius 1.90 m and mass 30.0 kg rotates counterclockwise in a horizontal plane with an initial angular speed of 4π rad/s. The fixed turntable bearing is frictionless. A lump of clay of mass 2.25 kg and negligible size is dropped onto the turntable from a small distance above it and immediately sticks to the turntable at a point 1.80 m to the east of the axis. (a) Find the final angular speed of the clay and turntable. (b) Is mechanical energy of the turntable-clay system conserved in this process? Explain and use numerical results to verify your answer. (c) Is momentum of the system conserved in this process? Explain your answer.

32. A student sits on a freely rotating stool holding two dumbbells, each of mass 3.00 kg (Fig. P11.32). When the student's arms are extended horizontally (Fig. P11.32a), the dumbbells are 1.00 m from the axis of rotation and the student rotates with an angular speed of 0.750 rad/s. The moment of inertia of the student plus stool is 3.00 kg·m² and is assumed to be constant. The student pulls the dumbbells inward horizontally to a position 0.300 m from the rotation axis (Fig. P11.32b). (a) Find the new angular speed of the student. (b) Find the kinetic energy of the rotating system before and after he pulls the dumbbells inward.

Figure P11.32

33. A playground merry-go-round of radius $R = 2.00$ m has a moment of inertia $I = 250$ kg·m² and is rotating at 10.0 rev/min about a frictionless vertical axle. Facing the axle, a 25.0-kg child hops onto the merry-go-round and manages to sit down on the edge. What is the new angular speed of the merry-go-round?

34. ● A uniform rod of mass 300 g and length 50.0 cm rotates in a horizontal plane about a fixed, vertical, frictionless pin through its center. Two small, dense beads, each of mass m, are mounted on the rod so that they can slide without friction along its length. Initially, the beads are held by catches at positions 10.0 cm on each side of the center, and the system is rotating at an angular speed of 36.0 rad/s. The catches are released simultaneously, and the beads slide outward along the rod. (a) Find the angular speed ω_f of the system at the instant the beads slide off the ends of the rod as it depends on m. (b) What are the maximum and minimum possible values for ω_f and the values of m to which they correspond? Describe the shape of a graph of ω_f versus m.

35. ● ▲ A 60.0-kg woman stands at the western rim of a horizontal turntable having a moment of inertia of 500 kg·m² and a radius of 2.00 m. The turntable is initially at rest and is free to rotate about a frictionless, vertical axle through its center. The woman then starts walking around the rim clockwise (as viewed from above the system) at a constant speed of 1.50 m/s relative to the Earth. (a) Consider the woman-turntable system as motion begins. Is mechanical energy of the system conserved? Is momentum of the system conserved? Is angular momentum of the system conserved? (b) In what direction and with what angular speed does the turntable rotate? (c) How much chemical energy does the woman's body convert into mechanical energy as the woman sets herself and the turntable into motion?

36. A puck of mass 80.0 g and radius 4.00 cm glides across an air table at a speed of 1.50 m/s as shown in Figure P11.36a. It makes a glancing collision with a second puck of radius 6.00 cm and mass 120 g (initially at rest) such that their rims just touch. Because their rims are coated with instant-acting glue, the pucks stick together and spin after the collision (Fig. P11.36b). (a) What is the angular momentum of the system relative to the center of mass? (b) What is the angular speed about the center of mass?

1.50 m/s

(a)   (b)

Figure P11.36

37. A wooden block of mass M resting on a frictionless, horizontal surface is attached to a rigid rod of length ℓ and of negligible mass (Fig. P11.37). The rod is pivoted at the other end. A bullet of mass m traveling parallel to the horizontal surface and perpendicular to the rod with speed v hits the block and becomes embedded in it. (a) What is the angular momentum of the bullet–block system? (b) What fraction of the original kinetic energy is converted into internal energy in the collision?

M ℓ

$\vec{v}$

Figure P11.37

38. A space station shaped like a giant wheel has a radius of 100 m and a moment of inertia of 5.00×10^8 kg·m². A crew of 150 is living on the rim, and the station's rotation causes the crew to experience an apparent free-fall acceleration of g (Fig. P11.27). When 100 people move to the center of the station for a union meeting, the angular speed changes. What apparent free-fall acceleration is experienced by the managers remaining at the rim? Assume the average mass of each inhabitant is 65.0 kg.

39. ● A wad of sticky clay with mass m and velocity $\vec{v}_i$ is fired at a solid cylinder of mass M and radius R (Figure P11.39). The cylinder is initially at rest and is mounted on a fixed horizontal axle that runs through its center of mass. The line of motion of the projectile is perpendicular to the axle and at a distance $d < R$ from the center. (a) Find the angular speed of the system just after the clay strikes and sticks to the surface of the cylinder. (b) Is mechanical energy of the clay-cylinder system conserved in this process? Explain your answer. (c) Is momentum of the clay-cylinder system conserved in this process? Explain your answer.

m $\vec{v}_i$

d

R M

Figure P11.39

40. A thin uniform rectangular signboard hangs vertically above the door of a shop. The sign is hinged to a stationary horizontal rod along its top edge. The mass of the sign is 2.40 kg, and its vertical dimension is 50.0 cm. The sign is swinging without friction, so it is a tempting target for children armed with snowballs. The maximum angular displacement of the sign is 25.0° on both sides of the vertical. At a moment when the sign is vertical and moving to the left, a snowball of mass 400 g, traveling horizontally with a velocity of 160 cm/s to the right, strikes perpendicularly at the lower edge of the sign and sticks there. (a) Calculate the angular speed of the sign immediately before the impact. (b) Calculate its angular speed immediately after the impact. (c) The spattered sign will swing up through what maximum angle?

41. Suppose a meteor of mass 3.00×10^{13} kg, moving at 30.0 km/s relative to the center of the Earth, strikes the Earth. What is the order of magnitude of the maximum possible decrease in the angular speed of the Earth due to this collision? Explain your answer.

Section 11.5 The Motion of Gyroscopes and Tops

42. A spacecraft is in empty space. It carries on board a gyroscope with a moment of inertia of $I_g = 20.0$ kg·m² about the axis of the gyroscope. The moment of inertia of the spacecraft around the same axis is $I_s = 5.00 \times 10^5$ kg·m². Neither the spacecraft nor the gyroscope is originally rotating. The gyroscope can be powered up in a negligible period of time to an angular speed of 100 s^{-1}. If the orientation of the spacecraft is to be changed by 30.0°, for what time interval should the gyroscope be operated?

43. The angular momentum vector of a precessing gyroscope sweeps out a cone as shown in Figure 11.13b. Its angular

speed, called its precessional frequency, is given by $\omega_p = \tau/L$, where τ is the magnitude of the torque on the gyroscope and L is the magnitude of its angular momentum. In the motion called *precession of the equinoxes*, the Earth's axis of rotation precesses about the perpendicular to its orbital plane with a period of 2.58×10^4 yr. Model the Earth as a uniform sphere and calculate the torque on the Earth that is causing this precession.

Additional Problems

44. We have all complained that there aren't enough hours in a day. In an attempt to fix that, suppose all the people in the world line up at the equator, and all start running east at 2.50 m/s relative to the surface of the Earth. By how much does the length of a day increase? Assume the world population to be 7.00×10^9 people with an average mass of 55.0 kg each and the Earth to be a solid homogeneous sphere. In addition, you may use the approximation $1/(1 - x) \approx 1 + x$ for small x.

45. An American football game has been canceled because of bad weather in Cleveland, and two retired players are sliding like children on a frictionless ice-covered parking lot. William "Refrigerator" Perry, mass 162 kg, is gliding to the right at 8.00 m/s, and Doug Flutie, mass 81.0 kg, is gliding to the left at 11.0 m/s along the same line. When they meet, they grab each other and hang on. (a) What is their velocity immediately thereafter? (b) What fraction of their original kinetic energy is still mechanical energy after their collision? The athletes had so much fun that they repeat the collision with the same original velocities, this time moving along parallel lines 1.20 m apart. At closest approach they lock arms and start rotating about their common center of mass. Model the men as particles and their arms as a cord that does not stretch. (c) Find the velocity of their center of mass. (d) Find their angular speed. (e) What fraction of their original kinetic energy is still mechanical energy after they link arms?

46. ● A skateboarder with his board can be modeled as a particle of mass 76.0 kg, located at his center of mass. As shown in Figure P8.37 of Chapter 8, the skateboarder starts from rest in a crouching position at one lip of a half-pipe (point Ⓐ). The half-pipe forms one half of a cylinder of radius 6.80 m with its axis horizontal. On his descent, the skateboarder moves without friction and maintains his crouch so that his center of mass moves through one quarter of a circle of radius 6.30 m. (a) Find his speed at the bottom of the half-pipe (point Ⓑ). (b) Find his angular momentum about the center of curvature. (c) Immediately after passing point Ⓑ, he stands up and raises his arms, lifting his center of gravity from 0.500 m to 0.950 m above the concrete (point Ⓒ). Explain why his angular momentum is constant in this maneuver, whereas his linear momentum and his mechanical energy are not constant. (d) Find his speed immediately after he stands up, when his center of mass is moving in a quarter circle of radius 5.85 m. (e) How much chemical energy in the skateboarder's legs was converted into mechanical energy as he stood up? Next, the skateboarder glides upward with his center of mass moving in a quarter circle of radius 5.85 m. His body is horizontal when he passes point Ⓓ, the far lip of the half-pipe. (f) Find his speed at this location. At last he goes ballistic, twisting around

while his center of mass moves vertically. (g) How high above point Ⓓ does he rise? (h) Over what time interval is he airborne before he touches down, facing downward and again in a crouch, 2.34 m below the level of point Ⓓ? (i) Compare the solution to this problem with the solution to Problem 8.37. Which is more accurate? Why? *Caution:* Do not try this stunt yourself without the required skill and protective equipment, or in a drainage channel to which you do not have legal access.

47. A rigid, massless rod has three particles with equal masses attached to it as shown in Figure P11.47. The rod is free to rotate in a vertical plane about a frictionless axle perpendicular to the rod through the point P and is released from rest in the horizontal position at $t = 0$. Assuming m and d are known, find (a) the moment of inertia of the system (rod plus particles) about the pivot, (b) the torque acting on the system at $t = 0$, (c) the angular acceleration of the system at $t = 0$, (d) the linear acceleration of the particle labeled 3 at $t = 0$, (e) the maximum kinetic energy of the system, (f) the maximum angular speed reached by the rod, (g) the maximum angular momentum of the system, and (h) the maximum speed reached by the particle labeled 2.

Figure P11.47

48. ● A light rope passes over a light, frictionless pulley. One end is fastened to a bunch of bananas of mass M, and a monkey of mass M clings to the other end (Fig. P11.48). The monkey climbs the rope in an attempt to reach the bananas. (a) Treating the system as consisting of the monkey, bananas, rope, and pulley, evaluate the net torque about the pulley axis. (b) Using the results of (a), determine the total angular momentum about the pulley axis and describe the motion of the system. Will the monkey reach the bananas?

Figure P11.48

49. Comet Halley moves about the Sun in an elliptical orbit, with its closest approach to the Sun being about 0.590 AU and its greatest distance 35.0 AU (1 AU = the Earth–Sun distance). The comet's speed at closest approach is 54.0 km/s. What is its speed when it is farthest from the Sun? The angular momentum of the comet about the Sun is conserved because no torque acts on the comet.

The gravitational force exerted by the Sun has zero moment arm.

50. A projectile of mass m moves to the right with a speed v_i (Fig. P11.50a). The projectile strikes and sticks to the end of a stationary rod of mass M, length d, pivoted about a frictionless axle through its center (Fig. P11.50b). (a) Find the angular speed of the system right after the collision. (b) Determine the fractional loss in mechanical energy due to the collision.

Figure P11.50

51. A puck of mass m is attached to a cord passing through a small hole in a frictionless, horizontal surface (Fig. P11.51). The puck is initially orbiting with speed v_i in a circle of radius r_i. The cord is then slowly pulled from below, decreasing the radius of the circle to r. (a) What is the speed of the puck when the radius is r? (b) Find the tension in the cord as a function of r. (c) How much work W is done in moving m from r_i to r? *Note:* The tension depends on r. (d) Obtain numerical values for v, T, and W when $r = 0.100$ m, $m = 50.0$ g, $r_i = 0.300$ m, and $v_i = 1.50$ m/s.

Figure P11.51

52. ● Two children are playing on stools at a restaurant counter. Their feet do not reach the footrests, and the tops of the stools are free to rotate without friction on pedestals fixed to the floor. One of the children catches a tossed ball in a process described by the equation

$(0.730 \text{ kg} \cdot \text{m}^2)(2.40\hat{\mathbf{j}} \text{ rad/s})$

$+ (0.120 \text{ kg})(0.350\hat{\mathbf{i}} \text{ m}) \times (4.30\hat{\mathbf{k}} \text{ m/s})$

$= [0.730 \text{ kg} \cdot \text{m}^2 + (0.120 \text{ kg})(0.350 \text{ m})^2] \vec{\boldsymbol{\omega}}$

(a) Solve the equation for the unknown $\vec{\boldsymbol{\omega}}$. (b) Complete the statement of the problem to which this equation applies. Your statement must include the given numerical information and specification of the unknown to be determined. (c) Could the equation equally well describe the other child throwing the ball? Explain your answer.

53. ▲ Two astronauts (Fig. P11.53), each having a mass of 75.0 kg, are connected by a 10.0-m rope of negligible mass. They are isolated in space, orbiting their center of mass at speeds of 5.00 m/s. Treating the astronauts as par-

ticles, calculate (a) the magnitude of the angular momentum of the system and (b) the rotational energy of the system. By pulling on the rope, one astronaut shortens the distance between them to 5.00 m. (c) What is the new angular momentum of the system? (d) What are the astronauts' new speeds? (e) What is the new rotational energy of the system? (f) How much work does the astronaut do in shortening the rope?

Figure P11.53   Problems 53 and 54.

54. Two astronauts (Fig. P11.53), each having a mass M, are connected by a rope of length d having negligible mass. They are isolated in space, orbiting their center of mass at speeds v. Treating the astronauts as particles, calculate (a) the magnitude of the angular momentum of the system and (b) the rotational energy of the system. By pulling on the rope, one astronaut shortens the distance between them to $d/2$. (c) What is the new angular momentum of the system? (d) What are the astronauts' new speeds? (e) What is the new rotational energy of the system? (f) How much work does the astronaut do in shortening the rope?

55. ● Native people throughout North and South America used a *bola* to hunt for birds and animals. A bola can consist of three stones, each with mass m, at the ends of three light cords, each with length ℓ. The other ends of the cords are tied together to form a Y. The hunter holds one stone and swings the other two stones above her head (Fig. P11.55a). Both stones move together in a horizontal circle of radius 2ℓ with speed v_0. At a moment when the horizontal component of their velocity is directed toward the quarry, the hunter releases the stone in her hand. As the bola flies through the air, the cords quickly take a stable arrangement with constant 120-degree angles between them (Fig. P11.55b). In the vertical direction, the bola is in free fall. Gravitational forces exerted by the Earth make the junction of the cords move with the downward acceleration $\vec{\mathbf{g}}$. You may ignore the vertical motion as you proceed to describe the horizontal motion of the bola. In

(a)   (b)

Figure P11.55

2 = intermediate;   3 = challenging;   □ = SSM/SG;   ▲ = ThomsonNOW;   ▨ = symbolic reasoning;   ● = qualitative reasoning

terms of m, ℓ, and v_0, calculate (a) the magnitude of the momentum, (b) the horizontal speed of the center of mass, (c) the angular momentum about the center of mass, and (d) the angular speed of the bola about its center of mass. Calculate the kinetic energy of the bola (e) at the instant of release and (f) in its stable Y shape. (g) Explain how the conservation laws apply to the bola as its configuration changes. Robert Beichner suggested the idea for this problem.

56. A solid cube of wood of side $2a$ and mass M is resting on a horizontal surface. The cube is constrained to rotate about a fixed axis AB (Fig. P11.56). A bullet of mass m and speed v is shot at the face opposite $ABCD$ at a height of $4a/3$. The bullet becomes embedded in the cube. Find the minimum value of v required to tip the cube so that it falls on face $ABCD$. Assume $m \ll M$.

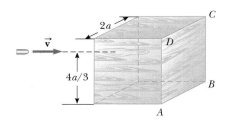

Figure P11.56

57. ● Global warming is a cause for concern because even small changes in the Earth's temperature can have significant consequences. For example, if the Earth's polar ice caps were to melt entirely, the resulting additional water in the oceans would flood many coastal areas. Calculate the resulting change in the duration of one day. Model the polar ice as having mass 2.30×10^{19} kg and forming two flat disks of radius 6.00×10^5 m. Assume the water spreads into an unbroken thin spherical shell after it melts. Is the change in the duration of a day appreciable?

58. A uniform solid disk is set into rotation with an angular speed ω_i about an axis through its center. While still rotating at this speed, the disk is placed into contact with a horizontal surface and released as shown in Figure

P11.58. (a) What is the angular speed of the disk once pure rolling takes place? (b) Find the fractional loss in kinetic energy from the moment the disk is released until pure rolling occurs. *Suggestion:* Consider torques about the center of mass.

Figure P11.58 Problems 58 and 59.

59. Suppose a solid disk of radius R is given an angular speed ω_i about an axis through its center and then lowered to a horizontal surface and released as shown in Figure P11.58. Furthermore, assume the coefficient of friction between disk and surface is μ. (a) Show that the time interval before pure rolling motion occurs is $R\omega_i/3\mu g$. (b) Show that the distance the disk travels before pure rolling occurs is $R^2\omega_i^2/18\mu g$.

60. A solid cube of side $2a$ and mass M is sliding on a frictionless surface with uniform velocity $\vec{v}$ as shown in Figure P11.60a. It hits a small obstacle at the end of the table that causes the cube to tilt as shown in Figure P11.60b. Find the minimum value of $\vec{v}$ such that the cube falls off the table. The moment of inertia of the cube about an axis along one of its edges is $8Ma^2/3$. *Note:* The cube undergoes an inelastic collision at the edge.

(a)   (b)

Figure P11.60

Answers to Quick Quizzes

11.1 (d). Because of the $\sin\theta$ function, $|\vec{A} \times \vec{B}|$ is either equal to or smaller than AB, depending on the angle θ.

11.2 (i), (a). If $\vec{p}$ and $\vec{r}$ are parallel or antiparallel, the angular momentum is zero. For a nonzero angular momentum, the linear momentum vector must be offset from the rotation axis. (ii), (c). The angular momentum is the product of the linear momentum and the perpendicular distance from the rotation axis to the line along which the linear momentum vector lies.

11.3 (b). The hollow sphere has a larger moment of inertia than the solid sphere.

11.4 (i), (a). The diver is an isolated system, so the product $I\omega$ remains constant. Because her moment of inertia decreases, her angular speed increases. (ii), (a). As the moment of inertia of the diver decreases, the angular speed increases by the same factor. For example, if I goes down by a factor of 2, then ω goes up by a factor of 2. The rotational kinetic energy varies as the square of ω. If I is halved, then ω^2 increases by a factor of 4 and the energy increases by a factor of 2.

Balanced Rock in Arches National Park, Utah, is a 3 000 000-kg boulder that has been in stable equilibrium for several millennia. It had a smaller companion nearby, called "Chip Off the Old Block," that fell during the winter of 1975. Balanced Rock appeared in an early scene of the movie *Indiana Jones and the Last Crusade.* We will study the conditions under which an object is in equilibrium in this chapter. (John W. Jewett Jr.)

12 Static Equilibrium and Elasticity

In Chapters 10 and 11, we studied the dynamics of rigid objects. Part of this chapter addresses the conditions under which a rigid object is in equilibrium. The term *equilibrium* implies either that the object is at rest or that its center of mass moves with constant velocity relative to an observer in an inertial reference frame. We deal here only with the former case, in which the object is in *static equilibrium.* Static equilibrium represents a common situation in engineering practice, and the principles it involves are of special interest to civil engineers, architects, and mechanical engineers. If you are an engineering student, you will undoubtedly take an advanced course in statics in the near future.

The last section of this chapter deals with how objects deform under load conditions. An *elastic* object returns to its original shape when the deforming forces are removed. Several elastic constants are defined, each corresponding to a different type of deformation.

12.1 The Rigid Object in Equilibrium

In Chapter 5, we discussed the particle in equilibrium model, in which a particle moves with constant velocity because the net force acting on it is zero. The situation with real (extended) objects is more complex because these objects often cannot

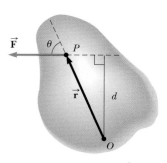

Figure 12.1   A single force $\vec{F}$ acts on a rigid object at the point P.

be modeled as particles. For an extended object to be in equilibrium, a second condition must be satisfied. This second condition involves the net torque acting on the extended object.

Consider a single force $\vec{F}$ acting on a rigid object as shown in Figure 12.1. The effect of the force depends on the location of its point of application P. If $\vec{r}$ is the position vector of this point relative to O, the torque associated with the force $\vec{F}$ about an axis through O is given by Equation 11.1:

$$\vec{\tau} = \vec{r} \times \vec{F}$$

Recall from the discussion of the vector product in Section 11.1 that the vector $\vec{\tau}$ is perpendicular to the plane formed by $\vec{r}$ and $\vec{F}$. You can use the right-hand rule to determine the direction of $\vec{\tau}$ as shown in Figure 11.2. Hence, in Figure 12.1, $\vec{\tau}$ is directed toward you out of the page.

As you can see from Figure 12.1, the tendency of $\vec{F}$ to rotate the object about an axis through O depends on the moment arm d as well as the magnitude of $\vec{F}$. Recall that the magnitude of $\vec{\tau}$ is Fd (see Eq. 10.19). According to Equation 10.21, the net torque on a rigid object causes it to undergo an angular acceleration.

In this discussion, we investigate those rotational situations in which the angular acceleration of a rigid object is zero. Such an object is in **rotational equilibrium**. Because $\Sigma\,\tau = I\alpha$ for rotation about a fixed axis, the necessary condition for rotational equilibrium is that **the net torque about any axis must be zero.** We now have two necessary conditions for equilibrium of an object:

1. The net external force on the object must equal zero:

$$\sum \vec{F} = 0 \tag{12.1}$$

2. The net external torque on the object about *any* axis must be zero:

$$\sum \vec{\tau} = 0 \tag{12.2}$$

These conditions describe the **rigid object in equilibrium** analysis model. The first condition is a statement of translational equilibrium; it states that the translational acceleration of the object's center of mass must be zero when viewed from an inertial reference frame. The second condition is a statement of rotational equilibrium; it states that the angular acceleration about any axis must be zero. In the special case of **static equilibrium,** which is the main subject of this chapter, the object in equilibrium is at rest relative to the observer and so has no translational or angular speed (that is, $v_{CM} = 0$ and $\omega = 0$).

PITFALL PREVENTION 12.1
Zero Torque

Zero net torque does not mean an absence of rotational motion. An object that is rotating at a constant angular speed can be under the influence of a net torque of zero. This possibility is analogous to the translational situation: zero net force does not mean an absence of translational motion.

Quick Quiz 12.1   Consider the object subject to the two forces in Figure 12.2. Choose the correct statement with regard to this situation. (a) The object is in force equilibrium but not torque equilibrium. (b) The object is in torque equilibrium but not force equilibrium. (c) The object is in both force equilibrium and torque equilibrium. (d) The object is in neither force equilibrium nor torque equilibrium.

Figure 12.2   (Quick Quiz 12.1) Two forces of equal magnitude are applied at equal distances from the center of mass of a rigid object.

Quick Quiz 12.2   Consider the object subject to the three forces in Figure 12.3. Choose the correct statement with regard to this situation. (a) The object is in force equilibrium but not torque equilibrium. (b) The object is in torque equilibrium but not force equilibrium. (c) The object is in both force equilibrium and torque equilibrium. (d) The object is in neither force equilibrium nor torque equilibrium.

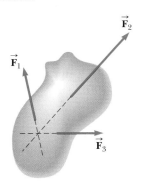

Figure 12.3   (Quick Quiz 12.2) Three forces act on an object. Notice that the lines of action of all three forces pass through a common point.

The two vector expressions given by Equations 12.1 and 12.2 are equivalent, in general, to six scalar equations: three from the first condition for equilibrium and three from the second (corresponding to x, y, and z components). Hence, in a complex system involving several forces acting in various directions, you could be faced with solving a set of equations with many unknowns. Here, we restrict our discussion to situations in which all the forces lie in the xy plane. (Forces whose vector representations are in the same plane are said to be *coplanar*.) With this restriction, we must deal with only three scalar equations. Two come from balancing the forces in the x and y directions. The third comes from the torque equation, namely that the net torque about a perpendicular axis through *any* point in the xy plane must be zero. Hence, the two conditions of the rigid object in equilibrium model provide the equations

$$\sum F_x = 0 \qquad \sum F_y = 0 \qquad \sum \tau_z = 0 \qquad \textbf{(12.3)}$$

where the location of the axis of the torque equation is arbitrary, as we now show.

Regardless of the number of forces that are acting, if an object is in translational equilibrium and the net torque is zero about one axis, the net torque must also be zero about any other axis. The axis can pass through a point that is inside or outside the object's boundaries. Consider an object being acted on by several forces such that the resultant force $\sum \vec{F} = \vec{F}_1 + \vec{F}_2 + \vec{F}_3 + \cdots = 0$. Figure 12.4 describes this situation (for clarity, only four forces are shown). The point of application of $\vec{F}_1$ relative to O is specified by the position vector $\vec{r}_1$. Similarly, the points of application of $\vec{F}_2, \vec{F}_3, \ldots$ are specified by $\vec{r}_2, \vec{r}_3, \ldots$ (not shown). The net torque about an axis through O is

$$\sum \vec{\tau}_O = \vec{r}_1 \times \vec{F}_1 + \vec{r}_2 \times \vec{F}_2 + \vec{r}_3 \times \vec{F}_3 + \cdots$$

Now consider another arbitrary point O' having a position vector $\vec{r}'$ relative to O. The point of application of $\vec{F}_1$ relative to O' is identified by the vector $\vec{r}_1 - \vec{r}'$. Likewise, the point of application of $\vec{F}_2$ relative to O' is $\vec{r}_2 - \vec{r}'$ and so forth. Therefore, the torque about an axis through O' is

$$\sum \vec{\tau}_{O'} = (\vec{r}_1 - \vec{r}') \times \vec{F}_1 + (\vec{r}_2 - \vec{r}') \times \vec{F}_2 + (\vec{r}_3 - \vec{r}') \times \vec{F}_3 + \cdots$$

$$= \vec{r}_1 \times \vec{F}_1 + \vec{r}_2 \times \vec{F}_2 + \vec{r}_3 \times \vec{F}_3 + \cdots - \vec{r}' \times (\vec{F}_1 + \vec{F}_2 + \vec{F}_3 + \cdots)$$

Because the net force is assumed to be zero (given that the object is in translational equilibrium), the last term vanishes, and we see that the torque about an axis through O' is equal to the torque about an axis through O. Hence, **if an object is in translational equilibrium and the net torque is zero about one axis, the net torque must be zero about any other axis.**

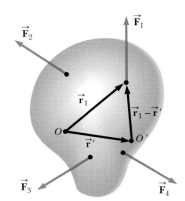

Figure 12.4   Construction showing that if the net torque is zero about an axis through the origin O, it is also zero about an axis through any other origin, such as O'.

Figure 12.5 An object can be divided into many small particles, each having a specific mass and specific coordinates. These particles can be used to locate the center of mass.

12.2 More on the Center of Gravity

Whenever we deal with a rigid object, one of the forces we must consider is the gravitational force acting on it, and we must know the point of application of this force. As we learned in Section 9.5, associated with every object is a special point called its center of gravity. The combination of the various gravitational forces acting on all the various mass elements of the object is equivalent to a single gravitational force acting through this point. Therefore, to compute the torque due to the gravitational force on an object of mass M, we need only consider the force $M\vec{\mathbf{g}}$ acting at the object's center of gravity.

How do we find this special point? As mentioned in Section 9.5, if we assume that $\vec{\mathbf{g}}$ is uniform over the object, the center of gravity of the object coincides with its center of mass. To see why, consider an object of arbitrary shape lying in the xy plane as illustrated in Figure 12.5. Suppose the object is divided into a large number of particles of masses m_1, m_2, m_3, ... having coordinates (x_1, y_1), (x_2, y_2), (x_3, y_3), ... In Equation 9.28, we defined the x coordinate of the center of mass of such an object to be

$$x_{CM} = \frac{m_1 x_1 + m_2 x_2 + m_3 x_3 + \cdots}{m_1 + m_2 + m_3 + \cdots} = \frac{\sum_i m_i x_i}{\sum_i m_i}$$

We use a similar equation to define the y coordinate of the center of mass, replacing each x with its y counterpart.

Let us now examine the situation from another point of view by considering the gravitational force exerted on each particle as shown in Figure 12.6. Each particle contributes a torque about an axis through the origin equal in magnitude to the particle's weight mg multiplied by its moment arm. For example, the magnitude of the torque due to the force $m_1 \vec{\mathbf{g}}_1$ is $m_1 g_1 x_1$, where g_1 is the value of the gravitational acceleration at the position of the particle of mass m_1. We wish to locate the center of gravity, the point at which application of the single gravitational force $M\vec{\mathbf{g}}_{CG}$ (where $M = m_1 + m_2 + m_3 + \cdots$ is the total mass of the object and $\vec{\mathbf{g}}_{CG}$ is the acceleration due to gravity at the location of the center of gravity) has the same effect on rotation as does the combined effect of all the individual gravitational forces $m_i \vec{\mathbf{g}}_i$. Equating the torque resulting from $M\vec{\mathbf{g}}_{CG}$ acting at the center of gravity to the sum of the torques acting on the individual particles gives

$$(m_1 + m_2 + m_3 + \cdots)g_{CG}x_{CG} = m_1 g_1 x_1 + m_2 g_2 x_2 + m_3 g_3 x_3 + \cdots$$

This expression accounts for the possibility that the value of g can in general vary over the object. If we assume uniform g over the object (as is usually the case), the g terms cancel and we obtain

$$x_{CG} = \frac{m_1 x_1 + m_2 x_2 + m_3 x_3 + \cdots}{m_1 + m_2 + m_3 + \cdots} \tag{12.4}$$

Comparing this result with Equation 9.29 shows that **the center of gravity is located at the center of mass as long as $\vec{\mathbf{g}}$ is uniform over the entire object.** Several examples in the next section deal with homogeneous, symmetric objects. The center of gravity for any such object coincides with its geometric center.

Figure 12.6 The gravitational force on an object is located at the center of gravity, which is the average position of the gravitational forces on all particles from which the object is made.

Quick Quiz 12.3 A meterstick is hung from a string tied at the 25-cm mark. A 0.50-kg object is hung from the zero end of the meterstick, and the meterstick is balanced horizontally. What is the mass of the meterstick? (a) 0.25 kg (b) 0.50 kg (c) 0.75 kg (d) 1.0 kg (e) 2.0 kg (f) impossible to determine

12.3   Examples of Rigid Objects in Static Equilibrium

The photograph of the one-bottle wine holder in Figure 12.7 shows one example of a balanced mechanical system that seems to defy gravity. For the system (wine holder plus bottle) to be in equilibrium, the net external force must be zero (see Eq. 12.1) and the net external torque must be zero (see Eq. 12.2). The second condition can be satisfied only when the center of gravity of the system is directly over the support point.

Figure 12.7   This one-bottle wine holder is a surprising display of static equilibrium. The center of gravity of the system (bottle plus holder) is directly over the support point.

PROBLEM-SOLVING STRATEGY   **Rigid Object in Equilibrium**

When analyzing a rigid object in equilibrium under the action of several external forces, use the following procedure.

1. *Conceptualize.* Think about the object that is in equilibrium and identify all the forces on it. Imagine what effect each force would have on the rotation of the object if it were the only force acting.

2. *Categorize.* Confirm that the object under consideration is indeed a rigid object in equilibrium.

3. *Analyze.* Draw a free-body diagram and label all external forces acting on the object. Try to guess the correct direction for each force.

   Resolve all forces into rectangular components, choosing a convenient coordinate system. Then apply the first condition for equilibrium, Equation 12.1. Remember to keep track of the signs of the various force components.

   Choose a convenient axis for calculating the net torque on the rigid object. Remember that the choice of the axis for the torque equation is arbitrary; therefore, choose an axis that simplifies your calculation as much as possible. Usually, the most convenient axis for calculating torques is one through a point at which several forces act, so their torques around this axis are zero. If you don't know a force or don't need to know a force, it is often beneficial to choose an axis through the point at which this force acts. Apply the second condition for equilibrium, Equation 12.2.

   Solve the simultaneous equations for the unknowns in terms of the known quantities.

4. *Finalize.* Make sure your results are consistent with the free-body diagram. If you selected a direction that leads to a negative sign in your solution for a force, do not be alarmed; it merely means that the direction of the force is the opposite of what you guessed. Add up the vertical and horizontal forces on the object and confirm that each set of components adds to zero. Add up the torques on the object and confirm that the sum equals zero.

EXAMPLE 12.1   **The Seesaw Revisited**

A seesaw consisting of a uniform board of mass M and length ℓ supports at rest a father and daughter with masses m_f and m_d, respectively, as shown in Figure 12.8. The support (called the *fulcrum*) is under the center of gravity of the board, the father is a distance d from the center, and the daughter is a distance $\ell/2$ from the center.

(A) Determine the magnitude of the upward force $\vec{\mathbf{n}}$ exerted by the support on the board.

Figure 12.8
(Example 12.1) A balanced system.

SOLUTION

Conceptualize Let us focus our attention on the board and consider the gravitational forces on the father and daughter as forces applied directly to the board. The daughter would cause a clockwise rotation of the board around the support, whereas the father would cause a counterclockwise rotation.

Categorize Because the text of the problem states that the system is at rest, we model the board as a rigid object in equilibrium. Because we will only need the first condition of equilibrium to solve this part of the problem, however, we model the board as a particle in equilibrium.

Analyze Define upward as the positive y direction and substitute the forces on the board into Equation 12.1:

$$n - m_f g - m_d g - Mg = 0$$

Solve for the magnitude of the force $\vec{n}$:

$$n = m_f g + m_d g + Mg = \boxed{(m_f + m_d + M)g}$$

(B) Determine where the father should sit to balance the system at rest.

SOLUTION

Categorize This part of the problem requires the introduction of torque to find the position of the father, so we model the board as a rigid object in equilibrium.

Analyze The board's center of gravity is at its geometric center because we are told that the board is uniform. If we choose a rotation axis perpendicular to the page through the center of gravity of the board, the torques produced by $\vec{n}$ and the gravitational force about this axis are zero.

Substitute expressions for the torques on the board due to the father and daughter into Equation 12.2:

$$(m_f g)(d) - (m_d g)\frac{\ell}{2} = 0$$

Solve for d:

$$d = \boxed{\left(\frac{m_d}{m_f}\right)\tfrac{1}{2}\ell}$$

Finalize This result is the same one we obtained in Example 11.6 by evaluating the angular acceleration of the system and setting the angular acceleration equal to zero.

What If? Suppose we had chosen another point through which the rotation axis were to pass. For example, suppose the axis is perpendicular to the page and passes through the location of the father. Does that change the results to parts (A) and (B)?

Answer Part (A) is unaffected because the calculation of the net force does not involve a rotation axis. In part (B), we would conceptually expect there to be no change if a different rotation axis is chosen because the second condition of equilibrium claims that the torque is zero about any rotation axis.

Let's verify this answer mathematically. Recall that the sign of the torque associated with a force is positive if that force tends to rotate the system counterclockwise, whereas the sign of the torque is negative if the force tends to rotate the system clockwise. Let's choose a rotation axis passing through the location of the father.

Apply the condition for rotational equilibrium, $\Sigma \tau = 0$:

$$n(d) - (Mg)(d) - (m_d g)\left(d + \frac{\ell}{2}\right) = 0$$

Substitute $n = (m_f + m_d + M)g$ from part (A) and solve for d:

$$(m_f + m_d + M)g(d) - (Mg)(d) - (m_d g)\left(d + \frac{\ell}{2}\right) = 0$$

$$(m_f g)(d) - (m_d g)\left(\frac{\ell}{2}\right) = 0 \quad \rightarrow \quad d = \left(\frac{m_d}{m_f}\right)\tfrac{1}{2}\ell$$

This result is in agreement with the one obtained in part (B).

EXAMPLE 12.2   Standing on a Horizontal Beam

A uniform horizontal beam with a length of 8.00 m and a weight of 200 N is attached to a wall by a pin connection. Its far end is supported by a cable that makes an angle of 53.0° with the beam (Fig. 12.9a). A 600-N person stands 2.00 m from the wall. Find the tension in the cable as well as the magnitude and direction of the force exerted by the wall on the beam.

SOLUTION

Conceptualize   Imagine that the person in Figure 12.9a moves outward on the beam. It seems reasonable that the farther he moves outward, the larger the torque he applies about the pivot and the larger the tension in the cable must be to balance this torque.

Categorize   Because the system is at rest, we categorize the beam as a rigid object in equilibrium.

(a)

(b)

Figure 12.9   (Example 12.2) (a) A uniform beam supported by a cable. A person walks outward on the beam. (b) The free-body diagram for the beam. (c) The free-body diagram for the beam showing the components of $\vec{R}$ and $\vec{T}$.

Analyze   We identify all the external forces acting on the beam: the 200-N gravitational force, the force $\vec{T}$ exerted by the cable, the force $\vec{R}$ exerted by the wall at the pivot, and the 600-N force that the person exerts on the beam. These forces are all indicated in the free-body diagram for the beam shown in Figure 12.9b. When we assign directions for forces, it is sometimes helpful to imagine what would happen if a force were suddenly removed. For example, if the wall were to vanish suddenly, the left end of the beam would move to the left as it begins to fall. This scenario tells us that the wall is not only holding the beam up but is also pressing outward against it. Therefore, we draw the vector $\vec{R}$ as shown in Figure 12.9b. Figure 12.9c shows the horizontal and vertical components of $\vec{T}$ and $\vec{R}$.

Substitute expressions for the forces on the beam into Equation 12.1:

$$(1) \quad \sum F_x = R\cos\theta - T\cos 53.0° = 0$$

$$(2) \quad \sum F_y = R\sin\theta + T\sin 53.0° - 600\text{ N} - 200\text{ N} = 0$$

where we have chosen rightward and upward as our positive directions. Because R, T, and θ are all unknown, we cannot obtain a solution from these expressions alone. (To solve for the unknowns, the number of simultaneous equations must equal the number of unknowns.)

Now let's invoke the condition for rotational equilibrium. A convenient axis to choose for our torque equation is the one that passes through the pin connection. The feature that makes this axis so convenient is that the force $\vec{R}$ and the horizontal component of $\vec{T}$ both have a moment arm of zero; hence, these forces produce no torque about this axis. The moment arms of the 600-N, 200-N, and $T\sin 53.0°$ forces about this axis are 2.00 m, 4.00 m, and 8.00 m, respectively.

Substitute expressions for the torques on the beam into Equation 12.2:

$$(3) \quad \sum \tau = (T\sin 53.0°)(8.00\text{ m}) - (600\text{ N})(2.00\text{ m}) - (200\text{ N})(4.00\text{ m}) = 0$$

Solve for T:

$$T = \boxed{313\text{ N}}$$

Substitute this value into Equations (1) and (2):

$$R\cos\theta - (313\text{ N})\cos 53.0° = 0$$

$$R\sin\theta + (313\text{ N})\sin 53.0° - 600\text{ N} - 200\text{ N} = 0$$

Solve for $R\cos\theta$ and $R\sin\theta$:

$$(4) \quad R\cos\theta = (313\text{ N})\cos 53.0° = 188\text{ N}$$

$$(5) \quad R\sin\theta = 600\text{ N} + 200\text{ N} - (313\text{ N})\sin 53.0° = 550\text{ N}$$

Divide Equation (5) by Equation (4):

$$\frac{R\sin\theta}{R\cos\theta} = \tan\theta = \frac{550\text{ N}}{188\text{ N}} = 2.93$$

Determine the angle θ:

$$\theta = \boxed{71.1°}$$

Solve Equation (4) for R:

$$R = \frac{188 \text{ N}}{\cos \theta} = \frac{188 \text{ N}}{\cos 71.1°} = \boxed{580 \text{ N}}$$

Finalize The positive value for the angle θ indicates that our estimate of the direction of $\vec{R}$ was accurate.

Had we selected some other axis for the torque equation, the solution might differ in the details but the answers would be the same. For example, had we chosen an axis through the center of gravity of the beam, the torque equation would involve both T and R. This equation, coupled with Equations (1) and (2), however, could still be solved for the unknowns. Try it!

What If? What if the person walks farther out on the beam? Does T change? Does R change? Does θ change?

Answer T must increase because the weight of the person exerts a larger torque about the pin connection, which must be countered by a larger torque in the opposite direction due to an increased value of T. If T increases, the vertical component of $\vec{R}$ decreases to maintain force equilibrium in the vertical direction. Force equilibrium in the horizontal direction, however, requires an increased horizontal component of $\vec{R}$ to balance the horizontal component of the increased $\vec{T}$. This fact suggests that θ becomes smaller, but it is hard to predict what happens to R. Problem 20 asks you to explore the behavior of R.

EXAMPLE 12.3 **The Leaning Ladder**

A uniform ladder of length ℓ rests against a smooth, vertical wall (Fig. 12.10a). The mass of the ladder is m, and the coefficient of static friction between the ladder and the ground is $\mu_s = 0.40$. Find the minimum angle θ_{min} at which the ladder does not slip.

SOLUTION

Conceptualize Think about any ladders you have climbed. Do you want a large friction force between the bottom of the ladder and the surface or a small one? If the friction force is zero, will the ladder stay up? Simulate a ladder with a ruler leaning against a vertical surface. Does the ruler slip at some angles and stay up at others?

Categorize We do not wish the ladder to slip, so we model it as a rigid object in equilibrium.

Analyze The free-body diagram showing all the external forces acting on the ladder is illustrated in Figure 12.10b. The force exerted by the ground on the ladder is the vector sum of a normal force $\vec{n}$ and the force of static friction $\vec{f}_s$. The force $\vec{P}$ exerted by the wall on the ladder is horizontal because the wall is frictionless.

(a)

(b)

Figure 12.10 (Example 12.3) (a) A uniform ladder at rest, leaning against a smooth wall. The ground is rough. (b) The free-body diagram for the ladder.

Apply the first condition for equilibrium to the ladder:

(1) $\sum F_x = f_s - P = 0$

(2) $\sum F_y = n - mg = 0$

Solve Equation (1) for P:

(3) $P = f_s$

Solve Equation (2) for n:

(4) $n = mg$

When the ladder is on the verge of slipping, the force of static friction must have its maximum value, which is given by $f_{s,\max} = \mu_s n$. Combine this equation with Equations (3) and (4):

$$P = f_{s,\max} = \mu_s n = \mu_s mg$$

Apply the second condition for equilibrium to the ladder, taking torques about an axis through O:

$$(5) \quad \sum \tau_O = P\ell \sin \theta_{\min} - mg \frac{\ell}{2} \cos \theta_{\min} = 0$$

Solve for $\tan \theta_{\min}$:

$$\frac{\sin \theta_{\min}}{\cos \theta_{\min}} = \tan \theta_{\min} = \frac{mg}{2P} = \frac{mg}{2\mu_s mg} = \frac{1}{2\mu_s} = 1.25$$

Solve for the angle $\theta_{\min}$:

$$\theta_{\min} = \tan^{-1}(1.25) = \boxed{51°}$$

Finalize Notice that the angle depends only on the coefficient of friction, not on the mass or length of the ladder.

EXAMPLE 12.4 | Negotiating a Curb

(A) Estimate the magnitude of the force $\vec{F}$ a person must apply to a wheelchair's main wheel to roll up over a sidewalk curb (Fig. 12.11a). This main wheel that comes in contact with the curb has a radius r, and the height of the curb is h.

SOLUTION

Conceptualize Think about wheelchair access to buildings. Generally, there are ramps built for individuals in wheelchairs. Steplike structures such as curbs are serious barriers to a wheelchair.

Categorize Imagine that the person exerts enough force so that the bottom of the wheel just loses contact with the lower surface and hovers at rest. We model the wheel in this situation as a rigid object in equilibrium.

Analyze Usually, the person's hands supply the required force to a slightly smaller wheel that is concentric with the main wheel. For simplicity, let's assume the radius of this second wheel is the same as the radius of the main wheel. Let's estimate a combined weight of $mg = 1\ 400$ N for the person and the wheelchair and choose a wheel radius of $r = 30$ cm. We also pick a curb height of $h = 10$ cm. Let's also assume the wheelchair and occupant are symmetric and each wheel supports a weight of 700 N. We then proceed to analyze only one of the wheels. Figure 12.11b shows the geometry for a single wheel.

(a)   (b)   (c)   (d)

Figure 12.11 (Example 12.4) (a) A person in a wheelchair attempts to roll up over a curb. (b) Details of the wheel and curb. The person applies a force $\vec{F}$ to the top of the wheel. (c) The free-body diagram for the wheel when it is just about to be raised. Three forces act on the wheel at this instant: $\vec{F}$, which is exerted by the hand; $\vec{R}$, which is exerted by the curb; and the gravitational force $m\vec{g}$. (d) The vector sum of the three external forces acting on the wheel is zero.

When the wheel is just about to be raised from the street, the normal force exerted by the ground on the wheel at point B goes to zero. Hence, at this time only three forces act on the wheel as shown in the free-body diagram in Figure 12.11c. The force $\vec{R}$, which is the force exerted by the curb on the wheel, acts at point A, so if we choose to have our axis of rotation pass through point A, we do not need to include $\vec{R}$ in our torque equation. The moment arm of $\vec{F}$ relative to an axis through A is $2r - h$ (see Fig. 12.11c).

Use the triangle OAC in Figure 12.11b to find the moment arm d of the gravitational force $m\vec{g}$ acting on the wheel relative to an axis through point A:

$$(1) \quad d = \sqrt{r^2 - (r - h)^2} = \sqrt{2rh - h^2}$$

Apply the second condition for equilibrium to the wheel, taking torques about an axis through A:

$$(2) \quad \sum \tau_A = mgd - F(2r - h) = 0$$

Substitute for d from Equation (1):

$$mg\sqrt{2rh - h^2} - F(2r - h) = 0$$

Solve for F:

$$F = \frac{mg\sqrt{2rh - h^2}}{2r - h}$$

Substitute the known values:

$$F = \frac{(700 \text{ N})\sqrt{2(0.3 \text{ m})(0.1 \text{ m}) - (0.1 \text{ m})^2}}{2(0.3 \text{ m}) - 0.1 \text{ m}}$$

$$= \boxed{3 \times 10^2 \text{ N}}$$

(B) Determine the magnitude and direction of $\vec{R}$.

SOLUTION

Apply the first condition for equilibrium to the wheel:

$$\sum F_x = F - R\cos\theta = 0$$

$$\sum F_y = R\sin\theta - mg = 0$$

Divide the second equation by the first:

$$\frac{R\sin\theta}{R\cos\theta} = \tan\theta = \frac{mg}{F} = \frac{700 \text{ N}}{300 \text{ N}} = 2.33$$

Solve for the angle θ:

$$\theta = \tan^{-1}(2.33) = \boxed{70°}$$

Use the right triangle shown in Figure 12.11d to obtain R:

$$R = \sqrt{(mg)^2 + F^2} = \sqrt{(700 \text{ N})^2 + (300 \text{ N})^2} = \boxed{8 \times 10^2 \text{ N}}$$

Finalize Notice that we have kept only one digit as significant. (We have written the angle as 70° because $7 \times 10^{1°}$ is awkward!) The results indicate that the force that must be applied to each wheel is substantial. You may want to estimate the force required to roll a wheelchair up a typical sidewalk accessibility ramp for comparison.

What If? Would it be easier to negotiate the curb if the person grabbed the wheel at point D in Figure 12.11c and pulled *upward*?

Answer If the force $\vec{F}$ in Figure 12.11c is rotated counterclockwise by 90° and applied at D, its moment arm is $d + r$. Let's call the magnitude of this new force F'.

Modify Equation (2) for this situation:

$$\sum \tau_A = mgd - F'(d + r) = 0$$

Solve this equation for F' and substitute for d:

$$F' = \frac{mgd}{d + r} = \frac{mg\sqrt{2rh - h^2}}{\sqrt{2rh - h^2} + r}$$

Take the ratio of this force to the original force that we calculated and express the result in terms of h/r, the ratio of the curb height to the wheel radius:

$$\frac{F'}{F} = \frac{\dfrac{mg\sqrt{2rh - h^2}}{\sqrt{2rh - h^2} + r}}{\dfrac{mg\sqrt{2rh - h^2}}{2r - h}} = \frac{2r - h}{\sqrt{2rh - h^2} + r} = \frac{2 - \left(\dfrac{h}{r}\right)}{\sqrt{2\left(\dfrac{h}{r}\right) - \left(\dfrac{h}{r}\right)^2} + 1}$$

Substitute the ratio $h/r = 0.33$ from the given values:

$$\frac{F'}{F} = \frac{2 - 0.33}{\sqrt{2(0.33) - (0.33)^2} + 1} = 0.96$$

This result tells us that, *for these values*, it is slightly easier to pull upward at D than horizontally at the top of the wheel. For very high curbs, so that h/r is close to 1, the ratio F'/F drops to about 0.5 because point A is located near the right edge of the wheel in Figure 12.11b. The force at D is applied at distance of about $2r$ from A, whereas the force at the top of the wheel has a moment arm of only about r. For high curbs, then, it is best to pull upward at D, although a large value of the force is required. For small curbs, it is best to apply the force at the top of the wheel. The ratio F'/F becomes larger than 1 at about $h/r = 0.3$ because point A is now close to the bottom of the wheel and the force applied at the

top of the wheel has a larger moment arm than when applied at D.

Finally, let's comment on the validity of these mathematical results. Consider Figure 12.11d and imagine that the vector $\vec{F}$ is upward instead of to the right. There is no way the three vectors can add to equal zero as required by the first equilibrium condition. Therefore, our results above may be qualitatively valid, but not exact quantitatively. To cancel the horizontal component of $\vec{R}$, the force at D must be applied at an angle to the vertical rather than straight upward. This feature makes the calculation more complicated and requires both conditions of equilibrium.

12.4   Elastic Properties of Solids

Except for our discussion about springs in earlier chapters, we have assumed that objects remain rigid when external forces act on them. In Section 9.7, we explored deformable systems. In reality, all objects are deformable to some extent. That is, it is possible to change the shape or the size (or both) of an object by applying external forces. As these changes take place, however, internal forces in the object resist the deformation.

We shall discuss the deformation of solids in terms of the concepts of *stress* and *strain*. **Stress** is a quantity that is proportional to the force causing a deformation; more specifically, stress is the external force acting on an object per unit cross-sectional area. The result of a stress is **strain,** which is a measure of the degree of deformation. It is found that, for sufficiently small stresses, **stress is proportional to strain;** the constant of proportionality depends on the material being deformed and on the nature of the deformation. We call this proportionality constant the **elastic modulus.** The elastic modulus is therefore defined as the ratio of the stress to the resulting strain:

$$\text{Elastic modulus} \equiv \frac{\text{stress}}{\text{strain}} \qquad \textbf{(12.5)}$$

The elastic modulus in general relates what is done to a solid object (a force is applied) to how that object responds (it deforms to some extent). It is similar to the spring constant k in Hooke's law (Eq. 7.9) that relates a force applied to a spring and the resultant deformation of the spring, measured by its extension or compression.

We consider three types of deformation and define an elastic modulus for each:

1. **Young's modulus** measures the resistance of a solid to a change in its length.
2. **Shear modulus** measures the resistance to motion of the planes within a solid parallel to each other.
3. **Bulk modulus** measures the resistance of solids or liquids to changes in their volume.

ACTIVE FIGURE 12.12

A long bar clamped at one end is stretched by an amount ΔL under the action of a force $\vec{F}$.

Sign in at www.thomsonedu.com and go to ThomsonNOW to adjust the values of the applied force and Young's modulus and observe the change in length of the bar.

Young's Modulus: Elasticity in Length

Consider a long bar of cross-sectional area A and initial length L_i that is clamped at one end as in Active Figure 12.12. When an external force is applied perpendicular to the cross section, internal forces in the bar resist distortion ("stretching"), but the bar reaches an equilibrium situation in which its final length L_f is greater

TABLE 12.1

Typical Values for Elastic Moduli

Substance	Young's Modulus (N/m²)	Shear Modulus (N/m²)	Bulk Modulus (N/m²)
Tungsten	35×10^{10}	14×10^{10}	20×10^{10}
Steel	20×10^{10}	8.4×10^{10}	6×10^{10}
Copper	11×10^{10}	4.2×10^{10}	14×10^{10}
Brass	9.1×10^{10}	3.5×10^{10}	6.1×10^{10}
Aluminum	7.0×10^{10}	2.5×10^{10}	7.0×10^{10}
Glass	6.5–7.8×10^{10}	2.6–3.2×10^{10}	5.0–5.5×10^{10}
Quartz	5.6×10^{10}	2.6×10^{10}	2.7×10^{10}
Water	—	—	0.21×10^{10}
Mercury	—	—	2.8×10^{10}

than L_i and in which the external force is exactly balanced by internal forces. In such a situation, the bar is said to be stressed. We define the **tensile stress** as the ratio of the magnitude of the external force F to the cross-sectional area A. The **tensile strain** in this case is defined as the ratio of the change in length ΔL to the original length L_i. We define **Young's modulus** by a combination of these two ratios:

Young's modulus ▶

$$Y \equiv \frac{\text{tensile stress}}{\text{tensile strain}} = \frac{F/A}{\Delta L/L_i} \qquad \textbf{(12.6)}$$

Young's modulus is typically used to characterize a rod or wire stressed under either tension or compression. Because strain is a dimensionless quantity, Y has units of force per unit area. Typical values are given in Table 12.1.

For relatively small stresses, the bar returns to its initial length when the force is removed. The **elastic limit** of a substance is defined as the maximum stress that can be applied to the substance before it becomes permanently deformed and does not return to its initial length. It is possible to exceed the elastic limit of a substance by applying a sufficiently large stress as seen in Figure 12.13. Initially, a stress-versus-strain curve is a straight line. As the stress increases, however, the curve is no longer a straight line. When the stress exceeds the elastic limit, the object is permanently distorted and does not return to its original shape after the stress is removed. As the stress is increased even further, the material ultimately breaks.

Figure 12.13 Stress-versus-strain curve for an elastic solid.

Shear Modulus: Elasticity of Shape

Another type of deformation occurs when an object is subjected to a force parallel to one of its faces while the opposite face is held fixed by another force (Active Fig. 12.14a). The stress in this case is called a shear stress. If the object is originally a rectangular block, a shear stress results in a shape whose cross section is a parallelogram. A book pushed sideways as shown in Active Figure 12.14b is an example of an object subjected to a shear stress. To a first approximation (for small distortions), no change in volume occurs with this deformation.

We define the **shear stress** as F/A, the ratio of the tangential force to the area A of the face being sheared. The **shear strain** is defined as the ratio $\Delta x/h$, where Δx is the horizontal distance that the sheared face moves and h is the height of the object. In terms of these quantities, the **shear modulus** is

Shear modulus ▶

$$S \equiv \frac{\text{shear stress}}{\text{shear strain}} = \frac{F/A}{\Delta x/h} \qquad \textbf{(12.7)}$$

Values of the shear modulus for some representative materials are given in Table 12.1. Like Young's modulus, the unit of shear modulus is the ratio of that for force to that for area.

(a)   (b)

ACTIVE FIGURE 12.14

(a) A shear deformation in which a rectangular block is distorted by two forces of equal magnitude but opposite directions applied to two parallel faces. (b) A book is under shear stress when a hand placed on the cover applies a horizontal force away from the spine.

Sign in at www.thomsonedu.com and go to ThomsonNOW to adjust the values of the applied force and the shear modulus and observe the change in shape of the block in (a).

Bulk Modulus: Volume Elasticity

Bulk modulus characterizes the response of an object to changes in a force of uniform magnitude applied perpendicularly over the entire surface of the object as shown in Active Figure 12.15. (We assume here that the object is made of a single substance.) As we shall see in Chapter 14, such a uniform distribution of forces occurs when an object is immersed in a fluid. An object subject to this type of deformation undergoes a change in volume but no change in shape. The **volume stress** is defined as the ratio of the magnitude of the total force F exerted on a surface to the area A of the surface. The quantity $P = F/A$ is called **pressure,** which we shall study in more detail in Chapter 14. If the pressure on an object changes by an amount $\Delta P = \Delta F/A$, the object experiences a volume change ΔV. The **volume strain** is equal to the change in volume ΔV divided by the initial volume V_i. Therefore, from Equation 12.5, we can characterize a volume ("bulk") compression in terms of the **bulk modulus,** which is defined as

$$B \equiv \frac{\text{volume stress}}{\text{volume strain}} = -\frac{\Delta F/A}{\Delta V/V_i} = -\frac{\Delta P}{\Delta V/V_i}   \qquad \textbf{(12.8)}$$

◀   **Bulk modulus**

A negative sign is inserted in this defining equation so that B is a positive number. This maneuver is necessary because an increase in pressure (positive ΔP) causes a decrease in volume (negative ΔV) and vice versa.

   Table 12.1 lists bulk moduli for some materials. If you look up such values in a different source, you may find the reciprocal of the bulk modulus listed. The reciprocal of the bulk modulus is called the **compressibility** of the material.

   Notice from Table 12.1 that both solids and liquids have a bulk modulus. No shear modulus and no Young's modulus are given for liquids, however, because a liquid does not sustain a shearing stress or a tensile stress. If a shearing force or a tensile force is applied to a liquid, the liquid simply flows in response.

Quick Quiz 12.4   For the three parts of this Quick Quiz, choose from the following choices the correct answer for the elastic modulus that describes the relationship between stress and strain for the system of interest, which is in italics: (a) Young's modulus   (b) shear modulus   (c) bulk modulus   (d) none of these choices   (i) A *block of iron* is sliding across a horizontal floor. The friction force between the block and the floor causes the block to deform. (ii) A trapeze artist swings through a circular arc. At the bottom of the swing, the *wires* supporting the trapeze are longer than when the trapeze artist simply hangs from the trapeze due to the increased tension in them. (iii) A spacecraft carries a *steel sphere* to a planet on which atmospheric pressure is much higher than on the Earth. The higher pressure causes the radius of the sphere to decrease.

ACTIVE FIGURE 12.15

When a solid is under uniform pressure, it undergoes a change in volume but no change in shape. This cube is compressed on all sides by forces normal to its six faces.

Sign in at www.thomsonedu.com and go to ThomsonNOW to adjust the values of the applied force and the bulk modulus and observe the change in volume of the cube.

Figure 12.16 (a) A concrete slab with no reinforcement tends to crack under a heavy load. (b) The strength of the concrete is increased by using steel reinforcement rods. (c) The concrete is further strengthened by prestressing it with steel rods under tension.

Prestressed Concrete

If the stress on a solid object exceeds a certain value, the object fractures. The maximum stress that can be applied before fracture occurs—called the *tensile strength*, *compressive strength*, or *shear strength*—depends on the nature of the material and on the type of applied stress. For example, concrete has a tensile strength of about 2×10^6 N/m², a compressive strength of 20×10^6 N/m², and a shear strength of 2×10^6 N/m². If the applied stress exceeds these values, the concrete fractures. It is common practice to use large safety factors to prevent failure in concrete structures.

Concrete is normally very brittle when it is cast in thin sections. Therefore, concrete slabs tend to sag and crack at unsupported areas as shown in Figure 12.16a. The slab can be strengthened by the use of steel rods to reinforce the concrete as illustrated in Figure 12.16b. Because concrete is much stronger under compression (squeezing) than under tension (stretching) or shear, vertical columns of concrete can support very heavy loads, whereas horizontal beams of concrete tend to sag and crack. A significant increase in shear strength is achieved, however, if the reinforced concrete is prestressed as shown in Figure 12.16c. As the concrete is being poured, the steel rods are held under tension by external forces. The external forces are released after the concrete cures; the result is a permanent tension in the steel and hence a compressive stress on the concrete. The concrete slab can now support a much heavier load.

EXAMPLE 12.5 | **Stage Design**

In Example 8.2, we analyzed a cable used to support an actor as he swung onto the stage. Now suppose the tension in the cable is 940 N as the actor reaches the lowest point. What diameter should a 10-m-long steel cable have if we do not want it to stretch more than 0.50 cm under these conditions?

SOLUTION

Conceptualize Look back at Example 8.2 to recall what is happening in this situation. We ignored any stretching of the cable there, but we wish to address this phenomenon in this example.

Categorize We perform a simple calculation involving Equation 12.6, so we categorize this example as a substitution problem.

Solve Equation 12.6 for the cross-sectional area of the cable:

$$A = \frac{FL_i}{Y\Delta L}$$

Substitute the known values:

$$A = \frac{(940 \text{ N})(10 \text{ m})}{(20 \times 10^{10} \text{ N/m}^2)(0.005\ 0 \text{ m})} = 9.4 \times 10^{-6} \text{ m}^2$$

Assuming that the cross section is circular, find the radius of the cable from $A = \pi r^2$:

$$r = \sqrt{\frac{A}{\pi}} = \sqrt{\frac{9.4 \times 10^{-6} \text{ m}^2}{\pi}} = 1.7 \times 10^{-3} \text{ m} = 1.7 \text{ mm}$$

Find the diameter of the cable:

$$d = 2r = 2(1.7 \text{ mm}) = \boxed{3.4 \text{ mm}}$$

To provide a large margin of safety, you would probably use a flexible cable made up of many smaller wires having a total cross-sectional area substantially greater than our calculated value.

EXAMPLE 12.6   Squeezing a Brass Sphere

A solid brass sphere is initially surrounded by air, and the air pressure exerted on it is 1.0×10^5 N/m² (normal atmospheric pressure). The sphere is lowered into the ocean to a depth where the pressure is 2.0×10^7 N/m². The volume of the sphere in air is 0.50 m³. By how much does this volume change once the sphere is submerged?

SOLUTION

Conceptualize Think about movies or television shows you have seen in which divers go to great depths in the water in submersible vessels. These vessels must be very strong to withstand the large pressure under water. This pressure squeezes the vessel and reduces its volume.

Categorize We perform a simple calculation involving Equation 12.8, so we categorize this example as a substitution problem.

Solve Equation 12.8 for the volume change of the sphere:

$$\Delta V = -\frac{V_i \Delta P}{B}$$

Substitute the numerical values:

$$\Delta V = -\frac{(0.50 \text{ m}^3)(2.0 \times 10^7 \text{ N/m}^2 - 1.0 \times 10^5 \text{ N/m}^2)}{6.1 \times 10^{10} \text{ N/m}^2}$$

$$= \boxed{-1.6 \times 10^{-4} \text{ m}^3}$$

The negative sign indicates that the volume of the sphere decreases.

Summary

DEFINITIONS

The gravitational force exerted on an object can be considered as acting at a single point called the **center of gravity.** An object's center of gravity coincides with its center of mass if the object is in a uniform gravitational field.

We can describe the elastic properties of a substance using the concepts of stress and strain. **Stress** is a quantity proportional to the force producing a deformation; **strain** is a measure of the degree of deformation. Stress is proportional to strain, and the constant of proportionality is the **elastic modulus:**

$$\text{Elastic modulus} \equiv \frac{\text{stress}}{\text{strain}} \qquad \textbf{(12.5)}$$

CONCEPTS AND PRINCIPLES

Three common types of deformation are represented by (1) the resistance of a solid to elongation under a load, characterized by **Young's modulus** Y; (2) the resistance of a solid to the motion of internal planes sliding past each other, characterized by the **shear modulus** S; and (3) the resistance of a solid or fluid to a volume change, characterized by the **bulk modulus** B.

ANALYSIS MODEL FOR PROBLEM SOLVING

Rigid Object in Equilibrium A rigid object in equilibrium exhibits no translational or angular acceleration. The net external force acting on it is zero, and the net external torque on it is zero about any axis:

$$\sum \vec{F} = 0 \qquad \textbf{(12.1)}$$

$$\sum \vec{\tau} = 0 \qquad \textbf{(12.2)}$$

The first condition is the condition for translational equilibrium, and the second is the condition for rotational equilibrium.

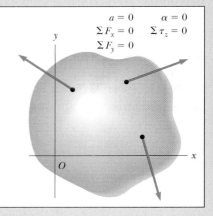

Questions

☐ denotes answer available in *Student Solutions Manual/Study Guide;* **O** denotes objective question

1. **O** Assume a single 300-N force is exerted on a bicycle frame as shown in Figure Q12.1. Consider the torque produced by this force about axes perpendicular to the plane of the paper and through each of the points A through F,

Figure Q12.1

where F is the center of mass of the frame. Rank the torques τ_A, τ_B, τ_C, τ_D, τ_E, and τ_F from largest to smallest, noting that zero is greater than a negative quantity. If two torques are equal, note their equality in your ranking.

2. Stand with your back against a wall. Why can't you put your heels firmly against the wall and then bend forward without falling?

3. Can an object be in equilibrium if it is in motion? Explain.

4. (a) Give an example in which the net force acting on an object is zero and yet the net torque is nonzero. (b) Give an example in which the net torque acting on an object is zero and yet the net force is nonzero.

5. **O** Consider the object in Figure 12.1. A single force is exerted on the object. The line of action of the force does

not pass through the object's center of mass. The acceleration of the center of mass of the object due to this force (a) is the same as if the force were applied at the center of mass, (b) is larger than the acceleration would be if the force were applied at the center of mass, (c) is smaller than the acceleration would be if the force were applied at the center of mass, or (d) is zero because the force causes only angular acceleration about the center of mass.

6. The center of gravity of an object may be located outside the object. Give a few examples for which this case is true.

7. Assume you are given an arbitrarily shaped piece of plywood, together with a hammer, nail, and plumb bob. How could you use these items to locate the center of gravity of the plywood? *Suggestion:* Use the nail to suspend the plywood.

8. **O** In the cabin of a ship, a soda can rests in a saucer-shaped indentation in a built-in counter. The can tilts as the ship slowly rolls. In which case is the can most stable against tipping over? (a) It is most stable when it is full. (b) It is most stable when it is half full. (c) It is most stable when it is empty. (d) It is most stable in two of these cases. (e) It is equally stable in all cases.

9. **O** The acceleration due to gravity becomes weaker by about three parts in ten million for each meter of increased elevation above the Earth's surface. Suppose a skyscraper is 100 stories tall, with the same floor plan for each story and with uniform average density. Compare the location of the building's center of mass and the location of its center of gravity. Choose one. (a) Its center of mass is higher by a distance of several meters. (b) Its center of mass is higher by a distance of several millimeters. (c) Its center of mass is higher by an infinitesimally small amount. (d) Its center of mass and its center of gravity are in the same location. (e) Its center of gravity is higher by a distance of several millimeters. (f) Its center of gravity is higher by a distance of several meters.

10. A girl has a large, docile dog she wishes to weigh on a small bathroom scale. She reasons that she can determine her dog's weight with the following method. First she puts the dog's two front feet on the scale and records the scale reading. Then she places the dog's two back feet on the scale and records the reading. She thinks that the sum of the readings will be the dog's weight. Is she correct? Explain your answer.

11. **O** The center of gravity of an ax is on the centerline of the handle, close to the head. Assume you saw across the handle through the center of gravity and weigh the two parts. What will you discover? (a) The handle side is heavier than the head side. (b) The head side is heavier than the handle side. (c) The two parts are equally heavy. (d) Their comparative weights cannot be predicted.

12. A ladder stands on the ground, leaning against a wall. Would you feel safer climbing up the ladder if you were told that the ground is frictionless but the wall is rough or if you were told that the wall is frictionless but the ground is rough? Justify your answer.

13. **O** In analyzing the equilibrium of a flat, rigid object, consider the step of choosing an axis about which to calculate torques. (a) No choice needs to be made. (b) The axis should pass through the object's center of mass. (c) The axis should pass through one end of the object. (d) The axis should be either the x axis or the y axis. (e) The axis needs to be an axle, hinge pin, pivot point, or fulcrum. (f) The axis should pass through any point within the object. (g) Any axis within or outside the object can be chosen.

14. **O** A certain wire, 3 m long, stretches by 1.2 mm when under tension 200 N. **(i)** An equally thick wire 6 m long, made of the same material and under the same tension, stretches by (a) 4.8 mm (b) 2.4 mm (c) 1.2 mm (d) 0.6 mm (e) 0.3 mm (f) 0 **(ii)** A wire with twice the diameter, 3 m long, made of the same material and under the same tension, stretches by what amount? Choose from the same possibilities (a) through (f).

15. What kind of deformation does a cube of Jell-O exhibit when it jiggles?

Problems

WebAssign The Problems from this chapter may be assigned online in WebAssign.

ThomsonNOW™ Sign in at **www.thomsonedu.com** and go to ThomsonNOW to assess your understanding of this chapter's topics with additional quizzing and conceptual questions.

1, 2, 3 denotes straightforward, intermediate, challenging;   ☐ denotes full solution available in *Student Solutions Manual/Study Guide;*   ▲ denotes coached solution with hints available at **www.thomsonedu.com;**   denotes developing symbolic reasoning;   ● denotes asking for qualitative reasoning;   ▪ denotes computer useful in solving problem

Section 12.1 The Rigid Object in Equilibrium

1. ▲ A uniform beam of mass m_b and length ℓ supports blocks with masses m_1 and m_2 at two positions as shown in Figure P12.1. The beam rests on two knife edges. For what value of x will the beam be balanced at P such that the normal force at O is zero?

Figure P12.1

2. Write the necessary conditions for equilibrium of the object shown in Figure P12.2. Calculate torques about an axis through point O.

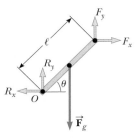

Figure P12.2

Section 12.2 More on the Center of Gravity

Problems 35, 37, 39, and 40 in Chapter 9 can also be assigned with this section.

3. A carpenter's square has the shape of an L as shown in Figure P12.3. Locate its center of gravity.

Figure P12.3

4. A circular pizza of radius R has a circular piece of radius $R/2$ removed from one side as shown in Figure P12.4. The center of gravity has moved from C to C' along the x axis. Show that the distance from C to C' is $R/6$. Assume the thickness and density of the pizza are uniform throughout.

Figure P12.4

5. ▲ Consider the following distribution of objects: a 5.00-kg object with its center of gravity at (0, 0) m, a 3.00-kg object at (0, 4.00) m, and a 4.00-kg object at (3.00, 0) m. Where should a fourth object of mass 8.00 kg be placed so that the center of gravity of the four-object arrangement will be at (0, 0)?

6. Pat builds a track for his model car out of solid wood as shown in Figure P12.6. The track is 5.00 cm wide, 1.00 m high, and 3.00 m long. The runway is cut so that it forms a parabola with the equation $y = (x - 3)^2/9$. Locate the horizontal coordinate of the center of gravity of this track.

Figure P12.6

7. Figure P12.7 shows three uniform objects: a rod, a right triangle, and a square. Their masses and their coordinates in meters are given. Determine the center of gravity for the three-object system.

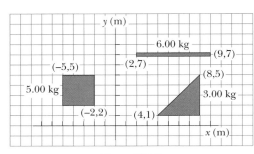

Figure P12.7

Section 12.3 Examples of Rigid Objects in Static Equilibrium

Problems 12, 17, 18, 19, 20, 21, 22, 23, 30, 40, 44, 47, 57, 61, 65, and 71 in Chapter 5 can also be assigned with this section.

8. A mobile is constructed of light rods, light strings, and beach souvenirs as shown in Figure P12.8. Determine the masses of the objects (a) m_1, (b) m_2, and (c) m_3.

Figure P12.8

9. Find the mass m of the counterweight needed to balance the 1 500-kg truck on the incline shown in Figure P12.9. Assume all pulleys are frictionless and massless.

Figure P12.9

10. Figure P12.10 shows a claw hammer being used to pull a nail out of a horizontal board. A force of 150 N is exerted horizontally as shown. Find (a) the force exerted by the hammer claws on the nail and (b) the force exerted by the surface on the point of contact with the hammer head. Assume the force the hammer exerts on the nail is parallel to the nail.

Figure P12.10

11. A 15.0-m uniform ladder weighing 500 N rests against a frictionless wall. The ladder makes a 60.0° angle with the horizontal. (a) Find the horizontal and vertical forces the ground exerts on the base of the ladder when an 800-N firefighter is 4.00 m from the bottom. (b) If the ladder is just on the verge of slipping when the firefighter is 9.00 m up, what is the coefficient of static friction between ladder and ground?

12. A uniform ladder of length L and mass m_1 rests against a frictionless wall. The ladder makes an angle θ with the horizontal. (a) Find the horizontal and vertical forces the ground exerts on the base of the ladder when a firefighter of mass m_2 is a distance x from the bottom. (b) If the ladder is just on the verge of slipping when the firefighter is a distance d from the bottom, what is the coefficient of static friction between ladder and ground?

13. A 1 500-kg automobile has a wheel base (the distance between the axles) of 3.00 m. The automobile's center of mass is on the centerline at a point 1.20 m behind the front axle. Find the force exerted by the ground on each wheel.

14. ● A 20.0-kg floodlight in a park is supported at the end of a horizontal beam of negligible mass that is hinged to a pole as shown in Figure P12.14. A cable at an angle of

30.0° with the beam helps support the light. Consider the equilibrium of the beam, drawing a free-body diagram of that object. Compute torques about an axis at the hinge at its left-hand end. Find (a) the tension in the cable, (b) the horizontal component of the force exerted by the pole on the beam, and (c) the vertical component of this force. Now solve the same problem from the same free-body diagram by computing torques around the junction between the cable and the beam at the right-hand end of the beam. Find (d) the vertical component of the force exerted by the pole on the beam, (e) the tension in the cable, and (f) the horizontal component of the force exerted by the pole on the beam. (g) Compare the solution to parts (a) through (c) with the solution to parts (d) through (f). Is either solution more accurate? Simpler? Taking together the whole set of equations read from the free-body diagram in both solutions, how many equations do you have? How many unknown quantities can be determined?

Figure P12.14

15. A flexible chain weighing 40.0 N hangs between two hooks located at the same height (Fig. P12.15). At each hook, the tangent to the chain makes an angle $\theta = 42.0°$ with the horizontal. Find (a) the magnitude of the force each hook exerts on the chain and (b) the tension in the chain at its midpoint. *Suggestion:* for part (b), make a free-body diagram for half of the chain.

Figure P12.15

16. Sir Lost-a-Lot dons his armor and sets out from the castle on his trusty steed in his quest to improve communication between damsels and dragons (Fig. P12.16). Unfortunately, his squire lowered the drawbridge too far and finally stopped it 20.0° below the horizontal. Lost-a-Lot

Figure P12.16   Problems 16 and 17.

and his horse stop when their combined center of mass is 1.00 m from the end of the bridge. The uniform bridge is 8.00 m long and has mass 2 000 kg. The lift cable is attached to the bridge 5.00 m from the hinge at the castle end and to a point on the castle wall 12.0 m above the bridge. Lost-a-Lot's mass combined with his armor and steed is 1 000 kg. Determine (a) the tension in the cable and the (b) horizontal and (c) vertical force components acting on the bridge at the hinge.

17. **Review problem.** In the situation described in Problem 16 and illustrated in Figure P12.16, the lift cable suddenly breaks! The hinge between the castle wall and the bridge is frictionless, and the bridge swings freely until it is vertical. (a) Find the angular acceleration of the bridge once it starts to move. (b) Find the angular speed of the bridge when it strikes the vertical castle wall below the hinge. (c) Find the force exerted by the hinge on the bridge immediately after the cable breaks. (d) Find the force exerted by the hinge on the bridge immediately before it strikes the castle wall.

18. Stephen is pushing his sister Joyce in a wheelbarrow when it is stopped by a brick 8.00 cm high (Fig. P12.18). The wheelbarrow handles make an angle of 15.0° below the horizontal. A downward force of 400 N is exerted on the wheel, which has a radius of 20.0 cm. (a) What force must Stephen apply along the handles to just start the wheel over the brick? (b) What is the force (magnitude and direction) that the brick exerts on the wheel just as the wheel begins to lift over the brick? In both parts (a) and (b), assume the brick remains fixed and does not slide along the ground.

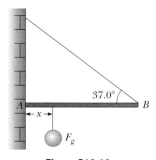

Figure P12.18

19. One end of a uniform 4.00-m-long rod of weight F_g is supported by a cable. The other end rests against the wall, where it is held by friction, as shown in Figure P12.19. The coefficient of static friction between the wall and the rod is $\mu_s = 0.500$. Determine the minimum distance x from point A at which an additional object, also with the same weight F_g, can be hung without causing the rod to slip at point A.

Figure P12.19

20. In the **What If?** section of Example 12.2, let x represent the distance in meters between the person and the hinge at the left end of the beam. (a) Show that the cable tension in newtons is given by $T = 93.9x + 125$. Argue that T increases as x increases. (b) Show that the direction angle θ of the hinge force is described by

$$\tan\theta = \left(\frac{32}{3x+4} - 1\right)\tan 53.0°$$

How does θ change as x increases? (c) Show that the magnitude of the hinge force is given by

$$R = \sqrt{8.82 \times 10^3 x^2 - 9.65 \times 10^4 x + 4.96 \times 10^5}$$

How does R change as x increases?

21. A vaulter holds a 29.4-N pole in equilibrium by exerting an upward force $\vec{U}$ with her leading hand and a downward force $\vec{D}$ with her trailing hand as shown in Figure P12.21. Point C is the center of gravity of the pole. What are the magnitudes of $\vec{U}$ and $\vec{D}$?

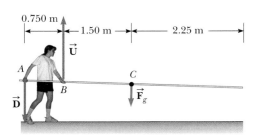

Figure P12.21

Section 12.4 Elastic Properties of Solids

22. Evaluate Young's modulus for the material whose stress-strain curve is shown in Figure 12.13.

23. A 200-kg load is hung on a wire of length 4.00 m, cross-sectional area 0.200×10^{-4} m², and Young's modulus 8.00×10^{10} N/m². What is its increase in length?

24. Assume Young's modulus for bone is 1.50×10^{10} N/m². The bone breaks if stress greater than 1.50×10^8 N/m² is imposed on it. (a) What is the maximum force that can be exerted on the femur bone in the leg if it has a minimum effective diameter of 2.50 cm? (b) If this much force is applied compressively, by how much does the 25.0-cm-long bone shorten?

25. A child slides across a floor in a pair of rubber-soled shoes. The friction force acting on each foot is 20.0 N. The footprint area of each shoe sole is 14.0 cm², and the thickness of each sole is 5.00 mm. Find the horizontal distance by which the upper and lower surfaces of each sole are offset. The shear modulus of the rubber is 3.00 MN/m².

26. A steel wire of diameter 1 mm can support a tension of 0.2 kN. A cable to support a tension of 20 kN should have diameter of what order of magnitude?

27. ▲ Assume that if the shear stress in steel exceeds about 4.00×10^8 N/m², the steel ruptures. Determine the shearing force necessary to (a) shear a steel bolt 1.00 cm in diameter and (b) punch a 1.00-cm-diameter hole in a steel plate 0.500 cm thick.

28. **Review problem.** A 30.0-kg hammer, moving with speed 20.0 m/s, strikes a steel spike 2.30 cm in diameter. The hammer rebounds with speed 10.0 m/s after 0.110 s. What is the average strain in the spike during the impact?

29. When water freezes, it expands by about 9.00%. What pressure increase would occur inside your automobile engine block if the water in it froze? (The bulk modulus of ice is 2.00×10^9 N/m^2.)

30. **Review problem.** A 2.00-m-long cylindrical steel wire with a cross-sectional diameter of 4.00 mm is placed over a light, frictionless pulley, with one end of the wire connected to a 5.00-kg object and the other end connected to a 3.00-kg object. By how much does the wire stretch while the objects are in motion?

31. A walkway suspended across a hotel lobby is supported at numerous points along its edges by a vertical cable above each point and a vertical column underneath. The steel cable is 1.27 cm in diameter and is 5.75 m long before loading. The aluminum column is a hollow cylinder with an inside diameter of 16.14 cm, an outside diameter of 16.24 cm, and unloaded length of 3.25 m. When the walkway exerts a load force of 8 500 N on one of the support points, how much does the point move down?

32. ● The deepest point in any ocean is in the Mariana Trench, which is about 11 km deep, in the Pacific. The pressure at this depth is huge, about 1.13×10^8 N/m^2. (a) Calculate the change in volume of 1.00 m^3 of seawater carried from the surface to this deepest point. (b) The density of seawater at the surface is 1.03×10^3 kg/m^3. Find its density at the bottom. (c) Explain whether or when it is a good approximation to think of water as incompressible.

Additional Problems

33. A bridge of length 50.0 m and mass 8.00×10^4 kg is supported on a smooth pier at each end as shown in Figure P12.33. A truck of mass 3.00×10^4 kg is located 15.0 m from one end. What are the forces on the bridge at the points of support?

Figure P12.33

34. ● A new General Electric kitchen stove has a mass of 68.0 kg and the dimensions shown in Figure P12.34. The stove comes with a warning that it can tip forward if a person stands or sits on the oven door when it is open. What can you conclude about the weight of such a person? Could it be a child? List the assumptions you make in solving this problem. The stove is supplied with a wall bracket to prevent the accident.

Figure P12.34

35. A uniform pole is propped between the floor and the ceiling of a room. The height of the room is 7.80 ft, and the coefficient of static friction between the pole and the ceiling is 0.576. The coefficient of static friction between the pole and the floor is greater than that. What is the length of the longest pole that can be propped between the floor and the ceiling?

36. Refer to Figure 12.16c. A lintel of prestressed reinforced concrete is 1.50 m long. The cross-sectional area of the concrete is 50.0 cm^2. The concrete encloses one steel reinforcing rod with cross-sectional area 1.50 cm^2. The rod joins two strong end plates. Young's modulus for the concrete is 30.0×10^9 N/m^2. After the concrete cures and the original tension T_1 in the rod is released, the concrete is to be under compressive stress 8.00×10^6 N/m^2. (a) By what distance will the rod compress the concrete when the original tension in the rod is released? (b) What is the new tension T_2 in the rod? (c) The rod will then be how much longer than its unstressed length? (d) When the concrete was poured, the rod should have been stretched by what extension distance from its unstressed length? (e) Find the required original tension T_1 in the rod.

37. A hungry bear weighing 700 N walks out on a beam in an attempt to retrieve a basket of food hanging at the end of the beam (Fig. P12.37). The beam is uniform, weighs 200 N, and is 6.00 m long; the basket weighs 80.0 N. (a) Draw a free-body diagram for the beam. (b) When the bear is at $x = 1.00$ m, find the tension in the wire and the components of the force exerted by the wall on the left end of the beam. (c) **What If?** If the wire can withstand a maximum tension of 900 N, what is the maximum distance the bear can walk before the wire breaks?

Figure P12.37

2 = intermediate;   3 = challenging;   □ = SSM/SG;   ▲ = ThomsonNOW;   ░ = symbolic reasoning;   ● = qualitative reasoning

38. The following equations are obtained from a free-body diagram of a rectangular farm gate, supported by two hinges on the left-hand side. A bucket of grain is hanging from the latch.

$$-A + C = 0$$

$$+B - 392 \text{ N} - 50.0 \text{ N} = 0$$

$$A(0) + B(0) + C(1.80 \text{ m}) - 392 \text{ N}(1.50 \text{ m})$$
$$- 50.0 \text{ N}(3.00 \text{ m}) = 0$$

(a) Draw the free-body diagram and complete the statement of the problem, specifying the unknowns. (b) Determine the values of the unknowns and state the physical meaning of each.

39. ▲ A uniform sign of weight F_g and width $2L$ hangs from a light, horizontal beam hinged at the wall and supported by a cable (Fig. P12.39). Determine (a) the tension in the cable and (b) the components of the reaction force exerted by the wall on the beam, in terms of F_g, d, L, and θ.

Figure P12.39

40. A 1 200-N uniform boom is supported by a cable as shown in Figure P12.40. The boom is pivoted at the bottom, and a 2 000-N object hangs from its top. Find the tension in the cable and the components of the reaction force exerted by the floor on the boom.

Figure P12.40

41. A crane of mass 3 000 kg supports a load of 10 000 kg as shown in Figure P12.41. The crane is pivoted with a frictionless pin at A and rests against a smooth support at B. Find the reaction forces at A and B.

Figure P12.41

42. ● Assume a person bends forward to lift a load "with his back" as shown in Figure P12.42a. The person's spine pivots mainly at the fifth lumbar vertebra, with the principal supporting force provided by the erector spinalis muscle in the back. To estimate the magnitude of the forces involved, consider the model shown in Figure P12.42b for a person bending forward to lift a 200-N object. The person's spine and upper body are represented as a uniform horizontal rod of weight 350 N, pivoted at the base of the spine. The erector spinalis muscle, attached at a point two thirds of the way up the spine, maintains the position of the back. The angle between the spine and this muscle is 12.0°. Find (a) the tension in the back muscle and (b) the compressional force in the spine. (c) Is this method a good way to lift a load? Explain your answer, using the results of parts (a) and (b). It can be instructive to compare a human to other animals. Can you suggest a better method to lift a load?

Figure P12.42

43. A 10 000-N shark is supported by a cable attached to a 4.00 m rod that can pivot at the base. Calculate the tension in the tie rope between the rod and the wall, assuming the tie rope is holding the system in the position shown in Figure P12.43. Find the horizontal and vertical forces exerted on the base of the rod. Ignore the weight of the rod.

Figure P12.43

44. A uniform rod of weight F_g and length L is supported at its ends by a frictionless trough as shown in Figure P12.44. (a) Show that the center of gravity of the rod must be vertically over point O when the rod is in equilibrium. (b) Determine the equilibrium value of the angle θ.

Figure P12.44

45. A force is exerted on a uniform rectangular cabinet weighing 400 N as shown in Figure P12.45. (a) The cabinet slides with constant speed when $F = 200$ N and $h = 0.400$ m. Find the coefficient of kinetic friction and the position of the resultant normal force. (b) Taking $F = 300$ N, find the value of h for which the cabinet just begins to tip.

$w = 60.0$ cm

$\ell = 100$ cm

Al's Cabinets

$\vec{\mathbf{F}}$

37.0°

h

Figure P12.45

46. Consider the rectangular cabinet of Problem 45, but with a force $\vec{\mathbf{F}}$ applied horizontally at the upper edge. (a) What is the minimum force required to start to tip the cabinet? (b) What is the minimum coefficient of static friction required for the cabinet not to slide with the application of a force of this magnitude? (c) Find the magnitude and direction of the minimum force required to tip the cabinet if the point of application can be chosen anywhere on the cabinet.

47. A uniform beam of mass m is inclined at an angle θ to the horizontal. Its upper end produces a 90° bend in a very rough rope tied to a wall, and its lower end rests on a rough floor (Fig. P12.47). (a) Let μ_s represent the coefficient of static friction between beam and floor. Assume μ_s is less than the cotangent of θ. Determine an expression for the maximum mass M that can be suspended from the top before the beam slips. (b) Determine the magnitude of the reaction force at the floor and the magnitude of the force exerted by the beam on the rope at P in terms of m, M, and μ_s.

P

M

m

θ

Figure P12.47

48. ● Consider a light truss, with weight negligible compared with the load it supports. Suppose it is formed from struts lying in a plane and joined by smooth hinge pins at their ends. External forces act on the truss only at the joints. Figure P12.48 shows one example of the simplest truss, with three struts and three pins. State reasoning to prove that the force any strut exerts on a pin must be directed along the length of the strut, as a force of tension or compression.

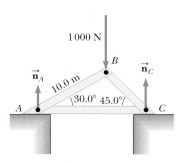

1 000 N

B

$\vec{\mathbf{n}}_A$ $\vec{\mathbf{n}}_C$

10.0 m

A 30.0° 45.0° C

Figure P12.48

49. Figure P12.48 shows a truss that supports a downward force of 1 000 N applied at the point B. The truss has negligible weight. The piers at A and C are smooth. (a) Apply the conditions of equilibrium to prove that $n_A = 366$ N and $n_C = 634$ N. (b) Use the result proved in Problem 48 to identify the directions of the forces that the bars exert on the pins joining them. Find the force of tension or of compression in each of the three bars.

50. One side of a plant shelf is supported by a bracket mounted on a vertical wall by a single screw as shown in Figure P12.50. Ignore the weight of the bracket. (a) Find the horizontal component of the force that the screw exerts on the bracket when an 80.0 N vertical force is applied as shown. (b) As your grandfather waters his geraniums, the 80.0-N load force is increasing at the rate 0.150 N/s. At what rate is the force exerted by the screw changing? *Suggestions:* Imagine that the bracket is slightly loose. You can do parts (a) and (b) most efficiently if you call the load force W and solve symbolically for the screw force F.

80.0 N   5.00 cm

3.00 cm

6.00 cm

Figure P12.50

51. A stepladder of negligible weight is constructed as shown in Figure P12.51. A painter of mass 70.0 kg stands on the ladder 3.00 m from the bottom. Assume the floor is frictionless. Find (a) the tension in the horizontal bar

C

2.00 m

3.00 m

2.00 m

A 2.00 m B

Figure P12.51

connecting the two halves of the ladder, (b) the normal forces at *A* and *B*, and (c) the components of the reaction force at the single hinge *C* that the left half of the ladder exerts on the right half. *Suggestion:* Treat the ladder as a single object, but also each half of the ladder separately.

52. ● Figure P12.52 shows a vertical force applied tangentially to a uniform cylinder of weight F_g. The coefficient of static friction between the cylinder and all surfaces is 0.500. In terms of F_g, find the maximum force *P* that can be applied without causing the cylinder to rotate. As a first step, explain why both friction forces will be at their maximum values when the cylinder is on the verge of slipping.

Figure P12.52

53. ▲ **Review problem.** A wire of length *L*, Young's modulus *Y*, and cross-sectional area *A* is stretched elastically by an amount ΔL. By Hooke's law, the restoring force is $-k\,\Delta L$. (a) Show that $k = YA/L$. (b) Show that the work done in stretching the wire by an amount ΔL is

$$W = \tfrac{1}{2} YA \frac{(\Delta L)^2}{L}$$

54. Two racquetballs each having a mass of 170 g are placed in a glass jar as shown in Figure P12.54. Their centers and the point *A* lie on a straight line. Assume the walls are frictionless. (a) Determine P_1, P_2, and P_3. (b) Determine the magnitude of the force exerted by the left ball on the right ball.

Figure P12.54

55. In exercise physiology studies, it is sometimes important to determine the location of a person's center of mass. This determination can be done with the arrangement shown in Figure P12.55. A light plank rests on two scales,

Figure P12.55

which read $F_{g1} = 380$ N and $F_{g2} = 320$ N. A distance of 2.00 m separates the scales. How far from the woman's feet is her center of mass?

56. A steel cable 3.00 cm² in cross-sectional area has a mass of 2.40 kg per meter of length. If 500 m of the cable is hung over a vertical cliff, how much does the cable stretch under its own weight? Take $Y_{\text{steel}} = 2.00 \times 10^{11}$ N/m².

57. (a) Estimate the force with which a karate master strikes a board, assuming the hand's speed at the moment of impact is 10.0 m/s, decreasing to 1.00 m/s during a 0.002 00-s time interval of contact between the hand and the board. The mass of his hand and arm is 1.00 kg. (b) Estimate the shear stress, assuming this force is exerted on a 1.00-cm-thick pine board that is 10.0 cm wide. (c) If the maximum shear stress a pine board can support before breaking is 3.60×10^6 N/m², will the board break?

58. **Review problem.** An aluminum wire is 0.850 m long and has a circular cross section of diameter 0.780 mm. Fixed at the top end, the wire supports a 1.20-kg object that swings in a horizontal circle. Determine the angular velocity required to produce a strain of 1.00×10^{-3}.

59. **Review problem.** A trailer with loaded weight $\vec{F}_g$ is being pulled by a vehicle with a force $\vec{P}$ as shown in Figure P12.59. The trailer is loaded such that its center of mass is located as shown. Ignore the force of rolling friction and let *a* represent the *x* component of the acceleration of the trailer. (a) Find the vertical component of $\vec{P}$ in terms of the given parameters. (b) Assume $a = 2.00$ m/s² and $h = 1.50$ m. What must be the value of *d* so that $P_y = 0$ (no vertical load on the vehicle)? (c) Find the values of P_x and P_y given that $F_g = 1\,500$ N, $d = 0.800$ m, $L = 3.00$ m, $h = 1.50$ m, and $a = -2.00$ m/s².

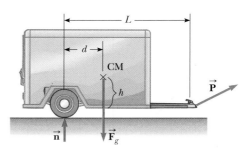

Figure P12.59

60. **Review problem.** A car moves with speed *v* on a horizontal circular track of radius *R*. A head-on view of the car is shown in Figure P12.60. The height of the car's center of mass above the ground is *h*, and the separation between its inner and outer wheels is *d*. The road is dry, and the

Figure P12.60

car does not skid. Show that the maximum speed the car can have without overturning is given by

$$v_{max} = \sqrt{\frac{gRd}{2h}}$$

To reduce the risk of rollover, should one increase or decrease h? Should one increase or decrease the width d of the wheel base?

Answers to Quick Quizzes

12.1 (a). The unbalanced torques due to the forces in Figure 12.2 cause an angular acceleration even though the translational acceleration is zero.

12.2 (b). The lines of action of all the forces in Figure 12.3 intersect at a common point. Therefore, the net torque about this point is zero. This zero value of the net torque is independent of the values of the forces. Because no force has a downward component, there is a net force and the object is not in force equilibrium.

12.3 (b). Both the object and the center of gravity of the meterstick are 25 cm from the pivot point. Therefore, the meterstick and the object must have the same mass for the system to be balanced.

12.4 (i), (b). The friction force on the block as it slides along the surface is parallel to the lower surface and will cause the block to undergo a shear deformation. (ii), (a). The stretching of the wire due to the increased tension is described by Young's modulus. (iii), (c). The pressure of the atmosphere results in a force of uniform magnitude perpendicular at all points on the surface of the sphere.

The red supergiant V838 Monocerotis is 20 000 lightyears from Earth. In 2002, the star exhibited a major outburst of energy typical of a nova event. Following the outburst, however, the variable behavior of infrared radiation from the star did not follow the typical nova pattern. Models of gravitational interaction leading to the merging of the star with a binary companion or its own planets have been proposed to explain the unusual behavior. (©STScI/NASA/Corbis)

13 Universal Gravitation

Before 1687, a large amount of data had been collected on the motions of the Moon and the planets, but a clear understanding of the forces related to these motions was not available. In that year, Isaac Newton provided the key that unlocked the secrets of the heavens. He knew, from his first law, that a net force had to be acting on the Moon because without such a force the Moon would move in a straight-line path rather than in its almost circular orbit. Newton reasoned that this force was the gravitational attraction exerted by the Earth on the Moon. He realized that the forces involved in the Earth–Moon attraction and in the Sun–planet attraction were not something special to those systems, but rather were particular cases of a general and universal attraction between objects. In other words, Newton saw that the same force of attraction that causes the Moon to follow its path around the Earth also causes an apple to fall from a tree. It was the first time that "earthly" and "heavenly" motions were unified.

In this chapter, we study the law of universal gravitation. We emphasize a description of planetary motion because astronomical data provide an important test of this law's validity. We then show that the laws of planetary motion developed by Johannes Kepler follow from the law of universal gravitation and the principle of conservation of angular momentum. We conclude by deriving a general expression for gravitational potential energy and examining the energetics of planetary and satellite motion.

13.1   Newton's Law of Universal Gravitation

You may have heard the legend that, while napping under a tree, Newton was struck on the head by a falling apple. This alleged accident supposedly prompted him to imagine that perhaps all objects in the Universe were attracted to each other in the same way the apple was attracted to the Earth. Newton analyzed astronomical data on the motion of the Moon around the Earth. From that analysis, he made the bold assertion that the force law governing the motion of planets was the *same* as the force law that attracted a falling apple to the Earth.

In 1687, Newton published his work on the law of gravity in his treatise *Mathematical Principles of Natural Philosophy*. **Newton's law of universal gravitation** states that

> every particle in the Universe attracts every other particle with a force that is directly proportional to the product of their masses and inversely proportional to the square of the distance between them.

◀ The law of universal gravitation

If the particles have masses m_1 and m_2 and are separated by a distance r, the magnitude of this gravitational force is

$$F_g = G\frac{m_1 m_2}{r^2} \tag{13.1}$$

where G is a constant, called the *universal gravitational constant*. Its value in SI units is

$$G = 6.673 \times 10^{-11}\ \text{N} \cdot \text{m}^2/\text{kg}^2 \tag{13.2}$$

Henry Cavendish (1731–1810) measured the universal gravitational constant in an important 1798 experiment. Cavendish's apparatus consists of two small spheres, each of mass m, fixed to the ends of a light, horizontal rod suspended by a fine fiber or thin metal wire as illustrated in Figure 13.1. When two large spheres, each of mass M, are placed near the smaller ones, the attractive force between smaller and larger spheres causes the rod to rotate and twist the wire suspension to a new equilibrium orientation. The angle of rotation is measured by the deflection of a light beam reflected from a mirror attached to the vertical suspension.

The form of the force law given by Equation 13.1 is often referred to as an **inverse-square law** because the magnitude of the force varies as the inverse square of the separation of the particles.[1] We shall see other examples of this type of force law in subsequent chapters. We can express this force in vector form by defining a unit vector $\hat{\mathbf{r}}_{12}$ (Active Fig. 13.2). Because this unit vector is directed from particle 1 toward particle 2, the force exerted by particle 1 on particle 2 is

$$\vec{\mathbf{F}}_{12} = -G\frac{m_1 m_2}{r^2}\,\hat{\mathbf{r}}_{12} \tag{13.3}$$

where the negative sign indicates that particle 2 is attracted to particle 1; hence, the force on particle 2 must be directed toward particle 1. By Newton's third law, the force exerted by particle 2 on particle 1, designated $\vec{\mathbf{F}}_{21}$, is equal in magnitude to $\vec{\mathbf{F}}_{12}$ and in the opposite direction. That is, these forces form an action–reaction pair, and $\vec{\mathbf{F}}_{21} = -\vec{\mathbf{F}}_{12}$.

Two features of Equation 13.3 deserve mention. First, the gravitational force is a field force that always exists between two particles, regardless of the medium that separates them. Because the force varies as the inverse square of the distance between the particles, it decreases rapidly with increasing separation.

Equation 13.3 can also be used to show that **the gravitational force exerted by a finite-size, spherically symmetric mass distribution on a particle outside the**

Figure 13.1   Cavendish apparatus for measuring G. The dashed line represents the original position of the rod.

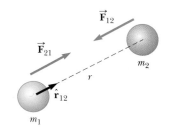

ACTIVE FIGURE 13.2

The gravitational force between two particles is attractive. The unit vector $\hat{\mathbf{r}}_{12}$ is directed from particle 1 toward particle 2. Notice that $\vec{\mathbf{F}}_{21} = -\vec{\mathbf{F}}_{12}$.

Sign in at www.thomsonedu.com and go to ThomsonNOW to change the masses of the particles and the separation distance between the particles and see the effect on the gravitational force.

---

[1] An *inverse* proportionality between two quantities x and y is one in which $y = k/x$, where k is a constant. A *direct* proportion between x and y exists when $y = kx$.

distribution is the same as if the entire mass of the distribution were concentrated at the center. For example, the magnitude of the force exerted by the Earth on a particle of mass *m* near the Earth's surface is

$$F_g = G\frac{M_E m}{R_E^2} \tag{13.4}$$

where M_E is the Earth's mass and R_E its radius. This force is directed toward the center of the Earth.

Quick Quiz 13.1 A planet has two moons of equal mass. Moon 1 is in a circular orbit of radius *r*. Moon 2 is in a circular orbit of radius 2*r*. What is the magnitude of the gravitational force exerted by the planet on Moon 2? (a) four times as large as that on Moon 1 (b) twice as large as that on Moon 1 (c) equal to that on Moon 1 (d) half as large as that on Moon 1 (e) one-fourth as large as that on Moon 1

EXAMPLE 13.1   Billiards, Anyone?

Three 0.300-kg billiard balls are placed on a table at the corners of a right triangle as shown in Figure 13.3. The sides of the triangle are of lengths *a* = 0.400 m, *b* = 0.300 m, and *c* = 0.500 m. Calculate the gravitational force vector on the cue ball (designated m_1) resulting from the other two balls as well as the magnitude and direction of this force.

SOLUTION

Conceptualize Notice in Figure 13.3 that the cue ball is attracted to both other balls by the gravitational force. We can see graphically that the net force should point upward and toward the right. We locate our coordinate axes as shown in Figure 13.3, placing our origin at the position of the cue ball.

Categorize This problem involves evaluating the gravitational forces on the cue ball using Equation 13.3. Once these forces are evaluated, it becomes a vector addition problem to find the net force.

Figure 13.3 (Example 13.1) The resultant gravitational force acting on the cue ball is the vector sum $\vec{\mathbf{F}}_{21} + \vec{\mathbf{F}}_{31}$.

Analyze Find the force exerted by m_2 on the cue ball:

$$\vec{\mathbf{F}}_{21} = G\frac{m_2 m_1}{r_{21}^2}\hat{\mathbf{j}}$$

$$= (6.67 \times 10^{-11}\ \text{N} \cdot \text{m}^2/\text{kg}^2)\frac{(0.300\ \text{kg})(0.300\ \text{kg})}{(0.400\ \text{m})^2}\hat{\mathbf{j}}$$

$$= 3.75 \times 10^{-11}\hat{\mathbf{j}}\ \text{N}$$

Find the force exerted by m_3 on the cue ball:

$$\vec{\mathbf{F}}_{31} = G\frac{m_3 m_1}{r_{31}^2}\hat{\mathbf{i}}$$

$$= (6.67 \times 10^{-11}\ \text{N} \cdot \text{m}^2/\text{kg}^2)\frac{(0.300\ \text{kg})(0.300\ \text{kg})}{(0.300\ \text{m})^2}\hat{\mathbf{i}}$$

$$= 6.67 \times 10^{-11}\hat{\mathbf{i}}\ \text{N}$$

Find the net gravitational force on the cue ball by adding these force vectors:

$$\vec{\mathbf{F}} = \vec{\mathbf{F}}_{31} + \vec{\mathbf{F}}_{21} = (6.67\hat{\mathbf{i}} + 3.75\hat{\mathbf{j}}) \times 10^{-11}\ \text{N}$$

Find the magnitude of this force:

$$F = \sqrt{F_{31}^2 + F_{21}^2} = \sqrt{(6.67)^2 + (3.75)^2} \times 10^{-11}\ \text{N}$$

$$= 7.65 \times 10^{-11}\ \text{N}$$

Find the tangent of the angle θ for the net force vector:

$$\tan \theta = \frac{F_y}{F_x} = \frac{F_{21}}{F_{31}} = \frac{3.75 \times 10^{-11} \text{ N}}{6.67 \times 10^{-11} \text{ N}} = 0.562$$

Evaluate the angle θ:

$$\theta = \tan^{-1}(0.562) = \boxed{29.3°}$$

Finalize   The result for F shows that the gravitational forces between everyday objects have extremely small magnitudes.

13.2   Free-Fall Acceleration and the Gravitational Force

Because the magnitude of the force acting on a freely falling object of mass m near the Earth's surface is given by Equation 13.4, we can equate this force to that given by Equation 5.6, $F_g = mg$, to obtain

$$mg = G\frac{M_E m}{R_E^2}$$

$$g = G\frac{M_E}{R_E^2} \tag{13.5}$$

Now consider an object of mass m located a distance h above the Earth's surface or a distance r from the Earth's center, where $r = R_E + h$. The magnitude of the gravitational force acting on this object is

$$F_g = G\frac{M_E m}{r^2} = G\frac{M_E m}{(R_E + h)^2}$$

The magnitude of the gravitational force acting on the object at this position is also $F_g = mg$, where g is the value of the free-fall acceleration at the altitude h. Substituting this expression for F_g into the last equation shows that g is given by

$$g = \frac{GM_E}{r^2} = \frac{GM_E}{(R_E + h)^2} \tag{13.6}$$

◀ Variation of g with altitude

Therefore, it follows that g *decreases* with *increasing altitude*. Values of g at various altitudes are listed in Table 13.1. Because an object's weight is mg, we see that as $r \to \infty$, the weight approaches zero.

TABLE 13.1

Free-Fall Acceleration g at Various Altitudes Above the Earth's Surface

Altitude h (km)	g (m/s²)
1 000	7.33
2 000	5.68
3 000	4.53
4 000	3.70
5 000	3.08
6 000	2.60
7 000	2.23
8 000	1.93
9 000	1.69
10 000	1.49
50 000	0.13
∞	0

Quick Quiz 13.2   Superman stands on top of a very tall mountain and throws a baseball horizontally with a speed such that the baseball goes into a circular orbit around the Earth. While the baseball is in orbit, what is the magnitude of the acceleration of the ball? (a) It depends on how fast the baseball is thrown. (b) It is zero because the ball does not fall to the ground. (c) It is slightly less than 9.80 m/s². (d) It is equal to 9.80 m/s².

EXAMPLE 13.2   **Variation of g with Altitude h**

The International Space Station operates at an altitude of 350 km. Plans for the final construction show that 4.22×10^6 N of material, measured at the Earth's surface, will have been lifted off the surface by various spacecraft. What is the weight of the space station when in orbit?

SOLUTION

Conceptualize The mass of the space station is fixed; it is independent of its location. Based on the discussion in this section, we realize that the value of g will be reduced at the height of the space station's orbit. Therefore, its weight will be smaller than that at the surface of the Earth.

Categorize This example is a relatively simple substitution problem.

Find the mass of the space station from its weight at the surface of the Earth:

$$m = \frac{F_g}{g} = \frac{4.22 \times 10^6 \text{ N}}{9.80 \text{ m/s}^2} = 4.31 \times 10^5 \text{ kg}$$

Use Equation 13.6 with $h = 350$ km to find g at the orbital location:

$$g = \frac{GM_E}{(R_E + h)^2}$$

$$= \frac{(6.67 \times 10^{-11} \text{ N} \cdot \text{m}^2/\text{kg}^2)(5.98 \times 10^{24} \text{ kg})}{(6.37 \times 10^6 \text{ m} + 0.350 \times 10^6 \text{ m})^2} = 8.83 \text{ m/s}^2$$

Use this value of g to find the space station's weight in orbit:

$$mg = (4.31 \times 10^5 \text{ kg})(8.83 \text{ m/s}^2) = \boxed{3.80 \times 10^6 \text{ N}}$$

EXAMPLE 13.3 **The Density of the Earth**

Using the known radius of the Earth and that $g = 9.80$ m/s² at the Earth's surface, find the average density of the Earth.

SOLUTION

Conceptualize Assume the Earth is a perfect sphere. The density of material in the Earth varies, but let's adopt a simplified model in which we assume the density to be uniform throughout the Earth. The resulting density is the average density of the Earth.

Categorize This example is a relatively simple substitution problem.

Solve Equation 13.5 for the mass of the Earth:

$$M_E = \frac{gR_E^2}{G}$$

Substitute this mass into the definition of density (Eq. 1.1):

$$\rho_E = \frac{M_E}{V_E} = \frac{(gR_E^2/G)}{\frac{4}{3}\pi R_E^3} = \frac{3}{4}\frac{g}{\pi G R_E}$$

$$= \frac{3}{4}\frac{9.80 \text{ m/s}^2}{\pi(6.67 \times 10^{-11} \text{ N} \cdot \text{m}^2/\text{kg}^2)(6.37 \times 10^6 \text{ m})} = \boxed{5.51 \times 10^3 \text{ kg/m}^3}$$

What If? What if you were told that a typical density of granite at the Earth's surface were 2.75×10^3 kg/m³. What would you conclude about the density of the material in the Earth's interior?

Answer Because this value is about half the density we calculated as an average for the entire Earth, we would conclude that the inner core of the Earth has a density much higher than the average value. It is most amazing that the Cavendish experiment—which determines G and can be done on a tabletop—combined with simple free-fall measurements of g, provides information about the core of the Earth!

13.3   Kepler's Laws and the Motion of Planets

Humans have observed the movements of the planets, stars, and other celestial objects for thousands of years. In early history, these observations led scientists to regard the Earth as the center of the Universe. This *geocentric model* was elaborated and formalized by the Greek astronomer Claudius Ptolemy (c. 100–c. 170) in the second century and was accepted for the next 1 400 years. In 1543, Polish astronomer Nicolaus Copernicus (1473–1543) suggested that the Earth and the other planets revolved in circular orbits around the Sun (the *heliocentric model*).

Danish astronomer Tycho Brahe (1546–1601) wanted to determine how the heavens were constructed and pursued a project to determine the positions of both stars and planets. Those observations of the planets and 777 stars visible to the naked eye were carried out with only a large sextant and a compass. (The telescope had not yet been invented.)

German astronomer Johannes Kepler was Brahe's assistant for a short while before Brahe's death, whereupon he acquired his mentor's astronomical data and spent 16 years trying to deduce a mathematical model for the motion of the planets. Such data are difficult to sort out because the moving planets are observed from a moving Earth. After many laborious calculations, Kepler found that Brahe's data on the revolution of Mars around the Sun led to a successful model.

Kepler's complete analysis of planetary motion is summarized in three statements known as **Kepler's laws:**

1. All planets move in elliptical orbits with the Sun at one focus.
2. The radius vector drawn from the Sun to a planet sweeps out equal areas in equal time intervals.
3. The square of the orbital period of any planet is proportional to the cube of the semimajor axis of the elliptical orbit.

◀   Kepler's laws

JOHANNES KEPLER
German astronomer (1571–1630)
Kepler is best known for developing the laws of planetary motion based on the careful observations of Tycho Brahe.

Kepler's First Law

We are familiar with circular orbits of objects around gravitational force centers from our discussions in this chapter. Kepler's first law indicates that the circular orbit is a very special case and elliptical orbits are the general situation. This notion was difficult for scientists of the time to accept because they believed that perfect circular orbits of the planets reflected the perfection of heaven.

Active Figure 13.4 shows the geometry of an ellipse, which serves as our model for the elliptical orbit of a planet. An ellipse is mathematically defined by choosing two points F_1 and F_2, each of which is a called a **focus,** and then drawing a curve through points for which the sum of the distances r_1 and r_2 from F_1 and F_2, respectively, is a constant. The longest distance through the center between points on the ellipse (and passing through each focus) is called the **major axis,** and this distance is $2a$. In Active Figure 13.4, the major axis is drawn along the x direction. The distance a is called the **semimajor axis.** Similarly, the shortest distance through the center between points on the ellipse is called the **minor axis** of length $2b$, where the distance b is the **semiminor axis.** Either focus of the ellipse is located at a distance c from the center of the ellipse, where $a^2 = b^2 + c^2$. In the elliptical orbit of a planet around the Sun, the Sun is at one focus of the ellipse. There is nothing at the other focus.

The **eccentricity** of an ellipse is defined as $e = c/a$, and it describes the general shape of the ellipse. For a circle, $c = 0$, and the eccentricity is therefore zero. The smaller b is compared to a, the shorter the ellipse is along the y direction compared with its extent in the x direction in Active Figure 13.4. As b decreases, c increases and the eccentricity e increases. Therefore, higher values of eccentricity correspond to longer and thinner ellipses. The range of values of the eccentricity for an ellipse is $0 < e < 1$.

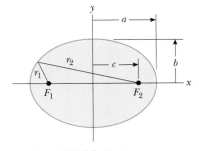

ACTIVE FIGURE 13.4

Plot of an ellipse. The semimajor axis has length a, and the semiminor axis has length b. Each focus is located at a distance c from the center on each side of the center.

Sign in at www.thomsonedu.com and go to ThomsonNOW to move the focal points or enter values for a, b, c, and the eccentricity $e = c/a$ and see the resulting elliptical shape.

PITFALL PREVENTION 13.2
Where Is the Sun?

The Sun is located at one focus of the elliptical orbit of a planet. It is *not* located at the center of the ellipse.

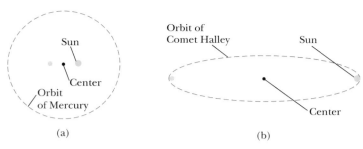

Figure 13.5 (a) The shape of the orbit of Mercury, which has the highest eccentricity ($e = 0.21$) among the eight planets in the solar system. The Sun is located at the large yellow dot, which is a focus of the ellipse. There is nothing physical located at the center (the small dot) or the other focus (the blue dot). (b) The shape of the orbit of Comet Halley.

Eccentricities for planetary orbits vary widely in the solar system. The eccentricity of the Earth's orbit is 0.017, which makes it nearly circular. On the other hand, the eccentricity of Mercury's orbit is 0.21, the highest of the eight planets. Figure 13.5a shows an ellipse with an eccentricity equal to that of Mercury's orbit. Notice that even this highest-eccentricity orbit is difficult to distinguish from a circle, which is one reason Kepler's first law is an admirable accomplishment. The eccentricity of the orbit of Comet Halley is 0.97, describing an orbit whose major axis is much longer than its minor axis, as shown in Figure 13.5b. As a result, Comet Halley spends much of its 76-year period far from the Sun and invisible from the Earth. It is only visible to the naked eye during a small part of its orbit when it is near the Sun.

Now imagine a planet in an elliptical orbit such as that shown in Active Figure 13.4, with the Sun at focus F_2. When the planet is at the far left in the diagram, the distance between the planet and the Sun is $a + c$. At this point, called the *aphelion*, the planet is at its maximum distance from the Sun. (For an object in orbit around the Earth, this point is called the *apogee*.) Conversely, when the planet is at the right end of the ellipse, the distance between the planet and the Sun is $a - c$. At this point, called the *perihelion* (for an Earth orbit, the *perigee*), the planet is at its minimum distance from the Sun.

Kepler's first law is a direct result of the inverse square nature of the gravitational force. We have already discussed circular and elliptical orbits, the allowed shapes of orbits for objects that are *bound* to the gravitational force center. These objects include planets, asteroids, and comets that move repeatedly around the Sun, as well as moons orbiting a planet. There are also *unbound* objects, such as a meteoroid from deep space that might pass by the Sun once and then never return. The gravitational force between the Sun and these objects also varies as the inverse square of the separation distance, and the allowed paths for these objects include parabolas ($e = 1$) and hyperbolas ($e > 1$).

Kepler's Second Law

Kepler's second law can be shown to be a consequence of angular momentum conservation as follows. Consider a planet of mass M_p moving about the Sun in an elliptical orbit (Active Fig. 13.6a). Let us consider the planet as a system. We model the Sun to be so much more massive than the planet that the Sun does not move. The gravitational force exerted by the Sun on the planet is a central force, always along the radius vector, directed toward the Sun (Active Fig. 13.6a). The torque on the planet due to this central force is clearly zero because $\vec{F}_g$ is parallel to $\vec{r}$.

Recall that the external net torque on a system equals the time rate of change of angular momentum of the system; that is, $\Sigma \vec{\tau} = d\vec{L}/dt$ (Eq. 11.13). Therefore, because the external torque on the planet is zero, it is modeled as an isolated system for angular momentum and **the angular momentum $\vec{L}$ of the planet is a constant of the motion:**

$$\vec{L} = \vec{r} \times \vec{p} = M_p \vec{r} \times \vec{v} = \text{constant}$$

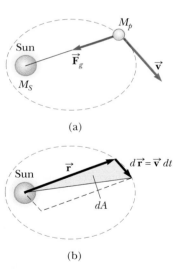

(a)

(b)

ACTIVE FIGURE 13.6

(a) The gravitational force acting on a planet is directed toward the Sun. (b) As a planet orbits the Sun, the area swept out by the radius vector in a time interval dt is equal to half the area of the parallelogram formed by the vectors $\vec{r}$ and $d\vec{r} = \vec{v} \, dt$.

Sign in at www.thomsonedu.com and go to ThomsonNOW to assign a value of the eccentricity and see the resulting motion of the planet around the Sun.

We can relate this result to the following geometric consideration. In a time interval dt, the radius vector $\vec{r}$ in Active Figure 13.6b sweeps out the area dA, which equals half the area $|\vec{r} \times d\vec{r}|$ of the parallelogram formed by the vectors $\vec{r}$ and $d\vec{r}$. Because the displacement of the planet in the time interval dt is given by $d\vec{r} = \vec{v}\,dt$,

$$dA = \tfrac{1}{2}|\vec{r} \times d\vec{r}| = \tfrac{1}{2}|\vec{r} \times \vec{v}\,dt| = \frac{L}{2M_p}\,dt$$

$$\frac{dA}{dt} = \frac{L}{2M_p} \tag{13.7}$$

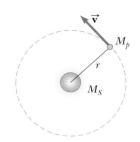

Figure 13.7   A planet of mass M_p moving in a circular orbit around the Sun. The orbits of all planets except Mercury are nearly circular.

where L and M_p are both constants. This result shows that that **the radius vector from the Sun to any planet sweeps out equal areas in equal times.**

This conclusion is a result of the gravitational force being a central force, which in turn implies that angular momentum of the planet is constant. Therefore, the law applies to *any* situation that involves a central force, whether inverse square or not.

Kepler's Third Law

Kepler's third law can be predicted from the inverse-square law for circular orbits. Consider a planet of mass M_p that is assumed to be moving about the Sun (mass M_S) in a circular orbit as in Figure 13.7. Because the gravitational force provides the centripetal acceleration of the planet as it moves in a circle, we use Newton's second law for a particle in uniform circular motion,

$$F_g = \frac{GM_S M_p}{r^2} = M_p a = \frac{M_p v^2}{r}$$

The orbital speed of the planet is $2\pi r/T$, where T is the period; therefore, the preceding expression becomes

$$\frac{GM_S}{r^2} = \frac{(2\pi r/T)^2}{r}$$

$$T^2 = \left(\frac{4\pi^2}{GM_S}\right) r^3 = K_S r^3$$

where K_S is a constant given by

$$K_S = \frac{4\pi^2}{GM_S} = 2.97 \times 10^{-19} \text{ s}^2/\text{m}^3$$

This equation is also valid for elliptical orbits if we replace r with the length a of the semimajor axis (Active Fig. 13.4):

$$T^2 = \left(\frac{4\pi^2}{GM_S}\right) a^3 = K_S a^3 \tag{13.8}$$

◀ Kepler's third law

Equation 13.8 is Kepler's third law. Because the semimajor axis of a circular orbit is its radius, this equation is valid for both circular and elliptical orbits. Notice that the constant of proportionality K_S is independent of the mass of the planet. Equation 13.8 is therefore valid for *any* planet.[2] If we were to consider the orbit of a satellite such as the Moon about the Earth, the constant would have a different value, with the Sun's mass replaced by the Earth's mass, that is, $K_E = 4\pi^2/GM_E$.

Table 13.2 is a collection of useful data for planets and other objects in the solar system. The far-right column verifies that the ratio T^2/r^3 is constant for all objects orbiting the Sun. The small variations in the values in this column are the result of uncertainties in the data measured for the periods and semimajor axes of the objects.

Recent astronomical work has revealed the existence of a large number of solar system objects beyond the orbit of Neptune. In general, these objects lie in the

[2] Equation 13.8 is indeed a proportion because the ratio of the two quantities T^2 and a^3 is a constant. The variables in a proportion are not required to be limited to the first power only.

TABLE 13.2

Useful Planetary Data

Body	Mass (kg)	Mean Radius (m)	Period of Revolution (s)	Mean Distance from the Sun (m)	$\dfrac{T^2}{r^3}$ (s²/m³)
Mercury	3.18×10^{23}	2.43×10^6	7.60×10^6	5.79×10^{10}	2.97×10^{-19}
Venus	4.88×10^{24}	6.06×10^6	1.94×10^7	1.08×10^{11}	2.99×10^{-19}
Earth	5.98×10^{24}	6.37×10^6	3.156×10^7	1.496×10^{11}	2.97×10^{-19}
Mars	6.42×10^{23}	3.37×10^6	5.94×10^7	2.28×10^{11}	2.98×10^{-19}
Jupiter	1.90×10^{27}	6.99×10^7	3.74×10^8	7.78×10^{11}	2.97×10^{-19}
Saturn	5.68×10^{26}	5.85×10^7	9.35×10^8	1.43×10^{12}	2.99×10^{-19}
Uranus	8.68×10^{25}	2.33×10^7	2.64×10^9	2.87×10^{12}	2.95×10^{-19}
Neptune	1.03×10^{26}	2.21×10^7	5.22×10^9	4.50×10^{12}	2.99×10^{-19}
Pluto[a]	$\approx 1.4 \times 10^{22}$	$\approx 1.5 \times 10^6$	7.82×10^9	5.91×10^{12}	2.96×10^{-19}
Moon	7.36×10^{22}	1.74×10^6	—	—	—
Sun	1.991×10^{30}	6.96×10^8	—	—	—

[a] In August, 2006, the International Astronomical Union adopted a definition of a planet that separates Pluto from the other eight planets. Pluto is now defined as a "dwarf planet" like the asteroid Ceres.

Kuiper belt, a region that extends from about 30 AU (the orbital radius of Neptune) to 50 AU. (An AU is an *astronomical unit,* equal to the radius of the Earth's orbit.) Current estimates identify at least 70 000 objects in this region with diameters larger than 100 km. The first Kuiper belt object (KBO) is Pluto, discovered in 1930, and formerly classified as a planet. Starting in 1992, many more have been detected, such as Varuna (diameter about 900–1 000 km, discovered in 2000), Ixion (diameter about 900–1 000 km, discovered in 2001), and Quaoar (diameter about 800 km, discovered in 2002). Others do not yet have names, but are currently indicated by their date of discovery, such as 2003 EL61, 2004 DW, and 2005 FY9. One KBO, 2003 UP313, is thought to be larger than Pluto.

A subset of about 1 400 KBOs are called "Plutinos" because, like Pluto, they exhibit a resonance phenomenon, orbiting the Sun two times in the same time interval as Neptune revolves three times. The contemporary application of Kepler's laws and such exotic proposals as planetary angular momentum exchange and migrating planets[3] suggest the excitement of this active area of current research.

Quick Quiz 13.3 An asteroid is in a highly eccentric elliptical orbit around the Sun. The period of the asteroid's orbit is 90 days. Which of the following statements is true about the possibility of a collision between this asteroid and the Earth? (a) There is no possible danger of a collision. (b) There is a possibility of a collision. (c) There is not enough information to determine whether there is danger of a collision.

EXAMPLE 13.4 **The Mass of the Sun**

Calculate the mass of the Sun noting that the period of the Earth's orbit around the Sun is 3.156×10^7 s and its distance from the Sun is 1.496×10^{11} m.

SOLUTION

Conceptualize Based on Kepler's third law, we realize that the mass of the Sun is related to the orbital size and period of a planet.

Categorize This example is a relatively simple substitution problem.

[3] R. Malhotra, "Migrating Planets," *Scientific American,* **281**(3): 56–63, September 1999.

Solve Equation 13.8 for the mass of the Sun:

$$M_S = \frac{4\pi^2 r^3}{GT^2}$$

Substitute the known values:

$$M_S = \frac{4\pi^2(1.496 \times 10^{11}\ \text{m})^3}{(6.67 \times 10^{-11}\ \text{N}\cdot\text{m}^2/\text{kg}^2)(3.156 \times 10^7\ \text{s})^2} = \boxed{1.99 \times 10^{30}\ \text{kg}}$$

In Example 13.3, an understanding of gravitational forces enabled us to find out something about the density of the Earth's core, and now we have used this understanding to determine the mass of the Sun!

EXAMPLE 13.5   **A Geosynchronous Satellite**

Consider a satellite of mass m moving in a circular orbit around the Earth at a constant speed v and at an altitude h above the Earth's surface as illustrated in Figure 13.8.

(A) Determine the speed of the satellite in terms of G, h, R_E (the radius of the Earth), and M_E (the mass of the Earth).

SOLUTION

Conceptualize Imagine the satellite moving around the Earth in a circular orbit under the influence of the gravitational force.

Categorize The satellite must have a centripetal acceleration. Therefore, we categorize the satellite as a particle under a net force and a particle in uniform circular motion.

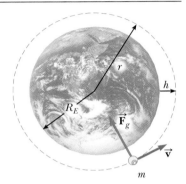

Figure 13.8 (Example 13.5) A satellite of mass m moving around the Earth in a circular orbit of radius r with constant speed v. The only force acting on the satellite is the gravitational force $\vec{F}_g$. (Not drawn to scale.)

Analyze The only external force acting on the satellite is the gravitational force, which acts toward the center of the Earth and keeps the satellite in its circular orbit.

Apply Newton's second law to the satellite:

$$F_g = G\frac{M_E m}{r^2} = ma = m\frac{v^2}{r}$$

Solve for v, noting that the distance r from the center of the Earth to the satellite is $r = R_E + h$:

$$(1)\quad v = \sqrt{\frac{GM_E}{r}} = \sqrt{\frac{GM_E}{R_E + h}}$$

(B) If the satellite is to be *geosynchronous* (that is, appearing to remain over a fixed position on the Earth), how fast is it moving through space?

SOLUTION

To appear to remain over a fixed position on the Earth, the period of the satellite must be 24 h = 86 400 s and the satellite must be in orbit directly over the equator.

Solve Kepler's third law (with $a = r$ and $M_S \rightarrow M_E$) for r:

$$r = \left(\frac{GM_E T^2}{4\pi^2}\right)^{1/3}$$

Substitute numerical values:

$$r = \left[\frac{(6.67 \times 10^{-11}\ \text{N}\cdot\text{m}^2/\text{kg}^2)(5.98 \times 10^{24}\ \text{kg})(86\ 400\ \text{s})^2}{4\pi^2}\right]^{1/3}$$

$$= 4.23 \times 10^7\ \text{m}$$

Use Equation (1) to find the speed of the satellite:

$$v = \sqrt{\frac{(6.67 \times 10^{-11} \text{ N} \cdot \text{m}^2/\text{kg}^2)(5.98 \times 10^{24} \text{ kg})}{4.23 \times 10^7 \text{ m}}}$$

$$= 3.07 \times 10^3 \text{ m/s}$$

Finalize The value of r calculated here translates to a height of the satellite above the surface of the Earth of almost 36 000 km. Therefore, geosynchronous satellites have the advantage of allowing an earthbound antenna to be aimed in a fixed direction, but there is a disadvantage in that the signals between Earth and the satellite must travel a long distance. It is difficult to use geosynchronous satellites for optical observation of the Earth's surface because of their high altitude.

What If? What if the satellite motion in part (A) were taking place at height h above the surface of another planet more massive than the Earth but of the same radius? Would the satellite be moving at a higher speed or a lower speed than it does around the Earth?

Answer If the planet exerts a larger gravitational force on the satellite due to its larger mass, the satellite must move with a higher speed to avoid moving toward the surface. This conclusion is consistent with the predictions of Equation (1), which shows that because the speed v is proportional to the square root of the mass of the planet, the speed increases as the mass of the planet increases.

13.4 The Gravitational Field

When Newton published his theory of universal gravitation, it was considered a success because it satisfactorily explained the motion of the planets. Since 1687, the same theory has been used to account for the motions of comets, the deflection of a Cavendish balance, the orbits of binary stars, and the rotation of galaxies. Nevertheless, both Newton's contemporaries and his successors found it difficult to accept the concept of a force that acts at a distance. They asked how it was possible for two objects to interact when they were not in contact with each other. Newton himself could not answer that question.

An approach to describing interactions between objects that are not in contact came well after Newton's death. This approach enables us to look at the gravitational interaction in a different way, using the concept of a **gravitational field** that exists at every point in space. When a particle of mass m is placed at a point where the gravitational field is $\vec{\mathbf{g}}$, the particle experiences a force $\vec{\mathbf{F}}_g = m\vec{\mathbf{g}}$. In other words, we imagine that the field exerts a force on the particle rather than consider a direct interaction between two particles. The gravitational field $\vec{\mathbf{g}}$ is defined as

Gravitational field ▶

$$\vec{\mathbf{g}} \equiv \frac{\vec{\mathbf{F}}_g}{m} \tag{13.9}$$

That is, the gravitational field at a point in space equals the gravitational force experienced by a *test particle* placed at that point divided by the mass of the test particle. We call the object creating the field the *source particle*. (Although the Earth is not a particle, it is possible to show that we can model the Earth as a particle for the purpose of finding the gravitational field that it creates.) Notice that the presence of the test particle is not necessary for the field to exist: the source particle creates the gravitational field. We can detect the presence of the field and measure its strength by placing a test particle in the field and noting the force exerted on it. In essence, we are describing the "effect" that any object (in this case, the Earth) has on the empty space around itself in terms of the force that *would* be present *if* a second object were somewhere in that space.[4]

[4] We shall return to this idea of mass affecting the space around it when we discuss Einstein's theory of gravitation in Chapter 39.

As an example of how the field concept works, consider an object of mass m near the Earth's surface. Because the gravitational force acting on the object has a magnitude $GM_E m/r^2$ (see Eq. 13.4), the field $\vec{\mathbf{g}}$ at a distance r from the center of the Earth is

$$\vec{\mathbf{g}} = \frac{\vec{\mathbf{F}}_g}{m} = -\frac{GM_E}{r^2}\,\hat{\mathbf{r}} \qquad \textbf{(13.10)}$$

where $\hat{\mathbf{r}}$ is a unit vector pointing radially outward from the Earth and the negative sign indicates that the field points toward the center of the Earth as illustrated in Figure 13.9a. The field vectors at different points surrounding the Earth vary in both direction and magnitude. In a small region near the Earth's surface, the downward field $\vec{\mathbf{g}}$ is approximately constant and uniform as indicated in Figure 13.9b. Equation 13.10 is valid at all points *outside* the Earth's surface, assuming the Earth is spherical. At the Earth's surface, where $r = R_E$, $\vec{\mathbf{g}}$ has a magnitude of 9.80 N/kg. (The unit N/kg is the same as m/s².)

13.5   Gravitational Potential Energy

In Chapter 8, we introduced the concept of gravitational potential energy, which is the energy associated with the configuration of a system of objects interacting via the gravitational force. We emphasized that the gravitational potential energy function mgy for a particle–Earth system is valid only when the particle is near the Earth's surface, where the gravitational force is constant. Because the gravitational force between two particles varies as $1/r^2$, we expect that a more general potential energy function—one that is valid without the restriction of having to be near the Earth's surface—will be different from $U = mgy$.

Recall from Equation 7.26 that the change in the gravitational potential energy of a system associated with a given displacement of a member of the system is defined as the negative of the work done by the gravitational force on that member during the displacement:

$$\Delta U = U_f - U_i = -\int_{r_i}^{r_f} F(r)\,dr \qquad \textbf{(13.11)}$$

We can use this result to evaluate the gravitational potential energy function. Consider a particle of mass m moving between two points Ⓐ and Ⓑ above the Earth's surface (Fig. 13.10). The particle is subject to the gravitational force given by Equation 13.1. We can express this force as

$$F(r) = -\frac{GM_E m}{r^2}$$

where the negative sign indicates that the force is attractive. Substituting this expression for $F(r)$ into Equation 13.11, we can compute the change in the gravitational potential energy function for the particle–Earth system:

$$U_f - U_i = GM_E m \int_{r_i}^{r_f} \frac{dr}{r^2} = GM_E m\left[-\frac{1}{r}\right]_{r_i}^{r_f}$$

$$U_f - U_i = -GM_E m\left(\frac{1}{r_f} - \frac{1}{r_i}\right) \qquad \textbf{(13.12)}$$

As always, the choice of a reference configuration for the potential energy is completely arbitrary. It is customary to choose the reference configuration for zero potential energy to be the same as that for which the force is zero. Taking $U_i = 0$ at $r_i = \infty$, we obtain the important result

$$U(r) = -\frac{GM_E m}{r} \qquad \textbf{(13.13)}$$

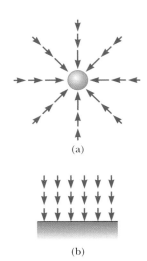

(a)

(b)

Figure 13.9 (a) The gravitational field vectors in the vicinity of a uniform spherical mass such as the Earth vary in both direction and magnitude. The vectors point in the direction of the acceleration a particle would experience if it were placed in the field. The magnitude of the field vector at any location is the magnitude of the free-fall acceleration at that location. (b) The gravitational field vectors in a small region near the Earth's surface are uniform in both direction and magnitude.

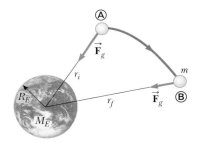

Figure 13.10 As a particle of mass m moves from Ⓐ to Ⓑ above the Earth's surface, the gravitational potential energy of the particle–Earth system changes according to Equation 13.12.

◀ Gravitational potential energy of the Earth–particle system

Figure 13.11 Graph of the gravitational potential energy U versus r for the system of an object above the Earth's surface. The potential energy goes to zero as r approaches infinity.

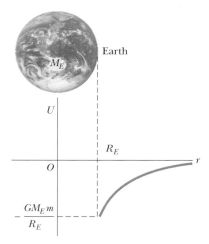

This expression applies when the particle is separated from the center of the Earth by a distance r, provided that $r \geq R_E$. The result is not valid for particles inside the Earth, where $r < R_E$. Because of our choice of U_i, the function U is always negative (Fig. 13.11).

Although Equation 13.13 was derived for the particle–Earth system, it can be applied to any two particles. That is, the gravitational potential energy associated with any pair of particles of masses m_1 and m_2 separated by a distance r is

$$U = -\frac{Gm_1 m_2}{r} \tag{13.14}$$

This expression shows that the gravitational potential energy for any pair of particles varies as $1/r$, whereas the force between them varies as $1/r^2$. Furthermore, the potential energy is negative because the force is attractive and we have chosen the potential energy as zero when the particle separation is infinite. Because the force between the particles is attractive, an external agent must do positive work to increase the separation between them. The work done by the external agent produces an increase in the potential energy as the two particles are separated. That is, U becomes less negative as r increases.

When two particles are at rest and separated by a distance r, an external agent has to supply an energy at least equal to $+Gm_1 m_2/r$ to separate the particles to an infinite distance. It is therefore convenient to think of the absolute value of the potential energy as the *binding energy* of the system. If the external agent supplies an energy greater than the binding energy, the excess energy of the system is in the form of kinetic energy of the particles when the particles are at an infinite separation.

We can extend this concept to three or more particles. In this case, the total potential energy of the system is the sum over all pairs of particles. Each pair contributes a term of the form given by Equation 13.14. For example, if the system contains three particles as in Figure 13.12,

Figure 13.12 Three interacting particles.

$$U_{\text{total}} = U_{12} + U_{13} + U_{23} = -G\left(\frac{m_1 m_2}{r_{12}} + \frac{m_1 m_3}{r_{13}} + \frac{m_2 m_3}{r_{23}}\right) \tag{13.15}$$

The absolute value of U_{total} represents the work needed to separate the particles by an infinite distance.

EXAMPLE 13.6 **The Change in Potential Energy**

A particle of mass m is displaced through a small vertical distance Δy near the Earth's surface. Show that in this situation the general expression for the change in gravitational potential energy given by Equation 13.12 reduces to the familiar relationship $\Delta U = mg\, \Delta y$.

SOLUTION

Conceptualize Compare the two different situations for which we have developed expressions for gravitational potential energy: (1) a planet and an object that are far apart for which the energy expression is Equation 13.12 and (2) a small object at the surface of a planet for which the energy expression is Equation 7.19. We wish to show that these two expressions are equivalent.

Categorize This example is a substitution problem.

Combine the fractions in Equation 13.12:

$$(1) \quad \Delta U = -GM_E m \left(\frac{1}{r_f} - \frac{1}{r_i} \right) = GM_E m \left(\frac{r_f - r_i}{r_i r_f} \right)$$

Evaluate $r_f - r_i$ and $r_i r_f$ if both the initial and final positions of the particle are close to the Earth's surface:

$$r_f - r_i = \Delta y \qquad r_i r_f \approx R_E^2$$

Substitute these expressions into Equation (1):

$$\Delta U \approx \frac{GM_E m}{R_E^2} \Delta y = mg \, \Delta y$$

where $g = GM_E/R_E^2$ (Eq. 13.5).

What If? Suppose you are performing upper-atmosphere studies and are asked by your supervisor to find the height in the Earth's atmosphere at which the "surface equation" $\Delta U = mg \, \Delta y$ gives a 1.0% error in the change in the potential energy. What is this height?

Answer Because the surface equation assumes a constant value for g, it will give a ΔU value that is larger than the value given by the general equation, Equation 13.12.

Set up a ratio reflecting a 1.0% error:

$$\frac{\Delta U_{\text{surface}}}{\Delta U_{\text{general}}} = 1.010$$

Substitute the expressions for each of these changes ΔU:

$$\frac{mg \, \Delta y}{GM_E m (\Delta y / r_i r_f)} = \frac{g r_i r_f}{GM_E} = 1.010$$

Substitute for r_i, r_f, and g from Equation 13.5:

$$\frac{(GM_E/R_E^2) R_E (R_E + \Delta y)}{GM_E} = \frac{R_E + \Delta y}{R_E} = 1 + \frac{\Delta y}{R_E} = 1.010$$

Solve for Δy:

$$\Delta y = 0.010 R_E = 0.010(6.37 \times 10^6 \text{ m}) = 6.37 \times 10^4 \text{ m} = 63.7 \text{ km}$$

13.6 Energy Considerations in Planetary and Satellite Motion

Consider an object of mass m moving with a speed v in the vicinity of a massive object of mass M, where $M \gg m$. The system might be a planet moving around the Sun, a satellite in orbit around the Earth, or a comet making a one-time flyby of the Sun. If we assume the object of mass M is at rest in an inertial reference frame, the total mechanical energy E of the two-object system when the objects are separated by a distance r is the sum of the kinetic energy of the object of mass m and the potential energy of the system, given by Equation 13.14:

$$E = K + U$$

$$E = \tfrac{1}{2}mv^2 - \frac{GMm}{r} \qquad\qquad \textbf{(13.16)}$$

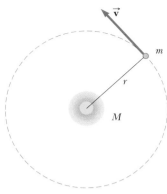

Figure 13.13 An object of mass m moving in a circular orbit about a much larger object of mass M.

Equation 13.16 shows that E may be positive, negative, or zero, depending on the value of v. For a bound system such as the Earth–Sun system, however, E is necessarily *less than zero* because we have chosen the convention that $U \to 0$ as $r \to \infty$.

We can easily establish that $E < 0$ for the system consisting of an object of mass m moving in a circular orbit about an object of mass $M >> m$ (Fig. 13.13). Newton's second law applied to the object of mass m gives

$$F_g = \frac{GMm}{r^2} = ma = \frac{mv^2}{r}$$

Multiplying both sides by r and dividing by 2 gives

$$\tfrac{1}{2}mv^2 = \frac{GMm}{2r} \tag{13.17}$$

Substituting this equation into Equation 13.16, we obtain

$$E = \frac{GMm}{2r} - \frac{GMm}{r}$$

◀ **Total energy for circular orbits**

$$E = -\frac{GMm}{2r} \quad \text{(circular orbits)} \tag{13.18}$$

This result shows that **the total mechanical energy is negative in the case of circular orbits.** Notice that **the kinetic energy is positive and equal to half the absolute value of the potential energy.** The absolute value of E is also equal to the binding energy of the system because this amount of energy must be provided to the system to move the two objects infinitely far apart.

The total mechanical energy is also negative in the case of elliptical orbits. The expression for E for elliptical orbits is the same as Equation 13.18 with r replaced by the semimajor axis length a:

◀ **Total energy for elliptical orbits**

$$E = -\frac{GMm}{2a} \quad \text{(elliptical orbits)} \tag{13.19}$$

Furthermore, the total energy is constant if we assume the system is isolated. Therefore, as the object of mass m moves from Ⓐ to Ⓑ in Figure 13.10, the total energy remains constant and Equation 13.16 gives

$$E = \tfrac{1}{2}mv_i^2 - \frac{GMm}{r_i} = \tfrac{1}{2}mv_f^2 - \frac{GMm}{r_f} \tag{13.20}$$

Combining this statement of energy conservation with our earlier discussion of conservation of angular momentum, we see that **both the total energy and the total angular momentum of a gravitationally bound, two-object system are constants of the motion.**

Quick Quiz 13.4 A comet moves in an elliptical orbit around the Sun. Which point in its orbit (perihelion or aphelion) represents the highest value of (a) the speed of the comet, (b) the potential energy of the comet–Sun system, (c) the kinetic energy of the comet, and (d) the total energy of the comet–Sun system?

EXAMPLE 13.7 | **Changing the Orbit of a Satellite**

A space transportation vehicle releases a 470-kg communications satellite while in an orbit 280 km above the surface of the Earth. A rocket engine on the satellite boosts it into a geosynchronous orbit. How much energy does the engine have to provide?

SOLUTION

Conceptualize Notice that the height of 280 km is much lower than that for a geosynchronous satellite, 36 000 km, as mentioned in Example 13.5. Therefore, energy must be expended to raise the satellite to this much higher position.

Categorize   This example is a substitution problem.

Find the initial radius of the satellite's orbit when it is still in the shuttle's cargo bay:

$$r_i = R_E + 280 \text{ km} = 6.65 \times 10^6 \text{ m}$$

Use Equation 13.18 to find the difference in energies for the satellite–Earth system with the satellite at the initial and final radii:

$$\Delta E = E_f - E_i = -\frac{GM_E m}{2r_f} - \left(-\frac{GM_E m}{2r_i} \right) = -\frac{GM_E m}{2} \left(\frac{1}{r_f} - \frac{1}{r_i} \right)$$

Substitute numerical values, using $r_f = 4.23 \times 10^7$ m from Example 13.5:

$$\Delta E = -\frac{(6.67 \times 10^{-11} \text{ N} \cdot \text{m}^2/\text{kg}^2)(5.98 \times 10^{24} \text{ kg})(470 \text{ kg})}{2}$$

$$\times \left(\frac{1}{4.23 \times 10^7 \text{ m}} - \frac{1}{6.65 \times 10^6 \text{ m}} \right)$$

$$= \boxed{1.19 \times 10^{10} \text{ J}}$$

which is the energy equivalent of 89 gal of gasoline. NASA engineers must account for the changing mass of the spacecraft as it ejects burned fuel, something we have not done here. Would you expect the calculation that includes the effect of this changing mass to yield a greater or a lesser amount of energy required from the engine?

Escape Speed

Suppose an object of mass m is projected vertically upward from the Earth's surface with an initial speed v_i as illustrated in Figure 13.14. We can use energy considerations to find the minimum value of the initial speed needed to allow the object to move infinitely far away from the Earth. Equation 13.16 gives the total energy of the system at any point. At the surface of the Earth, $v = v_i$ and $r = r_i = R_E$. When the object reaches its maximum altitude, $v = v_f = 0$ and $r = r_f = r_{\text{max}}$. Because the total energy of the object–Earth system is conserved, substituting these conditions into Equation 13.20 gives

$$\tfrac{1}{2}mv_i^2 - \frac{GM_E m}{R_E} = -\frac{GM_E m}{r_{\text{max}}}$$

Solving for v_i^2 gives

$$v_i^2 = 2GM_E \left(\frac{1}{R_E} - \frac{1}{r_{\text{max}}} \right) \qquad \textbf{(13.21)}$$

For a given maximum altitude $h = r_{\text{max}} - R_E$, we can use this equation to find the required initial speed.

We are now in a position to calculate **escape speed,** which is the minimum speed the object must have at the Earth's surface to approach an infinite separation distance from the Earth. Traveling at this minimum speed, the object continues to move farther and farther away from the Earth as its speed asymptotically approaches zero. Letting $r_{\text{max}} \to \infty$ in Equation 13.21 and taking $v_i = v_{\text{esc}}$ gives

$$v_{\text{esc}} = \sqrt{\frac{2GM_E}{R_E}} \qquad \textbf{(13.22)}$$

This expression for v_{esc} is independent of the mass of the object. In other words, a spacecraft has the same escape speed as a molecule. Furthermore, the result is independent of the direction of the velocity and ignores air resistance.

If the object is given an initial speed equal to v_{esc}, the total energy of the system is equal to zero. Notice that when $r \to \infty$, the object's kinetic energy and the potential energy of the system are both zero. If v_i is greater than v_{esc}, the total energy of the system is greater than zero and the object has some residual kinetic energy as $r \to \infty$.

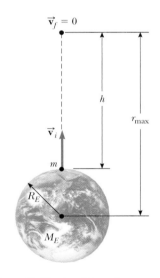

Figure 13.14   An object of mass m projected upward from the Earth's surface with an initial speed v_i reaches a maximum altitude h.

PITFALL PREVENTION 13.3
You Can't Really Escape

Although Equation 13.22 provides the "escape speed" from the Earth, *complete* escape from the Earth's gravitational influence is impossible because the gravitational force is of infinite range. No matter how far away you are, you will always feel some gravitational force due to the Earth.

EXAMPLE 13.8   **Escape Speed of a Rocket**

Calculate the escape speed from the Earth for a 5 000-kg spacecraft and determine the kinetic energy it must have at the Earth's surface to move infinitely far away from the Earth.

SOLUTION

Conceptualize   Imagine projecting the spacecraft from the Earth's surface so that it moves farther and farther away, traveling more and more slowly, with its speed approaching zero. Its speed will never reach zero, however, so the object will never turn around and come back.

Categorize   This example is a substitution problem.

Use Equation 13.22 to find the escape speed:

$$v_{esc} = \sqrt{\frac{2GM_E}{R_E}} = \sqrt{\frac{2(6.67 \times 10^{-11} \text{ N} \cdot \text{m}^2/\text{kg}^2)(5.98 \times 10^{24} \text{ kg})}{6.37 \times 10^6 \text{ m}}}$$

$$= \boxed{1.12 \times 10^4 \text{ m/s}}$$

Evaluate the kinetic energy of the spacecraft from Equation 7.16:

$$K = \tfrac{1}{2}mv_{esc}^2 = \tfrac{1}{2}(5.00 \times 10^3 \text{ kg})(1.12 \times 10^4 \text{ m/s})^2$$

$$= \boxed{3.14 \times 10^{11} \text{ J}}$$

The calculated escape speed corresponds to about 25 000 mi/h. The kinetic energy of the spacecraft is equivalent to the energy released by the combustion of about 2 300 gal of gasoline.

What If?   What if you want to launch a 1 000-kg spacecraft at the escape speed? How much energy would that require?

Answer   In Equation 13.22, the mass of the object moving with the escape speed does not appear. Therefore, the escape speed for the 1 000-kg spacecraft is the same as that for the 5 000-kg spacecraft. The only change in the kinetic energy is due to the mass, so the 1 000-kg spacecraft requires one-fifth of the energy of the 5 000-kg spacecraft:

$$K = \tfrac{1}{5}(3.14 \times 10^{11} \text{ J}) = 6.28 \times 10^{10} \text{ J}$$

Equations 13.21 and 13.22 can be applied to objects projected from any planet. That is, in general, the escape speed from the surface of any planet of mass M and radius R is

$$v_{esc} = \sqrt{\frac{2GM}{R}} \tag{13.23}$$

Escape speeds for the planets, the Moon, and the Sun are provided in Table 13.3. The values vary from 2.3 km/s for the Moon to about 618 km/s for the Sun. These results, together with some ideas from the kinetic theory of gases (see Chapter 21), explain why some planets have atmospheres and others do not. As we shall see later, at a given temperature the average kinetic energy of a gas molecule depends only on the mass of the molecule. Lighter molecules, such as hydrogen and helium, have a higher average speed than heavier molecules at the same temperature. When the average speed of the lighter molecules is not much less than the escape speed of a planet, a significant fraction of them have a chance to escape.

This mechanism also explains why the Earth does not retain hydrogen molecules and helium atoms in its atmosphere but does retain heavier molecules, such as oxygen and nitrogen. On the other hand, the very large escape speed for Jupiter enables that planet to retain hydrogen, the primary constituent of its atmosphere.

TABLE 13.3

Escape Speeds from the Surfaces of the Planets, Moon, and Sun

Planet	v_{esc} (km/s)
Mercury	4.3
Venus	10.3
Earth	11.2
Mars	5.0
Jupiter	60
Saturn	36
Uranus	22
Neptune	24
Moon	2.3
Sun	618

Black Holes

In Example 11.7, we briefly described a rare event called a supernova, the catastrophic explosion of a very massive star. The material that remains in the central core of such an object continues to collapse, and the core's ultimate fate depends on its mass. If the core has a mass less than 1.4 times the mass of our Sun, it gradually cools down and ends its life as a white dwarf star. If the core's mass is greater than this value, however, it may collapse further due to gravitational forces. What remains is a neutron star, discussed in Example 11.7, in which the mass of a star is compressed to a radius of about 10 km. (On the Earth, a teaspoon of this material would weigh about 5 billion tons!)

An even more unusual star death may occur when the core has a mass greater than about three solar masses. The collapse may continue until the star becomes a very small object in space, commonly referred to as a **black hole.** In effect, black holes are remains of stars that have collapsed under their own gravitational force. If an object such as a spacecraft comes close to a black hole, the object experiences an extremely strong gravitational force and is trapped forever.

The escape speed for a black hole is very high because of the concentration of the star's mass into a sphere of very small radius (see Eq. 13.23). If the escape speed exceeds the speed of light c, radiation from the object (such as visible light) cannot escape and the object appears to be black (hence the origin of the terminology "black hole"). The critical radius R_S at which the escape speed is c is called the **Schwarzschild radius** (Fig. 13.15). The imaginary surface of a sphere of this radius surrounding the black hole is called the **event horizon,** which is the limit of how close you can approach the black hole and hope to escape.

Although light from a black hole cannot escape, light from events taking place near the black hole should be visible. For example, it is possible for a binary star system to consist of one normal star and one black hole. Material surrounding the ordinary star can be pulled into the black hole, forming an **accretion disk** around the black hole as suggested in Figure 13.16. Friction among particles in the accretion disk results in transformation of mechanical energy into internal energy. As a result, the temperature of the material above the event horizon rises. This high-temperature material emits a large amount of radiation, extending well into the x-ray region of the electromagnetic spectrum. These x-rays are characteristic of a black hole. Several possible candidates for black holes have been identified by observation of these x-rays.

There is also evidence that supermassive black holes exist at the centers of galaxies, with masses very much larger than the Sun. (There is strong evidence of a supermassive black hole of mass 2–3 million solar masses at the center of our galaxy.) Theoretical models for these bizarre objects predict that jets of material should be evident along the rotation axis of the black hole. Figure 13.17 (page 380) shows a Hubble Space Telescope photograph of galaxy M87. The jet of material coming from this galaxy is believed to be evidence for a supermassive black hole at the center of the galaxy.

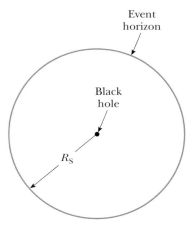

Figure 13.15   A black hole. The distance R_S equals the Schwarzschild radius. Any event occurring within the boundary of radius R_S, called the event horizon, is invisible to an outside observer.

Figure 13.16   A binary star system consisting of an ordinary star on the left and a black hole on the right. Matter pulled from the ordinary star forms an accretion disk around the black hole, in which matter is raised to very high temperatures, resulting in the emission of x-rays.

H. Ford et al. & NASA

Figure 13.17 Hubble Space Telescope images of the galaxy M87. The inset shows the center of the galaxy. The wider view shows a jet of material moving away from the center of the galaxy toward the upper right of the figure at about one tenth of the speed of light. Such jets are believed to be evidence of a supermassive black hole at the galaxy center.

Summary

ThomsonNOW™ Sign in at **www.thomsonedu.com** and go to ThomsonNOW to take a practice test for this chapter.

DEFINITIONS

The **gravitational field** at a point in space is defined as the gravitational force experienced by any test particle located at that point divided by the mass of the test particle:

$$\vec{\mathbf{g}} \equiv \frac{\vec{\mathbf{F}}_g}{m} \tag{13.9}$$

CONCEPTS AND PRINCIPLES

Newton's law of universal gravitation states that the gravitational force of attraction between any two particles of masses m_1 and m_2 separated by a distance r has the magnitude

$$F_g = G\frac{m_1 m_2}{r^2} \tag{13.1}$$

where $G = 6.673 \times 10^{-11}$ N·m²/kg² is the **universal gravitational constant.** This equation enables us to calculate the force of attraction between masses under many circumstances.

An object at a distance h above the Earth's surface experiences a gravitational force of magnitude mg, where g is the free-fall acceleration at that elevation:

$$g = \frac{GM_E}{r^2} = \frac{GM_E}{(R_E + h)^2} \tag{13.6}$$

In this expression, M_E is the mass of the Earth and R_E is its radius. Therefore, the weight of an object decreases as the object moves away from the Earth's surface.

(*continued*)

Kepler's laws of planetary motion state:

1. All planets move in elliptical orbits with the Sun at one focus.
2. The radius vector drawn from the Sun to a planet sweeps out equal areas in equal time intervals.
3. The square of the orbital period of any planet is proportional to the cube of the semimajor axis of the elliptical orbit.

Kepler's third law can be expressed as

$$T^2 = \left(\frac{4\pi^2}{GM_S}\right)a^3 \qquad \textbf{(13.8)}$$

where M_S is the mass of the Sun and a is the semimajor axis. For a circular orbit, a can be replaced in Equation 13.8 by the radius r. Most planets have nearly circular orbits around the Sun.

The **gravitational potential energy** associated with two particles separated by a distance r is

$$U = -\frac{Gm_1 m_2}{r} \qquad \textbf{(13.14)}$$

where U is taken to be zero as $r \to \infty$.

If an isolated system consists of an object of mass m moving with a speed v in the vicinity of a massive object of mass M, the total energy E of the system is the sum of the kinetic and potential energies:

$$E = \tfrac{1}{2}mv^2 - \frac{GMm}{r} \qquad \textbf{(13.16)}$$

The total energy of the system is a constant of the motion. If the object moves in an elliptical orbit of semimajor axis a around the massive object and $M >> m$, the total energy of the system is

$$E = -\frac{GMm}{2a} \qquad \textbf{(13.19)}$$

For a circular orbit, this same equation applies with $a = r$.

The **escape speed** for an object projected from the surface of a planet of mass M and radius R is

$$v_{\text{esc}} = \sqrt{\frac{2GM}{R}} \qquad \textbf{(13.23)}$$

Questions

□ denotes answer available in *Student Solutions Manual/Study Guide;* **O** denotes objective question

1. **O** Rank the magnitudes of the following gravitational forces from largest to smallest. If two forces are equal, show their equality in your list. (a) The force exerted by a 2-kg object on a 3-kg object 1 m away. (b) The force exerted by a 2-kg object on a 9-kg object 1 m away. (c) The force exerted by a 2-kg object on a 9-kg object 2 m away. (d) The force exerted by a 9-kg object on a 2-kg object 2 m away. (e) The force exerted by a 4-kg object on another 4-kg object 2 m away.

2. **O** The gravitational force exerted on an astronaut on the Earth's surface is 650 N directed downward. When she is in the International Space Station, what is the gravitational force on her? (a) several times larger (b) slightly larger (c) precisely the same (d) slightly smaller (e) several times smaller (f) nearly but not exactly zero (g) precisely zero (h) up instead of down

3. **O** Imagine that nitrogen and other atmospheric gases were more soluble in water so that the atmosphere of the Earth were entirely absorbed by the oceans. Atmospheric pressure would then be zero, and outer space would start at the planet's surface. Would the Earth then have a gravitational field? (a) yes; at the surface it would be larger in magnitude than 9.8 N/kg (b) yes, essentially the same as the current value (c) yes, somewhat less than 9.8 N/kg (d) yes, much less than 9.8 N/kg (e) no

4. The gravitational force exerted by the Sun on you is downward into the Earth at night and upward into the sky during the day. If you had a sensitive enough bathroom scale, would you expect to weigh more at night than during the day? Note also that you are farther away from the Sun at night than during the day. Would you expect to weigh less?

5. **O** Suppose the gravitational acceleration at the surface of a certain satellite A of Jupiter is 2 m/s². Satellite B has twice the mass and twice the radius of satellite A. What is the gravitational acceleration at its surface? (a) 16 m/s² (b) 8 m/s² (c) 4 m/s² (d) 2 m/s² (e) 1 m/s² (f) 0.5 m/s² (g) 0.25 m/s²

6. **O** A satellite originally moves in a circular orbit of radius R around the Earth. Suppose it is moved into a circular orbit of radius $4R$. **(i)** What does the force exerted on the satellite then become? (a) 16 times larger (b) 8 times larger (c) 4 times larger (d) 2 times larger (e) unchanged (f) 1/2 as large (g) 1/4 as large (h) 1/8 as large (i) 1/16 as large **(ii)** What happens to the speed of the satellite? Choose from the same possibilities (a) through (i). **(iii)** What happens to its period? Choose from the same possibilities (a) through (i).

7. **O** The vernal equinox and the autumnal equinox are associated with two points 180° apart in the Earth's orbit.

That is, the Earth is on precisely opposite sides of the Sun when it passes through these two points. From the vernal equinox, 185.4 days elapse before the autumnal equinox. Only 179.8 days elapse from the autumnal equinox until the next vernal equinox. In the year 2007, for example, the vernal equinox is 8 minutes after midnight Greenwich Mean Time on March 21, 2007, and the autumnal equinox is 9:51 p.m. September 23. Why is the interval from the March to the September equinox (which contains the summer solstice) longer than the interval from the September to the March equinox, rather than being equal to that interval? (a) They are really the same, but the Earth spins faster during the "summer" interval, so the days are shorter. (b) Over the "summer" interval the Earth moves slower because it is farther from the Sun. (c) Over the March-to-September interval the Earth moves slower because it is closer to the Sun. (d) The Earth has less kinetic energy when it is warmer. (e) The Earth has less orbital angular momentum when it is warmer. (f) Other objects do work to speed up and slow down the Earth's orbital motion.

8. A satellite in orbit around the Earth is not truly traveling through a vacuum. Rather, it moves through very thin air. Does the resulting air friction cause the satellite to slow down?

9. **O** A system consists of five particles. How many terms appear in the expression for the total gravitational potential energy? (a) 4 (b) 5 (c) 10 (d) 20 (e) 25 (f) 120

10. Explain why it takes more fuel for a spacecraft to travel from the Earth to the Moon than for the return trip. Estimate the difference.

11. **O** Rank the following quantities of energy from the largest to the smallest. State if any are equal. (a) the absolute value of the average potential energy of the Sun–Earth system (b) the average kinetic energy of the Earth in its orbital motion relative to the Sun (c) the absolute value of the total energy of the Sun–Earth system

12. Why don't we put a geosynchronous weather satellite in orbit around the 45th parallel? Wouldn't such a satellite be more useful in the United States than one in orbit around the equator?

13. Explain why the force exerted on a particle by a uniform sphere must be directed toward the center of the sphere. Would this statement be true if the mass distribution of the sphere were not spherically symmetric?

14. At what position in its elliptical orbit is the speed of a planet a maximum? At what position is the speed a minimum?

15. You are given the mass and radius of planet X. How would you calculate the free-fall acceleration on the surface of this planet?

16. If a hole could be dug to the center of the Earth, would the force on an object of mass m still obey Equation 13.1 there? What do you think the force on m would be at the center of the Earth?

17. In his 1798 experiment, Cavendish was said to have "weighed the Earth." Explain this statement.

18. Is the gravitational force a conservative or a nonconservative force? Each *Voyager* spacecraft was accelerated toward escape speed from the Sun by the gravitational force exerted by Jupiter on the spacecraft. Does the interaction of the spacecraft with Jupiter meet the definition of an elastic collision? How could the spacecraft be moving faster after the collision?

Problems

WebAssign   The Problems from this chapter may be assigned online in WebAssign.

ThomsonNOW   Sign in at **www.thomsonedu.com** and go to ThomsonNOW to assess your understanding of this chapter's topics with additional quizzing and conceptual questions.

1, 2, 3 denotes straightforward, intermediate, challenging;   ☐ denotes full solution available in *Student Solutions Manual/Study Guide;*   ▲ denotes coached solution with hints available at **www.thomsonedu.com;**   denotes developing symbolic reasoning;   ● denotes asking for qualitative reasoning;   ☗ denotes computer useful in solving problem

Section 13.1 Newton's Law of Universal Gravitation

1. Determine the order of magnitude of the gravitational force that you exert on another person 2 m away. In your solution, state the quantities you measure or estimate and their values.

2. Two ocean liners, each with a mass of 40 000 metric tons, are moving on parallel courses 100 m apart. What is the magnitude of the acceleration of one of the liners toward the other due to their mutual gravitational attraction? Model the ships as particles.

3. A 200-kg object and a 500-kg object are separated by 0.400 m. (a) Find the net gravitational force exerted by these objects on a 50.0-kg object placed midway between them. (b) At what position (other than an infinitely remote one) can the 50.0-kg object be placed so as to experience a net force of zero?

4. Two objects attract each other with a gravitational force of magnitude 1.00×10^{-8} N when separated by 20.0 cm. If the total mass of the two objects is 5.00 kg, what is the mass of each?

5. Three uniform spheres of mass 2.00 kg, 4.00 kg, and 6.00 kg are placed at the corners of a right triangle as shown in Figure P13.5. Calculate the resultant gravitational force on the 4.00-kg object, assuming the spheres are isolated from the rest of the Universe.

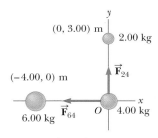

Figure P13.5

6. ● During a solar eclipse, the Moon, Earth, and Sun all lie on the same line, with the Moon between the Earth and the Sun. (a) What force is exerted by the Sun on the Moon? (b) What force is exerted by the Earth on the Moon? (c) What force is exerted by the Sun on the Earth? (d) Compare the answers to parts (a) and (b). Why doesn't the Sun capture the Moon away from the Earth?

7. ▲ In introductory physics laboratories, a typical Cavendish balance for measuring the gravitational constant G uses lead spheres with masses of 1.50 kg and 15.0 g whose centers are separated by about 4.50 cm. Calculate the gravitational force between these spheres, treating each as a particle located at the center of the sphere.

8. ● A student proposes to measure the gravitational constant G by suspending two spherical objects from the ceiling of a tall cathedral and measuring the deflection of the cables from the vertical. Draw a free-body diagram of one of the objects. Assume two 100.0-kg objects are suspended at the lower ends of cables 45.00 m long and the cables are attached to the ceiling 1.000 m apart. What is the separation of the objects? Is there more than one equilibrium separation distance? Explain.

Section 13.2 Free-Fall Acceleration and the Gravitational Force

9. ▲ When a falling meteoroid is at a distance above the Earth's surface of 3.00 times the Earth's radius, what is its acceleration due to the Earth's gravitation?

10. Review problem. Miranda, a satellite of Uranus, is shown in Figure P13.10a. It can be modeled as a sphere of radius 242 km and mass 6.68×10^{19} kg. (a) Find the free-fall acceleration on its surface. (b) A cliff on Miranda is 5.00 km high. It appears on the limb at the 11 o'clock position in Figure P13.10a and is magnified in Figure P13.10b. A devotee of extreme sports runs horizontally off

(a)   (b)

Figure P13.10

Courtesy of NASA/JPL

the top of the cliff at 8.50 m/s. For what time interval is he in flight? (Or is he in orbit?) (c) How far from the base of the vertical cliff does he strike the icy surface of Miranda? (d) What is his vector impact velocity?

11. The free-fall acceleration on the surface of the Moon is about one-sixth that on the surface of the Earth. The radius of the Moon is about $0.250R_E$. Find the ratio of their average densities, $\rho_{\text{Moon}}/\rho_{\text{Earth}}$.

Section 13.3 Kepler's Laws and the Motion of Planets

12. ● A particle of mass m moves along a straight line with constant speed in the x direction, a distance b from the x axis (Fig. P13.12). Does the particle possess any angular momentum about the origin? Explain why the amount of its angular momentum should change or should stay constant. Show that Kepler's second law is satisfied by showing that the two shaded triangles in the figure have the same area when $t_4 - t_3 = t_2 - t_1$.

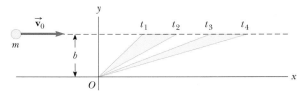

Figure P13.12

13. Plaskett's binary system consists of two stars that revolve in a circular orbit about a center of mass midway between them. This statement implies that the masses of the two stars are equal (Fig. P13.13). Assume the orbital speed of each star is 220 km/s and the orbital period of each is 14.4 days. Find the mass M of each star. (For comparison, the mass of our Sun is 1.99×10^{30} kg.)

Figure P13.13

14. Comet Halley (Fig. P13.14) approaches the Sun to within 0.570 AU, and its orbital period is 75.6 years. (AU is the symbol for astronomical unit, where 1 AU = 1.50×10^{11} m is the mean Earth–Sun distance.) How far from the

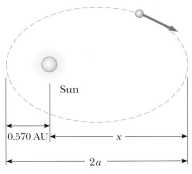

Figure P13.14

Sun will Halley's comet travel before it starts its return journey?

15. ▲ Io, a satellite of Jupiter, has an orbital period of 1.77 days and an orbital radius of 4.22×10^5 km. From these data, determine the mass of Jupiter.

16. Two planets X and Y travel counterclockwise in circular orbits about a star as shown in Figure P13.16. The radii of their orbits are in the ratio 3:1. At one moment, they are aligned as shown in Figure P13.16a, making a straight line with the star. During the next five years the angular displacement of planet X is 90.0° as shown in Figure P13.16b. Where is planet Y at this moment?

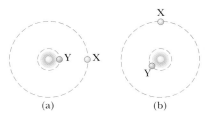

(a)   (b)

Figure P13.16

17. A synchronous satellite, which always remains above the same point on a planet's equator, is put in orbit around Jupiter to study the famous red spot. Jupiter rotates once every 9.84 h. Use the data of Table 13.2 to find the altitude of the satellite.

18. Neutron stars are extremely dense objects formed from the remnants of supernova explosions. Many rotate very rapidly. Suppose the mass of a certain spherical neutron star is twice the mass of the Sun and its radius is 10.0 km. Determine the greatest possible angular speed it can have so that the matter at the surface of the star on its equator is just held in orbit by the gravitational force.

19. Suppose the Sun's gravity were switched off. Objects in the solar system would leave their orbits and fly away in straight lines as described by Newton's first law. Would Mercury ever be farther from the Sun than Pluto? If so, find how long it would take for Mercury to achieve this passage. If not, give a convincing argument that Pluto is always farther from the Sun.

20. ● Given that the period of the Moon's orbit about the Earth is 27.32 d and the nearly constant distance between the center of the Earth and the center of the Moon is 3.84×10^8 m, use Equation 13.8 to calculate the mass of the Earth. Why is the value you calculate a bit too large?

Section 13.4 The Gravitational Field

21. Three objects of equal mass are located at three corners of a square of edge length ℓ as shown in Figure P13.21. Find the gravitational field at the fourth corner due to these objects.

Figure P13.21

22. A spacecraft in the shape of a long cylinder has a length of 100 m, and its mass with occupants is 1 000 kg. It has strayed too close to a black hole having a mass 100 times that of the Sun (Fig. P13.22). The nose of the spacecraft points toward the black hole, and the distance between the nose and the center of the black hole is 10.0 km. (a) Determine the total force on the spacecraft. (b) What is the difference in the gravitational fields acting on the occupants in the nose of the ship and on those in the rear of the ship, farthest from the black hole? This difference in accelerations grows rapidly as the ship approaches the black hole. It puts the body of the ship under extreme tension and eventually tears it apart.

Figure P13.22

23. ● (a) Compute the vector gravitational field at a point P on the perpendicular bisector of the line joining two objects of equal mass separated by a distance $2a$ as shown in Figure P13.23. (b) Explain physically why the field should approach zero as $r \to 0$. (c) Prove mathematically that the answer to part (a) behaves in this way. (d) Explain physically why the magnitude of the field should approach $2GM/r^2$ as $r \to \infty$. (e) Prove mathematically that the answer to part (a) behaves correctly in this limit.

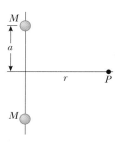

Figure P13.23

Section 13.5 Gravitational Potential Energy

In problems 24–39, assume $U = 0$ at $r = \infty$.

24. A satellite of the Earth has a mass of 100 kg and is at an altitude of 2.00×10^6 m. (a) What is the potential energy of the satellite–Earth system? (b) What is the magnitude of the gravitational force exerted by the Earth on the satellite? (c) **What If?** What force, if any, does the satellite exert on the Earth?

25. After our Sun exhausts its nuclear fuel, its ultimate fate may be to collapse to a *white dwarf* state. In this state, it would have approximately the same mass as it has now but a radius equal to the radius of the Earth. Calculate (a) the average density of the white dwarf, (b) the surface free-fall acceleration, and (c) the gravitational potential energy associated with a 1.00-kg object at its surface.

26. At the Earth's surface a projectile is launched straight up at a speed of 10.0 km/s. To what height will it rise? Ignore air resistance and the rotation of the Earth.

27. ● A system consists of three particles, each of mass 5.00 g, located at the corners of an equilateral triangle with sides of 30.0 cm. (a) Calculate the potential energy of the system. (b) Assume the particles are released simultaneously. Describe the subsequent motion of each. Will any collisions take place? Explain.

28. How much work is done by the Moon's gravitational field on a 1 000-kg meteor as it comes in from outer space and impacts on the Moon's surface?

29. ⚓ An object is released from rest at an altitude h above the surface of the Earth. (a) Show that its speed at a distance r from the Earth's center, where $R_E \le r \le R_E + h$, is

$$v = \sqrt{2GM_E\left(\frac{1}{r} - \frac{1}{R_E + h}\right)}$$

(b) Assume the release altitude is 500 km. Perform the integral

$$\Delta t = \int_i^f dt = -\int_i^f \frac{dr}{v}$$

to find the time of fall as the object moves from the release point to the Earth's surface. The negative sign appears because the object is moving opposite to the radial direction, so its speed is $v = -dr/dt$. Perform the integral numerically.

Section 13.6 Energy Considerations in Planetary and Satellite Motion

30. (a) What is the minimum speed, relative to the Sun, necessary for a spacecraft to escape the solar system, if it starts at the Earth's orbit? (b) *Voyager 1* achieved a maximum speed of 125 000 km/h on its way to photograph Jupiter. Beyond what distance from the Sun is this speed sufficient to escape the solar system?

31. ▲ A space probe is fired as a projectile from the Earth's surface with an initial speed of 2.00×10^4 m/s. What will its speed be when it is very far from the Earth? Ignore friction and the rotation of the Earth.

32. ● A 1 000-kg satellite orbits the Earth at a constant altitude of 100 km. How much energy must be added to the system to move the satellite into a circular orbit with altitude 200 km? Discuss the changes in kinetic energy, potential energy, and total energy.

33. A "treetop satellite" moves in a circular orbit just above the surface of a planet, assumed to offer no air resistance. Show that its orbital speed v and the escape speed from the planet are related by the expression $v_{esc} = \sqrt{2}v$.

34. ● Ganymede is the largest of Jupiter's moons. Consider a rocket on the surface of Ganymede, at the point farthest from the planet (Fig. P13.34). Does the presence of Ganymede make Jupiter exert a larger, smaller, or same-size force on the rocket compared with the force it would exert if Ganymede were not interposed? Determine the escape speed for the rocket from the planet–satellite system. The radius of Ganymede is 2.64×10^6 m, and its mass is 1.495×10^{23} kg. The distance between Jupiter and Ganymede is 1.071×10^9 m, and the mass of Jupiter is 1.90×10^{27} kg. Ignore the motion of Jupiter and Ganymede as they revolve about their center of mass.

Ganymede

Jupiter

Figure P13.34

35. A satellite of mass 200 kg is placed in Earth orbit at a height of 200 km above the surface. (a) Assuming a circular orbit, how long does the satellite take to complete one orbit? (b) What is the satellite's speed? (c) Starting from the satellite on the Earth's surface, what is the minimum energy input necessary to place this satellite in orbit? Ignore air resistance, but include the effect of the planet's daily rotation.

36. ● A satellite of mass m, originally on the surface of the Earth, is placed into Earth orbit at an altitude h. (a) Assuming a circular orbit, how long does the satellite take to complete one orbit? (b) What is the satellite's speed? (c) What is the minimum energy input necessary to place this satellite in orbit? Ignore air resistance, but include the effect of the planet's daily rotation. At what location on the Earth's surface and in what direction should the satellite be launched to minimize the required energy investment? Represent the mass and radius of the Earth as M_E and R_E.

37. An object is fired vertically upward from the surface of the Earth (of radius R_E) with an initial speed v_i that is comparable to but less than the escape speed v_{esc}. (a) Show that the object attains a maximum height h given by

$$h = \frac{R_E v_i^2}{v_{esc}^2 - v_i^2}$$

(b) A space vehicle is launched vertically upward from the Earth's surface with an initial speed of 8.76 km/s, which is less than the escape speed of 11.2 km/s. What maximum height does it attain? (c) A meteorite falls toward the Earth. It is essentially at rest with respect to the Earth when it is at a height of 2.51×10^7 m. With what speed does the meteorite strike the Earth? (d) **What If?** Assume a baseball is tossed up with an initial speed that is very small compared with the escape speed. Show that the equation from part (a) is consistent with Equation 4.12.

38. A satellite moves around the Earth in a circular orbit of radius r. (a) What is the speed v_0 of the satellite? Suddenly, an explosion breaks the satellite into two pieces, with masses m and $4m$. Immediately after the explosion the smaller piece of mass m is stationary with respect to the Earth and falls directly toward the Earth. (b) What is the speed v_i of the larger piece immediately after the explosion? (c) Because of the increase in its speed, this larger piece now moves in a new elliptical orbit. Find its distance away from the center of the Earth when it reaches the other end of the ellipse.

39. A comet of mass 1.20×10^{10} kg moves in an elliptical orbit around the Sun. Its distance from the Sun ranges between 0.500 AU and 50.0 AU. (a) What is the eccentricity of its orbit? (b) What is its period? (c) At aphelion what is the

potential energy of the comet–Sun system? *Note:* 1 AU = one astronomical unit = the average distance from Sun to Earth = 1.496×10^{11} m.

Additional Problems

40. ● Assume you are agile enough to run across a horizontal surface at 8.50 m/s, independently of the value of the gravitational field. What would be (a) the radius and (b) the mass of an airless spherical asteroid of uniform density 1.10×10^3 kg/m³ on which you could launch yourself into orbit by running? (c) What would be your period? (d) Would your running significantly affect the rotation of the asteroid? Explain.

41. The Solar and Heliospheric Observatory (SOHO) spacecraft has a special orbit, chosen so that its view of the Sun is never eclipsed and it is always close enough to the Earth to transmit data easily. It moves in a near-circle around the Sun that is smaller than the Earth's circular orbit. Its period, however, is not less than 1 yr but rather is just equal to 1 yr. It is always located between the Earth and the Sun along the line joining them. Both objects exert gravitational forces on the observatory. Show that its distance from the Earth must be between 1.47×10^9 m and 1.48×10^9 m. In 1772, Joseph Louis Lagrange determined theoretically the special location allowing this orbit. The SOHO spacecraft took this position on February 14, 1996. *Suggestion:* Use data that are precise to four digits. The mass of the Earth is 5.983×10^{24} kg.

42. Let Δg_M represent the difference in the gravitational fields produced by the Moon at the points on the Earth's surface nearest to and farthest from the Moon. Find the fraction $\Delta g_M/g$, where g is the Earth's gravitational field. (This difference is responsible for the occurrence of the *lunar tides* on the Earth.)

43. **Review problem.** Two identical hard spheres, each of mass m and radius r, are released from rest in otherwise empty space with their centers separated by the distance R. They are allowed to collide under the influence of their gravitational attraction. (a) Show that the magnitude of the impulse received by each sphere before they make contact is given by $[Gm^3(1/2r - 1/R)]^{1/2}$. (b) **What If?** Find the magnitude of the impulse each receives during their contact if they collide elastically.

44. Two spheres having masses M and $2M$ and radii R and $3R$, respectively, are released from rest when the distance between their centers is $12R$. How fast will each sphere be moving when they collide? Assume the two spheres interact only with each other.

45. A ring of matter is a familiar structure in planetary and stellar astronomy. Examples include Saturn's rings and a ring nebula. Consider a large uniform ring having a mass of 2.36×10^{20} kg and radius 1.00×10^8 m. An object of mass 1 000 kg is placed at a point A on the axis of the ring, 2.00×10^8 m from the center of the ring (Fig. P13.45). When the object is released, the attraction of the ring makes the object move along the axis toward the center of the ring (point B). (a) Calculate the gravitational potential energy of the object–ring system when the object is at A. (b) Calculate the gravitational potential energy of the system when the object is at B. (c) Calculate the object's speed as it passes through B.

Figure P13.45

46. (a) Show that the rate of change of the free-fall acceleration with distance above the Earth's surface is

$$\frac{dg}{dr} = -\frac{2GM_E}{R_E^3}$$

This rate of change over distance is called a *gradient*. (b) Assuming that h is small in comparison to the radius of the Earth, show that the difference in free-fall acceleration between two points separated by vertical distance h is

$$|\Delta g| = \frac{2GM_E h}{R_E^3}$$

(c) Evaluate this difference for $h = 6.00$ m, a typical height for a two-story building.

47. As an astronaut, you observe a small planet to be spherical. After landing on the planet, you set off, walking always straight ahead, and find yourself returning to your spacecraft from the opposite side after completing a lap of 25.0 km. You hold a hammer and a falcon feather at a height of 1.40 m, release them, and observe that they fall together to the surface in 29.2 s. Determine the mass of the planet.

48. A certain quaternary star system consists of three stars, each of mass m, moving in the same circular orbit of radius r about a central star of mass M. The stars orbit in the same sense and are positioned one-third of a revolution apart from one another. Show that the period of each of the three stars is

$$T = 2\pi\sqrt{\frac{r^3}{G(M + m/\sqrt{3})}}$$

49. **Review problem.** A cylindrical habitat in space 6.00 km in diameter and 30 km long has been proposed (by G. K. O'Neill, 1974). Such a habitat would have cities, land, and lakes on the inside surface and air and clouds

in the center. They would all be held in place by rotation of the cylinder about its long axis. How fast would the cylinder have to rotate to imitate the Earth's gravitational field at the walls of the cylinder?

50. ● Many people assume air resistance acting on a moving object will always make the object slow down. It can, however, actually be responsible for making the object speed up. Consider a 100-kg Earth satellite in a circular orbit at an altitude of 200 km. A small force of air resistance makes the satellite drop into a circular orbit with an altitude of 100 km. (a) Calculate its initial speed. (b) Calculate its final speed in this process. (c) Calculate the initial energy of the satellite–Earth system. (d) Calculate the final energy of the system. (e) Show that the system has lost mechanical energy and find the amount of the loss due to friction. (f) What force makes the satellite's speed increase? You will find a free-body diagram to be useful in explaining your answer.

51. ▲ Two hypothetical planets of masses m_1 and m_2 and radii r_1 and r_2, respectively, are nearly at rest when they are an infinite distance apart. Because of their gravitational attraction, they head toward each other on a collision course. (a) When their center-to-center separation is d, find expressions for the speed of each planet and for their relative speed. (b) Find the kinetic energy of each planet just before they collide, taking m_1 = 2.00 × 10^{24} kg, m_2 = 8.00 × 10^{24} kg, r_1 = 3.00 × 10^6 m, and r_2 = 5.00 × 10^6 m. *Note:* Both energy and momentum of the system are conserved.

52. The maximum distance from the Earth to the Sun (at aphelion) is 1.521 × 10^{11} m, and the distance of closest approach (at perihelion) is 1.471 × 10^{11} m. The Earth's orbital speed at perihelion is 3.027 × 10^4 m/s. Determine (a) the Earth's orbital speed at aphelion, (b) the kinetic and potential energies of the Earth–Sun system at perihelion, and (c) the kinetic and potential energies at aphelion. Is the total energy of the system constant? (Ignore the effect of the Moon and other planets.)

53. Studies of the relationship of the Sun to its galaxy—the Milky Way—have revealed that the Sun is located near the outer edge of the galactic disk, about 30 000 ly from the center. The Sun has an orbital speed of approximately 250 km/s around the galactic center. (a) What is the period of the Sun's galactic motion? (b) What is the order of magnitude of the mass of the Milky Way galaxy? Suppose the galaxy is made mostly of stars of which the Sun is typical. What is the order of magnitude of the number of stars in the Milky Way?

54. X-ray pulses from Cygnus X-1, a celestial x-ray source, have been recorded during high-altitude rocket flights. The signals can be interpreted as originating when a blob of ionized matter orbits a black hole with a period of 5.0 ms. If the blob is in a circular orbit about a black hole whose mass is $20M_{\text{Sun}}$, what is the orbit radius?

55. Astronomers detect a distant meteoroid moving along a straight line that, if extended, would pass at a distance $3R_E$ from the center of the Earth, where R_E is the radius of the Earth. What minimum speed must the meteoroid have if the Earth's gravitation is not to deflect the meteoroid to make it strike the Earth?

56. The oldest artificial satellite in orbit is *Vanguard I*, launched March 3, 1958. Its mass is 1.60 kg. In its initial orbit, its minimum distance from the center of the Earth was 7.02 Mm and its speed at this perigee point was 8.23 km/s. (a) Find the total energy of the satellite–Earth system. (b) Find the magnitude of the angular momentum of the satellite. (c) At apogee, find its speed and its distance from the center of the Earth. (d) Find the semi-major axis of its orbit. (e) Determine its period.

57. Two stars of masses M and m, separated by a distance d, revolve in circular orbits about their center of mass (Fig. P13.57). Show that each star has a period given by

$$T^2 = \frac{4\pi^2 d^3}{G(M + m)}$$

Proceed by applying Newton's second law to each star. Note that the center-of-mass condition requires that $Mr_2 = mr_1$, where $r_1 + r_2 = d$.

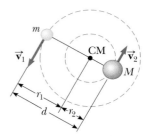

Figure P13.57

58. Show that the minimum period for a satellite in orbit around a spherical planet of uniform density ρ is

$$T_{\text{min}} = \sqrt{\frac{3\pi}{G\rho}}$$

independent of the radius of the planet.

59. Two identical particles, each of mass 1 000 kg, are coasting in free space along the same path. At one instant their separation is 20.0 m and each has precisely the same velocity of 800$\hat{\mathbf{i}}$ m/s. What are their velocities when they are 2.00 m apart?

60. (a) Consider an object of mass m, not necessarily small compared with the mass of the Earth, released at a distance of 1.20 × 10^7 m from the center of the Earth. Assume the objects behave as a pair of particles, isolated from the rest of the Universe. Find the magnitude of the acceleration a_{rel} with which each starts to move relative to the other. Evaluate the acceleration (b) for m = 5.00 kg, (c) for m = 2 000 kg, and (d) for m = 2.00 × 10^{24} kg. (e) Describe the pattern of variation of a_{rel} with m.

61. As thermonuclear fusion proceeds in its core, the Sun loses mass at a rate of 3.64 × 10^9 kg/s. During the 5 000-yr period of recorded history, by how much has the length of the year changed due to the loss of mass from the Sun? *Suggestions:* Assume the Earth's orbit is circular. No external torque acts on the Earth–Sun system, so angular momentum is conserved. If x is small compared with 1, then $(1 + x)^n$ is nearly equal to $1 + nx$.

Answers to Quick Quizzes

13.1 (e). The gravitational force follows an inverse-square behavior, so doubling the distance causes the force to be one-fourth as large.

13.2 (c). An object in orbit is simply falling while it moves around the Earth. The acceleration of the object is that due to gravity. Because the object was launched from a very tall mountain, the value for g is slightly less than that at the surface.

13.3 (a). From Kepler's third law and the given period, the major axis of the asteroid can be calculated. It is found to be 1.2×10^{11} m. Because this value is smaller than the Earth–Sun distance, the asteroid cannot possibly collide with the Earth.

13.4 (a) Perihelion. Because of conservation of angular momentum, the speed of the comet is highest at its closest position to the Sun. (b) Aphelion. The potential energy of the comet–Sun system is highest when the comet is at its farthest distance from the Sun. (c) Perihelion. The kinetic energy is highest at the point at which the speed of the comet is highest. (d) All points. The total energy of the system is the same regardless of where the comet is in its orbit.

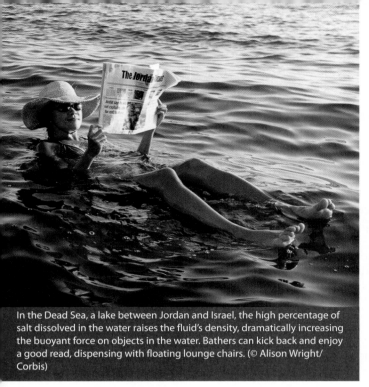

In the Dead Sea, a lake between Jordan and Israel, the high percentage of salt dissolved in the water raises the fluid's density, dramatically increasing the buoyant force on objects in the water. Bathers can kick back and enjoy a good read, dispensing with floating lounge chairs. (© Alison Wright/Corbis)

14 Fluid Mechanics

Matter is normally classified as being in one of three states: solid, liquid, or gas. From everyday experience we know that a solid has a definite volume and shape, a liquid has a definite volume but no definite shape, and an unconfined gas has neither a definite volume nor a definite shape. These descriptions help us picture the states of matter, but they are somewhat artificial. For example, asphalt and plastics are normally considered solids, but over long time intervals they tend to flow like liquids. Likewise, most substances can be a solid, a liquid, or a gas (or a combination of any of these three), depending on the temperature and pressure. In general, the time interval required for a particular substance to change its shape in response to an external force determines whether we treat the substance as a solid, a liquid, or a gas.

A **fluid** is a collection of molecules that are randomly arranged and held together by weak cohesive forces and by forces exerted by the walls of a container. Both liquids and gases are fluids.

In our treatment of the mechanics of fluids, we'll be applying principles we have already discussed. First, we consider the mechanics of a fluid at rest, that is, *fluid statics*, and then study fluids in motion, that is, *fluid dynamics.*

Figure 14.1 At any point on the surface of a submerged object, the force exerted by the fluid is perpendicular to the surface of the object. The force exerted by the fluid on the walls of the container is perpendicular to the walls at all points.

Definition of pressure ▶

Figure 14.2 A simple device for measuring the pressure exerted by a fluid.

PITFALL PREVENTION 14.1
Force and Pressure

Equations 14.1 and 14.2 make a clear distinction between force and pressure. Another important distinction is that *force is a vector* and *pressure is a scalar*. There is no direction associated with pressure, but the direction of the force associated with the pressure is perpendicular to the surface on which the pressure acts.

14.1 Pressure

Fluids do not sustain shearing stresses or tensile stresses; therefore, the only stress that can be exerted on an object submerged in a static fluid is one that tends to compress the object from all sides. In other words, the force exerted by a static fluid on an object is always perpendicular to the surfaces of the object as shown in Figure 14.1.

The pressure in a fluid can be measured with the device pictured in Figure 14.2. The device consists of an evacuated cylinder that encloses a light piston connected to a spring. As the device is submerged in a fluid, the fluid presses on the top of the piston and compresses the spring until the inward force exerted by the fluid is balanced by the outward force exerted by the spring. The fluid pressure can be measured directly if the spring is calibrated in advance. If F is the magnitude of the force exerted on the piston and A is the surface area of the piston, the **pressure** P of the fluid at the level to which the device has been submerged is defined as the ratio of the force to the area:

$$P \equiv \frac{F}{A} \tag{14.1}$$

Pressure is a scalar quantity because it is proportional to the magnitude of the force on the piston.

If the pressure varies over an area, the infinitesimal force dF on an infinitesimal surface element of area dA is

$$dF = P \, dA \tag{14.2}$$

where P is the pressure at the location of the area dA. To calculate the total force exerted on a surface of a container, we must integrate Equation 14.2 over the surface.

The units of pressure are newtons per square meter (N/m^2) in the SI system. Another name for the SI unit of pressure is the **pascal** (Pa):

$$1 \, \text{Pa} \equiv 1 \, \text{N/m}^2 \tag{14.3}$$

For a tactile demonstration of the definition of pressure, hold a tack between your thumb and forefinger, with the point of the tack on your thumb and the head of the tack on your forefinger. Now *gently* press your thumb and forefinger together. Your thumb will begin to feel pain immediately while your forefinger will not. The tack is exerting the same force on both your thumb and forefinger, but the pressure on your thumb is much larger because of the small area over which the force is applied.

Quick Quiz 14.1 Suppose you are standing directly behind someone who steps back and accidentally stomps on your foot with the heel of one shoe. Would you be better off if that person were (a) a large, male professional basketball player wearing sneakers or (b) a petite woman wearing spike-heeled shoes?

EXAMPLE 14.1   **The Water Bed**

The mattress of a water bed is 2.00 m long by 2.00 m wide and 30.0 cm deep.

(A) Find the weight of the water in the mattress.

SOLUTION

Conceptualize Think about carrying a jug of water and how heavy it is. Now imagine a sample of water the size of a water bed. We expect the weight to be relatively large.

Categorize This example is a substitution problem.

Find the volume of the water filling the mattress:

$$V = (2.00 \text{ m})(2.00 \text{ m})(0.300 \text{ m}) = 1.20 \text{ m}^3$$

Use Equation 1.1 and the density of fresh water (see Table 14.1) to find the mass of the water bed:

$$M = \rho V = (1\,000 \text{ kg/m}^3)(1.20 \text{ m}^3) = 1.20 \times 10^3 \text{ kg}$$

Find the weight of the bed:

$$Mg = (1.20 \times 10^3 \text{ kg})(9.80 \text{ m/s}^2) = \boxed{1.18 \times 10^4 \text{ N}}$$

which is approximately 2 650 lb. (A regular bed, including mattress, box springs, and metal frame, weighs approximately 300 lb.) Because this load is so great, it is best to place a water bed in the basement or on a sturdy, well-supported floor.

(B) Find the pressure exerted by the water on the floor when the water bed rests in its normal position. Assume the entire lower surface of the bed makes contact with the floor.

SOLUTION

When the water bed is in its normal position, the area in contact with the floor is 4.00 m². Use Equation 14.1 to find the pressure:

$$P = \frac{1.18 \times 10^4 \text{ N}}{4.00 \text{ m}^2} = \boxed{2.94 \times 10^3 \text{ Pa}}$$

What If? What if the water bed is replaced by a 300-lb regular bed that is supported by four legs? Each leg has a circular cross section of radius 2.00 cm. What pressure does this bed exert on the floor?

Answer The weight of the regular bed is distributed over four circular cross sections at the bottom of the legs. Therefore, the pressure is

$$P = \frac{F}{A} = \frac{mg}{4(\pi r^2)} = \frac{300 \text{ lb}}{4\pi(0.020\,0 \text{ m})^2}\left(\frac{1 \text{ N}}{0.225 \text{ lb}}\right)$$

$$= 2.65 \times 10^5 \text{ Pa}$$

This result is almost 100 times larger than the pressure due to the water bed! The weight of the regular bed, even though it is much less than the weight of the water bed, is applied over the very small area of the four legs. The high pressure on the floor at the feet of a regular bed could cause dents in wood floors or permanently crush carpet pile.

14.2 Variation of Pressure with Depth

As divers well know, water pressure increases with depth. Likewise, atmospheric pressure decreases with increasing altitude; for this reason, aircraft flying at high altitudes must have pressurized cabins for the comfort of the passengers.

TABLE 14.1

Densities of Some Common Substances at Standard Temperature (0°C) and Pressure (Atmospheric)

Substance	ρ (kg/m³)	Substance	ρ (kg/m³)
Air	1.29	Ice	0.917×10^3
Aluminum	2.70×10^3	Iron	7.86×10^3
Benzene	0.879×10^3	Lead	11.3×10^3
Copper	8.92×10^3	Mercury	13.6×10^3
Ethyl alcohol	0.806×10^3	Oak	0.710×10^3
Fresh water	1.00×10^3	Oxygen gas	1.43
Glycerin	1.26×10^3	Pine	0.373×10^3
Gold	19.3×10^3	Platinum	21.4×10^3
Helium gas	1.79×10^{-1}	Seawater	1.03×10^3
Hydrogen gas	8.99×10^{-2}	Silver	10.5×10^3

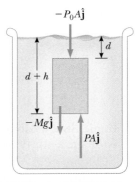

Figure 14.3 A parcel of fluid (darker region) in a larger volume of fluid is singled out. The net force exerted on the parcel of fluid must be zero because it is in equilibrium.

We now show how the pressure in a liquid increases with depth. As Equation 1.1 describes, the *density* of a substance is defined as its mass per unit volume; Table 14.1 lists the densities of various substances. These values vary slightly with temperature because the volume of a substance is dependent on temperature (as shown in Chapter 19). Under standard conditions (at 0°C and at atmospheric pressure), the densities of gases are about $\frac{1}{1\,000}$ the densities of solids and liquids. This difference in densities implies that the average molecular spacing in a gas under these conditions is about ten times greater than that in a solid or liquid.

Now consider a liquid of density ρ at rest as shown in Figure 14.3. We assume ρ is uniform throughout the liquid, which means the liquid is incompressible. Let us select a sample of the liquid contained within an imaginary cylinder of cross-sectional area A extending from depth d to depth $d + h$. The liquid external to our sample exerts forces at all points on the surface of the sample, perpendicular to the surface. The pressure exerted by the liquid on the bottom face of the sample is P, and the pressure on the top face is P_0. Therefore, the upward force exerted by the outside fluid on the bottom of the cylinder has a magnitude PA, and the downward force exerted on the top has a magnitude $P_0 A$. The mass of liquid in the cylinder is $M = \rho V = \rho A h$; therefore, the weight of the liquid in the cylinder is $Mg = \rho A h g$. Because the cylinder is in equilibrium, the net force acting on it must be zero. Choosing upward to be the positive y direction, we see that

$$\sum \vec{\mathbf{F}} = PA\hat{\mathbf{j}} - P_0 A\hat{\mathbf{j}} - Mg\hat{\mathbf{j}} = 0$$

or

$$PA - P_0 A - \rho A h g = 0$$

$$P = P_0 + \rho g h \tag{14.4}$$

◀ **Variation of pressure with depth**

That is, **the pressure P at a depth h below a point in the liquid at which the pressure is P_0 is greater by an amount $\rho g h$.** If the liquid is open to the atmosphere and P_0 is the pressure at the surface of the liquid, then P_0 is atmospheric pressure. In our calculations and working of end-of-chapter problems, we usually take atmospheric pressure to be

$$P_0 = 1.00 \text{ atm} = 1.013 \times 10^5 \text{ Pa}$$

Equation 14.4 implies that the pressure is the same at all points having the same depth, independent of the shape of the container.

Because the pressure in a fluid depends on depth and on the value of P_0, any increase in pressure at the surface must be transmitted to every other point in the fluid. This concept was first recognized by French scientist Blaise Pascal (1623–1662) and is called **Pascal's law: a change in the pressure applied to a fluid is transmitted undiminished to every point of the fluid and to the walls of the container.**

◀ **Pascal's law**

An important application of Pascal's law is the hydraulic press illustrated in Figure 14.4a. A force of magnitude F_1 is applied to a small piston of surface area A_1. The pressure is transmitted through an incompressible liquid to a larger piston of surface area A_2. Because the pressure must be the same on both sides, $P = F_1/A_1 = F_2/A_2$. Therefore, the force F_2 is greater than the force F_1 by a factor A_2/A_1. By designing a hydraulic press with appropriate areas A_1 and A_2, a large output force can be applied by means of a small input force. Hydraulic brakes, car lifts, hydraulic jacks, and forklifts all make use of this principle (Fig. 14.4b).

Because liquid is neither added to nor removed from the system, the volume of liquid pushed down on the left in Figure 14.4a as the piston moves downward through a displacement Δx_1 equals the volume of liquid pushed up on the right as the right piston moves upward through a displacement Δx_2. That is, $A_1 \Delta x_1 = A_2 \Delta x_2$; therefore, $A_2/A_1 = \Delta x_1/\Delta x_2$. We have already shown that $A_2/A_1 = F_2/F_1$. Therefore, $F_2/F_1 = \Delta x_1/\Delta x_2$, so $F_1 \Delta x_1 = F_2 \Delta x_2$. Each side of this equation is the work done by the force on its respective piston. Therefore, the work done by $\vec{\mathbf{F}}_1$ on the input piston equals the work done by $\vec{\mathbf{F}}_2$ on the output piston, as it must to conserve energy.

(a)   (b)

Figure 14.4   (a) Diagram of a hydraulic press. Because the increase in pressure is the same on the two sides, a small force $\vec{F}_1$ at the left produces a much greater force $\vec{F}_2$ at the right. (b) A vehicle undergoing repair is supported by a hydraulic lift in a garage.

Quick Quiz 14.2   The pressure at the bottom of a filled glass of water ($\rho = $ 1 000 kg/m^3) is P. The water is poured out, and the glass is filled with ethyl alcohol ($\rho = 806$ kg/m^3). What is the pressure at the bottom of the glass? (a) smaller than P (b) equal to P (c) larger than P (d) indeterminate

---

EXAMPLE 14.2	**The Car Lift**

In a car lift used in a service station, compressed air exerts a force on a small piston that has a circular cross section and a radius of 5.00 cm. This pressure is transmitted by a liquid to a piston that has a radius of 15.0 cm. What force must the compressed air exert to lift a car weighing 13 300 N? What air pressure produces this force?

SOLUTION

Conceptualize   Review the material just discussed about Pascal's law to understand the operation of a car lift.

Categorize   This example is a substitution problem.

Solve $F_1/A_1 = F_2/A_2$ for F_1:

$$F_1 = \left(\frac{A_1}{A_2}\right)F_2 = \frac{\pi(5.00 \times 10^{-2}\text{ m})^2}{\pi(15.0 \times 10^{-2}\text{ m})^2}\,(1.33 \times 10^4\text{ N})$$

$$= \quad 1.48 \times 10^3\text{ N}$$

Use Equation 14.1 to find the air pressure that produces this force:

$$P = \frac{F_1}{A_1} = \frac{1.48 \times 10^3\text{ N}}{\pi(5.00 \times 10^{-2}\text{ m})^2}$$

$$= \quad 1.88 \times 10^5\text{ Pa}$$

This pressure is approximately twice atmospheric pressure.

EXAMPLE 14.3	**A Pain in Your Ear**

Estimate the force exerted on your eardrum due to the water when you are swimming at the bottom of a pool that is 5.0 m deep.

SOLUTION

Conceptualize   As you descend in the water, the pressure increases. You may have noticed this increased pressure in your ears while diving in a swimming pool, a pond, or the ocean. We can find the pressure difference exerted on the eardrum from the depth given in the problem; then, after estimating the eardrum's surface area, we can determine the net force the water exerts on it.

Categorize This example is a substitution problem.

The air inside the middle ear is normally at atmospheric pressure P_0. Therefore, to find the net force on the eardrum, we must consider the difference between the total pressure at the bottom of the pool and atmospheric pressure. Let's estimate the surface area of the eardrum to be approximately $1 \text{ cm}^2 = 1 \times 10^{-4} \text{ m}^2$.

Use Equation 14.4 to find this pressure difference:

$$P_{\text{bot}} - P_0 = \rho g h$$
$$= (1.00 \times 10^3 \text{ kg/m}^3)(9.80 \text{ m/s}^2)(5.0 \text{ m}) = 4.9 \times 10^4 \text{ Pa}$$

Use Equation 14.1 to find the net force on the ear:

$$F = (P_{\text{bot}} - P_0)A = (4.9 \times 10^4 \text{ Pa})(1 \times 10^{-4} \text{ m}^2) \approx \boxed{5 \text{ N}}$$

Because a force of this magnitude on the eardrum is extremely uncomfortable, swimmers often "pop their ears" while under water, an action that pushes air from the lungs into the middle ear. Using this technique equalizes the pressure on the two sides of the eardrum and relieves the discomfort.

EXAMPLE 14.4 | The Force on a Dam

Water is filled to a height H behind a dam of width w (Fig. 14.5). Determine the resultant force exerted by the water on the dam.

SOLUTION

Conceptualize Because pressure varies with depth, we cannot calculate the force simply by multiplying the area by the pressure.

Categorize Because of the variation of pressure with depth, we must use integration to solve this example, so we categorize it as an analysis problem.

Analyze Let's imagine a vertical y axis, with $y = 0$ at the bottom of the dam. We divide the face of the dam into narrow horizontal strips at a distance y above the bottom, such as the red strip in Figure 14.5. The pressure on each such strip is due only to the water; atmospheric pressure acts on both sides of the dam.

Figure 14.5 (Example 14.4) Water exerts a force on a dam.

Use Equation 14.4 to calculate the pressure due to the water at the depth h:

$$P = \rho g h = \rho g(H - y)$$

Use Equation 14.2 to find the force exerted on the shaded strip of area $dA = w \, dy$:

$$dF = P \, dA = \rho g(H - y)w \, dy$$

Integrate to find the total force on the dam:

$$F = \int P \, dA = \int_0^H \rho g(H - y)w \, dy = \boxed{\tfrac{1}{2}\rho g w H^2}$$

Finalize Notice that the thickness of the dam shown in Figure 14.5 increases with depth. This design accounts for the greater pressure the water exerts on the dam at greater depths.

What If? What if you were asked to find this force without using calculus? How could you determine its value?

Answer We know from Equation 14.4 that the pressure varies linearly with depth. Therefore, the average pressure due to the water over the face of the dam is the average of the pressure at the top and the pressure at the bottom:

$$P_{\text{avg}} = \frac{P_{\text{top}} + P_{\text{bottom}}}{2} = \frac{0 + \rho g H}{2} = \tfrac{1}{2}\rho g H$$

The total force on the dam is equal to the product of the average pressure and the area of the face of the dam:

$$F = P_{avg}A = \left(\tfrac{1}{2}\rho gH\right)(Hw) = \tfrac{1}{2}\rho gwH^2$$

which is the same result we obtained using calculus.

14.3   Pressure Measurements

During the weather report on a television news program, the *barometric pressure* is often provided. This reading is the current pressure of the atmosphere, which varies over a small range from the standard value provided earlier. How is this pressure measured?

One instrument used to measure atmospheric pressure is the common barometer, invented by Evangelista Torricelli (1608–1647). A long tube closed at one end is filled with mercury and then inverted into a dish of mercury (Fig. 14.6a). The closed end of the tube is nearly a vacuum, so the pressure at the top of the mercury column can be taken as zero. In Figure 14.6a, the pressure at point A, due to the column of mercury, must equal the pressure at point B, due to the atmosphere. If that were not the case, there would be a net force that would move mercury from one point to the other until equilibrium is established. Therefore, $P_0 = \rho_{Hg}gh$, where ρ_{Hg} is the density of the mercury and h is the height of the mercury column. As atmospheric pressure varies, the height of the mercury column varies, so the height can be calibrated to measure atmospheric pressure. Let us determine the height of a mercury column for one atmosphere of pressure, $P_0 = 1$ atm $= 1.013 \times 10^5$ Pa:

$$P_0 = \rho_{Hg}gh \quad \rightarrow \quad h = \frac{P_0}{\rho_{Hg}g} = \frac{1.013 \times 10^5 \text{ Pa}}{(13.6 \times 10^3 \text{ kg/m}^3)(9.80 \text{ m/s}^2)} = 0.760 \text{ m}$$

(a)

(b)

Figure 14.6   Two devices for measuring pressure: (a) a mercury barometer and (b) an open-tube manometer.

Based on such a calculation, one atmosphere of pressure is defined to be the pressure equivalent of a column of mercury that is exactly 0.760 0 m in height at 0°C.

A device for measuring the pressure of a gas contained in a vessel is the open-tube manometer illustrated in Figure 14.6b. One end of a U-shaped tube containing a liquid is open to the atmosphere, and the other end is connected to a system of unknown pressure P. In an equilibrium situation, the pressures at points A and B must be the same (otherwise, the curved portion of the liquid would experience a net force and would accelerate), and the pressure at A is the unknown pressure of the gas. Therefore, equating the unknown pressure P to the pressure at point B, we see that $P = P_0 + \rho gh$. The difference in pressure $P - P_0$ is equal to ρgh. The pressure P is called the **absolute pressure,** and the difference $P - P_0$ is called the **gauge pressure.** For example, the pressure you measure in your bicycle tire is gauge pressure.

Quick Quiz 14.3   Several common barometers are built, with a variety of fluids. For which of the following fluids will the column of fluid in the barometer be the highest? (a) mercury   (b) water   (c) ethyl alcohol   (d) benzene

---

14.4   Buoyant Forces and Archimedes's Principle

Have you ever tried to push a beach ball down under water (Fig. 14.7a, page 396)? It is extremely difficult to do because of the large upward force exerted by the water on the ball. The upward force exerted by a fluid on any immersed object is called a **buoyant force.** We can determine the magnitude of a buoyant force by

(a)   (b)

Figure 14.7   (a) A swimmer pushes a beach ball underwater. (b) The forces on a beach ball–sized parcel of water. The buoyant force $\vec{\mathbf{B}}$ on a beach ball that replaces this parcel is exactly the same as the buoyant force on the parcel.

ARCHIMEDES
Greek Mathematician, Physicist, and Engineer (c. 287–212 BC)
Archimedes was perhaps the greatest scientist of antiquity. He was the first to compute accurately the ratio of a circle's circumference to its diameter, and he also showed how to calculate the volume and surface area of spheres, cylinders, and other geometric shapes. He is well known for discovering the nature of the buoyant force and was also a gifted inventor. One of his practical inventions, still in use today, is Archimedes's screw, an inclined, rotating, coiled tube used originally to lift water from the holds of ships. He also invented the catapult and devised systems of levers, pulleys, and weights for raising heavy loads. Such inventions were successfully used to defend his native city, Syracuse, during a two-year siege by Romans.

applying some logic. Imagine a beach ball–sized parcel of water beneath the water surface as in Figure 14.7b. Because this parcel is in equilibrium, there must be an upward force that balances the downward gravitational force on the parcel. This upward force is the buoyant force, and its magnitude is equal to the weight of the water in the parcel. The buoyant force is the resultant force on the parcel due to all forces applied by the fluid surrounding the parcel.

Now imagine replacing the beach ball–sized parcel of water with a beach ball of the same size. The net force applied by the fluid surrounding the beach ball is the same, regardless of whether it is applied to a beach ball or to a parcel of water. Consequently, **the magnitude of the buoyant force on an object always equals the weight of the fluid displaced by the object.** This statement is known as **Archimedes's principle.**

With the beach ball under water, the buoyant force, equal to the weight of a beach ball–sized parcel of water, is much larger than the weight of the beach ball. Therefore, there is a large net upward force, which explains why it is so hard to hold the beach ball under the water. Note that Archimedes's principle does not refer to the makeup of the object experiencing the buoyant force. The object's composition is not a factor in the buoyant force because the buoyant force is exerted by the fluid.

To better understand the origin of the buoyant force, consider a cube immersed in a liquid as in Figure 14.8. According to Equation 14.4, the pressure P_{bot} at the bottom of the cube is greater than the pressure P_{top} at the top by an amount $\rho_{\text{fluid}}gh$, where h is the height of the cube and ρ_{fluid} is the density of the fluid. The pressure at the bottom of the cube causes an *upward* force equal to $P_{\text{bot}}A$, where A is the area of the bottom face. The pressure at the top of the cube causes a *downward* force equal to $P_{\text{top}}A$. The resultant of these two forces is the buoyant force $\vec{\mathbf{B}}$ with magnitude

$$B = (P_{\text{bot}} - P_{\text{top}})A = (\rho_{\text{fluid}}gh)A$$

Buoyant force ▶

$$B = \rho_{\text{fluid}}gV \tag{14.5}$$

where $V = Ah$ is the volume of the fluid displaced by the cube. Because the product $\rho_{\text{fluid}}V$ is equal to the mass of fluid displaced by the object,

$$B = Mg$$

where Mg is the weight of the fluid displaced by the cube. This result is consistent with our initial statement about Archimedes's principle above, based on the discussion of the beach ball.

Under normal conditions, the weight of a fish is slightly greater than the buoyant force on the fish. Hence, the fish would sink if it did not have some mechanism for adjusting the buoyant force. The fish accomplishes that by internally regulating the size of its air-filled swim bladder to increase its volume and the magnitude of the buoyant force acting on it, according to Equation 14.5. In this manner, fish are able to swim to various depths.

Before we proceed with a few examples, it is instructive to discuss two common situations: a totally submerged object and a floating (partly submerged) object.

Case 1: Totally Submerged Object When an object is totally submerged in a fluid of density ρ_{fluid}, the magnitude of the upward buoyant force is $B = \rho_{\text{fluid}}gV = \rho_{\text{fluid}}gV_{\text{obj}}$, where V_{obj} is the volume of the object. If the object has a mass M and density ρ_{obj}, its weight is equal to $F_g = Mg = \rho_{\text{obj}}gV_{\text{obj}}$, and the net force on the object is $B - F_g = (\rho_{\text{fluid}} - \rho_{\text{obj}})gV_{\text{obj}}$. Hence, if the density of the object is less than the density of the fluid, the downward gravitational force is less than the buoyant force and the unsupported object accelerates upward (Active Fig. 14.9a). If the density of the object is greater than the density of the fluid, the upward buoyant force is less than the downward gravitational force and the unsupported object sinks (Active Fig. 14.9b). If the density of the submerged object equals the density of the fluid, the net force on the object is zero and the object remains in equilibrium. Therefore, **the direction of motion of an object submerged in a fluid is determined only by the densities of the object and the fluid.**

Case 2: Floating Object Now consider an object of volume V_{obj} and density $\rho_{\text{obj}} < \rho_{\text{fluid}}$ in static equilibrium floating on the surface of a fluid, that is, an object that is only *partially* submerged (Active Fig. 14.10). In this case, the upward buoyant force is balanced by the downward gravitational force acting on the object. If V_{fluid} is the volume of the fluid displaced by the object (this volume is the same as the volume of that part of the object beneath the surface of the fluid), the buoyant force has a magnitude $B = \rho_{\text{fluid}}gV_{\text{fluid}}$. Because the weight of the object is $F_g = Mg = \rho_{\text{obj}}gV_{\text{obj}}$ and because $F_g = B$, we see that $\rho_{\text{fluid}}gV_{\text{fluid}} = \rho_{\text{obj}}gV_{\text{obj}}$, or

$$\frac{V_{\text{fluid}}}{V_{\text{obj}}} = \frac{\rho_{\text{obj}}}{\rho_{\text{fluid}}} \tag{14.6}$$

This equation shows that **the fraction of the volume of a floating object that is below the fluid surface is equal to the ratio of the density of the object to that of the fluid.**

Quick Quiz 14.4   You are shipwrecked and floating in the middle of the ocean on a raft. Your cargo on the raft includes a treasure chest full of gold that you found before your ship sank, and the raft is just barely afloat. To keep you floating as high as possible in the water, should you (a) leave the treasure chest on top of the raft, (b) secure the treasure chest to the underside of the raft, or (c) hang the treasure chest in the water with a rope attached to the raft? (Assume throwing the treasure chest overboard is not an option you wish to consider.)

Figure 14.8 The external forces acting on the cube of liquid are the gravitational force $\vec{F}_g$ and the buoyant force $\vec{B}$. Under equilibrium conditions, $B = F_g$.

PITFALL PREVENTION 14.2
Buoyant Force Is Exerted by the Fluid

Remember that **the buoyant force is exerted by the fluid.** It is not determined by properties of the object except for the amount of fluid displaced by the object. Therefore, if several objects of different densities but the same volume are immersed in a fluid, they will all experience the same buoyant force. Whether they sink or float is determined by the relationship between the buoyant force and the gravitational force.

ACTIVE FIGURE 14.9

(a) A totally submerged object that is less dense than the fluid in which it is submerged experiences a net upward force. (b) A totally submerged object that is denser than the fluid experiences a net downward force and sinks.

Sign in at www.thomsonedu.com and go to ThomsonNOW to move the object to new positions as well as change the density of the object and see the results.

ACTIVE FIGURE 14.10

An object floating on the surface of a fluid experiences two forces, the gravitational force $\vec{F}_g$ and the buoyant force $\vec{B}$. Because the object floats in equilibrium, $B = F_g$.

Sign in at www.thomsonedu.com and go to ThomsonNOW to change the densities of the object and the fluid.

| EXAMPLE 14.5 | **Eureka!** |

Archimedes supposedly was asked to determine whether a crown made for the king consisted of pure gold. According to legend, he solved this problem by weighing the crown first in air and then in water as shown in Figure 14.11. Suppose the scale read 7.84 N when the crown was in air and 6.84 N when it was in water. What should Archimedes have told the king?

SOLUTION

Conceptualize   Figure 14.11 helps us imagine what is happening in this example. Because of the buoyant force, the scale reading is smaller in Figure 14.11b than in Figure 14.11a.

Categorize   This problem is an example of Case 1 discussed earlier because the crown is completely submerged. The scale reading is a measure of one of the forces on the crown, and the crown is stationary. Therefore, we can categorize the crown as a particle in equilibrium.

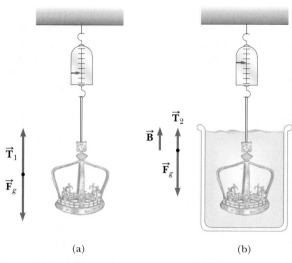

Figure 14.11   (Example 14.5) (a) When the crown is suspended in air, the scale reads its true weight because $T_1 = F_g$ (the buoyancy of air is negligible). (b) When the crown is immersed in water, the buoyant force $\vec{B}$ changes the scale reading to a lower value $T_2 = F_g - B$.

Analyze   When the crown is suspended in air, the scale reads the true weight $T_1 = F_g$ (neglecting the small buoyant force due to the surrounding air). When the crown is immersed in water, the buoyant force $\vec{B}$ reduces the scale reading to an *apparent* weight of $T_2 = F_g - B$.

Apply the force equilibrium condition to the crown in water:

$$\sum F = B + T_2 - F_g = 0$$

Solve for B and substitute the known values:

$$B = F_g - T_2 = 7.84 \text{ N} - 6.84 \text{ N} = 1.00 \text{ N}$$

Because this buoyant force is equal in magnitude to the weight of the displaced water, $\rho_w g V_w = 1.00$ N, where V_w is the volume of the displaced water and ρ_w is its density. Also, the volume of the crown V_c is equal to the volume of the displaced water because the crown is completely submerged.

Find the volume of the crown:

$$V_c = V_w = \frac{1.00 \text{ N}}{\rho_w g} = \frac{1.00 \text{ N}}{(1\ 000 \text{ kg/m}^3)(9.80 \text{ m/s}^2)} = 1.02 \times 10^{-4} \text{ m}^3$$

Find the density of the crown from Equation 1.1:

$$\rho_c = \frac{m_c}{V_c} = \frac{m_c g}{V_c g} = \frac{7.84 \text{ N}}{(1.02 \times 10^{-4} \text{ m}^3)(9.80 \text{ m/s}^2)}$$

$$= 7.84 \times 10^3 \text{ kg/m}^3$$

Finalize   From Table 14.1 we see that the density of gold is 19.3×10^3 kg/m^3. Therefore, Archimedes should have reported that the king had been cheated. Either the crown was hollow, or it was not made of pure gold.

What If?   Suppose the crown has the same weight but is indeed pure gold and not hollow. What would the scale reading be when the crown is immersed in water?

Answer   Find the volume of the solid gold crown:

$$V_c = \frac{m_c}{\rho_c} = \frac{m_c g}{\rho_c g} = \frac{7.84 \text{ N}}{(19.3 \times 10^3 \text{ kg/m}^3)(9.80 \text{ m/s}^2)}$$

$$= 4.15 \times 10^{-5} \text{ m}^3$$

Find the buoyant force on the crown:

$$B = \rho_w g V_w = \rho_w g V_c$$
$$= (1.00 \times 10^3 \text{ kg/m}^3)(9.80 \text{ m/s}^2)(4.15 \times 10^{-5} \text{ m}^3) = 0.406 \text{ N}$$

Find the tension in the string hanging from the scale:

$$T_2 = F_g - B = 7.84 \text{ N} - 0.406 \text{ N} = 7.43 \text{ N}$$

EXAMPLE 14.6   A Titanic Surprise

An iceberg floating in seawater as shown in Figure 14.12a is extremely dangerous because most of the ice is below the surface. This hidden ice can damage a ship that is still a considerable distance from the visible ice. What fraction of the iceberg lies below the water level?

SOLUTION

Conceptualize You are likely familiar with the phrase, "That's only the tip of the iceberg." The origin of this popular saying is that most of the volume of a floating iceberg is beneath the surface of the water (Fig. 14.12b).

Categorize This example corresponds to Case 2. It is also a simple substitution problem involving Equation 14.6.

(a)   (b)

Figure 14.12 (Example 14.6) (a) Much of the volume of this iceberg is beneath the water. (b) A ship can be damaged even when it is not near the visible ice.

Evaluate Equation 14.6 using the densities of ice and seawater (Table 14.1):

$$f = \frac{V_{\text{seawater}}}{V_{\text{ice}}} = \frac{\rho_{\text{ice}}}{\rho_{\text{seawater}}} = \frac{917 \text{ kg/m}^3}{1\,030 \text{ kg/m}^3} = \boxed{0.890 \text{ or } 89.0\%}$$

Therefore, the visible fraction of ice above the water's surface is about 11%. It is the unseen 89% below the water that represents the danger to a passing ship.

14.5   Fluid Dynamics

Thus far, our study of fluids has been restricted to fluids at rest. We now turn our attention to fluids in motion. When fluid is in motion, its flow can be characterized as being one of two main types. The flow is said to be **steady,** or **laminar,** if each particle of the fluid follows a smooth path such that the paths of different particles never cross each other as shown in Figure 14.13. In steady flow, every fluid particle arriving at a given point has the same velocity.

Above a certain critical speed, fluid flow becomes **turbulent.** Turbulent flow is irregular flow characterized by small whirlpool-like regions as shown in Figure 14.14 (page 400).

The term **viscosity** is commonly used in the description of fluid flow to characterize the degree of internal friction in the fluid. This internal friction, or *viscous force,* is associated with the resistance that two adjacent layers of fluid have to moving relative to each other. Viscosity causes part of the fluid's kinetic energy to be converted to internal energy. This mechanism is similar to the one by which an object sliding on a rough horizontal surface loses kinetic energy.

Figure 14.13 Laminar flow around an automobile in a test wind tunnel.

Figure 14.14 Hot gases from a cigarette made visible by smoke particles. The smoke first moves in laminar flow at the bottom and then in turbulent flow above.

Because the motion of real fluids is very complex and not fully understood, we make some simplifying assumptions in our approach. In our model of **ideal fluid flow,** we make the following four assumptions:

1. **The fluid is nonviscous.** In a nonviscous fluid, internal friction is neglected. An object moving through the fluid experiences no viscous force.
2. **The flow is steady.** In steady (laminar) flow, all particles passing through a point have the same velocity.
3. **The fluid is incompressible.** The density of an incompressible fluid is constant.
4. **The flow is irrotational.** In irrotational flow, the fluid has no angular momentum about any point. If a small paddle wheel placed anywhere in the fluid does not rotate about the wheel's center of mass, the flow is irrotational.

The path taken by a fluid particle under steady flow is called a **streamline.** The velocity of the particle is always tangent to the streamline as shown in Figure 14.15. A set of streamlines like the ones shown in Figure 14.15 form a *tube of flow.* Fluid particles cannot flow into or out of the sides of this tube; if they could, the streamlines would cross one another.

Consider ideal fluid flow through a pipe of nonuniform size as illustrated in Figure 14.16. The particles in the fluid move along streamlines in steady flow. In a time interval Δt, a short element of the fluid at the bottom end of the pipe moves a distance $\Delta x_1 = v_1 \Delta t$. If A_1 is the cross-sectional area in this region, the mass of fluid contained in the left shaded region in Figure 14.16 is $m_1 = \rho A_1 \Delta x_1 = \rho A_1 v_1 \Delta t$, where ρ is the (unchanging) density of the ideal fluid. Similarly, the fluid that moves through the upper end of the pipe in the time interval Δt has a mass $m_2 = \rho A_2 v_2 \Delta t$. Because the fluid is incompressible and the flow is steady, however, the mass of fluid that crosses A_1 in a time interval Δt must equal the mass that crosses A_2 in the same time interval. That is, $m_1 = m_2$ or $\rho A_1 v_1 = \rho A_2 v_2$, which means that

$$A_1 v_1 = A_2 v_2 = \text{constant} \tag{14.7}$$

Figure 14.15 A particle in laminar flow follows a streamline, and at each point along its path the particle's velocity is tangent to the streamline.

This expression is called the **equation of continuity for fluids.** It states that the product of the area and the fluid speed at all points along a pipe is constant for an incompressible fluid. Equation 14.7 shows that the speed is high where the tube is constricted (small A) and low where the tube is wide (large A). The product Av, which has the dimensions of volume per unit time, is called either the *volume flux* or the *flow rate.* The condition $Av = $ constant is equivalent to the statement that the volume of fluid that enters one end of a tube in a given time interval equals the volume leaving the other end of the tube in the same time interval if no leaks are present.

You demonstrate the equation of continuity each time you water your garden with your thumb over the end of a garden hose as in Figure 14.17. By partially blocking the opening with your thumb, you reduce the cross-sectional area through which the water passes. As a result, the speed of the water increases as it exits the hose, and it can be sprayed over a long distance.

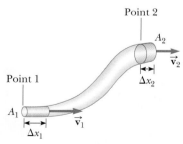

Figure 14.16 A fluid moving with steady flow through a pipe of varying cross-sectional area. The volume of fluid flowing through area A_1 in a time interval Δt must equal the volume flowing through area A_2 in the same time interval. Therefore, $A_1 v_1 = A_2 v_2$.

Figure 14.17 The speed of water spraying from the end of a garden hose increases as the size of the opening is decreased with the thumb.

| EXAMPLE 14.7 | **Watering a Garden** |

A gardener uses a water hose 2.50 cm in diameter to fill a 30.0-L bucket. The gardener notes that it takes 1.00 min to fill the bucket. A nozzle with an opening of cross-sectional area 0.500 cm² is then attached to the hose. The nozzle is held so that water is projected horizontally from a point 1.00 m above the ground. Over what horizontal distance can the water be projected?

SOLUTION

Conceptualize   Imagine any past experience you have with projecting water from a hose or a pipe. The faster the water is traveling as it leaves the hose, the farther it will land on the ground from the end of the hose.

Categorize   Once the water leaves the hose, it is in free fall. Therefore, we categorize a given element of the water as a projectile. The element is modeled as a particle under constant acceleration (due to gravity) in the vertical direction and a particle under constant velocity in the horizontal direction. The horizontal distance over which the element is projected depends on the speed with which it is projected. This example involves a change in area for the pipe, so we also categorize it as one in which we use the equation of continuity for fluids.

Analyze   We first find the speed of the water in the hose from the bucket-filling information.

Find the cross-sectional area of the hose:

$$A = \pi r^2 = \pi \frac{d^2}{4} = \pi \left[\frac{(2.50 \text{ cm})^2}{4} \right] = 4.91 \text{ cm}^2$$

Evaluate the volume flow rate in cm³/s:

$$Av = 30.0 \text{ L/min} = \frac{30.0 \times 10^3 \text{ cm}^3}{60.0 \text{ s}} = 500 \text{ cm}^3/\text{s}$$

Solve for the speed of the water in the hose:

$$v_1 = \frac{500 \text{ cm}^3/\text{s}}{A} = \frac{500 \text{ cm}^3/\text{s}}{4.91 \text{ cm}^2} = 102 \text{ cm/s} = 1.02 \text{ m/s}$$

We have labeled this speed v_1 because we identify point 1 within the hose. We identify point 2 in the air just outside the nozzle. We must find the speed $v_2 = v_{xi}$ with which the water exits the nozzle. The subscript i anticipates that it will be the *initial* velocity component of the water projected from the hose, and the subscript x indicates that the initial velocity vector of the projected water is horizontal.

Solve the continuity equation for fluids for v_2:

$$v_2 = v_{xi} = \frac{A_1}{A_2} v_1$$

Substitute numerical values:

$$v_{xi} = \frac{4.91 \text{ cm}^2}{0.500 \text{ cm}^2} (1.02 \text{ m/s}) = 10.0 \text{ m/s}$$

We now shift our thinking away from fluids and to projectile motion. In the vertical direction, an element of the water starts from rest and falls through a vertical distance of 1.00 m.

Write Equation 2.16 for the vertical position of an element of water, modeled as a particle under constant acceleration:

$$y_f = y_i + v_{yi}t - \tfrac{1}{2}gt^2$$

Substitute numerical values:

$$-1.00 \text{ m} = 0 + 0 - \tfrac{1}{2}(9.80 \text{ m/s}^2)t^2$$

Solve for the time at which the element of water lands on the ground:

$$t = \sqrt{\frac{2(1.00 \text{ m})}{9.80 \text{ m/s}^2}} = 0.452 \text{ s}$$

Use Equation 2.7 to find the horizontal position of the element at this time, modeled as a particle under constant velocity:

$$x_f = x_i + v_{xi}t = 0 + (10.0 \text{ m/s})(0.452 \text{ s}) = \boxed{4.52 \text{ m}}$$

Finalize The time interval for the element of water to fall to the ground is unchanged if the projection speed is changed because the projection is horizontal. Increasing the projection speed results in the water hitting the ground farther from the end of the hose, but requires the same time interval to strike the ground.

14.6 Bernoulli's Equation

DANIEL BERNOULLI
Swiss physicist (1700–1782)
Bernoulli made important discoveries in fluid dynamics. Born into a family of mathematicians, he was the only member of his family to make a mark in physics.

Bernoulli's most famous work, *Hydrodynamica,* was published in 1738; it is both a theoretical and a practical study of equilibrium, pressure, and speed in fluids. He showed that as the speed of a fluid increases, its pressure decreases. Referred to as "Bernoulli's principle," Bernoulli's work is used to produce a partial vacuum in chemical laboratories by connecting a vessel to a tube through which water is running rapidly.

In *Hydrodynamica,* Bernoulli also attempted the first explanation of the behavior of gases with changing pressure and temperature; this step was the beginning of the kinetic theory of gases, a topic we study in Chapter 21.

You have probably experienced driving on a highway and having a large truck pass you at high speed. In this situation, you may have had the frightening feeling that your car was being pulled in toward the truck as it passed. We will investigate the origin of this effect in this section.

As a fluid moves through a region where its speed or elevation above the Earth's surface changes, the pressure in the fluid varies with these changes. The relationship between fluid speed, pressure, and elevation was first derived in 1738 by Swiss physicist Daniel Bernoulli. Consider the flow of a segment of an ideal fluid through a nonuniform pipe in a time interval Δt as illustrated in Figure 14.18. At the beginning of the time interval, the segment of fluid consists of the blue shaded portion (portion 1) at the left and the unshaded portion. During the time interval, the left end of the segment moves to the right by a distance Δx_1, which is the length of the blue shaded portion at the left. Meanwhile, the right end of the segment moves to the right through a distance Δx_2, which is the length of the blue shaded portion (portion 2) at the upper right of Figure 14.18. Therefore, at the end of the time interval, the segment of fluid consists of the unshaded portion and the blue shaded portion at the upper right.

Now consider forces exerted on this segment by fluid to the left and the right of the segment. The force exerted by the fluid on the left end has a magnitude P_1A_1. The work done by this force on the segment in a time interval Δt is $W_1 = F_1 \, \Delta x_1 = P_1A_1 \, \Delta x_1 = P_1V$, where V is the volume of portion 1. In a similar manner, the work done by the fluid to the right of the segment in the same time interval Δt is $W_2 = -P_2A_2 \, \Delta x_2 = -P_2V$. (The volume of portion 1 equals the volume of portion 2 because the fluid is incompressible.) This work is negative because the force on the segment of fluid is to the left and the displacement is to the right. Therefore, the net work done on the segment by these forces in the time interval Δt is

$$W = (P_1 - P_2)V$$

Part of this work goes into changing the kinetic energy of the segment of fluid, and part goes into changing the gravitational potential energy of the segment–Earth system. Because we are assuming streamline flow, the kinetic energy K_{uns} of the unshaded portion of the segment in Figure 14.18 is unchanged during the time interval. Therefore, the change in the kinetic energy of the segment of fluid is

$$\Delta K = \left(\tfrac{1}{2}mv_2^{\,2} + K_{uns}\right) - \left(\tfrac{1}{2}mv_1^{\,2} + K_{uns}\right) = \tfrac{1}{2}mv_2^{\,2} - \tfrac{1}{2}mv_1^{\,2}$$

where m is the mass of both portion 1 and portion 2. (Because the volumes of both portions are the same, they also have the same mass.)

Considering the gravitational potential energy of the segment–Earth system, once again there is no change during the time interval for the gravitational potential energy U_{uns} associated with the unshaded portion of the fluid. Consequently, the change in gravitational potential energy is

$$\Delta U = (mgy_2 + U_{uns}) - (mgy_1 + U_{uns}) = mgy_2 - mgy_1$$

From Equation 8.2, the total work done on the system by the fluid outside the segment is equal to the change in mechanical energy of the system: $W = \Delta K + \Delta U$. Substituting for each of these terms gives

$$(P_1 - P_2)V = \tfrac{1}{2}mv_2^{\,2} - \tfrac{1}{2}mv_1^{\,2} + mgy_2 - mgy_1$$

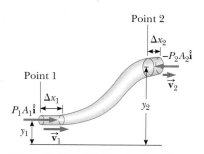

Figure 14.18 A fluid in laminar flow through a constricted pipe. The volume of the shaded portion on the left is equal to the volume of the shaded portion on the right.

If we divide each term by the portion volume V and recall that $\rho = m/V$, this expression reduces to

$$P_1 - P_2 = \tfrac{1}{2}\rho v_2{}^2 - \tfrac{1}{2}\rho v_1{}^2 + \rho g y_2 - \rho g y_1$$

Rearranging terms gives

$$P_1 + \tfrac{1}{2}\rho v_1{}^2 + \rho g y_1 = P_2 + \tfrac{1}{2}\rho v_2{}^2 + \rho g y_2 \qquad (14.8)$$

which is **Bernoulli's equation** as applied to an ideal fluid. This equation is often expressed as

$$P + \tfrac{1}{2}\rho v^2 + \rho g y = \text{constant} \qquad (14.9)$$

◀ Bernoulli's equation

Bernoulli's equation shows that the pressure of a fluid decreases as the speed of the fluid increases. In addition, the pressure decreases as the elevation increases. This latter point explains why water pressure from faucets on the upper floors of a tall building is weak unless measures are taken to provide higher pressure for these upper floors.

When the fluid is at rest, $v_1 = v_2 = 0$ and Equation 14.8 becomes

$$P_1 - P_2 = \rho g(y_2 - y_1) = \rho g h$$

This result is in agreement with Equation 14.4.

Although Equation 14.9 was derived for an incompressible fluid, the general behavior of pressure with speed is true even for gases: as the speed increases, the pressure decreases. This *Bernoulli effect* explains the experience with the truck on the highway at the opening of this section. As air passes between you and the truck, it must pass through a relatively narrow channel. According to the continuity equation, the speed of the air is higher. According to the Bernoulli effect, this higher-speed air exerts less pressure on your car than the slower-moving air on the other side of your car. Therefore, there is a net force pushing you toward the truck!

Quick Quiz 14.5   You observe two helium balloons floating next to each other at the ends of strings secured to a table. The facing surfaces of the balloons are separated by 1–2 cm. You blow through the small space between the balloons. What happens to the balloons? (a) They move toward each other. (b) They move away from each other. (c) They are unaffected.

EXAMPLE 14.8   **The Venturi Tube**

The horizontal constricted pipe illustrated in Figure 14.19, known as a *Venturi tube*, can be used to measure the flow speed of an incompressible fluid. Determine the flow speed at point 2 of Figure 14.19a if the pressure difference $P_1 - P_2$ is known.

SOLUTION

Conceptualize   Bernoulli's equation shows how the pressure of a fluid decreases as its speed increases. Therefore, we should be able to calibrate a device to give us the fluid speed if we can measure pressure.

Categorize   Because the problem states that the fluid is incompressible, we can categorize it as one in which we can use the equation of continuity for fluids and Bernoulli's equation.

Figure 14.19   (Example 14.8) (a) Pressure P_1 is greater than pressure P_2 because $v_1 < v_2$. This device can be used to measure the speed of fluid flow. (b) A Venturi tube, located at the top of the photograph. The higher level of fluid in the middle column shows that the pressure at the top of the column, which is in the constricted region of the Venturi tube, is lower.

Analyze Apply Equation 14.8 to points 1 and 2, noting that $y_1 = y_2$ because the pipe is horizontal:

$$(1) \quad P_1 + \tfrac{1}{2}\rho v_1^2 = P_2 + \tfrac{1}{2}\rho v_2^2$$

Solve the equation of continuity for v_1:

$$v_1 = \frac{A_2}{A_1} v_2$$

Substitute this expression into Equation (1):

$$P_1 + \tfrac{1}{2}\rho\left(\frac{A_2}{A_1}\right)^2 v_2^2 = P_2 + \tfrac{1}{2}\rho v_2^2$$

Solve for v_2:

$$v_2 = A_1\sqrt{\frac{2(P_1 - P_2)}{\rho(A_1^2 - A_2^2)}}$$

Finalize From the design of the tube (areas A_1 and A_2) and measurements of the pressure difference $P_1 - P_2$, we can calculate the speed of the fluid with this equation. To see the relationship between fluid speed and pressure difference, place two empty soda cans on their sides about 2 cm apart on a table. Gently blow a stream of air horizontally between the cans and watch them roll together slowly due to a modest pressure difference between the stagnant air on their outside edges and the moving air between them. Now blow more strongly and watch the increased pressure difference move the cans together more rapidly.

EXAMPLE 14.9 | **Torricelli's Law**

An enclosed tank containing a liquid of density ρ has a hole in its side at a distance y_1 from the tank's bottom (Fig. 14.20). The hole is open to the atmosphere, and its diameter is much smaller than the diameter of the tank. The air above the liquid is maintained at a pressure P. Determine the speed of the liquid as it leaves the hole when the liquid's level is a distance h above the hole.

SOLUTION

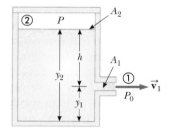

Figure 14.20 (Example 14.9) A liquid leaves a hole in a tank at speed v_1.

Conceptualize Imagine that the tank is a fire extinguisher. When the hole is opened, liquid leaves the hole with a certain speed. If the pressure P at the top of the liquid is increased, the liquid leaves with a higher speed. If the pressure P falls too low, the liquid leaves with a low speed and the extinguisher must be replaced.

Categorize Looking at Figure 14.20, we know the pressure at two points and the velocity at one of those points. We wish to find the velocity at the second point. Therefore, we can categorize this example as one in which we can apply Bernoulli's equation.

Analyze Because $A_2 \gg A_1$, the liquid is approximately at rest at the top of the tank, where the pressure is P. At the hole P_1 is equal to atmospheric pressure P_0.

Apply Bernoulli's equation between points 1 and 2:

$$P_0 + \tfrac{1}{2}\rho v_1^2 + \rho g y_1 = P + \rho g y_2$$

Solve for v_1, noting that $y_2 - y_1 = h$:

$$v_1 = \sqrt{\frac{2(P - P_0)}{\rho} + 2gh}$$

Finalize When P is much greater than P_0 (so that the term $2gh$ can be neglected), the exit speed of the water is mainly a function of P. If the tank is open to the atmosphere, then $P = P_0$ and $v_1 = \sqrt{2gh}$. In other words, for an open tank, the speed of liquid leaving a hole a distance h below the surface is equal to that acquired by an object falling freely through a vertical distance h. This phenomenon is known as **Torricelli's law.**

What If? What if the position of the hole in Figure 14.20 could be adjusted vertically? If the tank is open to the atmosphere and sitting on a table, what position of the hole would cause the water to land on the table at the farthest distance from the tank?

Answer   Model a parcel of water exiting the hole as a projectile. Find the time at which the parcel strikes the table from a hole at an arbitrary position:

$$y_f = y_i + v_{yi}t - \tfrac{1}{2}gt^2$$

$$0 = y_1 + 0 - \tfrac{1}{2}gt^2$$

$$t = \sqrt{\frac{2y_1}{g}}$$

Find the horizontal position of the parcel at the time it strikes the table:

$$x_f = x_i + v_{xi}t = 0 + \sqrt{2g(y_2 - y_1)}\sqrt{\frac{2y_1}{g}}$$

$$= 2\sqrt{(y_2 y_1 - y_1{}^2)}$$

Maximize the horizontal position by taking the derivative of x_f with respect to y_1 (because y_1, the height of the hole, is the variable that can be adjusted) and setting it equal to zero:

$$\frac{dx_f}{dy_1} = \tfrac{1}{2}(2)(y_2 y_1 - y_1{}^2)^{-1/2}(y_2 - 2y_1) = 0$$

Solve for y_1:

$$y_1 = \tfrac{1}{2}y_2$$

Therefore, to maximize the horizontal distance, the hole should be halfway between the bottom of the tank and the upper surface of the water. Below this location, the water is projected at a higher speed but falls for a short time interval, reducing the horizontal range. Above this point, the water is in the air for a longer time interval but is projected with a smaller horizontal speed.

14.7   Other Applications of Fluid Dynamics

Consider the streamlines that flow around an airplane wing as shown in Figure 14.21. Let's assume the airstream approaches the wing horizontally from the right with a velocity $\vec{v}_1$. The tilt of the wing causes the airstream to be deflected downward with a velocity $\vec{v}_2$. Because the airstream is deflected by the wing, the wing must exert a force on the airstream. According to Newton's third law, the airstream exerts a force $\vec{F}$ on the wing that is equal in magnitude and opposite in direction. This force has a vertical component called **lift** (or aerodynamic lift) and a horizontal component called **drag.** The lift depends on several factors, such as the speed of the airplane, the area of the wing, the wing's curvature, and the angle between the wing and the horizontal. The curvature of the wing surfaces causes the pressure above the wing to be lower than that below the wing due to the Bernoulli effect. This pressure difference assists with the lift on the wing. As the angle between the wing and the horizontal increases, turbulent flow can set in above the wing to reduce the lift.

In general, an object moving through a fluid experiences lift as the result of any effect that causes the fluid to change its direction as it flows past the object. Some factors that influence lift are the shape of the object, its orientation with respect to the fluid flow, any spinning motion it might have, and the texture of its surface. For example, a golf ball struck with a club is given a rapid backspin due to the slant of the club. The dimples on the ball increase the friction force between the ball and the air so that air adheres to the ball's surface. Figure 14.22 (page 406) shows air adhering to the ball and being deflected downward as a result. Because the ball pushes the air down, the air must push up on the ball. Without the dimples, the friction force is lower and the golf ball does not travel as far. It may seem counterintuitive to increase the range by increasing the friction force, but the lift gained by spinning the ball more than compensates for the loss of range due to

Figure 14.21   Streamline flow around a moving airplane wing. The air approaching from the right is deflected downward by the wing. By Newton's third law, this deflection must coincide with an upward force on the wing from the air: *lift*. Because of air resistance, there is also a force opposite the velocity of the wing: *drag.*

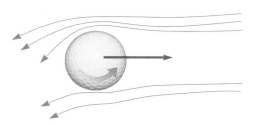

Figure 14.22 Because of the deflection of air, a spinning golf ball experiences a lifting force that allows it to travel much farther than it would if it were not spinning.

Figure 14.23 A stream of air passing over a tube dipped into a liquid causes the liquid to rise in the tube.

the effect of friction on the translational motion of the ball. For the same reason, a baseball's cover helps the spinning ball "grab" the air rushing by and helps deflect it when a "curve ball" is thrown.

A number of devices operate by means of the pressure differentials that result from differences in a fluid's speed. For example, a stream of air passing over one end of an open tube, the other end of which is immersed in a liquid, reduces the pressure above the tube as illustrated in Figure 14.23. This reduction in pressure causes the liquid to rise into the air stream. The liquid is then dispersed into a fine spray of droplets. You might recognize that this so-called atomizer is used in perfume bottles and paint sprayers.

Summary

ThomsonNOW™ Sign in at **www.thomsonedu.com** and go to ThomsonNOW to take a practice test for this chapter.

DEFINITIONS

The **pressure** P in a fluid is the force per unit area exerted by the fluid on a surface:

$$P \equiv \frac{F}{A} \qquad (14.1)$$

In the SI system, pressure has units of newtons per square meter (N/m²), and 1 N/m² = 1 **pascal** (Pa).

CONCEPTS AND PRINCIPLES

The pressure in a fluid at rest varies with depth h in the fluid according to the expression

$$P = P_0 + \rho g h \qquad (14.4)$$

where P_0 is the pressure at $h = 0$ and ρ is the density of the fluid, assumed uniform.

Pascal's law states that when pressure is applied to an enclosed fluid, the pressure is transmitted undiminished to every point in the fluid and to every point on the walls of the container.

When an object is partially or fully submerged in a fluid, the fluid exerts on the object an upward force called the **buoyant force**. According to **Archimedes's principle,** the magnitude of the buoyant force is equal to the weight of the fluid displaced by the object:

$$B = \rho_{\text{fluid}} g V \qquad (14.5)$$

The flow rate (volume flux) through a pipe that varies in cross-sectional area is constant; that is equivalent to stating that the product of the cross-sectional area A and the speed v at any point is a constant. This result is expressed in the **equation of continuity for fluids:**

$$A_1 v_1 = A_2 v_2 = \text{constant} \qquad (14.7)$$

The sum of the pressure, kinetic energy per unit volume, and gravitational potential energy per unit volume has the same value at all points along a streamline for an ideal fluid. This result is summarized in **Bernoulli's equation:**

$$P + \tfrac{1}{2}\rho v^2 + \rho g y = \text{constant} \qquad (14.9)$$

Questions

☐ denotes answer available in *Student Solutions Manual/Study Guide;* **O** denotes objective question

1. **O** Figure Q14.1 shows aerial views from directly above two dams. Both dams are equally wide (the vertical dimension in the diagram) and equally high (into the page in the diagram). The dam on the left holds back a very large lake, and the dam on the right holds back a narrow river. Which dam has to be built more strongly? (a) the dam on the left (b) the dam on the right (c) both the same (d) cannot be predicted

Dam   Dam

Figure Q14.1

2. Two thin-walled drinking glasses having equal base areas but different shapes, with very different cross-sectional areas above the base, are filled to the same level with water. According to the expression $P = P_0 + \rho g h$, the pressure is the same at the bottom of both glasses. In view of this equality, why does one glass weigh more than the other?

3. Because atmospheric pressure is about 10^5 N/m^2 and the area of a person's chest is about 0.13 m^2, the force of the atmosphere on one's chest is around 13 000 N. In view of this enormous force, why don't our bodies collapse?

4. A fish rests on the bottom of a bucket of water while the bucket is being weighed on a scale. When the fish begins to swim around, does the scale reading change?

5. You are a passenger on a spacecraft. For your survival and comfort, the interior contains air just like that at the surface of the Earth. The spacecraft is coasting through a very empty region of space. That is, a nearly perfect vacuum exists just outside the wall. Suddenly, a meteoroid pokes a hole, about the size of a large coin, right through the wall next to your seat. What happens? Is there anything you can or should do about it?

6. Does a ship float higher in the water of an inland lake or in the ocean? Why?

7. **O** An apple is held completely submerged just below the surface of water in a container. The apple is then moved to a deeper point in the water. Compared with the force needed to hold the apple just below the surface, what is the force needed to hold it at the deeper point? (a) larger (b) the same (c) smaller (d) impossible to determine

8. When an object is immersed in a liquid at rest, why is the net force on the object in the horizontal direction equal to zero?

9. A barge is carrying a load of gravel along a river. The barge approaches a low bridge, and the captain realizes that the top of the pile of gravel is not going to make it under the bridge. The captain orders the crew to shovel gravel from the pile into the water. Is that a good decision?

10. An empty metal soap dish barely floats in water. A bar of Ivory soap floats in water. When the soap is stuck in the soap dish, the combination sinks. Explain why.

11. **O** A beach ball is made of thin plastic. It has been inflated with air, but the plastic is not stretched. By swimming with fins on, you manage to take the ball from the surface of a pool to the bottom. Once the ball is completely submerged, what happens to the buoyant force exerted on the beach ball as you take it deeper? (a) increases (b) remains constant (c) decreases (d) is impossible to determine

12. If you release a ball while inside a freely falling elevator, the ball remains in front of you rather than falling to the floor because the ball, the elevator, and you all experience the same downward gravitational acceleration. What happens if you repeat this experiment with a helium-filled balloon? (This question is tricky.)

13. **O** A small piece of steel is tied to a block of wood. When the wood is placed in a tub of water with the steel on top, half of the block is submerged. Now the block is inverted so that the steel is under water. **(i)** Does the amount of the block submerged (a) increase, (b) decrease, or (c) remain the same? **(ii)** What happens to the water level in the tub when the block is inverted? (a) It rises. (b) It falls. (c) It remains the same.

14. How would you determine the density of an irregularly shaped rock?

15. **O** Rank the buoyant forces exerted on the following seven objects, from the largest to the smallest. Assume the objects have been dropped into a swimming pool and allowed to come to mechanical equilibrium. If any buoyant forces are equal, state that in your ranking. (a) a block of solid oak (b) an aluminum block of equal volume to the wood (c) a beach ball made of thin plastic and inflated with air, of equal volume (d) an iron block of equal volume (e) a thin-walled, sealed bottle of water equal in volume to the wood (f) an aluminum block having the same mass as the wood (g) an iron block of equal mass

16. **O** A person in a boat floating in a small pond throws an anchor overboard. What happens to the level of the pond? (a) It rises. (b) It falls. (c) It remains the same.

17. Is the buoyant force a conservative force? Is a potential energy associated with it? Explain your answers.

18. An unopened can of diet cola floats when placed in a tank of water, whereas a can of regular cola of the same brand sinks in the tank. What do you suppose could explain this behavior?

19. **O** A piece of unpainted porous wood floats in a container partly filled with water. The container is sealed and pressurized above atmospheric pressure. What happens to the wood? (a) It rises. (b) It falls. (c) It remains at the same level.

20. The water supply for a city is often provided from reservoirs built on high ground. Water flows from the reservoir, through pipes, and into your home when you turn

the tap on your faucet. Why is the water flow more rapid out of a faucet on the first floor of a building than in an apartment on a higher floor?

21. If the airstream from a hair dryer is directed over a table-tennis ball, the ball can be levitated. Explain.

22. When ski jumpers are airborne (Fig. Q14.22), they bend their bodies forward and keep their hands at their sides. Why?

Figure Q14.22

23. Why do airplane pilots prefer to take off with the airplane facing into the wind?

24. **O** A water supply maintains a constant rate of flow for water in a hose. You want to change the opening of the nozzle so that water leaving the nozzle reaches a height that is four times the current maximum height the water reaches with the nozzle vertical. To do so, what should you do? (a) decrease the area of the opening by a factor of 16 (b) decrease the area by a factor of 8 (c) decrease the area by a factor of 4 (d) decrease the area by a factor of 2 (e) give up because it cannot be done

25. Prairie dogs (Fig. Q14.25) ventilate their burrows by building a mound around one entrance, which is open to a stream of air when wind blows from any direction. A second entrance at ground level is open to almost stagnant air. How does this construction create an airflow through the burrow?

Figure Q14.25

26. In Figure Q14.26, an airstream moves from right to left through a tube that is constricted at the middle. Three table-tennis balls are levitated in equilibrium above the vertical columns through which the air escapes. (a) Why is the ball at the right higher than the one in the middle? (b) Why is the ball at the left lower than the ball at the right even though the horizontal tube has the same dimensions at these two points?

Figure Q14.26

27. **O** (i) A glass of water contains floating ice cubes. When the ice melts, does the water level in the glass (a) go up, (b) go down, or (c) remain the same? (ii) One of the predicted problems due to global warming is that ice in the polar ice caps will melt and raise sea level everywhere in the world. Is that more of a worry for ice (a) at the north pole, where most of the ice floats on water; (b) at the south pole, where most of the ice sits on land; (c) both at the north and the south poles equally; or (d) at neither pole?

Problems

WebAssign The Problems from this chapter may be assigned online in WebAssign.

ThomsonNOW™ Sign in at **www.thomsonedu.com** and go to ThomsonNOW to assess your understanding of this chapter's topics with additional quizzing and conceptual questions.

1, 2, 3 denotes straightforward, intermediate, challenging; ☐ denotes full solution available in *Student Solutions Manual/Study Guide;* ▲ denotes coached solution with hints available at **www.thomsonedu.com;** denotes developing symbolic reasoning; ● denotes asking for qualitative reasoning; ⬛ denotes computer useful in solving problem

Section 14.1 Pressure

1. Calculate the mass of a solid iron sphere that has a diameter of 3.00 cm.

2. Find the order of magnitude of the density of the nucleus of an atom. What does this result suggest concerning the structure of matter? Model a nucleus as consisting of protons and neutrons closely packed together. Each has mass 1.67×10^{-27} kg and radius on the order of 10^{-15} m.

3. A 50.0-kg woman balances on one heel of a pair of high-heeled shoes. If the heel is circular and has a radius of 0.500 cm, what pressure does she exert on the floor?

4. What is the total mass of the Earth's atmosphere? (The radius of the Earth is 6.37×10^6 m, and atmospheric pressure at the surface is 1.013×10^5 N/m².)

Section 14.2 Variation of Pressure with Depth

5. The spring of the pressure gauge shown in Figure 14.2 has a force constant of 1 000 N/m, and the piston has a diameter of 2.00 cm. As the gauge is lowered into water, what change in depth causes the piston to move in by 0.500 cm?

6. (a) Calculate the absolute pressure at an ocean depth of 1 000 m. Assume the density of seawater is 1 024 kg/m³ and the air above exerts a pressure of 101.3 kPa. (b) At this depth, what force must the frame around a circular submarine porthole having a diameter of 30.0 cm exert to counterbalance the force exerted by the water?

7. ▲ What must be the contact area between a suction cup (completely exhausted) and a ceiling if the cup is to support the weight of an 80.0-kg student?

8. The small piston of a hydraulic lift has a cross-sectional area of 3.00 cm² and its large piston has a cross-sectional area of 200 cm² (Fig. 14.4a). What force must be applied to the small piston for the lift to raise a load of 15.0 kN? (In service stations, this force is usually exerted by compressed air.)

9. For the basement of a new house, a hole is dug in the ground, with vertical sides going down 2.40 m. A concrete foundation wall is built across the 9.60-m width of the excavation. This foundation wall is 0.183 m from the front of the basement hole. During a rainstorm, drainage from the street fills up the space in front of the concrete wall, but not the basement behind the wall. The water does not soak into the clay soil. Find the force the water causes on the foundation wall. For comparison, the gravitational force exerted on the water is (2.40 m)(9.60 m)(0.183 m)(1 000 kg/m³)(9.80 m/s²) = 41.3 kN.

10. (a) A powerful vacuum cleaner has a hose 2.86 cm in diameter. With no nozzle on the hose, what is the weight of the heaviest brick that the cleaner can lift (Fig. P14.10a)? (b) **What If?** An octopus uses one sucker of diameter 2.86 cm on each of the two shells of a clam in an attempt to pull the shells apart (Fig. P14.10b). Find the greatest force the octopus can exert in seawater 32.3 m deep. *Caution:* Experimental verification can be interesting, but do not drop a brick on your foot. Do not overheat the motor of a vacuum cleaner. Do not get an octopus mad at you.

(a)	(b)

Figure P14.10

11. A swimming pool has dimensions 30.0 m × 10.0 m and a flat bottom. When the pool is filled to a depth of 2.00 m

with fresh water, what is the force caused by the water on the bottom? On each end? On each side?

12. The tank in Figure P14.12 is filled with water 2.00 m deep. At the bottom of one sidewall is a rectangular hatch 1.00 m high and 2.00 m wide that is hinged at the top of the hatch. (a) Determine the force the water causes on the hatch. (b) Find the torque caused by the water about the hinges.

Figure P14.12

13. **Review problem.** The Abbott of Aberbrothock paid for a bell moored to the Inchcape Rock to warn sailors away. Assume the bell was 3.00 m in diameter and cast from brass with a bulk modulus of 14.0 × 10¹⁰ N/m². The pirate Ralph the Rover cut loose the bell and threw it into the ocean. By how much did the diameter of the bell decrease as it sank to a depth of 10.0 km? Years later, the klutz drowned when his ship collided with the rock. *Note:* The brass is compressed uniformly, so you may model the bell as a sphere of diameter 3.00 m.

Section 14.3 Pressure Measurements

14. Figure P14.14 shows Superman attempting to drink water through a very long straw. With his great strength he achieves maximum possible suction. The walls of the tubular straw do not collapse. (a) Find the maximum height through which he can lift the water. (b) **What If?** Still thirsty, the Man of Steel repeats his attempt on the Moon, which has no atmosphere. Find the difference between the water levels inside and outside the straw.

Figure P14.14

15. ▲ ● Blaise Pascal duplicated Torricelli's barometer using a red Bordeaux wine, of density 984 kg/m³, as the working liquid (Fig. P14.15). What was the height *h* of the wine column for normal atmospheric pressure? Would you expect the vacuum above the column to be as good as for mercury?

Figure P14.15

16. Mercury is poured into a U-tube as shown in Figure P14.16a. The left arm of the tube has cross-sectional area A_1 of 10.0 cm², and the right arm has a cross-sectional area A_2 of 5.00 cm². One hundred grams of water are then poured into the right arm as shown in Figure P14.16b. (a) Determine the length of the water column in the right arm of the U-tube. (b) Given that the density of mercury is 13.6 g/cm³, what distance h does the mercury rise in the left arm?

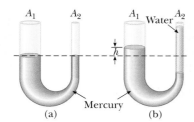

Figure P14.16

17. Normal atmospheric pressure is 1.013×10^5 Pa. The approach of a storm causes the height of a mercury barometer to drop by 20.0 mm from the normal height. What is the atmospheric pressure? (The density of mercury is 13.59 g/cm³.)

18. A tank with a flat bottom of area A and vertical sides is filled to a depth h with water. The pressure is 1 atm at the top surface. (a) What is the absolute pressure at the bottom of the tank? (b) Suppose an object of mass M and density less than the density of water is placed in the tank and floats. No water overflows. What is the resulting increase in pressure at the bottom of the tank? (c) Evaluate your results for a backyard swimming pool with depth 1.50 m and a circular base with diameter 6.00 m. Two persons with combined mass 150 kg enter the pool and float quietly there. Find the original absolute pressure and the pressure increase at the bottom of the pool.

19. ● The human brain and spinal cord are immersed in the cerebrospinal fluid. The fluid is normally continuous between the cranial and spinal cavities and exerts a pressure of 100 to 200 mm of H_2O above the prevailing atmospheric pressure. In medical work, pressures are often measured in units of millimeters of H_2O because body fluids, including the cerebrospinal fluid, typically have the same density as water. The pressure of the cerebrospinal fluid can be measured by means of a *spinal tap* as illustrated in Figure P14.19. A hollow tube is inserted into the spinal column, and the height to which the fluid rises is observed. If the fluid rises to a height of 160 mm, we write its gauge pressure as 160 mm H_2O. (a) Express this pressure in pascals, in atmospheres, and in millimeters of mercury. (b) Sometimes it is necessary to determine whether an accident victim has suffered a crushed vertebra that is blocking flow of the cerebrospinal fluid in the spinal column. In other cases, a physician may suspect that a tumor or other growth is blocking the spinal column and inhibiting flow of cerebrospinal fluid. Such conditions can be investigated by means of *Queckenstedt's test*. In this procedure, the veins in the patient's neck are compressed to make the blood pressure rise in the brain. The increase in pressure in the blood vessels is transmitted to the cerebrospinal fluid. What should be the normal effect on the height of the fluid in the spinal tap? (c) Suppose compressing the veins had no effect on the fluid level. What might account for this result?

Figure P14.19

Section 14.4 Buoyant Forces and Archimedes's Principle

20. (a) A light balloon is filled with 400 m³ of helium. At 0°C, the balloon can lift a payload of what mass? (b) **What If?** In Table 14.1, observe that the density of hydrogen is nearly one-half the density of helium. What load can the balloon lift if filled with hydrogen?

21. A table-tennis ball has a diameter of 3.80 cm and average density of 0.084 0 g/cm³. What force is required to hold it completely submerged under water?

22. The gravitational force exerted on a solid object is 5.00 N. When the object is suspended from a spring scale and submerged in water, the scale reads 3.50 N (Fig. P14.22). Find the density of the object.

Figure P14.22 Problems 22 and 23.

23. A 10.0-kg block of metal measuring 12.0 cm × 10.0 cm × 10.0 cm is suspended from a scale and immersed in water as shown in Figure P14.22b. The 12.0-cm dimension is vertical, and the top of the block is 5.00 cm below the surface of the water. (a) What are the forces acting on the top and on the bottom of the block? (Take $P_0 = 101.30$ kPa.) (b) What is the reading of the spring scale? (c) Show that the buoyant force equals the difference between the forces at the top and bottom of the block.

24. ● The weight of a rectangular block of low-density material is 15.0 N. With a thin string, the center of the horizontal bottom face of the block is tied to the bottom of a beaker partly filled with water. When 25.0% of the block's volume is submerged, the tension in the string is 10.0 N. (a) Sketch a free-body diagram for the block, showing all forces acting on it. (b) Find the buoyant force on the block. (c) Oil of density 800 kg/m³ is now steadily added to the beaker, forming a layer above the water and surrounding the block. The oil exerts forces on each of the four sidewalls of the block that the oil touches. What are the directions of these forces? (d) What happens to the string tension as the oil is added? Explain how the oil has this effect on the string tension. (e) The string breaks when its tension reaches 60.0 N. At this moment, 25.0% of the block's volume is still below the waterline. What additional fraction of the block's volume is below the top surface of the oil? (f) After the string breaks, the block comes to a new equilibrium position in the beaker. It is now in contact only with the oil. What fraction of the block's volume is submerged?

25. Preparing to anchor a buoy at the edge of a swimming area, a worker uses a rope to lower a cubical concrete block, 0.250 m on each edge, into ocean water. The block moves down at a constant speed of 1.90 m/s. You can accurately model the concrete and the water as incompressible. (a) At what rate is the force the water exerts on one face of the block increasing? (b) At what rate is the buoyant force on the block increasing?

26. To an order of magnitude, how many helium-filled toy balloons would be required to lift you? Because helium is an irreplaceable resource, develop a theoretical answer rather than an experimental answer. In your solution, state what physical quantities you take as data and the values you measure or estimate for them.

27. ☐ ▲ A cube of wood having an edge dimension of 20.0 cm and a density of 650 kg/m³ floats on water. (a) What is the distance from the horizontal top surface of the cube to the water level? (b) What mass of lead should be placed on the cube so that the top of the cube will be just level with the water?

28. A spherical aluminum ball of mass 1.26 kg contains an empty spherical cavity that is concentric with the ball. The ball barely floats in water. Calculate (a) the outer radius of the ball and (b) the radius of the cavity.

29. Determination of the density of a fluid has many important applications. A car battery contains sulfuric acid, for which density is a measure of concentration. For the battery to function properly, the density must be within a range specified by the manufacturer. Similarly, the effectiveness of antifreeze in your car's engine coolant depends on the density of the mixture (usually ethylene glycol and water). When you donate blood to a blood bank, its screening includes determination of the density of the blood because higher density correlates with higher hemoglobin content. A *hydrometer* is an instrument used to determine liquid density. A simple one is sketched in Figure P14.29. The bulb of a syringe is squeezed and released to let the atmosphere lift a sample of the liquid of interest into a tube containing a calibrated rod of known density. The rod, of length L and average density ρ_0, floats partially immersed in the liquid of density ρ. A length h of the rod protrudes above the surface of the liquid. Show that the density of the liquid is

$$\rho = \frac{\rho_0 L}{L - h}$$

Figure P14.29 Problems 29 and 30.

30. ● Refer to Problem 29 and Figure P14.29. A hydrometer is to be constructed with a cylindrical floating rod. Nine fiduciary marks are to be placed along the rod to indicate densities having values of 0.98 g/cm³, 1.00 g/cm³, 1.02 g/cm³, 1.04 g/cm³, . . ., 1.14 g/cm³. The row of marks is to start 0.200 cm from the top end of the rod and end 1.80 cm from the top end. (a) What is the required length of the rod? (b) What must be its average density? (c) Should the marks be equally spaced? Explain your answer.

31. How many cubic meters of helium are required to lift a balloon with a 400-kg payload to a height of 8 000 m? (Take $\rho_{He} = 0.180$ kg/m³.) Assume the balloon maintains a constant volume and the density of air decreases with the altitude z according to the expression $\rho_{air} = \rho_0 e^{-z/8\,000}$, where z is in meters and $\rho_0 = 1.25$ kg/m³ is the density of air at sea level.

32. A bathysphere used for deep-sea exploration has a radius of 1.50 m and a mass of 1.20×10^4 kg. To dive, this submarine takes on mass in the form of seawater. Determine the amount of mass the submarine must take on if it is to descend at a constant speed of 1.20 m/s, when the resistive force on it is 1 100 N in the upward direction. The density of seawater is 1.03×10^3 kg/m³.

33. A plastic sphere floats in water with 50.0% of its volume submerged. This same sphere floats in glycerin with 40.0% of its volume submerged. Determine the densities of the glycerin and the sphere.

34. The United States possesses the eight largest warships in the world—aircraft carriers of the *Nimitz* class—and is building two more. Suppose one of the ships bobs up to float 11.0 cm higher in the water when 50 fighter planes take off from it in 25 minutes, at a location where the free-fall acceleration is 9.78 m/s². Bristling with bombs and missiles, the planes have an average mass of 29 000 kg. Find the horizontal area enclosed by the waterline of the $4-billion ship. By comparison, its flight deck has area 18 000 m². Below decks are passageways hundreds of meters long, so narrow that two large men cannot pass each other.

Section 14.5 Fluid Dynamics

Section 14.6 Bernoulli's Equation

35. A large storage tank, open at the top and filled with water, develops a small hole in its side at a point 16.0 m below the water level. The rate of flow from the leak is 2.50×10^{-3} m³/min. Determine (a) the speed at which the water leaves the hole and (b) the diameter of the hole.

36. A village maintains a large tank with an open top, containing water for emergencies. The water can drain from the tank through a hose of diameter 6.60 cm. The hose ends with a nozzle of diameter 2.20 cm. A rubber stopper is inserted into the nozzle. The water level in the tank is kept 7.50 m above the nozzle. (a) Calculate the friction force exerted on the stopper by the nozzle. (b) The stopper is removed. What mass of water flows from the nozzle in 2.00 h? (c) Calculate the gauge pressure of the flowing water in the hose just behind the nozzle.

37. Water flows through a fire hose of diameter 6.35 cm at a rate of 0.012 0 m³/s. The fire hose ends in a nozzle of inner diameter 2.20 cm. What is the speed with which the water exits the nozzle?

38. Water moves through a constricted pipe in steady, ideal flow. At one point as shown in Figure 14.16 where the pressure is 2.50×10^4 Pa, the diameter is 8.00 cm. At another point 0.500 m higher, the pressure is equal to 1.50×10^4 Pa and the diameter is 4.00 cm. Find the speed of flow (a) in the lower section and (b) in the upper section. (c) Find the volume flow rate through the pipe.

39. Figure P14.39 shows a stream of water in steady flow from a kitchen faucet. At the faucet, the diameter of the stream is 0.960 cm. The stream fills a 125-cm³ container in 16.3 s. Find the diameter of the stream 13.0 cm below the opening of the faucet.

40. Water falls over a dam of height h with a mass flow rate of R, in units of kilograms per second. (a) Show that the power available from the water is

$$\mathcal{P} = Rgh$$

where g is the free-fall acceleration. (b) Each hydroelectric unit at the Grand Coulee Dam takes in water at a rate of 8.50×10^5 kg/s from a height of 87.0 m. The power developed by the falling water is converted to electric power with an efficiency of 85.0%. How much electric power does each hydroelectric unit produce?

41. A legendary Dutch boy saved Holland by plugging a 1.20-cm diameter hole in a dike with his finger. If the hole was 2.00 m below the surface of the North Sea (density 1 030 kg/m³), (a) what was the force on his finger? (b) If he pulled his finger out of the hole, during what time interval would the released water fill 1 acre of land to a depth of 1 ft? Assume the hole remained constant in size. (A typical U.S. family of four uses 1 acre-foot of water, 1 234 m³, in 1 year.)

42. ● In ideal flow, a liquid of density 850 kg/m³ moves from a horizontal tube of radius 1.00 cm into a second horizontal tube of radius 0.500 cm. A pressure difference ΔP exists between the tubes. (a) Find the volume flow rate as a function of ΔP. Evaluate the volume flow rate (b) for $\Delta P = 6.00$ kPa and (c) for $\Delta P = 12.0$ kPa. (d) State how the volume flow rate depends on ΔP.

43. Water is pumped up from the Colorado River to supply Grand Canyon Village, located on the rim of the canyon. The river is at an elevation of 564 m, and the village is at an elevation of 2 096 m. Imagine that the water is pumped through a single long pipe 15.0 cm in diameter, driven by a single pump at the bottom end. (a) What is the minimum pressure at which the water must be pumped if it is to arrive at the village? (b) If 4 500 m³ of water is pumped per day, what is the speed of the water in the pipe? (c) What additional pressure is necessary to deliver this flow? *Note:* Assume the free-fall acceleration and the density of air are constant over this range of elevations. The pressures you calculate are too high for an ordinary pipe. The water is actually lifted in stages by several pumps through shorter pipes.

44. ● Old Faithful Geyser in Yellowstone National Park erupts at approximately 1-h intervals, and the height of the water column reaches 40.0 m (Fig. P14.44). (a) Model the rising stream as a series of separate drops. Analyze the free-fall motion of one of the drops to determine the speed at which the water leaves the ground. (b) **What If?** Model the rising stream as an ideal fluid in streamline

Figure P14.39

Figure P14.44

flow. Use Bernoulli's equation to determine the speed of the water as it leaves ground level. (c) How does the answer from part (a) compare with the answer from part (b)? (d) What is the pressure (above atmospheric) in the heated underground chamber if its depth is 175 m? Assume the chamber is large compared with the geyser's vent.

45. A Venturi tube may be used as a fluid flowmeter (see Fig. 14.19). Taking the difference in pressure as $P_1 - P_2 = 21.0$ kPa, find the fluid flow rate in cubic meters per second given that the radius of the outlet tube is 1.00 cm, the radius of the inlet tube is 2.00 cm, and the fluid is gasoline ($\rho = 700$ kg/m³).

Section 14.7 Other Applications of Fluid Dynamics

46. An airplane has a mass of 1.60×10^4 kg, and each wing has an area of 40.0 m². During level flight, the pressure on the lower wing surface is 7.00×10^4 Pa. Determine the pressure on the upper wing surface.

47. A siphon of uniform diameter is used to drain water from a tank as illustrated in Figure P14.47. Assume steady flow without friction. (a) If $h = 1.00$ m, find the speed of outflow at the end of the siphon. (b) **What If?** What is the limitation on the height of the top of the siphon above the water surface? (For the flow of the liquid to be continuous, the pressure must not drop below the vapor pressure of the liquid.)

Figure P14.47

48. An airplane is cruising at altitude 10 km. The pressure outside the craft is 0.287 atm; within the passenger compartment, the pressure is 1.00 atm and the temperature is 20°C. A small leak occurs in one of the window seals in the passenger compartment. Model the air as an ideal fluid to find the speed of the stream of air flowing through the leak.

49. A hypodermic syringe contains a medicine having the density of water (Fig. P14.49). The barrel of the syringe has a cross-sectional area $A = 2.50 \times 10^{-5}$ m², and the needle has a cross-sectional area $a = 1.00 \times 10^{-8}$ m². In the absence of a force on the plunger, the pressure every-

where is 1 atm. A force $\vec{F}$ of magnitude 2.00 N acts on the plunger, making medicine squirt horizontally from the needle. Determine the speed of the medicine as it leaves the needle's tip.

50. The Bernoulli effect can have important consequences for the design of buildings. For example, wind can blow around a skyscraper at remarkably high speed, creating low pressure. The higher atmospheric pressure in the still air inside the buildings can cause windows to pop out. As originally constructed, the John Hancock Building in Boston popped windowpanes that fell many stories to the sidewalk below. (a) Suppose a horizontal wind blows with a speed of 11.2 m/s outside a large pane of plate glass with dimensions 4.00 m × 1.50 m. Assume the density of the air to be 1.30 kg/m³. The air inside the building is at atmospheric pressure. What is the total force exerted by air on the windowpane? (b) **What If?** If a second skyscraper is built nearby, the airspeed can be especially high where wind passes through the narrow separation between the buildings. Solve part (a) again with a wind speed of 22.4 m/s, twice as high.

Additional Problems

51. A helium-filled balloon is tied to a 2.00-m-long, 0.050 0-kg uniform string. The balloon is spherical with a radius of 0.400 m. When released, it lifts a length h of string and then remains in equilibrium as shown in Figure P14.51. Determine the value of h. The envelope of the balloon has a mass of 0.250 kg.

Figure P14.51

52. Figure P14.52 shows a water tank with a valve at the bottom. If this valve is opened, what is the maximum height attained by the water stream coming out of the right side of the tank? Assume $h = 10.0$ m, $L = 2.00$ m, and $\theta = 30.0°$ and assume the cross-sectional area at A is very large compared with that at B.

Figure P14.49

Figure P14.52

53. The true weight of an object can be measured in a vacuum, where buoyant forces are absent. An object of volume V is weighed in air on an equal-arm balance with the use of counterweights of density ρ. Representing the density of air as ρ_{air} and the balance reading as F_g', show that the true weight F_g is

$$F_g = F_g' + \left(V - \frac{F_g'}{\rho g}\right)\rho_{air}g$$

54. Water is forced out of a fire extinguisher by air pressure as shown in Figure P14.54. How much gauge air pressure in the tank (above atmospheric) is required for the water jet to have a speed of 30.0 m/s when the water level is 0.500 m below the nozzle?

Figure P14.54

55. A light spring of constant k = 90.0 N/m is attached vertically to a table (Fig. P14.55a). A 2.00-g balloon is filled with helium (density = 0.180 kg/m³) to a volume of 5.00 m³ and is then connected to the spring, causing the spring to stretch as shown in Figure P14.55b. Determine the extension distance L when the balloon is in equilibrium.

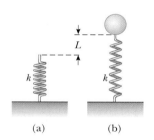

Figure P14.55

56. ● *We can't call it Flubber.* Assume a certain liquid, with density 1 230 kg/m³, exerts no friction force on spherical objects. A ball of mass 2.10 kg and radius 9.00 cm is dropped from rest into a deep tank of this liquid from a height of 3.30 m above the surface. (a) Find the speed at which the ball enters the liquid. (b) What two forces are exerted on the ball as it moves through the liquid? (c) Explain why the ball moves down only a limited distance into the liquid and calculate this distance. (d) With what speed does the ball pop up out of the liquid? (e) How does the time interval Δt_{down}, during which the ball moves from the surface down to its lowest point, compare with the time interval Δt_{up} for the return trip between the same two points? (f) **What If?** Now modify the model to suppose the liquid exerts a small friction force on the ball, opposite in direction to its motion. In this case, how do the time intervals Δt_{down} and Δt_{up} compare? Explain your answer with a conceptual argument rather than a numerical calculation.

57. ● As a 950-kg helicopter hovers, its horizontal rotor pushes a column of air downward at 40.0 m/s. What can you say about the quantity of this air? Explain your answer. You may model the air motion as ideal flow.

58. Evangelista Torricelli was the first person to realize that we live at the bottom of an ocean of air. He correctly surmised that the pressure of our atmosphere is attributable to the weight of the air. The density of air at 0°C at the Earth's surface is 1.29 kg/m³. The density decreases with increasing altitude (as the atmosphere thins). On the other hand, if we assume the density is constant at 1.29 kg/m³ up to some altitude h and is zero above that altitude, then h would represent the depth of the ocean of air. Use this model to determine the value of h that gives a pressure of 1.00 atm at the surface of the Earth. Would the peak of Mount Everest rise above the surface of such an atmosphere?

59. ▲ **Review problem.** With reference to Figure 14.5, show that the total torque exerted by the water behind the dam about a horizontal axis through O is $\frac{1}{6}\rho gwH^3$. Show that the effective line of action of the total force exerted by the water is at a distance $\frac{1}{3}H$ above O.

60. In about 1657, Otto von Guericke, inventor of the air pump, evacuated a sphere made of two brass hemispheres. Two teams of eight horses each could pull the hemispheres apart only on some trials and then "with greatest difficulty," with the resulting sound likened to a cannon firing (Fig. P14.60). (a) Show that the force F required to pull the thin-walled evacuated hemispheres apart is $\pi R^2(P_0 - P)$, where R is the radius of the hemispheres and P is the pressure inside the hemispheres, which is much less than P_0. (b) Determine the force for $P = 0.100P_0$ and $R = 0.300$ m.

Figure P14.60   The colored engraving, dated 1672, illustrates Otto von Guericke's demonstration of the force due to air pressure as it might have been performed before Emperor Ferdinand III.

2 = intermediate;   3 = challenging;   □ = SSM/SG;   ▲ = ThomsonNOW;   ▓ = symbolic reasoning;   ● = qualitative reasoning

61. A 1.00-kg beaker containing 2.00 kg of oil (density = 916.0 kg/m³) rests on a scale. A 2.00-kg block of iron suspended from a spring scale is completely submerged in the oil as shown in Figure P14.61. Determine the equilibrium readings of both scales.

Figure P14.61   Problems 61 and 62.

62. A beaker of mass m_b containing oil of mass m_o and density ρ_o rests on a scale. A block of iron of mass m_{Fe} suspended from a spring scale is completely submerged in the oil as shown in Figure P14.61. Determine the equilibrium readings of both scales.

63. In 1983, the United States began coining the cent piece out of copper-clad zinc rather than pure copper. The mass of the old copper penny is 3.083 g and that of the new cent is 2.517 g. Calculate the percent of zinc (by volume) in the new cent. The density of copper is 8.960 g/cm³ and that of zinc is 7.133 g/cm³. The new and old coins have the same volume.

64. Show that the variation of atmospheric pressure with altitude is given by $P = P_0 e^{-\alpha y}$, where $\alpha = \rho_0 g/P_0$, P_0 is atmospheric pressure at some reference level $y = 0$, and ρ_0 is the atmospheric density at this level. Assume the decrease in atmospheric pressure over an infinitesimal change in altitude (so that the density is approximately uniform) is given by $dP = -\rho g\, dy$ and that the density of air is proportional to the pressure.

65. Review problem. A uniform disk of mass 10.0 kg and radius 0.250 m spins at 300 rev/min on a low-friction axle. It must be brought to a stop in 1.00 min by a brake pad that makes contact with the disk at an average distance of 0.220 m from the axis. The coefficient of friction between the pad and the disk is 0.500. A piston in a cylinder of diameter 5.00 cm presses the brake pad against the disk. Find the pressure required for the brake fluid in the cylinder.

66. A cube of ice whose edges measure 20.0 mm is floating in a glass of ice-cold water, and one of the ice cube's faces is parallel to the water's surface. (a) How far below the water surface is the bottom face of the ice cube? (b) Ice-cold ethyl alcohol is gently poured onto the water surface to form a layer 5.00 mm thick above the water. The alcohol does not mix with the water. When the ice cube again attains hydrostatic equilibrium, what is the distance from the top of the water to the bottom face of the block? (c) Additional cold ethyl alcohol is poured onto the water's surface until the top surface of the alcohol coincides with the top surface of the ice cube (in hydrostatic equilibrium). How thick is the required layer of ethyl alcohol?

67. An incompressible, nonviscous fluid is initially at rest in the vertical portion of the pipe shown in Figure P14.67a, where $L = 2.00$ m. When the valve is opened, the fluid flows into the horizontal section of the pipe. What is the speed of the fluid when it is all in the horizontal section as shown in Figure P14.67b? Assume the cross-sectional area of the entire pipe is constant.

Figure P14.67

68. The water supply of a building is fed through a main pipe 6.00 cm in diameter. A 2.00-cm-diameter faucet tap, located 2.00 m above the main pipe, is observed to fill a 25.0-L container in 30.0 s. (a) What is the speed at which the water leaves the faucet? (b) What is the gauge pressure in the 6-cm main pipe? (Assume the faucet is the only "leak" in the building.)

69. A U-tube open at both ends is partially filled with water (Fig. P14.69a). Oil having a density 750 kg/m³ is then poured into the right arm and forms a column $L = 5.00$ cm high (Fig. P14.69b). (a) Determine the difference h in the heights of the two liquid surfaces. (b) The right arm is then shielded from any air motion while air is blown across the top of the left arm until the surfaces of the two liquids are at the same height (Fig. P14.69c). Determine the speed of the air being blown across the left arm. Take the density of air as 1.29 kg/m³.

Figure P14.69

70. A woman is draining her fish tank by siphoning the water into an outdoor drain as shown in Figure P14.70 (page 416). The rectangular tank has footprint area A and depth h. The drain is located a distance d below the surface of the water in the tank, where $d \gg h$. The cross-sectional area of the siphon tube is A'. Model the water as flowing without friction. (a) Show that the time interval required to empty the tank is

$$\Delta t = \frac{Ah}{A'\sqrt{2gd}}$$

(b) Evaluate the time interval required to empty the tank if it is a cube 0.500 m on each edge, taking $A' = 2.00$ cm^2 and $d = 10.0$ m.

Figure P14.70

71. The hull of an experimental boat is to be lifted above the water by a hydrofoil mounted below its keel as shown in Figure P14.71. The hydrofoil is shaped like an airplane wing. Its area projected onto a horizontal surface is A. When the boat is towed at sufficiently high speed, water of density ρ moves in streamline flow so that its average speed at the top of the hydrofoil is n times larger than its speed v_b below the hydrofoil. (a) Ignoring the buoyant force, show that the upward lift force exerted by the water on the hydrofoil has a magnitude

$$F \approx \tfrac{1}{2}(n^2 - 1)\rho v_b^2 A$$

(b) The boat has mass M. Show that the liftoff speed is

$$v \approx \sqrt{\frac{2Mg}{(n^2 - 1)A\rho}}$$

(c) Assume an 800-kg boat is to lift off at 9.50 m/s. Evaluate the area A required for the hydrofoil if its design yields $n = 1.05$.

Figure P14.71

Answers to Quick Quizzes

14.1 (a). Because the basketball player's weight is distributed over the larger surface area of the shoe, the pressure (F/A) he applies is relatively small. The woman's lesser weight is distributed over the very small cross-sectional area of the spiked heel, so the pressure is high.

14.2 (a). Because both fluids have the same depth, the one with the smaller density (alcohol) will exert the smaller pressure.

14.3 (c). All barometers will have the same pressure at the bottom of the column of fluid: atmospheric pressure. Therefore, the barometer with the highest column will be the one with the fluid of lowest density.

14.4 (b) or (c). In all three cases, the weight of the treasure chest causes a downward force on the raft that makes the raft sink into the water. In (b) and (c), however, the treasure chest also displaces water, which provides a buoyant force in the upward direction, reducing the effect of the chest's weight.

14.5 (a). The high-speed air between the balloons results in low pressure in this region. The higher pressure on the outer surfaces of the balloons pushes them toward each other.

TABLE A.1

Conversion Factors

Length

	m	cm	km	in.	ft	mi
1 meter	1	10^2	10^{-3}	39.37	3.281	6.214×10^{-4}
1 centimeter	10^{-2}	1	10^{-5}	0.393 7	3.281×10^{-2}	6.214×10^{-6}
1 kilometer	10^3	10^5	1	3.937×10^4	3.281×10^3	0.621 4
1 inch	2.540×10^{-2}	2.540	2.540×10^{-5}	1	8.333×10^{-2}	1.578×10^{-5}
1 foot	0.304 8	30.48	3.048×10^{-4}	12	1	1.894×10^{-4}
1 mile	1 609	1.609×10^5	1.609	6.336×10^4	5 280	1

Mass

	kg	g	slug	u
1 kilogram	1	10^3	6.852×10^{-2}	6.024×10^{26}
1 gram	10^{-3}	1	6.852×10^{-5}	6.024×10^{23}
1 slug	14.59	1.459×10^4	1	8.789×10^{27}
1 atomic mass unit	1.660×10^{-27}	1.660×10^{-24}	1.137×10^{-28}	1

Note: 1 metric ton = 1 000 kg.

Time

	s	min	h	day	yr
1 second	1	1.667×10^{-2}	2.778×10^{-4}	1.157×10^{-5}	3.169×10^{-8}
1 minute	60	1	1.667×10^{-2}	6.994×10^{-4}	1.901×10^{-6}
1 hour	3 600	60	1	4.167×10^{-2}	1.141×10^{-4}
1 day	8.640×10^4	1 440	24	1	2.738×10^{-5}
1 year	3.156×10^7	5.259×10^5	8.766×10^3	365.2	1

Speed

	m/s	cm/s	ft/s	mi/h
1 meter per second	1	10^2	3.281	2.237
1 centimeter per second	10^{-2}	1	3.281×10^{-2}	2.237×10^{-2}
1 foot per second	0.304 8	30.48	1	0.681 8
1 mile per hour	0.447 0	44.70	1.467	1

Note: 1 mi/min = 60 mi/h = 88 ft/s.

Force

	N	lb
1 newton	1	0.224 8
1 pound	4.448	1

(*Continued*)

TABLE A.1

Conversion Factors   (*Continued*)

Energy, Energy Transfer

	J	ft · lb	eV
1 joule	1	0.737 6	6.242×10^{18}
1 foot-pound	1.356	1	8.464×10^{18}
1 electron volt	1.602×10^{-19}	1.182×10^{-19}	1
1 calorie	4.186	3.087	2.613×10^{19}
1 British thermal unit	1.055×10^3	7.779×10^2	6.585×10^{21}
1 kilowatt-hour	3.600×10^6	2.655×10^6	2.247×10^{25}

	cal	Btu	kWh
1 joule	0.238 9	9.481×10^{-4}	2.778×10^{-7}
1 foot-pound	0.323 9	1.285×10^{-3}	3.766×10^{-7}
1 electron volt	3.827×10^{-20}	1.519×10^{-22}	4.450×10^{-26}
1 calorie	1	3.968×10^{-3}	1.163×10^{-6}
1 British thermal unit	2.520×10^2	1	2.930×10^{-4}
1 kilowatt-hour	8.601×10^5	3.413×10^2	1

Pressure

	Pa	atm
1 pascal	1	9.869×10^{-6}
1 atmosphere	1.013×10^5	1
1 centimeter mercury[a]	1.333×10^3	1.316×10^{-2}
1 pound per square inch	6.895×10^3	6.805×10^{-2}
1 pound per square foot	47.88	4.725×10^{-4}

	cm Hg	lb/in.²	lb/ft²
1 pascal	7.501×10^{-4}	1.450×10^{-4}	2.089×10^{-2}
1 atmosphere	76	14.70	2.116×10^3
1 centimeter mercury[a]	1	0.194 3	27.85
1 pound per square inch	5.171	1	144
1 pound per square foot	3.591×10^{-2}	6.944×10^{-3}	1

[a]At 0°C and at a location where the free-fall acceleration has its "standard" value, 9.806 65 m/s².

TABLE A.2

Symbols, Dimensions, and Units of Physical Quantities

Quantity	Common Symbol	Unit[a]	Dimensions[b]	Unit in Terms of Base SI Units
Acceleration	$\vec{\mathbf{a}}$	m/s²	L/T^2	m/s²
Amount of substance	n	MOLE		mol
Angle	θ, ϕ	radian (rad)	1	
Angular acceleration	$\vec{\boldsymbol{\alpha}}$	rad/s²	T^{-2}	s^{-2}
Angular frequency	ω	rad/s	T^{-1}	s^{-1}
Angular momentum	$\vec{\mathbf{L}}$	kg · m²/s	ML^2/T	kg · m²/s
Angular velocity	$\vec{\boldsymbol{\omega}}$	rad/s	T^{-1}	s^{-1}
Area	A	m²	L^2	m²
Atomic number	Z			
Capacitance	C	farad (F)	Q^2T^2/ML^2	A² · s⁴/kg · m²
Charge	q, Q, e	coulomb (C)	Q	A · s

(*Continued*)

TABLE A.2

Symbols, Dimensions, and Units of Physical Quantities (*Continued*)

Charge density				
Line	λ	C/m	Q/L	A · s/m
Surface	σ	C/m^2	Q/L^2	A · s/m^2
Volume	ρ	C/m^3	Q/L^3	A · s/m^3
Conductivity	σ	$1/\Omega \cdot$m	Q^{2}T/ML^3	A^2 · s^3/kg · m^3
Current	I	AMPERE	Q/T	A
Current density	J	A/m^2	Q/TL^2	A/m^2
Density	ρ	kg/m^3	M/L^3	kg/m^3
Dielectric constant	κ			
Electric dipole moment	$\vec{\mathbf{p}}$	C · m	QL	A · s · m
Electric field	$\vec{\mathbf{E}}$	V/m	ML/QT^2	kg · m/A · s^3
Electric flux	Φ_E	V · m	ML^3/QT^2	kg · m^3/A · s^3
Electromotive force	$\boldsymbol{\varepsilon}$	volt (V)	ML^2/QT^2	kg · m^2/A · s^3
Energy	E, U, K	joule (J)	ML^2/T^2	kg · m^2/s^2
Entropy	S	J/K	ML^2/T^{2}K	kg · m^2/s^2 · K
Force	$\vec{\mathbf{F}}$	newton (N)	ML/T^2	kg · m/s^2
Frequency	f	hertz (Hz)	T^{-1}	s^{-1}
Heat	Q	joule (J)	ML^2/T^2	kg · m^2/s^2
Inductance	L	henry (H)	ML^2/Q^2	kg · m^2/A^2 · s^2
Length	ℓ, L	METER	L	m
Displacement	$\Delta x, \Delta \vec{\mathbf{r}}$			
Distance	d, h			
Position	$x, y, z, \vec{\mathbf{r}}$			
Magnetic dipole moment	$\vec{\boldsymbol{\mu}}$	N · m/T	QL^2/T	A · m^2
Magnetic field	$\vec{\mathbf{B}}$	tesla (T) (= Wb/m^2)	M/QT	kg/A · s^2
Magnetic flux	Φ_B	weber (Wb)	ML^2/QT	kg · m^2/A · s^2
Mass	m, M	KILOGRAM	M	kg
Molar specific heat	C	J/mol · K		kg · m^2/s^2 · mol · K
Moment of inertia	I	kg · m^2	ML^2	kg · m^2
Momentum	$\vec{\mathbf{p}}$	kg · m/s	ML/T	kg · m/s
Period	T	s	T	s
Permeability of free space	μ_0	N/A^2 (= H/m)	ML/Q^2	kg · m/A^2 · s^2
Permittivity of free space	ϵ_0	C^2/N · m^2 (= F/m)	Q^{2}T^2/ML^3	A^2 · s^4/kg · m^3
Potential	V	volt (V) (= J/C)	ML^2/QT^2	kg · m^2/A · s^3
Power	$\mathscr{P}$	watt (W) (= J/s)	ML^2/T^3	kg · m^2/s^3
Pressure	P	pascal (Pa) (= N/m^2)	M/LT^2	kg/m · s^2
Resistance	R	ohm (Ω) (= V/A)	ML^2/Q^{2}T	kg · m^2/A^2 · s^3
Specific heat	c	J/kg · K	L^2/T^{2}K	m^2/s^2 · K
Speed	v	m/s	L/T	m/s
Temperature	T	KELVIN	K	K
Time	t	SECOND	T	s
Torque	$\vec{\boldsymbol{\tau}}$	N · m	ML^2/T^2	kg · m^2/s^2
Velocity	$\vec{\mathbf{v}}$	m/s	L/T	m/s
Volume	V	m^3	L^3	m^3
Wavelength	λ	m	L	m
Work	W	joule (J) (= N · m)	ML^2/T^2	kg · m^2/s^2

[a]The base SI units are given in uppercase letters.

[b]The symbols M, L, T, K, and Q denote mass, length, time, temperature, and charge, respectively.

This appendix in mathematics is intended as a brief review of operations and methods. Early in this course, you should be totally familiar with basic algebraic techniques, analytic geometry, and trigonometry. The sections on differential and integral calculus are more detailed and are intended for students who have difficulty applying calculus concepts to physical situations.

B.1 Scientific Notation

Many quantities used by scientists often have very large or very small values. The speed of light, for example, is about 300 000 000 m/s, and the ink required to make the dot over an i in this textbook has a mass of about 0.000 000 001 kg. Obviously, it is very cumbersome to read, write, and keep track of such numbers. We avoid this problem by using a method incorporating powers of the number 10:

$$10^0 = 1$$

$$10^1 = 10$$

$$10^2 = 10 \times 10 = 100$$

$$10^3 = 10 \times 10 \times 10 = 1\,000$$

$$10^4 = 10 \times 10 \times 10 \times 10 = 10\,000$$

$$10^5 = 10 \times 10 \times 10 \times 10 \times 10 = 100\,000$$

and so on. The number of zeros corresponds to the power to which ten is raised, called the **exponent** of ten. For example, the speed of light, 300 000 000 m/s, can be expressed as 3.00×10^8 m/s.

In this method, some representative numbers smaller than unity are the following:

$$10^{-1} = \frac{1}{10} = 0.1$$

$$10^{-2} = \frac{1}{10 \times 10} = 0.01$$

$$10^{-3} = \frac{1}{10 \times 10 \times 10} = 0.001$$

$$10^{-4} = \frac{1}{10 \times 10 \times 10 \times 10} = 0.000\,1$$

$$10^{-5} = \frac{1}{10 \times 10 \times 10 \times 10 \times 10} = 0.000\,01$$

In these cases, the number of places the decimal point is to the left of the digit 1 equals the value of the (negative) exponent. Numbers expressed as some power of ten multiplied by another number between one and ten are said to be in **scientific notation.** For example, the scientific notation for 5 943 000 000 is 5.943×10^9 and that for 0.000 083 2 is 8.32×10^{-5}.

When numbers expressed in scientific notation are being multiplied, the following general rule is very useful:

$$10^n \times 10^m = 10^{n+m} \tag{B.1}$$

where n and m can be *any* numbers (not necessarily integers). For example, $10^2 \times 10^5 = 10^7$. The rule also applies if one of the exponents is negative: $10^3 \times 10^{-8} = 10^{-5}$.

When dividing numbers expressed in scientific notation, note that

$$\frac{10^n}{10^m} = 10^n \times 10^{-m} = 10^{n-m} \qquad \textbf{(B.2)}$$

Exercises

With help from the preceding rules, verify the answers to the following equations:

1. $86\ 400 = 8.64 \times 10^4$
2. $9\ 816\ 762.5 = 9.816\ 762\ 5 \times 10^6$
3. $0.000\ 000\ 039\ 8 = 3.98 \times 10^{-8}$
4. $(4.0 \times 10^8)(9.0 \times 10^9) = 3.6 \times 10^{18}$
5. $(3.0 \times 10^7)(6.0 \times 10^{-12}) = 1.8 \times 10^{-4}$
6. $\dfrac{75 \times 10^{-11}}{5.0 \times 10^{-3}} = 1.5 \times 10^{-7}$
7. $\dfrac{(3 \times 10^6)(8 \times 10^{-2})}{(2 \times 10^{17})(6 \times 10^5)} = 2 \times 10^{-18}$

B.2   Algebra

Some Basic Rules

When algebraic operations are performed, the laws of arithmetic apply. Symbols such as x, y, and z are usually used to represent unspecified quantities, called the **unknowns.**

First, consider the equation

$$8x = 32$$

If we wish to solve for x, we can divide (or multiply) each side of the equation by the same factor without destroying the equality. In this case, if we divide both sides by 8, we have

$$\frac{8x}{8} = \frac{32}{8}$$

$$x = 4$$

Next consider the equation

$$x + 2 = 8$$

In this type of expression, we can add or subtract the same quantity from each side. If we subtract 2 from each side, we have

$$x + 2 - 2 = 8 - 2$$

$$x = 6$$

In general, if $x + a = b$, then $x = b - a$.

Now consider the equation

$$\frac{x}{5} = 9$$

If we multiply each side by 5, we are left with x on the left by itself and 45 on the right:

$$\left(\frac{x}{5}\right)(5) = 9 \times 5$$

$$x = 45$$

In all cases, *whatever operation is performed on the left side of the equality must also be performed on the right side.*

The following rules for multiplying, dividing, adding, and subtracting fractions should be recalled, where a, b, c, and d are four numbers:

	Rule	Example
Multiplying	$\left(\dfrac{a}{b}\right)\left(\dfrac{c}{d}\right) = \dfrac{ac}{bd}$	$\left(\dfrac{2}{3}\right)\left(\dfrac{4}{5}\right) = \dfrac{8}{15}$
Dividing	$\dfrac{(a/b)}{(c/d)} = \dfrac{ad}{bc}$	$\dfrac{2/3}{4/5} = \dfrac{(2)(5)}{(4)(3)} = \dfrac{10}{12}$
Adding	$\dfrac{a}{b} \pm \dfrac{c}{d} = \dfrac{ad \pm bc}{bd}$	$\dfrac{2}{3} - \dfrac{4}{5} = \dfrac{(2)(5) - (4)(3)}{(3)(5)} = -\dfrac{2}{15}$

Exercises

In the following exercises, solve for x.

Answers

1. $a = \dfrac{1}{1 + x}$ $x = \dfrac{1 - a}{a}$

2. $3x - 5 = 13$ $x = 6$

3. $ax - 5 = bx + 2$ $x = \dfrac{7}{a - b}$

4. $\dfrac{5}{2x + 6} = \dfrac{3}{4x + 8}$ $x = -\dfrac{11}{7}$

Powers

When powers of a given quantity x are multiplied, the following rule applies:

$$x^n x^m = x^{n+m} \tag{B.3}$$

For example, $x^2 x^4 = x^{2+4} = x^6$.

When dividing the powers of a given quantity, the rule is

$$\frac{x^n}{x^m} = x^{n-m} \tag{B.4}$$

For example, $x^8/x^2 = x^{8-2} = x^6$.

A power that is a fraction, such as $\frac{1}{3}$, corresponds to a root as follows:

$$x^{1/n} = \sqrt[n]{x} \tag{B.5}$$

For example, $4^{1/3} = \sqrt[3]{4} = 1.587\ 4$. (A scientific calculator is useful for such calculations.) Finally, any quantity x^n raised to the mth power is

$$(x^n)^m = x^{nm} \tag{B.6}$$

Table B.1 summarizes the rules of exponents.

TABLE B.1

Rules of Exponents

$$x^0 = 1$$
$$x^1 = x$$
$$x^n x^m = x^{n+m}$$
$$x^n/x^m = x^{n-m}$$
$$x^{1/n} = \sqrt[n]{x}$$
$$(x^n)^m = x^{nm}$$

Exercises

Verify the following equations:

1. $3^2 \times 3^3 = 243$

2. $x^5 x^{-8} = x^{-3}$

3. $x^{10}/x^{-5} = x^{15}$

4. $5^{1/3} = 1.709\ 976$ (Use your calculator.)

5. $60^{1/4} = 2.783\ 158$ (Use your calculator.)

6. $(x^4)^3 = x^{12}$

Factoring

Some useful formulas for factoring an equation are the following:

$$ax + ay + az = a(x + y + z) \quad \text{common factor}$$

$$a^2 + 2ab + b^2 = (a + b)^2 \quad \text{perfect square}$$

$$a^2 - b^2 = (a + b)(a - b) \quad \text{differences of squares}$$

Quadratic Equations

The general form of a quadratic equation is

$$ax^2 + bx + c = 0 \tag{B.7}$$

where x is the unknown quantity and a, b, and c are numerical factors referred to as **coefficients** of the equation. This equation has two roots, given by

$$x = \frac{-b \pm \sqrt{b^2 - 4ac}}{2a} \tag{B.8}$$

If $b^2 \geq 4ac$, the roots are real.

EXAMPLE B.1

The equation $x^2 + 5x + 4 = 0$ has the following roots corresponding to the two signs of the square-root term:

$$x = \frac{-5 \pm \sqrt{5^2 - (4)(1)(4)}}{2(1)} = \frac{-5 \pm \sqrt{9}}{2} = \frac{-5 \pm 3}{2}$$

$$x_+ = \frac{-5 + 3}{2} = -1 \quad x_- = \frac{-5 - 3}{2} = -4$$

where x_+ refers to the root corresponding to the positive sign and x_- refers to the root corresponding to the negative sign.

Exercises

Solve the following quadratic equations:

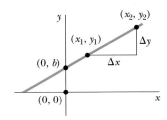

Figure B.1 A straight line graphed on an xy coordinate system. The slope of the line is the ratio of Δy to Δx.

		Answers	
1.	$x^2 + 2x - 3 = 0$	$x_+ = 1$	$x_- = -3$
2.	$2x^2 - 5x + 2 = 0$	$x_+ = 2$	$x_- = \frac{1}{2}$
3.	$2x^2 - 4x - 9 = 0$	$x_+ = 1 + \sqrt{22}/2$	$x_- = 1 - \sqrt{22}/2$

Linear Equations

A linear equation has the general form

$$y = mx + b \tag{B.9}$$

where m and b are constants. This equation is referred to as linear because the graph of y versus x is a straight line as shown in Figure B.1. The constant b, called the **y-intercept,** represents the value of y at which the straight line intersects the y axis. The constant m is equal to the **slope** of the straight line. If any two points on the straight line are specified by the coordinates (x_1, y_1) and (x_2, y_2) as in Figure B.1, the slope of the straight line can be expressed as

$$\text{Slope} = \frac{y_2 - y_1}{x_2 - x_1} = \frac{\Delta y}{\Delta x} \tag{B.10}$$

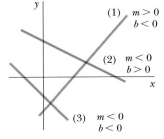

Figure B.2 The brown line has a positive slope and a negative y-intercept. The blue line has a negative slope and a positive y-intercept. The green line has a negative slope and a negative y-intercept.

Note that m and b can have either positive or negative values. If $m > 0$, the straight line has a *positive* slope as in Figure B.1. If $m < 0$, the straight line has a *negative* slope. In Figure B.1, both m and b are positive. Three other possible situations are shown in Figure B.2.

Exercises

1. Draw graphs of the following straight lines: (a) $y = 5x + 3$ (b) $y = -2x + 4$ (c) $y = -3x - 6$

2. Find the slopes of the straight lines described in Exercise 1.

Answers   (a) 5   (b) -2 (c) -3

3. Find the slopes of the straight lines that pass through the following sets of points: (a) $(0, -4)$ and $(4, 2)$ (b) $(0, 0)$ and $(2, -5)$ (c) $(-5, 2)$ and $(4, -2)$

Answers   (a) $\frac{3}{2}$ (b) $-\frac{5}{2}$ (c) $-\frac{4}{9}$

Solving Simultaneous Linear Equations

Consider the equation $3x + 5y = 15$, which has two unknowns, x and y. Such an equation does not have a unique solution. For example, $(x = 0, y = 3)$, $(x = 5, y = 0)$, and $(x = 2, y = \frac{9}{5})$ are all solutions to this equation.

If a problem has two unknowns, a unique solution is possible only if we have *two* equations. In general, if a problem has n unknowns, its solution requires n equations. To solve two simultaneous equations involving two unknowns, x and y, we solve one of the equations for x in terms of y and substitute this expression into the other equation.

EXAMPLE **B.2**

Solve the two simultaneous equations

$$(1) \qquad 5x + y = -8$$

$$(2) \qquad 2x - 2y = 4$$

Solution   From Equation (2), $x = y + 2$. Substitution of this equation into Equation (1) gives

$$5(y + 2) + y = -8$$

$$6y = -18$$

$$y = \boxed{-3}$$

$$x = y + 2 = \boxed{-1}$$

Alternative Solution   Multiply each term in Equation (1) by the factor 2 and add the result to Equation (2):

$$10x + 2y = -16$$

$$\underline{2x - 2y = 4}$$

$$12x \qquad = -12$$

$$x = \boxed{-1}$$

$$y = x - 2 = \boxed{-3}$$

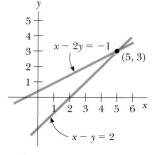

Figure B.3   A graphical solution for two linear equations.

Two linear equations containing two unknowns can also be solved by a graphical method. If the straight lines corresponding to the two equations are plotted in a conventional coordinate system, the intersection of the two lines represents the solution. For example, consider the two equations

$$x - y = 2$$

$$x - 2y = -1$$

These equations are plotted in Figure B.3. The intersection of the two lines has the coordinates $x = 5$ and $y = 3$, which represents the solution to the equations. You should check this solution by the analytical technique discussed earlier.

Exercises

Solve the following pairs of simultaneous equations involving two unknowns:

Answers

1. $x + y = 8$ $x = 5, y = 3$
$x - y = 2$

2. $98 - T = 10a$ $T = 65, a = 3.27$
$T - 49 = 5a$

3. $6x + 2y = 6$ $x = 2, y = -3$
$8x - 4y = 28$

Logarithms

Suppose a quantity x is expressed as a power of some quantity a:

$$x = a^y \tag{B.11}$$

The number a is called the **base** number. The **logarithm** of x with respect to the base a is equal to the exponent to which the base must be raised to satisfy the expression $x = a^y$:

$$y = \log_a x \tag{B.12}$$

Conversely, the **antilogarithm** of y is the number x:

$$x = \text{antilog}_a y \tag{B.13}$$

In practice, the two bases most often used are base 10, called the *common* logarithm base, and base $e = 2.718\,282$, called Euler's constant or the *natural* logarithm base. When common logarithms are used,

$$y = \log_{10} x \quad (\text{or } x = 10^y) \tag{B.14}$$

When natural logarithms are used,

$$y = \ln x \quad (\text{or } x = e^y) \tag{B.15}$$

For example, $\log_{10} 52 = 1.716$, so antilog$_{10}$ $1.716 = 10^{1.716} = 52$. Likewise, $\ln 52 = 3.951$, so antiln $3.951 = e^{3.951} = 52$.

In general, note you can convert between base 10 and base e with the equality

$$\ln x = (2.302\,585) \log_{10} x \tag{B.16}$$

Finally, some useful properties of logarithms are the following:

$$\left. \begin{aligned} \log(ab) &= \log a + \log b \\ \log(a/b) &= \log a - \log b \\ \log(a^n) &= n \log a \end{aligned} \right\} \text{ any base}$$

$$\ln e = 1$$

$$\ln e^a = a$$

$$\ln\left(\frac{1}{a}\right) = -\ln a$$

B.3   Geometry

The **distance** d between two points having coordinates (x_1, y_1) and (x_2, y_2) is

$$d = \sqrt{(x_2 - x_1)^2 + (y_2 - y_1)^2} \tag{B.17}$$

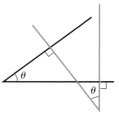

Figure B.4 The angles are equal because their sides are perpendicular.

Figure B.5 The angle θ in radians is the ratio of the arc length s to the radius r of the circle.

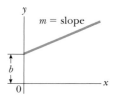

Figure B.6 A straight line with a slope of m and a y-intercept of b.

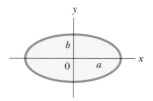

Figure B.7 An ellipse with semimajor axis a and semiminor axis b.

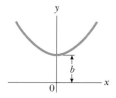

Figure B.8 A parabola with its vertex at $y = b$.

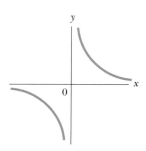

Figure B.9 A hyperbola.

TABLE B.2

Useful Information for Geometry

Shape	Area or Volume	Shape	Area or Volume
Rectangle	$\text{Area} = \ell w$	Sphere	Surface area $= 4\pi r^2$ Volume $= \frac{4\pi r^3}{3}$
Circle	$\text{Area} = \pi r^2$ $\text{Circumference} = 2\pi r$	Cylinder	Lateral surface area $= 2\pi r\ell$ Volume $= \pi r^2 \ell$
Triangle	$\text{Area} = \frac{1}{2}bh$	Rectangular box	Surface area $=$ $2(\ell h + \ell w + hw)$ Volume $= \ell wh$

Two angles are equal if their sides are perpendicular, right side to right side and left side to left side. For example, the two angles marked θ in Figure B.4 are the same because of the perpendicularity of the sides of the angles. To distinguish the left and right sides of an angle, imagine standing at the angle's apex and facing into the angle.

Radian measure: The arc length s of a circular arc (Fig. B.5) is proportional to the radius r for a fixed value of θ (in radians):

$$s = r\theta$$
$$\theta = \frac{s}{r} \tag{B.18}$$

Table B.2 gives the **areas** and **volumes** for several geometric shapes used throughout this text.

The equation of a **straight line** (Fig. B.6) is

$$y = mx + b \tag{B.19}$$

where b is the y-intercept and m is the slope of the line.

The equation of a **circle** of radius R centered at the origin is

$$x^2 + y^2 = R^2 \tag{B.20}$$

The equation of an **ellipse** having the origin at its center (Fig. B.7) is

$$\frac{x^2}{a^2} + \frac{y^2}{b^2} = 1 \tag{B.21}$$

where a is the length of the semimajor axis (the longer one) and b is the length of the semiminor axis (the shorter one).

The equation of a **parabola** the vertex of which is at $y = b$ (Fig. B.8) is

$$y = ax^2 + b \tag{B.22}$$

The equation of a **rectangular hyperbola** (Fig. B.9) is

$$xy = \text{constant} \tag{B.23}$$

B.4 Trigonometry

That portion of mathematics based on the special properties of the right triangle is called trigonometry. By definition, a right triangle is a triangle containing a 90° angle. Consider the right triangle shown in Figure B.10, where side a is opposite the angle θ, side b is adjacent to the angle θ, and side c is the hypotenuse of the triangle. The three basic trigonometric functions defined by such a triangle are the sine (sin), cosine (cos), and tangent (tan). In terms of the angle θ, these functions are defined as follows:

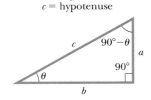

a = opposite side
b = adjacent side
c = hypotenuse

$$\sin \theta = \frac{\text{side opposite } \theta}{\text{hypotenuse}} = \frac{a}{c} \qquad \textbf{(B.24)}$$

$$\cos \theta = \frac{\text{side adjacent to } \theta}{\text{hypotenuse}} = \frac{b}{c} \qquad \textbf{(B.25)}$$

$$\tan \theta = \frac{\text{side opposite } \theta}{\text{side adjacent to } \theta} = \frac{a}{b} \qquad \textbf{(B.26)}$$

Figure B.10   A right triangle, used to define the basic functions of trigonometry.

The Pythagorean theorem provides the following relationship among the sides of a right triangle:

$$c^2 = a^2 + b^2 \qquad \textbf{(B.27)}$$

From the preceding definitions and the Pythagorean theorem, it follows that

$$\sin^2 \theta + \cos^2 \theta = 1$$

$$\tan \theta = \frac{\sin \theta}{\cos \theta}$$

The cosecant, secant, and cotangent functions are defined by

$$\csc \theta = \frac{1}{\sin \theta} \quad \sec \theta = \frac{1}{\cos \theta} \quad \cot \theta = \frac{1}{\tan \theta}$$

The following relationships are derived directly from the right triangle shown in Figure B.10:

$$\sin \theta = \cos (90° - \theta)$$

$$\cos \theta = \sin (90° - \theta)$$

$$\cot \theta = \tan (90° - \theta)$$

Some properties of trigonometric functions are the following:

$$\sin (-\theta) = -\sin \theta$$

$$\cos (-\theta) = \cos \theta$$

$$\tan (-\theta) = -\tan \theta$$

The following relationships apply to *any* triangle as shown in Figure B.11:

$$\alpha + \beta + \gamma = 180°$$

Law of cosines
$$\begin{cases} a^2 = b^2 + c^2 - 2bc \cos \alpha \\ b^2 = a^2 + c^2 - 2ac \cos \beta \\ c^2 = a^2 + b^2 - 2ab \cos \gamma \end{cases}$$

Law of sines
$$\frac{a}{\sin \alpha} = \frac{b}{\sin \beta} = \frac{c}{\sin \gamma}$$

Table B.3 (page A-12) lists a number of useful trigonometric identities.

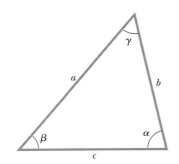

Figure B.11   An arbitrary, nonright triangle.

EXAMPLE **B.3**

Consider the right triangle in Figure B.12 in which $a = 2.00$, $b = 5.00$, and c is unknown. From the Pythagorean theorem, we have

$$c^2 = a^2 + b^2 = 2.00^2 + 5.00^2 = 4.00 + 25.0 = 29.0$$

$$c = \sqrt{29.0} = 5.39$$

Figure B.12   (Example B.3)

To find the angle θ, note that

$$\tan \theta = \frac{a}{b} = \frac{2.00}{5.00} = 0.400$$

Using a calculator, we find that

$$\theta = \tan^{-1}(0.400) = \boxed{21.8°}$$

where $\tan^{-1}(0.400)$ is the notation for "angle whose tangent is 0.400," sometimes written as arctan (0.400).

TABLE B.3

Some Trigonometric Identities

$\sin^2 \theta + \cos^2 \theta = 1$	$\csc^2 \theta = 1 + \cot^2 \theta$
$\sec^2 \theta = 1 + \tan^2 \theta$	$\sin^2 \dfrac{\theta}{2} = \frac{1}{2}(1 - \cos \theta)$
$\sin 2\theta = 2 \sin \theta \cos \theta$	$\cos^2 \dfrac{\theta}{2} = \frac{1}{2}(1 + \cos \theta)$
$\cos 2\theta = \cos^2 \theta - \sin^2 \theta$	$1 - \cos \theta = 2 \sin^2 \dfrac{\theta}{2}$
$\tan 2\theta = \dfrac{2 \tan \theta}{1 - \tan^2 \theta}$	$\tan \dfrac{\theta}{2} = \sqrt{\dfrac{1 - \cos \theta}{1 + \cos \theta}}$

$$\sin (A \pm B) = \sin A \cos B \pm \cos A \sin B$$
$$\cos (A \pm B) = \cos A \cos B \mp \sin A \sin B$$
$$\sin A \pm \sin B = 2 \sin \left[\tfrac{1}{2}(A \pm B)\right] \cos \left[\tfrac{1}{2}(A \mp B)\right]$$
$$\cos A + \cos B = 2 \cos \left[\tfrac{1}{2}(A + B)\right] \cos \left[\tfrac{1}{2}(A - B)\right]$$
$$\cos A - \cos B = 2 \sin \left[\tfrac{1}{2}(A + B)\right] \sin \left[\tfrac{1}{2}(B - A)\right]$$

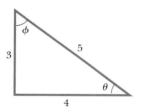

Figure B.13   (Exercise 1)

Exercises

1. In Figure B.13, identify (a) the side opposite θ (b) the side adjacent to ϕ and then find (c) $\cos \theta$, (d) $\sin \phi$, and (e) $\tan \phi$.

Answers   (a) 3   (b) 3   (c) $\frac{4}{5}$ (d) $\frac{4}{5}$ (e) $\frac{4}{3}$

2. In a certain right triangle, the two sides that are perpendicular to each other are 5.00 m and 7.00 m long. What is the length of the third side?

Answer   8.60 m

3. A right triangle has a hypotenuse of length 3.0 m, and one of its angles is 30°. (a) What is the length of the side opposite the 30° angle? (b) What is the side adjacent to the 30° angle?

Answers   (a) 1.5 m   (b) 2.6 m

B.5   Series Expansions

$$(a + b)^n = a^n + \frac{n}{1!} a^{n-1}b + \frac{n(n - 1)}{2!} a^{n-2}b^2 + \cdots$$

$$(1 + x)^n = 1 + nx + \frac{n(n - 1)}{2!} x^2 + \cdots$$

$$e^x = 1 + x + \frac{x^2}{2!} + \frac{x^3}{3!} + \cdots$$

$$\ln(1 \pm x) = \pm x - \tfrac{1}{2}x^2 \pm \tfrac{1}{3}x^3 - \cdots$$

$$\left.\begin{array}{l} \sin x = x - \dfrac{x^3}{3!} + \dfrac{x^5}{5!} - \cdots \\[2mm] \cos x = 1 - \dfrac{x^2}{2!} + \dfrac{x^4}{4!} - \cdots \\[2mm] \tan x = x + \dfrac{x^3}{3} + \dfrac{2x^5}{15} + \cdots \quad |x| < \dfrac{\pi}{2} \end{array}\right\} \quad x \text{ in radians}$$

For $x \ll 1$, the following approximations can be used:[1]

$$(1 + x)^n \approx 1 + nx \qquad \sin x \approx x$$

$$e^x \approx 1 + x \qquad \cos x \approx 1$$

$$\ln(1 \pm x) \approx \pm x \qquad \tan x \approx x$$

B.6   Differential Calculus

In various branches of science, it is sometimes necessary to use the basic tools of calculus, invented by Newton, to describe physical phenomena. The use of calculus is fundamental in the treatment of various problems in Newtonian mechanics, electricity, and magnetism. In this section, we simply state some basic properties and "rules of thumb" that should be a useful review to the student.

First, a **function** must be specified that relates one variable to another (e.g., a coordinate as a function of time). Suppose one of the variables is called y (the dependent variable), and the other x (the independent variable). We might have a function relationship such as

$$y(x) = ax^3 + bx^2 + cx + d$$

If a, b, c, and d are specified constants, y can be calculated for any value of x. We usually deal with continuous functions, that is, those for which y varies "smoothly" with x.

The **derivative** of y with respect to x is defined as the limit as Δx approaches zero of the slopes of chords drawn between two points on the y versus x curve. Mathematically, we write this definition as

$$\frac{dy}{dx} = \lim_{\Delta x \to 0} \frac{\Delta y}{\Delta x} = \lim_{\Delta x \to 0} \frac{y(x + \Delta x) - y(x)}{\Delta x} \tag{B.28}$$

where Δy and Δx are defined as $\Delta x = x_2 - x_1$ and $\Delta y = y_2 - y_1$ (Fig. B.14). Note that dy/dx *does not* mean dy divided by dx, but rather is simply a notation of the limiting process of the derivative as defined by Equation B.28.

A useful expression to remember when $y(x) = ax^n$, where a is a *constant* and n is *any* positive or negative number (integer or fraction), is

$$\frac{dy}{dx} = nax^{n-1} \tag{B.29}$$

If $y(x)$ is a polynomial or algebraic function of x, we apply Equation B.29 to *each* term in the polynomial and take $d[\text{constant}]/dx = 0$. In Examples B.4 through B.7, we evaluate the derivatives of several functions.

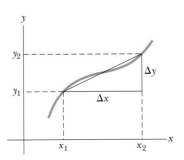

Figure B.14   The lengths Δx and Δy are used to define the derivative of this function at a point.

[1]The approximations for the functions sin x, cos x, and tan x are for $x \leq 0.1$ rad.

TABLE B.4

Derivative for Several Functions

$$\frac{d}{dx}(a) = 0$$

$$\frac{d}{dx}(ax^n) = nax^{n-1}$$

$$\frac{d}{dx}(e^{ax}) = ae^{ax}$$

$$\frac{d}{dx}(\sin ax) = a\cos ax$$

$$\frac{d}{dx}(\cos ax) = -a\sin ax$$

$$\frac{d}{dx}(\tan ax) = a\sec^2 ax$$

$$\frac{d}{dx}(\cot ax) = -a\csc^2 ax$$

$$\frac{d}{dx}(\sec x) = \tan x \sec x$$

$$\frac{d}{dx}(\csc x) = -\cot x \csc x$$

$$\frac{d}{dx}(\ln ax) = \frac{1}{x}$$

$$\frac{d}{dx}(\sin^{-1} ax) = \frac{a}{\sqrt{1 - a^2x^2}}$$

$$\frac{d}{dx}(\cos^{-1} ax) = \frac{-a}{\sqrt{1 - a^2x^2}}$$

$$\frac{d}{dx}(\tan^{-1} ax) = \frac{a}{1 + a^2x^2}$$

Note: The symbols a and n represent constants.

Special Properties of the Derivative

A. Derivative of the product of two functions   If a function $f(x)$ is given by the product of two functions—say, $g(x)$ and $h(x)$—the derivative of $f(x)$ is defined as

$$\frac{d}{dx}f(x) = \frac{d}{dx}[g(x)h(x)] = g\frac{dh}{dx} + h\frac{dg}{dx} \qquad \text{(B.30)}$$

B. Derivative of the sum of two functions   If a function $f(x)$ is equal to the sum of two functions, the derivative of the sum is equal to the sum of the derivatives:

$$\frac{d}{dx}f(x) = \frac{d}{dx}[g(x) + h(x)] = \frac{dg}{dx} + \frac{dh}{dx} \qquad \text{(B.31)}$$

C. Chain rule of differential calculus   If $y = f(x)$ and $x = g(z)$, then dy/dz can be written as the product of two derivatives:

$$\frac{dy}{dz} = \frac{dy}{dx}\frac{dx}{dz} \qquad \text{(B.32)}$$

D. The second derivative   The second derivative of y with respect to x is defined as the derivative of the function dy/dx (the derivative of the derivative). It is usually written as

$$\frac{d^2y}{dx^2} = \frac{d}{dx}\left(\frac{dy}{dx}\right) \qquad \text{(B.33)}$$

Some of the more commonly used derivatives of functions are listed in Table B.4.

EXAMPLE B.4

Suppose $y(x)$ (that is, y as a function of x) is given by

$$y(x) = ax^3 + bx + c$$

where a and b are constants. It follows that

$$y(x + \Delta x) = a(x + \Delta x)^3 + b(x + \Delta x) + c$$

$$= a(x^3 + 3x^2 \Delta x + 3x \Delta x^2 + \Delta x^3) + b(x + \Delta x) + c$$

so

$$\Delta y = y(x + \Delta x) - y(x) = a(3x^2 \Delta x + 3x \Delta x^2 + \Delta x^3) + b \Delta x$$

Substituting this into Equation B.28 gives

$$\frac{dy}{dx} = \lim_{\Delta x \to 0} \frac{\Delta y}{\Delta x} = \lim_{\Delta x \to 0}\left[3ax^2 + 3ax \Delta x + a \Delta x^2\right] + b$$

$$\frac{dy}{dx} = 3ax^2 + b$$

EXAMPLE B.5

Find the derivative of

$$y(x) = 8x^5 + 4x^3 + 2x + 7$$

Solution Applying Equation B.29 to each term independently and remembering that d/dx (constant) $= 0$, we have

$$\frac{dy}{dx} = 8(5)x^4 + 4(3)x^2 + 2(1)x^0 + 0$$

$$\frac{dy}{dx} = 40x^4 + 12x^2 + 2$$

EXAMPLE B.6

Find the derivative of $y(x) = x^3/(x+1)^2$ with respect to x.

Solution We can rewrite this function as $y(x) = x^3(x+1)^{-2}$ and apply Equation B.30:

$$\frac{dy}{dx} = (x+1)^{-2} \frac{d}{dx}(x^3) + x^3 \frac{d}{dx}(x+1)^{-2}$$

$$= (x+1)^{-2} 3x^2 + x^3(-2)(x+1)^{-3}$$

$$\frac{dy}{dx} = \frac{3x^2}{(x+1)^2} - \frac{2x^3}{(x+1)^3}$$

EXAMPLE B.7

A useful formula that follows from Equation B.30 is the derivative of the quotient of two functions. Show that

$$\frac{d}{dx}\left[\frac{g(x)}{h(x)}\right] = \frac{h\dfrac{dg}{dx} - g\dfrac{dh}{dx}}{h^2}$$

Solution We can write the quotient as gh^{-1} and then apply Equations B.29 and B.30:

$$\frac{d}{dx}\left(\frac{g}{h}\right) = \frac{d}{dx}(gh^{-1}) = g\frac{d}{dx}(h^{-1}) + h^{-1}\frac{d}{dx}(g)$$

$$= -gh^{-2}\frac{dh}{dx} + h^{-1}\frac{dg}{dx}$$

$$= \frac{h\dfrac{dg}{dx} - g\dfrac{dh}{dx}}{h^2}$$

B.7   Integral Calculus

We think of integration as the inverse of differentiation. As an example, consider the expression

$$f(x) = \frac{dy}{dx} = 3ax^2 + b \qquad \text{(B.34)}$$

which was the result of differentiating the function

$$y(x) = ax^3 + bx + c$$

in Example B.4. We can write Equation B.34 as $dy = f(x) \, dx = (3ax^2 + b) \, dx$ and obtain $y(x)$ by "summing" over all values of x. Mathematically, we write this inverse operation as

$$y(x) = \int f(x) \, dx$$

For the function $f(x)$ given by Equation B.34, we have

$$y(x) = \int (3ax^2 + b) \, dx = ax^3 + bx + c$$

where c is a constant of the integration. This type of integral is called an *indefinite integral* because its value depends on the choice of c.

A general **indefinite integral** $I(x)$ is defined as

$$I(x) = \int f(x) \, dx \qquad \text{(B.35)}$$

where $f(x)$ is called the *integrand* and $f(x) = dI(x)/dx$.

For a *general continuous* function $f(x)$, the integral can be described as the area under the curve bounded by $f(x)$ and the x axis, between two specified values of x, say, x_1 and x_2, as in Figure B.15.

The area of the blue element in Figure B.15 is approximately $f(x_i) \, \Delta x_i$. If we sum all these area elements between x_1 and x_2 and take the limit of this sum as $\Delta x_i \rightarrow 0$, we obtain the *true* area under the curve bounded by $f(x)$ and the x axis, between the limits x_1 and x_2:

$$\text{Area} = \lim_{\Delta x_i \to 0} \sum_i f(x_i) \Delta x_i = \int_{x_1}^{x_2} f(x) \, dx \qquad \text{(B.36)}$$

Integrals of the type defined by Equation B.36 are called **definite integrals.**

Figure B.15   The definite integral of a function is the area under the curve of the function between the limits x_1 and x_2.

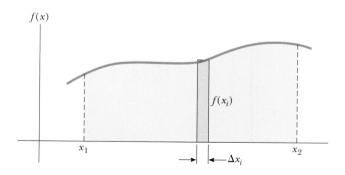

One common integral that arises in practical situations has the form

$$\int x^n \, dx = \frac{x^{n+1}}{n+1} + c \quad (n \neq -1) \tag{B.37}$$

This result is obvious, being that differentiation of the right-hand side with respect to x gives $f(x) = x^n$ directly. If the limits of the integration are known, this integral becomes a *definite integral* and is written

$$\int_{x_1}^{x_2} x^n \, dx = \frac{x^{n+1}}{n+1} \bigg|_{x_1}^{x_2} = \frac{x_2^{n+1} - x_1^{n+1}}{n+1} \quad (n \neq -1) \tag{B.38}$$

EXAMPLES

1. $\displaystyle\int_0^a x^2 \, dx = \frac{x^3}{3} \bigg]_0^a = \frac{a^3}{3}$

3. $\displaystyle\int_3^5 x \, dx = \frac{x^2}{2} \bigg]_3^5 = \frac{5^2 - 3^2}{2} = 8$

2. $\displaystyle\int_0^b x^{3/2} \, dx = \frac{x^{5/2}}{5/2} \bigg]_0^b = \tfrac{2}{5} b^{5/2}$

Partial Integration

Sometimes it is useful to apply the method of *partial integration* (also called "integrating by parts") to evaluate certain integrals. This method uses the property

$$\int u \, dv = uv - \int v \, du \tag{B.39}$$

where u and v are *carefully* chosen so as to reduce a complex integral to a simpler one. In many cases, several reductions have to be made. Consider the function

$$I(x) = \int x^2 e^x \, dx$$

which can be evaluated by integrating by parts twice. First, if we choose $u = x^2$, $v = e^x$, we obtain

$$\int x^2 e^x \, dx = \int x^2 \, d(e^x) = x^2 e^x - 2 \int e^x x \, dx + c_1$$

Now, in the second term, choose $u = x$, $v = e^x$, which gives

$$\int x^2 e^x \, dx = x^2 e^x - 2x e^x + 2 \int e^x \, dx + c_1$$

or

$$\int x^2 e^x \, dx = x^2 e^x - 2x e^x + 2e^x + c_2$$

TABLE B.5

Some Indefinite Integrals (An arbitrary constant should be added to each of these integrals.)

$$\int x^n \, dx = \frac{x^{n+1}}{n+1} \quad \text{(provided } n \neq 1\text{)}$$

$$\int \frac{dx}{x} = \int x^{-1} \, dx = \ln x$$

$$\int \frac{dx}{a+bx} = \frac{1}{b} \ln (a+bx)$$

$$\int \frac{x \, dx}{a+bx} = \frac{x}{b} - \frac{a}{b^2} \ln (a+bx)$$

$$\int \frac{dx}{x(x+a)} = -\frac{1}{a} \ln \frac{x+a}{x}$$

$$\int \frac{dx}{(a+bx)^2} = -\frac{1}{b(a+bx)}$$

$$\int \frac{dx}{a^2 + x^2} = \frac{1}{a} \tan^{-1} \frac{x}{a}$$

$$\int \frac{dx}{a^2 - x^2} = \frac{1}{2a} \ln \frac{a+x}{a-x} \quad (a^2 - x^2 > 0)$$

$$\int \frac{dx}{x^2 - a^2} = \frac{1}{2a} \ln \frac{x-a}{x+a} \quad (x^2 - a^2 > 0)$$

$$\int \frac{x \, dx}{a^2 \pm x^2} = \pm \tfrac{1}{2} \ln (a^2 \pm x^2)$$

$$\int \frac{dx}{\sqrt{a^2 - x^2}} = \sin^{-1} \frac{x}{a} = -\cos^{-1} \frac{x}{a} \quad (a^2 - x^2 > 0)$$

$$\int \frac{dx}{\sqrt{x^2 + a^2}} = \ln (x + \sqrt{x^2 \pm a^2})$$

$$\int \frac{x \, dx}{\sqrt{a^2 - x^2}} = -\sqrt{a^2 - x^2}$$

$$\int \frac{x \, dx}{\sqrt{x^2 \pm a^2}} = \sqrt{x^2 \pm a^2}$$

$$\int \sqrt{a^2 - x^2} \, dx = \tfrac{1}{2} \left(x\sqrt{a^2 - x^2} + a^2 \sin^{-1} \frac{x}{a} \right)$$

$$\int x\sqrt{a^2 - x^2} \, dx = -\tfrac{1}{3}(a^2 - x^2)^{3/2}$$

$$\int \sqrt{x^2 \pm a^2} \, dx = \tfrac{1}{2}\left[x\sqrt{x^2 \pm a^2} \pm a^2 \ln (x + \sqrt{x^2 \pm a^2}) \right]$$

$$\int x(\sqrt{x^2 \pm a^2}) \, dx = \tfrac{1}{3}(x^2 \pm a^2)^{3/2}$$

$$\int e^{ax} \, dx = \frac{1}{a} e^{ax}$$

$$\int \ln ax \, dx = (x \ln ax) - x$$

$$\int xe^{ax} \, dx = \frac{e^{ax}}{a^2} \, (ax - 1)$$

$$\int \frac{dx}{a + be^{cx}} = \frac{x}{a} - \frac{1}{ac} \ln (a + be^{cx})$$

$$\int \sin ax \, dx = \frac{1}{a} \cos ax$$

$$\int \cos ax \, dx = \frac{1}{a} \sin ax$$

$$\int \tan ax \, dx = -\frac{1}{a} \ln (\cos ax) = \frac{1}{a} \ln (\sec ax)$$

$$\int \cot ax \, dx = \frac{1}{a} \ln (\sin ax)$$

$$\int \sec ax \, dx = \frac{1}{a} \ln (\sec ax + \tan ax) = \frac{1}{a} \ln \left[\tan \left(\frac{ax}{2} + \frac{\pi}{4} \right) \right]$$

$$\int \csc ax \, dx = \frac{1}{a} \ln (\csc ax - \cot ax) = \frac{1}{a} \ln \left(\tan \frac{ax}{2} \right).$$

$$\int \sin^2 ax \, dx = \frac{x}{2} + \frac{\sin 2ax}{4a}$$

$$\int \cos^2 ax \, dx = \frac{x}{2} + \frac{\sin 2ax}{4a}$$

$$\int \frac{dx}{\sin^2 ax} = -\frac{1}{a} \cot ax$$

$$\int \frac{dx}{\cos^2 ax} = \frac{1}{a} \tan ax$$

$$\int \tan^2 ax \, dx = \frac{1}{a} (\tan ax) - x$$

$$\int \cot^2 ax \, dx = -\frac{1}{a} (\cot ax) - x$$

$$\int \sin^{-1} ax \, dx = x(\sin^{-1} ax) + \frac{\sqrt{1 - a^2 x^2}}{a}$$

$$\int \cos^{-1} ax \, dx = x(\cos^{-1} ax) - \frac{\sqrt{1 - a^2 x^2}}{a}$$

$$\int \frac{dx}{(x^2 + a^2)^{3/2}} = \frac{x}{a^2 \sqrt{x^2 + a^2}}$$

$$\int \frac{x \, dx}{(x^2 + a^2)^{3/2}} = -\frac{1}{\sqrt{x^2 + a^2}}$$

TABLE B.6

**Gauss's Probability Integral
and Other Definite Integrals**

$$\int_0^\infty x^n e^{-ax}\,dx = \frac{n!}{a^{n+1}}$$

$$I_0 = \int_0^\infty e^{-ax^2}dx = \frac{1}{2}\sqrt{\frac{\pi}{a}} \qquad \text{(Gauss's probability integral)}$$

$$I_1 = \int_0^\infty xe^{-ax^2}\,dx = \frac{1}{2a}$$

$$I_2 = \int_0^\infty x^2 e^{-ax^2}dx = -\frac{dI_0}{da} = \frac{1}{4}\sqrt{\frac{\pi}{a^3}}$$

$$I_3 = \int_0^\infty x^3 e^{-ax^2}\,dx = -\frac{dI_1}{da} = \frac{1}{2a^2}$$

$$I_4 = \int_0^\infty x^4 e^{-ax^2}dx = \frac{d^2 I_0}{da^2} = \frac{3}{8}\sqrt{\frac{\pi}{a^5}}$$

$$I_5 = \int_0^\infty x^5 e^{-ax^2}\,dx = \frac{d^2 I_1}{da^2} = \frac{1}{a^3}$$

$$\vdots$$

$$I_{2n} = (-1)^n \frac{d^n}{da^n} I_0$$

$$I_{2n+1} = (-1)^n \frac{d^n}{da^n} I_1$$

The Perfect Differential

Another useful method to remember is that of the *perfect differential*, in which we look for a change of variable such that the differential of the function is the differential of the independent variable appearing in the integrand. For example, consider the integral

$$I(x) = \int \cos^2 x \, \sin x \, dx$$

This integral becomes easy to evaluate if we rewrite the differential as $d(\cos x) = -\sin x\,dx$. The integral then becomes

$$\int \cos^2 x \, \sin x \, dx = -\int \cos^2 x \, d(\cos x)$$

If we now change variables, letting $y = \cos x$, we obtain

$$\int \cos^2 x \, \sin x \, dx = -\int y^2 \, dy = -\frac{y^3}{3} + c = -\frac{\cos^3 x}{3} + c$$

Table B.5 (page A-18) lists some useful indefinite integrals. Table B.6 gives Gauss's probability integral and other definite integrals. A more complete list can be found in various handbooks, such as *The Handbook of Chemistry and Physics* (Boca Raton, FL: CRC Press, published annually).

B.8   Propagation of Uncertainty

In laboratory experiments, a common activity is to take measurements that act as raw data. These measurements are of several types—length, time interval, temperature, voltage, and so on—and are taken by a variety of instruments. Regardless of the measurement and the quality of the instrumentation, **there is always uncertainty associated with a physical measurement.** This uncertainty is a combination of that associated with the instrument and that related to the system being measured. An example of the former is the inability to exactly determine the position of a length measurement between the lines on a meterstick. An example of uncertainty related to the system being measured is the variation of temperature within a sample of water so that a single temperature for the sample is difficult to determine.

Uncertainties can be expressed in two ways. **Absolute uncertainty** refers to an uncertainty expressed in the same units as the measurement. Therefore, the length of a computer disk label might be expressed as (5.5 ± 0.1) cm. The uncertainty of ± 0.1 cm by itself is not descriptive enough for some purposes, however. This uncertainty is large if the measurement is 1.0 cm, but it is small if the measurement is 100 m. To give a more descriptive account of the uncertainty, **fractional uncertainty** or **percent uncertainty** is used. In this type of description, the uncertainty is divided by the actual measurement. Therefore, the length of the computer disk label could be expressed as

$$\ell = 5.5 \text{ cm } \pm \frac{0.1 \text{ cm}}{5.5 \text{ cm}} = 5.5 \text{ cm } \pm 0.018 \quad \text{(fractional uncertainty)}$$

or as

$$\ell = 5.5 \text{ cm } \pm 1.8\% \quad \text{(percent uncertainty)}$$

When combining measurements in a calculation, the percent uncertainty in the final result is generally larger than the uncertainty in the individual measurements. This is called **propagation of uncertainty** and is one of the challenges of experimental physics.

Some simple rules can provide a reasonable estimate of the uncertainty in a calculated result:

Multiplication and division: When measurements with uncertainties are multiplied or divided, add the *percent uncertainties* to obtain the percent uncertainty in the result.

Example: The Area of a Rectangular Plate

$$A = \ell w = (5.5 \text{ cm } \pm 1.8\%) \times (6.4 \text{ cm } \pm 1.6\%) = 35 \text{ cm}^2 \pm 3.4\%$$

$$= (35 \pm 1) \text{ cm}^2$$

Addition and subtraction: When measurements with uncertainties are added or subtracted, add the *absolute uncertainties* to obtain the absolute uncertainty in the result.

Example: A Change in Temperature

$$\Delta T = T_2 - T_1 = (99.2 \pm 1.5)°C - (27.6 \pm 1.5)°C = (71.6 \pm 3.0)°C$$

$$= 71.6°C \pm 4.2\%$$

Powers: If a measurement is taken to a power, the percent uncertainty is multiplied by that power to obtain the percent uncertainty in the result.

Example: The Volume of a Sphere

$$V = \tfrac{4}{3}\pi r^3 = \tfrac{4}{3}\pi (6.20 \text{ cm } \pm 2.0\%)^3 = 998 \text{ cm}^3 \pm 6.0\%$$

$$= (998 \pm 60) \text{ cm}^3$$

For complicated calculations, many uncertainties are added together, which can cause the uncertainty in the final result to be undesirably large. Experiments should be designed such that calculations are as simple as possible.

Notice that uncertainties in a calculation always add. As a result, an experiment involving a subtraction should be avoided if possible, especially if the measurements being subtracted are close together. The result of such a calculation is a small difference in the measurements and uncertainties that add together. It is possible that the uncertainty in the result could be larger than the result itself!

Group I	Group II					Transition elements			

H 1
1.007 9
1s

Li 3	**Be** 4
6.941	9.0122
$2s^1$	$2s^2$

| Symbol — **Ca** 20 — Atomic number |
| Atomic mass† — 40.078 |
| $4s^2$ — Electron configuration |

Na 11	**Mg** 12
22.990	24.305
$3s^1$	$3s^2$

K 19	**Ca** 20	**Sc** 21	**Ti** 22	**V** 23	**Cr** 24	**Mn** 25	**Fe** 26	**Co** 27
39.098	40.078	44.956	47.867	50.942	51.996	54.938	55.845	58.933
$4s^1$	$4s^2$	$3d^14s^2$	$3d^24s^2$	$3d^34s^2$	$3d^54s^1$	$3d^54s^2$	$3d^64s^2$	$3d^74s^2$

Rb 37	**Sr** 38	**Y** 39	**Zr** 40	**Nb** 41	**Mo** 42	**Tc** 43	**Ru** 44	**Rh** 45
85.468	87.62	88.906	91.224	92.906	95.94	(98)	101.07	102.91
$5s^1$	$5s^2$	$4d^15s^2$	$4d^25s^2$	$4d^45s^1$	$4d^55s^1$	$4d^55s^2$	$4d^75s^1$	$4d^85s^1$

Cs 55	**Ba** 56	57–71*	**Hf** 72	**Ta** 73	**W** 74	**Re** 75	**Os** 76	**Ir** 77
132.91	137.33		178.49	180.95	183.84	186.21	190.23	192.2
$6s^1$	$6s^2$		$5d^26s^2$	$5d^36s^2$	$5d^46s^2$	$5d^56s^2$	$5d^66s^2$	$5d^76s^2$

Fr 87	**Ra** 88	89–103**	**Rf** 104	**Db** 105	**Sg** 106	**Bh** 107	**Hs** 108	**Mt** 109
(223)	(226)		(261)	(262)	(266)	(264)	(277)	(268)
$7s^1$	$7s^2$		$6d^27s^2$	$6d^37s^2$				

*Lanthanide series

La 57	**Ce** 58	**Pr** 59	**Nd** 60	**Pm** 61	**Sm** 62
138.91	140.12	140.91	144.24	(145)	150.36
$5d^16s^2$	$5d^14f^16s^2$	$4f^36s^2$	$4f^46s^2$	$4f^56s^2$	$4f^66s^2$

**Actinide series

Ac 89	**Th** 90	**Pa** 91	**U** 92	**Np** 93	**Pu** 94
(227)	232.04	231.04	238.03	(237)	(244)
$6d^17s^2$	$6d^27s^2$	$5f^26d^17s^2$	$5f^36d^17s^2$	$5f^46d^17s^2$	$5f^66d^07s^2$

Note: Atomic mass values given are averaged over isotopes in the percentages in which they exist in nature.

†For an unstable element, mass number of the most stable known isotope is given in parentheses.

††Elements 112 and 114 have not yet been named.

†††For a description of the atomic data, visit *physics.nist.gov/PhysRefData/Elements/per_text.html*

			Group III	Group IV	Group V	Group VI	Group VII	Group 0
							H 1 1.007 9 $1s^1$	**He** 2 4.002 6 $1s^2$
			B 5 10.811 $2p^1$	**C** 6 12.011 $2p^2$	**N** 7 14.007 $2p^3$	**O** 8 15.999 $2p^4$	**F** 9 18.998 $2p^5$	**Ne** 10 20.180 $2p^6$
			Al 13 26.982 $3p^1$	**Si** 14 28.086 $3p^2$	**P** 15 30.974 $3p^3$	**S** 16 32.066 $3p^4$	**Cl** 17 35.453 $3p^5$	**Ar** 18 39.948 $3p^6$
Ni 28 58.693 $3d^84s^2$	**Cu** 29 63.546 $3d^{10}4s^1$	**Zn** 30 65.41 $3d^{10}4s^2$	**Ga** 31 69.723 $4p^1$	**Ge** 32 72.64 $4p^2$	**As** 33 74.922 $4p^3$	**Se** 34 78.96 $4p^4$	**Br** 35 79.904 $4p^5$	**Kr** 36 83.80 $4p^6$
Pd 46 106.42 $4d^{10}$	**Ag** 47 107.87 $4d^{10}5s^1$	**Cd** 48 112.41 $4d^{10}5s^2$	**In** 49 114.82 $5p^1$	**Sn** 50 118.71 $5p^2$	**Sb** 51 121.76 $5p^3$	**Te** 52 127.60 $5p^4$	**I** 53 126.90 $5p^5$	**Xe** 54 131.29 $5p^6$
Pt 78 195.08 $5d^96s^1$	**Au** 79 196.97 $5d^{10}6s^1$	**Hg** 80 200.59 $5d^{10}6s^2$	**Tl** 81 204.38 $6p^1$	**Pb** 82 207.2 $6p^2$	**Bi** 83 208.98 $6p^3$	**Po** 84 (209) $6p^4$	**At** 85 (210) $6p^5$	**Rn** 86 (222) $6p^6$
Ds 110 (271)	**Rg** 111 (272)	112[††] (285)		114[††] (289)				

Eu 63 151.96 $4f^76s^2$	**Gd** 64 157.25 $4f^75d^16s^2$	**Tb** 65 158.93 $4f^85d^16s^2$	**Dy** 66 162.50 $4f^{10}6s^2$	**Ho** 67 164.93 $4f^{11}6s^2$	**Er** 68 167.26 $4f^{12}6s^2$	**Tm** 69 168.93 $4f^{13}6s^2$	**Yb** 70 173.04 $4f^{14}6s^2$	**Lu** 71 174.97 $4f^{14}5d^16s^2$
Am 95 (243) $5f^77s^2$	**Cm** 96 (247) $5f^76d^17s^2$	**Bk** 97 (247) $5f^86d^17s^2$	**Cf** 98 (251) $5f^{10}7s^2$	**Es** 99 (252) $5f^{11}7s^2$	**Fm** 100 (257) $5f^{12}7s^2$	**Md** 101 (258) $5f^{13}7s^2$	**No** 102 (259) $5f^{14}7s^2$	**Lr** 103 (262) $6d^15f^{14}7s^2$

TABLE D.1

SI Units

Base Quantity	SI Base Unit	
	Name	**Symbol**
Length	meter	m
Mass	kilogram	kg
Time	second	s
Electric current	ampere	A
Temperature	kelvin	K
Amount of substance	mole	mol
Luminous intensity	candela	cd

TABLE D.2

Some Derived SI Units

Quantity	Name	Symbol	Expression in Terms of Base Units	Expression in Terms of Other SI Units
Plane angle	radian	rad	m/m	
Frequency	hertz	Hz	s^{-1}	
Force	newton	N	$kg \cdot m/s^2$	J/m
Pressure	pascal	Pa	$kg/m \cdot s^2$	N/m^2
Energy	joule	J	$kg \cdot m^2/s^2$	$N \cdot m$
Power	watt	W	$kg \cdot m^2/s^3$	J/s
Electric charge	coulomb	C	$A \cdot s$	
Electric potential	volt	V	$kg \cdot m^2/A \cdot s^3$	W/A
Capacitance	farad	F	$A^2 \cdot s^4/kg \cdot m^2$	C/V
Electric resistance	ohm	Ω	$kg \cdot m^2/A^2 \cdot s^3$	V/A
Magnetic flux	weber	Wb	$kg \cdot m^2/A \cdot s^2$	$V \cdot s$
Magnetic field	tesla	T	$kg/A \cdot s^2$	
Inductance	henry	H	$kg \cdot m^2/A^2 \cdot s^2$	$T \cdot m^2/A$

CHAPTER 1

1. 5.52×10^3 kg/m^3, between the density of aluminum and iron and greater than the densities of typical surface rocks

3. 23.0 kg

5. 7.69 cm

7. (b) only

9. The units of G are m^3/kg $\cdot$ s^2.

11. 1.39×10^3 m^2

13. Not with the pages from Volume 1, but yes with the pages from the full version. Each page has area 0.059 m^2. The room has wall area 37 m^2, requiring 630 sheets, which would be counted as 1 260 pages.

15. 11.4×10^3 kg/m^3

17. (a) 250 yr (b) 3.09×10^4 times

19. 1.00×10^{10} lb

21. 151 μm

23. 2.86 cm

25. $\sim 10^6$ balls

27. $\sim 10^2$ kg; $\sim 10^3$ kg

29. $\sim 10^2$ tuners

31. (a) 3 (b) 4 (c) 3 (d) 2

33. (a) 797 (b) 1.1 (c) 17.66

35. 8.80%

37. 9

39. 63

41. 108° and 288°

43. 48.6 kg

45. (a) smaller by nine times (b) Δt is inversely proportional to d^2. (c) Plot Δt on the vertical axis and $1/d^2$ on the horizontal axis. (d) $4QL/[k\pi(T_h - T_c)]$

47. (a) $m = 346$ g $- (14.5$ g/cm$^3)a^3$ (b) $a = 0$ (c) 346 g (d) yes (e) $a = 2.60$ cm (f) 90.6 g (g) yes (h) 218 g (i) No; 218 g is not equal to 314 g. (j) Parts (b), (c), and (d) describe a uniform solid sphere with $\rho = 4.70$ g/cm^3 as a approaches zero. Parts (e), (f), and (g) describe a uniform liquid drop with $\rho = 1.23$ g/cm^3 as a approaches 2.60 cm. The function $m(a)$ is not a linear function, so a halfway between 0 and 2.60 cm does not give a value for m halfway between the minimum and maximum values. The graph of m versus a starts at $a = 0$ with a horizontal tangent. Then it curves down more and more steeply as a increases. The liquid drop of radius 1.30 cm has only one eighth the volume of the whole sphere, so its presence brings down the mass by only a small amount, from 346 g to 314 g. (k) The answer would not change as long as the wall of the shell is unbroken.

49. 5.0 m

51. $0.579t$ ft^3/s $+ (1.19 \times 10^{-9})t^2$ ft^3/s^2

53. 3.41 m

55. 0.449%

57. (a) 0.529 cm/s (b) 11.5 cm/s

59. 1×10^{10} gal/yr

CHAPTER 2

1. (a) 5 m/s (b) 1.2 m/s (c) -2.5 m/s (d) -3.3 m/s (e) 0

3. (a) 3.75 m/s (b) 0

5. (a) -2.4 m/s (b) -3.8 m/s (c) 4.0 s

7. (a) and (c)

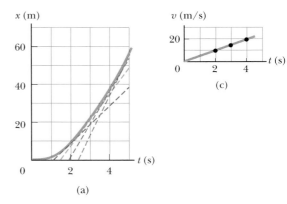

(a)

(b) $v_{t=5.0\text{ s}} = 23$ m/s, $v_{t=4.0\text{ s}} = 18$ m/s, $v_{t=3.0\text{ s}} = 14$ m/s, $v_{t=2.0\text{ s}} = 9.0$ m/s (c) 4.6 m/s^2 (d) 0

9. 5.00 m

11. (a) 20.0 m/s, 5.00 m/s (b) 262 m

13. (a) 2.00 m (b) -3.00 m/s (c) -2.00 m/s^2

15. (a) 13.0 m/s (b) 10.0 m/s, 16.0 m/s (c) 6.00 m/s^2 (d) 6.00 m/s^2

17.

(a)

19. (a) 9.00 m/s (b) 5.00 m/s (c) 3.00 m/s (d) -3.00 m/s (e) 17.0 m/s (f) The graph of velocity versus time is a straight line passing through 13 m/s at 10:05 a.m. and sloping downward, decreasing by 4 m/s for each second thereafter. (g) If and only if we know the object's velocity at one instant of time, knowing its acceleration tells us its velocity at every other moment, as long as the acceleration is constant.

21. -16.0 cm/s^2

23. (a) 20.0 s (b) It cannot; it would need a longer runway.

25. 3.10 m/s

27. (a) -202 m/s^2 (b) 198 m

29. (a) 4.98×10^{-9} s (b) 1.20×10^{15} m/s^2

31. (a) False unless the acceleration is zero. We define constant acceleration to mean that the velocity is changing steadily in time. Then the velocity cannot be changing steadily in space. (b) True. Because the velocity is changing steadily in time, the velocity halfway through an interval is equal to the average of its initial and final values.

33. (a) 3.45 s (b) 10.0 ft

35. (a) 19.7 cm/s (b) 4.70 cm/s^2 (c) The time interval required for the speed to change between Ⓐ and Ⓑ is sufficient to find the acceleration, more directly than we could find it from the distance between the points.

37. We ignore air resistance. We assume the worker's flight time, "a mile," and "a dollar" were measured to three-digit precision. We have interpreted "up in the sky" as referring to free-fall time, not to the launch and landing times. Therefore, the wage was $99.3/h.

39. (a) 10.0 m/s up   (b) 4.68 m/s down

41. (a) 29.4 m/s   (b) 44.1 m

43. (a) 7.82 m   (b) 0.782 s

45. 38.2 m

47. (a) $a_x(t) = a_{xi} + Jt$, $v_x(t) = v_{xi} + a_{xi}t + \frac{1}{2}Jt^2$,
$x(t) = x_i + v_{xi}t + \frac{1}{2}a_{xi}t^2 + \frac{1}{6}Jt^3$

49. (a) 0   (b) 6.0 m/s²   (c) −3.6 m/s²   (d) 6 s and 18 s
(e) 18 s   (f) 84 m   (g) 204 m

51. (a) 41.0 s   (b) 1.73 km   (c) −184 m/s

53. (a) 5.43 m/s² and 3.83 m/s²   (b) 10.9 m/s and 11.5 m/s
(c) Maggie by 2.62 m

55. 155 s, 129 s

57. (a) 3.00 s   (b) −15.3 m/s   (c) 31.4 m/s down and
34.8 m/s down

59. (a) 5.46 s   (b) 73.0 m   (c) $v_{\text{Stan}} = 22.6$ m/s,
$v_{\text{Kathy}} = 26.7$ m/s

61. (a) yes, to two significant digits   (b) 0.742 s   (c) Yes; the braking distance is proportional to the square of the original speed.   (d) −19.7 ft/s² = −6.01 m/s²

63. 0.577v

CHAPTER 3

1. (−2.75, −4.76) m

3. (a) 2.24 m   (b) 2.24 m at 26.6°

5. (a) r, 180° − θ (b) 2r, 180° + θ (c) 3r, −θ

7. 70.0 m

9. (a) 10.0 m   (b) 15.7 m   (c) 0

11. (a) 5.2 m at 60°   (b) 3.0 m at 330°   (c) 3.0 m at 150°
(d) 5.2 m at 300°

13. approximately 420 ft at −3°

15. 47.2 units at 122°

17. Yes. The speed of the camper should be 28.3 m/s or greater.

19. (a) $(-11.1\hat{\mathbf{i}} + 6.40\hat{\mathbf{j}})$ m   (b) $(1.65\hat{\mathbf{i}} + 2.86\hat{\mathbf{j}})$ cm
(c) $(-18.0\hat{\mathbf{i}} - 12.6\hat{\mathbf{j}})$ in.

21. 358 m at 2.00° S of E

23. 196 cm at 345°

25. (a) $2.00\hat{\mathbf{i}} - 6.00\hat{\mathbf{j}}$ (b) $4.00\hat{\mathbf{i}} + 2.00\hat{\mathbf{j}}$ (c) 6.32
(d) 4.47   (e) 288°, 26.6°

27. 9.48 m at 166°

29. 4.64 m at 78.6° N of E

31. (a) 185 N at 77.8° from the +x axis
(b) $(-39.3\hat{\mathbf{i}} - 181\hat{\mathbf{j}})$ N

33. $|\vec{\mathbf{B}}| = 7.81$, $\theta_x = 59.2°$, $\theta_y = 39.8°$, $\theta_z = 67.4°$

35. (a) 5.92 m is the magnitude of
$(5.00\hat{\mathbf{i}} - 1.00\hat{\mathbf{j}} - 3.00\hat{\mathbf{k}})$ m. (b) 19.0 m is the magnitude
of $(4.00\hat{\mathbf{i}} - 11.0\hat{\mathbf{j}} - 15.0\hat{\mathbf{k}})$ m.

37. (a) $8.00\hat{\mathbf{i}} + 12.0\hat{\mathbf{j}} - 4.00\hat{\mathbf{k}}$ (b) $2.00\hat{\mathbf{i}} + 3.00\hat{\mathbf{j}} - 1.00\hat{\mathbf{k}}$
(c) $-24.0\hat{\mathbf{i}} - 36.0\hat{\mathbf{j}} + 12.0\hat{\mathbf{k}}$

39. (a) $(3.12\hat{\mathbf{i}} + 5.02\hat{\mathbf{j}} - 2.20\hat{\mathbf{k}})$ km   (b) 6.31 km

41. (a) $-3.00\hat{\mathbf{i}} + 2.00\hat{\mathbf{j}}$ (b) 3.61 at 146°
(c) $3.00\hat{\mathbf{i}} - 6.00\hat{\mathbf{j}}$

43. (a) $49.5\hat{\mathbf{i}} + 27.1\hat{\mathbf{j}}$ (b) 56.4 units at 28.7°

45. (a) $[(5 + 11f)\hat{\mathbf{i}} + (3 + 9f)\hat{\mathbf{j}}]$ m   (b) $(5\hat{\mathbf{i}} + 3\hat{\mathbf{j}})$ m is reasonable because it is the starting point. (c) $(16\hat{\mathbf{i}} + 12\hat{\mathbf{j}})$ m is reasonable because it is the endpoint.

47. 1.15°

49. 2.29 km

51. (a) 7.17 km   (b) 6.15 km

53. 390 mi/h at 7.37° N of E

55. $(0.456\hat{\mathbf{i}} - 0.708\hat{\mathbf{j}})$ m

57. 240 m at 237°

59. (a) (10.0 m, 16.0 m)   (b) You will arrive at the treasure if you take the trees in any order. The directions take you to the average position of the trees.

61. 106°

CHAPTER 4

1. (a) 4.87 km at 209° from E   (b) 23.3 m/s
(c) 13.5 m/s at 209°

3. 2.50 m/s

5. (a) $(0.800\hat{\mathbf{i}} - 0.300\hat{\mathbf{j}})$ m/s²   (b) 339°
(c) $(360\hat{\mathbf{i}} - 72.7\hat{\mathbf{j}})$ m, −15.2°

7. (a) $\vec{\mathbf{v}} = 5\hat{\mathbf{i}} + 4t^{3/2}\hat{\mathbf{j}}$ (b) $\vec{\mathbf{r}} = 5t\hat{\mathbf{i}} + 1.6t^{5/2}\hat{\mathbf{j}}$

9. (a) $3.34\hat{\mathbf{i}}$ m/s   (b) −50.9°

11. $(7.23 \times 10^3 \text{ m}, 1.68 \times 10^3 \text{ m})$

13. 53.1°

15. (a) 22.6 m   (b) 52.3 m   (c) 1.18 s

17. (a) The ball clears by 0.889 m. (b) while descending

19. (a) 18.1 m/s   (b) 1.13 m   (c) 2.79 m

21. 9.91 m/s

23. $\tan^{-1}[(2gh)^{1/2}/v]$

25. 377 m/s²

27. (a) 6.00 rev/s   (b) 1.52 km/s²   (c) 1.28 km/s²

29. 1.48 m/s² inward and 29.9° backward

31. (a) 13.0 m/s²   (b) 5.70 m/s   (c) 7.50 m/s²

33. (a) 57.7 km/h at 60.0° W of vertical
(b) 28.9 km/h downward

35. 2.02×10^3 s; 21.0% longer

37. $t_{\text{Alan}} = \dfrac{2L/c}{1 - v^2/c^2}$, $t_{\text{Beth}} = \dfrac{2L/c}{\sqrt{1 - v^2/c^2}}$. Beth returns first.

39. 15.3 m

41. 27.7° E of N

43. (a) 9.80 m/s² down   (b) 3.72 m

45. (a) 41.7 m/s   (b) 3.81 s
(c) $(34.1\hat{\mathbf{i}} - 13.4\hat{\mathbf{j}})$ m/s; 36.7 m/s

47. (a) 25.0 m/s²; 9.80 m/s²
(b)

25.0 m/s²

9.80 m/s² $\vec{\mathbf{a}}$

(c) 26.8 m/s² inward at 21.4° below the horizontal

49. (a)

t (s)	0	1	2	3	4	5
r (m)	0	45.7	82.0	109	127	136

t (s)	6	7	8	9	10
r (m)	138	133	124	117	120

(b) The vector $\vec{v}$ tells how $\vec{r}$ is changing. If $\vec{v}$ at a particular point has a component along $\vec{r}$, then $\vec{r}$ will be increasing in magnitude (if $\vec{v}$ is at an angle less than $90°$ from $\vec{r}$) or decreasing (if the angle between $\vec{v}$ and $\vec{r}$ is more than $90°$). To be at a maximum, the distance from the origin must be momentarily staying constant, and the only way that can happen is if the angle between velocity and position is a right angle. Then $\vec{r}$ will be changing in direction at that point, but not in magnitude. (c) The requirement for perpendicularity can be defined as equality between the tangent of the angle between $\vec{v}$ and the x direction and the tangent of the angle between $\vec{r}$ and the y direction. In symbols, this equality can be written $(9.8t - 49)/12 = 12t/(49t - 4.9t^2)$, which has the solution $t = 5.70$ s, giving, in turn, $r = 138$ m. Alternatively, we can require $dr^2/dt = 0 = (d/dt)[(12t)^2 + (49t - 4.9t^2)^2]$, which results in the same equation with the same solution.

51. (a) $26.6°$ (b) 0.949
53. (a) 6.80 km   (b) 3.00 km vertically above the impact point   (c) $66.2°$
55. (a) 46.5 m/s   (b) $-77.6°$ (c) 6.34 s
57. (a) 20.0 m/s, 5.00 s   (b) $(16.0\hat{\mathbf{i}} - 27.1\hat{\mathbf{j}})$ m/s
    (c) 6.53 s   (d) $24.5\hat{\mathbf{i}}$ m
59. (a) 43.2 m   (b) $(9.66\hat{\mathbf{i}} - 25.5\hat{\mathbf{j}})$ m/s. Air resistance would ordinarily make the jump distance smaller and the final horizontal and vertical velocity components both somewhat smaller. When the skilled jumper makes his body into an airfoil, he deflects downward the air through which he passes so that it deflects him upward, giving him more time in the air and a longer jump.
61. Safe distances are less than 270 m or greater than 3.48×10^3 m from the western shore.

CHAPTER 5

1. $(6.00\hat{\mathbf{i}} + 15.0\hat{\mathbf{j}})$ N; 16.2 N
3. (a) $(2.50\hat{\mathbf{i}} + 5.00\hat{\mathbf{j}})$ N (b) 5.59 N
5. (a) 3.64×10^{-18} N   (b) 8.93×10^{-30} N is 408 billion times smaller
7. 2.55 N for an 88.7-kg person
9. (a) 5.00 m/s^2 at $36.9°$ (b) 6.08 m/s^2 at $25.3°$
11. (a) $\sim 10^{-22}$ m/s^2 (b) $\sim 10^{-23}$ m
13. (a) 15.0 lb up   (b) 5.00 lb up   (c) 0
15. (a) 3.43 kN   (b) 0.967 m/s horizontally forward
17.

613 N

19. (a) $P\cos 40° - n = 0$ and $P\sin 40° - 220$ N $= 0$; $P = 342$ N and $n = 262$ N   (b) $P - n\cos 40° - (220$ N$)\sin 40° = 0$ and $n\sin 40 - (220$ N$)\cos 40° = 0$; $n = 262$ N and $P = 342$ N   (c) The results agree. The methods have a similar level of difficulty. Each involves one equation in one unknown and one equation in two unknowns. If we are interested in finding n without finding P, method (b) is simpler.
23. (a) 49.0 N   (b) 49.0 N   (c) 98.0 N   (d) 24.5 N
25. 8.66 N east
27. (a) 646 N up   (b) 646 N up   (c) 627 N up
    (d) 589 N up

29. 3.73 m
31. (a) $F_x > 19.6$ N   (b) $F_x \le -78.4$ N
    (c)

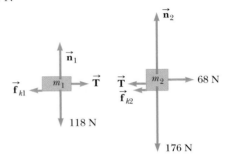

33. (a) 706 N   (b) 814 N   (c) 706 N   (d) 648 N
35. (a) 256 m   (b) 42.7 m
37. (a) no   (b) 16.9 N backwards $+ 37.2$ N upward $= 40.9$ N upward and backward at $65.6°$ with the horizontal
39. (a) 1.78 m/s^2 (b) 0.368 (c) 9.37 N   (d) 2.67 m/s
41. 37.8 N
43. (a)

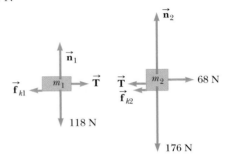

(b) 27.2 N, 1.29 m/s^2
45. (a) $a = 0$ if $P < 8.11$ N; $a = -3.33$ m/s$^2 + (1.41/$kg$)P$ to the right if $P > 8.11$ N   (b) $a = 0$; 3.99 N horizontally backward   (c) 10.8 m/s^2 to the right; 3.45 N to the left   (d) The acceleration is zero for all values of P less than 8.11 N. When P passes this threshold, the acceleration jumps to its minimum nonzero value of 8.14 m/s^2. From there it increases linearly with P toward arbitrarily high values.
47. 72.0 N
49. (a) 2.94 m/s^2 forward (b) 2.45 m/s^2 forward (c) 1.19 m/s^2 up the incline   (d) 0.711 m/s^2 up the incline   (e) $16.7°$ (f) The mass makes no difference. Mathematically, the mass divides out in determinations of acceleration. If several packages of dishes were placed in the truck, they would all slide together, whether they were tied to one another or not.
51. (a)

(b) 0.408 m/s^2 (c) 83.3 N
53. (a) 3.00 s   (b) 20.1 m   (c) $(18.0\hat{\mathbf{i}} - 9.00\hat{\mathbf{j}})$ m

55. (a) $a = 12$ N$/(4$ kg $+ m_1)$ forward   (b) 12 N$/(1 + m_1/4$ kg) forward   (c) 2.50 m/s^2 forward and 10.0 N forward   (d) The force approaches zero   (e) The force approaches 12.0 N   (f) The tension in a cord of negligible mass is constant along its length.

57. (a) $Mg/2$, $Mg/2$, $Mg/2$, $3Mg/2$, Mg (b) $Mg/2$

59. (a) Both are equal respectively.   (b) 1.61×10^4 N   (c) 2.95×10^4 N   (d) 0 N; 3.51 m/s upward. The first 3.50 m/s of the speed of 3.51 m/s needs no dynamic cause; the motion of the cable continues on its own, as described by the law of "inertia" or "pigheadedness." The increase from 3.50 m/s to 3.51 m/s must be caused by some total upward force on the section of cable. Because its mass is very small compared to a thousand kilograms, however, the force is very small compared to 1.61×10^4 N, the nearly uniform tension of this section of cable.

61. (b)

θ	0	15°	30°	45°	60°
P (N)	40.0	46.4	60.1	94.3	260

63. (a) The net force on the cushion is in a fixed direction, downward and forward making angle $\tan^{-1}(F/mg)$ with the vertical. Starting from rest, it will move along this line with (b) increasing speed. Its velocity changes in magnitude. (c) 1.63 m   (d) It will move along a parabola. The axis of the parabola is parallel to the dashed line in the problem figure. If the cushion is thrown in a direction above the dashed line, its path will be concave downward, making its velocity become more and more nearly parallel to the dashed line over time. If the cushion is thrown down more steeply, its path will be concave upward, again making its velocity turn toward the fixed direction of its acceleration.

65. (a) $19.3°$ (b) 4.21 N

67. $(M + m_1 + m_2)(m_2g/m_1)$

69. (a) $30.7°$ (b) 0.843 N

71. (a) $T_1 = \dfrac{2mg}{\sin\theta_1}$, $T_2 = \dfrac{mg}{\sin\theta_2} = \dfrac{mg}{\sin\left[\tan^{-1}\left(\frac{1}{2}\tan\theta_1\right)\right]}$,

$T_3 = \dfrac{2mg}{\tan\theta_1}$

(b) $\theta_2 = \tan^{-1}\left(\dfrac{\tan\theta_1}{2}\right)$

CHAPTER 6

1. Any speed up to 8.08 m/s
3. (a) 8.32×10^{-8} N toward the nucleus   (b) 9.13×10^{22} m/s^2 inward
5. (a) static friction   (b) $0.085\ 0$
7. 2.14 rev/min
9. $v \le 14.3$ m/s
11. (a) 108 N   (b) 56.2 N
13. (a) 4.81 m/s   (b) 700 N up
15. No. Tarzan needs a vine of tensile strength 1.38 kN.
17. 3.13 m/s
19. (a) 3.60 m/s^2 (b) zero   (c) An observer in the car (a noninertial frame) claims an 18.0-N force toward the left and an 18.0-N force toward the right. An inertial observer (outside the car) claims only an 18.0-N force toward the right.
21. (a) $17.0°$ (b) 5.12 N
23. (a) 491 N   (b) 50.1 kg   (c) 2.00 m/s
25. $0.092\ 8°$
27. (a) 32.7 s^{-1} (b) 9.80 m/s^2 down   (c) 4.90 m/s^2 down
29. 3.01 N up

31. (a) 1.47 N·s/m   (b) 2.04×10^{-3} s   (c) 2.94×10^{-2} N
33. (a) 78.3 m/s   (b) 11.1 s   (c) 121 m
35. (a) $x = k^{-1}\ln(1 + kv_0\,t)$ (b) $v = v_0e^{-kx}$
37. (a) $0.034\ 7$ s^{-1} (b) 2.50 m/s   (c) $a = -cv$
39. $v = v_0e^{-bt/m}$

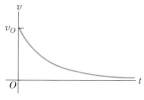

In this model, the object keeps moving forever. It travels a finite distance in an infinite time interval.

41. (a) 106 N up the incline   (b) 0.396
43. (a) 11.5 kN   (b) 14.1 m/s
45. (a) $0.016\ 2$ kg/m   (b) $\frac{1}{2}D\rho A$ (c) 0.778 (d) 1.5% (e) For stacked coffee filters falling in air at terminal speed, the graph of air resistance force as a function of the square of speed demonstrates that the force is proportional to the speed squared, within the experimental uncertainty estimated as 2%. This proportionality agrees with the theoretical model of air resistance at high speeds. The drag coefficient of a coffee filter is $D = 0.78 \pm 2\%$.
47. $g(\cos\phi\tan\theta - \sin\phi)$
49. (b) 732 N down at the equator and 735 N down at the poles
51. (a) The only horizontal force on the car is the force of friction, with a maximum value determined by the surface roughness (described by the coefficient of static friction) and the normal force (here equal to the gravitational force on the car). (b) 34.3 m   (c) 68.6 m   (d) Braking is better. You should not turn the wheel. If you used any of the available friction force to change the direction of the car, it would be unavailable to slow the car and the stopping distance would be longer.   (e) The conclusion is true in general. The radius of the curve you can barely make is twice your minimum stopping distance.
53. (a) 5.19 m/s   (b) $T = 555$ N

55. (b) 2.54 s; 23.6 rev/min   (c) The gravitational and friction forces remain constant. The normal force increases. The person remains in motion with the wall. (d) The gravitational force remains constant. The normal and friction forces decrease. The person slides relative to the wall and downward into the pit.
57. (a) $v_{\min} = \sqrt{\dfrac{Rg(\tan\theta - \mu_s)}{1 + \mu_s\tan\theta}}$, $v_{\max} = \sqrt{\dfrac{Rg(\tan\theta + \mu_s)}{1 - \mu_s\tan\theta}}$

(b) $\mu_s = \tan\theta$ (c) 8.57 m/s $\le v \le 16.6$ m/s
59. (a) $0.013\ 2$ m/s   (b) 1.03 m/s   (c) 6.87 m/s
61. 12.8 N

CHAPTER 7

1. (a) 31.9 J   (b) 0   (c) 0   (d) 31.9 J
3. −4.70 kJ
7. (a) 16.0 J   (b) 36.9°
9. (a) 11.3°   (b) 156°   (c) 82.3°
11. $\vec{A}$ = 7.05 m at 28.4°
13. (a) 24.0 J   (b) −3.00 J   (c) 21.0 J
15. (a) 7.50 J   (b) 15.0 J   (c) 7.50 J   (d) 30.0 J
17. (a) 0.938 cm   (b) 1.25 J
19. 7.37 N/m
21. 0.299 m/s
23. (a) 0.020 4 m   (b) 720 N/m
25. (b) mgR
27. (a) 0.600 J   (b) −0.600 J   (c) 1.50 J
29. (a) 1.20 J   (b) 5.00 m/s   (c) 6.30 J
31. (a) 60.0 J   (b) 60.0 J
33. 878 kN up
35. (a) 4.56 kJ   (b) 6.34 kN   (c) 422 km/s²   (d) 6.34 kN
    (e) The forces are the same. The two theories agree.
37. (a) 259 kJ, 0, −259 kJ   (b) 0, −259 kJ, −259 kJ
39. (a) −196 J   (b) −196 J   (c) −196 J. The force is
    conservative.
41. (a) 125 J   (b) 50.0 J   (c) 66.7 J   (d) The force is
    nonconservative. The results differ.
43. (a) 40.0 J   (b) −40.0 J   (c) 62.5 J
45. (A/r^2) away from the other particle
47. (a) + at Ⓑ, − at Ⓓ, 0 at Ⓐ, Ⓒ, and Ⓔ
    (b) Ⓒ stable; Ⓐ and Ⓔ unstable
    (c)

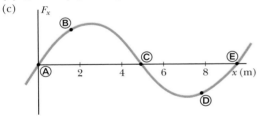

49. (c) U (J)   Equilibrium at $x = 0$

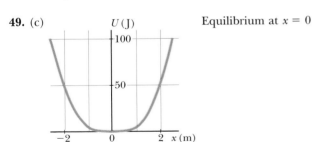

    (d) 0.823 m/s
51. 90.0 J
53. (a) $x = (3.62\ m)/(4.30 − 23.4m)$ where x is in meters and
    m is in kilograms   (b) 0.095 1 m (c) 0.492 m   (d) 6.85 m
    (e) The situation is impossible.   (f) The extension is
    directly proportional to m when m is only a few grams.
    Then it grows faster and faster, diverging to infinity for
    $m = 0.184$ kg.
55. $U(x) = 1 + 4e^{-2x}$. The force must be conservative because
    the work the force does on the object on which it acts
    depends only on the original and final positions of the
    object, not on the path between them.
57. 1.68 m/s
59. 0.799 J

CHAPTER 8

1. (a) $\Delta E_{int} = Q + T_{ET} + T_{ER}$ (b) $\Delta K + \Delta U + \Delta E_{int} =$
    $W + Q + T_{MW} + T_{MT}$ (c) $\Delta U = Q + T_{MT}$
    (d) $0 = Q + T_{MT} + T_{ET} + T_{ER}$
3. (a) $v = (3gR)^{1/2}$ (b) 0.098 0 N down
5. 10.2 m
7. (a) 4.43 m/s   (b) 5.00 m
9. 5.49 m/s
11. (a) 25.8 m   (b) 27.1 m/s²
13. (a) 650 J   (b) 588 J   (c) 0   (d) 0   (e) 62.0 J
    (f) 1.76 m/s
15. (a) −168 J   (b) 184 J   (c) 500 J   (d) 148 J   (e) 5.65 m/s
17. 2.04 m
19. 3.74 m/s
21. (a) −160 J   (b) 73.5 J   (c) 28.8 N   (d) 0.679
23. (a) 1.40 m/s   (b) 4.60 cm after release   (c) 1.79 m/s
25. (a) 0.381 m   (b) 0.143 m   (c) 0.371 m
27. (a) $a_x = -\mu_k gx/L$ (b) $v = (\mu_k gL)^{1/2}$
29. 875 W
31. ~ 10⁴ W
33. $46.2
35. (a) 10.2 kW   (b) 10.6 kW   (c) 5.82 MJ
37. (a) 11.1 m/s   (b) 19.6 m/s² upward   (c) 2.23 × 10³ N
    upward   (d) 1.01 × 10³ J   (e) 5.14 m/s   (f) 1.35 m
    (g) 1.39 s
39. (a) $(2 + 24t^2 + 72t^4)$ J   (b) $12t$ m/s²; $48t$ N
    (c) $(48t + 288t^3)$ W   (d) 1 250 J
41. (a) 1.38 × 10⁴ J   (b) 3.02 × 10⁴ W
43. (a) 4.12 m   (b) 3.35 m
45. (a) 2.17 kW   (b) 58.6 kW
47. (a) $x = -4.0$ mm   (b) −1.0 cm
49. 33.4 kW
51. (a) 0.225 J   (b) $\Delta E_{mech} = -0.363$ J   (c) No. The normal
    force changes in a complicated way.
53. (a) 100 J   (b) 0.410 m   (c) 2.84 m/s   (d) −9.80 mm
    (e) 2.85 m/s
55. 0.328
57. 1.24 m/s
59. (a) 0.400 m   (b) 4.10 m/s   (c) The block stays on the
    track.
61. $2m$
65. (a) 14.1 m/s   (b) −7.90 kJ   (c) 800 N   (d) 771 N
    (e) 1.57 kN up

CHAPTER 9

1. (a) $(9.00\hat{i} − 12.0\hat{j})$ kg·m/s   (b) 15.0 kg · m/s at 307°
3. ~ 10⁻²³ m/s
5. (b) $p = \sqrt{2mK}$
7. (a) 13.5 N·s   (b) 9.00 kN   (c) 18.0 kN
9. 260 N normal to the wall
11. (a) $12.0\hat{i}$ N·s   (b) $4.80\hat{i}$ m/s   (c) $2.80\hat{i}$ m/s
    (d) $2.40\hat{i}$ N
13. (b) small   (d) large   (e) no difference
15. 301 m/s
17. (a) 2.50 m/s   (b) 37.5 kJ   (c) Each process is the time-
    reversal of the other. The same momentum conservation
    equation describes both.
19. 0.556 m
21. (a) $\vec{v}_g = 1.15\hat{i}$ m/s   (b) $\vec{v}_p = -0.346\hat{i}$ m/s
23. (a) 0.284   (b) 115 fJ and 45.4 fJ

25. 91.2 m/s

27. 2.50 m/s at $-60.0°$

29. $v_{orange} = 3.99$ m/s, $v_{yellow} = 3.01$ m/s

31. $(3.00\hat{i} - 1.20\hat{j})$ m/s

33. (a) $(-9.33\hat{i} - 8.33\hat{j})$ Mm/s   (b) 439 fJ

35. $\vec{r}_{CM} = (0\hat{i} + 1.00\hat{j})$ m

37. $\vec{r}_{CM} = (11.7\hat{i} + 13.3\hat{j})$ cm

39. (a) 15.9 g   (b) 0.153 m

41. (a) $(1.40\hat{i} + 2.40\hat{j})$ m/s   (b) $(7.00\hat{i} + 12.0\hat{j})$ kg·m/s

43. 0.700 m

45. (a) Yes. $18.0\hat{i}$ kg·m/s.   (b) No. The floor does zero work.   (c) Yes. We could say that the final momentum of the cart came from the floor or from the Earth through the floor.   (d) No. The kinetic energy came from the original gravitational energy of the elevated load, in amount 27.0 J.   (e) Yes. The acceleration is caused by the static friction force exerted by the floor that prevents the caterpillar tracks from slipping backward.

47. (b) 2.06 m/s   (c) Yes. The bumper continues to exert a force to the left until the particle has swung down to its lowest point.

49. (a) 3.75 kg·m/s² to the right   (b) 3.75 N to the right   (c) 3.75 N   (d) 2.81 J   (e) 1.41 J   (f) Friction between sand and belt converts half of the input work into extra internal energy.

51. (a) 39.0 MN   (b) 3.20 m/s² up

53. (a) 442 metric tons   (b) 19.2 metric tons. This amount is much less than the value suggested. Mathematically, the logarithm in the rocket propulsion equation is not a linear function. Physically, a higher exhaust speed has an extra-large cumulative effect on the rocket frame's final speed, by counting again and again in the speed the frame attains second after second during its burn.

55. 240 s

57. $\left(\dfrac{M+m}{m}\right)\sqrt{\dfrac{gd^2}{2h}}$

59. (a) 0; inelastic
(b) $(-0.250\hat{i} + 0.750\hat{j} - 2.00\hat{k})$ m/s; perfectly inelastic
(c) either $a = -6.74$ with $\vec{v} = -0.419\,\hat{k}$ m/s or $a = 2.74$ with $\vec{v} = -3.58\,\hat{k}$ m/s

61. (a) $m/M = 0.403$ (b) no changes; no difference

63. (b) 0.042 9   (c) 1.00   (d) Energy is an entirely different thing from momentum. A comparison: When children eat their soup, they do not eat the tablecloth. Another comparison: When a photographer's single-use flashbulb flashes, a magnesium filament oxidizes. Chemical energy disappears. (Internal energy appears and light carries some energy away.) The measured mass of the flashbulb is the same before and after. It can be the same despite the 100% energy conversion because energy and mass are totally different things in classical physics. In the ballistic pendulum, conversion of energy from mechanical into internal does not upset conservation of mass or conservation of momentum.

65. (a) $-0.256\hat{i}$ m/s and $0.128\hat{i}$ m/s
(b) $-0.064\,2\hat{i}$ m/s and 0   (c) 0 and 0

67. (a) 100 m/s   (b) 374 J

69. $(3Mgx/L)\hat{j}$

CHAPTER 10

1. (a) 5.00 rad, 10.0 rad/s, 4.00 rad/s²   (b) 53.0 rad, 22.0 rad/s, 4.00 rad/s²

3. (a) 4.00 rad/s²   (b) 18.0 rad

5. (a) 5.24 s   (b) 27.4 rad

7. (a) 7.27×10^{-5} rad/s   (b) 2.57×10^4 s = 428 min

9. 50.0 rev

11. $\sim 10^7$ rev

13. (a) 8.00 rad/s   (b) 8.00 m/s, $a_r = -64.0$ m/s², $a_t = 4.00$ m/s²   (c) 9.00 rad

15. (a) $(-2.73\hat{i} + 1.24\hat{j})$ m   (b) in the second quadrant, at 156°   (c) $(-1.85\hat{i} - 4.10\hat{j})$ m/s   (d) toward the third quadrant, at 246°

(e) $(6.15\hat{i} - 2.78\hat{j})$ m/s²   (f) $(24.6\hat{i} - 11.1\hat{j})$ N

17. (a) 126 rad/s   (b) 3.77 m/s   (c) 1.26 km/s²   (d) 20.1 m

19. 0.572

21. (a) 143 kg·m²   (b) 2.57 kJ

25. (a) 24.5 m/s   (b) no; no; no; no; yes

27. 1.28 kg·m²

29. $\sim 10^0$ kg·m²

33. -3.55 N·m

35. (a) 24.0 N·m   (b) 0.035 6 rad/s²   (c) 1.07 m/s²

37. (a) 0.309 m/s²   (b) 7.67 N and 9.22 N

39. 21.5 N

41. 24.5 km

43. 149 rad/s

45. (a) 1.59 m/s   (b) 53.1 rad/s

47. (a) 11.4 N, 7.57 m/s², 9.53 m/s down   (b) 9.53 m/s

51. (a) $2(Rg/3)^{1/2}$ (b) $4(Rg/3)^{1/2}$ (c) $(Rg)^{1/2}$

53. (a) 500 J   (b) 250 J   (c) 750 J

55. (a) $\frac{2}{3}g \sin\theta$ for the disk, larger than $\frac{1}{2}g \sin\theta$ for the hoop   (b) $\frac{1}{3}\tan\theta$

57. 1.21×10^{-4} kg·m²; height is unnecessary

59. $\frac{1}{3}\ell$

61. (a) 4.00 J   (b) 1.60 s   (c) yes

63. (a) $\omega = 3F\ell/b$ (b) $\alpha = 3F\ell/mL^2$ (c) and (d) Both larger. A component of the thrust force, exerted by the water about to spray from the ends of the arms, causes a forward torque on the rotor. Notice also that the rotor with bent arms has a slightly smaller moment of inertia than it would if the same metal tubes were straight.

65. (a) $(3g/L)^{1/2}$ (b) $3g/2L$ (c) $-\frac{3}{2}g\hat{i} - \frac{3}{4}g\hat{j}$
(d) $-\frac{3}{2}Mg\hat{i} + \frac{1}{4}Mg\hat{j}$

67. -0.322 rad/s²

71. (a) 118 N and 156 N   (b) 1.17 kg·m²

73. (a) $\alpha = -0.176$ rad/s²   (b) 1.29 rev   (c) 9.26 rev

75. (a) $\omega(2h^3/g)^{1/2}$ (b) 0.011 6 m   (c) Yes; the deflection is only 0.02% of the original height.

79. (a) 2.70R   (b) $\Sigma F_x = -20mg/7$, $\Sigma F_y = -5mg/7$

81. (a) $(3gh/4)^{1/2}$ (b) $(3gh/4)^{1/2}$

83. (c) $(8Fd/3M)^{1/2}$

85. to the left

CHAPTER 11

1. $-7.00\hat{\mathbf{i}} + 16.0\hat{\mathbf{j}} - 10.0\hat{\mathbf{k}}$

3. (a) $-17.0\hat{\mathbf{k}}$ (b) $70.6°$

5. 0.343 N · m horizontally north

7. $45.0°$

9. $F_3 = F_1 + F_2$; no

11. $17.5\hat{\mathbf{k}}$ kg · m^2/s

13. $(60.0\hat{\mathbf{k}})$ kg · m^2/s

15. $mvR[\cos(vt/R) + 1]\hat{\mathbf{k}}$

17. (a) zero (b) $(-mv_i^3 \sin^2\theta \cos\theta/2g)\hat{\mathbf{k}}$
  (c) $(-2mv_i^3 \sin^2\theta \cos\theta/g)\hat{\mathbf{k}}$ (d) The downward gravitational force exerts a torque in the $-z$ direction.

19. (a) $-m\ell gt \cos\theta\hat{\mathbf{k}}$ (b) The planet exerts a gravitational torque on the ball. (c) $-mg\ell \cos\theta\hat{\mathbf{k}}$

23. (a) 0.360 kg · m^2/s (b) 0.540 kg · m^2/s

25. (a) 0.433 kg · m^2/s (b) 1.73 kg · m^2/s

27. (a) 1.57×10^8 kg · m^2/s (b) 6.26×10^3 s = 1.74 h

29. (a) $\omega_f = \omega_i I_1/(I_1 + I_2)$ (b) $I_1/(I_1 + I_2)$

31. (a) 11.1 rad/s counterclockwise (b) No. 507 J is transformed into internal energy. (c) No. The turntable bearing promptly imparts impulse 44.9 kg · m/s north into the turntable-clay system and thereafter keeps changing the system momentum.

33. 7.14 rev/min

35. (a) Mechanical energy is not conserved; some chemical energy is converted into mechanical energy. Momentum is not conserved. The turntable bearing exerts an external northward force on the axle. Angular momentum is conserved. (b) 0.360 rad/s counterclockwise (c) 99.9 J

37. (a) $mv\ell$ down (b) $M/(M + m)$

39. (a) $\omega = 2mv_i d/[M + 2m]R^2$ (b) No; some mechanical energy changes into internal energy. (c) Momentum is not conserved. The axle exerts a backward force on the cylinder.

41. $\sim 10^{-13}$ rad/s

43. 5.45×10^{22} N · m

45. (a) $1.67\hat{\mathbf{i}}$ m/s (b) $0.033\ 5 = 3.35\%$ (c) $1.67\hat{\mathbf{i}}$ m/s
  (d) 15.8 rad/s (e) $1.00 = 100\%$

47. (a) $7md^2/3$ (b) $mgd\hat{\mathbf{k}}$ (c) $3g/7d$ counterclockwise
  (d) $2g/7$ upward (e) mgd (f) $\sqrt{6g/7d}$ (g) $m\sqrt{14gd^3}/3$
  (h) $\sqrt{2gd/21}$

49. 0.910 km/s

51. (a) $v_i r_i/r$ (b) $T = (mv_i^2 r_i^2)r^{-3}$ (c) $\frac{1}{2}mv_i^2(r_i^2/r^2 - 1)$
  (d) 4.50 m/s, 10.1 N, 0.450 J

53. (a) $3\ 750$ kg · m^2/s (b) 1.88 kJ (c) $3\ 750$ kg · m^2/s
  (d) 10.0 m/s (e) 7.50 kJ (f) 5.62 kJ

55. (a) $2mv_0$ (b) $2v_0/3$ (c) $4m\ell v_0/3$ (d) $4v_0/9\ell$ (e) mv_0^2
  (f) $26mv_0^2/27$ (g) No horizontal forces act on the bola from outside after release, so the horizontal momentum stays constant. Its center of mass moves steadily with the horizontal velocity it had at release. No torques about its axis of rotation act on the bola, so its spin angular momentum stays constant. Internal forces cannot affect momentum conservation and angular momentum conservation, but they can affect mechanical energy. Energy $mv_0^2/27$ changes from mechanical energy into internal energy as the bola takes its stable configuration.

57. An increase of 0.550 s. It is not a significant change.

CHAPTER 12

1. $[(m_1 + m_b)d + m_1\ell/2]/m_2$

3. $(3.85$ cm, 6.85 cm$)$

5. $(-1.50$ m, -1.50 m$)$

7. $(2.54$ m, 4.75 m$)$

9. 177 kg

11. (a) $f_s = 268$ N, $n = 1\ 300$ N (b) 0.324

13. 2.94 kN on each rear wheel and 4.41 kN on each front wheel

15. (a) 29.9 N (b) 22.2 N

17. (a) 1.73 rad/s^2 (b) 1.56 rad/s
  (c) $(-4.72\hat{\mathbf{i}} + 6.62\hat{\mathbf{j}})$ kN (d) $38.9\hat{\mathbf{j}}$ kN

19. 2.82 m

21. 88.2 N and 58.8 N

23. 4.90 mm

25. 23.8 μm

27. (a) 3.14×10^4 N (b) 6.28×10^4 N

29. 1.65×10^8 N/m^2

31. 0.860 mm

33. $n_A = 5.98 \times 10^5$ N, $n_B = 4.80 \times 10^5$ N

35. 9.00 ft

37. (a)

  (b) $T = 343$ N, $R_x = 171$ N to the right, $R_y = 683$ N up
  (c) 5.13 m

39. (a) $T = F_g(L + d)/[\sin\theta\,(2L + d)]$
  (b) $R_x = F_g(L + d)\cot\theta/(2L + d)$, $R_y = F_gL/(2L + d)$

41. $\vec{\mathbf{F}}_A = (-6.47 \times 10^5\hat{\mathbf{i}} + 1.27 \times 10^5\hat{\mathbf{j}})$ N,
  $\vec{\mathbf{F}}_B = 6.47 \times 10^5\hat{\mathbf{i}}$ N

43. 5.08 kN, $R_x = 4.77$ kN, $R_y = 8.26$ kN

45. (a) 20.1 cm to the left of the front edge; $\mu_k = 0.571$
  (b) 0.501 m

47. (a) $M = (m/2)(2\mu_s \sin\theta - \cos\theta)(\cos\theta - \mu_s \sin\theta)^{-1}$
  (b) $R = (m + M)g(1 + \mu_s^2)^{1/2}$
  $F = g[M^2 + \mu_s^2(m + M)^2]^{1/2}$

49. (b) AB compression 732 N, AC tension 634 N, BC compression 897 N

51. (a) 133 N (b) $n_A = 429$ N and $n_B = 257$ N
  (c) $R_x = 133$ N and $R_y = -257$ N

55. 1.09 m

57. (a) $4\ 500$ N (b) 4.50×10^6 N/m^2 (c) The board will break.

59. (a) $P_y = (F_g/L)(d - ah/g)$ (b) 0.306 m
  (c) $(-306\hat{\mathbf{i}} + 553\hat{\mathbf{j}})$ N

CHAPTER 13

1. $\sim 10^{-7}$ N toward you

3. (a) 2.50×10^{-5} N toward the 500-kg object (b) between the objects and 0.245 m from the 500-kg object

5. $(-100\hat{\mathbf{i}} + 59.3\hat{\mathbf{j}})$ pN

7. 7.41×10^{-10} N

9. 0.613 m/s^2 toward the Earth

11. $\rho_{\text{Moon}}/\rho_{\text{Earth}} = \frac{2}{3}$

13. 1.26×10^{32} kg

15. 1.90×10^{27} kg

17. 8.92×10^7 m

19. After 3.93 yr, Mercury would be farther from the Sun than Pluto.

21. $\vec{g} = \dfrac{Gm}{\ell^2}\left(\frac{1}{2} + \sqrt{2}\right)$ toward the opposite corner

23. (a) $\vec{g} = 2MGr(r^2 + a^2)^{-3/2}$ toward the center of mass
(b) At $r = 0$, the fields of the two objects are equal in magnitude and opposite in direction, to add to zero.
(d) When r is much greater than a, the fact that the two masses are separate is unimportant. They create a total field like that of a single object of mass $2M$.

25. (a) 1.84×10^9 kg/m^3 (b) 3.27×10^6 m/s^2
(c) -2.08×10^{13} J

27. (a) -1.67×10^{-14} J   (b) Each object will slowly accelerate toward the center of the triangle, where the three will simultaneously collide.

29. (b) 340 s

31. 1.66×10^4 m/s

35. (a) 5.30×10^3 s   (b) 7.79 km/s   (c) 6.43×10^9 J

37. (b) 1.00×10^7 m   (c) 1.00×10^4 m/s

39. (a) 0.980   (b) 127 yr   (c) -2.13×10^{17} J

43. (b) $2[Gm^3(1/2r - 1/R)]^{1/2}$

45. (a) -7.04×10^4 J   (b) -1.57×10^5 J   (c) 13.2 m/s

47. 7.79×10^{14} kg

49. $\omega = 0.057\ 2$ rad/s or 1 rev in 110 s

51. (a) $m_2(2G/d)^{1/2}(m_1 + m_2)^{-1/2}$ and
$m_1(2G/d)^{1/2}(m_1 + m_2)^{-1/2}$; relative speed
$(2G/d)^{1/2}(m_1 + m_2)^{1/2}$ (b) 1.07×10^{32} J and 2.67×10^{31} J

53. (a) 200 Myr   (b) $\sim 10^{41}$ kg; $\sim 10^{11}$ stars

55. $(GM_E/4R_E)^{1/2}$

59. $(800 + 1.73 \times 10^{-4})\hat{\mathbf{i}}$ m/s and $(800 - 1.73 \times 10^{-4})\hat{\mathbf{i}}$ m/s

61. 18.2 ms

CHAPTER 14

1. 0.111 kg

3. 6.24 MPa

5. 1.62 m

7. 7.74×10^{-3} m^2

9. 271 kN horizontally backward

11. 5.88×10^6 N down; 196 kN outward; 588 kN outward

13. 0.722 mm

15. 10.5 m; no because some alcohol and water evaporate

17. 98.6 kPa

19. (a) 1.57 Pa, 1.55×10^{-2} atm, 11.8 mm Hg   (b) The fluid level in the tap should rise.   (c) blockage of flow of the cerebrospinal fluid

21. 0.258 N down

23. (a) $1.017\ 9 \times 10^3$ N down, $1.029\ 7 \times 10^3$ N up   (b) 86.2 N
(c) By either method of evaluation, the buoyant force is 11.8 N up.

25. (a) 1.20×10^3 N/s   (b) 0

27. (a) 7.00 cm   (b) 2.80 kg

31. 1 430 m^3

33. 1 250 kg/m^3 and 500 kg/m^3

35. (a) 17.7 m/s   (b) 1.73 mm

37. 31.6 m/s

39. 0.247 cm

41. (a) 2.28 N toward Holland   (b) 1.74×10^6 s

43. (a) 1 atm + 15.0 MPa   (b) 2.95 m/s   (c) 4.34 kPa

45. 2.51×10^{-3} m^3/s

47. (a) 4.43 m/s   (b) The siphon can be no higher than 10.3 m.

49. 12.6 m/s

51. 1.91 m

55. 0.604 m

57. If the helicopter could create the air it expels downward, the mass flow rate of the air would have to be at least 233 kg/s. In reality, the rotor takes in air from above, which is moving over a larger area with lower speed, and blows it downward at higher speed. The amount of this air has to be at least a few times larger than 233 kg every second.

61. 17.3 N and 31.7 N

63. 90.04%

65. 758 Pa

67. 4.43 m/s

69. (a) 1.25 cm   (b) 13.8 m/s

71. (c) 1.70 m^2

CHAPTER 15

1. (a) The motion repeats precisely.   (b) 1.81 s   (c) No, the force is not in the form of Hooke's law

3. (a) 1.50 Hz, 0.667 s   (b) 4.00 m   (c) π rad   (d) 2.83 m

5. (b) 18.8 cm/s, 0.333 s   (c) 178 cm/s^2, 0.500 s
(d) 12.0 cm

7. 40.9 N/m

9. 18.8 m/s, 7.11 km/s^2

11. (a) 40.0 cm/s, 160 cm/s^2 (b) 32.0 cm/s, -96.0 cm/s^2
(c) 0.232 s

13. 0.628 m/s

15. 2.23 m/s

17. (a) 28.0 mJ   (b) 1.02 m/s   (c) 12.2 mJ   (d) 15.8 mJ

19. 2.60 cm and -2.60 cm

21. (a) at 0.218 s and at 1.09 s   (b) 0.014 6 W

23. (b) 0.628 s

25. Assuming simple harmonic motion, (a) 0.820 m/s, (b) 2.57 rad/s^2, and (c) 0.641 N. More precisely, (a) 0.817 m/s, (b) 2.54 rad/s^2, and (c) 0.634 N. The answers agree to two digits. The answers computed from conservation of energy and from Newton's second law are more precisely correct. With this amplitude, the motion of the pendulum is approximately simple harmonic.

29. 0.944 kg · m^2

33. (a) 5.00×10^{-7} kg · m^2 (b) 3.16×10^{-4} N · m/rad

35. 1.00×10^{-3} s^{-1}

37. (a) 7.00 Hz   (b) 2.00%   (c) 10.6 s

39. (a) 1.00 s   (b) 5.09 cm

41. 318 N

43. 1.74 Hz

45. (a) 2.09 s   (b) 0.477 Hz   (c) 36.0 cm/s
(d) $(0.064\ 8\ \text{m}^2/\text{s}^2)\,m$ (e) $(9.00/\text{s}^2)\,m$
(f) Period, frequency, and maximum speed are all independent of mass in this situation. The energy and the force constant are directly proportional to mass.

47. (a) $2Mg$, $Mg(1 + y/L)$ (b) $T = (4\pi/3)(2L/g)^{1/2}$, 2.68 s

49. 6.62 cm

51. 9.19×10^{13} Hz

53. (a)

(b) $\dfrac{dT}{dt} = \dfrac{\pi \, dM/dt}{2\rho a^2 g^{1/2}[L_i + (dM/dt)t/2\rho a^2]^{1/2}}$

(c) $T = 2\pi g^{-1/2}\left[L_i + \left(\dfrac{dM}{dt}\right)\left(\dfrac{t}{2\rho a^2}\right)\right]^{1/2}$

55. $f = (2\pi L)^{-1}\left(gL + \dfrac{kh^2}{M}\right)^{1/2}$

57. (b) 1.23 Hz

59. (a) 3.00 s   (b) 14.3 J   (c) 25.5°

61. If the cyclist goes over washboard bumps at one certain speed, they can excite a resonance vibration of the bike, so large in amplitude as to make the rider lose control. $\sim 10^1$ m

69. (b) after 42.2 minutes

CHAPTER 16

1. $y = 6\,[(x - 4.5t)^2 + 3]^{-1}$

3. (a) the P wave   (b) 665 s

5. (a) $(3.33\hat{\mathbf{i}})$ m/s   (b) -5.48 cm   (c) 0.667 m, 5.00 Hz
(d) 11.0 m/s

7. 0.319 m

9. 2.00 cm, 2.98 m, 0.576 Hz, 1.72 m/s

11. (a) 31.4 rad/s   (b) 1.57 rad/m
(c) $y = (0.120 \text{ m}) \sin (1.57x - 31.4t)$ where x is in meters and t is in seconds   (d) 3.77 m/s   (e) 118 m/s²

13. (a) 0.250 m   (b) 40.0 rad/s   (c) 0.300 rad/m   (d) 20.9 m
(e) 133 m/s   (f) $+x$

15. (a) $y = (8.00 \text{ cm}) \sin (7.85x + 6\pi t)$
(b) $y = (8.00 \text{ cm}) \sin (7.85x + 6\pi t - 0.785)$

17. (a) -1.51 m/s, 0   (b) 16.0 m, 0.500 s, 32.0 m/s

19. (a) 0.500 Hz, 3.14 rad/s   (b) 3.14 rad/m
(c) $(0.100 \text{ m}) \sin (3.14\ x/\text{m} - 3.14\ t/\text{s})$
(d) $(0.100 \text{ m}) \sin (-3.14\ t/\text{s})$
(e) $(0.100 \text{ m}) \sin (4.71 \text{ rad} - 3.14\ t/\text{s})$ (f) 0.314 m/s

21. 80.0 N

23. 520 m/s

25. 1.64 m/s²

27. 13.5 N

29. 185 m/s

31. 0.329 s

35. 55.1 Hz

37. (a) 62.5 m/s   (b) 7.85 m   (c) 7.96 Hz   (d) 21.1 W

39. $\sqrt{2}\,\mathcal{P}_0$

41. (a) $A = 40$ (b) $A = 7.00$, $B = 0$, $C = 3.00$. One can take the dot product of the given equation with each one of $\hat{\mathbf{i}}, \hat{\mathbf{j}}$, and $\hat{\mathbf{k}}$.   (c) $A = 0$, $B = 7.00$ mm, $C = 3.00/\text{m}$, $D = 4.00/\text{s}$, $E = 2.00$. Consider the average value of both sides of the given equation to find A. Then consider the maximum value of both sides to find B. You can evaluate the partial derivative of both sides of the given equation with respect to x and separately with respect to t to obtain equations yielding C and D upon chosen substitutions for x and t. Then substitute $x = 0$ and $t = 0$ to obtain E.

45. ~ 1 min

47. 0.456 m/s

49. (a) 39.2 N   (b) 0.892 m   (c) 83.6 m/s

51. (a) The energy a wave crest carries is constant in the absence of absorption. Then the rate at which energy moves beyond a fixed distance from the source, which is the power of the wave, is constant. The power is proportional to the square of the amplitude and to the wave

speed. The speed decreases as the wave moves into shallower water near shore, so the amplitude must increase. (b) 8.31 m   (c) As the water depth goes to zero, our model would predict zero speed and infinite amplitude. The amplitude must be finite as the wave comes ashore. As the speed decreases, the wavelength also decreases. When it becomes comparable to the water depth, or smaller, the expression $v = \sqrt{gd}$ no longer applies.

53. (a) $\mathcal{P} = (0.050\ 0 \text{ kg/s})v_{y,\text{max}}^2$ (b) The power is proportional to the square of the maximum element speed. (c) $(7.5 \times 10^{-4} \text{ kg})v_{y,\text{max}}^2 = \frac{1}{2}m_3 v_{y,\text{max}}^2$ (d) $(0.300 \text{ kg})v_{y,\text{max}}^2$

55. 0.084 3 rad

59. (a) $(0.707)2(L/g)^{1/2}$ (b) $L/4$

61. 3.86×10^{-4}

63. (a) $\dfrac{\mu\omega^3}{2k}A_0^2 e^{-2bx}$ (b) $\dfrac{\mu\omega^3}{2k}A_0^2$ (c) e^{-2bx}

65. (a) $\mu_0 + (\mu_L - \mu_0)x/L$

CHAPTER 17

1. 5.56 km. As long as the speed of light is much greater than the speed of sound, its actual value does not matter.

3. 0.196 s

5. 7.82 m

7. (a) 826 m   (b) 1.47 s

9. (a) 0.625 mm   (b) 1.50 mm to 75.0 μm

11. (a) 2.00 μm, 40.0 cm, 54.6 m/s   (b) -0.433 μm
(c) 1.72 mm/s

13. $\Delta P = (0.200 \text{ N/m}^2) \sin (62.8x/\text{m} - 2.16 \times 10^4 t/\text{s})$

15. 5.81 m

17. 66.0 dB

19. (a) 3.75 W/m²   (b) 0.600 W/m²

21. (a) 2.34 m and 0.390 m   (b) 0.161 N/m² for both notes
(c) 4.25×10^{-7} m and 7.09×10^{-8} m   (d) The wavelengths and displacement amplitudes would be larger by a factor of 1.09. The answer to part (b) would be unchanged.

23. (a) 1.32×10^{-4} W/m²   (b) 81.2 dB

25. (a) 0.691 m   (b) 691 km

27. 65.6 dB

29. (a) 30.0 m   (b) 9.49×10^5 m

31. (a) 332 J   (b) 46.4 dB

33. (a) 3.04 kHz   (b) 2.08 kHz   (c) 2.62 kHz, 2.40 kHz

35. 26.4 m/s

37. 19.3 m

39. (a) 56.3 s   (b) 56.6 km farther along

41. 2.82×10^8 m/s

43. It is unreasonable, implying a sound level of 123 dB. Nearly all the missing mechanical energy becomes internal energy in the latch.

45. (a) f is a few hundred hertz. $\lambda \sim 1$ m, duration ~ 0.1 s. (b) Yes. The frequency can be close to 1 000 Hz. If the person clapping his or her hands is at the base of the pyramid, the echo can drop somewhat in frequency and in loudness as sound returns, with the later cycles coming from the smaller and more distant upper risers. The sound could imitate some particular bird and could in fact be a recording of the call.

49. (a) 0.515/min   (b) 0.614/min

51. (a) 55.8 m/s   (b) 2 500 Hz

53. 1 204.2 Hz

55. (a) 0.642 W   (b) $0.004\ 28 = 0.428\%$

57. (a) The sound through the metal arrives first.
(b) (365 m/s) Δt (c) 46.3 m   (d) The answer becomes

$$\ell = \frac{\Delta t}{\dfrac{1}{331 \text{ m/s}} - \dfrac{1}{v_r}}$$

where v_r is the speed of sound in the rod. As v_r goes to infinity, the travel time in the rod becomes negligible. The answer approaches (331 m/s) Δt, which is the distance the sound travels in air during the delay time.
59. (a) $0.948°$ (b) $4.40°$
61. 1.34×10^4 N
63. (a) 6.45   (b) 0

CHAPTER 18

1. (a) -1.65 cm   (b) -6.02 cm   (c) 1.15 cm
3. (a) $+x, -x$ (b) 0.750 s   (c) 1.00 m
5. (a) 9.24 m   (b) 600 Hz
7. (a) 2   (b) 9.28 m and 1.99 m
9. (a) $156°$ (b) 0.058 4 cm
11. 15.7 m, 31.8 Hz, 500 m/s
13. At 0.089 1 m, 0.303 m, 0.518 m, 0.732 m, 0.947 m, 1.16 m from one speaker
15. (a) 4.24 cm   (b) 6.00 cm   (c) 6.00 cm
(d) 0.500 cm, 1.50 cm, 2.50 cm
17. 0.786 Hz, 1.57 Hz, 2.36 Hz, 3.14 Hz
19. (a) 350 Hz   (b) 400 kg
21. (a) 163 N   (b) 660 Hz
23. $\dfrac{Mg}{4Lf^2 \tan \theta}$
25. (a) 3 loops   (b) 16.7 Hz   (c) 1 loop
27. (a) 3.66 m/s   (b) 0.200 Hz
29. (a) 0.357 m   (b) 0.715 m
31. 0.656 m and 1.64 m
33. $n(206 \text{ Hz})$ for $n = 1$ to 9 and $n(84.5 \text{ Hz})$ for $n = 2$ to 23
35. 50.0 Hz, 1.70 m
37. (a) 350 m/s   (b) 1.14 m
39. (21.5 ± 0.1) m. The data suggest 0.6-Hz uncertainty in the frequency measurements, which is only a little more than 1%.
41. (a) 1.59 kHz   (b) odd-numbered harmonics   (c) 1.11 kHz
43. 5.64 beats/s
45. (a) 1.99 beats/s   (b) 3.38 m/s
47. The second harmonic of E is close to the third harmonic of A, and the fourth harmonic of $C^\#$ is close to the fifth harmonic of A.
49. (a) The yo-yo's downward speed is $dL/dt = (0.8 \text{ m/s}^2)(1.2 \text{ s})$ $= 0.960$ m/s. The instantaneous wavelength of the fundamental string wave is given by $d_{NN} = \lambda/2 = L$, so $\lambda = 2L$ and $d\lambda/dt = 2\, dL/dt = 2(0.96 \text{ m/s}) = 1.92$ m/s. (b) For the second harmonic, the wavelength is equal to the length of the string. Then the rate of change of wavelength is equal to $dL/dt = 0.960$ m/s, half as much as for the first harmonic. (c) A yo-yo of different mass will hold the string under different tension to make each string wave vibrate with a different frequency, but the geometrical argument given in parts (a) and (b) still applies to the wavelength. The answers are unchanged: $d\lambda_1/dt = 1.92$ m/s and $d\lambda_2/dt = 0.960$ m/s.
51. (a) 34.8 m/s   (b) 0.977 m
53. 3.85 m/s away from the station or 3.77 m/s toward the station

55. (a) 59.9 Hz   (b) 20.0 cm
57. (a) $\frac{1}{2}$ (b) $[n/(n + 1)]^2 T$ (c) $\frac{9}{16}$
59. $y_1 + y_2 = 11.2 \sin (2.00x - 10.0t + 63.4°)$
61. (a) 78.9 N   (b) 211 Hz

CHAPTER 19

1. (a) $-274°C$ (b) 1.27 atm   (c) 1.74 atm
3. (a) $-320°F$ (b) 77.3 K
5. 3.27 cm
7. (a) 0.176 mm   (b) 8.78 μm   (c) 0.093 0 cm^3
9. (a) $-179°C$ is attainable.   (b) $-376°C$ is below 0 K and unattainable.
11. (a) 99.8 mL   (b) about 6% of the volume change of the acetone
13. (a) 99.4 cm^3 (b) 0.943 cm
15. 5 336 images
17. (a) 400 kPa   (b) 449 kPa
19. 1.50×10^{29} molecules
21. 472 K
23. (a) 41.6 mol   (b) 1.20 kg, nearly in agreement with the tabulated density
25. (a) 1.17 g   (b) 11.5 mN   (c) 1.01 kN
(d) The molecules must be moving very fast.
27. 4.39 kg
29. (a) 7.13 m   (b) The open end of the tube should be at the bottom after the bird surfaces so that the water can drain out. There is no other requirement. Air does not tend to bubble out of a narrow tube.
31. (a) 94.97 cm   (b) 95.03 cm
33. 3.55 cm
35. It falls by 0.094 3 Hz.
37. (a) Expansion makes density drop.   (b) $5 \times 10^{-5}(°C)^{-1}$
39. (a) $h = nRT/(mg + P_0A)$ (b) 0.661 m
41. We assume $\alpha\, \Delta T$ is much less than 1.
43. Yes, as long as the coefficients of expansion remain constant. The lengths L_C and L_S at $0°C$ need to satisfy $17L_C = 11L_S$. Then the steel rod must be longer. With $L_S - L_C = 5.00$ cm, the only possibility is $L_S = 14.2$ cm and $L_C = 9.17$ cm.
45. (a) 0.340%   (b) 0.480%
47. 2.74 m
49. (b) 1.33 kg/m^3
53. No. Steel would need to be 2.30 times stronger.
55. (a) $L_f = L_i e^{\alpha \Delta T}$ (b) 2.00×10^{-4}%; 59.4%
57. (a) 6.17×10^{-3} kg/m   (b) 632 N   (c) 580 N; 192 Hz
59. 4.54 m

CHAPTER 20

1. $(10.0 + 0.117)°C$
3. 0.234 kJ/kg $\cdot$ °C
5. 1.78×10^4 kg
7. $29.6°C$
9. (a) 0.435 cal/g $\cdot$ °C   (b) We cannot make a definite identification. The material might be an unknown alloy or a material not listed in the table. It might be beryllium.
11. $23.6°C$
13. 1.22×10^5 J
15. 0.294 g
17. 0.414 kg
19. (a) $0°C$ (b) 114 g
21. -1.18 MJ

23. -466 J

25. (a) $-4P_iV_i$ (b) It is proportional to the square of the volume, according to $T = (P_i/nRV_i)V^2$.

27. $Q = -720$ J

29.

	Q	W	ΔE_{int}
BC	$-$	0	$-$
CA	$-$	$+$	$-$
AB	$+$	$-$	$+$

31. (a) 7.50 kJ   (b) 900 K

33. -3.10 kJ, 37.6 kJ

35. (a) 0.041 0 m^3 (b) $+5.48$ kJ   (c) -5.48 kJ

37. 10.0 kW

39. 51.2°C

41. 74.8 kJ

43. (a) 0.964 kg or more   (b) The test samples and the inner surface of the insulation can be prewarmed to 37.0°C as the box is assembled. Then nothing changes in temperature during the test period, and the masses of the test samples and insulation make no difference.

45. 3.49×10^3 K

47. Intensity is defined as power per area perpendicular to the direction of energy flow. The direction of sunlight is along the line from the Sun to the object. The perpendicular area is the projected flat, circular area enclosed by the *terminator*, the line that separates day and night on the object. The object radiates infrared light outward in all directions. The area perpendicular to this energy flow is its spherical surface area. The steady-state surface temperature is 279 K = 6°C. We find this temperature to be chilly, well below comfortable room temperatures.

49. 2.27 km

51. (a) 16.8 L   (b) 0.351 L/s

53. $c = \mathcal{P}/\rho R\,\Delta T$

55. 5.87×10^{4}°C

57. 5.31 h

59. 1.44 kg

61. 38.6 m^3/d

63. 9.32 kW

65. (a) The equation $dT/dr = \mathcal{P}/4\pi kr^2$ represents the law of thermal conduction, incorporating the definition of thermal conductivity, applied to a spherical surface within the shell. The rate of energy transfer $\mathcal{P}$ must be the same for all radii so that each bit of material stays at a temperature that is constant in time.   (b) We separate the variables T and r in the thermal conduction equation and integrate the equation between points on the interior and exterior surfaces.   (c) 18.5 W   (d) With $\mathcal{P}$ now known, we separate the variables again and integrate between a point on the interior surface and any point within the shell.   (e) $T = 5$°C $+ 184$ cm $\cdot$ °C $[1/(3$ cm$) - 1/r]$ (f) 29.5°C

CHAPTER 21

1. (a) 4.00 u $= 6.64 \times 10^{-24}$ g   (b) 55.9 u $= 9.28 \times 10^{-23}$ g
   (c) 207 u $= 3.44 \times 10^{-22}$ g

3. 0.943 N, 1.57 Pa

5. 3.21×10^{12} molecules

7. 3.32 mol

9. (a) 3.54×10^{23} atoms   (b) 6.07×10^{-21} J   (c) 1.35 km/s

11. (a) 8.76×10^{-21} J for both   (b) 1.62 km/s for helium and 514 m/s for argon

13. (a) 3.46 kJ   (b) 2.45 kJ   (c) -1.01 kJ

15. Between 10^{-2}°C and 10^{-3}°C

17. $13.5PV$

19. (a) 1.39 atm   (b) 366 K, 253 K   (c) 0, -4.66 kJ, -4.66 kJ

21. 227 K

23. (a)

   (b) 8.77 L   (c) 900 K   (d) 300 K   (e) -336 J

25. (a) 28.0 kJ   (b) 46.0 kJ   (c) isothermal process: $P_f = 10.0$ atm; adiabatic process: $P_f = 25.1$ atm

27. (a) 9.95 cal/K, 13.9 cal/K   (b) 13.9 cal/K, 17.9 cal/K

29. Sulfur dioxide is the gas in Table 21.2 with the greatest molecular mass. If the effective spring constants for various chemical bonds are comparable, SO_2 can then be expected to have low frequencies of atomic vibration. Vibration can be excited at lower temperature for sulfur dioxide than for the other gases. Some vibration may be going on at 300 K.

31. (a) 6.80 m/s   (b) 7.41 m/s   (c) 7.00 m/s

35. (a) 2.37×10^4 K   (b) 1.06×10^3 K

37. (b) 0.278

39. (a) 100 kPa, 66.5 L, 400 K, 5.82 kJ, 7.48 kJ, -1.66 kJ
   (b) 133 kPa, 49.9 L, 400 K, 5.82 kJ, 5.82 kJ, 0
   (c) 120 kPa, 41.6 L, 300 K, 0, -909 J, $+909$ J
   (d) 120 kPa, 43.3 L, 312 K, 722 J, 0, $+722$ J

41. (b) 447 J/kg·°C agrees with the tabulated value within 0.3%.   (c) 127 J/kg·°C agrees with the tabulated value within 2%.

43. (b) The expressions are equal because $PV = nRT$ and $\gamma = (C_V + R)/C_V = 1 + R/C_V$ give $R = (\gamma - 1)C_V$, so $PV = n(\gamma - 1)C_VT$ and $PV/(\gamma - 1) = nC_VT$

45. 510 K and 290 K

47. 0.623

49. (a) Pressure increases as volume decreases.
   (d) 0.500 atm^{-1}, 0.300 atm^{-1}

51. (a) 7.27×10^{-20} J   (b) 2.20 km/s   (c) 3 510 K. The evaporating molecules are exceptional, at the high-speed tail of the distribution of molecular speeds. The average speed of molecules in the liquid and in the vapor is appropriate only to room temperature.

53. (a) 0.514 m^3 (b) 2.06 m^3 (c) 2.38×10^3 K   (d) -480 kJ
   (e) 2.28 MJ

55. 1.09×10^{-3}, 2.69×10^{-2}, 0.529, 1.00, 0.199, 1.01×10^{-41}, $1.25 \times 10^{-1\,082}$

59. (a) 0.203 mol   (b) $T_B = T_C = 900$ K, $V_C = 15.0$ L

(c, d)	P, atm	V, L	T, K	E_{int}, kJ
A	1.00	5.00	300	0.760
B	3.00	5.00	900	2.28
C	1.00	15.0	900	2.28
A	1.00	5.00	300	0.760

   (e) Lock the piston in place and put the cylinder into an oven at 900 K. Keep the gas in the oven while gradually letting the gas expand to lift a load on the piston as far as it can. Move the cylinder from the oven back to the 300-K room and let the gas cool and contract.

(f, g)	Q, kJ	W, kJ	ΔE_{int}, kJ
AB	1.52	0	1.52
BC	1.67	-1.67	0
CA	-2.53	$+1.01$	-1.52
$ABCA$	0.656	-0.656	0

61. (b) 1.60×10^4 K

CHAPTER 22

1. (a) 6.94%   (b) 335 J
3. (a) 10.7 kJ   (b) 0.533 s
5. 55.4%
7. 77.8 W
9. (a) 67.2%   (b) 58.8 kW
11. The actual efficiency of 0.069 8 is less than four-tenths of the Carnot efficiency of 0.177.
13. (a) 741 J   (b) 459 J
15. (a) 564 K   (b) 212 kW   (c) 47.5%
17. (b) $1 - T_c/T_h$, the same as for a single reversible engine   (c) $(T_c + T_h)/2$ (d) $(T_h T_c)^{1/2}$
19. 9.00
23. 72.2 J
25. 23.1 mW
27. (a) 244 kPa   (b) 192 J
29. (a) 51.2%   (b) 36.2%
33. 195 J/K
35. 1.02 kJ/K
37. $\sim 10^0$ W/K from metabolism; much more if you are using high-power electric appliances or an automobile
39. 5.76 J/K; the temperature is constant if the gas is ideal.
41. (a) 1   (b) 6
43. (a)

Result	Number of ways to draw
All R	1
2 R, 1 G	3
1 R, 2 G	3
All G	1

(b)

Result	Number of ways to draw
All R	1
4R, 1G	5
3R, 2G	10
2R, 3G	10
1R, 4G	5
All G	1

45. (a) 214 J, 64.3 J   (b) -35.7 J, -35.7 J. The net effect would be the transport of energy by heat from the cold to the hot reservoir without expenditure of external work. (c) 333 J, 233 J   (d) 83.3 J, 83.3 J, 0. The net effect would be converting energy, taken in by heat, entirely into energy output by work in a cyclic process.   (e) -0.111 J/K. The entropy of the Universe would have decreased.

47. (a) 5.00 kW   (b) 763 W
49. (a) $2nRT_i \ln 2$ (b) 0.273
51. 5.97×10^4 kg/s
53. (a) 8.48 kW   (b) 1.52 kW   (c) 1.09×10^4 J/K (d) The COP drops by 20.0%.
55. (a) $10.5nRT_i$ (b) $8.50nRT_i$ (c) 0.190 (d) This efficiency is much less than the 0.833 for a Carnot engine operating between the temperatures used here.
57. (a) $nC_P \ln 3$ (b) Both ask for the change in entropy between the same two states of the same system. Entropy is a state variable. The change in entropy does not depend on path, but only on original and final states.
61. (a) 20.0°C   (c) $\Delta S = +4.88$ J/K   (d) The mixing is irreversible. It is clear that warm water and cool water do not come unmixed, and the entropy change is positive.

CHAPTER 23

1. (a) $+160$ zC, 1.01 u   (b) $+160$ zC, 23.0 u   (c) -160 zC, 35.5 u   (d) $+320$ zC, 40.1 u   (e) -480 zC, 14.0 u (f) $+640$ zC, 14.0 u   (g) $+1.12$ aC, 14.0 u   (h) -160 zC, 18.0 u
3. The force is $\sim 10^{26}$ N.
5. (a) 1.59 nN away from the other   (b) 1.24×10^{36} times larger   (c) 8.61×10^{-11} C/kg
7. 0.872 N at 330°
9. (a) 2.16×10^{-5} N toward the other   (b) 8.99×10^{-7} N away from the other
11. (a) 82.2 nN toward the other particle   (b) 2.19 Mm/s
13. (a) 55.8 pN/C down   (b) 102 nN/C up
15. The field at the origin can be to the right if the unknown charge is $-9Q$, or the field can be to the left if and only if the unknown charge is $+27Q$.
17. (a) $5.91k_e q/a^2$ at 58.8°   (b) $5.91k_e q^2/a^2$ at 58.8°
19. (a) $k_e Qx\hat{\mathbf{i}}/(R^2 + x^2)^{3/2}$ (b) As long as the charge is symmetrically placed, the number of charges does not matter. A continuous ring corresponds to n becoming larger without limit.
21. 1.59×10^6 N/C toward the rod
23. (a) $6.64\hat{\mathbf{i}}$ MN/C   (b) $24.1\hat{\mathbf{i}}$ MN/C   (c) $6.40\hat{\mathbf{i}}$ MN/C (d) $0.664\hat{\mathbf{i}}$ MN/C, taking the axis of the ring as the x axis
25. (a) 93.6 MN/C; the near-field approximation is 104 MN/C, about 11% high.   (b) 0.516 MN/C; the charged-particle approximation is 0.519 MN/C, about 0.6% high.
27. $-21.6\hat{\mathbf{i}}$ MN/C
31. (a) 86.4 pC for each   (b) 324 pC, 459 pC, 459 pC, 432 pC (c) 57.6 pC, 106 pC, 154 pC, 96.0 pC
33.

35. (a)

The field is zero at the center of the triangle.   (b) $1.73 k_e q\hat{\mathbf{j}}/a^2$

37. (a) 61.3 Gm/s^2 (b) $19.5\ \mu$s   (c) 11.7 m   (d) 1.20 fJ
39. K/ed in the direction of motion
41. (a) 111 ns   (b) 5.68 mm   (c) $(450\hat{\mathbf{i}} + 102\hat{\mathbf{j}})$ km/s

43. (a) 21.8 μm (b) 2.43 cm
45. (a) 10.9 nC (b) 5.44 mN
47. 40.9 N at 263°

49. $Q = 2L\sqrt{\dfrac{k(L - L_i)}{k_e}}$

53. $-707\hat{\mathbf{j}}$ mN
55. (a) $\theta_1 = \theta_2$
57. (a) 0.307 s (b) Yes. Ignoring gravity makes a difference of 2.28%.
59. (a) $\vec{\mathbf{F}} = 1.90(k_e q^2/s^2)(\hat{\mathbf{i}} + \hat{\mathbf{j}} + \hat{\mathbf{k}})$ (b) $\vec{\mathbf{F}} = 3.29(k_e q^2/s^2)$ in the direction away from the diagonally opposite vertex

65. $\dfrac{k_e \lambda_0}{2x_0}(-\hat{\mathbf{i}})$

CHAPTER 24

1. 4.14 MN/C
3. (a) aA (b) bA (c) 0
5. 1.87 kN$\cdot$m²/C
7. (a) -6.89 MN$\cdot$m²/C (b) The number of lines entering exceeds the number leaving by 2.91 times or more.
9. $-Q/\epsilon_0$ for S_1; 0 for S_2; $-2Q/\epsilon_0$ for S_3; 0 for S_4
11. (a) $+Q/2\epsilon_0$ (b) $-Q/2\epsilon_0$
13. -18.8 kN$\cdot$m²/C
15. 0 if $R \le d$; $(2\lambda/\epsilon_0)\sqrt{R^2 - d^2}$ if $R > d$
17. (a) 3.20 MN$\cdot$m²/C (b) 19.2 MN$\cdot$m²/C (c) The answer to part (a) could change, but the answer to part (b) would stay the same.
19. 2.33×10^{21} N/C
21. 508 kN/C up
23. -2.48 μC/m²
25. 5.94×10^5 m/s
27. $\vec{\mathbf{E}} = \rho r/2\epsilon_0$ away from the axis
29. (a) 0 (b) 7.19 MN/C away from the center
31. (a) 51.4 kN/C outward (b) 646 N$\cdot$m²/C
33. (a) 0 (b) 5 400 N/C outward (c) 540 N/C outward
35. (a) $+708$ nC/m² and -708 nC/m² (b) $+177$ nC and -177 nC
37. 2.00 N
39. (a) $-\lambda, +3\lambda$ (b) $3\lambda/2\pi\epsilon_0 r$ radially outward
41. (a) 80.0 nC/m² on each face (b) $9.04\hat{\mathbf{k}}$ kN/C (c) $-9.04\hat{\mathbf{k}}$ kN/C
43. (b) $Q/2\epsilon_0$ (c) Q/ϵ_0
45. (a) The charge on the exterior surface is -55.7 nC distributed uniformly. (b) The charge on the interior surface is $+55.7$ nC. It might have any distribution. (c) The charge within the shell is -55.7 nC. It might have any distribution.
47. (a) $\rho r/3\epsilon_0$, $Q/4\pi\epsilon_0 r^2$, 0, $Q/4\pi\epsilon_0 r^2$, all radially outward (b) $-Q/4\pi b^2$ and $+Q/4\pi c^2$
49. $\theta = \tan^{-1}[qQ/(2\pi\epsilon_0 dmv^2)]$
51. (a) σ/ϵ_0 away from both plates (b) 0 (c) σ/ϵ_0 away from both plates
53. $\sigma/2\epsilon_0$ radially outward
57. $\vec{\mathbf{E}} = a/2\epsilon_0$ radially outward
61. (b) $\vec{\mathbf{g}} = GM_E r/R_E^3$ radially inward
63. (a) -4.00 nC (b) $+9.56$ nC (c) $+4.00$ nC and $+5.56$ nC
65. (a) If the volume charge density is nonzero, the field cannot be uniform in magnitude. (b) The field must be uniform in magnitude along any line in the direction of the field. The field magnitude can vary between points in a plane perpendicular to the field lines.

CHAPTER 25

1. (a) 152 km/s (b) 6.49 Mm/s
3. 1.67 MN/C
5. 38.9 V; the origin
7. (a) $2QE/k$ (b) QE/k (c) $2\pi\sqrt{m/k}$ (d) $2(QE - \mu_k mg)/k$
9. (a) 0.400 m/s (b) It is the same. Each bit of the rod feels a force of the same size as before.
11. (a) 1.44×10^{-7} V (b) -7.19×10^{-8} V (c) -1.44×10^{-7} V, $+7.19 \times 10^{-8}$ V
13. (a) 6.00 m (b) -2.00 μC
15. -11.0 MV
17. 8.95 J
21. (a) no point at a finite distance from the particles (b) $2k_e q/a$
23. (a) 10.8 m/s and 1.55 m/s (b) Greater. The conducting spheres will polarize each other, with most of the positive charge of one and of the negative charge of the other on their inside faces. Immediately before they collide, their centers of charge will be closer than their geometric centers, so they will have less electric potential energy and more kinetic energy.
25. $5k_e q^2/9d$

27. $\left[\left(1 + \sqrt{\tfrac{1}{8}}\right)\dfrac{k_e q^2}{mL}\right]^{1/2}$

29. (a) 10.0 V, -11.0 V, -32.0 V (b) 7.00 N/C in the $+x$ direction
31. $\vec{\mathbf{E}} = (-5 + 6xy)\hat{\mathbf{i}} + (3x^2 - 2z^2)\hat{\mathbf{j}} - 4yz\hat{\mathbf{k}}$; 7.07 N/C

33. $E_y = \dfrac{k_e Q}{y\sqrt{\ell^2 + y^2}}$

35. (a) C/m² (b) $k_e \alpha[L - d\ln(1 + L/d)]$
37. -1.51 MV
39. (a) 0, 1.67 MV (b) 5.84 MN/C away, 1.17 MV (c) 11.9 MN/C away, 1.67 MV
41. (a) 248 nC/m² (b) 496 nC/m²
43. (a) 450 kV (b) 7.51 μC
45. (a) 1.42 mm (b) 9.20 kV/m
47. 253 MeV
49. (a) -27.2 eV (b) -6.80 eV (c) 0
51. (a) Yes. The inverse proportionality of potential to radius is sufficient to show that $200R = 150(R + 10$ cm$)$, so $R = 30.0$ cm. Then $Q = 6.67$ nC. (b) Almost but not quite. Two possibilities exist: $R = 29.1$ cm with $Q = 6.79$ nC and $R = 3.44$ cm with $Q = 804$ pC.
53. 4.00 nC at $(-1.00$ m, 0$)$ and -5.01 nC at $(0, 2.00$ m$)$
55. $k_e Q^2/2R$
57. $V_2 - V_1 = (-\lambda/2\pi\epsilon_0)\ln(r_2/r_1)$
61. (b) $E_r = 2k_e p\cos\theta/r^3$; $E_\theta = k_e p\sin\theta/r^3$; yes; no (c) $V = k_e py(x^2 + y^2)^{-3/2}$; $\vec{\mathbf{E}} = 3k_e pxy(x^2 + y^2)^{-5/2}\hat{\mathbf{i}} + k_e p(2y^2 - x^2)(x^2 + y^2)^{-5/2}\hat{\mathbf{j}}$

63. $V = \pi k_e C\left[R\sqrt{x^2 + R^2} + x^2\ln\left(\dfrac{x}{R + \sqrt{x^2 + R^2}}\right)\right]$

65. (a) 488 V (b) 78.1 aJ (c) 306 km/s (d) 390 Gm/s² toward the negative plate (e) 651 aN toward the negative plate (f) 4.07 kN/C
67. Outside the sphere, $E_x = 3E_0 a^3 xz(x^2 + y^2 + z^2)^{-5/2}$, $E_y = 3E_0 a^3 yz(x^2 + y^2 + z^2)^{-5/2}$, and $E_z = E_0 + E_0 a^3(2z^2 - x^2 - y^2)(x^2 + y^2 + z^2)^{-5/2}$. Inside the sphere, $E_x = E_y = E_z = 0$.

CHAPTER 26

1. (a) 48.0 μC (b) 6.00 μC
3. (a) 1.33 μC/m^2 (b) 13.3 pF
5. (a) 11.1 kV/m toward the negative plate (b) 98.3 nC/m^2
   (c) 3.74 pF (d) 74.7 pC
7. 4.42 μm
9. (a) 2.68 nF (b) 3.02 kV
11. (a) 15.6 pF (b) 256 kV
13. (a) 3.53 μF (b) 6.35 V and 2.65 V (c) 31.8 μC on each
15. 6.00 pF and 3.00 pF
17. (a) 5.96 μF (b) 89.5 μC on 20 μF, 63.2 μC on 6 μF, 26.3 μC on 15 μF and on 3 μF
19. 120 μC; 80.0 μC and 40.0 μC
21. ten
23. 6.04 μF
25. 12.9 μF
27. (a) 216 μJ (b) 54.0 μJ
31. (a) 1.50 μC (b) 1.83 kV
35. 9.79 kg
37. (a) 81.3 pF (b) 2.40 kV
39. 1.04 m
41. 22.5 V
43. (b) -8.78×10^6 N/C·m; $-5.53 \times 10^{-2}\hat{\mathbf{i}}$ N
45. 19.0 kV
47. (a) 11.2 pF (b) 134 pC (c) 16.7 pF (d) 66.9 pC
49. (a) 40.0 μJ (b) 500 V
51. 0.188 m^2
55. Gasoline has 194 times the specific energy content of the battery and 727 000 times that of the capacitor.
57. (a) $Q_0^2 d(\ell - x)/(2\ell^3\epsilon_0)$ (b) $Q_0^2 d/(2\ell^3\epsilon_0)$ to the right (c) $Q_0^2/(2\ell^4\epsilon_0)$ (d) $Q_0^2/(2\ell^4\epsilon_0)$; they are precisely the same.
59. 4.29 μF
61. (a) The additional energy comes from work done by the electric field in the wires as it forces more charge onto the already-charged plates. (b) The charge increases according to $Q/Q_0 = \kappa$.
63. 750 μC on C_1 and 250 μC on C_2
65. $\frac{4}{3}C$

CHAPTER 27

1. 7.50×10^{15} electrons
3. (a) $0.632 I_0\tau$ (b) $0.999\,95 I_0\tau$ (c) $I_0\tau$
5. (a) 17.0 A (b) 85.0 kA/m^2
7. (a) 2.55 A/m^2 (b) 5.31×10^{10} m^{-3} (c) 1.20×10^{10} s
9. (a) 221 nm (b) No. The deuterons are so far apart that one does not produce a significant potential at the location of the next.
11. 6.43 A
13. (a) 1.82 m (b) 280 μm
15. $6.00 \times 10^{-15}/\Omega \cdot$m
17. 0.180 V/m
19. (a) 31.5 n$\Omega \cdot$m (b) 6.35 MA/m^2 (c) 49.9 mA
   (d) 659 μm/s (e) 0.400 V
21. 0.125
23. 5.00 A, 24.0 Ω
25. 5.49 Ω
27. 36.1%
29. (a) 3.17 m (b) 340 W
31. (a) 0.660 kWh (b) $0.039 6
33. $0.232
35. $0.269/day

37. (a) 184 W (b) 461°C
39. ~ $1
41. Any diameter d and length ℓ related by $d^2 = (4.77 \times 10^{-8}$ m)ℓ, such as length 0.900 m and diameter 0.207 mm. Yes.
45. Experimental resistivity = 1.47 $\mu\Omega \cdot$m $\pm4\%$, in agreement with 1.50 $\mu\Omega \cdot$m
47. (a) 8.00 V/m in the x direction (b) 0.637 Ω (c) 6.28 A
   (d) 200 MA/m^2 in the x direction
49. (a) 667 A (b) 50.0 km
51.

Material	$\alpha' = \alpha/(1 - 20\alpha)$
Silver	$4.1 \times 10^{-3}/°$C
Copper	$4.2 \times 10^{-3}/°$C
Gold	$3.6 \times 10^{-3}/°$C
Aluminum	$4.2 \times 10^{-3}/°$C
Tungsten	$4.9 \times 10^{-3}/°$C
Iron	$5.6 \times 10^{-3}/°$C
Platinum	$4.25 \times 10^{-3}/°$C
Lead	$4.2 \times 10^{-3}/°$C
Nichrome	$0.4 \times 10^{-3}/°$C
Carbon	$-0.5 \times 10^{-3}/°$C
Germanium	$-24 \times 10^{-3}/°$C
Silicon	$-30 \times 10^{-3}/°$C

53. It is exact. The resistance can be written $R = \rho L^2/V$ and the stretched length as $L = L_i(1 + \delta)$. Then the result follows directly.
55. (b) Charge is conducted by current in the direction of decreasing potential. Energy is conducted by heat in the direction of decreasing temperature.
59. Coat the surfaces of entry and exit with a material of much higher conductivity than the bulk material of the object. The electric potential will be essentially uniform over each of these electrodes. Current will be distributed over the whole area where each electrode is in contact with the resistive object.
61. (a) $\dfrac{\epsilon_0\ell}{2d} (\ell + 2x + \kappa\ell - 2\kappa x)$

   (b) $\dfrac{\epsilon_0\ell v \, \Delta V(\kappa - 1)}{d}$ clockwise

63. 2.71 MΩ
65. 2 020°C

CHAPTER 28

1. (a) 6.73 Ω (b) 1.97 Ω
3. (a) 12.4 V (b) 9.65 V
5. (a) 17.1 Ω (b) 1.99 A for 4 Ω and 9 Ω, 1.17 A for 7 Ω, 0.818 A for 10 Ω
7. (a) 227 mA (b) 5.68 V
9. (a) 75.0 V (b) 25.0 W, 6.25 W, and 6.25 W; 37.5 W
11. $R_1 = 1.00$ kΩ, $R_2 = 2.00$ kΩ, $R_3 = 3.00$ kΩ
13. It decreases. Closing the switch opens a new path with resistance of only 20 Ω. $R = 14.0$ Ω
15. 14.2 W to 2 Ω, 28.4 W to 4 Ω, 1.33 W to 3 Ω, 4.00 W to 1 Ω
17. 846 mA down in the 8-Ω resistor; 462 mA down in the middle branch; 1.31 A up in the right-hand branch
19. (a) -222 J and 1.88 kJ (b) 687 J, 128 J, 25.6 J, 616 J, 205 J (c) 1.66 kJ of chemical energy is transformed into internal energy.

21. 0.395 A and 1.50 V

23. 1.00 A up in 200 Ω, 4.00 A up in 70 Ω, 3.00 A up in 80 Ω, 8.00 A down in 20 Ω, 200 V

25. (a) 909 mA   (b) -1.82 V $= V_b - V_a$

27. (a) 5.00 s   (b) 150 μC   (c) 4.06 μA

29. (a) -61.6 mA   (b) 0.235 μC   (c) 1.96 A

31. (a) 6.00 V   (b) 8.29 μs

33. 0.302 Ω

35. 16.6 kΩ

37. (a) 12.5 A, 6.25 A, 8.33 A   (b) No. Together they would require 27.1 A.

39. (a) 1.02 A down   (b) 0.364 A down   (c) 1.38 A up   (d) 0   (e) 66.0 μC

41. 2.22 h

43. a is 4.00 V higher

45. 87.3 %

47. 6.00 Ω, 3.00 Ω

49. (a) $I_1 = \dfrac{IR_2}{R_1 + R_2}$, $I_2 = \dfrac{IR_1}{R_1 + R_2}$

51. (a) $R \le 1\,050$ Ω   (b) $R \ge 10.0$ Ω

53. (a) 9.93 μC   (b) 33.7 nA   (c) 334 nW   (d) 337 nW

55. (a) 40.0 W   (b) 80.0 V, 40.0 V, 40.0 V

57. (a) 9.30 V, 2.51 Ω   (b) 186 V and 3.70 A   (c) 1.09 A   (d) 143 W   (e) 0.162 Ω   (f) 3.00 mW   (g) 2.21 W   (h) The power output of the emf depends on the resistance connected to it. A question about "the rest of the power" is not meaningful when it compares circuits with different currents. The net emf produces more current in the circuit where the copper wire is used. The net emf delivers more power when the copper wire is used, 687 W rather than 203 W without the wire. Nearly all this power results in extra internal energy in the internal resistance of the batteries, which rapidly rise to a high temperature. The circuit with the copper wire is unsafe because the batteries overheat. The circuit without the copper wire is unsafe because it delivers an electric shock to the experimenter.

61. (a) 0 in 3 kΩ and 333 μA in 12 kΩ and 15 kΩ   (b) 50.0 μC   (c) $(278\ \mu A)e^{-t/180\ ms}$ (d) 290 ms

63. (a) $R_x = R_2 - R_1/4$ (b) $R_x = 2.75$ Ω. The station is inadequately grounded.

65. (a) $2\Delta t/3$ (b) $3\Delta t$

CHAPTER 29

1. (a) up   (b) toward you, out of the plane of the paper   (c) no deflection   (d) into the plane of the paper

3. $(-20.9\hat{\mathbf{j}})$ mT

5. 48.9° or 131°

7. 2.34 aN

9. (a) 49.6 aN south   (b) 1.29 km

11. $r_\alpha = r_d = \sqrt{2}r_p$

13. (a) 5.00 cm   (b) 8.78×10^6 m/s

15. 7.88 pT

17. 244 kV/m

19. 0.278 m

21. (a) 4.31×10^7 rad/s   (b) 51.7 Mm/s

23. 70.1 mT

25. 0.245 T east

27. (a) 4.73 N   (b) 5.46 N   (c) 4.73 N

29. 1.07 m/s

31. $2\pi rIB \sin \theta$ up

33. 2.98 μN west

35. 9.98 N · m clockwise as seen looking down from above

37. (a) Minimum: pointing north at 48.0° below the horizontal; maximum: pointing south at 48.0° above the horizontal. (b) 1.07 μJ

39. The magnetic moment cannot go to infinity. Its maximum value is 5.37 mA · m² for a single-turn circle. Smaller by 21% and by 40% are the magnetic moments for the single-turn square and triangle. Circular coils with several turns have magnetic moments inversely proportional to the number of turns, approaching zero as the number of turns goes to infinity.

41. 43.1 μT

43. (a) The electric current experiences a magnetic force. (c) no, no, no

45. 12.5 km. It will not hit the Earth, but it will perform a hairpin turn and go back parallel to its original direction.

47. (a) -8.00×10^{-21} kg · m/s   (b) 8.90°

49. (a) $(3.52\hat{\mathbf{i}} - 1.60\hat{\mathbf{j}})$ aN   (b) 24.4°

51. 128 mT north at an angle of 78.7° below the horizontal

53. 0.588 T

55. 0.713 A counterclockwise as seen from above

57. 2.75 Mrad/s

59. 3.70×10^{-24} N · m

61. (a) 1.33 m/s   (b) Positive ions moving toward you in magnetic field to the right feel upward magnetic force and migrate upward in the blood vessel. Negative ions moving toward you feel downward magnetic force and accumulate at the bottom of this section of vessel. Therefore, both species can participate in the generation of the emf.

63. (a) $v = qBh/m$. If its speed is slightly less than the critical value, the particle moves in a semicircle of radius h and leaves the field with velocity $-v\hat{\mathbf{j}}$. If its speed is incrementally greater, the particle moves in a quarter circle of the same radius and moves along the boundary outside the field with velocity $v\hat{\mathbf{i}}$. (b) The particle moves in a smaller semicircle of radius mv/qB, attaining final velocity $-v\hat{\mathbf{j}}$. (c) The particle moves in a circular arc of radius $r = mv/qB$, leaving the field with velocity $v \sin \theta \hat{\mathbf{i}} + v \cos \theta \hat{\mathbf{j}}$, where $\theta = \sin^{-1} (h/r)$.

65. (a) For small angular displacements, the torque on the dipole is equal to a negative constant times the displacement.

(b) $f = \dfrac{1}{2\pi}\sqrt{\dfrac{\mu B}{I}}$

(c) The equilibrium orientation of the needle shows the direction of the field. In a stronger field, the frequency is higher. The frequency is easy to measure precisely over a wide range of values. 2.04 mT.

CHAPTER 30

1. 12.5 T

3. (a) 28.3 μT into the paper   (b) 24.7 μT into the paper

5. $\dfrac{\mu_0 I}{4\pi x}$ into the paper

7. (a) $2I_1$ out of the page   (b) $6I_1$ into the page

9. (a) along the line ($y = -0.420$ m, $z = 0$)   (b) $(-34.7\hat{\mathbf{j}})$ mN   (c) $(17.3\hat{\mathbf{j}})$ kN/C

11. at A, 53.3 μT toward the bottom of the page; at B, 20.0 μT toward the bottom of the page; at C, zero.

13. (a) $4.5\dfrac{\mu_0 I}{\pi L}$

(b) Stronger. Each of the two sides meeting at the nearby vertex contributes more than twice as much to the net field at the new point.

15. $(-13.0\hat{\mathbf{j}})\,\mu\text{T}$

17. $(-27.0\hat{\mathbf{i}})\,\mu\text{N}$

19. parallel to the wires and 0.167 m below the upper wire

21. (a) opposite directions   (b) 67.8 A   (c) Smaller. A smaller gravitational force would be pulling down on the wires, therefore tending to reduce the angle.

23. 20.0 μT toward the bottom of the page

25. at a, 200 μT toward the top of the page; at b, 133 μT toward the bottom of the page

27. (a) 6.34 mN/m inward   (b) Greater. The magnetic field increases toward the outside of the bundle, where more net current lies inside a particular radius. The larger field exerts a stronger force on the strand we choose to monitor.

29. (a) 0

   (b) $\dfrac{\mu_0 I}{2\pi R}$ tangent to the wall in a counterclockwise sense

   (c) $\dfrac{\mu_0 I^2}{(2\pi R)^2}$ inward

31. (a) $\mu_0 b r_1^2/3$ (b) $\mu_0 b R^3/3 r_2$

35. 31.8 mA

37. 226 μN away from the center of the loop, 0

39. (a) 3.13 mWb   (b) 0

41. (a) 7.40 μWb   (b) 2.27 μWb

43. 2.02

45. (a) 8.63×10^{45} electrons   (b) 4.01×10^{20} kg

47. $\dfrac{\mu_0 I}{2\pi w}\ln\left(1 + \dfrac{w}{b}\right)\hat{\mathbf{k}}$

49. $(-12.0\hat{\mathbf{k}})$ mN

51. 143 pT

57. (a) 2.46 N upward   (b) The magnetic field at the center of the loop or on its axis is much weaker than the magnetic field immediately outside the wire. The wire has negligible curvature on the scale of 1 mm, so we model the lower loop as a long, straight wire to find the field it creates at the location of the upper wire. (c) 107 m/s² upward

59. (a) 274 μT   (b) $(-274\hat{\mathbf{j}})\,\mu$T   (c) $(1.15\hat{\mathbf{i}})$ mN   (d) $(0.384\hat{\mathbf{i}})$ m/s²   (e) acceleration is constant   (f) $(0.999\hat{\mathbf{i}})$ m/s

61. $\dfrac{\mu_0 I_1 I_2 L}{\pi R}$ to the right

65. $\frac{1}{3}\rho\mu_0\omega R^2$

67. (a) $\dfrac{\mu_0 I(2r^2 - a^2)}{\pi r(4r^2 - a^2)}$ to the left

   (b) $\dfrac{\mu_0 I(2r^2 + a^2)}{\pi r(4r^2 + a^2)}$ toward the top of the page

CHAPTER 31

1. (a) 101 μV tending to produce clockwise current as seen from above (b) It is twice as large in magnitude and in the opposite sense.

3. 9.82 mV

5. (b) 3.79 mV   (c) 28.0 mV

7. 160 A

9. (a) 1.60 A counterclockwise   (b) 20.1 μT   (c) left

11. $-(14.2\text{ mV})\cos(120t)$

13. 283 μA upward

15. $(68.2\text{ mV})e^{-1.6t}$, tending to produce counterclockwise current

17. 272 m

19. 13.3 mA counterclockwise in the lower loop and clockwise in the upper loop

21. (a) 1.18 mV. The wingtip on the pilot's left is positive. (b) no change   (c) No. If we try to connect the wings into a circuit with the lightbulb, we run an extra insulated wire along the wing. In a uniform field, the total emf generated in the one-turn coil is zero.

23. (a) 3.00 N to the right   (b) 6.00 W

25. 24.1 V with the outer contact positive

27. 2.83 mV

29. (a) $F = N^2 B^2 w^2 v/R$ to the left   (b) 0
   (c) $F = N^2 B^2 w^2 v/R$ to the left

31. 145 μA upward in the picture

33. 1.80 mN/C upward and to the left, perpendicular to r_1

35. (a) 7.54 kV   (b) The plane of the loop is parallel to $\vec{\mathbf{B}}$.

37. $(28.6\text{ mV})\sin(4\pi t)$

39. (a) 110 V   (b) 8.53 W   (c) 1.22 kW

41. Both are correct. The current in the magnet creates an upward magnetic field 🖑, so the N and S poles on the solenoid core are shown correctly. On the rail in front of the brake, the upward magnetic flux increases as the coil approaches, so a current is induced here to create downward magnetic field 🤚. This current is clockwise, so the S pole on the rail is shown correctly. On the rail behind the brake, the upward magnetic flux is decreasing. The induced current in the rail will produce upward magnetic field by being counterclockwise 🖐 as the picture correctly shows.

43. (b) Larger R makes current smaller, so the loop must travel faster to maintain equality of magnetic force and weight. (c) The magnetic force is proportional to the product of field and current, while the current is itself proportional to field. If B becomes two times smaller, the speed must become four times larger to compensate.

45. $-(7.22\text{ mV})\cos(2\pi\,523t/\text{s})$

47.

(a) Doubling N doubles amplitude. (b) Doubling ω doubles the amplitude and halves the period. (c) Doubling ω and halving N leaves the amplitude the same and cuts the period in half.

49. (a) 3.50 A up in 2 Ω, and 1.40 A up in 5 Ω (b) 34.3 W   (c) 4.29 N

51. $\sim 10^{-4}$ V, by reversing a 20-turn coil of diameter 3 cm in 0.1 s in a field of 10^{-3} T

53. 1.20 μC

55. (a) 0.900 A from *b* toward *a*   (b) 0.108 N   (c) *b*   (d) No. Instead of decreasing downward magnetic flux to induce clockwise current, the new loop will see increasing downward flux to cause counterclockwise current, but the current in the resistor is still from *b* to *a*.

57. (a) $C\pi a^2 K$ (b) the upper plate   (c) The changing magnetic field within the loop induces an electric field around the circumference, which pushes on charged particles in the wire.

59. (a) 36.0 V   (b) 600 mWb/s   (c) 35.9 V   (d) 4.32 N · m

63. 6.00 A

67. $(-87.1$ mV$)$ cos $(200\pi t + \phi)$

CHAPTER 32

1. 100 V

3. $-(18.8$ V$)$ cos $(377t)$

5. -0.421 A/s

7. (a) 188 μT   (b) 33.3 nT · m²   (c) 0.375 mH   (d) B and Φ_B are proportional to current; L is independent of current

9. $\mathcal{E}_0/k^2L$

11. (a) 0.139 s   (b) 0.461 s

13. (a) 2.00 ms   (b) 0.176 A   (c) 1.50 A   (d) 3.22 ms

15. (a) 0.800   (b) 0

17. (a) 6.67 A/s   (b) 0.332 A/s

19. (a) 1.00 kΩ (b) 3.00 ms

21. (a) 5.66 ms   (b) 1.22 A   (c) 58.1 ms

23. 2.44 μJ

25. 44.2 nJ/m³ for the $\vec{\mathbf{E}}$ field and 995 μJ/m³ for the $\vec{\mathbf{B}}$ field

27. (a) 66.0 W   (b) 45.0 W   (c) 21.0 W   (d) At all instants after the connection is made, the battery power is equal to the sum of the power delivered to the resistor and the power delivered to the magnetic field. Immediately after $t = 0$, the resistor power is nearly zero and nearly all the battery power is going into the magnetic field. Long after the connection is made, the magnetic field is absorbing no more power and the battery power is going into the resistor.

29. $\dfrac{2\pi B_0^2 R^3}{\mu_0} = 2.70 \times 10^{18}$ J

31. 1.00 V

33. (a) 18.0 mH   (b) 34.3 mH   (c) -9.00 mV

35. $M = \dfrac{N_1 N_2 \pi \mu_0 R_1^2 R_2^2}{2(x^2 + R_1^2)^{3/2}}$

37. 400 mA

39. 281 mH

41. 608 pF

43. (a) 6.03 J   (b) 0.529 J   (c) 6.56 J

45. (a) 4.47 krad/s   (b) 4.36 krad/s   (c) 2.53%

47. (a) 0.693$(2L/R)$ (b) 0.347$(2L/R)$

49. (a) -20.0 mV   (b) $-(10.0$ MV/s²$)t^2$ (c) 63.2 μs

51. $(Q/2N)(3L/C)^{1/2}$

53. (a) Immediately after the circuit is connected, the potential difference across the resistor is zero and the emf across the coil is 24.0 V. (b) After several seconds, the potential difference across the resistor is 24.0 V and that across the coil is 0. (c) The two voltages are equal to each other, both being 12.0 V, only once, at 0.578 ms after the circuit is connected. (d) As the current decays, the potential difference across the resistor is always equal to the emf across the coil.

55.

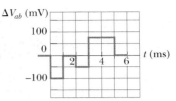

57. (b) 91.2 μH   (c) 90.9 μH is only 0.3% smaller

61. (a) 72.0 V; *b*

(b)

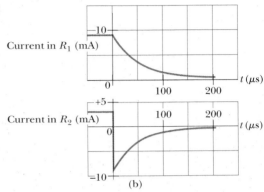

(c) 75.2 μs

63. 300 Ω

65. (a) 62.5 GJ   (b) 2 000 N

67. (a) 2.93 mT up   (b) 3.42 Pa   (c) The supercurrents must be clockwise to produce a downward magnetic field that cancels the upward field of the current in the windings. (d) The field of the windings is upward and radially outward around the top of the solenoid. It exerts a force radially inward and upward on each bit of the clockwise supercurrent. The total force on the supercurrents in the bar is upward. (e) 1.30 mN

CHAPTER 33

1. $\Delta v(t) = (283$ V$)$ sin $(628t)$

3. 2.95 A, 70.7 V

5. 14.6 Hz

7. (a) 42.4 mH   (b) 942 rad/s

9. 5.60 A

11. 0.450 Wb

13. (a) 141 mA   (b) 235 mA

15. 100 mA

17. (a) 194 V   (b) current leads by 49.9°

19. (a) 78.5 Ω (b) 1.59 kΩ (c) 1.52 kΩ (d) 138 mA   (e) $-84.3°$

21. (a) 17.4°   (b) The voltage leads the current.

23. 1.88 V

25.

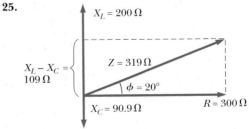

27. 8.00 W

29. (a) 16.0 Ω (b) -12.0 Ω

31. (a) 39.5 V · m/ΔV (b) The diameter is inversely proportional to the potential difference. (c) 26.3 mm   (d) 13.2 kV

33. $11(\Delta V_{rms})^2/14R$

35. 1.82 pF

37. 242 mJ

39. 0.591 and 0.987; the circuit in Problem 21

41. 687 V

43. (a) 29.0 kW   (b) 5.80×10^{-3} (c) If the generator were limited to 4 500 V, no more than 17.5 kW could be delivered to the load, never 5 000 kW.

45. (b) 0; 1   (c) $f_h = (10.88RC)^{-1}$

47. (a) 613 μF   (b) 0.756

49. (a) 580 μH and 54.6 μF   (b) 1   (c) 894 Hz   (d) Δv_{out} leads Δv_{in} by 60.0° at 200 Hz. Δv_{out} and Δv_{in} are in phase at 894 Hz. Δv_{out} lags Δv_{in} by 60.0° at 4 000 Hz.   (e) 1.56 W, 6.25 W, 1.56 W   (f) 0.408

51. (a) X_C could be 53.8 Ω or it could be 1.35 kΩ. (b) X_C must be 53.8 Ω. (c) X_C must be 1.43 kΩ.

53. 56.7 W

55. Tension T and separation d must be related by $T = (274$ N/m$^2)d^2$. One possibility is $T = 10.9$ N and $d = 0.200$ m.

57. (a) 225 mA   (b) 450 mA

59. (a) 1.25 A   (b) The current lags the voltage by 46.7°.

61. (a) 200 mA; voltage leads by 36.8°   (b) 40.0 V; $\phi = 0°$ (c) 20.0 V; $\phi = -90.0°$ (d) 50.0 V; $\phi = +90.0°$

63. (b) 31.6

67. (a)

f (Hz)	X_L (Ω)	X_C (Ω)	Z (Ω)
300	283	12 600	12 300
600	565	6 280	5 720
800	754	4 710	3 960
1 000	942	3 770	2 830
1 500	1 410	2 510	1 100
2 000	1 880	1 880	40.0
3 000	2 830	1 260	1 570
4 000	3 770	942	2 830
6 000	5 650	628	5 020
10 000	9 420	377	9 040

(b) Impedance (kΩ)

69. (a) and (b) 19.7 cm at 35.0°. The answers are identical.
   (c) 9.36 cm at 169°

CHAPTER 34

1. (a) 11.3 GV · m/s   (b) 0.100 A

3. 1.85 aT up

5. $(-2.87\hat{\mathbf{j}} + 5.75\hat{\mathbf{k}})$ Gm/s^2

7. (a) the year 2.69×10^3 (b) 499 s   (c) 2.56 s
   (d) 0.133 s   (e) 33.3 μs

9. (a) 6.00 MHz   (b) $(-73.3\hat{\mathbf{k}})$ nT
   (c) $\vec{\mathbf{B}} = [(-73.3\hat{\mathbf{k}})$ nT$] \cos (0.126x - 3.77 \times 10^7 t)$

11. (a) 0.333 μT   (b) 0.628 μm   (c) 477 THz

13. 75.0 MHz

15. 3.33 μJ/m^3

17. 307 μW/m^2

19. 3.33×10^3 m^2

21. (a) 332 kW/m^2 radially inward   (b) 1.88 kV/m and 222 μT

23. (a) $\vec{\mathbf{E}} \cdot \vec{\mathbf{B}} = 0$ (b) $(11.5\hat{\mathbf{i}} - 28.6\hat{\mathbf{j}})$ W/m^2

25. (a) 2.33 mT   (b) 650 MW/m^2 (c) 510 W

27. (a) 88.8 nW/m^2 (b) 11.3 MW

29. 83.3 nPa

31. (a) 1.90 kN/C   (b) 50.0 pJ   (c) 1.67×10^{-19} kg · m/s

33. (a) 590 W/m^2 (b) 2.10×10^{16} W   (c) 70.1 MN
   (d) The gravitational force is $\sim 10^{13}$ times stronger and in the opposite direction. (e) On the Earth, the Sun's gravitational force is also $\sim 10^{13}$ times stronger than the light-pressure force and in the opposite direction.

35. (a) 134 m   (b) 46.9 m

37. (a) away along the perpendicular bisector of the line segment joining the antennas   (b) along the extensions of the line segment joining the antennas

39. (a) $\vec{\mathbf{E}} = \frac{1}{2}\mu_0 c J_{max}[\cos (kx - \omega t)]\hat{\mathbf{j}}$
   (b) $\vec{\mathbf{S}} = \frac{1}{4}\mu_0 c J_{max}^2[\cos^2 (kx - \omega t)]\hat{\mathbf{i}}$
   (c) $I = \dfrac{\mu_0 c J_{max}^2}{8}$ (d) 3.48 A/m

41. (a) 6.00 pm   (b) 7.50 cm

43. (a) 4.17 m to 4.55 m   (b) 3.41 m to 3.66 m
   (c) 1.61 m to 1.67 m

45. 1.00 Mm = 621 mi; not very practical

47. (a) 3.85×10^{26} W   (b) 1.02 kV/m and 3.39 μT

49. (a)

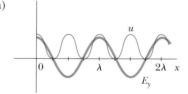

(b), (c) $u_E = u_B = \frac{1}{2}\epsilon_0 E_{max}^2 \cos^2 (kx)$
   (d) $u = \epsilon_0 E_{max}^2 \cos^2 (kx)$ (e) $E_\lambda = \frac{1}{2}A\lambda\epsilon_0 E_{max}^2$

   (f) $I = \frac{1}{2}c\epsilon_0 E_{max}^2 = \frac{1}{2}\sqrt{\dfrac{\epsilon_0}{\mu_0}} E_{max}^2$. This result agrees with

   $I = \dfrac{E_{max}^2}{2\mu_0 c}$ in Equation 34.24.

51. (a) 6.67×10^{-16} T   (b) 5.31×10^{-17} W/m^2
   (c) 1.67×10^{-14} W   (d) 5.56×10^{-23} N

53. 95.1 mV/m

55. (a) $B_{max} = 583$ nT, $k = 419$ rad/m, $\omega = 126$ Grad/s;
   $\vec{\mathbf{B}}$ vibrates in xz plane   (b) $\vec{\mathbf{S}}_{avg} = (40.6\hat{\mathbf{i}})$ W/m^2
   (c) 271 nPa   (d) $(406\hat{\mathbf{i}})$ nm/s^2

57. (a) 22.6 h   (b) 30.6 s

59. (a) 8.32×10^7 W/m^2 (b) 1.05 kW

61. (b) 17.6 Tm/s^2, 1.75×10^{-27} W   (c) 1.80×10^{-24} W

63. (a) $2\pi^2 r^2 fB_{max} \cos\theta$, where θ is the angle between the magnetic field and the normal to the loop   (b) The loop should be in the vertical plane containing the line of sight to the transmitter.

65. (a) 388 K   (b) 363 K

CHAPTER 35

1. 300 Mm/s. The sizes of the objects need to be accounted for; otherwise, the answer would be too large by 2%.
3. 114 rad/s
5. (a) 1.94 m   (b) 50.0° above the horizontal
7. 23.3°
9. 25.5°, 442 nm
11. 19.5° above the horizon
13. 22.5°
15. (a) 181 Mm/s   (b) 225 Mm/s   (c) 136 Mm/s
17. 30.0° and 19.5° at entry; 19.5° and 30.0° at exit
19. 3.88 mm
21. 30.4° and 22.3°
23. (a) yes, if the angle of incidence is 58.9°   (b) No. Both the reduction in speed and the bending toward the normal reduce the component of velocity parallel to the interface. This component cannot remain constant unless the angle of incidence is 0°.
25. 86.8°
27. 27.9°
29. (b) 37.2°   (c) 37.3°   (d) 37.3°
31. 4.61°
33. (a) 24.4°   (b) 37.0°   (c) 49.8°
35. 1.000 08
37. (a) $dn/(n-1)$ (b) yes; yes; yes   (c) 350 μm
39. Skylight incident from above travels down the plastic. If the index of refraction of the plastic is greater than 1.41, the rays close in direction to the vertical are totally reflected from the side walls of the slab and from both facets at the bottom of the plastic, where it is not immersed in gasoline. This light returns up inside the plastic and makes it look bright. Unless the index of refraction of the plastic is unrealistically large (greater than about 2.1), total internal reflection is frustrated where the plastic is immersed in gasoline. There the downward-propagating light passes from the plastic out into the gasoline. Little light is reflected up, and the gauge looks dark.
41. Scattered light leaving the photograph in all forward horizontal directions in air is gathered by refraction into a fan in the water of half-angle 48.6°. At larger angles, you see things on the other side of the globe, reflected by total internal reflection at the back surface of the cylinder.
43. 77.5°
45. 2.27 m
47. 62.2%
49. 82 reflections
51. 27.5°
53. (a) Total internal reflection occurs for all values of θ, or the maximum angle is 90°. (b) 30.3°   (c) Total internal reflection never occurs as the light moves from lower-index polystyrene into higher-index carbon disulfide.
55. 2.36 cm
57. $\theta = \sin^{-1}\left[\dfrac{L}{R^2}\left(\sqrt{n^2R^2 - L^2} - \sqrt{R^2 - L^2}\right)\right]$
61. (a) nR_1 (b) R_2
63. (a) 1.20   (b) 3.40 ns

CHAPTER 36

1. $\sim 10^{-9}$ s younger
3. 35.0 in.
5. (a) $-(p_1 + h)$ (b) virtual   (c) upright   (d) 1.00   (e) no
7. (a) -12.0 cm; 0.400   (b) -15.0 cm; 0.250   (c) upright
9. (a) $q = 45.0$ cm; $M = -0.500$
(b) $q = -60.0$ cm; $M = 3.00$
(c) Image (a) is real, inverted, and diminished. Image (b) is virtual, upright, and enlarged.

11. (a) 2.22 cm   (b) 10.0
13. (a) 160 mm   (b) $R = -267$ mm
15. (a) convex   (b) at the 30.0 cm mark   (c) -20.0 cm
17. (a) a concave mirror with radius of curvature 2.08 m
(b) 1.25 m from the object
19. (a) The image starts 60.0 cm above the mirror and moves up faster and faster, running out to an infinite distance above the mirror. At that moment, the image rays are parallel and the image is equally well described as infinitely far below the mirror. From there, the image moves up, slowing down as it moves, to reach the mirror vertex.
(b) at 0.639 s and 0.782 s
21. 38.2 cm below the top surface of the ice
23. 8.57 cm
25. (a) inside the tank, 24.9 cm behind the front wall; virtual, right side up, enlarged   (b) inside the tank, 93.9 cm behind the front wall; virtual, right side up, enlarged
(c) 1.10 and 1.39   (d) 9.92 cm and 12.5 cm   (e) The plastic has uniform thickness, so the surfaces of entry and exit for any particular ray are very nearly parallel. The ray is slightly displaced, but it would not be changed in direction by going through the plastic wall with air on both sides. Only the difference between the air and water is responsible for the refraction of the light.
27. (a) 16.4 cm   (b) 16.4 cm
29. (a) $q = 40.0$ cm, real and inverted, actual size $M = -1.00$
(b) $q = \infty$, $M = \infty$, no image is formed   (c) $q = -20.0$ cm, upright, virtual, enlarged $M = +2.00$
31. 2.84 cm
33. (a) -12.3 cm, to the left of the lens   (b) 0.615
(c)

35. (a) 5.36 cm   (b) -18.8 cm   (c) virtual, right side up, enlarged (d) A magnifying glass with focal length 7.50 cm is used to form an image of a stamp, enlarged 3.50 times. Find the object distance. Locate and describe the image.

37. (a) $p = \dfrac{d}{2} \pm \sqrt{\dfrac{d^2}{4} - fd}$

(b) Both images are real and inverted. One is enlarged, the other diminished.

39. 2.18 mm away from the film plane

41. 21.3 cm

43. −4.00 diopters, a diverging lens

45. (a) at 4.17 cm   (b) 6.00

47. (a) −800   (b) image is inverted

49. 3.38 min

51. −40.0 cm

53. −25.0 cm

55. $x' = (1\ 024\ \text{cm} - 58x)\ \text{cm}/(6\ \text{cm} - x)$. The image starts at the position $x'_i = 171$ cm and moves in the positive x direction, faster and faster, until it is out at infinity when the object is at the position $x = 6$ cm. At this instant, the rays from the top of the object are parallel as they leave the lens. Their intersection point can be described as at $x' = \infty$ to the right or equally well as at $x' = -\infty$ on the left. From $x' = -\infty$, the image continues moving to the right, now slowing down. It reaches, for example, −280 cm when the object is at 8 cm and −55 cm when the object is finally at 12 cm. The image has traveled always to the right, to infinity and beyond.

57. Align the lenses on the same axis and 9.00 cm apart. Let the light pass first through the diverging lens and then through the converging lens. The diameter increases by a factor of 1.75.

59. 0.107 m to the right of the vertex of the hemispherical face

61. 8.00 cm. Ray diagram:

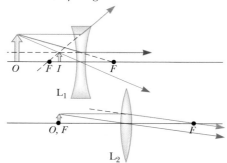

63. 1.50 m in front of the mirror; 1.40 cm (inverted)

65. (a) 30.0 cm and 120 cm   (b) 24.0 cm   (c) real, inverted, diminished with $M = -0.250$

67. (a) 20.0 cm to the right of the second lens, −6.00
(b) inverted   (c) 6.67 cm to the right of the second lens, −2.00, inverted

CHAPTER 37

1. 1.58 cm

3. (a) 55.7 m   (b) 124 m

5. 1.54 mm

7. (a) 2.62 mm   (b) 2.62 mm

9. 36.2 cm

11. (a) 10.0 m (b) 516 m (c) Only the runway centerline is a maximum for the interference patterns for both frequencies. If the frequencies were related by a ratio of small integers k/ℓ, the plane could by mistake fly along the kth side maximum of one signal, where it coincides with the

ℓth side maximum of the other. The plane cannot make a sharp turn at the end of the runway, so it would then be headed in the wrong direction to land.

13. (a) 13.2 rad (b) 6.28 rad (c) 0.012 7 degree
(d) 0.059 7 degree

15. (a) 1.93 μm (b) 3.00λ (c) It corresponds to a maximum. The path difference is an integer multiple of the wavelength.

17. 48.0 μm

19. $E_1 + E_2 = 10.0 \sin (100\pi t + 0.927)$

21. (a) 7.95 rad (b) 0.453

23. (a) green (b) violet

25. 512 nm

27. 96.2 nm

29. (a) 238 nm (b) The wavelength increases because of thermal expansion of the filter material. (c) 328 nm

31. 4.35 μm

33. 1.20 mm

35. 39.6 μm

37. 1.62 cm

39. 1.25 m

41. (a) $\sim 10^{-3}$ degree   (b) $\sim 10^{11}$ Hz, microwave

43. 2.52 cm

45. 20.0×10^{-6} °C^{-1}

47. 3.58°

49. 1.62 km

51. 421 nm

55. (b) 266 nm

57. $y' = (n - 1)tL/d$

59. (a) 70.6 m   (b) 136 m

61. (a) 14.7 μm   (b) 1.53 cm   (c) −16.0 m

63. (a) 4.86 cm from the top   (b) 78.9 nm and 128 nm
(c) 2.63×10^{-6} rad

65. 0.505 mm

67. 0.498 mm

CHAPTER 38

1. 4.22 mm

3. 0.230 mm

5. three maxima, at 0° and near 46° on both sides

7. 0.016 2

9.

11. 1.00 mrad

13. 3.09 m

15. 13.1 m

17. Neither. It can resolve no objects closer than several centimeters apart.

19. 7.35°

21. 5.91° in first order, 13.2° in second order, 26.5° in third order

23. (a) 478.7 nm, 647.6 nm, and 696.6 nm (b) 20.51°, 28.30°, and 30.66°

25. three, at 0° and at 45.2° to the right and left.

27. (a) five orders   (b) ten orders in the short-wavelength region

29. 2

31. 14.4°

33. The crystal cannot produce diffracted beams of visible light. Bragg's law cannot be satisfied for a wavelength much larger than the distance between atomic planes in the crystal.

35. (a) 54.7°   (b) 63.4°   (c) 71.6°

37. 60.5°

39. (b) For light confined to a plane, yes.

$$\left| \tan^{-1}\left(\frac{n_3}{n_2}\right) - \tan^{-1}\left(\frac{n_1}{n_2}\right) \right|$$

41. (a) 0.875 (b) 0.789 (c) 0.670 (d) You can get more and more of the incident light through the stack of ideal filters, approaching 50%, by reducing the angle between the axes of each one and the next.

43. (a) 6   (b) 7.50°

45. (a) 0.045 0   (b) 0.016 2

47. 632.8 nm

49. (a) 25.6°   (b) 19.0°

51. 545 nm

53. (a) 3.53×10^3 grooves/cm   (c) 11 maxima

55. $4.58 \ \mu m < d < 5.23 \ \mu m$

57. 15.4

59. (a) 41.8°   (b) 0.593   (c) 0.262 m

61. (b) 3.77 nm/cm

63. (b) 15.3 μm

65. $\phi = 1.391\ 557\ 4$ after 17 steps or fewer

67. $a = 99.5 \ \mu m \pm 1\%$

CHAPTER 39

5. $0.866c$

7. 1.54 ns

9. $0.800c$

11. (a) 39.2 μs (b) It was accurate to one digit. Cooper aged 1.78 μs less in each single orbit.

13. (a) 20.0 m   (b) 19.0 m   (c) $0.312c$

15. 11.3 kHz

17. (b) $0.050\ 4c$

19. (a) $0.943c$ (b) 2.55 km

21. B occurred 4.44×10^{-7} s before A

23. $0.960c$

25. (a) 2.73×10^{-24} kg·m/s   (b) 1.58×10^{-22} kg·m/s   (c) 5.64×10^{-22} kg·m/s

27. 4.50×10^{-14}

29. $0.285c$

31. (a) 5.37×10^{-11} J   (b) 1.33×10^{-9} J

33. 1.63×10^3 MeV/c

35. (a) 938 MeV   (b) 3.00 GeV   (c) 2.07 GeV

39. (a) $0.979c$ (b) $0.065\ 2c$ (c) $0.914c = 274$ Mm/s   (d) $0.999\ 999\ 97c$; $0.948c$; $0.052\ 3c = 15.7$ Mm/s

41. 4.08 MeV and 29.6 MeV

43. smaller by 3.18×10^{-12} kg, which is too small a fraction of 9 g to be measured

45. 4.28×10^9 kg/s

47. (a) 26.6 Mm   (b) 3.87 km/s   (c) -8.34×10^{-11} (d) 5.29×10^{-10} (e) $+4.46 \times 10^{-10}$

49. (a) a few hundred seconds   (b) $\sim 10^8$ km

51. (a) $u = c \left(\dfrac{2H + H^2}{1 + 2H + H^2} \right)^{1/2}$, where $H = K/mc^2$

(b) u goes to 0 as K goes to 0. (c) u approaches c as K increases without limit.

(d) $a = \dfrac{\mathscr{P}}{mcH^{1/2}(2 + H)^{1/2}(1 + H)^2}$

(e) $a = \dfrac{\mathscr{P}}{mc\,(2H)^{1/2}} = \dfrac{\mathscr{P}}{(2mK)^{1/2}}$, in agreement with the non-relativistic case.

(f) a approaches $\mathscr{P}/mcH^3 = \mathscr{P}m^2c^5/K^3$ (g) As energy is steadily imparted to the particle, the particle's acceleration decreases. It decreases steeply, proportionally to $1/K^3$ at high energy. In this way, the particle's speed cannot reach or surpass a certain upper limit, which is the speed of light in vacuum.

53. 0.712%

55. (a) 76.0 min   (b) 52.1 min

57. (a) $0.946c$ (b) 0.160 ly   (c) 0.114 yr   (d) 7.50×10^{22} J

59. yes, with 18.8 m to spare

61. (b) For u small compared with c, the relativistic expression agrees with the classical expression. As u approaches c, the acceleration approaches zero, so the object can never reach or surpass the speed of light.
(c) Perform the operation $\int(1 - u^2/c^2)^{-3/2}du = (qE/m)\int dt$ to obtain $u = qEct(m^2c^2 + q^2E^2t^2)^{-1/2}$ and then $\int dx = \int qEct(m^2c^2 + q^2E^2t^2)^{-1/2}dt$ to obtain $x = (c/qE)[(m^2c^2 + q^2E^2t^2)^{1/2} - mc]$

63. (a) $M = \dfrac{2m\sqrt{4 - u^2/c^2}}{3\sqrt{1 - u^2/c^2}}$

(b) $M = 4m/3$. The result agrees with the arithmetic sum of the masses of the two colliding particles.

65. (a) The refugees conclude that Tau Ceti exploded 16.0 yr before the Sun. (b) A stationary observer at the midpoint concludes that Tau Ceti and the Sun exploded simultaneously.

67. 1.82×10^{-3} eV

CHAPTER 40

1. 5.18×10^3 K

3. approximately 5 200 K. A firefly cannot be at this temperature, so its light cannot be blackbody radiation.

5. 1.30×10^{15}/s

7. (a) 5.78×10^3 K   (b) 501 nm

9. (a) 2.57 eV (b) 12.8 μeV (c) 191 neV (d) 484 nm (visible), 9.68 cm, and 6.52 m (radio waves)

11. 2.27×10^{30} photons/s

15. (a) 1.90 eV (b) 0.216 V

17. (a) We find the energy of a photon with wavelength 400 nm and check whether it exceeds the work function. Of these metals, only lithium shows the photoelectric effect. (b) 0.808 eV

19. 8.41 pC

21. 1.78 eV, 9.47×10^{-28} kg $\cdot$ m/s

23. 70.0°

25. (a) 43.0° (b) 602 keV, 3.21×10^{-22} kg $\cdot$ m/s (c) 278 keV, 3.21×10^{-22} kg $\cdot$ m/s

27. (a) 2.88 pm (b) 101°

29. It is sufficient because Compton's equation and the conservation of vector momentum give three independent equations in the unknowns λ', λ_0, and u. Wavelength is 3.82 pm

31. (a) 0.667 (b) 0.001 09

33. (a) 14.0 kV/m, 46.8 μT (b) 4.19 nN (c) 10.2 g

35. (a) 0.174 nm (b) 5.37 pm or 5.49 pm ignoring relativistic correction

37. (a) $\sim$ 100 MeV or more (b) $\sim$ -1 MeV. No. With kinetic energy much larger than the magnitude of its negative electric potential energy, the electron would immediately escape.

39. (b) No. $\lambda^{-2} + \lambda_C^{-2}$ cannot be equal to λ^{-2}.

41. (a) 14.9 keV or, ignoring relativistic correction, 15.1 keV (b) 124 keV

43. (a) 3.91×10^4 (b) 20.0 GeV/c = 1.07×10^{-17} kg $\cdot$ m/s (c) 6.22×10^{-17} m, small compared with the size of the nucleus. The scattering of the electrons can give information about the particles forming the nucleus.

47. (a) 993 nm (b) 4.96 mm (c) If its detection forms part of an interference pattern, the neutron must have passed through both slits. If we test to see which slit a particular neutron passes through, the neutron will not form part of the interference pattern.

49. Within 1.16 mm for the electron, 5.28×10^{-32} m for the bullet

51. 3.79×10^{28} m, 190 times the diameter of the observable Universe

53. (b) 519 am

55. (a)

Maximum photoelectron energy increasing linearly with photon frequency

(b) 6.4×10^{-34} J $\cdot$ s $\pm$ 8% (c) 1.4 eV

57. $\dfrac{hc}{\lambda} - \dfrac{e^2 B^2 R^2}{2m_e}$

63. 0.143 nm. The wavelength is comparable to the distance between atoms in a crystal, so diffraction can be observed.

67. 2.81×10^{-8}

CHAPTER 41

1. (a) 126 pm (b) 5.27×10^{-24} kg $\cdot$ m/s (c) 95.5 eV

3. (a) 0.434 nm (b) 6.00 eV

5. (a)

(b) 2.20 nm, 2.75 nm, 4.12 nm, 4.71 nm, 6.60 nm, 11.0 nm

7. 0.793 nm

9. 6.16 MeV, 202 fm, a gamma ray

11. 0.513 MeV, 2.05 MeV, 4.62 MeV. They do; the MeV is the natural unit for energy radiated by an atomic nucleus.

13. (a) $\Delta p \approx \hbar/2L$ (b) $E \approx \hbar^2/8mL^2$. This estimate is too low by $4\pi^2 \approx 40$ times. It correctly displays the pattern of dependence of the energy on the mass and on the length of the well.

17. At $L/4$ and at $3L/4$. We look for $\sin(2\pi x/L)$ taking on its extreme values 1 and -1 so that the squared wave function is as large as it can be.

19. (a) 0.196 (b) 0.609 (c) The classical probability, $\frac{1}{3}$, is very different.

23. (a) $E = \hbar^2/mL^2$

(b) $\displaystyle\int_{-L}^{L} A^2(1 - x^2/L^2)^2 dx = 1$ gives $A = \left(\dfrac{15}{16L}\right)^{1/2}$.

(c) $\frac{47}{81} = 0.580$

27. (a)

(b) $2L$

29. By 0.959 nm, to 1.91 nm

31. (a) 0.010 3 (b) 0.990

33. 1.35

37. 600 nm

39. (b) The acceleration is equal to a negative constant times the excursion from equilibrium. The frequency is $\dfrac{1}{2\pi}\sqrt{\dfrac{k}{\mu}}$.

41. $\sim 10^{-10^{30}}$

43. (a)

(b)

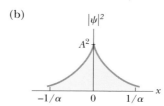

(c) The wave function is continuous. It shows localization by approaching zero as $x \to \pm\infty$. It is everywhere finite and can be normalized. (d) $A = \sqrt{\alpha}$ (e) 0.632

45. (b) For the transition from level 2 to level 1, $\lambda = 1.38\ \mu m$ infrared. For level 4 to level 1, $\lambda = 276$ nm ultraviolet. For level 3 to level 2, $\lambda = 827$ nm infrared. For level 4 to level 2, $\lambda = 344$ nm near ultraviolet. For level 4 to level 3, $\lambda = 590$ nm yellow-orange visible.

47. 0.029 4

49. (a) 434 THz   (b) 691 nm   (c) 165 peV or more

53. (a)

$$\frac{2}{a}\ |\psi|^2 = (2/a)\,e^{-2x/a}$$

(b) 0   (c) 0.865

55. (a) $-7k_e e^2/3d$ (b) $h^2/36m_e d^2$ (c) 49.9 pm   (d) The lithium interatomic spacing of 280 pm is 5.62 times larger. Therefore, it is of the same order of magnitude as the interatomic spacing $2d$ here.

57. (a) $A = \left(\dfrac{2}{17L}\right)^{1/2}$ (b) $|A|^2 + |B|^2 = 1/a$

59. 2.25

CHAPTER 42

1. (a) 5   (b) no; no

3. (b) 0.846 ns

5. (a) 1.89 eV, 656 nm   (b) 3.40 eV, 365 nm

7. (a) 0.212 nm   (b) 9.95×10^{-25} kg·m/s
   (c) 2.11×10^{-34} kg·m²/s   (d) 3.40 eV   (e) -6.80 eV
   (f) -3.40 eV

9. (a) $E_n = -54.4$ eV/n^2 for $n = 1, 2, 3, \ldots$

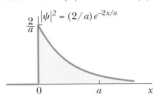

n	E (eV)
∞	0
4	-3.40
3	-6.05
2	-13.6
1	-54.4

ENERGY

(b) 54.4 eV

11. $r_n = (0.106\ \text{nm})\,n^2$, $E_n = -6.80$ eV/n^2, for $n = 1, 2, 3, \ldots$

13. (a) 1.31 μm   (b) 164 nm

15. (a) $\Delta p \geq \hbar/2r$ (b) Choosing $p \approx \hbar/r$, we find that $E = K + U = \hbar^2/2m_e r^2 - k_e e^2/r$. (c) $r = \hbar^2/m_e k_e e^2 = a_0$ and $E = -13.6$ eV, in agreement with the Bohr theory

17. (b) 0.497

19. It does, with $E = -k_e e^2/2a_0$.

21. (a)

n	ℓ	m_ℓ	m_s
3	2	2	$\frac{1}{2}$
3	2	2	$-\frac{1}{2}$
3	2	1	$\frac{1}{2}$
3	2	1	$-\frac{1}{2}$
3	2	0	$\frac{1}{2}$
3	2	0	$-\frac{1}{2}$
3	2	-1	$\frac{1}{2}$
3	2	-1	$-\frac{1}{2}$
3	2	-2	$\frac{1}{2}$
3	2	-2	$-\frac{1}{2}$

(b)

n	ℓ	m_ℓ	m_s
3	1	1	$\frac{1}{2}$
3	1	1	$-\frac{1}{2}$
3	1	0	$\frac{1}{2}$
3	1	0	$-\frac{1}{2}$
3	1	-1	$\frac{1}{2}$
3	1	-1	$-\frac{1}{2}$

23. (a) Find the orbital quantum number of an electron in a state in which it has orbital angular momentum equal to 4.714×10^{-34} J·s. (b) orbital quantum number = 4

25. (a) 2   (b) 8   (c) 18   (d) 32   (e) 50

27. (a) 3.99×10^{17} kg/m³   (b) 81.7 am   (c) 1.77 Tm/s
   (d) It is $5.91 \times 10^3 c$, which is huge compared with the speed of light and impossible.

29. $n = 3$; $\ell = 2$; $m_\ell = -2, -1, 0, 1$, or 2; $s = 1$; $m_s = -1, 0$, or 1, for a total of 15 states

31. The $4s$ subshell is filled first. We would expect $[Ar]3d^44s^2$ to have lower energy, but $[Ar]3d^54s^1$ has more unpaired spins and lower energy according to Hund's rule. It is the ground-state configuration of chromium.

33. aluminum

35. (a) $1s, 2s, 2p, 3s, 3p, 4s, 3d, 4p, 5s, 4d, 5p, 6s, 4f, 5d, 6p, 7s$
   (b) Element 15 should have valence $+5$ or -3, and it does. Element 47 should have valence -1, but it has valence $+1$. Element 86 should be inert, and it is.

37. 18.4 T

39. 1.4 and 1.0. When the outermost electron in sodium is promoted from the $3s$ state into a $3p$ state, its wave function still overlaps somewhat with the ten electrons below it. It therefore sees the $+11e$ nuclear charge not fully screened and on average moves in an electric field like that created by a particle with charge $+11e - 9.6e = 1.4e$. When this valence electron is lifted farther to a $3p$ state, it is essentially entirely outside the cloud of ten electrons below it and moves in the field of a net charge $+11e - 10e = 1e$.

41. 0.072 5 nm

43. iron

45. 28.2 THz, 10.6 μm, infrared

47. 3.49×10^{16} photons

49. (a) 217 nm   (b) 93.1 nm

51. (a) 609 μeV   (b) 6.9 μeV   (c) 147 GHz, 2.04 mm

53. The classical frequency is $4\pi^2 m_e k_e^2 e^4/h^3 n^3$.

55. (a) -8.16 eV, -2.04 eV, -0.902 eV, -0.508 eV, -0.325 eV
   (b) 1 090 nm, 811 nm, 724 nm, 609 nm   (d) The spectrum

could be that of hydrogen, Doppler-shifted by motion away from us at speed $0.471c$.

57. (a) 1.57×10^{14} m$^{-3/2}$ (b) 2.47×10^{28} m^{-3}
(c) 8.69×10^8 m^{-1}

59. (a) 4.20 mm   (b) 1.05×10^{19} photons
(c) 8.82×10^{16}/mm^3

61. $3h^2/4mL^2$

65. 5.39 keV

67. 0.125

69. 9.79 GHz

CHAPTER 43

1. (a) 921 pN toward the other ion   (b) -2.88 eV

3. (a) $(2A/B)^{1/6}$ (b) $B^2/4A$ (c) 74.2 pm, 4.46 eV

5. ~ 10 K

7. (a) 40.0 μeV, 9.66 GHz   (b) If r is 10% too small, then f is 20% too large.

9. 5.63 Trad/s

13. 2.72×10^{-47} kg $\cdot$ m^2

15. 0.358 eV

17. $(18.4 \ \mu\text{eV})J(J+1)$, where $J = 0, 1, 2, 3, \ldots$

19. 2.9×10^{-47} kg $\cdot$ m^2

21. only 64.1 THz

23. -7.84 eV

27. An average atom contributes 0.981 electron to the conduction band.

29. (a) 1.57 Mm/s   (b) It is larger by ten orders of magnitude.

31. (a) 4.23 eV   (b) 3.27×10^4 K

33. 5.28 eV

37. (a) 1.10 (b) 1.47×10^{-25}. It is vastly smaller. Very few states well above the Fermi energy are occupied at room temperature.

39. (a) 275 THz   (b) 1.09 μm

41. The gap should be less than or equal to 1.24 eV. Silicon's energy gap of 1.14 eV means that it can absorb the energy of nearly all the photons in sunlight and is an appropriate material for a solar energy collector.

43. 226 nm

45. (a) 59.5 mV   (b) -59.5 mV

47. 4.19 mA

49. 203 A to produce a magnetic field in the direction of the original field

51. (a)

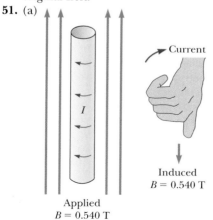

Applied
$B = 0.540$ T

(b) 10.7 kA

53. (a) 6.15×10^{13} Hz   (b) 1.59×10^{-46} kg $\cdot$ m^2
(c) 4.79 μm or 4.96 μm

55. 7

59. (a) 0.350 nm   (b) -7.02 eV   (c) $-1.20\hat{\mathbf{i}}$ nN

61. (a) r_0 (b) B (c) $(a/\pi)[B/2\mu]^{1/2}$
(d) $B - (ha/\pi)[B/8\mu]^{1/2}$

CHAPTER 44

1. $\sim 10^{28}$; $\sim 10^{28}$; $\sim 10^{28}$

3. (a) 2.81×10^{-5} (b) 1.38×10^{-14}

5. (a) 455 fm   (b) 6.04 Mm/s

7. 16.0 km

9. (a) 1.11 MeV/nucleon   (b) 7.07 MeV/nucleon
(c) 8.79 MeV/nucleon   (d) 7.57 MeV/nucleon

11. (a) $^{139}_{55}$Cs   (b) $^{139}_{57}$La   (c) $^{139}_{55}$Cs

13. greater for $^{15}_{7}$N by 3.54 MeV

15. 7.93 MeV

17. 200 MeV

19. 1.16 ks

21. (a) 1.55×10^{-5}/s, 12.4 h   (b) 2.39×10^{13} atoms
(c) 1.88 mCi

23. 9.47×10^9 nuclei

25. 1.41

27. 2.66 d

29. 4.27 MeV

31. (a) $N_d = 10^6(1 - e^{-0.069 \ 3t})$, where t is in hours   (b) The number of daughter nuclei starts from zero at $t = 0$. It first increases most rapidly, at 6.93×10^4/h, and then more and more slowly. Its rate of change approaches zero while the number asymptotically approaches 1.00×10^6 as t increases without limit.

33. (a) e$^-$ + p $\rightarrow$ n + ν (b) $^{15}_{8}$O atom $\rightarrow$ $^{15}_{7}$N atom + ν
(c) 2.75 MeV

35.

37. (a) 148 Bq/m^3 (b) 7.05×10^7 atoms/m^3
(c) 2.17×10^{-17}

39. (a) $^{21}_{10}$Ne   (b) $^{144}_{54}$Xe   (c) $^0_1$e$^+$ + ν

41. $^{197}_{79}$Au + $^1_0$n $\rightarrow$ $^{198}_{80}$Hg + $^0_{-1}$e$^-$ + $\bar{\nu}$ (b) 7.89 MeV

43. 8.005 3 u; 10.013 5 u

45. (a) 29.2 MHz   (b) 42.6 MHz   (c) 2.13 kHz

47. (a) 5.70 MeV   (b) 3.27 MeV, exothermic

49. (b) 1.53 MeV

51. Find the reaction energy (Q value) of the reaction $^{10}_{5}$B + $^4_2$He $\rightarrow$ $^{13}_{6}$C + $^1_1$H. Solving, $Q = 4.06$ MeV is the energy released by the reaction as it is converted from rest energy into other forms.

53. (a) The process cannot occur because energy input would be required.   (b) can occur
(c) K_e between 0 and 156 keV

55. (a) conservation of energy   (b) Electric potential energy of the parent nucleus can supply the required energy.
(c) 1.20 MeV

57. (a) 61.8 Bq/L   (b) 40.3 d

59. 5.94 Gyr
61. 2.20 μeV
63. 0.400%
65. (a) 3.91 Gyr   (b) It could be no older. We must make some assumption about the original quantity of radioactive material. In part (a), we assumed the rock originally contained no strontium.

CHAPTER 45

1. 0.387 g
3. $^{144}_{54}$Xe, $^{143}_{54}$Xe, and $^{142}_{54}$Xe
5. $^1_0$n + ^{232}Th $\rightarrow$ ^{233}Th $\rightarrow$ ^{233}Pa + e$^-$ + $\bar{\nu}$,
   ^{233}Pa $\rightarrow$ ^{233}U + e$^-$ + $\bar{\nu}$
7. 5.80 Mm
9. approximately 3 000 yr
11. 2.68×10^5
13. (a) 4.55×10^{-24} kg·m/s   (b) 0.146 nm. This size is the same order of magnitude as an atom's outer electron cloud and is vastly larger than a nucleus.
15. (a) 31.9 g/h   (b) 122 g/h
17. (a) 3.24 fm   (b) 444 keV   (c) $\frac{2}{5}v_i$ (d) 740 keV
   (e) possibly by tunneling
19. (a) 2.22 Mm/s   (b) $\sim 10^{-7}$ s
21. (a) 10^{14} cm^{-3} (b) 1.24×10^5 J/m^3 (c) 1.77 T
23. 1.66×10^3 yr
25. (a) 2.5 mrem per x-ray image   (b) The technician's occupational exposure is high compared to background radiation; it is 38 times 0.13 rem/yr.
27. 2.09×10^6 s
29. 1.14 rad
31. 3.96×10^{-4} J/kg
33. (a) 3.12×10^7 (b) 3.12×10^{10} electrons
35. 4.45×10^{-8} kg/h
37. (b) R/λ
39. (a) 8×10^4 eV   (b) 4.62 MeV and 13.9 MeV
   (c) 1.03×10^7 kWh
41. (a) 177 MeV   (b) $K_{Br} = 112$ MeV, $K_{La} = 65.4$ MeV
   (c) $v_{Br} = 15.8$ Mm/s, $v_{La} = 9.20$ Mm/s
43. 482 Ci, less than the fission inventory by on the order of a hundred million times
45. 2.56×10^4 kg
47. (a) 333 μCi, 15.5 μCi, 312 μCi   (b) 50.4%, 2.35%, 47.3%
   (c) It is potentially dangerous, notably if the material is inhaled as a powder. With precautions to minimize human contact, microcurie sources can be routinely used in laboratories.
49. (a) 2.65 GJ   (b) The fusion energy is 78.0 times larger.
51. (a) 4.91×10^8 kg/h $= 4.91 \times 10^5$ m^3/h   (b) 0.141 kg/h
53. (a) 15.5 cm   (b) 51.7 MeV   (c) The number of decays per second is the decay rate R, and the energy released in each decay is Q. Then the energy released per unit time interval is $\mathcal{P} = QR$.   (d) 227 kJ/yr   (e) 3.18 J/yr
55. 14.0 MeV or, ignoring relativistic correction, 14.1 MeV
57. (a) 2.24×10^7 kWh   (b) 17.6 MeV   (c) 2.34×10^8 kWh
   (d) 9.36 kWh   (e) Coal is cheap at this moment in human history. We hope that safety and waste disposal problems can be solved so that nuclear energy can be affordable before scarcity drives up the price of fossil fuels.
59. (b) 26.7 MeV
61. (a) 5×10^7 K   (b) 1.94 MeV, 1.20 MeV, 1.02 MeV, 7.55 MeV, 7.30 MeV, 1.73 MeV, 1.02 MeV, 4.97 MeV,

26.7 MeV   (c) Most of the neutrinos leave the star directly after their creation, without interacting with any other particles.
63. (b) 1.00 μs   (c) 2.83 km/s   (d) 14.6 μs
   (e) yes; 107 kilotons of TNT

CHAPTER 46

1. 453 ZHz; 662 am
3. (a) 558 TJ   (b) 2.17×10^7
5. 118 MeV
7. $\sim 10^{-18}$ m
9. 67.5 MeV, 67.5 MeV/c, 16.3 ZHz
11. (a) 0.782 MeV   (b) $v_e = 0.919c$, $v_p = 380$ km/s   (c) The electron is moving faster than one-tenth the speed of light, and the proton is not. Relativistic kinetic energy and momentum equations need be used only for the electron.
13. (a) muon lepton number L_μ and electron lepton number L_e (b) charge   (c) baryon number   (d) baryon number   (e) charge
15. (a) $\bar{\nu}_\mu$ (b) ν_μ (c) $\bar{\nu}_e$ (d) ν_e (e) ν_μ (f) $\bar{\nu}_e + \nu_\mu$
17. Reactions (a), (c), and (f) violate baryon number conservation. Reactions (b), (d), and (e) can occur. Reaction (f) violates muon lepton number conservation.
19. (b) $E_e = E_\gamma = 469$ MeV, $p_e = p_\gamma = 469$ MeV/c
   (c) 0.999 999 4c
21. Reactions (b) and (c) conserve strangeness. Reactions (a), (d), (e), and (f) violate strangeness conservation.
23. (a) electron and muon lepton numbers   (b) electron lepton number   (c) charge and strangeness   (d) baryon number   (e) strangeness
25. (a) baryon number, charge, L_e and L_τ (b) baryon number, charge, L_e, L_μ, and L_τ (c) strangeness, charge, L_e, L_μ, and L_τ (d) baryon number, strangeness, charge, L_e, L_μ, and L_τ (e) baryon number, strangeness, charge, L_e, L_μ, and L_τ (f) baryon number, strangeness, charge, L_e, L_μ, and L_τ
27. 9.26 cm
29. (b) 5.63 GeV   (c) 768 MeV   (d) 280 MeV   (e) 4.43 TeV
35. (a) The reaction $\bar{u}d$ + uud $\rightarrow$ $\bar{s}d$ + uds has a total of 1 u, 2 d, and 0 s quarks originally and finally. (b) The reaction $\bar{d}u$ + uud $\rightarrow$ $\bar{s}u$ + uus has a net of 3 u, 0 d, and 0 s before and after. (c) The reaction $\bar{u}s$ + uud $\rightarrow$ $\bar{s}u$ + $\bar{s}d$ + sss shows conservation at 1 u, 1 d, and 1 s quark. (d) The process uud + uud $\rightarrow$ $\bar{s}d$ + uud + $\bar{d}u$ + uds nets 4 u, 2 d, and 0 s quarks initially and finally; the mystery particle is a Λ^0 or a Σ^0.
37. (a) Σ^+ (b) π^- (c) K^0 (d) Ξ^-
39. (a) 3.32 am/s   (b) 690 pm/s
41. (a) 0.160c (b) 2.82×10^9 ly
43. (a) 590.07 nm   (b) 597 nm   (c) 661 nm
45. (a) 8.41×10^6 kg   (b) No. It is only the fraction 4.23×10^{-24} of the mass of the Sun.
47. 3.15 μW/m^2
49. (a) $\sim 10^{13}$ K   (b) $\sim 10^{10}$ K
51. (b) 11.8 Gyr
53. (a) 1.61×10^{-35} m   (b) 5.38×10^{-44} s, of the same order of magnitude as the ultrahot epoch   (c) Yes. The opaque fireball of the Big Bang, measured as the cosmic microwave background radiation, prevents us from receiving visible light from things before the Universe was a few hundred thousand years old. Walls of more profound fire hide all information from still earlier times.

55. $19 \text{ eV}/c^2$

57. one part in 50 000 000

59. (a) $2Nmc$ (b) $3^{1/2}Nmc$ (c) method (a)

61. 5.35 MeV and 32.3 MeV

63. 74.4 MeV

65. 29.8 MeV

67. Diagram (a): electron–positron annihilation; e^-. Diagram (b): a neutrino collides with a neutron, producing a proton and a muon; W^+

69. (a) 127 MeV   (b) 1.06 mm   (c) 1.17 meV
    (d) 5.81×10^{19} eV

Locator note: **boldface** indicates a definition; *italics* indicates a figure; *t* indicates a table.

Standard Abbreviations and Symbols for Units

Symbol	Unit	Symbol	Unit
A	ampere	K	kelvin
u	atomic mass unit	kg	kilogram
atm	atmosphere	kmol	kilomole
Btu	British thermal unit	L	liter
C	coulomb	lb	pound
°C	degree Celsius	ly	lightyear
cal	calorie	m	meter
d	day	min	minute
eV	electron volt	mol	mole
°F	degree Fahrenheit	N	newton
F	farad	Pa	pascal
ft	foot	rad	radian
G	gauss	rev	revolution
g	gram	s	second
H	henry	T	tesla
h	hour	V	volt
hp	horsepower	W	watt
Hz	hertz	Wb	weber
in.	inch	yr	year
J	joule	Ω	ohm

Mathematical Symbols Used in the Text and Their Meaning

Symbol	Meaning
$=$	is equal to
$\equiv$	is defined as
$\neq$	is not equal to
$\propto$	is proportional to
$\sim$	is on the order of
$>$	is greater than
$<$	is less than
$\gg (\ll)$	is much greater (less) than
$\approx$	is approximately equal to
Δx	the change in x
$\sum_{i=1}^{N} x_i$	the sum of all quantities x_i from $i = 1$ to $i = N$
$|x|$	the magnitude of x (always a nonnegative quantity)
$\Delta x \to 0$	Δx approaches zero
$\dfrac{dx}{dt}$	the derivative of x with respect to t
$\dfrac{\partial x}{\partial t}$	the partial derivative of x with respect to t
$\int$	integral